Dear Ivy Tech Automotive Students,

The Ivy Tech Automotive Technology Program has partnered with Pearson Learning Solutions to create a custom textbook for the AUTC 100, 113, 123, and 243 course sequence. This allows us to use only the content needed for your course from the following four textbooks:

Introduction to Automotive Service

Automotive Technology: Principles, Diagnosis and Service

Automotive Electricity and Electronics

Advanced Automotive Electricity and Electronics

Your book includes a custom Table of Contents, a Custom Index, and all pages, diagrams, tables, photographs, and illustrations have been renumbered so your book flows seamlessly from start to finish.
   We are confident that this approach will save you money while still providing you with the best content resource for use in these courses.

Sincerely,

The Ivy Tech Automotive Technology Program and Pearson Learning Solutions

Electricity and Electronics for the Automotive Industry

A Pearson Learning Solutions Publication
for Ivy Tech Community College

Taken from:
Advanced Automotive Electricity and Electronics
by James D. Halderman

Introduction to Automotive Service
by James D. Halderman and Darrell Deeter

Automotive Electricity and Electronics, Third Edition
by James D. Halderman

Automotive Technology: Principles, Diagnosis, and Service, Fourth Edition
by James D. Halderman

Front cover photograph courtesy of Lunamarina/dreamstime.com.
Back cover photograph courtesy of Berlinphoto/dreamstime.com.

Taken from:

Advanced Automotive Electricity and Electronics
by James D. Halderman
Copyright © 2013 by Pearson Education, Inc.
Published by Prentice Hall
Upper Saddle River, New Jersey 07458

Introduction to Automotive Service
by James D. Halderman and Darrell Deeter
Copyright © 2013 by Pearson Education, Inc.
Published by Prentice Hall

Automotive Electricity and Electronics, Third Edition
by James D. Halderman
Copyright © 2011, 2009, 2005 by Pearson Education, Inc.
Published by Prentice Hall

Automotive Technology: Principles, Diagnosis, and Service, Fourth Edition
by James D. Halderman
Copyright © 2012, 2009, 2003, 1999 by Pearson Education, Inc.
Published by Prentice Hall

This special edition published in cooperation with Pearson Learning Solutions.

All trademarks, service marks, registered trademarks, and registered service marks are the property of their respective owners and are used herein for identification purposes only.

Pearson Learning Solutions, 501 Boylston Street, Suite 900, Boston, MA 02116
A Pearson Education Company
www.pearsoned.com

Printed in the United States of America

3 4 5 6 7 8 9 10 0BRV 17 16 15 14 13 12

0002000010271657481

ES/LP

ISBN 10: 1-256-73039-4
ISBN 13: 978-1-256-73039-2

JIM HALDERMAN brings a world of experience, knowledge, and talent to his work. His automotive service experience includes working as a flat-rate technician, a business owner, and a professor of automotive technology at a leading U.S. community college for more than 20 years.

He has a Bachelor of Science degree from Ohio Northern University and a Master's degree in Education from Miami University in Oxford, Ohio. Jim also holds a U.S. patent for an electronic transmission control device. He is an ASE-certified Master Automotive Technician and is also Advanced Engine Performance (L1) ASE certified. Jim is the author of many automotive textbooks, all published by Pearson Prentice Hall Publishing Company. Jim has presented numerous technical seminars to national audiences, including the California Automotive Teachers (CAT) and the Illinois College Automotive Instructor Association (ICAIA). He is also a member and presenter at the North American Council of Automotive Teachers (NACAT). Jim was also named Regional Teacher of the Year by General Motors Corporation and outstanding alumni of Ohio Northern University. Jim and his wife, Michelle, live in Dayton, Ohio. They have two children. You can reach Jim at

jim@jameshalderman.com

DARRELL DEETER has been an automotive machinist, an automotive technician, and a shop owner, and is currently a Professor of Automotive Technology at Saddleback College in Mission Viejo, California. Darrell has a Bachelor's degree from California State University, Long Beach, and a Master's in Vocational Education from the University of Alaska, Anchorage. Darrell is an ASE-certified Master Auto, Master Medium/Heavy Vehicle, M1-M3 Machinist, plus L1 and L2. Darrell has also presented technical seminars at the North American Council of Automotive Teachers (NACAT) and at the California Automotive Teachers (CAT) conferences. Darrell was named by CAT as the Outstanding College Instructor for 2009 and by NACAT as its MVP in 2010. When not working on cars, Darrell and his wife Beth can be found touring the continent on their motorcycle.

BRIEF CONTENTS

CONTENTS

chapter 14
VEHICLE LIFTING AND HOISTING   131

Taken from: *Automotive Technology: Principles, Diagnosis, and Service,* Fourth Edition by James D. Halderman

chapter 15
SCIENTIFIC PRINCIPLES AND MATERIALS   138

chapter 16
MATH, CHARTS, AND CALCULATIONS   149

Taken from: *Automotive Electricity and Electronics,* Third Edition by James D. Halderman

chapter 17
ELECTRICAL FUNDAMENTALS   155

chapter 24
AUDIO SYSTEM OPERATION AND DIAGNOSIS 213

Taken from: *Advanced Automotive Electricity and Electronics* by James D. Halderman

chapter 25
CIRCUIT TESTERS AND DIGITAL METERS 229

chapter 26
OSCILLOSCOPES AND GRAPHING MULTIMETERS 247

chapter 27
AUTOMOTIVE WIRING AND WIRE REPAIR 255

chapter 37
LIGHTING AND SIGNALING CIRCUITS 401

chapter 38
DRIVER INFORMATION AND NAVIGATION SYSTEMS 424

chapter 39
HORN, WIPER, AND BLOWER MOTOR CIRCUITS 449

chapter 1

AUTOMOTIVE BACKGROUND AND OVERVIEW

OBJECTIVES: After studying Chapter 1, the reader will be able to: • Explain the evolution of the automobile. • Discuss the major components of a vehicle. • Describe the evolution of engines. • List the common components of most vehicles. • List the eight areas of automotive service according to ASE/NATEF.

KEY TERMS: • Air filter 5 • Body 2 • Body-on-frame (BOF) 3 • Carbon monoxide (CO) 5 • Catalytic converter 5 • Chassis 2 • Coolant 5 • Drive shaft 6 • Double overhead camshaft (DOHC) 4 • Evaporative emission system (EVAP) 5 • Exhaust gas recirculation (EGR) 5 • Flathead 4 • Frames 3 • Hydrocarbon (HC) 5 • Ignition control module (ICM) 5 • Inline engine 4 • Intake manifold 5 • Internal combustion engine 4 • Malfunction indicator light (MIL) 6 • Manufacturer's suggested retail price (MSRP) 4 • OBD-II 6 • Oil filter 5 • Oil galleries 5 • Oil pan 5 • Oil pump 5 • Oil sump 5 • Overhead camshaft (OHC) 4 • Overhead valve (OHV) 4 • Oxides of nitrogen (NOX) 5 • PCV valve 5 • Pillars 3 • Positive crankcase ventilation (PCV) 5 • Propeller shaft 6 • Radiator 5 • Scan tool 6 • Self-propelled vehicle 1 • Single overhead camshaft (SOHC) 4 • Thermostat 5 • Transaxle 6 • Transfer case 6 • Unibody 3 • Universal joints (U-joints) 6 • Water jackets 5 • Water pump 5

HISTORICAL BACKGROUND

For centuries, man either walked or used animals to provide power for transportation. After the invention of electric, steam, and gasoline propulsion systems, people used **self-propelled vehicles**, which are vehicles that moved under their own power.

Major milestones in vehicle development include:

1876	The OTTO four-stroke cycle engine was developed by a German engineer, Nikolaus Otto.
1885	The first automobile was powered by an OTTO cycle gasoline engine designed by Karl Friedrick Beary (1844–1929).
1892	Rudolf Diesel (1858–1913) received a patent for a compression ignition engine. The first diesel engine was built in 1897.
1896	Henry Ford (1863–1947) built his first car, called the Quadricycle. ● **SEE FIGURE 1–1**.
1900	About 4,200 total automobiles were sold, including: • 40% were steam powered • 38% were battery/electric powered • 22% were gasoline engine powered
1902	Oldsmobile, founded by Ransom E. Olds (1864–1950), produced the first large-scale, affordable vehicle.
1908	William Durant (1861–1947) formed General Motors.
1908	The Ford Model T was introduced.
1912	The electric starter was invented by Charles F. Kettering (1876–1958) of Dayton, Ohio, first used on a Cadillac. The starter was produced by a new company called Delco, which stood for Dayton Engineering Laboratories Company.
1914	First car with a 100% steel body was made by the Budd Corporation for Dodge. Before 1914, all car bodies had wood components in them.
1922	The first vehicle to have four-wheel hydraulically operated brakes was a Duesenberg built in Indianapolis, Indiana.
1940	The first fully automatic transmission was introduced by Oldsmobile.
1973	Airbags were offered as an option on some General Motors vehicles.
1985	Lincoln offers the first four-wheel antilock braking system.
1997	The first vehicle with electronic stability control was offered by Cadillac.

FIGURE 1–1 A Ford Quadricycle built by Henry Ford.

FIGURE 1–2 Most vehicle bodies were constructed with a wood framework until the 1920s.

BODIES

Early motor vehicles evolved from horse-drawn carriages. The engine and powertrain were attached to a modified carriage leading to the term "horseless carriage".

The bodies evolved until in the 1930s, all-steel-enclosed bodies became the most used type. All bodies depended on a frame of wood or steel to support the chassis components. ● SEE FIGURE 1–2.

CHASSIS SYSTEMS OVERVIEW

The **chassis** system of the vehicle includes the following components:

1. Frame or **body** of the vehicle, which is used to provide the support for the suspension and steering components as well as the powertrain.

2. The suspension system of the vehicle, which provides a smooth ride to the driver and passengers and helps the tires remain on the road even when the vehicle is traveling over rough roads. The suspension system includes springs and control arms which allow the wheels to move up and down and keep the tires on the road.

3. The braking system of the vehicle is used to slow and stop the rotation of the wheels, which in turn stops the vehicle. The braking system includes the brake pedal, master cylinder, plus wheel brakes at each wheel. Two types of wheel brakes are used. Disc brakes include a caliper, which applies force to brake pads on both sides of a rotating disc or rotor. Drum brakes use brake shoes which are applied by hydraulic pressure outward against a rotating brake drum. The brake drum is attached to and stops the rotation of the wheels. Drum brakes are often used on the rear of most vehicles.

4. Wheels and tires—The wheels are attached to the bearing hubs on the axles. The tires must provide traction for accelerating, braking, and cornering, as well as provide a comfortable ride. Wheels are constructed of steel or aluminum alloy and mount to the hubs of the vehicle using lug nuts, which must be tightened correctly to the proper torque.

The chassis components include:

■ Front and rear suspension
■ Axles and hubs (to support the wheels and tires)
■ Steering mechanism
■ Engine and transmission
■ Final drive differential and axles

Often, these chassis were so complete that they could be driven without a body. ● FIGURE 1–3.

Many of the expensive automakers in the 1920s and 1930s had bodies built by another company. Eventually, most bodies were constructed of steel and many without the need for a frame to support the drivetrain and suspension.

FIGURE 1–3 A chassis of a 1950s era vehicle showing the engine, drivetrain, frame, and suspension.

FIGURE 1–4 Body and terms.

BODY TERMS The roof of a vehicle is supported by **pillars** and they are labeled A, B, C, and D from the front to the rear of the vehicle. All vehicles have an A pillar at the windshield but many, such as a hardtop, do not have a B pillar. Station wagons and sport utility vehicles (SUVs) often have a D pillar at the rear of the vehicle. ● **SEE FIGURE 1–4.**

FRAMES

Frame construction usually consists of channel-shaped steel beams welded and/or fastened together. Vehicles with a separate frame and body are usually called **body-on-frame** vehicles (**BOF**). Many terms are used to label or describe the frame of a vehicle, including:

UNIT-BODY CONSTRUCTION Unit-body construction (sometimes called **unibody**) is a design that combines the body with the structure of the frame. The body is composed of many individual stamped-steel panels welded together. The strength of this type of construction lies in the *shape* of the assembly. The typical vehicle uses 300 separate stamped-steel panels that are spot-welded together to form a vehicle's body. ● **SEE FIGURE 1–5.**

NOTE: A typical vehicle contains about 10,000 separate individual parts.

FIGURE 1–5 Note the ribbing and the many different pieces of sheet metal used in the construction of this body.

SPACE-FRAME CONSTRUCTION Space-frame construction consists of formed sheet steel used to construct a framework of the entire vehicle. The vehicle is drivable without the body, which uses plastic or steel panels to cover the steel framework. ● **SEE FIGURE 1–6.**

FIGURE 1–6 A Corvette without the body. Notice that the vehicle is complete enough to be driven. This photo was taken at the Corvette Museum in Bowling Green, Kentucky.

FIGURE 1–7 A Ford flathead V-8 engine. This engine design was used by Ford Motor Company from 1932 through 1953. In a flathead design, the valves located next to (beside) the cylinders.

TECH TIP

Treat a Vehicle Body with Respect

Do not sit on a vehicle. The metal can easily be distorted, which could cost hundreds of dollars to repair. This includes sitting on the hood, roof, and deck (trunk) lid, as well as fenders. Also, do not hang on any opened door as this can distort the hinge area causing the door not to close properly.

ENGINE DESIGN EVOLUTION

All gasoline and diesel engines are called **internal combustion engines** and were designed to compress an ignitable mixture. This mixture was ignited by using a spark (gasoline) or by heat of compression (diesel). Early engines used valves that were in the engine block, which also contained the round cylinders where pistons were fitted. The pistons are connected to a crankshaft, which converts the up and down motion of the pistons to a rotary force which is used to propel the vehicle.

INLINE VERSUS V-TYPE DESIGN Most early engines used four or six cylinders arranged inline. These were called **inline engines** and are still produced today. Some engines with 4, 6, 8, 10, 12, or 16 cylinders were arranged with half of the cylinders on each set of a "V" and connected to a common crankshaft in the bottom of the "V." The crankshaft changed the up-and-down motion of the piston to rotary motion, allowing the engine to power the drive wheels.

VALVE LOCATION DESIGN The design where the valves were located in the engine block is called **flathead** design because the cylinder head simply covered the combustion chamber and included a hole for the spark plug. The engine block contains passages for coolant as well as lubricating oil and is the support for all other engine systems. ● SEE FIGURE 1–7.

By the 1950s, most engine designs placed the valves in the cylinder head. This is called an **overhead valve or OHV** design.

Even newer engine designs feature **overhead camshafts (OHC)**, called **single overhead camshaft (SOHC)** designs and engines that use two overhead camshafts per bank of cylinders called **double overhead camshaft (DOHC)** designs. The placement of the camshaft, which results in better flow of intake air into and exhaust out of the engine.

FREQUENTLY ASKED QUESTION

What Is the Monroney Label?

The Monroney label is the sticker on the vehicle that lists the **manufacturer's suggested retail price**, usually abbreviated **MSRP**. The law that requires this label on all vehicles is called the Monroney Law, named for the congressman who sponsored the bill, Almer S. Monroney (1902–1980), a U.S. farm representative from Oklahoma from 1939–1951 and a U.S. Senator from 1951 to 1969.

Before the Monroney label law was passed in 1958, the price of a vehicle was unknown to new vehicle buyers who had to rely on the dealer for pricing. Besides all of the standard and optional equipment on the vehicle, the Monroney label also includes fuel economy and exhaust emission information.
● SEE FIGURE 1–8.

FIGURE 1–8 A Monroney label as shown on the side window of a new vehicle.

The need for reduced emissions and greater fuel economy led to advances in engine design. These changes included:

- Electronic ignition systems
- Electronic fuel injection
- Computerized engine controls
- Emission control devices, including the catalytic converter used in the exhaust system to reduce emissions
- Improved engine oils that help reduce friction and reduce emissions

ENGINE SYSTEMS OVERVIEW

Every engine requires many systems to function correctly.

COOLING SYSTEM While some older engines were air cooled, all engines currently in production are liquid cooled. Coolant is circulated by a **water pump** through passages in the cylinder block and head called **water jackets**. The **coolant** is a mixture of antifreeze and water to provide corrosion and freezing protection. After the coolant picks up the heat from the engine, it flows through a **radiator**, which cools the coolant by releasing the heat into the air. The temperature of the coolant is maintained by using a **thermostat** located in the coolant passage, which opens to allow coolant to flow to the radiator or closes until the coolant is hot enough to need cooling.

LUBRICATION SYSTEM All engines need a supply of lubricating oil to reduce friction and help to cool the engine. Most engines are equipped with an **oil pan**, also called an **oil sump**, containing 3 to 7 quarts (liters) of oil. An engine driven **oil pump** forces the oil under pressure through an **oil filter**, then to passages in the block and head called **oil galleries**, and then to all of the moving parts.

AIR INTAKE SYSTEM All engines, both gasoline and diesel engines, draw air from the atmosphere. It requires about 9,000 gallons of air for each gallon of gasoline used. The air must be drawn where deep water in the road cannot be drawn into the engine. The air is then filtered by a replaceable **air filter**. After the air is filtered, it passes through a throttle valve and then into the engine through an **intake manifold**.

FUEL SYSTEM The fuel system includes the following components and systems:

- Fuel tank
- Fuel lines and filter(s)
- Fuel injectors
- Electronic control of the fuel pump and fuel injection

The fuel injectors are designed to atomize the liquid gasoline into small droplets so they can be mixed with the air entering the engine. This mixture of fuel and air is then ignited by the spark plug.

STARTING AND CHARGING SYSTEM Engine starting and charging systems, which include the battery, starting (cranking) system and charging system components and circuits.

IGNITION SYSTEM The ignition system includes the ignition coil(s), which creates a high voltage spark by stepping up battery voltage using an **ignition control module (ICM)**. The arc across the electrodes of the spark plug ignites the air-fuel mixture in the combustion chamber and the resulting pressure pushes the piston down on the power stroke.

EMISSION CONTROL SYSTEM The control of vehicle emissions includes controlling gasoline vapors from being released into the atmosphere in addition to reducing the emissions from the exhaust. Unburned gasoline emissions are called **hydrocarbon (HC)** emissions and exhaust gases that are controlled include **carbon monoxide (CO)** and **oxides of nitrogen (NOX)**. The **evaporative emission control system**, usually called the **EVAP system**, is designed to prevent gasoline fumes and vapors from being released. Other emission control systems include:

- **Positive crankcase ventilation (PCV)**. This system uses a valve called a **PCV valve** to regulate the flow of gases created in the crankcase of a running engine, which are routed back into the intake manifold. The engine will then draw these gases into the combustion chamber where they are burned to help prevent the release of the gases into the atmosphere.
- **Exhaust gas recirculation (EGR)**. The EGR system meters about 3% to 7% of the exhaust gases back into the intake where the gases reduce the peak combustion temperature and prevent the oxygen (O2) and nitrogen (NO) from the air from combining to form oxides of nitrogen.
- **Catalytic converter**. The catalytic converter is a unit located in the exhaust system usually close to the engine, which causes chemical changes in the exhaust gases.

- On-board diagnostics means that the engine as well as the engine management systems can test itself for proper operation and alert the driver if a fault is detected. The warning lamp is called the **malfunction indicator light (MIL)** and is labeled "Check Engine" or "Service Engine Soon." The on-board diagnostic system is currently in the second generation and is called **OBD-II**. Electronic hand-held testers, called **scan tools**, are needed to access (retrieve) stored diagnostic trouble codes (DTCs) and view sensor and system data.

POWERTRAIN OVERVIEW

The purpose of the powertrain is to transfer the torque output of the engine to the drive wheels.

REAR-WHEEL-DRIVE POWERTRAIN
A rear-wheel-drive vehicle uses the following components to transfer engine torque to the rear drive wheels:

- Transmission. An automatic transmission usually uses planetary gear sets and electronic controls to change gear ratios. In a manually shifted transmission, the drivetrain contains a clutch assembly, which allows the driver to disengage engine torque from the transmission to allow the driver to shift from one gear ratio to another. The transmission contains gears and other assemblies that provide high torque output at low speeds for acceleration and lower torque output but at higher speeds for maximum fuel economy at highway speeds.
- Drive Shaft. A **drive shaft**, also called a **propeller shaft**, is used to connect and transmit engine torque from the transmission to the rear differential. **Universal joints (U-joints)** are used to allow the rear differential to move up and down on the rear suspension and still be able to transmit engine torque.
- Differential. A differential is used at the rear of the vehicle and performs three functions:
  - Allows different axle speeds for cornering.
  - The differential increases the torque applied to the rear drive wheels by reducing the speed.
  - The differential also changes the direction of the applied engine torque and uses axle shafts to transfer the torque to the drive wheels.

FRONT-WHEEL-DRIVE POWERTRAIN
A front-wheel-drive vehicle uses a **transaxle**, which is a combination of a transmission and differential in one assembly. Drive axle shafts then transfer the engine torque to the front drive wheels from the output of the transaxle.

FOUR-WHEEL-DRIVE SYSTEM
There are many types of methods of powering all four wheels. Many include a

FIGURE 1–9 A dash control panel used by the driver to control the four-wheel-drive system.

transfer case to split engine torque to both the front and the rear wheels. ● **SEE FIGURE 1–9.**

ELECTRICAL/ELECTRONIC SYSTEMS OVERVIEW

Early vehicles did not have an electrical system because even the ignition did not require a battery. Early engines used a magneto to create a spark instead of using electrical power from a battery as used today.

The first electrical components on vehicles were battery-powered lights, not only for the driver to see the road, but also so others could see an approaching vehicle at night.

Only after 1912 and the invention of the self-starter did the use of a battery become commonplace. Charles F. Kettering also invented the point-type ignition system about the same time as the self-starter. Therefore, the early batteries were often referred to as SLI batteries meaning starting, lighting, and ignition. From the 1920s into the 1950s other electrical components were added, such as radios, defroster fans, and horns. It was not until the 1960s that electrical accessories, such as air conditioning, power seats, and power windows, became common.

Today's vehicles require alternators that are capable of producing a higher amount of electricity than was needed in the past, and the number of electronic components has grown to include every system in the vehicle, including:

- A tire pressure monitoring system for the tires
- Heated and cooled seats
- Automatic climate control
- Power windows
- Security systems
- Electric power steering
- Electronic suspension

● **SEE FIGURE 1–10.**

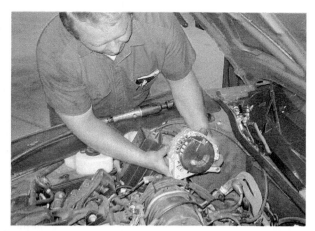

FIGURE 1–10 The alternator is in the heart of the electrical system.

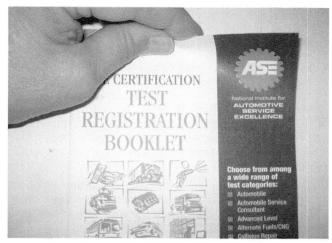

FIGURE 1–11 Test registration booklet that includes details on all vehicle-related certification tests given by ASE.

HEATING, VENTILATION, AND AIR CONDITIONING OVERVIEW

Early model vehicles did not include any heaters or other methods to provide comfort for the driver and passengers. Most early vehicles were open with a simple removable top. Some had optional side curtains that provided all-weather protection. In the 1930s and 1940s when fully enclosed bodies became common, the vehicle manufacturers started to include heaters, which were small radiators with engine coolant flowing through them. About the same time and into the 1950s, about the only options that many vehicles had were a radio and heater, abbreviated R & H.

Today, air conditioning systems are on most vehicles and incorporate defrosters and passenger compartment heating, often in two zones for maximum comfort of the driver and passenger. Additional related comfort options today include heated and cooled seats and heated steering wheels.

EIGHT AREAS OF AUTOMOTIVE SERVICE

In 1972, the National Institute for Automotive Service Excellence, a non-profit organization known as simply ASE, created a series of eight tests that cover the major vehicle systems. ● **SEE FIGURE 1–11.**

ENGINE REPAIR (A1) This content area includes questions related to engine block and cylinder head diagnosis and service, as well as the lubrication, cooling, fuel, ignition, and exhaust systems inspection and service.

AUTOMATIC TRANSMISSION (A2) This content area includes general automatic transmission/transaxle diagnosis, including hydraulic and electronic related systems.

MANUAL DRIVE TRAIN AND AXLES (A3) This content area includes clutch diagnosis and repair, manual transmission diagnosis and repair, as well as drive shaft, universal, and constant velocity joint diagnosis and service. Also included in this content area are rear differential diagnosis and repair plus four-wheel-drive component diagnosis and repair.

SUSPENSION AND STEERING (A4) This content area includes steering and suspension system diagnosis and repair, including wheel alignment diagnosis and adjustments plus wheel and tire diagnosis and repair procedures.

BRAKES (A5) The brake content area includes the diagnosis and repair of the hydraulic system, drum and disc brake systems, plus power assist units, antilock braking, and traction control systems.

ELECTRICAL/ELECTRONIC SYSTEMS (A6) This content area includes many systems, including the battery, starting, charging, lighting, gauges, and accessory circuit diagnosis and repair.

HEATING AND AIR CONDITIONING (A7) The heating and air conditioning content area includes air conditioning service, refrigeration systems, heating and engine cooling systems diagnosis and repair, as well as refrigerant recovery, recycling, handling, and retrofit.

ENGINE PERFORMANCE (A8) The engine performance content area includes diagnosis and testing of those systems responsible for the proper running and operation of the engine. Included in this area are general engine diagnosis, ignition and fuel systems, as well as emission control and computerized engine control diagnosis and repair.

This textbook covers the content of all eight ASE areas plus all of the background and fundamental information needed by technicians.

SUMMARY

1. Major automobile milestones include: the OTTO cycle engine (1876), the first diesel engine (1892), Henry Ford's first car (1896), Oldsmobile's large-scale production (1902), the first Model T Ford (1908), the first car with four-wheel hydraulic brakes (1922), the first automatic transmission (1940), the first vehicle to use a four-wheel antilock braking system (1985), and the first vehicle with electronic stability control (1997).

2. The chassis of the vehicle consists of a frame or body, which has attached to it the front and rear suspension, the brake system, the engine and transmission, as well as the steering system.

3. A vehicle frame is the main structural support for the body.

4. Engine design has changed from inline flathead 4-, 6-, and 8-cylinder engines to new double-overhead camshaft designs, which are computer controlled.

5. The engine consists of the following systems: air intake, cooling, lubrication, fuel, ignition, and emission control.

6. Major advances have also been made to electrical systems and controls from no electrical circuits in the early days of self-propelled vehicles to computer-controlled accessory and climate control systems today.

7. The eight areas of automotive service include: engine repair (A1), automatic transmission/transaxle (A2), manual transmission/transaxle (A3), suspension and steering (A4), brakes (A5), electrical and electronic systems (A6), heating and air conditioning (A7), and engine performance (A8).

REVIEW QUESTIONS

1. In 1900, what was the most produced vehicle powered by?

2. What parts are included in the vehicle chassis?

3. Why were early engines called flat heads?

4. What is the difference between a unit-body and body-on-frame vehicle?

5. The powertrain consists of what components?

6. What are the eight ASE automotive service content areas?

CHAPTER QUIZ

1. The first self-propelled vehicle that used an OTTO cycle four-stroke gasoline engine was produced in _____.
   - **a.** 1885
   - **b.** 1900
   - **c.** 1902
   - **d.** 1908

2. Early vehicles were constructed mostly of what material?
   - **a.** Steel
   - **b.** Cast iron
   - **c.** Wood
   - **d.** Tin

3. Which component is *not* part of the chassis system?
   - **a.** Frame
   - **b.** Electrical system
   - **c.** Suspension
   - **d.** Brakes

4. Early engines were called flat head design because they_____.
   - **a.** Were only inline engines
   - **b.** Did not include valves
   - **c.** Used valves beside the cylinder
   - **d.** Used spark plugs at the top of the cylinders

5. A V-type engine could have how many cylinders?
   - **a.** 4
   - **b.** 6
   - **c.** 8
   - **d.** All of the above

6. What component regulates the temperature of the coolant in an engine?
   - **a.** Cooling (water) jackets
   - **b.** Thermostat
   - **c.** Cooling fan(s)
   - **d.** Radiator

7. A malfunction indicator light (MIL) on the dash may be labeled _____.
   - **a.** Check engine
   - **b.** Service vehicle soon
   - **c.** MIL
   - **d.** MAL

8. To retrieve stored diagnostic trouble codes, a service technician needs a _____.
   - **a.** Paper clip
   - **b.** Desktop computer
   - **c.** Wireless connection to an electronic tester
   - **d.** Scan tool

9. A four-wheel drive vehicle often uses a _____ to transmit torque to all four wheels.
   - **a.** Drive shaft
   - **b.** U-joint
   - **c.** Transaxle
   - **d.** Transfer case

10. Automotive service systems are generally separated into how many content areas?
   - **a.** 4
   - **b.** 6
   - **c.** 8
   - **d.** 10

chapter 2

CAREERS IN THE AUTOMOTIVE SERVICE INDUSTRY

OBJECTIVES: After studying Chapter 2, the reader will be able to: • Describe automotive service-related positions. • Discuss the level of training and experience needed for each position. • Describe the technical skills needed for each position. • Explain the relationship of the service manager to others in a shop and company. • Prepare and complete a work order. • Discuss vehicle warranty policies.

KEY TERMS: • Entrepreneur 16 • On-the-job training (OJT) 11 • Parts counter person 15 • Service advisor 13 • Service consultant 13 • Service manager 14 • Service writer 13 • Shop foreman 13 • Team leader 13 • Technician (tech) 9 • Vehicle Identification Number (VIN) 12 • Work order 12

THE NEED FOR AUTOMOTIVE TECHNICIANS

The need for trained and skilled automotive **technicians** is greater than ever for several reasons, including:

- Vehicles are becoming more complex and require a higher level of knowledge and skills.
- Electrical and electronic components and sensors are included throughout the vehicle.
- Construction of parts and materials being used has changed over the last few years, meaning that all service work must be done to specified procedures to help avoid damage being done to the vehicle.
- Increasing numbers of different types of lubricants and coolants make even routine service challenging.

All of the above issues require proper training and the ability to follow factory specified procedures to ensure customer satisfaction. The number of service technicians needed is increasing due to more vehicles on the road. A good service technician can find work in almost any city or town in the country, making the career as a professional service technician an excellent choice.

THE NEED FOR CONTINUOUS VEHICLE SERVICE

Vehicles are lasting longer due to improved materials and more exacting tolerances. Every year, vehicles are being driven farther than ever before. It used to be (in the 1950s) that the life

of a vehicle was considered to be 100,000 miles or 10 years. Now achieving 200,000 miles without a major repair is common with proper maintenance and routine service. However, even the amount of needed routine service has been reduced due to changes in the vehicles, such as radial tires that now last 40,000 miles instead of older tires which were worn out and needed to be replaced every 15,000 miles.

WARRANTIES A warranty is a guarantee to the purchaser of a vehicle that it will function as specified. The warranty covers the quality and performance of the product and states the conditions under which the warranty will be honored. Vehicle warranties vary but all warranties indicate a time and mileage restriction. The expressed warranties often include the following areas:

- New vehicle limited warranty that covers most components and is commonly called a bumper-to-bumper policy.
- Powertrain warranty covers the engine, transmission/transaxle, and final drive units. This coverage usually is longer than the bumper-to-bumper coverage.
- Sheet metal rust through warranty is usually longer than the bumper-to-bumper and powertrain warranty and covers rust if a hole occurs starting from inside the outer metal surface of the body.
- Emission control device warranties depend on the emission rating, the warranty coverage of the powertrain control module (PCM), and the catalytic converter and are covered for 8 years and 80,000 miles up to 10 years and 150,000 miles.

Vehicle warranties, unless an emergency repair, must be performed at a dealership, which is certified by the vehicle manufacturer to perform the repairs. At the dealership, the technician performing the repair must also be certified by the vehicle manufacturer.

All technicians should be familiar with what may be covered by the factory warranties to help ensure that the customer does not have to pay for a repair that may be covered. While warranties do cover many components of the vehicle, wear and service items are not covered by a warranty in most cases and therefore, offer excellent opportunity for additional service work for trained automotive technicians.

INCREASING AGE OF A VEHICLE The average age of a vehicle on the road today has increased to older than nine years. This trend means that more vehicles than ever are not covered by a factory warranty and are often in need of repair. Aftermarket warranties also can be used at most repair facilities, making it very convenient for vehicle owners.

TECHNICIAN WORK SITES

Service technician work takes place in a variety of work sites, including:

NEW VEHICLE DEALERSHIPS Most dealerships handle one or more brands of vehicle, and the technician employed at dealerships usually has to meet minimum training standards. The training is usually provided at no cost online or at regional training centers. The dealer usually pays the service technician for the day(s) spent in training as well as provides or pays for transportation, meals, and lodging. Most dealerships offer in house on-line training with minimum off-site training. ● **SEE FIGURE 2–1.**

INDEPENDENT SERVICE FACILITIES These small-to medium-size repair facilities usually work on a variety of vehicles. Technicians employed at independent service facilities usually have to depend on aftermarket manufacturers' seminars or the local vocational school or college to keep technically up-to-date. ● **SEE FIGURE 2–2.**

FIGURE 2–1 A service technician checking for a noise of a vehicle in a new-vehicle dealership service department.

FIGURE 2–2 A typical independent service facility. Independent garages often work on a variety of vehicles and perform many different types of vehicle repairs and service. Some independent garages specialize in just one or two areas of service work or in just one or two makes of vehicles.

FIGURE 2–3 This NAPA parts store also performs service work from the garage area on the side of the building.

MASS MERCHANDISER Large national chains of vehicle repair facilities are common in most medium- and large-size cities. Some examples of these chains include Sears, Goodyear, Firestone, and NAPA, as shown in the figure. ● **SEE FIGURE 2–3.** Technicians employed by these chains usually work on a wide variety of vehicles. Many of the companies have their own local or regional training sites designed to train beginning service technicians and to provide update training for existing technicians.

SPECIALTY SERVICE FACILITIES Specialty service facilities usually limit their service work to selected systems or components of the vehicle and/or to a particular brand of vehicle. Examples of specialty service facilities include Midas, Speedy, and AAMCO Transmissions. Many of the franchised specialty facilities have their own technician training for both beginning and advanced technicians. ● **SEE FIGURE 2–4.**

FLEET FACILITIES Many city, county, and state governments have their own vehicle service facilities for the maintenance and repair of their vehicles. Service technicians are usually employees of the city, county, or state and are usually paid by the hour rather than on a commission basis. ● **SEE FIGURE 2–5.**

FIGURE 2–4 Midas is considered to be a specialty service shop.

TECHNICIAN JOB CLASSIFICATIONS

There are many positions and jobs in the vehicle service industry. In smaller service facilities (shops), the duties of many positions may be combined in one job. A large city dealership may have all of the following vehicle service positions. A technician is often referred to as a tech.

LUBE TECH/QUICK SERVICE TECHNICIAN A lubrication technician should be trained in the proper use of hand tools and instructed how to properly service various types of vehicles. The training could be **on-the-job (OTJ)** or could be the result of high school or college automotive training. Some larger companies provide in-house training for new technicians and as a result they are trained to perform according to a specified standard. It is important that the lubrication technician double-check the work to be certain that the correct viscosity oil has been installed and to the specified level. The oil plug and oil filter must also be checked for leakage.

Lubrication technicians are trained to perform routine services, including:

- Oil and oil filter change
- Chassis lubrication
- Fluids check and refill
- Tire inflation checks
- Accessory drive belt inspection
- Air filter check and replacement
- Cabin filter replacement
- Windshield wiper blade replacement

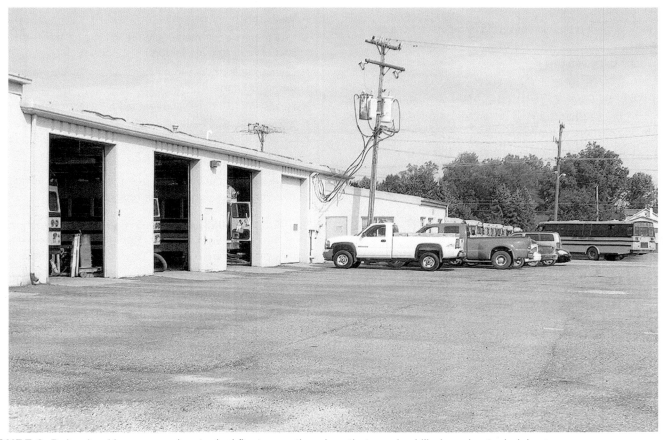

FIGURE 2–5 A school bus garage is a typical fleet operation shop that needs skilled service technicians.

As a result of these tasks the lubrication technician should be skilled in hoisting the vehicle and able to handle the tasks efficiently and in minimum time.

NEW VEHICLE PREPARATION FOR DELIVERY An entry-level position at a dealership often includes preparing new vehicles for delivery to the customer. This is often referred to as "new car prep." The duties performed for new vehicle preparation are generally learned on the job. The vehicle manufacturer publishes guidelines that should be followed and it is the responsibility of the new vehicle preparation person to see that all items are checked and serviced, and all associated paperwork is completed. The activities normally associated with preparing a new vehicle for delivery include:

- Installing wheel center caps or wheel covers (if used)
- Installing roof racks, running boards, and other dealer-installed options
- Checking and correcting tire pressures

  NOTE: Many vehicle manufacturers ship the vehicles to the dealer with the tires overinflated to help prevent movement of the vehicle during shipping.

- Checking all fluids
- Checking that everything works, including the remote key fob and all accessories
- Ordering any parts found to be broken, missing, and damaged in transit
- Removing all protective covering and plastic from the seats, carpet, and steering wheel
- Washing the vehicle

GENERAL SERVICE TECHNICIAN A general service technician usually has training as an automotive technician either in one or more of the following:

- High school—Technical or vocational school or a comprehensive high school that has an Automotive Youth Education System (AYES) program or NATEF certification.
- College or technical school—Usually a two-year program that can earn the student an associate's degree.
- Career college or institute—Usually a 6-month to 12-month program earning the graduate a certificate.

Automotive service technicians perform preventative maintenance, diagnose faults, and repair automotive vehicles and light trucks.

Automotive service technicians adjust, test, and repair engines, steering systems, braking systems, drivetrains, vehicle suspensions, electrical systems and air conditioning systems, and perform wheel alignments. In large shops, some technicians specialize in repairing, rebuilding, and servicing specific parts, such as braking systems, suspension, and steering systems. In smaller shops, automotive service technicians may work on a wider variety of repair jobs.

Automotive service technicians begin by reading the work order and examining the vehicle. To locate the cause of faulty operation and repair it, a technician will:

- Verify customer concern
- Use testing equipment, take the vehicle for a test-drive, and/or refer to manufacturer's specifications and manuals
- Dismantle faulty assemblies, repair, or replace worn or damaged parts
- Reassemble, adjust, and test the repaired mechanism

Automotive service technicians also may:

- Perform scheduled maintenance services, such as oil changes, lubrications, and filter replacement
- Advise customers on work performed, general vehicle conditions, and future repair requirements

WORKING CONDITIONS. Most automotive service technicians work a 40-hour, five-day week. Some evening, weekend, or holiday work may be required. The work is sometimes noisy and dirty. There is some risk of injury involved in working with power tools and near exhaust gases.

SKILLS AND ABILITIES. The work is most rewarding for those who enjoy doing precise work that is varied and challenging. Also, technicians usually achieve job security and a feeling of independence.

To be successful in the trade, automotive service technicians need:

- Good hearing, eyesight, and manual dexterity (ability to work with hands)
- Mechanical aptitude and interest

- The ability to lift between 25 and 50 pounds (11 and 25 kilograms)
- The willingness to keep up-to-date with changing technology

A working knowledge of electricity, electronics, and computers is also required for many service procedures.

EMPLOYMENT AND ADVANCEMENT. Automotive service technicians are employed by automotive repair shops, specialty repair shops, service facilities, car and truck dealerships, and by large organizations that own fleets of vehicles.

Experienced automotive service technicians may advance to service manager or shop foreman. Some automotive service technicians open their own repair facilities.

Many technicians can also start work in a shop or dealership and learn on the job. Most technicians keep up-to-date by attending update seminars or training classes on specific topics throughout the year.

Specific tasks performed by a general service technician can include the following:

- All of the tasks performed by the lubrication technician.
- Engine repairs, including intake manifold gasket replacement; cylinder head replacement; and oil and water pump replacement plus other engine-related tasks.
- Brake system service and repair, including disc brakes; drum brakes; parking brake; and antilock brake (ABS) diagnosis and service.
- Suspension-related service, including tire inspection and replacement; shock and strut replacement; servicing or replacing wheel bearings; performing steering component inspection and parts replacement; and performing wheel alignment and vibration diagnosis.
- Electrical-related diagnosis and repair, including starting and charging problems; correcting lighting and accessory faults; and general service such as light bulb replacement and key fob reprogramming.
- Heating, ventilation, and air conditioning work usually involves the use of diagnostic and service equipment that requires special training and certification if working with refrigerants.
- Engine performance-related diagnosis and repair, including replacing fuel pumps and filters; cleaning or replacing fuel injectors; service ignition system components; solving emissions-related failures; and determining the cause and correcting "Check Engine" lights.
- Manual transmission service and repairs, including replacing clutches; adjusting, or replacing clutch linkage; servicing differentials and performing four-wheel drive diagnosis and service procedures.
- Automatic transmission service and repairs, including performing routine automatic transmission service; removing and replacing automatic transmissions; transmissions/transaxles and performing diagnosis and service checks, including fluid pressure and scan tool diagnosis.

The vehicle is then driven by the service technician to verify the repair.

TECHNICIAN TEAM LEADER A **team leader** is an experienced service technician who is capable of performing most if not all of the work that the shop normally handles. The team leader then assigns work to others in the group based on the experience or competency of the technician. The team leader then checks the work after it has been completed to be sure that it has been correctly performed. The number of hours of labor for each member of the team is totaled each pay period. Each member of the team is paid an equal share of the time but at different rates. The team leader gets a higher per hour rate than the others on the team. The rate of pay per hour is based on the level of training and experience. A beginning technician may or may not be paid as part of the total team hours depending on how the team system is organized. While some shops do not use teams, many large shops or dealerships have two or more teams. The advantage of a team-type organization is that everyone on the team looks out and helps each other if needed because they are all paid based on the number of hours the team generates. The team leader performs the duties of a shop foreman but only for those members on the team and not the entire shop. The team leader is under the direction and control of the service manager.

SHOP FOREMAN A **shop foreman** (usually employed in larger dealerships and vehicle repair facilities) is an experienced service technician who is usually paid a salary (so much a week, month, or year). A shop foreman is a knowledgeable and experienced service technician who keeps up-to-date with the latest vehicle systems, tools, and equipment. Typical shop foreman's duties include:

- Test-driving the customer's vehicle to verify the customer concern (complaint)
- Assigning work to the service technicians
- Assisting the service technicians
- Helps maintain the shop and shop equipment
- Assisting the service manager
- Verifying that the repair is completed satisfactorily

The shop foreman is under the direction and control of the service manager.

SERVICE ADVISOR A **service advisor**, also called a **service writer** or **service consultant**, is the person at the dealership or shop designated to communicate the needs of the customer and accurately complete a work order.

A service advisor should:

- Have a professional appearance
- Be able to speak clearly
- Be able to listen carefully to the customer
- Write neatly and/or type accurately
- Be familiar with industry and shop standards and procedures

Most service advisors would benefit from taking a short course on service advising skill development and

Work Order (Figure 2–6)

HOME TOWN CHEVROLET
100 N. MAIN ST.

8993

Customer's Description of Problem/Repair:

This accurately describes the problem or symptom I am experiencing with my motor vehicle. Customer's Initials _____

COST	QUAN.	PART NUMBER / DESCRIPTION	PRICE	
	1	Battery Interstate 60 Month Battery	74	00
	1	Oil filter	11	25
	1	Air filter	36	59
	1	Seal Ring		25
	1	Ant Mast	67	97
			190	06

SUBLET REPAIRS

ALL PARTS ARE NEW UNLESS SPECIFIED OTHERWISE.

NAME	MR CUSTOMER	DATE RECEIVED	9/18/11
ADDRESS	444 W. 3rd St.	COMPLETION DATE	
CITY	STATE	ZIP	MILEAGE IN	52084
VIN	1G2NW51AA6S6201	ENGINE NO. 3.1 V–6	MAKE CHEVY	MILEAGE OUT
TYPE OR MODEL COBALT	YEAR 06	LICENSE NUMBER BQU449	PHONE WHEN READY YES ☐ NO ☐	
TERMS	ORDER ACCEPTED BY		PHONE	

			TECH ID # / INIT.	LABOR CHARGE
LUBRICATE	☐			
CHANGE OIL	☐			
CHANGE OIL FILTER CART.	☐			
CHANGE TRANS. OIL	☐			
CHANGE DIFF. OIL	☐			
PACK FRONT WHEEL BRGS.	☐			
ADJUST BRAKES	☐			
X TIRES	☐			
WASH	☐			
SAFETY INSPECTION	☐			

OPER. NO.	INSTRUCTIONS:		
1.0	45 K Service	450	00
.6	Check Battery Replace	22	50
.5	Ant Mast	22	50
.5	Check left front Headlight	22	50

This Facility charges _____ % of the Total _____ Charges, up to a Maximum of $ _____ , for Shop Materials.

WE WILL OFFER TO RETURN TO YOU ALL REPLACED PARTS, AS REQUIRED BY LAW, UNLESS THEY ARE TO BE REBUILT, SOLD, OR RETURNED TO THE MANUFACTURER.

I hereby authorize the repair work herein set forth to be done by you, together with the furnishing by you of the necessary parts and other material for such repair, and agree: that you are not responsible for any delays caused by unavailability or delayed availability of parts or material for any reason; that you neither assume nor authorize any other person to assume for you any liability in connection with such repair; that you shall not be responsible for loss of or damage to the above vehicle, or articles left therein, in case of fire, theft or other cause beyond your control; that an express mechanic's lien is hereby acknowledged on the above vehicle to secure the amount of repairs thereto; that your employees may operate the above vehicle on streets, highways or elsewhere for the purpose of testing and/or inspecting such vehicle.
I HEREBY ACKNOWLEDGE RECEIPT OF A COPY HEREOF.

X _____

ESTIMATE
(UNDER OHIO LAW) YOU HAVE THE RIGHT TO AN ESTIMATE IF THE EXPECTED COST OF REPAIRS OR SERVICES WILL BE MORE THAN TWENTY-FIVE DOLLARS. INITIAL YOUR CHOICE.
WRITTEN _____ ESTIMATE ORAL _____ ESTIMATE I DO NOT REQUEST _____ AN ESTIMATE

WARRANTY STATEMENT AND DISCLAIMER: THE DEALER HEREBY DISCLAIMS ALL WARRANTIES EXPRESS OR IMPLIED, INCLUDING ANY IMPLIED WARRANTIES OF MERCHANTABILITY OR FITNESS FOR A PARTICULAR PURPOSE, AND NEITHER ASSUMES NOR AUTHORIZES ANY OTHER PERSON TO ASSUME FOR IT ANY LIABILITY IN CONNECTION WITH THE SALE OF SAID PARTS OR THIS REPAIR. THIS DISCLAIMER IN NO WAY AFFECTS THE PROVISIONS OF ANY MANUFACTURER OR OTHER SUPPLIER WARRANTIES. IF DEALER PROVIDES A WRITTEN WARRANTY, ANY IMPLIED WARRANTIES ARE EXPRESSLY LIMITED TO THE TERM OF THE WRITTEN WARRANTY.

ORIGINAL ESTIMATE $ _____
AUTHORIZED ADDITIONS
$ _____

CUSTOMERS ACCEPTANCE
INITIAL HERE _____
DATE _____
TIME _____
BY _____

In the event that you, the customer, authorize commencement but do not authorize completion of a repair or service, a charge will be imposed for disassembly, reassembly or partially completed work. Such charge will be directly related to the actual amount of labor or parts involved in the inspection, repair or service.

	SALE	
TOTAL LABOR	517	50
TOTAL PARTS	190	06
GAS, OIL & GREASE	18	75
SUBLET REPAIRS		
	726	31
TAX 6.5%	47	21
TOTAL	773	52

FIGURE 2–6 Typical work order. *(Courtesy of Reynolds and Reynolds Company)*

---

interpersonal relationship building. A service advisor should be familiar with the operation of the vehicle, but not to the same level as a service technician. A service advisor should not diagnose the problem, but rather state clearly on the work order what, when, and where the problem occurs so that the service technician has all the needed information to make an accurate diagnosis. ● **SEE FIGURE 2–6** for an example of a typical work order.

The service advisor's duties include:

1. Recording the vehicle identification number (VIN) of the vehicle on the work order
2. Recording the make, model, year, and mileage on the work order
3. Carefully recording what the customer's complaint (concern) is so that the service technician can verify the complaint and make the proper repair
4. Reviewing the customer's vehicle history file and identifying additional required service
5. Keeping the customer informed as to the progress of the service work

A service advisor must be at the shop early in the morning to greet the customers and often needs to stay after the shop closes for business to be available when the customer returns at the end of the day.

SERVICE MANAGER The **service manager** rarely works on a vehicle but instead organizes the service facility and keeps it operating smoothly. A service manager can be a former service technician or in many larger dealerships, a business major graduate who is skilled at organization and record keeping. The service manager typically handles all of the paperwork associated with operating a service department.

NOTE: In a small shop, the shop owner usually performs all of the duties of a shop foreman and service manager, as well as the lead technician in many cases.

Typical duties of a service manager include:

- Establishing guidelines to determine the technicians' efficiency
- Supervising any warranty claims submitted to the vehicle manufacturer or independent insurer
- Evaluating and budgeting for shop tools and equipment
- Establishing service department hours of operation and employee schedules

TECH TIP

Check the Vehicle before Work Is Started

As part of the work order writing process, the service advisor should look over the vehicle and make a written note of any body damage that may already exist. If any damage is noted it should be mentioned to the customer and noted on the work order. Often the customer is not aware of any damage especially on the passenger side and thus would blame the shop for the damage after the service work was performed.

■ Assigning working hours and pay for technicians and others in the service department

■ Establishing procedures and policies to keep the service area clean and properly maintained

PARTS-RELATED POSITIONS

The parts manager at the service facility or other parts personnel such as the **parts counter person** are responsible for getting the correct part for the service technician.

PARTS COUNTER PERSON A parts counter person often learns job skills by on-the-job training. A good parts counter person must be able to greet and easily talk to customers and technicians. A parts counter person must also have computer skills and the willingness to help others.

The parts counter person usually has the following duties:

■ Greet the customer or technician

■ Locate the correct parts for the service technician or customer

■ Suggest related parts (retail customers)

■ Stock shelves

■ Check in delivered parts

■ Take inventory

■ Keep the parts department clean

■ Help the parts manager

● **SEE FIGURE 2–7.**

PARTS MANAGER The specific duties of a parts manager usually include:

■ Ordering parts from the vehicle manufacturers and aftermarket companies

■ Stocking parts

■ Organizing the parts department in a clear and orderly fashion

FIGURE 2–7 Parts counter people need to know many aspects of automotive repair to be effective with customers.

■ Locating parts quickly within the parts department

■ Developing contacts with parts departments in other local dealerships so that parts that are not in stock can be purchased quickly and at a reasonable cost

SALES JOBS—USED VEHICLES; NEW VEHICLES

SALESPERSON When a vehicle is sold, it generates a potential customer for the service department. New and many used vehicle sales dealerships employ salespeople to help the customer select and purchase a vehicle. The salesperson should have excellent interpersonal skills, as well as be familiar with the local and regional laws and taxes to be able to complete all of the paperwork associated with the sale of a vehicle. The usual duties of a vehicle salesperson include:

■ Greet the customer

■ Introduce yourself and welcome the customer to the store

■ Qualify the customer as to the ability to purchase a vehicle

■ Demonstrate and ride with the customer on a test-drive

■ Be able to find the answer to any question the customer may ask about the vehicle and/or financing

■ Be able to complete the necessary paperwork

■ Follow up the sale with a telephone call or card

SALES MANAGER A sales manager is an experienced salesperson who is able to organize and manage several individual salespeople. The duties of a sales manager include:

■ Establish a schedule where salespeople will be available during all hours of operation

- Consult with salespeople as needed on individual sales
- Train new salespeople
- Conduct sales promotion activities
- Attend or assign someone to attend vehicle auctions to sell and/or purchase vehicles
- Keep up-to-date with the automotive market
- Purchase vehicles that sell well in the local market
- Answer to the general manager or dealership principal

OTHER CAREERS IN THE AUTOMOTIVE INDUSTRY

Other careers in the automotive industry include:

- Sales representative for automotive tools and equipment
- Technical trainers
- Technical school instructors
- Wholesale parts warehouse management
- Insurance adjuster
- Automotive technical writer
- Warranty claim examiner

TYPICAL AUTOMOTIVE ORGANIZATION ARRANGEMENT

LARGE COMPREHENSIVE NEW VEHICLE DEALER A typical dealership includes many levels because there are many departments such as sales (new and used) as well

? FREQUENTLY ASKED QUESTION

What Is an Entrepreneur?

An **entrepreneur** is a person who starts and operates a business. Many service technicians want to eventually own their own shop and become an entrepreneur. However, operating a shop involves many duties and responsibilities that many service technicians lack, including:

- Bookkeeping and accounting skills
- Tax preparation (local, state, and federal)
- Sales tax collection and payment
- Health insurance arrangements for employees
- Unemployment compensation payments
- Workers' compensation payments
- Uniform payment
- Real estate taxes
- Garage keepers liability insurance

   While at first it may seem like owning your own shop would be great, a good technician can often make more money, and have fewer headaches, by simply working for someone else.

as the service, parts and body shops to manage. ● **SEE FIGURE 2–8**.

INDEPENDENT SHOP An independent shop may or may not have a shop foreman depending on the number of technicians and the volume of work. Larger independent shops have a shop foreman, whereas at smaller shops, the owner is the shop foreman. ● **SEE FIGURE 2–9**.

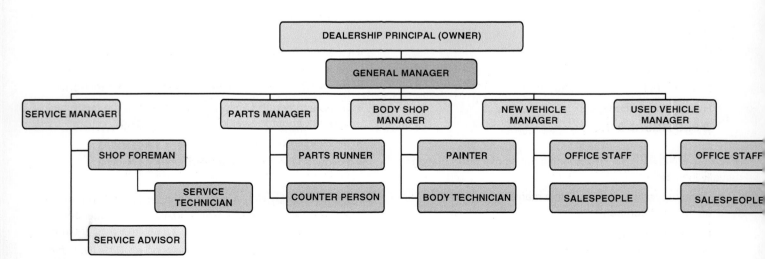

FIGURE 2–8 A typical large new vehicle dealership organizational chart.

FIGURE 2–9 A typical independent shop organizational chart.

SUMMARY

1. A service advisor is the person at a dealership or shop who greets the customer and writes the work order stating what repairs and service the customer wants.

2. A lube or quick service technician performs routine service, such as oil change, cabin and air filter replacement, and other common service procedures.

3. A new vehicle preparation technician is a person who prepares a new vehicle for delivery to the customer.

4. A general service technician has training and experience in a wide range of automotive systems, including engines, brakes, suspensions, manual transmissions, electrical, heat, air conditioning, engine performance, and automatic transmissions.

5. A shop foreman is an experienced service technician who performs diagnosis, as well as helping other technicians.

6. A service manager handles financial responsibilities associated with the proper operation of the service department or shop, including budgets, equipment purchases, and maintenance arrangement, as well as working hours, pay rate determination, and efficiency ratings.

7. Parts departments are a key part of a dealership and parts delivery and/or inventory is a large part of any shop operation.

8. Vehicle sales, both new and used, generate the need for vehicle service, and the salespeople must have good interpersonal skills.

REVIEW QUESTIONS

1. What should be included on a work order?

2. Why should a vehicle be inspected when the work order is being written?

3. What tasks are usually performed by a general service technician?

4. What duties are performed by the shop foreman and service manager?

5. What duties are performed by a parts counter person?

6. What duties are performed by vehicle salespeople?

CHAPTER QUIZ

1. A service advisor is called a _____
   a. Shop foreman
   b. Service manager
   c. Service writer
   d. Technician

2. What is *not* included on a work order?
   a. Customer's mother's maiden name
   b. VIN
   c. Mileage
   d. Description of work requested

3. All of the following are usual duties of a lube technician except _____
   a. Oil change
   b. Air filter replacement
   c. Water pump replacement
   d. Accessory drive belt inspection

4. New vehicle preparation is usually an entry-level vehicle service position and usually involves what duties?
   a. Installing dealer-installed options
   b. Correcting tire pressures
   c. Removal of all protective coverings and plastic
   d. All of the above

5. What is *not* a duty of a general service technician?
   a. Have the customer sign the work order
   b. Order the parts needed
   c. Diagnose the customer's concern
   d. Perform vehicle repair procedures

6. Which description best fits the role of a service advisor?
   a. A skilled technician
   b. A beginning technician
   c. A customer service representative
   d. A money manager

7. Two technicians are discussing the duties of a shop fore-man and a service manager. Technician A says that a shop foreman diagnoses vehicle problems. Technician B says that the service manager usually repairs vehicles. Which technician is correct?
   a. Technician A only
   b. Technician B only
   c. Both Technicians A and B
   d. Neither Technician A nor B

8. Who is the person that greets the service customer and completes the work order?
   a. Service manager   b. Service advisor
   c. Service writer   d. Either b or c

9. Which job would be concerned with the maintenance of the shop equipment?
   a. Service manager   b. Shop foreman
   c. Shop owner   d. Any of the above

10. Which job would be concerned with working hours and pay?
    a. Service manager   b. Shop foreman
    c. Service advisor   d. Service technician

chapter 3

STARTING A CAREER IN THE AUTOMOTIVE INDUSTRY

OBJECTIVES: **After studying Chapter 3, the reader will be able to:** • Explain the steps and processes for applying for a job. • Describe what the resume should include. • Explain why having a good driving record is important to a shop owner. • Discuss how to prepare for a career in the automotive industry.

KEY TERMS: • Apprentice program 20 • Clock-in 22 • Clock time 22 • Commission pay 23 • Cooperative education 20 • Entrepreneur 25 • Federal tax 23 • FICA 23 • Flat-rate 23 • Gross 23 • Housing expense 24 • Incentive pay 23 • Job shadowing 20 • Net 23 • Part-time employment 20 • Reference 21 • Resume 21 • Soft skills 20 • State tax 23 • Straight time 22

PREPARING FOR AN AUTOMOTIVE SERVICE CAREER

DESIRE AND INTEREST If a person has an interest in automobiles and trucks and likes computers, the automotive service field may be a good career choice. Computer skills are needed in addition to hands-on skills for several reasons, including:

- Service information, such as diagnostic procedures and specifications, is commonly available in electronic format.
- Work orders are commonly written and sent to the technician electronically. The technician therefore needs typing skills to type the steps taken during the service or repair procedures.
- Warranty claims are often submitted by the Internet and computer skills are needed to quickly and accurately submit claims and answer questions from the insurance company.

Interest in vehicles is also very important toward being successful as a professional service technician. Most technicians enjoy working on vehicles, not only professionally, but also during their spare time. Many technicians own a project vehicle, which could include:

- Drag race vehicle
- Race vehicle used in road racing
- A fun vehicle used on sunny weekend days and evenings
- Motorcycle
- Snowmobile or jet ski
- Truck for rock crawling

TECHNICAL KNOWLEDGE AND SKILLS The enjoyment of being involved with vehicles is very important because the job of servicing and repairing automobiles and trucks can be hard and dirty work. Many men and women enjoy being around and learning about the details of vehicle operation. With these desires and interest, working in the automotive service field is a great career. Technical information, skills, and tools needed include:

- **Hand tools and tool usage.** Owning and experience using hand tools is important for a service technician. All service technicians are expected to be able to remove and replace parts and components as needed in a timely manner using proper tools and techniques.
- **Technical knowledge.** While knowing how all aspects of the vehicle works is not expected of a beginning service technician, it is important that the technician have a basic understanding of the parts and procedures needed at least for routine service procedures.

 TECH TIP

If in Doubt, Ask

No one expects a beginning service technician to know everything, but other technicians do not know what you do or do not know. It is usually assumed that the beginning technician will ask for help if they think they need the help. However, asking for help is very rare and requires the beginning technician to admit that they do not know something. Not asking for help can cause harm to the vehicle or the service technician. If in doubt—always ask. No one will be upset and learning the answer to your question will help in the learning experience.

JOB SHADOWING   A great way to see what it is really like to work as a service technician is to follow a professional around for a day or more. **Job shadowing** is usually arranged through an automotive program, and the shop or dealership has agreed to allow someone into the shop area to observe.

While it does allow the student to observe, job shadowing does not allow the person to perform any work or help the technician in any way. During the day, the person who is job shadowing has to wear all personal protective equipment as required by the technician and must observe all safety regulations. The advantages of job shadowing include:

- Being able to observe a typical day in the life of an automotive technician
- Being able to talk to the working technician about what is being done and why
- Being able to observe other technicians and seeing the various skill levels that often exist in a shop

COOPERATIVE EDUCATION PROGRAMS   **Cooperative education** programs are formal programs of study at a high school or college where the student attends classes at the school, and also works at a local shop or dealership.

If a cooperative education program is held at the high school level, the work at the shop or dealership occurs during the afternoon or evening and during the summer between the junior and senior year. The most common high school cooperative program is called AYES, which means Automotive Youth Education System (see www.ayes.org). The vehicle manufacturers involved in this program include:

- General Motors
- Chrysler
- Toyota
- Honda
- Nissan
- BMW
- Kia
- Subaru
- Hyundai

If the cooperative education program is held at a community college, the work at the dealership occurs around the training sessions, usually the first or second half of a semester or on alternative semesters. The most common college programs include:

- General Motors ASEP (Automotive Service Educational Program) (see *www.gmasepbsep.com*)
- Ford ASSET (Automotive Student Service Educational Program) (see *www.fordasset.com*)
- Chrysler CAP (College Automotive Program) (see *www. chryslercap.com*)
- Toyota T-TEN (Toyota Technician Education Network) (see *www.toyota.com/about/tten/index.html*)

Another factory sponsored program open to those who have already completed a postsecondary automotive program is BMW STEP (Service Technician Education Program) (see *www.bmwusa.com/about/techtraining.html*).

APPRENTICE PROGRAMS   An **apprentice program** involves a beginning service technician working at a shop or dealership during the day and attending training classes in the evening. The key advantage to this type of program is that money is being earned due to full-time employment and getting on-the-job training (OJT) during the day. Often the shop or dealership will help pay for training. While this program usually takes more than two years to complete, the work performed at the shop or dealership usually becomes more technical as the apprentice becomes more knowledgeable and gets more experienced.

PART-TIME EMPLOYMENT   Working part time in the automotive service industry is an excellent way to get hands-on experience, which makes it easier to relate classroom knowledge to everyday problems and service issues. Working part time gives the student technician some flexibility as to college schedules and provides an income needed for expenses. Often **part-time employment** becomes full-time employment so it is important to keep attending technical classes toward becoming an asset to the company.

DEVELOPING AN EMPLOYMENT PLAN

An employment plan is an evaluation of your skills, interest, and talents. Selecting a career is different than getting a job. A typical job, while it does involve some training, usually can be learned in a few days to several months. However, a career requires many years to achieve competence. Therefore, selecting a career should require a thorough self-examination to determine what your true interest is in a particular career field. Some items that you should enjoy or would be willing and able to learn include:

- Working with your hands, using tools and equipment
- Computer usage, including typing skills
- Working in an area where lifting is often required
- Being able to read, understand, and follow service information, technical service bulletins, and work orders
- Being able to perform diagnostic work and figure out the root cause of a problem

SOFT SKILLS   In addition, any career, including being a service technician, requires many people skills, often called **soft skills**. These people-related skills include:

- Working cooperatively with other people
- Communicating effectively with others verbally (speech) and in writing
- Working as a member of a team for the benefit of all

- Being able to work by yourself to achieve a goal or complete a job assignment
- Being able to lead or supervise others
- Willingness to work with others with a different background or country of origin

While it is almost impossible to be able to answer all of these questions, just looking at these items and trying to identify your interests and talents will help in your selection of a career that gives you lifelong satisfaction.

LOCATING EMPLOYMENT POSSIBILITIES

Locating where you wish to work is a very important part of your career. Of course, where you would like to work may not have an opening and you may have to work hard to locate a suitable employer. First, try to select a shop or dealership where you think you would like to work because of location, vehicles serviced, or other factors. Ask other technicians who have worked or are presently working there to be sure that the location would meet your needs.

If looking for employment through a want ad in a newspaper or employment website, check the following:

- **Job description.** Is this a position that could advance into a more technical position?
- **Tools needed.** Most professional service technician positions require that the technician provide their own tools. (The shop or dealership provides the shop equipment.) Do you have the tools needed to do the job?
- **Hours needed.** Are you available during the hours specified in the ad?
- **Drug testing.** Is a drug test needed for employment and are you prepared to pass?

PREPARING A RESUME

A **resume** is usually a one-page description of your skills, talents, and education. It is used by prospective employers to help narrow the field of applicants for a job or position. The number one purpose of a resume is to obtain a job interview. A good resume should include the following items:

Personal Information
- Full given name (avoid nicknames)
- Mailing address (do not use a post office [PO] box)
- Telephone and/or cell phone number
- E-mail address
- Avoid using dates which could indicate your age

Educational Information
- Highest education level achieved
- Major, if in a college or in a training program

Experience and Skills
- Work or volunteer experience that may be helpful or useful to an employer. For example, if you took a course

in welding, this may be useful to a shop owner who is looking for a service technician who could do welding, even though this fact was not included in the job posting.
- A valid driver's license is a must for most professional service technicians.
- A good driving record. Often the shop insurance company will not allow a shop owner to hire a technician with a poor driving record.

REFERENCES

A **reference** is someone who is willing to tell a possible employer about you, including your skills and talents, as well as your truthfulness and work habits.

Most employers would like to see someone who is familiar with you and your family, such as a priest, minister, or elder in your church. Some teachers or coaches also can be asked to be a reference. Always ask the person for approval before including the person on your list of references. Ask the reference to supply you with a written recommendation. Some references prefer to simply fill out a reference questionnaire sent by many companies. If a reference sends you a written recommendation, have copies made so they can be included with your resume.

PREPARING A COVER LETTER

When answering an advertisement in a newspaper or magazine, be sure to include the details of where you saw the ad in your cover letter to the employer. For example: "I am applying for the position as an entry-level service technician as published in the August 15 edition of the Daily News."

If the requirements for the position are listed, be sure to include that you do have the specified training and/or experience and the tools needed for the job.

If calling about a position, be sure to state that you are applying for the position posted and ask to speak to the correct person or to the person mentioned in the ad.

CONTACTING POTENTIAL EMPLOYERS

When a job opening is posted in a newspaper or it is mentioned by a friend, most experts recommend that you visit the shop or dealership in person to see where the job is located, the condition of the buildings, and the surrounding areas. This trip could also be used for you to submit your resume and cover letter in person unless the company indicates otherwise. Be prepared to be interviewed when submitting your resume. Even if the position has already been filled, the trip gives you experience in meeting people and seeing the shop, which helps increase your

Always Be Truthful

No one is smart enough to be a liar. If you say something that is not true, then you have to remember what was said forever or your lie will often be discovered. If asked about your experience or knowledge, try to be as truthful as possible. Facts and skills can be learned and not knowing how to do everything that a shop may be involved with is not an indication that you will be rejected from the job opening.

confidence during the job search. Searching for a job is a full-time job in itself. Be prepared every day to answer ads, search employment websites and travel to shops or dealerships.

COMPLETING THE EMPLOYMENT APPLICATION

Most businesses require that an employment application be completed because it not only asks for all necessary personal information needed, but also references and emergency contacts. Most employment application forms ask for previous employers, the names and telephone numbers of contact people, and other information which you may not remember. It is wise to have all of the information written down ahead of time and take it with you for reference when completing the application. Always answer questions honestly and as thoroughly as possible. Never lie on an employment application.

THE INTERVIEW

When meeting for the job interview, be sure to dress appropriately for the position. For example, a suit and tie would not be appropriate for an interview for a service technician position. However, the following may be a helpful guide:

- Wear shoes that are not sneakers and be sure they are clean
- Wear slacks, not jeans
- Wear a shirt with a collar
- Do not wear a hat
- Be clean shaven or have beard/mustache neatly trimmed
- Have clean hair
- Avoid facial jewelry

During the interview, try to answer every question honestly. Emphasize what you are capable of providing to the shop, including:

- Enthusiasm
- Experience

- Willingness to work
- Willingness to work long hours and/or long weeks

AFTER THE INTERVIEW

After the interview, follow up with a letter thanking the shop for the interview. In the letter include when the interview occurred and that from the information you received, that you are very interested in becoming a part of the organization (shop or dealership). Also include contact information such as your cell phone number and e-mail address so the service manager can easily get in contact with you. A quick review of your skills and talent will also be helpful to the shop owner or service manager.

ACCEPTING EMPLOYMENT

When a job is offered, there will likely be some paperwork that needs to be filled out and decisions made. Some of the requested information could include:

- Social security number (social insurance number in Canada)
- W-4 tax withholding form
- Emergency contact people
- Retirement plan selection (This is usually given to you to study and return at a later date.)
- Other information that may be unique to the shop or dealership

After accepting the employment position, be sure to determine exactly what day and time you should report to work and try to determine where your tools should be placed. Most places will show you around and introduce you to others you will work with.

TECHNICIAN PAY METHODS

STRAIGHT-TIME PAY METHODS When the particular service or repair is not covered or mentioned in a flat-rate guide, it is common practice for the technician to **clock-in** and use the actual time spent on the repair as a basis for payment. The technician uses a flat-rate time ticket and a time clock to record the actual time. Being paid for the actual time spent is often called **straight time** or **clock time**. Difficult engine performance repairs are often calculated using the technician's straight time.

FLAT-RATE PAY METHODS Beginning service technicians are usually paid by the hour. The hourly rate can vary greatly depending on the experience of the technician and type of work being performed. Most experienced service technicians are paid by a method called **flat-rate**. The flat-rate method of pay is also called **incentive** or **commission pay**. "Flat-rate" means that the technician is paid a set amount of time (flat-rate) for every service operation. The amount of time allocated is published in a flat-rate manual. For example, if a bumper requires replacement, the flat-rate manual may call for 1.0 hour (time is always expressed in tenths of an hour). Each hour has 60 minutes. Each tenth of an hour is 1/10 of 60 or 6 minutes.

0.1 hour = 6 minutes
0.2 hour = 12 minutes
0.3 hour = 18 minutes
0.4 hour = 24 minutes
0.5 hour = 30 minutes
0.6 hour = 36 minutes
0.7 hour = 42 minutes
0.8 hour = 48 minutes
0.9 hour = 54 minutes
1.0 hour = 60 minutes

Many service operations are greater than 1 hour and are expressed as such:

2.4 hours = 2 hours and 24 minutes
3.6 hours = 3 hours and 36 minutes

The service technician would therefore get paid the flat-rate time regardless of how long it actually took to complete the job. Often, the technician can "beat flat-rate" by performing the operation in less time than the published time. It is therefore important that the technician not waste time and work efficiently to get paid the most for a day's work. The technician also has to be careful to perform the service procedure correctly because if the job needs to be done again due to an error, the technician does the repair at no pay. Therefore, the technician needs to be fast and careful at the same time.

The vehicle manufacturer determines the flat-rate for each labor operation by having a team of technicians perform the operation several times. The average of all of these times is often published as the allocated time. The flat-rate method was originally developed to determine a fair and equitable way to pay dealerships for covered warranty repairs. Because the labor rate differs throughout the country, a fixed dollar amount would not be fair compensation. However, if a time could be established for each operation, then the vehicle manufacturer could reimburse the dealership for the set number of hours multiplied by the labor rate approved for that dealership. For example, if the approved labor rate is $60.00 per hour and:

Technician A performed 6.2 hours × $60.00 = $372.00
Technician B performed 4.8 hours × $60.00 = $288.00
The total paid to the dealership by the   = $660.00
manufacturer

This does not mean that the service technician gets paid $60.00 per hour. Sorry, no! This means that the dealership gets reimbursed for labor at the $60.00 per hour rate. The service technician usually gets paid a lot less than half of the total labor charge.

Depending on the part of the country and the size of the dealership and community, the technician's flat-rate per hour income can vary from $7.00 to $20.00 or more per flat-rate hour. Remember, a high pay rate ($20 for example) does not necessarily mean that the service technician will be earning $800.00 per week (40 hours × $20.00 per hour = $800.00). If the dealership is not busy or it is a slow time of year, maybe the technician will only have the opportunity to "turn" 20 hours per week. So it is not really the pay rate that determines what a technician will earn but rather a combination of all of the following:

- Pay rate
- Number of service repairs performed
- Skill and speed of the service technician
- Type of service work (a routine brake service may be completed faster and easier than a difficult engine performance problem)

A service technician earns more at a busy dealership with a lower pay rate than at a smaller or less busy dealership with a higher pay rate.

PAYROLL DEDUCTIONS

GROSS VERSUS NET COMPENSATION

Most beginning technicians start by receiving a certain amount of money per hours worked. **Gross** earnings are the total amount you earned during the pay period. The paycheck you receive will be for an amount called **net** earnings. Taxes and deductions that are taken from your paycheck may include all or most of the following:

- **Federal** income **tax**
- **State** income **tax** (not all states)
- Social Security taxes (labeled **FICA**, which stands for Federal Insurance Contribution Act)
- Health/dental/eye insurance deductions

In addition to the above, uniform costs, savings plan deductions, parts account deductions, as well as weekly payments for tools, may also reduce the amount of your net or "take-home" pay.

RETIREMENT INFORMATION AND PAYMENTS

Some shops or dealerships offer some retirement savings plan but the most commonly used is an employer-sponsored 401(k) account named after a section of the U.S. Internal Revenue Code. A 401(k) account allows a worker to save for retirement while deferring taxes on the saved money and earnings until withdrawal. Most 401(k) plans allow the employer to select from stock mutual funds or other investments. A 401(k) retirement plan offers two advantages compared to a simple savings account.

- The contributions (money deposited into the account) are tax deferred. The amount will increase due to interest and no taxes are due until the money is withdrawn.
- Many employers provide matching contributions to your 401(k) account, which can range from 0% (no matching contributions) to 100%.

The savings really add up over time. For example, if you start saving at age 25 and your income averages $3,000 per month ($36,000 per year) and you contribute 6% of your pay and the employer contributes 3%, after 40 years at age 65, the account will be worth $1,700,000 (one million, seven hundred thousand dollars) assuming a 10% average return.

In retirement, most experts agree that 4% of the total can be withdrawn each year and not reduce the capital investment. Four percent of $1,700,000 is $68,000 per year or over $5,600 per month every month for the rest of your life.

ADDITIONAL SERVICE TECHNICIAN BENEFITS Many larger dealerships and service facilities often offer some or all of the following:

- Paid uniforms/cleaning
- Vacation time
- Update training (especially new vehicle dealerships)
- Some sort of retirement (usually a contributing 401(k)) program
- Health and dental insurance (usually not fully paid)
- Discounts on parts and vehicles purchased at the dealership or shop

Not all service facilities offer all of these additional benefits.

HOUSING AND LIVING EXPENSES

As a general guideline, **housing expenses** such as rent or a mortgage payment should not exceed 30% of the gross monthly income. For example,

Ten dollars per hour times 40 hours per week = $400 per week times 4 weeks in a month = $1600 per month. Thirty percent of $1600 is $480 per month for rent or a mortgage payment.

A vehicle payment should not exceed 25% of the gross earnings. In the example where the pay was $10 per hour, the maximum recommended vehicle payment should be $400 per month.

BECOMING A SHOP OWNER

Many service technicians want to start and operate their own shop. Becoming a shop owner results in handling many non-automotive-related duties that some technicians do not feel qualified to handle, including:

- Handling customers
- Ordering and paying for shop equipment and supplies
- Bookkeeping, including payroll
- Budgeting for and paying for garage owner's insurance and workers' compensation
- Paying rent, as well as heat/air conditioning bills
- Advertising expenses
- Hiring and firing employees

? FREQUENTLY ASKED QUESTION

Employee or Contract Labor?

Most shops and dealerships hire service technicians as employees. However, some shops or businesses will pay a technician for services performed on a contract basis. This means that they are not hiring you as an employee, but simply paying for a service similar to having a plumber repair a toilet. The plumber is performing a service and is paid for the job rather than as an employee of the shop. An employer–employee relationship exists if the shop meets two factors:

1. **Direction**—This means that the employer can direct the technician to report to work to perform service work.
2. **Control**—This means that the employer can direct the hours and days when the work is to be performed and at the employer's location.

A contract labor association exists if the repairs are performed without both direction and control of the shop.

If a contract labor basis is established, then no taxes are withheld. It is then the responsibility of the technician to make the necessary and required general tax payments and pay all taxes on time.

⚙ TECH TIP

Find Three Key People

An **entrepreneur** is a person who organizes and manages their own business assuming the risk for the sake of a profit. Many service technicians have the desire to own their own repair facility. The wise business owner (entrepreneur) seeks the advice of the following people when starting and operating their own business.

1. **Attorney (lawyer)**—This professional will help guide you to make sure that your employees and your customers are protected by the laws of your community, state, and federal regulations.
2. **Accountant**—This professional will help you with the journals and records that must be kept by all businesses and to help with elements such as payroll taxes, unemployment taxes, and workmen's compensation that all businesses have to pay.
3. **Insurance Agent**—This professional will help you select the coverage needed to protect you and your business from major losses.

SUMMARY

1. When applying for a job, list in your cover letter where you saw the opening and also mention that you meet all of the requirements for the position.
2. A resume is a brief description of your education and experience.
3. Present a professional appearance during an interview.
4. Net pay is gross pay minus all deductions, such as federal taxes and FICA.
5. Housing and vehicle payments each should not exceed 25% of your monthly income.
6. Becoming a shop owner involves more paperwork than most service technicians realize.

REVIEW QUESTIONS

1. What facts should be included on the resume?
2. What are five interviewing tips?
3. What is the difference between gross pay and net pay?
4. What taxes are usually withheld from a paycheck?
5. What are five duties of a shop owner?

CHAPTER QUIZ

1. A resume should be how many pages long?
    a. 1
    b. 2
    c. 3
    d. 4 or more
2. What personal information should *not* be included on the resume?
    a. Address
    b. Cell or telephone number
    c. Age
    d. Work experience

3. Why is having a good driving record good for the shop?
   a. Allows the use of a company vehicle
   b. Lowers insurance costs
   c. Allows you to drive customers' vehicles
   d. Permits you to use your vehicle to get parts

4. Which is *not* recommended during an interview?
   a. Wear shoes that are not sneakers
   b. Wear a shirt with a collar
   c. Have clean hair
   d. Wear jeans

5. During an interview, try to _____.
   a. Show enthusiasm
   b. Explain your work experience
   c. State your willingness to work
   d. All of the above

6. Ten dollars per hour is about how much income per year?
   a. $20,000   b. $25,000
   c. $30,000   d. $35,000

7. One of the deductions from a paycheck is for Social Security. This item is usually shown on the pay stub as_____.
   a. Social Security
   b. SSA
   c. FICA
   d. U.S. government deduction

8. Technician A says that the net pay amount is usually higher than the gross pay amount. Technician B says that the gross pay amount is usually higher than the net pay. Which technician is correct?
   a. Technician A only
   b. Technician B only
   c. Both Technicians A and B
   d. Neither Technician A nor B

9. A beginning service technician earns $400 per week. How much should the technician spend on a vehicle payment?
   a. $400 per month
   c. $800 per month
   b. $500 per month
   d. $1000 per month

10. Which activity does not allow a person to perform any work while at the shop?
    a. Cooperative education program
    b. Apprenticeship program
    c. Job shadowing
    d. Part-time employment

chapter 4

WORKING AS A PROFESSIONAL SERVICE TECHNICIAN

OBJECTIVES: **After studying Chapter 4, the reader will be able to:** • Discuss how to start a new job. • Describe the advantages of having a mentor. • Explain how a mentor can improve on-the-job learning. • Discuss the role of the trainee with a mentor. • Explain formal and informal evaluations. • Describe the role of a service technician. • Explain how the flat-rate pay plan works. • Describe the type and pricing of parts.

KEY TERMS: • Advisor 35 • Advocate 35 • Aftermarket parts 33 • Coach 35 • Core 33 • Core charge 33 • Counselor 35 • Critical thinking 36 • Customer pay (CP) 32 • Flagging 33 • Formal evaluation 37 • Informal evaluation 37 • Jobber 33 • Mentor 34 • Original equipment (OE) 33 • Rebuilt 34 • Remove and inspect (R & I) 33 • Remove and replace (R & R) 33 • Renewal parts 33 • Repair order (RO) 30 • Role model 35 • Service bay 30 • Stall 30 • Teacher 35 • Three Cs (concern, cause, correction) 30 • Trainee 34 • Warehouse distributor 33

PROFESSIONALISM

Professionalism and personal credibility are important and can determine success as a service technician or as a customer service provider. A true professional does the following on a regular basis.

1. **Practice consistency.** Be positive, professional, and warm at all times.

2. **Keep your word.** Follow through with the commitments that you make. People will not have faith in you if you break your promises.

3. **Develop technical expertise.** Become very knowledgeable about the vehicles being serviced. Attend regular update training classes to keep up with the latest technical information and equipment.

4. **Become a teammate with your coworkers.** Working successfully with others shows that you have common goals and can benefit from the specific skills of others.

5. **Be accountable.** Practice honesty all of the time, admit mistakes, and take responsibility for actions. Apologize if you are wrong.

ETHICS Ethics are a set of principles that govern the conduct of an individual or group. Sometimes ethical decisions are easy to recognize and are perceived as popular choices of behavior by the people around us. At times the range of

TECH TIP

Clean Clothes Are a Must

Anyone who meets the public in any business must not only be dressed appropriately, but the clothing should be clean. Service advisors and others that greet the public should also be sure that their shoes are shined. Dull, dirty, or scuffed shoes or messy appearance reflects an unprofessional look.

possible choices falls into gray areas in which the "right" or "wrong" course of action is difficult or nearly impossible to identify. When faced with an ethically challenging situation, ask yourself the following questions:

- Is it legal? (Is it against local, state, or federal laws?)

- Is it fair? (Is it harmful to me or to others?)

- How do I feel about it? (Is it against the teachings of my parents or my religion?)

- Would public opinion find my behavior incorrect? (Would it disappoint my family?)

- Am I fearful of what those I trust would say about my actions? (Would I be hurt or upset if someone did this to me?)

The above questions can be quite revealing when attempting to choose an ethical course of action.

The five main methods of communication used in effective customer service interaction include listening, talking, nonverbal communications, reading, and writing.

LISTENING   Active listening is the ability to hear and understand what the speaker is saying. To listen to your customers or other technicians is to show them that you care about and respect their questions and concerns. It is not easy to be a good listener; it takes practice and dedication to improve your listening techniques. Listening is a skill that must continuously be developed.

Several barriers to good listening exist. A listener may be distracted from what is being said, have a closed mind to the speaker and the message, won't stop talking, or is lazy and unwilling to make the commitment to be a good listener.

Listening requires the listener to stop talking and to hear what the speaker is saying. It has been said that humans were given two ears and one mouth because we are supposed to listen twice as much as we speak. The best way to keep your mind focused on the speaker and to avoid becoming distracted is to pay attention. We can think about 10 times faster than we can speak, so frequently we have processed what speakers have said and are waiting for them to catch up with us. By focusing on speakers and on what is being said we are less likely to miss the messages being delivered. Putting that into practice is not as easy as it sounds.

A good listener does the following:

- Focuses on the speaker and what is being said.
- Looks at the speaker and makes eye contact when possible.
- Listens with an open mind.
- Rephrases what was said to clarify that the intended message is understood.
- A good listener knows the joy of sharing and communicating with others. Work to become the best listener you can be.

VERBAL   Verbal means speaking, using words and terminology that others can comprehend. Eye contact is always important when we are communicating with others.

TECH TIP

Never Use Profanity

Regardless of the situation, a true professional never resorts to the use of profanity. If tensions are high and the discussion becomes heated, try to defuse the situation by turning the situation over to someone else.

Eye contact is allowing our eyes to make visual contact with someone else's. In our culture, eye contact conveys sincerity and interest. Avoiding eye contact may suggest a lack of concern or lack of honesty. Customers may perceive that a customer service provider is not interested in what they are saying if they do not periodically make eye contact with the customer.

When dealing with people from other cultures, customer service providers should be aware of cultural differences. In many other cultures eye avoidance is a sign of respect. Be sensitive to others but use eye contact whenever possible.

NONVERBAL COMMUNICATION   The tone and inflection of the voice, facial expressions, posture, hand movements, and eye contact are all forms of nonverbal communications. These nonverbal indicators can contradict the message conveyed through another method of communication.

Nonverbal communication includes body posture such as having the arms crossed. When a person crosses his or her arms, or looks at other things rather than paying attention to what you are discussing, these actions could indicate one of several things, including:

1. They are not interested in what you are saying
2. They don't believe what you are saying
3. They are not listening

If this type of nonverbal communication is noticed, there are several things that could be done to overcome this barrier, including:

1. Ask questions, which would require them to pay attention plus it shows that you are interested in what they think.
2. Give the customer options rather than just ask them what they want such as saying "would you prefer to have this work done all at the same time or spread out over several weeks?"

TELEPHONE COMMUNICATION   A large percentage of customers make first contact with a shop or dealer service department by telephone. Service technicians normally do not talk to customers directly but may be asked to help clarify a repair or a service procedure.

TECH TIP

Always Have Paper and a Pen When on the Telephone

When talking to a customer, whether in person or on the telephone, have paper and a pencil or pen to record the necessary information. In this case, the customer service representative at a dealer is using a preprinted form to record the service procedures to be performed on a customer's vehicle while talking on the phone. ● **SEE FIGURE 4–1.**

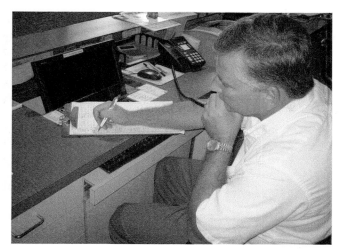

FIGURE 4–1 When answering the telephone, be sure to have paper and pen or pencil handy to record the customer information.

FIGURE 4–2 If you smile while talking on the telephone, your attitude will be transmitted to the customer.

Some suggestions when talking on the telephone include:

- Use proper titles for the people with whom you communicate. If in doubt about whether to use a first name, call the person by the more formal *Mr.* or *Ms.* If they prefer the more informal first name, they will say so. It is better to be a little too formal than overly familiar.

- Thank people for calling. "Thank you" is the most powerful phrase in human relations and it reassures customers that you are interested in serving.

- Try to avoid technical terms and abbreviations such as EGR and other terms commonly used in the trade but will not be understood by the customer. Try to phrase the technical description by saying that you replaced or serviced a part in the emission control system and include the entire name of the part such as the "exhaust gas recirculation valve."

- Keep your comments positive and focused toward solving the problem or concern.

- Avoid saying anything that makes people or your shop look unprofessional or uncaring. When dealing with customers, some words are more positive and appropriate to use. Some customer service providers find it helpful to list words to use and words to avoid on a card so that it is available for easy reference.

 TECH TIP

Smile While You Talk

If you smile while talking on the telephone, your voice will reflect a positive and helpful attitude, which customers or vendors will easily recognize over the telephone. ● **SEE FIGURE 4–2**.

- Speak clearly and distinctly. Hold the telephone mouthpiece about a half-inch from your lips. Speak naturally and comfortably. Talk to your caller as you would to a friend.

- Move to a quiet area if background noise level is high.

WRITING Writing is communicating by using the written word so that others can understand the intended message. Service technicians are required to document the work that was performed on a vehicle. For some technicians this is the most difficult part of the service. If writing, be sure it is legible and if not, then print all messages and information. Writing or typing in the description of the steps performed during the diagnosis and repair of the vehicle should be worded as if the technician is talking to the customer. For example, if a coolant leak was repaired by replacing the water pump the technician should write out the following steps and operations on the work order:

1. Visually verified coolant leaking.

2. Performed a pressure test of the cooling system and located the leak as coming from the water pump.

3. Replaced the water pump and added new coolant and bled the system of trapped air.

4. Pressure tested the cooling system to verify that the leak was corrected—no leaks found.

READING Reading means the ability to read and comprehend the written word. All service technicians need to be able to read, understand, and follow written instructions and repair procedures. If some words are not understood use a dictionary or ask another technician for help. For example, a beginning technician read in the service information that the wiring connector was "adjacent to the coolant reservoir." The technician did not understand what the word adjacent meant and found out from another technician that it meant "next or close to."

If reading a note from a customer written in another language you do not understand try to ask if someone else in the shop can read it for you.

Use Internet Translation

If the customer is non-English speaking, type the information into a text document and search for a translation on the Internet. Give the copy of the translated document to the customer. The customer request could also be translated into English, if needed, to help the shop understand exactly what the customer is requesting and needs.

Google Is Your Friend

If unsure as to how something works or if you need more detailed information about something, go to *www.google.com*® and search for the topic. Using the Internet can help with locating hard-to-find facts and can even be used to help with a service procedure that you have not done before. For a link to all factory service information, go to the website of National Automotive Service Task Force at *www.nastf.org*. Look at the work scheduled for the next day and try to determine as much about the job as possible so you can be prepared the next day to tackle the procedure. Using the International Automotive Technicians Network at *www.iatn.net* is also very helpful for technical information and can help pin down hard-to-find problems.

WHAT HAPPENS THE FIRST DAY?

The first day on the job, someone, usually the shop owner or shop foreman, should:

- Introduce the new technician to key people at the shop.
- Show the new technician the facility, parking, rules, and regulations of the organization.
- Establish the new technician's work area.
- Ask questions of the new technician regarding their skills and talents.

The shop owner or foreman should:

- Review the training tasks that were completed in school.
- Try to direct work to the new technician that covers their training or experience.

The first day on the job the beginning technician should:

- Smile and ask questions if needed to clarify procedures and regulations.

Don't Touch Other Technician's Tools

A beginning technician seldom has all of the tools needed to perform all of the service and repair tasks. A technician's tools are very important. If a tool needs to be borrowed, the beginning technician should ask for permission to borrow a tool. Then when the tool is returned, it should be clean and replaced back exactly where the technician asks for it to be returned.

Regulated Terms to Use

In some states or areas where automotive service is regulated, such as in California or Michigan, it is important that the term used to describe a labor operation is the term defined by the state agency. This means that some terms used in parts and time guides may not be the same terms used by the state. Always check that the terms used are in compliance with all regulations. Some terms that could be affected include rebuild, repair, overhaul, inspection and R & R (remove and replace), and safety inspection.

- Be prepared to take and pass a drug test.
- Assure the service manager or shop owner that you are serious about a career as an automotive technician.

A work order, also called a **repair order** or **RO** is assigned to a technician who is best qualified to perform the work. The technician gets the keys and drives the vehicle to an assigned **service bay** (also called a **stall**), performs the proper diagnosis, gets the necessary parts from the parts department, and completes the repair.

After the service work has been performed, the service technician should then fill out the work order and describe what work was performed. These are called the "**three Cs.**"

1. **Concern**—Write on the work order what was done to confirm the customer's concern. For example, "Drove the vehicle at highway speed and verified a vibration."
2. **Cause**—The service technician should write the cause of the problem. For example, "Used a scan tool and discovered that cylinder #3 was misfiring."
3. **Correction**—The service technician should write what was done to correct the problem. For example, "Removed the spark plug wire from cylinder number three and by visual inspection found that the boot had been arcing to the cylinder head. Replaced the spark plug wire and verified that the misfire was corrected."

DUTIES OF A SERVICE TECHNICIAN

READING THE WORK ORDER A work order is selected or assigned to a service technician who then performs the listed tasks. The work order should be written so that the technician knows exactly what needs to be done. However, if there is any doubt, the technician should clarify the needed task with the service advisor or the person who spoke to the customer.

TALKING TO CUSTOMERS The typical service technician usually does not talk directly to a customer except in some smaller shops. However, there may be cases where the technician will be asked to clarify a procedure or repair to a customer. Many technicians do not like to talk to the customers and fear that they may say too much or not enough. If a technician is asked to talk to a customer, try to keep the discussion to the following without being too technical.

- The service technician should repeat the original concern. This is to simply verify to the customer and the technician the goal of the service or repair.

 TECH TIP

If Late—Call

When running late, you may know that you will be just a few minutes late but your boss does not know how late you will be. If you are going to be late, even by a few minutes, call the shop and let them know. This does not eliminate your being late from your record, but does demonstrate your concern to your service manager and other technicians who are counting on you to being on time to work every day.

 TECH TIP

Ask Me about This

A good service advisor will document what the customer wants done on the work order. However, there are times when the explanation and description would take too long and too much space to be practical. In these cases, the wise service advisor simply states on the work order for the service technician to see the service advisor to discuss the situation. The service advisor can write the basic request to document what is needed.

- The cause of the fault should be mentioned. If further diagnostic steps needed to find the cause are requested, discuss the steps followed and the equipment or tools used.

- Discuss what was done to solve the concern, including what part or parts were replaced. This step may also include what other service operations were needed to complete the repair, such as reprogramming the computer.

NOTE: If the customer speaks a foreign language that you do not understand, excuse yourself and locate someone in the shop who can assist you with communicating with the customer. Avoid using slang or abbreviation of technical terms. Ask the person if they understand and be willing to restate, if needed, until the situation is understood. This can often be difficult if discussing technical situations to persons of another language or culture.

ESTIMATING A REPAIR Sometimes a service technician is asked to help create an estimate for the customer. It is usually the responsibility of the service advisor or shop owner to create estimates. The technician may be helpful by pointing out all of the operations that need to be performed to achieve a repair. The estimate for a repair includes:

- **Parts needed**—This list would also include any gaskets and/or supplies needed. The technician can help identify if extra supplies may be needed.

- **Labor**—A published time guide is usually used but many times options such as rear air conditioning or four-wheel drive may add substantial time to the operation. The technician can help with the estimate by making sure that the options are pointed out to the service advisor or shop owner.

DOCUMENTING THE WORK ORDER The service technician must document the work order. This means that the service technician must write (or type) what all was done to the vehicle, including documenting defective components or conditions that were found in the course of the diagnosis. The documentation is often called "telling the story" and should include the following:

- The test equipment used to diagnose the problem. For example: Used a Tech 2 scan tool to retrieve P0300 random misfire diagnostic trouble code.

 TECH TIP

Car, Truck, or Vehicle?

When discussing a vehicle with a customer, it is best to avoid creating problems. For example, if a technician asked about a customer's "car", the customer could become concerned because they drive a truck and many owners of trucks do not want their vehicle called a car. Use of the term "vehicle," a generic term, is often recommended when talking to customers to avoid possible concerns.

- Used a digital multimeter to determine a spark plug wire was defective.
- List what parts or service operations were performed. For example: Replaced the spark plug wire on cylinder number 3. Used a scan tool to clear the diagnostic trouble codes and verify that the engine is operating correctly.

FOLLOWING RECOMMENDED PROCEDURES
All service technicians should follow the diagnostic and service procedures specified by the vehicle manufacturer. Service information procedures to be followed include the following:

- Follow and document the diagnostic procedure. Writing down the test results helps the customer see all that was involved in the procedure and creates the proper paper trail for future reference, if needed.
- Follow the recommended removal and reinstallation (R & R) procedures. This step helps prevent the possibility of doing harm to the vehicle if an alternative method is attempted.
- Always torque fasteners to factory specifications. This step is very important because under- or overtightened fasteners can cause problems that were not present until after the repair. The wise technician will document torque specifications on the work order.

CUSTOMER PAY
Customer pay (CP) means that the customer will be paying for the service work at a dealership rather than the warranty. Often the same factory flat-rate number of hours is used to calculate the technician's pay, but customer pay often pays the service technician at a higher rate.

FREQUENTLY ASKED QUESTION

What Can a Service Technician Do to Earn More Money?

Because most service technicians are paid on a commission basis (flat-rate), the more work that is completed, the more hours the technician can "turn." Therefore, to earn the most money, the service technician could do the following to increase the amount of work performed:

- Keep up-to-date and learn the latest technical information
- Practice good habits that help avoid errors or incomplete repairs
- Learn from experienced and successful fellow technicians and try to approach the repair the same way the successful technician does
- Purchase the proper tools to do the work efficiently

NOTE: This does not mean that every technician needs to purchase all possible tools. Purchase only those tools that you know you will need and use.

For example, a service technician earning $15.00 per flat-rate hour for warranty work may be paid $18.00 per hour for customer-pay work. Obviously, service technicians prefer to work on vehicles that require customer-pay service work rather than factory-warranty service work.

NONDEALERSHIP FLAT-RATE Technicians who work for independent service facilities or at other nondealership locations use one or both of the following to set rates of pay:

- Mitchell, Motors, or Chilton parts and time guides
- Alldata, Shop-Key, Car-Quest, Auto Value, Mitchell, AC Delco, or other shop management software program.

These guides contain service operation and flat-rate times. Generally, these are about 20% higher (longer) than those specified by the factory flat-rate to compensate for rust or corrosion and other factors of time and mileage that often lengthen the time necessary to complete a repair. Again, the service technician is usually paid a dollar amount per flat-rate hour based on one of these aftermarket flat-rate guides. The guides also provide a list price for the parts for each vehicle. This information allows the service advisor to accurately estimate the total cost of the repair.

FLAGGING A WORK ORDER

When a service technician completes a service procedure or repair, a sticker or notification on the work order indicates the following:

- Technician number (number rather than a name is often used not only to shorten the identification but also to shield the actual identity of the technician from the customer)

TECH TIP

Technician Skill Level and Severe Service

Most aftermarket service information includes a guideline for the relative level of the technician's skill required to perform the listed service procedures. These include:

A = Highly skilled and experienced technician
B = Skilled technician who is capable of performing diagnosis of vehicle systems
C = Semiskilled technician who is capable of performing routine service work without direct supervision

Many time guides provide additional time for vehicles that may be excessively rusted due to climate conditions or have been subjected to abuse. Be sure to quote the higher rate if any of these conditions are present on the customer's vehicle.
● SEE FIGURE 4–3.

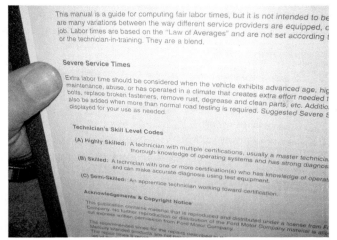

FIGURE 4–3 Note the skill levels of the technician and the extra time that should be added if work is being performed on a vehicle that has excessive rust or other factors as stated in the time guide.

- Work order number
- Actual clock time from a time clock record for certain jobs as needed
- Amount of time allocated to the repair expressed in hours and tenths of an hour

The application of the service technician's sticker to the back of the work order or completing the details of the repair into the electronic service record is called **flagging the work order.**

NOTE: The actual assignment of the time is often done by another person at the dealership or service facility. This procedure assures that the correct number of hours is posted to the work order and to the technician's ticket.

SUBLET REPAIRS

Often a repair (or a part of a repair) is performed by another person or company outside of the dealership or service facility. For example, an engine needing repair that also has a defective or leaking radiator would be repaired by the original repair facility, but the radiator may be sent to a specialty radiator repair shop. The radiator repair cost is then entered on the work order as a sublet repair.

PARTS REPLACEMENT

Parts replacement is often called **R & R,** meaning **remove and replace.**

NOTE: R & R can also mean remove and repair, but this meaning is generally not used as much now as it used to

be when components such as starters and air conditioning compressors were repaired rather than replaced as an assembly.

R & I is often used to indicate **remove and inspect** to check a component for damage. The old replaced part is often returned for remanufacturing and is called a **core.** A **core charge** is often charged by parts stores when a new (or remanufactured) part is purchased. This core charge usually represents the value of the old component. Because it is needed by the remanufacturer as a starting point for the remanufacturing process, the core charge is also an incentive to return the old part for credit (or refund) of the core charge.

NOTE: Most parts stores today require that all cores be returned in the original boxes. Be sure to place the defective part into the same box that was used for the new or remanufactured part to be sure that the shop gets the proper credit for the core.

ORIGINAL EQUIPMENT PARTS Parts at a new vehicle dealership come either directly from the vehicle manufacturer or a regional dealership. If one dealership purchases from another dealership, the cost of the part is higher, but no waiting is required. If a dealership orders a part from the manufacturer directly, the cost is lower, but there is often a 7- to 10-day waiting period. **Original equipment** parts, abbreviated **OE,** are generally of the highest quality because they have to meet performance and durability standards not required of replacement parts manufacturers.

NOTE: Many service technicians will use only OE parts for certain critical systems such as fuel injection and ignition system components because, in their experience, even though the price is often higher, the extra quality seems to be worth the cost not only to the owner of the vehicle but also to the service technician who does not have to worry about having to replace the same part twice.

AFTERMARKET PARTS Parts manufactured to be sold for use after the vehicle is made are often referred to as **aftermarket parts** or **renewal parts.** Most aftermarket parts are sold at automotive parts stores or **jobbers.** A jobber or parts retailer usually gets parts from a large regional **warehouse distributor.** The warehouse distributor can either purchase parts directly from the manufacturer or from an even larger central warehouse. Because each business needs to make a profit (typically, 35%), the cost to the end user may not be lower than it is for the same part purchased at a dealership (two-step process instead of the typical three-step process) even though it costs more to manufacture the original equipment part. To determine what a 35% margin increase is for any product, simply divide the cost by 0.65. To illustrate how this works, compare the end cost of a part (part A) from a dealership and a parts store.

Retail Parts Store	New Vehicle Dealership
Manufacturer's selling price = $17.00	Manufacturer's selling price = $25.00
Warehouse distributor's selling price = $26.15 ($17.00 ÷ 0.65 = $26.15)	Parts department selling price = $38.46 ($25.00 ÷ 0.65 = $38.46)
Retail store selling price = $40.23 ($26.15 ÷ 0.65 = $40.23)	

NOTE: The cost of the part to the customer where service work is performed is increased about 35% over the base cost of the part. For example, a part from a parts store that costs the repair facility $40.23 will be billed to the customer at about $61.00. The retail service customer at the dealer may pay $59.17 ($38.46 ÷ 0.65 = $59.17).

NEW VERSUS REMANUFACTURED PARTS

New parts are manufactured from raw materials and have never been used on a vehicle. A remanufactured component (also called **rebuilt**) has been used on a vehicle until the component wore out or failed. A remanufacturer totally disassembles the component, cleans, machines, and performs all the necessary steps to restore the part to a "like new" look and function. If properly remanufactured, the component can be expected to deliver the same length of service as a new component part.

The cost of a remanufactured component is often less than the cost of a new part.

CAUTION: Do not always assume that a remanufactured component is less expensive than a new component. Due to the three-step distribution process, the final cost to the end user (you) may be close to the same!

USED PARTS

Used parts offer another alternative to either new or remanufactured parts. The cost of a used component is typically one-half the cost of the component if purchased new. Wrecking and salvage yards use a Hollander manual that lists original equipment part numbers and cost and cross-references them to other parts that are the same.

WORKING WITH A MENTOR

A mentor is a person at the job site who helps the beginning service technician, also called the **trainee.** The word **mentor** comes from Greek mythology. In Homer's *The Odyssey,* Mentor was the faithful companion and friend of Ulysses (Odysseus), the King of Ithaca. Before Ulysses went to the Trojan Wars, he instructed Mentor to stay and take full charge of the royal household. This meant that Mentor had to be father figure,

 TECH TIP

Work Habit Hints

The following statements reflect the expectations of service managers or shop owners for their technicians:

1. Report to work every day on time. Being several minutes early every day is an easy way to show your service manager and fellow technicians that you are serious about your job and career.
2. If you *must* be late or absent, call your service manager as soon as possible.
3. Keep busy. If not assigned to a specific job, ask what activities the service manager or supervisor wants you to do.
4. Report any mistakes or accidents *immediately* to your supervisor or team leader. *Never* allow a customer to be the first to discover a mistake.
5. Never lie to your employer or to a customer.
6. Always return any borrowed tools as soon as you are done with them and in *clean* condition. *Show* the person you borrowed the tools from that you are returning them to the toolbox or workbench.
7. Keep your work area neat and orderly.
8. Always use fender covers when working under the hood.
9. Double-check your work to be sure that everything is correct.
   a. Remember: "If you are forcing something, you are probably doing something wrong."
   b. Ask for help if unclear as to what to do or how to do it.
10. Do not smoke in a customer's vehicle.
11. Avoid profanity.
12. DO NOT TOUCH THE RADIO! If the radio is turned on and prevents you from hearing noises, turn the volume down. Try to return the vehicle to the owner with the radio at the same volume as originally set.

NOTE: Some shops have a policy that requires employees to turn the radio off.

13. Keep yourself neatly groomed, including:
   a. Shirttail tucked into pants (unless shirt is designed to be worn outside)
   b. Daily bathing and use of deodorant
   c. Clean hair, regular haircuts, and hair tied back if long
   d. Men: daily shave or keep beard and/or mustache neatly trimmed
   e. Women: makeup and jewelry kept to a minimum

teacher, role model, counselor, trusted advisor, challenger, and encourager to the King's son in order that he become a wise and good ruler.

Therefore, a good definition of a mentor would be, "A highly qualified individual who is entrusted with the protection and development of an inexperienced technician."

A mentor therefore fulfills many roles, such as:

- **Teacher**—helps teach information and procedures
- **Coach**—has trainee practice service procedures
- **Counselor**—concerned about, but not trained to offer advice on personal life decisions.
- **Advisor**—helps with career-type decisions, such as what tools are needed
- **Advocate** (stands up for the trainee)—represents and helps the trainee's concerns be expressed to others
- **Role model**—presents a positive role model every day

QUALIFICATIONS OF A GOOD MENTOR A good mentor should be assigned to a new technician. Qualifications of a good mentor include:

- **Trade proficiency** —The person selected should be a highly skilled technician.
- **Good coaching/mentoring skills and techniques** —The mentor has to have patience and be willing to help the trainee by explaining each step needed to complete a service procedure.

 TECH TIP

Adhere to the Times

When starting a new job at a shop or dealership, be sure to ask about the following:

- **What time should I arrive at work?** This may be different than the scheduled work starting time. For example, the work day could start at 8 a.m. but the shop owner or service manager may want all technicians to arrive and start to get ready to work at 7:50 a.m.
- **When is break time?** Breaks may or may not be regularly scheduled and it is important for the beginning technician to know and adhere to break times.
- **When is lunch time?** In some busy shops, the lunch period is staggered to be sure that some technicians are always available for work. Always be willing to adhere to the requested lunch period.

- **Leadership/role model** —The mentor should take pride in being a professional service technician and have high ethical and professional standards.

Mentoring a trainee can be frustrating for an experienced technician. This occurs because the mentor needs to verify almost everything the trainee does until satisfied that competence has been achieved. Even very basic procedures need to be watched, such as hoisting the vehicle, changing the oil and oil filter, plus many other operations. As a result, the time taken to help the beginning technician will reduce the efficiency, and therefore, the pay of the mentor. However, after several weeks, the trainee can start helping the mentor, thereby increasing efficiency.

TEAMWORK

TEAM BUILDING A team is a group of individuals working together to achieve a common goal. Even shops or service departments that do not use a team system with a group of technicians is still a team. All members of the service department are really part of a team effort working together to achieve efficient vehicle service and customer satisfaction. The key to building a team that works together is selecting employees that are willing to work together. While the shop owner or service manager at a dealership has hiring authority, every technician should consider what is best for the entire group to help increase repeat business and satisfied customers.

LEADERSHIP ROLES As a technician gains experience, he or she often asks for guidance, not only for technical answers, but also for how to handle other issues in the shop, such as paperwork, use of aftermarket parts, and other issues. Therefore, the more experience the technician has, the more likely he or she will be placed in a leadership and role model position.

GOAL SETTING AND BUSINESS MEETINGS

GOAL SETTING The wise service technician sets goals to achieve during a career and life. The purpose of goal setting is to focus efforts on improving your personal and professional life. Goals can include: Career, physical, family, education, financial, and public service. There are many helpful websites that can be used to help set and track progress toward achieving goals. The hardest part of any goal is to write it down. Until it is written down, a goal is not real.

BUSINESS MEETINGS All service technicians attend business (shop) meetings. A good business meeting will have the following features:

1. An agenda (list of topics to be discussed) will be given out or displayed.

2. The meeting should start on time and end on time.

3. If someone is to give a report or be asked to do a project, this topic should be discussed with the designated person before the meeting to avoid that person from being surprised and made to feel uncomfortable.

4. The meeting should be held following the "Robert's Rule of Order" guidelines.

5. Often meetings include others from inside or outside the company or shop, so try to look your best and smile to make the best impression.

ADVANCEMENT SKILLS

The job of a service technician becomes more valuable to the shop or dealership if work can be accomplished quickly and without any mistakes. Therefore, being careful to avoid errors is the first consideration for any service technician. Then, with experience, the speed of accomplishing tasks can and will increase.

More than speed is needed to become a master technician. It requires problem solving and critical thinking skills, too. While beginning technicians are usually not required to diagnose problems, troubleshooting skills are very important toward becoming a master technician. Most master technicians follow a plan that includes:

1. Always verify the customer concern.

2. Perform a thorough visual inspection and check for possible causes of the problem, including damage from road debris or accidents.

3. Use a scan tool and check for stored diagnostic trouble codes (DTCs).

4. Check service information for technical service bulletins (TSBs).

5. Check service information and follow all diagnostic trouble charts.

6. Locate and correct the root cause of the problem.

7. Verify the repair and document the work order.

The hardest part of the diagnostic process is to locate the root cause of the problem. The process of analyzing and evaluating information and making a conclusion is called **critical thinking.**

HOUSEKEEPING DUTIES

A professional service technician is usually responsible for keeping his or her work area clean and tidy. Good housekeeping includes all of the following:

- **Clean floor**—If coolant or oil is spilled on the floor during a repair procedure, it should be cleaned before starting another job.

- **Tool box**—Keep work area and tool box clean and organized.

TECH TIP

Keeping "Things" off the Floor
To make cleaning easier and for a more professional shop appearance, keep only those items on the floor that have to be on the floor and find a place off the floor for all other items.

TECH TIP

Look at the Shop from a Customer's Point of View
To determine if the shop and other technicians look professional, step outside and enter the shop through the same door as a customer. Now look around. Look at the shop and the other technicians. Does the shop give the appearance of a professional service facility? If not, try to improve the look by asking the shop owner or service manager to do the same thing in an attempt to create a more professional-looking shop.

- **Items kept off the floor**—It is easy to allow parts and other items to be stored in and around the toolbox and in corners. However, having items on the floor makes keeping the area clean and neat looking very difficult.

- **Keep areas around exits and fire extinguishers clear.** Do not store or place parts, boxes, or shop equipment, such as floor jacks and testers, near exits and fire extinguishers. This helps ensure that people can have easy access to exits or the fire extinguishers in the event of an emergency.

- **Avoid spraying chemicals in the air.** To help keep the air in the shop clean, keep the use of spray chemicals, such as brake cleaner, to a minimum and avoid spraying where it could result in affecting the air others breathe.

SELF-MANAGEMENT

A professional service technician should try to maintain a professional appearance at all times. For example, if coolant or automatic transmission fluid (ATF) gets onto a shirt or pants, the wise technician would change into a clean uniform before working on another vehicle. Many shop owners and service managers recommend that shirttails always be tucked into pants to ensure a more professional appearance.

 TECH TIP

Write It Down

If a technician needs to have another technician finish a repair due to illness or some other reason, be sure to write down exactly what was done and what needs to be done. Verbal communication, while very effective, is often not a good way to explain multiple steps or processes. For example, the other technician could easily forget that the oil had not yet been added to the engine, which could cause a serious problem if the engine were to be started. If in doubt, write it down.

 TECH TIP

Don't Cover Up Mistakes

Everyone makes mistakes. While a damaged component or vehicle is never a good thing to have happen, the wise technician should notify the service manager or other person in charge as soon as a problem or accident occurs. Only then can work begin to correct the problem. If a mistake is hidden, eventually someone will learn about the error and then people will not think it was wise to ignore or to cover up the situation.

JOB EVALUATION

In most jobs, there is an evaluation of performance. A beginning technician is not expected to perform at the same level as an experienced master technician but should be able to do the following:

- **Follow instructions.** The trainee should follow the instructions of the mentor or service manager. This includes making sure that the person is notified when the job has been completed and if there were any problems.

- **Do no harm.** Avoid exerting a lot of force to door panels or other components to help avoid breaking clips or components. Always use the right tool for the job. For example, never use pliers to remove a bolt or nut, which could round off the flats of the fastener. Always think before acting, "Am I going to hurt something by doing this?"

- **Keep a neat and clean appearance.** It is normal to get dirty while performing service work on a vehicle. However, after each job is completed or even during the repair, try to keep as clean as possible.

- **Ask that your work be checked.** Even though the trainee thinks that the service or repair was done correctly, until confidence has been established, it is wise to ask to have all work double-checked.

CAUTION: Never allow a mistake to reach the customer. It is only a problem if it cannot be corrected.

FORMAL EVALUATION The mentor and/or service manager may or may not conduct a written evaluation on a regular basis. If a written evaluation is performed, this is called a **formal evaluation.** A formal evaluation usually includes many points of discussion. See the sample evaluation form.

INFORMAL EVALUATION In many cases, a beginning technician's activities are simply observed and noted, which is a type of **informal evaluation.** Both are usually done and both can influence the technician's pay.

NOTE: Most employees are fired from a job as the result of not being able to get along with others, rather than a lack of technical skills.

Technician Evaluation

Please check one of the spaces to the left of each characteristic which best expresses your judgment of the technician:

ATTITUDE-APPLICATION TO WORK
_____outstanding in enthusiasm
_____very interested and industrious
_____average in diligence and interest
_____somewhat indifferent
_____definitely not interested

DEPENDABILITY
_____completely dependable
_____above average in dependability
_____usually dependable
_____sometimes neglectful or careless
_____unreliable

QUALITY OF WORK
_____excellent
_____very good
_____average
_____below average
_____very poor

MATURITY
_____shows confidence
_____has good self-assurance
_____average maturity
_____seldom assertive
_____timid
_____brash

ABILITY TO LEARN
_____learned work exceptionally well
_____learned work readily
_____average in understanding work
_____rather slow in learning
_____very slow to learn

INITIATIVE
_____proceeds well on his or her own
_____proceeds independently at times
_____does all assigned work
_____hesitates
_____must be pushed frequently

RELATIONS WITH OTHERS
_____exceptionally well accepted
_____works well with others
_____gets along satisfactorily
_____has difficulty working with others
_____works very poorly with others

QUANTITY OF WORK
_____usually high output
_____more than average
_____normal amount
_____below average
_____low output, slow

JUDGMENT
_____exceptionally mature
_____above average
_____usually makes the right decision
_____often uses poor judgment

ATTENDANCE
_____regular
_____irregular

PUNCTUALITY
_____regular
_____irregular

SUMMARY

1. Professionalism and personal credibility are important to the success of any service technician.

2. A mentor is an experienced technician who helps a beginning technician in all aspects of the trade.

3. A mentor can help a beginning service technician to not only quickly learn how to perform automotive service and repair procedures but also can provide career and personal development guidance.

4. The beginning service technician (trainee) has the responsibility to ask questions and act in a professional manner.

5. Evaluations can be formal or informal.

6. Before a technician starts to work on a vehicle, the work order should be read carefully to determine exactly what service needs to be performed.

7. If a technician is asked to talk to a customer about a repair, discuss the original problem (concern), what was found (cause), and what was done to correct the fault (correction).

8. A technician should always document the work order and follow the vehicle manufacturer's recommended procedures.

REVIEW QUESTIONS

1. What factors are part of being a professional service technician?

2. What is a mentor?

3. What are the roles of a mentor?

4. What are the responsibilities the beginning technician has to the shop and/or mentor?

5. A formal evaluation could include what items?

6. What are the three Cs?

7. What should be included on the work order after the repair has been completed?

CHAPTER QUIZ

1. Professionalism includes which factor?
   a. Keeping your word
   b. Becoming a teammate with your coworkers
   c. Apologizing if you are wrong
   d. All of the above

2. Types of communications include _____
   a. Verbal
   b. Written
   c. Nonverbal
   d. All of the above

3. The three Cs include _____
   a. Correction, correct torque, and customer name
   b. Concern, cause, and correction
   c. Cause, cost, and caller name
   d. Captured data, cause, and cost (of the repair)

4. When documenting the work order, what things should be listed?
   a. The test equipment used in the diagnosis
   b. The test procedure that was followed
   c. The parts that were replaced
   d. All of the above

5. Technician A says that customer-pay rate is sometimes higher than the factory flat-rate. Technician B says that the factory flat-rate times are usually longer (given more time) compared to aftermarket flat-rate time guides. Which technician is correct?
   a. Technician A only
   b. Technician B only
   c. Both Technicians A and B
   d. Neither Technician A nor B

6. Housekeeping duties of a technician can include_____
   a. Cleaning the floor
   b. Keeping the work area clean and organized
   c. Keeping items off the floor whenever possible
   d. All of the above

7. If running late, the wise technician should_____
   a. Call the shop and let them know you will be late
   b. Speed up
   c. Call the shop and take the day off
   d. Stop and eat a good breakfast before going to the shop

8. Flat-rate pay means_____
   a. The same pay (flat-rate) every week
   b. The same number of hours every week
   c. The technician is paid according to the job, not by the number of hours worked
   d. The technician is paid overtime

9. Customer pay (CP) means_____
   a. Customer pays for the repair or service
   b. Warranty does not pay for the repair or service
   c. The technician often gets paid more for each job
   d. All of the above

10. A mentor performs all of the following except _____
    a. Helps guide diagnosis of a problem
    b. Signs paychecks
    c. Offers advice on how to do a job
    d. Advises on professional behavior

chapter 5

TECHNICIAN CERTIFICATION

OBJECTIVES: **After studying Chapter 5, the reader will be able to:** • Explain the requirements for becoming an ASE certified technician. • Describe the type of test questions asked on the certification tests. • Explain how to prepare to take the ASE certification tests. • Describe test taking skills needed to help pass the certification tests. • Explain how to register and take the ASE certification tests.

KEY TERMS: • Except-type questions 42 • ASE (National Institute for Automotive service Excellence) 40 • Distracter 41 • Experience-based questions 41 • IP certification 46 • Key 41 • Least-likely-type question 42 • ASE certified master 40 • Most-likely-type question 42 • Multiple-choice question 41 • Technician A and B question 42 • Work experience 41

AUTOMOBILE TECHNICIAN CERTIFICATION TESTS

Even though individual franchises and companies often certify their own technicians, there is a nationally recognized certification organization, the **National Institute for Automotive Service Excellence,** better known by its abbreviation, **ASE.**
● **SEE FIGURE 5–1.**

ASE is a nonprofit association founded in 1972, and its main goal is to improve the quality of vehicle service through standardized testing and volunteer certification.

WHAT AREAS OF VEHICLE SERVICE ARE COVERED BY THE ASE TESTS?
Automobile test service areas include:

A1 Engine Repair

A2 Automatic Transmission/Transaxle

A3 Manual Drivetrain and Axles

A4 Suspension and Steering

A5 Brakes

A6 Electrical/Electronic Systems

A7 Heating and Air Conditioning

A8 Engine Performance

If a technician takes and passes all eight of the automobile tests and has achieved two or more years of work experience, ASE will award the designation of **ASE Certified Master Automobile Technician.** Contact ASE for other certification areas.

FIGURE 5–1 The ASE logo. *(Courtesy of ASE)*

HOW CAN I CONTACT ASE?

ASE
101 Blue Seal Drive, SE
Suite 101
Leesburg, VA 20175

Toll-free: 1-800-390-6789
1-703-669-6600
website: www.ase.com

WHEN ARE THE TESTS GIVEN AND WHERE?

The ASE written tests are given at hundreds of test sites throughout the year for online testing.

NOTE: ASE offers tests at various times of the year electronically. Go to the ASE website for details.

Consult the ASE registration booklet or website for details and locations of the test sites.

WHAT DO I HAVE TO DO TO REGISTER?

You can register for the ASE tests in three ways:

1. Mail in the registration form that is in the registration booklet.
2. Register online at www.ase.com
3. Telephone at (866) 427-3273

Call ASE toll-free at 1-888-ASE-TEST or visit the website for details about cost and dates.

HOW MANY YEARS OF WORK EXPERIENCE ARE NEEDED?

ASE requires that you have two or more years of full-time, hands-on **working experience** either as an automobile, truck, truck equipment, or school bus technician, engine machinist, or in collision repair, refinishing, or damage analysis and estimating for certification, except as noted below. If you have *not* previously provided work experience information, you will receive a Work Experience Report Form with your admission ticket. You *must* complete and return this form to receive a certificate.

SUBSTITUTIONS FOR WORK EXPERIENCE. You may receive credit for up to one year of the two-year work experience requirement by substituting relevant formal training in one, or a combination, of the following:

High School Training: Three full years of training, either in automobile/truck/school bus repair or in ollision repair, refinishing, or damage estimating, may be substituted for one year of work experience.

Post-High School Training: Two full years of post-high school training in a public or private trade school, technical institute, community or four-year college, or in an apprenticeship program may be counted as one year of work experience.

Short Courses: For shorter periods of post-high school training, you may substitute two months of training for one month of work experience.

You may receive full credit for the two-year work experience requirement with the following:

Completion of Apprenticeship: Satisfactory completion of either a three- or four-year bona fide apprenticeship program.

ARE THERE ANY HANDS-ON ACTIVITIES ON THE ASE TEST?

No. All ASE tests are written using objective-type questions, meaning that you must select the correct answer from four possible alternatives.

WHO WRITES THE ASE QUESTIONS?

All ASE test questions are written by a panel of industry experts, educators, and experienced ASE certified service technicians. Each question is reviewed by the committee and it is checked for the following:

- **Technically accurate.** All test questions use the correct terms and only test for vehicle manufacturer's recommended service procedures. Slang is not used nor are any aftermarket accessories included on the ASE test.
- **Manufacturer neutral.** All efforts are made to avoid using vehicle or procedures that are manufacturer specific such as to General Motors vehicles or to Toyotas. A service technician should feel comfortable about being able to answer the questions regardless of the type or brand of vehicle.
- **Logical answers.** All effort is made to be sure that all answers (not just the correct answers) are possible. While this may seem to make the test tricky, it is designed to test for real knowledge of the subject.
- **Random answer.** All efforts are made to be sure that the correct answers are not always the longest answer or that one letter, such as **c,** is not used more than any other letter.
- **Experience-based questions.** The questions asked are generally not knowledge-based questions, but rather require experience to answer correctly. Specifications are not asked for, but instead a question as to what would most likely occur if the unit is out-of-specifications could be asked.

KEY AND DISTRACTER

The **key** is the correct answer. As part of the test writing sessions, the committee is asked to create other answers that sound feasible but are not correct. These incorrect answers are called **distracters.**

WHAT TYPES OF QUESTIONS ARE ASKED ON THE ASE TEST?

All ASE test questions are objective. This means that there will not be questions where you will have to write an answer. Instead, all you have to do is select one of the four possible answers and place a mark in the correct place on the score sheet.

- **Multiple-choice questions.** This type of question has one correct (or mostly correct) answer (called the key) and three incorrect answers. A multiple-choice question example:

  What part of an automotive engine does not move?

  a. Piston
  b. Connecting rod
  c. Block
  d. Valve

The correct answer is **c** (block). This type of question asks for a specific answer. Answer **a** (piston), **b** (connecting rod), and **d** (valve) all move during normal engine operation. The best answer is **c** (block) because even though it may vibrate, it does not move as the other parts do.

- **Technician A and Technician B questions.** This type of question is generally considered to be the most difficult according to service technicians who take the ASE test. A situation or condition is usually stated and two technicians (A and B) say what they think could be the correct answer and you must decide which technician is correct.

  a. Technician A only
  b. Technician B only
  c. Both Technicians A and B
  d. Neither Technician A nor B

The best way to answer this type of question is to carefully read the question and consider Technician A and Technician B answers to be solutions to a true or false question. If Technician A is correct, mark on the test by Technician A the letter T for true. If Technician B is also correct, write the letter T for true by Technician B. Then mark **c** on your test score sheet, for both technicians are correct.

Example:

Two technicians are discussing an engine that has lower than specified fuel pressure. Technician A says that the fuel pump could be the cause. Technician B says that the fuel pressure regulator could be the cause.

 Which technician is correct?

  a. Technician A only
  b. Technician B only
  c. Both Technicians A and B
  d. Neither Technician A nor B

Analysis:

Is Technician A correct? The answer is yes because if the fuel pump was defective, the pump pressure could be lower than specified by the vehicle manufacturer. Is Technician B correct? The answer is yes because a stuck open regulator with a weak spring could be the cause of lower than specified fuel pressure. The correct answer is therefore **c** (Both Technicians A and B are correct).

- **Most-likely-type questions.** This type of question asks which of the four possible items listed is the most likely to cause the problem or symptom. This type of question is often considered to be difficult because recent experience may lead you to answer the question incorrectly because even though it is possible, it is not the "most likely."

Example:

Which of the items below is the most likely to cause blue exhaust at engine start?

  a. Valve stem seals
  b. Piston rings
  c. Clogged PCV valve
  d. A stuck oil pump regulator valve

Analysis:

The correct answer is **a** because valve stem seals are the most likely to cause this problem. Answer **b** is not correct because even though worn piston rings can cause the engine to burn oil and produce blue exhaust smoke, it is not the most likely cause of blue smoke at engine start. Answers **c** and **d** are not correct because even though these items could contribute to the engine burning oil and producing blue exhaust smoke, they are not the most likely.

- **Except-type questions.** ASE will sometimes use a question that includes answers that are all correct except one. You have to determine which of the four answers is not correct.

Example:

A radiator is being pressure tested using a hand-operated tester. This test will check for leaks in all except:

  a. Radiator   b. Heater core
  c. Water pump   d. Evaporator

Analysis:

The correct answer is **d** because the evaporator is not included in the cooling system and will not be pressurized during this test. Answers **a** (radiator), **b** (heater core), and **c** (water pump) are all being tested under pressure exerted on the cooling system by the pressure tester.

- **Least-likely-type questions.** Another type of question asked on many ASE tests is a question that asks which of the following is least likely to be the cause of a problem or symptom. In other words, all of the answers are possible, but it is up to the reader to determine which answer is the least likely to be correct.

Example:

Which of the following is the least likely cause of low oil pressure?

  a. Clogged oil pump screen   b. Worn main bearing
  c. Worn camshaft bearing   d. Worn oil pump

Analysis:

The correct answer is **c** because even though worn camshaft bearings can cause low oil pressure, the other answers are more likely to be the cause.

QUESTIONS OFTEN ASKED

SHOULD I GUESS IF I DON'T KNOW THE ANSWER? Yes. ASE tests simply record the correct answers, and by guessing, you will have at least a 25% (1 out of 4) chance. If you leave the answer blank, it will be scored as being incorrect. Instead of guessing entirely, try to eliminate as many of the answers as possible as not being very likely. If you can eliminate two out of the four, you have increased your chance of guessing to 50% (two out of four).

IS EACH TEST THE SAME EVERY TIME I TAKE IT? No. ASE writes many questions for each area and selects from this "test bank" for each test session. You may see some of the same questions if you take the same test in the spring and then again in the fall, but you will also see many different questions.

CAN I SKIP QUESTIONS I DON'T KNOW AND COME BACK TO ANSWER LATER?

Yes. You may skip a question if you wish, but be sure to mark the question and return to answer the question later. It is often recommended to answer the question or guess and go on with the test so that you do not run out of time to go back over the questions.

HOW MUCH TIME DO I HAVE TO TAKE THE TESTS?

Each computer-based test will allow enough time for completion, usually between one and two hours for each test. The time allowed for each test is available on the ASE website.

WILL I HAVE TO KNOW SPECIFICATIONS AND GAUGE READINGS?

Yes and no. You will be asked the correct range for a particular component or operation and you must know about what the specification should be. Otherwise, the questions will state that the value is less than or greater than the allowable specification. The question will deal with how the service technician should proceed or what action should be taken.

CAN I TAKE A BREAK DURING THE TEST?

Yes, you may use the restroom after receiving permission from the proctor of the test site.

CAN I LEAVE EARLY IF I HAVE COMPLETED THE TEST(S)?

Yes, you may leave quietly after you have completed the test(s).

HOW ARE THE TESTS SCORED?

The ASE tests are machine scored and the results tabulated by American College Testing (ACT).

WHAT PERCENTAGE DO I NEED TO ACHIEVE TO PASS THE ASE TEST?

While there is no exact number of questions that must be answered correctly in each area, an analysis of the test results indicate that the percentage needed to pass varies from 61% to 69%. Therefore, in order to pass the Engine Repair (A1) ASE certification test, you will have to answer about 39 questions correct out of 60. In other words, you can miss about 21 questions and still pass.

WHAT HAPPENS IF I DO NOT PASS? DO I HAVE TO WAIT A YEAR BEFORE TRYING AGAIN?

No. If you fail to achieve a passing score on any ASE test, you can take the test again at the next testing session.

DO I HAVE TO PAY ANOTHER REGISTRATION FEE IF I ALREADY PAID IT ONCE?

Yes. The registration fee is due at every test session whether you select to take one or more ASE tests. Therefore, it is wise to take as many tests as you can at each test session.

WILL I RECEIVE NOTICE OF WHICH QUESTIONS I MISSED?

ASE sends out a summary of your test results, which shows how many questions you missed in each category, but not individual questions.

WILL ASE SEND ME THE CORRECT ANSWERS TO THE QUESTIONS I MISSED SO I WILL KNOW HOW TO ANSWER THEM IN THE FUTURE?

No. ASE will not send you the answers to test questions.

TEST-TAKING TIPS

START NOW

Even if you have been working on vehicles for a long time, taking an ASE certification test can be difficult. The questions will not include how things work or other "textbook" knowledge. The questions are based on "real-world" diagnosis and service. The tests may seem tricky to some because the wrong answers are designed to be similar to the correct answer.

If this is your first time taking the test or you are going to recertify, start now to prepare. Allocate time each day to study.

PRACTICE IS IMPORTANT

Many service technicians do not like taking tests. As a result, many technicians rush through the test to get the pain over with quickly. Also, many service technicians have lots of experience on many different vehicles. This is what makes them good at what they do, but when an everyday problem is put into a question format (multiple choice), the answer may not be as clear as your experience has taught you.

KEYS TO SUCCESS
The keys to successful test taking include:

- Practice answering similar-type questions.
- Carefully read each question two times to make sure you understand the question.
- Read each answer.
- Pick the best answer.
- Avoid reading too much into each question.
- Do not change an answer unless you are sure that the answer is definitely wrong.
- Look over the glossary of automotive terms for words that are not familiar to you.

The best preparation is practice, practice, and more practice. This is where using the ASE Test Prep practice tests can help.

PREPARE MENTALLY
Practicing also helps relieve another potential problem many people have called "chronic test syndrome." This condition is basically an inability to concentrate or focus during a test. The slightest noise, fear of failure, and worries about other things all contribute. The best medicine is practice, practice, and more practice. With practice, test taking becomes almost second nature.

PREPARE PHYSICALLY
Be prepared physically. Get enough sleep and eat right.

ONE MONTH BEFORE THE TEST

- Budget your time for studying. On average you will need four to six hours of study for each test that you are taking.
- Use the ASE Test Prep Online test preparation service three or more times a week for your practice.
- Study with a friend or a group if possible.

THE WEEK BEFORE THE TEST

- Studying should consist of about two hours of reviewing for each test being taken.
- Make sure you know how to get to the testing center. If possible, drive to the test site and locate the room.
- Get plenty of rest.

THE DAY OF THE TEST

- Study time is over.
- Keep your work schedule light or get the day off if possible.
- Eat a small, light meal the evening of the test.
- Drink a large glass of water one to two hours before the test. (The brain and body work on electrical impulses, and water is used as a conductor.)
- Arrive at least 30 minutes early at the test center. Be ready to start on time.

WHAT TO BRING TO THE TEST

- A photo ID.
- Your Entry Ticket that came with your ASE packet.

DURING THE TEST

- BREATHE (oxygen is the most important nutrient for the brain).
- Read every question TWICE.
- Read ALL the ANSWERS.
- If you have trouble with a question, leave it blank and continue. At the end of the test, go back and try any skipped questions. (Frequently, you will get a hint in another question that follows.)

There are eight automotive certifications including:

1. Engine Repair (A1) ASE Task List

Content Area	Questions in Test	Percentage of Test
A. General Engine Diagnosis	15	28%
B. Cylinder Head and Valve Train Diagnosis and Repair	10	23%
C. Engine Block Diagnosis and Repair	10	23%
D. Lubrication and Cooling Systems Diagnosis and Repair	8	14%
E. Fuel, Electrical, Ignition, and Exhaust Systems Inspection and Service	7	12%
Total	**50**	**100%**

2. Automatic Transmission/Transaxles (A2) ASE Task List

Content Area	Questions in Test	Percentage of Test
A. General Transmission/ Transaxle Diagnosis 1. Mechanical/Hydraulic Systems (11) 2. Electronic Systems (14)	25	50%
B. In-Vehicle Transmission/ Transaxle Repair	12	16%
C. Off-Vehicle Transmission/ Transaxle Repair 1. Removal, Disassembly, and Assembly (3) 2. Gear Train, Shafts, Bushings, Oil Pump, and Case (4) 3. Friction and Reaction Units (4)	13	26%
Total	**50**	**100%**

3. Manual Drivetrain and Axles (A3) ASE Task List

Content Area	Questions in Test	Percentage of Test
A. Clutch Diagnosis and Repair	6	15%
B. Transmission Diagnosis and Repair	7	18%
C. Transaxle Diagnosis and Repair	7	20%
D. Drive (Half) Shaft and Universal Joint/Constant Velocity (CV) Joint Diagnosis and Repair (Front- and Rear-wheel Drive)	5	13%

E. Rear Axle Diagnosis and Repair
  1. Ring and Pinion Gears (3)
  2. Differential Case Assembly (2)
  3. Limited Slip Differential (1)
  4. Axle Shafts (1)
	7	17%

F. Four-Wheel Drive Component Diagnosis and Repair	8	17%
Total	**40**	**100%**

4. Suspension and Steering (A4) ASE Task List

Content Area	Questions in Test	Percentage of Test

A. Steering Systems Diagnosis and Repair
  1. Steering Columns and Manual Steering Gears (3)
  2. Power-Assisted Steering Units (4)
  3. Steering Linkage (3)
	10	25%

B. Suspension Systems Diagnosis and Repair
  1. Front Suspensions (6)
  2. Rear Suspensions (5)
  3. Miscellaneous Service (2)
	11	28%

C. Related Suspension and Steering Service	2	5%
D. Wheel Alignment Diagnosis, Adjustment, and Repair	12	30%
E. Wheel and Tire Diagnosis and Repair	5	12%
Total	**40**	**100%**

5. Brakes (A5) ASE Task List

Content Area	Questions in Test	Percentage of Test

A. Hydraulic Systems Diagnosis and Repair
  1. Master Cylinders (non-ABS) (3)
  2. Fluids, Lines, and Hoses (3)
  3. Valves and Switches (non-ABS) (4)
  4. Bleeding, Flushing, and Leak Testing (non-ABS) (4)
	12	27%

B. Drum Brake Diagnosis and Repair	5	11%
C. Disc Brake Diagnosis and Repair	10	22%
D. Power Assist Units Diagnosis and Repair	4	8%
E. Miscellaneous Diagnosis and Repair	7	16%
F. Antilock Brake System Diagnosis and Repair	7	16%
Total	**45**	**100%**

6. Electrical Systems (A6) ASE Task List

Content Area	Questions in Test	Percentage of Test
A. General Electrical/Electronic System Diagnosis	13	26%
B. Battery Diagnosis and Service	4	8%
C. Starting System Diagnosis and Repair	5	10%
D. Charging System Diagnosis and Repair	5	10%

E. Lighting Systems Diagnosis and Repair
  1. Headlights, Parking Lights, Taillights, Dash Lights, and Courtesy Lights (3)
  2. Stoplights, Turn Signals, Hazard Lights, and Back-up Lights (3)
	6	12%

F. Gauges, Warning Devices, and Driver Information Systems Diagnosis and Repair	6	12%
G. Horn and Wiper/Washer Diagnosis and Repair	3	6%

H. Accessories Diagnosis and Repair
  1. Body (4)
  2. Miscellaneous (4)
	8	16%

Total	**50**	**100%**

7. Heating and Air Conditioning (A7) ASE Task List

Content Area	Questions in Test	Percentage of Test
A. A/C System Diagnosis and Repair	13	24%
B. Refrigeration System Component Diagnosis and Repair 1. Compressor and Clutch (5) 2. Evaporator, Condenser, and Related Components (5)	10	20%
C. Heating and Engine Cooling Systems Diagnosis and Repair	4	10%
D. Operating Systems and Related Controls Diagnosis and Repair 1. Electrical (9) 2. Vacuum/Mechanical (3) 3. Automatic and Semi-Automatic Heating, Ventilating, and A/C Systems (5)	19	34%
E. Refrigerant Recover, Recycling, and Handling	4	12%
Total	**50**	**100%**

8. Engine Performance (A8) ASE Task List

Content Area	Questions in Test	Percentage of Test
A. General Engine Diagnosis	12	17%
B. Ignition System Diagnosis and Repair	8	17%
C. Fuel, Air Induction, and Exhaust Systems Diagnosis and Repair	9	18%
D. Emissions Control Systems Diagnosis and Repair 1. Positive Crankcase Ventilation (1) 2. Exhaust Gas Recirculation (3) 3. Secondary Air Injector (AIR) and Catalytic Converter (2) 4. Evaporative Emissions Controls (3)	8	15%
E. Computerized Engine Controls Diagnosis and Repair (Including OBD II)	13	27%
Total	**50**	**100%**

To become certified by ASE, the service technician must have two years of experience and pass a test in each area. If a technician passes all eight automotive certification tests, then the technician is considered a master certified automobile service technician.

CANADA'S AUTOMOTIVE APPRENTICESHIP PROGRAM (RED SEAL)

In Canada, in all provinces and territories but Quebec and British Columbia, an **Inter-Provincial (IP) Certificate** is required. An apprenticeship program is in place that takes a minimum of four years, combining ten months in a shop and about two months in school training in each of the four years. Most apprentices must undergo 7200 hours of training before they can complete the IP examination. ASE certifications are currently used on a voluntary basis since 1993, however an IP Certificate is still required. Other licensing of automotive technicians may be required in some cases, such as environmental substances, liquefied petroleum gas, or steam operators.

NOTE: A valid driver's license is a must for any automotive service technician.

RECERTIFICATION

All ASE certifications expire after five years and the technician needs to take a recertification test to remain certified. As vehicles and technology change, it is important that all technicians attend update classes. Most experts recommend that each technician should have at least 40 hours (one full week) of update training every year. Update training classes can be found through many sources, including:

1. Many parts stores and warehouse distributors provide training classes throughout the year.
2. State or regional associations, such as the Automotive Service Association (www.asashop.org), offer update conferences.
3. Local colleges or training companies offer update training. Other training can be found listed on the International Automotive Technicians Network (www.iatn.net).

SUMMARY

1. ASE is an abbreviation for the National Institute for Automotive Service Excellence, a nonprofit association founded in 1972.

2. The eight ASE test content areas include: A1—Engine Repair, A2—Automatic Transmission, A3—Manual Drivetrain and Axles, A4—Suspension and Steering, A5—Brakes, A6— electrical/ Electronic Systems, A7—Heating and Air Conditioning, and A8—Engine Performance.

3. To become an ASE certified technician, two years of experience are required plus achieving a passing test score on one or more ASE certification tests.

4. The types of questions used on an ASE certification test include: multiple-choice questions, Technician A and Technician B questions, most-likely-type questions, except-type questions, and least-likely-type questions.

REVIEW QUESTIONS

1. What are the eight ASE test areas?
2. When are the written ASE tests given?
3. What types of questions are asked on the ASE certification tests?
4. What can a technician do to help prepare to take the certification tests?

CHAPTER QUIZ

1. Which ASE certification test would cover experience in lighting system diagnosis?
   a. A6
   b. A7
   c. A8
   d. All of the above are possible

2. How many ASE tests must be passed to become a master automotive technician?
   a. 8
   b. 6
   c. 4
   d. 2

3. How many years of experience are required to achieve ASE certification?
   a. 8
   b. 6
   c. 4
   d. 2

4. Credit for how many years of work experience can be substituted by attending automotive service training?
   a. None —no substitution for work experience is permitted
   b. 1 year
   c. 2 years
   d. 3 years

5. When taking an ASE certification test, _____.
   a. You can take a break after receiving permission
   b. The correct answers will be shown after you finish
   c. Only one test can be taken
   d. Some hands-on activities may be required

6. A type of test question *not* asked on the ASE certification test is_____.
   a. Most likely
   b. Least likely
   c. Fill in the blank
   d. Multiple choice

7. Which type of question is the same as two true-and-false-type questions?
   a. All except type
   b. Technician A and Technician B
   c. Least likely type
   d. Most likely type

8. Technician A says that you should guess if you do not know the correct answer. Technician B says that ASE will send you the correct answers to the questions you missed with your test results. Which technician is correct?
   a. Technician A only
   b. Technician B only
   c. Both Technicians A and B
   d. Neither Technician A nor B

9. ASE tests require knowledge of vehicle specifications for spark plug gap.
   a. True
   b. False

10. A technician should do all of the following to prepare to take the ASE certification test *except* _____.
    a. Get a good night's sleep the night before the test
    b. Try to keep work schedule light the day of the test
    c. Eat a big meal
    d. Have photo ID and entry ticket

chapter
6

SHOP SAFETY

OBJECTIVES: After studying Chapter 6, the reader should be able to: • Identify situations where hearing protection should be worn. • Discuss how to safely handle tools and shop equipment. • Describe how to properly use a fire extinguisher. • Discuss shop safety procedures.

KEY TERMS: • ANSI 48 • Bump cap 49 • Decibel (dB) 49 • Eye wash station 54 • Fire blankets 53 • Microbes 51 • "PASS" 52 • Personal protective equipment (PPE) 48 • Spontaneous combustion 50

PERSONAL PROTECTIVE EQUIPMENT

Safety is not just a buzzword on a poster in the work area. Safe work habits can reduce accidents and injuries, ease the workload, and keep employees pain free.

SAFETY GLASSES The most important **personal protective equipment (PPE)** a technician should wear all the time are safety glasses, which meet standard **ANSI** Z87.1. ● **SEE FIGURE 6–1.**

STEEL-TOED SHOES Steel-toed safety shoes are also a good investment. ● **SEE FIGURE 6–2.** If safety shoes are not available, then leather-topped shoes offer more protection than canvas or cloth covered shoes.

GLOVES Wear gloves to protect your hands from rough or sharp surfaces. Thin rubber gloves are recommended when working around automotive liquids such as engine oil, antifreeze,

transmission fluid, or any other liquids that may be hazardous. Several types of gloves and their characteristics include:

■ **Latex surgical gloves.** These gloves are relatively inexpensive, but tend to stretch, swell, and weaken when exposed to gas, oil, or solvents.

■ **Vinyl gloves.** These gloves are also inexpensive and are not affected by gas, oil, or solvents. ● **SEE FIGURE 6–3.**

■ **Polyurethane gloves.** These gloves are more expensive, yet very strong. Even though these gloves are also not affected by gas, oil, or solvents, they tend to be slippery.

■ **Nitrile gloves.** These gloves are exactly like latex gloves, but are not affected by gas, oil, or solvents, yet they tend to be expensive.

■ **Mechanic's gloves.** These gloves are usually made of synthetic leather and spandex and provide thermo protection, as well as protection from dirt and grime.

FIGURE 6–2 Steel-toed shoes are a worthwhile investment to help prevent foot injury due to falling objects. Even these well-worn shoes can protect the feet of this service technician.

FIGURE 6–1 Safety glasses should be worn at all times when working on or around any vehicle or servicing any component.

FIGURE 6-3 Protective gloves such as these vinyl gloves are available in several sizes. Select the size that allows the gloves to fit snugly. Vinyl gloves last a long time and often can be worn all day to help protect your hands from dirt and possible hazardous materials.

FIGURE 6-4 One version of a bump cap is this padded plastic insert that is worn inside a regular cloth cap.

BUMP CAP Service technicians working under a vehicle should wear a **bump cap** to protect the head against under-vehicle objects and the pads of the hoist. ● **SEE FIGURE 6-4.**

HANDS, JEWELRY, AND CLOTHING Remove jewelry that may get caught on something or act as a conductor to an exposed electrical circuit. ● **SEE FIGURE 6-5.**

Take care of your hands. Keep your hands clean by washing with soap and hot water that is at least 110°F (43°C). Avoid loose or dangling clothing. Also, ear protection should be worn if the sound around you requires that you raise your voice (sound level higher than 90 **decibels [dB]**).

NOTE: A typical lawnmower produces noise at a level of about 110 dB. This means that everyone who uses a lawnmower or other lawn or garden equipment should wear ear protection.

FIGURE 6-5 Remove all jewelry before performing service work on any vehicle.

 TECH TIP

Professional Behavior in the Shop Is a Must

To be respected as a professional service techni-cian and for safety, always behave in a professional manner. These behaviors include, but are not limited to the following:

- Show respect to other technicians and employees. For example, the shop owner or service manager may not always be right, but they are always the boss.
- Avoid horseplay or practical jokes.
- Act as if a customer is observing your behavior at all times because this is often the case.

SAFETY TIPS FOR TECHNICIANS

- When lifting any object, get a secure grip with solid footing. Keep the load close to your body to minimize the strain. Lift with your legs and arms, not your back.
- Do not twist your body when carrying a load. Instead, pivot your feet to help prevent strain on the spine.
- Ask for help when moving or lifting heavy objects.
- Push a heavy object rather than pull it. (This is oppo-site to the way you should work with tools—never push a wrench! If you do and a bolt or nut loosens,

FIGURE 6–6 Always connect an exhaust hose to the tailpipe of the engine of a vehicle to be run inside a building.

FIGURE 6–8 An electric pusher used to push vehicles into or around the shop.

FIGURE 6–7 A magnetic tray is a helpful item to keep needed tools up where they can be easily reached without having to bend over, saving time and energy over the course of a long day in the shop.

your entire weight is used to propel your hand(s) forward. This usually results in cuts, bruises, or other painful injury.)

- Always connect an exhaust hose to the tailpipe of any running vehicle to help prevent the buildup of carbon monoxide inside a closed garage space. ● **SEE FIGURE 6–6**.

- When standing, keep objects, parts, and tools with which you are working between chest height and waist height. If seated, work at tasks that are at elbow height. ● **SEE FIGURE 6–7**.

- Always be sure the hood is securely held open.

- Ask for help when pushing a vehicle or use a motorized pusher. ● **SEE FIGURE 6–8**.

SAFETY TIP

Shop Cloth Disposal

Always dispose of oily shop cloths in an enclosed container to prevent a fire. ● **SEE FIGURE 6–9**. Whenever oily cloths are thrown together on the floor or workbench, a chemical reaction can occur which can ignite the cloth even without an open flame. This process of ignition without an open flame is called **spontaneous combustion.**

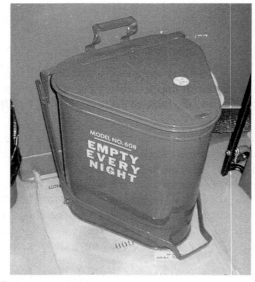

FIGURE 6–9 All oily shop cloths should be stored in a metal container equipped with a lid to help prevent spontaneous combustion.

TECH TIP

Pound with Something Softer

If you must pound on something, be sure to use a tool that is softer than what you are about to pound on to avoid damage. Examples are given in the following table.

The Material Being Pounded	What to Pound With
Steel or cast iron	Brass or aluminum hammer or punch
Aluminum	Plastic or rawhide mallet or plastic-covered dead-blow hammer
Plastic	Rawhide mallet or plastic dead-blow hammer

CLEANING METHODS AND PROCESSES

There are four basic types of cleaning methods and processes used in vehicle service.

POWER WASHING   Power washing uses an electric- or gasoline-powered compressor to increase the pressure of water and force it out of a nozzle. The pressure of the water itself is usually enough to remove dirt, grease, and grime from vehicle components. Sometimes a chemical cleaner, such as a detergent, is added to the water to help with cleaning.

SAFE USE OF POWER WASHERS.   Because water is being sprayed at high pressure, a face shield should be worn when using a power washer to protect not only the eyes but also the face in the event of the spray being splashed back toward the technician. Also use a pressure washer in an area where the runoff from the cleaning will not contaminate local groundwater or cause harm to plants or animals.

CHEMICAL/MICROBE CLEANING   Chemical cleaning involves one of several cleaning solutions, including detergent, solvents, or small, living microorganisms called **microbes** that eat oil and grease. The microbes live in water and eat the hydrocarbons that are the basis of grease and oil.

SAFE USE OF CHEMICAL CLEANING.   A face shield should be worn when cleaning parts using a chemical cleaner. Avoid spilling the cleaner on the floor to help prevent slipping accidents. Clean and replace the chemical cleaner regularly.

ABRASIVE CLEANING   Abrasive cleaning is used to clean disassembled parts, such as engine blocks. The abrasives used include steel shot, ground walnut shells, or in the case of cleaning paint from a vehicle body, baking soda can be used.

SAFE USE OF ABRASIVE CLEANERS.   Always wear a protective face shield and protective clothing, including gloves, long sleeves, and long pants.

THERMAL OVENS   Thermal cleaning uses heat to bake off grease and dirt with special high-temperature ovens. This method of cleaning requires the use of expensive equipment but does not use any hazardous chemicals and is environmentally safe.

SAFE USE OF THERMAL OVENS.   Because thermal ovens operate at high temperatures, often exceeding 600°F (315°C), the oven should be turned off and allowed to cool overnight before removing the parts from the oven to avoid being exposed to the high temperature.

ELECTRICAL CORD SAFETY

Use correctly grounded three-prong sockets and extension cords to operate power tools. Some tools use only two-prong plugs. Make sure these are double insulated and repair or replace any electrical cords that are cut or damaged to prevent the possibility of an electrical shock. When not in use, keep electrical cords off the floor to prevent tripping over them. Tape the cords down if they are placed in high foot traffic areas.

JUMP-STARTING AND BATTERY SAFETY

To jump-start another vehicle with a dead battery, connect good-quality copper jumper cables as indicated in ● **FIGURE 6–10** or use a jump box. The last connection made should always be on the engine block or an engine bracket as far from the battery as possible. It is normal for a spark to be created when the jumper cables finally complete the jumper cable connections, and this spark could cause an explosion of the gases around the battery. Many newer vehicles have special ground connections built away from the battery just for the purpose of jump-starting. Check the owner manual or service information for the exact location.

SAFETY TIP

Compressed Air Safety

Improper use of an air nozzle can cause blindness or deafness. Compressed air must be reduced to less than 30 PSI (206 kPa). ● **SEE FIGURE 6–11**. If an air nozzle is used to dry and clean parts, make sure the air stream is directed away from anyone else in the immediate area. Always use an OSHA-approved nozzle with side slits that limit the maximum pressure at the nozzle to 30 PSI. Coil and store air hoses when they are not in use.

FIGURE 6–10 Jumper cable usage guide.

FIGURE 6–11 The air pressure going to the nozzle should be reduced to 30 PSI or less.

FIGURE 6–12 A typical fire extinguisher designed to be used on type class A, B, or C fires.

Batteries contain acid and should be handled with care, to avoid tipping them greater than a 45-degree angle. Always remove jewelry when working around a battery to avoid the possibility of electrical shock or burns, which can occur when the metal comes in contact with a 12 volt circuit and ground, such as the body of the vehicle.

FIRE EXTINGUISHERS

There are four classes of fire extinguishers. Each class should be used on specific fires only.

- *Class A* is designed for use on general combustibles, such as cloth, paper, and wood.

- *Class B* is designed for use on flammable liquids and greases, including gasoline, oil, thinners, and solvents.
- *Class C* is used only on electrical fires.
- *Class D* is effective only on combustible metals such as powdered aluminum, sodium, or magnesium.

The class rating is clearly marked on the side of every fire extinguisher. Many extinguishers are good for multiple types of fires. ● **SEE FIGURE 6–12**.

When using a fire extinguisher, remember the word **"PASS."**

P = Pull the safety pin.

A = Aim the nozzle of the extinguisher at the base of the fire.

S = Squeeze the lever to actuate the extinguisher.

S = Sweep the nozzle from side to side.

● **SEE FIGURE 6–13**.

FIGURE 6–13 A CO$_2$ fire extinguisher being used on a fire set in an open steel drum during a demonstration at a fire department training center.

FIGURE 6–14 A treated wool blanket is kept in this easy-to-open wall-mounted holder and should be placed in a centralized location in the shop.

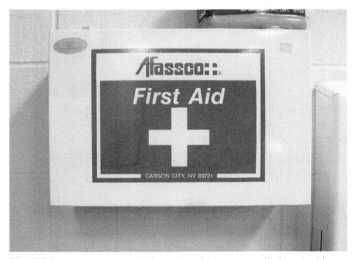

FIGURE 6–15 A first aid box should be centrally located in the shop and kept stocked with the recommended supplies.

TYPES OF FIRE EXTINGUISHERS Types of fire extinguishers include the following:

- **Water.** A water fire extinguisher, usually in a pressurized container, is good to use on Class A fires by reducing the temperature to the point where a fire cannot be sustained.

- **Carbon dioxide (CO$_2$).** A carbon dioxide fire extinguisher is good for almost any type of fire, especially Class B or Class C materials. A CO$_2$ fire extinguisher works by removing the oxygen from the fire and the cold CO$_2$ also helps reduce the temperature of the fire.

- **Dry chemical (yellow).** A dry chemical fire extinguisher is good for Class A, B, or C fires by coating the flammable materials, which eliminates the oxygen from the fire. A dry chemical fire extinguisher tends to be very corrosive and will cause damage to electronic devices.

FIRE BLANKETS

Fire blankets are required to be available in the shop areas. If a person is on fire, a fire blanket should be removed from its storage bag and thrown over and around the victim to smother the fire. ● **SEE FIGURE 6–14** showing a typical fire blanket.

FIRST AID AND EYE WASH STATIONS

All shop areas must be equipped with a first aid kit and an eye wash station centrally located and kept stocked with emergency supplies.

FIRST AID KIT A first aid kit should include:

- Bandages (variety)
- Gauze pads
- Roll gauze
- Iodine swab sticks
- Antibiotic ointment
- Hydrocortisone cream
- Burn gel packets
- Eye wash solution
- Scissors
- Tweezers
- Gloves
- First aid guide

● **SEE FIGURE 6–15.** Every shop should have a person trained in first aid. If there is an accident, call for help immediately.

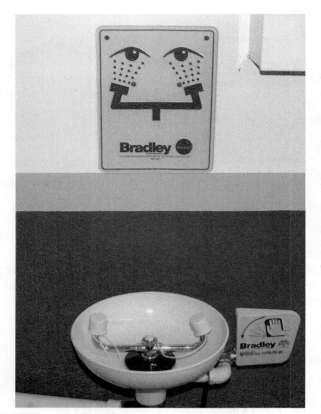

FIGURE 6–16 A typical eye wash station. Often a thorough flushing of the eyes with water is the best treatment in the event of eye contamination.

FIGURE 6–17 This area has been blocked off to help keep visitors from the dangerous work area.

EYE WASH STATION An **eye wash station** should be centrally located and used whenever any liquid or chemical gets into the eyes. If such an emergency does occur, keep eyes in a constant stream of water and call for professional assistance. ● **SEE FIGURE 6–16**.

 TECH TIP

Mark Off the Service Area
Some shops rope off the service bay area to help keep traffic and distractions to a minimum, which could prevent personal injury. ● **SEE FIGURE 6–17**.

SUMMARY

1. All service technicians should wear safety glasses that meet standard ANSI Z87.1.

2. Ear protection should be worn anytime the noise level is at 90 decibels (dB) or higher.

3. Safety should be exercised when working with electrical cords or when jump-starting another vehicle.

4. If a fire extinguisher is needed, remember: Pull the safety pin, aim the nozzle, squeeze the lever, and sweep the nozzle from side-to-side.

REVIEW QUESTIONS

1. List four items that are personal protective equipment (PPE).

2. What are the types of fire extinguishers and their usage?

3. What items are included in a typical first aid box?

1. What do you call the service technician's protective head cover?
   a. Cap
   b. Hat
   c. Bump cap
   d. Helmet

2. All safety glasses should meet the standards set by _____.
   a. ANSI
   b. SAE
   c. ASE
   d. DOT

3. When washing hands, the water should be at what temperature?
   a. 98°F (37°C)
   b. 110°F (43°C)
   c. 125°F (52°C)
   d. 135°F (57°C)

4. Hearing protection should be worn anytime the noise level exceeds _____.
   a. 60 dB
   b. 70 dB
   c. 80 dB
   d. 90 dB

5. Two technicians are discussing the safe use of a wrench. Technician A says that a wrench should be pulled toward you. Technician B says that a wrench should be pushed away from you. Which technician is correct?
   a. Technician A only
   b. Technician B only
   c. Both Technicians A and B
   d. Neither Technician A nor B

6. Exhaust hoses should be used because one of the exhaust gases is deadly in high concentration. This gas is _____.
   a. Carbon monoxide (CO)
   b. Carbon dioxide (CO_2)
   c. Hydrocarbons (HC)
   d. Oxides of nitrogen (NO_X)

7. The process of combustion occurring without an open flame is called _____.
   a. Direct ignition
   b. Non-open flame combustion
   c. Spontaneous combustion
   d. Cold fusion

8. When using a fire extinguisher, what word can be used to remember what to do?
   a. PASS
   b. FIRE
   c. RED
   d. LEVER

9. Which type of fire extinguisher can create a corrosive compound when discharged?
   a. CO_2
   b. Dry chemical
   c. Water
   d. CO

10. Which item is usually *not* included in a first aid kit?
    a. Eye wash solution
    b. Antibiotic cream
    c. Fire blanket
    d. Bandages

chapter 7
ENVIRONMENTAL AND HAZARDOUS MATERIALS

OBJECTIVES: **After studying Chapter 7, the reader should be able to:** • Prepare for the ASE assumed knowledge content required by all service technicians to adhere to environmentally appropriate actions and behavior. • Define the Occupational Safety and Health Act (OSHA). • Explain what is contained in the material safety data sheet (MSDS). • Identify hazardous waste materials in accordance with state and federal regulations and follow proper safety precautions while handling hazardous waste materials. • Define the steps required to safely handle and store automotive chemicals and waste.

KEYTERMS: • Aboveground storage tank (AGST) 59 • Asbestosis 58 • BCI 62 • CAA 57 • CFR 56 • EPA 56 • Hazardous waste material 56 • HEPA vacuum 58 • Mercury 64 • MSDS 57 • OSHA 56 • RCRA 57 • Right-to-know laws 57 • Solvent 58 • Underground storage tank (UST) 59 • Used oil 59 • WHMIS 57

HAZARDOUS WASTE

DEFINITION OF HAZARDOUS WASTE **Hazardous waste materials** are chemicals, or components, that the shop no longer needs that pose a danger to the environment and people if they are disposed of in ordinary garbage cans or sewers. However, no material is considered hazardous waste until the shop has finished using it and is ready to dispose of it.

PERSONAL PROTECTIVE EQUIPMENT (PPE) When handling hazardous waste material, one must always wear the proper protective clothing and equipment detailed in the right-to-know laws. This includes respirator equipment. All recommended procedures must be followed accurately. Personal injury may result from improper clothing, equipment, and procedures when handling hazardous materials.

FEDERAL AND STATE LAWS

OCCUPATIONAL SAFETY AND HEALTH ACT The United States Congress passed the **Occupational Safety and Health Act (OSHA)** in 1970. This legislation was designed to assist and encourage the citizens of the United States in their efforts to assure:

- Safe and healthful working conditions by providing research, information, education, and training in the field of occupational safety and health.

- Safe and healthful working conditions for working men and women by authorizing enforcement of the standards developed under the Act.

Because about 25% of workers are exposed to health and safety hazards on the job, the OSHA standards are necessary to monitor, control, and educate workers regarding health and safety in the workplace.

EPA The **Environmental Protection Agency (EPA)** publishes a list of hazardous materials that is included in the **Code of Federal Regulations (CFR)**. The EPA considers waste hazardous if it is included on the EPA list of hazardous materials, or it has one or more of the following characteristics:

- **Reactive.** Any material that reacts violently with water or other chemicals is considered hazardous.

- **Corrosive.** If a material burns the skin, or dissolves metals and other materials, a technician should consider it hazardous. A pH scale is used, with the number 7 indicating neutral. Pure water has a pH of 7. Lower numbers indicate an acidic solution and higher numbers indicate a caustic solution. If a material releases cyanide gas, hydrogen sulfide gas, or similar gases when exposed to low pH acid solutions, it is considered hazardous.

 WARNING

Hazardous waste disposal laws include serious penalties for anyone responsible for breaking these laws.

- **Toxic.** Materials are hazardous if they leak one or more of eight different heavy metals in concentrations greater than 100 times the primary drinking water standard.
- **Ignitable.** A liquid is hazardous if it has a flash point below 140°F (60°C), and a solid is hazardous if it ignites spontaneously.
- **Radioactive.** Any substance that emits measurable levels of radiation is radioactive. When individuals bring containers of a highly radioactive substance into the shop environment, qualified personnel with the appropriate equipment must test them.

RIGHT-TO-KNOW LAWS The **right-to-know laws** state that employees have a right to know when the materials they use at work are hazardous. The right-to-know laws started with the Hazard Communication Standard published by OSHA in 1983. Originally, this document was intended for chemical companies and manufacturers that required employees to handle hazardous materials in their work situation but the federal courts have decided to apply these laws to all companies, including automotive service shops. Under the right-to-know laws, the employer has responsibilities regarding the handling of hazardous materials by their employees. All employees must be trained about the types of hazardous materials they will encounter in the workplace. The employees must be informed about their rights under legislation regarding the handling of hazardous materials.

MATERIAL SAFETY DATA SHEETS (MSDS). All hazardous materials must be properly labeled, and information about each hazardous material must be posted on **material safety data sheets (MSDS)** available from the manufacturer. In Canada, MSDS information is called **Workplace Hazardous Materials Information Systems (WHMIS).**

The employer has a responsibility to place MSDS information where they are easily accessible by all employees. The MSDS information provide the following information about the hazardous material: chemical name, physical characteristics, protective handling equipment, explosion/fire hazards, incompatible materials, health hazards, medical conditions aggravated by exposure, emergency and first aid procedures, safe handling, and spill/leak procedures.

The employer also has a responsibility to make sure that all hazardous materials are properly labeled. The label information must include health, fire, and reactivity hazards posed by the material, as well as the protective equipment necessary to handle the material. The manufacturer must supply all warning and precautionary information about hazardous materials. This information must be read and understood by the employee before handling the material. ● **SEE FIGURE 7–1.**

RESOURCE CONSERVATION AND RECOVERY ACT (RCRA) Federal and state laws control the disposal of hazardous waste materials and every shop employee must be familiar with these laws. Hazardous waste disposal laws include the **Resource Conservation and Recovery Act (RCRA).** This law states that hazardous material users are responsible for hazardous materials from the time they become

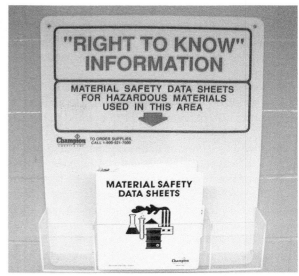

FIGURE 7–1 Material safety data sheets (MSDS) should be readily available for use by anyone in the area who may come into contact with hazardous materials.

a waste until the proper waste disposal is completed. Many shops hire an independent hazardous waste hauler to dispose of hazardous waste material. The shop owner, or manager, should have a written contract with the hazardous waste hauler. Rather than have hazardous waste material hauled to an approved hazardous waste disposal site, a shop may choose to recycle the material in the shop. Therefore, the user must store hazardous waste material properly and safely, and be responsible for the transportation of this material until it arrives at an approved hazardous waste disposal site, where it can be processed according to the law. The RCRA controls the following types of automotive waste:

- Paint and body repair products waste
- Solvents for parts and equipment cleaning
- Batteries and battery acid
- Mild acids used for metal cleaning and preparation
- Waste oil, and engine coolants or antifreeze
- Air conditioning refrigerants and oils
- Engine oil filters

CLEAN AIR ACT Air conditioning (A/C) systems and refrigerants are regulated by the **Clean Air Act (CAA),** Title VI, Section 609. Technician certification and service equipment is also regulated. Any technician working on automotive air conditioning systems must be certified. Air conditioning refrigerants must not be released or vented into the atmosphere, and used refrigerants must be recovered.

ASBESTOS HAZARDS

Friction materials such as brake and clutch linings often contain asbestos. While asbestos has been eliminated from most original equipment friction materials, the automotive service technician cannot know whether the vehicle being serviced is or is not equipped with friction materials containing asbestos. It is important that all friction materials be handled as if they do contain asbestos.

Asbestos exposure can cause scar tissue to form in the lungs. This condition is called **asbestosis.** It gradually causes increasing shortness of breath, and the scarring to the lungs is permanent.

Even low exposures to asbestos can cause *mesothelioma*, a type of fatal cancer of the lining of the chest or abdominal cavity. Asbestos exposure can also increase the risk of *lung cancer* as well as cancer of the voice box, stomach, and large intestine. It usually takes 15 to 30 years or more for cancer or asbestos lung scarring to show up after exposure. Scientists call this the *latency period*.

Government agencies recommend that asbestos exposure be eliminated or controlled to the lowest level possible. These agencies have developed recommendations and standards that the automotive service technician and equipment manufacturer should follow. These U.S. federal agencies include the National Institute for Occupational Safety and Health (NIOSH), Occupational Safety and Health Administration (OSHA), and Environmental Protection Agency (EPA).

ASBESTOS OSHA STANDARDS The Occupational Safety and Health Administration (OSHA) has established three levels of asbestos exposure. Any vehicle service establishment that does either brake or clutch work must limit employee exposure to asbestos to less than 0.2 fibers per cubic centimeter (cc) as determined by an air sample.

If the level of exposure to employees is greater than specified, corrective measures must be performed and a large fine may be imposed.

NOTE: Research has found that worn asbestos fibers such as those from automotive brakes or clutches may not be as hazardous as first believed. Worn asbestos fibers do not have sharp flared ends that can latch onto tissue, but rather are worn down to a dust form that resembles talc. Grinding or sawing operations on unworn brake shoes or clutch discs *will* contain *harmful* asbestos fibers. To limit health damage, always use proper handling procedures while working around any component that may contain asbestos.

ASBESTOS EPA REGULATIONS The federal Environmental Protection Agency (EPA) has established procedures for the removal and disposal of asbestos. The EPA procedures require that products containing asbestos be "wetted" to prevent the asbestos fibers from becoming airborne. According to the EPA, asbestos-containing materials can be disposed of as regular waste. Only when asbestos becomes airborne is it considered to be hazardous.

ASBESTOS HANDLING GUIDELINES The air in the shop area can be tested by a testing laboratory, but this can

FIGURE 7–2 All brakes should be moistened with water or solvent to help prevent brake dust from becoming airborne.

be expensive. Tests have determined that asbestos levels can easily be kept below the recommended levels by using a liquid, like water, or a special vacuum.

NOTE: The service technician cannot tell whether the old brake pads, shoes, or clutch discs contain asbestos. Therefore, to be safe, the technician should assume that all brake pads, shoes, or clutch discs contain asbestos.

HEPA VACUUM. A special **high-efficiency particulate air (HEPA) vacuum** system has been proven to be effective in keeping asbestos exposure levels below 0.1 fibers per cubic centimeter.

SOLVENT SPRAY. Many technicians use an aerosol can of brake cleaning solvent to wet the brake dust and prevent it from becoming airborne. A **solvent** is a liquid that is used to dissolve dirt, grime, or solid particles. Commercial brake cleaners are available that use a concentrated cleaner that is mixed with water. ● **SEE FIGURE 7–2.** The waste liquid is filtered, and when dry, the filter can be disposed of as solid waste.

DISPOSAL OF BRAKE DUST AND BRAKE SHOE. The hazard of asbestos occurs when asbestos fibers are airborne. Once the asbestos has been wetted down, it is then considered to be solid waste, rather than hazardous waste. Old brake shoes and pads should be enclosed, preferably in a plastic bag, to help prevent any of the brake material from becoming airborne. *Always follow current federal and local laws concerning disposal of all waste.*

 WARNING

Never use compressed air to blow brake dust. The fine talclike brake dust can create a health hazard even if asbestos is not present or is present in dust rather than fiber form.

USED BRAKE FLUID

Most brake fluid is made from polyglycol, is water soluble, and can be considered hazardous if it has absorbed metals from the brake system.

STORAGE AND DISPOSAL OF BRAKE FLUID

- Collect brake fluid in a container clearly marked to indicate that it is designated for that purpose.
- If the waste brake fluid is hazardous, be sure to manage it appropriately and use only an authorized waste receiver for its disposal.
- If the waste brake fluid is nonhazardous (such as old, but unused), determine from your local solid waste collection provider what should be done for its proper disposal.
- Do not mix brake fluid with used engine oil.
- Do not pour brake fluid down drains or onto the ground.
- Recycle brake fluid through a registered recycler.

USED OIL

Used oil is any petroleum-based or synthetic oil that has been used. During normal use, impurities such as dirt, metal scrapings, water, or chemicals can get mixed in with the oil. Eventually, this used oil must be replaced with virgin or re-refined oil. The EPA's used oil management standards include a three-pronged approach to determine if a substance meets the definition of *used oil*. To meet the EPA's definition of used oil, a substance must meet each of the following three criteria.

- **Origin.** The first criterion for identifying used oil is based on the oil's origin. Used oil must have been refined from crude oil or made from synthetic materials. Animal and vegetable oils are excluded from the EPA's definition of used oil.
- **Use.** The second criterion is based on whether and how the oil is used. Oils used as lubricants, hydraulic fluids, heat transfer fluids, and for other similar purposes are considered used oil. The EPA's definition also excludes products used as cleaning agents, as well as certain petroleum-derived products like antifreeze and kerosene.
- **Contaminants.** The third criterion is based on whether the oil is contaminated with either physical or chemical impurities. In other words, to meet the EPA's definition, used oil must become contaminated as a result of being used. This aspect of the EPA's definition includes residues and contaminants generated from handling, storing, and processing used oil.

NOTE: The release of only 1 gallon of used oil (a typical oil change) can make 1 million gallons of fresh water undrinkable.

If used oil is dumped down the drain and enters a sewage treatment plant, concentrations as small as 50 to 100 parts per million (ppm) in the wastewater can foul sewage treatment processes. Never mix a listed hazardous waste, gasoline, wastewater, halogenated solvent, antifreeze, or an unknown waste material with used oil. Adding any of these substances will cause the used oil to become contaminated, which classifies it as hazardous waste.

STORAGE AND DISPOSAL OF USED OIL Once oil has been used, it can be collected, recycled, and used over and over again. An estimated 380 million gallons of used oil are recycled each year. Recycled used oil can sometimes be used again for the same job or can take on a completely different task. For example, used engine oil can be re-refined and sold at some discount stores as engine oil or processed for furnace fuel oil. After collecting used oil in an appropriate container such as a 55 gallon steel drum, the material must be disposed of in one of two ways.

- Shipped offsite for recycling
- Burned in an onsite or offsite EPA-approved heater for energy recovery

Used oil must be stored in compliance with an existing **underground storage tank (UST)** or an **aboveground storage tank (AGST)** standard, or kept in separate containers. ● **SEE FIGURE 7–3.** Containers are portable receptacles, such as a 55 gallon steel drum.

KEEP USED OIL STORAGE DRUMS IN GOOD CONDITION. This means that they should be covered, secured from vandals, properly labeled, and maintained in compliance with local fire codes. Frequent inspections for leaks, corrosion, and spillage are an essential part of container maintenance.

NEVER STORE USED OIL IN ANYTHING OTHER THAN TANKS AND STORAGE CONTAINERS. Used oil may also be stored in units that are permitted to store regulated hazardous waste.

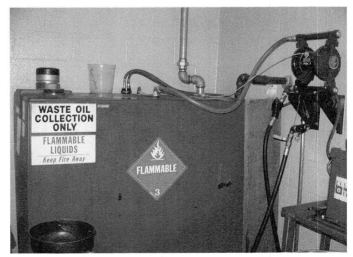

FIGURE 7–3 A typical aboveground oil storage tank.

USED OIL FILTER DISPOSAL REGULATIONS. Used oil filters contain used engine oil that may be hazardous. Before an oil filter is placed into the trash or sent to be recycled, it must be drained using one of the following hot-draining methods approved by the EPA.

- Puncture the filter antidrainback valve or filter dome end and hot drain for at least 12 hours
- Hot draining and crushing
- Dismantling and hot draining
- Any other hot-draining method, which will remove all the used oil from the filter

After the oil has been drained from the oil filter, the filter housing can be disposed of in any of the following ways.

- Sent for recycling
- Picked up by a service contract company
- Disposed of in regular trash

SOLVENTS

The major sources of chemical danger are liquid and aerosol brake cleaning fluids that contain chlorinated hydrocarbon solvents. Several other chemicals that do not deplete the ozone, such as heptane, hexane, and xylene, are now being used in nonchlorinated brake cleaning solvents. Some manufacturers are also producing solvents they describe as environmentally responsible, which are biodegradable and noncarcinogenic (not cancer causing).

There is no specific standard for physical contact with chlorinated hydrocarbon solvents or the chemicals replacing them. All contact should be avoided whenever possible. The law requires an employer to provide appropriate protective equipment and ensure proper work practices by an employee handling these chemicals.

EFFECTS OF CHEMICAL POISONING The effects of exposure to chlorinated hydrocarbon and other types of solvents can take many forms. Short-term exposure at low levels can cause symptoms such as:

- Headache
- Nausea

SAFETY TIP

Hand Safety

Service technicians should wash their hands with soap and water after handling engine oil, differential oil, or transmission fluids or wear protective rubber gloves. Another safety hint is that the service technician should not wear watches, rings, or other jewelry that could come in contact with electrical or moving parts of a vehicle. ● **SEE FIGURE 7–4.**

FIGURE 7–4 Washing hands and removing jewelry are two important safety habits all service technicians should practice.

- Drowsiness
- Dizziness
- Lack of coordination
- Unconsciousness

It may also cause irritation of the eyes, nose, and throat, and flushing of the face and neck. Short-term exposure to higher concentrations can cause liver damage with symptoms such as yellow jaundice or dark urine. Liver damage may not become evident until several weeks after the exposure.

HAZARDOUS SOLVENTS AND REGULATORY STATUS Most solvents are classified as hazardous wastes. Other characteristics of solvents include the following:

- Solvents with flash points below 140°F (60°C) are considered flammable and, like gasoline, are federally regulated by the Department of Transportation (DOT).
- Solvents and oils with flash points above 60°C are considered combustible and, like engine oil, are also regulated by the DOT. All flammable items must be stored in a fireproof container. ● **SEE FIGURE 7–5.**

? **FREQUENTLY ASKED QUESTION**

How Can You Tell If a Solvent Is Hazardous?

If a solvent or any of the ingredients of a product contains "fluor" or "chlor" then it is likely to be hazardous. Check the instructions on the label for proper use and disposal procedures.

It is the responsibility of the repair shop to determine if its spent solvent is hazardous waste. Solvent reclaimers are available that clean and restore the solvent so it lasts indefinitely.

FIGURE 7–5 Typical fireproof flammable storage cabinet.

FIGURE 7–6 Using a water-based cleaning system helps reduce the hazards from using strong chemicals.

USED SOLVENTS Used or spent solvents are liquid materials that have been generated as waste and may contain xylene, methanol, ethyl ether, and methyl isobutyl ketone (MIBK). These materials must be stored in OSHA-approved safety containers with the lids or caps closed tightly. Additional requirements include the following:

- Containers should be clearly labeled "Hazardous Waste" and the date the material was first placed into the storage receptacle should be noted.
- Labeling is not required for solvents being used in a parts washer.
- Used solvents will not be counted toward a facility's monthly output of hazardous waste if the vendor under contract removes the material.
- Used solvents may be disposed of by recycling with a local vendor, such as SafetyKleen®, to have the used solvent removed according to specific terms in the vendor agreement.
- Use aqueous-based (nonsolvent) cleaning systems to help avoid the problems associated with chemical solvents. ● **SEE FIGURE 7–6**.

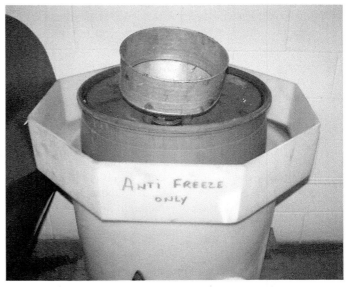

FIGURE 7–7 Used antifreeze coolant should be kept separate and stored in a leakproof container until it can be recycled or disposed of according to federal, state, and local laws. Note that the storage barrel is placed inside another container to catch any coolant that may spill out of the inside barrel.

COOLANT DISPOSAL

Coolant is a mixture of antifreeze and water. New antifreeze is not considered to be hazardous even though it can cause death if ingested. Used antifreeze may be hazardous due to dissolved metals from the engine and other components of the cooling system. These metals can include iron, steel, aluminum, copper, brass, and lead (from older radiators and heater cores). Coolant should be disposed of in one of the following ways:

- Coolant should be recycled either onsite or offsite.
- Used coolant should be stored in a sealed and labeled container. ● **SEE FIGURE 7–7**.
- Used coolant can often be disposed of into municipal sewers with a permit. Check with local authorities and obtain a permit before discharging used coolant into sanitary sewers.

LEAD-ACID BATTERY WASTE

About 70 million spent lead-acid batteries are generated each year in the United States alone. Lead is classified as a toxic metal and the acid used in lead-acid batteries is highly corrosive. The vast majority (95% to 98%) of these batteries are recycled through lead reclamation operations and secondary lead smelters for use in the manufacture of new batteries.

BATTERY DISPOSAL   Used lead-acid batteries must be reclaimed or recycled in order to be exempt from hazardous waste regulations. Leaking batteries must be stored and transported as hazardous waste. Some states have more strict regulations, which require special handling procedures and transportation. According to the **Battery Council International (BCI),** battery laws usually include the following rules.

1. Lead-acid battery disposal is prohibited in landfills or incinerators. Batteries are required to be delivered to a battery retailer, wholesaler, recycling center, or lead smelter.

2. All retailers of automotive batteries are required to post a sign that displays the universal recycling symbol and indicates the retailer's specific requirements for accepting used batteries.

3. Battery electrolyte contains sulfuric acid, which is a very corrosive substance capable of causing serious personal injury, such as skin burns and eye damage. In addition, the battery plates contain lead, which is highly poisonous. For this reason, disposing of batteries improperly can cause environmental contamination and lead to severe health problems.

BATTERY HANDLING AND STORAGE   Batteries, whether new or used, should be kept indoors if possible. The storage location should be an area specifically designated for battery storage and must be well ventilated (to the outside). If outdoor storage is the only alternative, a sheltered and secured area with acid-resistant secondary containment is strongly recommended. It is also advisable that acid-resistant secondary containment be used for indoor storage. In addition, batteries should be placed on acid-resistant pallets and never stacked.

FUEL SAFETY AND STORAGE

Gasoline is a very explosive liquid. The expanding vapors that come from gasoline are extremely dangerous. These vapors are present even in cold temperatures. Vapors formed in gasoline

tanks on many vehicles are controlled, but vapors from gasoline storage may escape from the can, resulting in a hazardous situation. Therefore, place gasoline storage containers in a well-ventilated space. Although diesel fuel is not as volatile as gasoline, the same basic rules apply to diesel fuel and gasoline storage. These rules include the following:

1. Use storage cans that have a flash-arresting screen at the outlet. These screens prevent external ignition sources from igniting the gasoline within the can when someone pours the gasoline or diesel fuel.

2. Use only a red approved gasoline container to allow for proper hazardous substance identification. ● **SEE FIGURE 7–8**.

3. Do not fill gasoline containers completely full. Always leave the level of gasoline at least 1 in. from the top of the container. This action allows expansion of the gasoline at higher temperatures. If gasoline containers are completely full, the gasoline will expand when the temperature increases. This expansion forces gasoline from the can and creates a dangerous spill. If gasoline or diesel fuel containers must be stored, place them in a designated storage locker or facility.

4. Never leave gasoline containers open, except while filling or pouring gasoline from the container.

5. Never use gasoline as a cleaning agent.

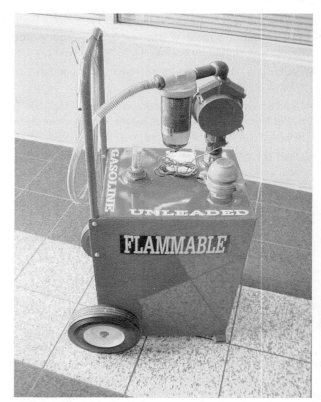

FIGURE 7–8 This red gasoline container holds about 30 gallons of gasoline and is used to fill vehicles used for training.

6. Always connect a ground strap to containers when filling or transferring fuel or other flammable products from one container to another to prevent static electricity that could result in explosion and fire. These ground wires prevent the buildup of a static electric charge, which could result in a spark and disastrous explosion.

AIRBAG HANDLING

Airbag modules are pyrotechnic devices that can be ignited if exposed to an electrical charge or if the body of the vehicle is subjected to a shock. Airbag safety should include the following precautions.

1. Disarm the airbag(s) if you will be working in the area where a discharged bag could make contact with any part of your body. Consult service information for the exact procedure to follow for the vehicle being serviced.
2. If disposing of an airbag, the usual procedure is to deploy the airbag using a 12 volt power supply, such as a jump-start box, using long wires to connect to the module to ensure a safe deployment.
3. Do not expose an airbag to extreme heat or fire.
4. Always carry an airbag pointing away from your body.
5. Place an airbag module facing upward.
6. Always follow the manufacturer's recommended procedure for airbag disposal or recycling, including the proper packaging to use during shipment.
7. Wear protective gloves if handling a deployed airbag.
8. Always wash your hands or body well if exposed to a deployed airbag. The chemicals involved can cause skin irritation and possible rash development.

USED TIRE DISPOSAL

Used tires are an environmental concern because of several reasons, including the following:

1. In a landfill, they tend to "float" up through the other trash and rise to the surface.
2. The inside of tires traps and holds rainwater, which is a breeding ground for mosquitoes. Mosquito-borne diseases include encephalitis, malaria and dengue fever.
3. Used tires present a fire hazard and, when burned, create a large amount of black smoke that contaminates the air.

Used tires should be disposed of in one of the following ways.

1. Used tires can be reused until the end of their useful life.
2. Tires can be retreaded.
3. Tires can be recycled or shredded for use in asphalt.
4. Derimmed tires can be sent to a landfill (most landfill operators will shred the tires because it is illegal in many states to landfill whole tires).
5. Tires can be burned in cement kilns or other power plants where the smoke can be controlled.
6. A registered scrap tire handler should be used to transport tires for disposal or recycling.

AIR CONDITIONING REFRIGERANT OIL DISPOSAL

Air conditioning refrigerant oil contains dissolved refrigerant and is therefore considered to be hazardous waste. This oil must be kept separated from other waste oil or the entire amount of oil must be treated as hazardous. Used refrigerant oil must be sent to a licensed hazardous waste disposal company for recycling or disposal. ● **SEE FIGURE 7–9**.

WASTE CHART All automotive service facilities create some waste and while most of it is handled properly, it is important that all hazardous and nonhazardous waste be accounted for and properly disposed. ● **SEE CHART 7–1** for a list of typical wastes generated at automotive shops, plus a checklist for keeping track of how these wastes are handled.

FIGURE 7–9 Air conditioning refrigerant oil must be kept separated from other oils because it contains traces of refrigerant and must be treated as hazardous waste.

WASTE STREAM	TYPICAL CATEGORY IF NOT MIXED WITH OTHER HAZARDOUS WASTE	IF DISPOSED IN LANDFILL AND NOT MIXED WITH A HAZARDOUS WASTE	IF RECYCLED
Used oil	Used oil	Hazardous waste	Used oil
Used oil filters	Nonhazardous solid waste, if completely drained	Nonhazardous solid waste, if completely drained	Used oil, if not drained
Used transmission fluid	Used oil	Hazardous waste	Used oil
Used brake fluid	Used oil	Hazardous waste	Used oil
Used antifreeze	Depends on characterization	Depends on characterization	Depends on characterization
Used solvents	Hazardous waste	Hazardous waste	Hazardous waste
Used citric solvents	Nonhazardous solid waste	Nonhazardous solid waste	Hazardous waste
Lead-acid automotive batteries	Not a solid waste if returned to supplier	Hazardous waste	Hazardous waste
Shop rags used for oil	Used oil	Depends on used oil characterization	Used oil
Shop rags used for solvent or gasoline spills	Hazardous waste	Hazardous waste	Hazardous waste
Oil spill absorbent material	Used oil	Depends on used oil characterization	Used oil
Spill material for solvent and gasoline	Hazardous waste	Hazardous waste	Hazardous waste
Catalytic converter	Not a solid waste if returned to supplier	Nonhazardous solid waste	Nonhazardous solid waste
Spilled or unused fuels	Hazardous waste	Hazardous waste	Hazardous waste
Spilled or unusable paints and thinners	Hazardous waste	Hazardous waste	Hazardous waste
Used tires	Nonhazardous solid waste	Nonhazardous solid waste	Nonhazardous solid waste

CHART 7–1

Typical wastes generated at auto repair shops and typical category (hazardous or nonhazardous) by disposal method.

 TECH TIP

Remove Components That Contain Mercury

Some vehicles have a placard near the driver's side door that lists the components that contain the heavy metal, mercury. **Mercury** can be absorbed through the skin and is a heavy metal that once absorbed by the body does not leave. ● SEE FIGURE 7–10.

These components should be removed from the vehicle before the rest of the body is sent to be recycled to help prevent releasing mercury into the environment.

This vehicle may include mercury-added devices installed by the manufacturer:
• REAR SEAT VIDEO DISPLAY
• NAVIGATION DISPLAY
• H.I.D. HEADLAMPS
Remove devices before vehicle disposal. Upon removal of devices please reuse, recycle or dispose as hazardous waste.
05020527AA

FIGURE 7–10 Placard near driver's door, including what devices in the vehicle contain mercury.

Hazardous Materials Identification Guide (HMIG)

TYPE HAZARD		DEGREE	
○	HEALTH	4 -	Extreme
○	FLAMMABILITY	3 -	Serious
○	REACTIVITY	2 -	Moderate
○	PROTECTIVE EQUIPMENT	1 -	Slight
		0 -	Minimal

HAZARD RATING AND PROTECTIVE EQUIPMENT

	Health		Flammable		Reactive
	Type of Possible Injury		Susceptibility of materials to burn		Susceptibility of materials to release energy
4	Highly Toxic. May be fatal on short-term exposure. Special protective equipment required.	4	Extremely flammable gas or liquid. Flash Point below 73°F.	4	Extreme. Explosive at room temperature.
3	Toxic. Avoid inhalation or skin contact.	3	Flammable. Flash Point 73°F to 100°F.	3	Serious. May explode if shocked, heated under confinement or mixed w/ water.
2	Moderately Toxic. May be harmful if inhaled or absorbed.	2	Combustible. Requires moderate heating to ignite. Flash Point 100°F to 200°F.	2	Moderate. Unstable, may react with water.
1	Slightly Toxic. May cause slight irritation.	1	Slightly Combustible. Requires strong heating to ignite.	1	Slight. May react if heated or mixed with water.
0	Minimal. All chemicals have a slight degree of toxicity.	0	Minimal. Will not burn under normal conditions.	0	Minimal. Normally stable, does not react with water.

Protective Equipment

A	Safety Glasses	E	Safety Glasses + Gloves + Dust Respirator	I	Safety Glasses + Gloves + Combination Dust & Vapor Respirator
B	Safety Glasses + Gloves	F	Safety Glasses + Gloves + Apron + Dust Respirator	J	Chemical Goggles + Gloves + Apron + Combination Dust & Vapor Respirator
C	Safety Glasses + Gloves + Apron	G	Safety Glasses + Gloves + Vapor Respirator	K	Apron + Gloves + Full Protection Suit + Boots
D	Faceshield + Gloves + Apron	H	Chemical Goggles + Gloves + Apron + Vapor Respirator	X	Ask your supervisor for guidance.

FIGURE 7–11 The Environmental Protection Agency (EPA) Hazardous Materials Identification Guide is a standardized listing of the hazards and the protective equipment needed.

TECH TIP

What Every Technician Should Know

The Hazardous Materials Identification Guide (HMIG) is the standard labeling for all materials. The service technician should be aware of the meaning of the label. ● **SEE FIGURE 7–11.**

SUMMARY

1. Hazardous materials include common automotive chemicals, liquids, and lubricants, especially those whose ingredients contain *chlor* or *fluor* in their name.
2. Right-to-know laws require that all workers have access to material safety data sheets (MSDS).
3. Asbestos fibers should be avoided and removed according to current laws and regulations.
4. Used engine oil contains metals worn from parts and should be handled and disposed of properly.
5. Solvents represent a serious health risk and should be avoided as much as possible.
6. Coolant should be disposed of properly or recycled.
7. Batteries are considered to be hazardous waste and should be discarded to a recycling facility.

REVIEW QUESTIONS

1. List five common automotive chemicals or products that may be considered hazardous materials.
2. The Resource Conservation and Recovery Act (RCRA) controls what types of automotive waste?

CHAPTER QUIZ

1. Hazardous materials include all of the following *except* _____.
   a. Engine oil
   b. Asbestos
   c. Water
   d. Brake cleaner
2. To determine if a product or substance being used is hazardous, consult _____.
   a. A dictionary
   b. An MSDS
   c. SAE standards
   d. EPA guidelinesu
3. Exposure to asbestos dust can cause what condition?
   a. Asbestosis
   b. Mesothelioma
   c. Lung cancer
   d. All of the above
4. Wetted asbestos dust is considered to be _____.
   a. Solid waste
   b. Hazardous waste
   c. Toxic
   d. Poisonous
5. An oil filter should be hot drained for how long before disposing of the filter?
   a. 30 to 60 minutes
   b. 4 hours
   c. 8 hours
   d. 12 hours
6. Used engine oil should be disposed of by all *except* the following methods.
   a. Disposed of in regular trash
   b. Shipped offsite for recycling
   c. Burned onsite in a waste oil-approved heater
   d. Burned offsite in a waste oil-approved heater
7. All of the following are the proper ways to dispose of a *drained* oil filter *except* _____.
   a. Sent for recycling
   b. Picked up by a service contract company
   c. Disposed of in regular trash
   d. Considered to be hazardous waste and disposed of accordingly
8. Which act or organization regulates air conditioning refrigerant?
   a. Clean Air Act (CAA)
   b. MSDS
   c. WHMIS
   d. Code of Federal Regulations (CFR)
9. Gasoline should be stored in approved containers that include what color(s)?
   a. A red container with yellow lettering
   b. A red container
   c. A yellow container
   d. A yellow container with red lettering
10. What automotive devices may contain mercury?
   a. Rear seat video displays
   b. Navigation displays
   c. HID headlights
   d. All of the above

chapter 8

HAND TOOLS

OBJECTIVES: After studying Chapter 8, the reader should be able to: • Explain the types, proper name and classification of hand tools • Describe what tool is the best to use for each job. • Discuss how to safely use hand tools. • Explain the difference between the brand name (trade name) and the proper name for tools. • Explain how to maintain hand tools.

KEY TERMS: • Adjustable wrench 67 • Aviation tin snips 75 • Beam-type torque wrench 69 • Box-end wrench 67 • Breaker bar (flex handle) 68 • Cheater bar 81 • Chisel 76 • Clicker-type torque wrench 69 • Close end 67 • Cold chisel 76 • Combination wrench 67 • Crowfoot socket 69 • Dead-blow hammer 73 • Diagonal (side-cut or dike) pliers 73 • Double-cut file 75 • Drive size 69 • Easy out 77 • Extension 69 • Files 75 • Fitting wrench 68 • Flare-nut wrench 68 • Flat-tip (straight blade) screwdriver 71 • Hacksaw 78 • Locking pliers 74 • Multigroove adjustable pliers 73 • Needle-nose pliers 73 • Nut splitter 76 • Offset left aviation snip 75 • Offset right aviation snip 75 • Open-end wrench 67 • Punch 76 • Ratchet 68 • Removers 76 • Screwdriver 71 • Seal driver 80 • Seal puller 80 • Single-cut file 75 • Slip-joint pliers 73 • Snap-ring pliers 74 • Socket 68 • Socket adapter 71 • Straight cut aviation snip 75 • Stud removal tool 76 • Stud remover 76 • Tin snips 75 • Torque wrench 69 • Tube-nut wrench 68 • Universal joint 69 • Utility knife 75 • Vise-Grip® 74 • Water pump pliers 73 • Wrench 67

WRENCHES

Wrenches are the most used hand tool by service technicians. Most wrenches are constructed of forged alloy steel, usually chrome-vanadium steel. ● **SEE FIGURE 8–1**.

After the wrench is formed, it is hardened, tempered to reduce brittleness, and then chrome plated. Wrenches are available in both fractional and metric sizes. There are several types of wrenches.

OPEN-END WRENCH An **open-end wrench** is often used to loosen or tighten bolts or nuts that do not require a lot of torque. An open-end wrench can be easily placed on a bolt or nut with an angle of 15 degrees, which allows the wrench to be flipped over and used again to continue to rotate the fastener. The major disadvantage of an open-end wrench is the lack of torque that can be applied due to the fact that the open jaws of the wrench only contact two flat surfaces of the fastener. An open-end wrench has two different sizes, one at each end. ● **SEE FIGURE 8–2**.

BOX-END WRENCH A **box-end wrench** is placed over the top of the fastener and grips the points of the fastener. A box-end wrench is angled 15 degrees to allow it to clear nearby objects.

Therefore, a box-end wrench should be used to loosen or to tighten fasteners. A box-end wrench is also called a **close-end**

FIGURE 8–1 A forged wrench after it has been forged but before the flashing, extra material around the wrench, has been removed.

wrench. A box-end wrench has two different sizes, one at each end. ● **SEE FIGURES 8–3 AND 8–4**.

COMBINATION WRENCH Most service technicians purchase **combination wrenches**, which have the open end at one end and the same size box end on the other. ● **SEE FIGURE 8–5**.

A combination wrench allows the technician to loosen or tighten a fastener using the box end of the wrench, turn it around, and use the open end to increase the speed of rotating the fastener.

ADJUSTABLE WRENCH An **adjustable wrench** is often used where the exact size wrench is not available or when a large nut, such as a wheel spindle nut, needs to be rotated but not tightened. An adjustable wrench should not be used to

FIGURE 8–2 A typical open-end wrench. The size is different on each end and notice that the head is angled 15 degrees at each end.

FIGURE 8–3 A typical box-end wrench is able to grip the bolt or nut at points completely around the fastener. Each end is a different size.

FIGURE 8–4 The end of a box-end wrench is angled 15 degrees to allow clearance for nearby objects or other fasteners.

FIGURE 8–5 A combination wrench has an open end at one end and a box end at the other with the same size at each end.

loosen or tighten fasteners because the torque applied to the wrench can cause the movable jaws to loosen their grip on the fastener, causing it to become rounded. ● SEE FIGURE 8–6.

LINE WRENCHES Line wrenches are also called **flare-nut wrenches**, **fitting wrenches**, or **tube-nut wrenches** and are designed to grip almost all the way around a nut used to retain a fuel or refrigerant line, and yet be able to be installed over the line. ● SEE FIGURE 8–7.

SAFE USE OF WRENCHES. Wrenches should be inspected before use to be sure they are not cracked, bent, or damaged.

FIGURE 8–6 An adjustable wrench. Adjustable wrenches are sized by the overall length of the wrench and not by how far the jaws open. Common sizes of adjustable wrenches include 8, 10, and 12 in.

FIGURE 8–7 The end of a typical line wrench, which shows that it is capable of grasping most of the head of the fitting.

All wrenches should be cleaned after use before being returned to the toolbox. Always use the correct size of wrench for the fastener being loosened or tightened to help prevent the rounding of the flats of the fastener. When attempting to loosen a fastener, pull a wrench—do not push a wrench. If a wrench is pushed, your knuckles can be hurt when forced into another object if the fastener breaks loose.

RATCHETS, SOCKETS, AND EXTENSIONS

A **socket** fits over the fastener and grips the points and/or flats of the bolt or nut. The socket is rotated (driven) using either a long bar called a **breaker bar (flex handle)** or a **ratchet**. ● SEE FIGURES 8–8 AND 8–9.

A ratchet turns the socket in only one direction and allows the rotating of the ratchet handle back and forth in a narrow

FIGURE 8–8 A typical ratchet used to rotate a socket. A ratchet makes a ratcheting noise when it is being rotated in the opposite direction from loosening or tightening. A knob or lever on the ratchet allows the user to switch directions.

FIGURE 8–9 A typical flex handle used to rotate a socket, also called a breaker bar because it usually has a longer handle than a ratchet and, therefore, can be used to apply more torque to a fastener than a ratchet.

space. Socket **extensions** and **universal joints** are also used with sockets to allow access to fasteners in restricted locations.

Sockets are available in various **drive sizes**, including 1/4 in., 3/8 in., and 1/2 in. sizes for most automotive use. ● **SEE FIGURES 8–10 AND 8–11.**

Many heavy-duty truck and/or industrial applications use 3/4 in. and 1 in. sizes. The drive size is the distance of each side of the square drive. Sockets and ratchets of the same size are designed to work together.

CROWFOOT SOCKETS
A **crowfoot socket** is a socket that is an open-end or line wrench to allow access to fasteners that cannot be reached using a conventional wrench. ● **SEE FIGURE 8–12.**

Crowfoot sockets are available in the following categories.

- Fractional inch open-end wrench
- Metric open-end wrench
- Fractional line wrench
- Metric line wrench

TECH TIP

Right to Tighten

It is sometimes confusing which way to rotate a wrench or screwdriver, especially when the head of the fastener is pointing away from you. To help visualize while looking at the fastener, say "righty tighty, lefty loosey."

FIGURE 8–10 The most commonly used socket drive sizes include 1/4 in., 3/8 in., and 1/2 in. drive.

FIGURE 8–11 A 6-point socket fits the head of the bolt or nut on all sides. A 12-point socket can round off the head of a bolt or nut if a lot of force is applied.

FIGURE 8–12 A crowfoot socket is designed to reach fasteners using a ratchet or breaker bar with an extension.

TORQUE WRENCHES
Torque wrenches are socket turning handles that are designed to apply a known amount of force to the fastener. There are two basic types of torque wrenches.

1. A **clicker-type torque wrench** is first set to the specified torque and then it "clicks" when the set torque value has been reached. When force is removed from the torque wrench handle, another click is heard. The setting on a clicker-type torque wrench should be set back to zero after use and checked for proper calibration regularly. ● **SEE FIGURE 8–13.**

2. A **beam- or dial-type torque wrench** is used to measure torque, but instead of presetting the value, the actual torque is displayed on the scale or dial of the wrench as the fastener is being tightened. Beam-type torque wrenches are available in 1/4 in., 3/8 in., and 1/2 in. drives and both English and metric units. ● **SEE FIGURE 8–14.**

FIGURE 8–13 Using a torque wrench to tighten connecting rod nuts on an engine.

FIGURE 8–14 A beam-type torque wrench that displays the torque reading on the face of the dial. The beam display is read as the beam deflects, which is in proportion to the amount of torque applied to the fastener.

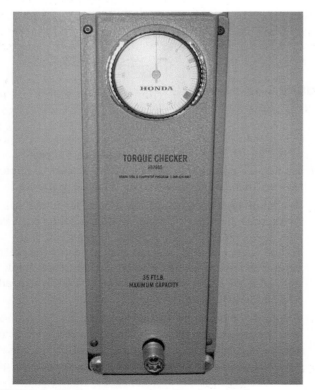

FIGURE 8–15 Torque wrench calibration checker.

FIGURE 8–16 Deep sockets allow access to the nut that has a stud plus other locations needing great depth, such as spark plugs.

 TECH TIP

Check Torque Wrench Calibration Regularly

Torque wrenches should be checked regularly. For example, Honda has a torque wrench calibration setup at each of their training centers. It is expected that a torque wrench be checked for accuracy before every use. Most experts recommend that torque wrenches be checked and adjusted as needed at least every year and more often if possible.
● **SEE FIGURE 8–15.**

SAFE USE OF SOCKETS AND RATCHETS. Always use the proper size socket that correctly fits the bolt or nut. All sockets and ratchets should be cleaned after use before being placed back into the toolbox. Sockets are available in short and deep well designs. ● **SEE FIGURE 8–16.**

Also select the appropriate drive size. For example, for small work, such as on the dash, select a 1/4 in. drive. For most general service work, use a 3/8 in. drive and for suspension and steering and other large fasteners, select a 1/2 in. drive. When loosening a fastener, always pull the ratchet toward you rather than push it outward.

 FREQUENTLY ASKED QUESTION

Is It Lb-Ft or Ft-Lb of Torque?

The unit for torque is expressed as a force times the distance (leverage) from the object. Therefore, the official unit for torque is lb-ft (pound-feet) or newton-meters (a force times a distance). However, it is commonly expressed in ft-lb and even some torque wrenches are labeled with this unit.

Double-Check the Specifications

Misreading torque specifications is easy to do but can have serious damaging results. Specifications for fasteners are commonly expressed lb-ft. Many smaller fasteners are tightened to specifications expressed in lb-in.

1 lb-ft = 12 lb-in.

Therefore, if a fastener were to be accidentally tightened to 24 lb-ft instead of 24 lb-in., the actual torque applied to the fastener will be 288 lb-in. instead of the specified 24 lb-in.

This extra torque will likely break the fastener, but it could also warp or distort the part being tightened. Always double-check the torque specifications.

Use Socket Adapters with Caution

Socket adapters are available and can be used for different drive size sockets on a ratchet. Combinations include:

- 1/4 in. drive—3/8 in. sockets
- 3/8 in. drive—1/4 in. sockets
- 3/8 in. drive—1/2 in. sockets
- 1/2 in. drive—3/8 in. sockets

Using a larger drive ratchet or breaker bar on a smaller size socket can cause the application of too much force to the socket, which could crack or shatter. Using a smaller size drive tool on a larger socket will usually not cause any harm, but would greatly reduce the amount of torque that can be applied to the bolt or nut.

Avoid Using "Cheater Bars"

Whenever a fastener is difficult to remove, some technicians will insert the handle of a ratchet or a breaker bar into a length of steel pipe. The extra length of the pipe allows the technician to exert more torque than can be applied using the drive handle alone. However, the extra torque can easily overload the socket and ratchet, causing them to break or shatter, which could cause personal injury.

SCREWDRIVERS

Many smaller fasteners are removed and installed by using a **screwdriver**. Screwdrivers are available in many sizes and tip shapes. The most commonly used screwdriver is called a **flat tip** or **straight blade**.

Flat-tip screwdrivers are sized by the width of the blade and this width should match the width of the slot in the screw. ● **SEE FIGURE 8–17**.

CAUTION: Do not use a screwdriver as a pry tool or as a chisel. Always use the proper tool for each application.

Another type of commonly used screwdriver is called a Phillips screwdriver, named for Henry F. Phillips, who invented the crosshead screw in 1934. Due to the shape of the crosshead screw and screwdriver, a Phillips screw can be driven with more torque than can be achieved with a slotted screw.

A Phillips head screwdriver is specified by the length of the handle and the size of the point at the tip. A #1 tip has a sharp point, a #2 tip is the most commonly used, and a #3 tip is blunt and is only used for larger sizes of Phillips head fasteners. For example, a #2 × 3 in. Phillips screwdriver would typically measure 6 in. from the tip of the blade to the end of the handle (3 in. long handle and 3 in. long blade) with a #2 tip.

Both straight blade and Phillips screwdrivers are available with a short blade and handle for access to fasteners with limited room. ● **SEE FIGURE 8–18**.

OFFSET SCREWDRIVERS Offset screwdrivers are used in places where a conventional screwdriver cannot fit. An offset screwdriver is bent at the ends and is used similar to a wrench. Most offset screwdrivers have a straight blade at one end and a Phillips end at the opposite end. ● **SEE FIGURE 8–19**.

IMPACT SCREWDRIVER An impact screwdriver is used to break loose or tighten a screw. A hammer is used to strike the end after the screwdriver holder is placed in the head of the screw and rotated in the desired direction. The force

BLADE WIDTH

FIGURE 8–17 A flat-tip (straight blade) screwdriver. The width of the blade should match the width of the slot in the fastener being loosened or tightened.

FIGURE 8–18 Two stubby screwdrivers that are used to access screws that have limited space above. A straight blade is on top and a #2 Phillips screwdriver is on the bottom.

FIGURE 8–19 An offset screwdriver is used to install or remove fasteners that do not have enough space above to use a conventional screwdriver.

FIGURE 8–20 An impact screwdriver used to remove slotted or Phillips head fasteners that cannot be broken loose using a standard screwdriver.

from the hammer blow does two things: It applies a force downward holding the tip of the screwdriver in the slot and then applies a twisting force to loosen (or tighten) the screw. ● SEE FIGURE 8–20.

SAFE USE OF SCREWDRIVERS. Always use the proper type and size screwdriver that matches the fastener. Try to avoid pressing down on a screwdriver because if it slips, the screwdriver tip could go into your hand, causing serious

personal injury. All screwdrivers should be cleaned after use. Do not use a screwdriver as a pry bar; always use the correct tool for the job.

HAMMERS AND MALLETS

HAMMERS Hammers and mallets are used to force objects together or apart. The shape of the back part of the hammer head (called the *peen*) usually determines the name. For example, a ball-peen hammer has a rounded end like a ball and it is used to straighten oil pans and valve covers, using the hammer head, and for shaping metal, using the ball peen. ● SEE FIGURE 8–21.

NOTE: A claw hammer has a claw used to remove nails and is not used for automotive service.

A hammer is usually sized by the weight of the head of the hammer and the length of the handle. For example, a commonly used ball-peen hammer has an 8 oz head with an 11 in. handle.

MALLETS Mallets are a type of hammer with a large striking surface, which allows the technician to exert force over a larger area than a hammer, so as not to harm the part or component.

FIGURE 8–21 A typical ball-peen hammer.

FIGURE 8–22 A rubber mallet used to deliver a force to an object without harming the surface.

FIGURE 8–23 A dead-blow hammer that was left outside in freezing weather. The plastic covering was damaged, which destroyed this hammer. The lead shot is encased in the metal housing and then covered.

Mallets are made from a variety of materials including rubber, plastic, or wood. ● SEE FIGURE 8–22.

A shot-filled plastic hammer is called a **dead-blow hammer**. The small lead balls (shot) inside a plastic head prevent the hammer from bouncing off of the object when struck. ● SEE FIGURE 8–23.

SAFE USE OF HAMMERS AND MALLETS. All mallets and hammers should be cleaned after use and not exposed to extreme temperatures. Never use a hammer or mallet that is damaged in any way and always use caution to avoid doing damage to the components and the surrounding area. Always follow the hammer manufacturer's recommended procedures and practices.

PLIERS

SLIP-JOINT PLIERS Pliers are capable of holding, twisting, bending, and cutting objects and are an extremely useful classification of tools. The common household type of pliers is called the **slip-joint pliers**. There are two different positions where the junction of the handles meets to achieve a wide range of sizes of objects that can be gripped. ● SEE FIGURE 8–24.

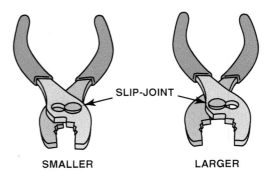

SMALLER   LARGER

FIGURE 8–24 Typical slip-joint pliers, which are also common household pliers. The slip joint allows the jaws to be opened to two different settings.

MULTI-GROOVES FOR JAW WIDTH ADJUSTMENT

FIGURE 8–25 Multigroove adjustable pliers are known by many names, including the trade name Channel Locks.

MULTIGROOVE ADJUSTABLE PLIERS For gripping larger objects, a set of **multigroove adjustable pliers** is a commonly used tool of choice by many service technicians. Originally designed to remove the various size nuts holding rope seals used in water pumps, the name **water pump pliers** is also used. ● SEE FIGURE 8–25.

LINESMAN'S PLIERS Linesman's pliers are specifically designed for cutting, bending, and twisting wire. While commonly used by construction workers and electricians, linesman's pliers are very useful tools for the service technician who deals with wiring. The center parts of the jaws are designed to grasp round objects such as pipe or tubing without slipping. ● SEE FIGURE 8–26.

DIAGONAL PLIERS **Diagonal pliers** are designed for cutting only. The cutting jaws are set at an angle to make it easier to cut wires. Diagonal pliers are also called **side cuts** or **dikes**. These pliers are constructed of hardened steel and they are used mostly for cutting wire. ● SEE FIGURE 8–27.

NEEDLE-NOSE PLIERS **Needle-nose pliers** are designed to grip small objects or objects in tight locations. Needle-nose pliers have long, pointed jaws, which allow the tips to reach into narrow openings or groups of small objects. ● SEE FIGURE 8–28.

FLAT GRIP

PIPE GRIP

SIDE CUTTERS

JOINT CUTTERS

CUTS SOFT WIRE

GRIPS SMALL OBJECTS

FIGURE 8–26 A linesman's pliers are very useful because they can help perform many automotive service jobs.

CUTTING WIRES CLOSE TO TERMINALS

PULLING OUT AND SPREADING COTTER PIN

FIGURE 8–27 Diagonal-cut pliers are another common tool that has many names.

FIGURE 8–28 Needle-nose pliers are used where there is limited access to a wire or pin that needs to be installed or removed.

Most needle-nose pliers have a wire cutter located at the base of the jaws near the pivot. There are several variations of needle-nose pliers, including right angle jaws or slightly angled to allow access to certain cramped areas.

 TECH TIP

Brand Name Versus Proper Term

Technicians often use slang or brand names of tools rather than the proper term. This results in some confusion for new technicians. Some examples are given in the following table.

Brand Name	Proper Term	Slang Name
Crescent wrench	Adjustable wrench	Monkey wrench
Vise Grip	Locking pliers	
Channel Locks	Water pump pliers or multigroove adjustable pliers	Pump pliers
	Diagonal cutting pliers	Dikes or side cuts

 TECH TIP

Use Chalk

Often soft metal particles can become stuck in a file, especially when using it to file aluminum or other soft metals. Rub some chalk into the file before using it to prevent this from happening.

LOCKING PLIERS **Locking pliers** are adjustable pliers that can be locked to hold objects from moving. Most locking pliers also have wire cutters built into the jaws near the pivot point. Locking pliers come in a variety of styles and sizes and are commonly referred to by their trade name **Vise-Grip**®. The size is the length of the pliers, not how far the jaws open. ● **SEE FIGURE 8–29.**

SAFE USE OF PLIERS. Pliers should not be used to remove any bolt or other fastener. Pliers should only be used when specified for use by the vehicle manufacturer.

SNAP-RING PLIERS **Snap-ring pliers** are used to remove and install snap rings. Many snap-ring pliers are designed to be able to remove and install inward, as well as outward,

RELEASE LEVER

FIGURE 8–29 Locking pliers are best known by their trade name Vise-Grip®.

expanding snap rings. Snap-ring pliers can be equipped with serrated-tipped jaws for grasping the opening in the snap ring, while others are equipped with points, which are inserted into the holes in the snap ring. ● SEE FIGURE 8–30.

FILES   **Files** are used to smooth metal and are constructed of hardened steel with diagonal rows of teeth. Files are available with a single row of teeth called a **single-cut file**, as well as two rows of teeth cut at an opposite angle called a **double-cut file**. Files are available in a variety of shapes and sizes from small flat files, half-round files, and triangular files. ● SEE FIGURE 8–31.

SAFE USE OF FILES.   Always use a file with a handle. Because files cut only when moved forward, a handle must be attached to prevent possible personal injury. After making a forward strike, lift the file and return the file to the starting position; avoid dragging the file backward.

CUTTERS

SNIPS   Service technicians are often asked to fabricate sheet metal brackets or heat shields and need to use one or more types of cutters available. The simplest is called **tin snips**, which are designed to make straight cuts in a variety of materials, such as sheet steel, aluminum, or even fabric. A variation of the tin snips is called **aviation tin snips**. There are three designs of aviation snips, including one designed to cut straight (called a **straight cut aviation snip**), one designed to cut left (called an **offset left aviation snip**), and one designed to cut right (called an **offset right aviation snip**). The handles are color coded for easy identification. These include yellow for straight, red for left, and green for right. ● SEE FIGURE 8–32.

UTILITY KNIFE   A **utility knife** uses a replaceable blade and is used to cut a variety of materials such as carpet, plastic, wood, and paper products, such as cardboard. ● SEE FIGURE 8–33.

INTERNAL SNAP RING

EXTERNAL SNAP RING

FIGURE 8–30 Snap-ring pliers are also called lock-ring pliers and are designed to remove internal and external snap rings (lock rings).

TRIANGULAR

HALF ROUND

ROUND

FLAT

HANDLE

FIGURE 8–31 Files come in many different shapes and sizes. Never use a file without a handle.

STRAIGHT CUT TIN SNIP

OFFSET RIGHT-HAND AVIATION SNIP

FIGURE 8–32 Tin snips are used to cut thin sheets of metal or carpet.

FIGURE 8–33 A utility knife uses replaceable blades and is used to cut carpet and other materials.

SAFE USE OF CUTTERS. Whenever using cutters, always wear eye protection or a face shield to guard against the possibility of metal pieces being ejected during the cut. Always follow recommended procedures.

PUNCHES AND CHISELS

PUNCHES
A **punch** is a small diameter steel rod that has a smaller diameter ground at one end. A punch is used to drive a pin out that is used to retain two components. Punches come in a variety of sizes, which are measured across the diameter of the machined end. Sizes include 1/16 in., 1/8 in., 3/16 in., and 1/4 in. ● **SEE FIGURE 8-34.**

CHISELS
A **chisel** has a straight, sharp cutting end that is used for cutting off rivets or to separate two pieces of an assembly. The most common design of chisel used for automotive service work is called a **cold chisel.**

SAFE USE OF PUNCHES AND CHISELS. Always wear eye protection when using a punch or a chisel because the hardened steel is brittle and parts of the punch could fly off and cause serious personal injury. See the warning stamped on the side of this automotive punch in ● **SEE FIGURE 8-35.**

FIGURE 8-34 A punch used to drive pins from assembled components. This type of punch is also called a pin punch.

FIGURE 8-35 Warning stamped in the side of a punch warning that goggles should be worn when using this tool. Always follow safety warnings.

FIGURE 8-36 Use a grinder or a file to remove the mushroom material on the end of a punch or chisel.

Punches and chisels can also have the top rounded off, which is called "mushroomed." This material must be ground off to help avoid the possibility that the overhanging material is loosened and becomes airborne during use. ● **SEE FIGURE 8-36.**

REMOVERS

Removers are tools used to remove damaged fasteners. A remover tool is not normally needed during routine service unless the fastener is corroded or has been broken or damaged by a previous attempt to remove the bolt or nut.

To help prevent the need for a remover tool, all rusted and corroded fasteners should be sprayed with penetrating oil. Penetrating oil is a low viscosity oil that is designed to flow in between the threads of a fastener or other small separation between two parts. Commonly used penetrating oils include WD-40®, Kroil®, and CRC 5-56.

CAUTION: Do not use penetrating oil as a lubricating oil because it is volatile and will evaporate soon after usage leaving little lubricant behind for protection.

Over time, rust and corrosion can cause the threads of the fastener to be attached to the nut or the casting making it very difficult to remove. There are several special tools that can be used to remove damaged fasteners. Which one to use depends on the type of damage.

DAMAGED HEADS If the bolt head or a nut becomes damaged or rounded, there are two special tools that can be used, including:

■ **Stud remover.** A **stud removal tool** grips the part of the stud above the surface and uses a cam or wedge to grip the stud as it is being rotated by a ratchet or breaker bar. ● **SEE FIGURE 8-37.**

■ **Nut splitter.** A **nut splitter** is used to remove the nut by splitting it from the bolt. A nut splitter is used by inserting the cutter against a flat of the nut and

FIGURE 8–37 A stud remover uses an offset serrated wheel to grasp the stud so it will be rotated when a ratchet or breaker bar is used to rotate the assembly.

FIGURE 8–38 A nut splitter is used to split a nut that cannot be removed. After the nut has been split, a chisel is then used to remove the nut.

tightening the threaded bolt of the splitter. The nut will be split away from the bolt and can then be removed. ● **SEE FIGURE 8–38.**

CAUTION: Do not rotate the entire nut splitter or damage to the cutting wedge will occur.

BROKEN BOLTS, STUDS, OR SCREWS
Often, bolts, studs, or screws break even with, or below the surface, making stud removal tools impossible to use. Bolt extractors are commonly called **easy outs.** An easy out is constructed of hardened steel with flutes or edges ground into the side in an opposite direction of most threads. ● **SEE FIGURE 8–39.**

NOTE: Always select the largest extractor that can be used to help avoid the possibility of breaking the extractor while attempting to remove the bolt.

A hole is drilled into the center of a broken bolt. Then, the extractor (easy out) is inserted into the hole and rotated counterclockwise using a wrench. As the extractor rotates, the grooves grip tighter into the wall of the hole drilled in the broken bolt. As a result, most extractors are capable of removing most broken bolts.

FIGURE 8–39 A set of bolt extractors, commonly called easy outs.

FIGURE 8–40 Removing plugs or bolts is easier if the plug is first heated to cherry red color, using a torch, and then applying wax. During cooling, the wax flows in between the threads, making it easier to remove.

 TECH TIP

The Wax Trick

Many times rusted fasteners can be removed by using heat to expand the metal and break the rust bond between the fastener and the nut or casting. Many technicians heat the fastener using a torch and then apply paraffin wax or a candle to the heated fastener. ● **SEE FIGURE 8–40.** The wax will melt and as the part cools, will draw the liquid wax down between the threads. After allowing the part to cool, attempt to remove the fastener. It will often be removed without any trouble.

I Broke Off an Easy Out—Now What?

An extractor (easy out) is hardened steel and removing this and the broken bolt is now a job for a professional machine shop. The part, which could be as large as an engine block, needs to be removed from the vehicle and taken to a machine shop that is equipped to handle this type of job. One method involves using an electrical discharge machine (EDM). An EDM uses a high amperage electrical current to produce thousands of arcs between the electrode and the broken tool. The part is submerged in a nonconducting liquid and each tiny spark vaporizes a small piece of the broken tool.

HACKSAWS

A **hacksaw** is used to cut metals, such as steel, aluminum, brass, or copper. The cutting blade of a hacksaw is replaceable and the sharpness and number of teeth can be varied to meet the needs of the job. Use 14 or 18 teeth per inch (tpi) for cutting plaster or soft metals, such as aluminum and copper. Use 24 or 32 teeth per inch for steel or pipe. Hacksaw blades should be installed with the teeth pointing away from the handle. This means that a hacksaw cuts while the blade is pushed in the forward direction, and then pressure should be released as the blade is pulled rearward before repeating the cutting operation. ● **SEE FIGURE 8–41.**

SAFE USE OF HACKSAWS. Check that the hacksaw is equipped with the correct blade for the job and that the teeth are pointed away from the handle. When using a hacksaw, move the hacksaw slowly away from you, then lift slightly and return for another cut.

REPLACEABLE BLADE

FIGURE 8–41 A typical hacksaw that is used to cut metal. If cutting sheet metal or thin objects, a blade with more teeth should be used.

BASIC HAND TOOL LIST

Hand tools are used to turn fasteners (bolts, nuts, and screws). The following is a list of hand tools every automotive technician should possess. Specialty tools are not included.

Safety glasses

Tool chest

1/4 in. drive socket set (1/4 to 9/16 in. standard and deep sockets; 6 to 15 mm standard and deep sockets)

1/4 in. drive ratchet

1/4 in. drive 2 in. extension

1/4 in. drive 6 in. extension

1/4 in. drive handle

3/8 in. drive socket set (3/8 to 7/8 in. standard and deep sockets; 10 to 19 mm standard and deep sockets)

3/8 in. drive Torx set (T40, T45, T50, and T55)

3/8 in. drive 13/16 in. plug socket

3/8 in. drive 5/8 in. plug socket

3/8 in. drive ratchet

3/8 in. drive 1 1/2 in. extension

3/8 in. drive 3 in. extension

3/8 in. drive 6 in. extension

3/8 in. drive 18 in. extension

3/8 in. drive universal

1/2 in. drive socket set (1/2 to 1 in. standard and deep sockets; 9 to 19 mm standard and deep metric sockets)

1/2 in. drive ratchet

1/2 in. drive breaker bar

1/2 in. drive 5 in. extension

1/2 in. drive 10 in. extension

3/8 to 1/4 in. adapter

1/2 to 3/8 in. adapter

3/8 to 1/2 in. adapter

Crowfoot set (fractional inch)

Crowfoot set (metric)

3/8 through 1 in. combination wrench set

10 through 19 mm combination wrench set

1/16 through 1/4 in. hex (Allen) wrench set

2 through 12 mm hex (Allen) wrench set

3/8 in. hex socket

13 to 14 mm flare nut wrench

15 to 17 mm flare nut wrench

5/16 to 3/8 in. flare nut wrench

7/16 to 1/2 in. flare nut wrench

1/2 to 9/16 in. flare nut wrench

Diagonal pliers

Needle pliers

Hide Those from the Boss

An apprentice technician started working for a dealership and put his top tool box on a work-bench. Another technician observed that, along with a complete set of good-quality tools, the box contained several adjustable wrenches. The more experienced technician said, "Hide those from the boss." If any adjustable wrench is used on a bolt or nut, the movable jaw often moves or loosens and starts to round the head of the fastener. If the head of the bolt or nut becomes rounded, it becomes that much more difficult to remove.

Need to Borrow a Tool More than Twice? Buy It!

Most service technicians agree that it is okay for a beginning technician to borrow a tool occasionally. However, if a tool has to be borrowed more than twice, then be sure to purchase it as soon as possible. Also, whenever a tool is borrowed, be sure that you clean the tool and let the technician you borrowed the tool from know that you are returning the tool. These actions will help in any future dealings with other technicians.

Adjustable-jaw pliers
Locking pliers
Snap-ring pliers
Stripping or crimping pliers
Ball-peen hammer
Rubber hammer
Dead-blow hammer'
Five-piece standard screwdriver set
Four-piece Phillips screwdriver set
#15 Torx screwdriver
#20 Torx screwdriver
File
Center punch
Pin punches (assorted sizes)
Chisel
Utility knife
Valve core tool
Filter wrench (large filters)
Filter wrench (smaller filters)
Test light
Feeler gauge
Scraper
Magnet

FIGURE 8–42 A typical beginning technician tool set that includes the basic tools to get started.

FIGURE 8–43 A typical large tool box, showing just one of many drawers.

TOOL SETS AND ACCESSORIES

A beginning service technician may wish to start with a small set of tools before spending a lot of money on an expensive, extensive tool box. See ● **SEE FIGURES 8–42 AND 8–43**.

The Valve Grinding Compound Trick

Apply a small amount of valve grinding compound to a Phillips or Torx screw or bolt head. The gritty valve grinding compound "grips" the screwdriver or tool bit and prevents the tool from slipping up and out of the screw head. Valve grinding compound is available in a tube from most automotive parts stores.

FIGURE 8–44 A seal puller being used to remove a seal from a rear axle.

FIGURE 8–45 A seal (boot) driver or installer is usually plastic and is designed to seat the seal.

SEAL PULLERS AND DRIVERS

SEAL PULLERS   Grease seals are located on many automotive components, including brake rotors, transmission housings, and differentials. A **seal puller** is used to properly remove grease seals, as shown in ● **SEE FIGURE 8–44**.

SEAL DRIVERS   A **seal driver** can be either plastic or metal, usually aluminum, and is used to seat the outer lip of a grease seal into the grease seal pocket. A seal is usually driven into position using a plastic mallet and a seal driver that is the same size as the outside diameter of the grease seal retainer. ● **SEE FIGURE 8–45**.

FIGURE 8–46 A typical 12 volt test light.

ELECTRICAL HAND TOOLS

TEST LIGHTS   A test light is used to test for electricity. A typical automotive test light consists of a clear plastic screwdriver-like handle that contains a light bulb. A wire is attached to one terminal of the bulb, which the technician connects to a clean metal part of the vehicle. The other end of the bulb is attached to a point that can be used to test for electricity at a connector or wire. When there is power at the point and a good connection at the other end, the light bulb lights. ● **SEE FIGURE 8–46**.

SOLDERING GUNS

- **Electric soldering gun**. This type of soldering gun is usually powered by 110 volt AC and often has two power settings expressed in watts. A typical electric soldering gun will produce from 85 to 300 watts of heat at the tip, which is more than adequate for soldering. ● **SEE FIGURE 8–47**.

- **Electric soldering pencil**. This type of soldering iron is less expensive and creates less heat than an electric soldering gun. A typical electric soldering pencil (iron) creates 30 to 60 watts of heat and is suitable for soldering smaller wires and connections.

- **Butane-powered soldering iron**. A butane-powered soldering iron is portable and very useful for automotive service work because an electrical cord is not needed. Most butane-powered soldering irons produce about 60 watts of heat, which is enough for most automotive soldering.

BUTANE-POWERED

ELECTRIC

FIGURE 8–47 An electric soldering gun used to make electrical repairs. Soldering guns are sold by the wattage rating. The higher the wattage, the greater amount of heat created. Most solder guns used for automotive electrical work usually fall within the 60 to 160 watt range.

In addition to a soldering iron, most service technicians who do electrical-related work should have the following:

- Wire cutters
- Wire strippers
- Wire crimpers
- Heat gun

A digital meter is a necessary tool for any electrical diagnosis and troubleshooting. A digital multimeter, abbreviated DMM, is usually capable of measuring the following units of electricity.

- DC volts
- AC volts
- Ohms
- Amperes

TECH TIP

It Just Takes a Second

Whenever removing any automotive component, it is wise to screw the bolts back into the holes a couple of threads by hand. This ensures that the right bolt will be used in its original location when the component or part is put back on the vehicle. Often, the same diameter of fastener is used on a component, but the length of the bolt may vary. Spending just a couple of seconds to put the bolts and nuts back where they belong when the part is removed can save a lot of time when the part is being reinstalled. Besides making certain that the right fastener is being installed in the right place, this method helps prevent bolts and nuts from getting lost or kicked away. How much time have you wasted looking for that lost bolt or nut?

SAFETY TIPS FOR USING HAND TOOLS

The following safety tips should be kept in mind whenever you are working with hand tools.

- Always *pull* a wrench toward you for best control and safety. Never push a wrench.
- Keep wrenches and all hand tools clean to help prevent rust and to allow for a better, firmer grip.
- Always use a 6-point socket or a box-end wrench to break loose a tight bolt or nut.
- Use a box-end wrench for torque and an open-end wrench for speed.
- Never use a pipe extension or other type of "**cheater bar**" on a wrench or ratchet handle. If more force is required, use a larger tool or use penetrating oil and/or heat on the frozen fastener. (If heat is used on a bolt or nut to remove it, always replace it with a new part.)
- Always use the proper tool for the job. If a specialized tool is required, use the proper tool and do not try to use another tool improperly.
- Never expose any tool to excessive heat. High temperatures can reduce the strength ("draw the temper") of metal tools.
- Never use a hammer on any wrench or socket handle unless you are using a special "staking face" wrench designed to be used with a hammer.
- Replace any tools that are damaged or worn.

HAND TOOL MAINTENANCE

Most hand tools are constructed of rust-resistant metals but they can still rust or corrode if not properly maintained. For best results and long tool life, the following steps should be taken.

- Clean each tool before placing it back into the tool box.
- Keep tools separated. Moisture on metal tools will start to rust more readily if the tools are in contact with another metal tool.
- Line the drawers of the tool box with a material that will prevent the tools from moving as the drawers are opened and closed. This helps to quickly locate the proper tool and size.

- Release the tension on all "clicker-type" torque wrenches after use.
- Keep the tool box secure.

FIGURE 8–48 A binder clip being used to keep a fender cover from falling.

SUMMARY

1. Wrenches are available in open end, box end, and combination open and box end.
2. An adjustable wrench should only be used where the proper size is not available.
3. Line wrenches are also called flare-nut wrenches, fitting wrenches, or tube-nut wrenches and are used to remove fuel or refrigerant lines.
4. Sockets are rotated by a ratchet or breaker bar, also called a flex handle.
5. Torque wrenches measure the amount of torque applied to a fastener.
6. Screwdriver types include straight blade (flat tip) Torx, and Phillips.
7. Hammers and mallets come in a variety of sizes and weights.
8. Pliers are a useful tool and are available in many different types, including slip-joint, multigroove, linesman's, diagonal, needle-nose, and locking pliers.
9. Other common hand tools include snap-ring pliers, files, cutters, punches, chisels, and hacksaws.

REVIEW QUESTIONS

1. Why are wrenches offset 15 degrees?
2. What are the other names for a line wrench?
3. What are the standard automotive drive sizes for sockets?
4. Which type of screwdriver requires the use of a hammer or mallet?
5. What is inside a dead-blow hammer?
6. What type of cutter is available in left and right cutters?

CHAPTER QUIZ

1. When working with hand tools, always _____.
   a. Push the wrench—don't pull toward you
   b. Pull a wrench—don't push a wrench

2. The proper term for Channel Locks is _____.
   a. Vise Grips
   b. Crescent wrench
   c. Locking pliers
   d. Multigroove adjustable pliers

3. The proper term for Vise Grips is _____.
   a. Locking pliers   c. Side cuts
   b. Slip-joint pliers   d. Multigroove adjustable pliers

4. Which tool listed is a brand name?
   a. Locking pliers
   b. Monkey wrench
   c. Side cutters
   d. Vise Grips

5. Two technicians are discussing torque wrenches. Technician A says that a torque wrench is capable of tightening a fastener with more torque than a conventional breaker bar or ratchet. Technician B says that a torque wrench should be calibrated regularly for the most accurate results. Which technician is correct?
   a. Technician A only
   b. Technician B only
   c. Both Technicians A and B
   d. Neither Technician A nor B

6. What type of screwdriver should be used if there is very limited space above the head of the fastener?
   a. Offset screwdriver
   b. Phillips screwdriver
   c. Impact screwdriver
   d. Robertson screwdriver

7. Where is the "peen" of the hammer?
   a. The striking face
   b. The handle
   c. The back part opposite the striking face
   d. The part that connects to the handle

8. What type of hammer is plastic coated, has a metal casing inside, and is filled with small lead balls?
   a. Dead-blow hammer
   b. Soft-blow hammer
   c. Sledge hammer
   d. Plastic hammer

9. Which type of pliers is capable of fitting over a large object?
   a. Slip-joint pliers
   b. Linesman's pliers
   c. Locking pliers
   d. Multigroove adjustable pliers

10. Which tool has a replaceable cutting edge?
   a. Side-cut pliers
   b. Tin snips
   c. Utility knife
   d. Aviation snips

chapter 9

POWER TOOLS AND SHOP EQUIPMENT

OBJECTIVES: **After studying Chapter 9, the reader should be able to:** • Identify commonly used power tools. • Identify commonly used shop equipment. • Discuss the proper use of power tools and shop equipment. • Describe the safety procedures that should be followed when working with power tools and shop equipment.

KEY TERMS: • Air-blow gun 86 • Air compressor 84 • Air drill 86 • Air ratchet 85 • Bearing splitter 88 • Bench grinder 87 • Bench vise 87 • Die grinder 85 • Engine stand 89 • Hydraulic press 88 • Impact wrench 85 • Incandescent light 86 • Light-emitting diode (LED) 87 • Portable crane 88 • Stone wheel 87 • Trouble light 86 • Wire brush wheel 87 • Work light 86

AIR COMPRESSOR

A shop air compressor is usually located in a separate room or an area away from the customer area of a shop. An **air compressor** is powered by a 220 V AC electric motor and includes a storage tank and the compressor itself, as well as the pressure switches, which are used to maintain a certain minimum level of air pressure in the system. The larger the storage tank, expressed in gallons, the longer an air tool can be operated in the shop without having the compressor start operating. ● **SEE FIGURE 9–1.**

SAFE USE OF COMPRESSED AIR. Air under pressure can create dangerous situations. For example, an object, such as a small piece of dirt, could be forced out of an air hose blow gun with enough force to cause serious personal injury. All OSHA-approved air nozzles have air vents drilled around the outside of the main discharge hole to help reduce the force of the air blast. Also, the air pressure used by an air nozzle (blow gun) must be kept to 30 PSI (207 kPa) or less. ● **SEE FIGURE 9–2.**

FIGURE 9–1 A typical shop compressor. It is usually placed out of the way, yet accessible to provide for maintenance to the unit.

FIGURE 9–2 Always use an air nozzle that is OSHA approved. The openings in the side are used to allow air to escape if the nozzle tip were to become clogged.

FIGURE 9–3 A typical 1/2 in. drive impact wrench.

FIGURE 9–4 This impact wrench features a variable torque setting using a rotary knob. The direction of rotation can be changed by pressing the button at the bottom.

FIGURE 9–5 A typical battery-powered 3/8 in. drive impact wrench.

FIGURE 9–6 A black impact socket. Always use impact-type sockets whenever using an impact wrench to avoid the possibility of shattering the socket, which can cause personal injury.

AIR AND ELECTRICALLY OPERATED TOOLS

IMPACT WRENCH An **impact wrench**, either air (pneumatic) or electrically powered, is a tool that is used to remove and install fasteners. The air-operated 1/2 in. drive impact wrench is the most commonly used unit. ● **SEE FIGURE 9–3.**

The direction of rotation is controlled by a switch. ● **SEE FIGURE 9–4.**

Electrically powered impact wrenches commonly include:

- Battery-powered units. ● **SEE FIGURE 9–5.**
- 110-volt AC-powered units. This type of impact wrench is very useful, especially if compressed air is not readily available.

CAUTION: Always use impact sockets with impact wrenches, and be sure to wear eye protection in case the

socket or fastener shatters. Impact sockets are thicker walled and constructed with premium alloy steel. They are hardened with a black oxide finish to help prevent corrosion and distinguish them from regular sockets. ● **SEE FIGURE 9–6.**

AIR RATCHET An **air ratchet** is used to remove and install fasteners that would normally be removed or installed using a ratchet and a socket. An air ratchet is much faster, yet has an air hose attached, which reduces accessibility to certain places. ● **SEE FIGURE 9–7.**

DIE GRINDER A **die grinder** is a commonly used air-powered tool, which can also be used to sand or remove gaskets and rust. ● **SEE FIGURE 9–8.**

FIGURE 9–7 An air ratchet is a very useful tool that allows fast removal and installation of fasteners, especially in areas that are difficult to reach or do not have room enough to move a hand ratchet wrench.

 REAL-WORLD FIX

The Case of the Rusty Air Impact Wrenches

In one busy shop, it was noticed by several technicians that water was being pumped through the air compressor lines and out of the vents of air impact wrenches whenever they were used. It is normal for moisture in the air to condense in the air storage tank of an air compressor. One of the routine service procedures is to drain the water from the air compressor. The water had been drained regularly from the air compressor at the rear of the shop, but the problem continued. Then someone remembered that there was a second air compressor mounted over the parts department. No one could remember ever draining the tank from that compressor. After that tank was drained, the problem of water in the lines was solved. The service manager assigned a person to drain the water from both compressors every day and to check the oil level. The oil in the compressor is changed every six months to help ensure long life of the expensive compressors.

AIR DRILL An **air drill** is a drill that rotates faster than electric drills (up to 20,000 RPM). Air drills are commonly used in auto body work when many holes need to be drilled for plug welding.

AIR-BLOW GUN An **air-blow gun** is used to clean equipment and other purposes where a stream of air would be needed. Automotive air-blow guns should meet OSHA requirements and include passages to allow air to escape outward at the nozzle, thereby relieving pressure if the nozzle were to become blocked.

AIR-OPERATED GREASE GUN An air-operated grease gun uses shop air to operate a plunger, which then applies a

FIGURE 9–8 This typical die grinder surface preparation kit includes the air-operated die grinder, as well as a variety of sanding discs for smoothing surfaces or removing rust.

force to the grease cartridge. Most air-operated grease guns use a 1/4 in. air inlet and operate on 90 PSI of air pressure.

BATTERY-POWERED GREASE GUN Battery-powered grease guns are more expensive than air-operated grease guns but offer the convenience of not having an air hose attached, making use easier. Many use rechargeable 14 to 18 volt batteries and use standard grease cartridges.

TROUBLE LIGHTS

INCANDESCENT **Incandescent lights** use a filament that produces light when electric current flows through the bulb. This was the standard **trouble light**, also called a **work light** for many years until safety issues caused most shops to switch to safer fluorescent or LED lights. If incandescent light bulbs are used, try to locate bulbs that are rated "rough service," which is designed to withstand shock and vibration more than conventional light bulbs.

FLUORESCENT A trouble light is an essential piece of shop equipment, and for safety, should be fluorescent rather than incandescent. Incandescent light bulbs can scatter or break if gasoline were to be splashed onto the bulb creating a serious fire hazard. Fluorescent light tubes are not as likely to be broken

 WARNING

Do not use incandescent trouble lights around gasoline or other flammable liquids. The liquids can cause the bulb to break and the hot filament can ignite the flammable liquid.

FIGURE 9–9 A fluorescent trouble light operates cooler and is safer to use in the shop because it is protected against accidental breakage where gasoline or other flammable liquids would happen to come in contact with the light.

and are usually protected by a clear plastic enclosure. Trouble lights are usually attached to a retractor, which can hold 20 to 50 ft of electrical cord. ● SEE FIGURE 9–9.

LED TROUBLE LIGHT Light-emitting diode (LED) trouble lights are excellent to use because they are shock resistant, long lasting, and do not represent a fire hazard. Some trouble lights are battery powered and therefore can be used in places where an attached electrical cord could present problems.

BENCH/PEDESTAL GRINDER

A grinder can be mounted on a workbench or on a stand-alone pedestal.

BENCH- OR PEDESTAL-MOUNTED GRINDER These high-powered grinders can be equipped with a wire brush wheel and/or a stone wheel.

- A **wire brush wheel** is used to clean steel or sheet metal parts.
- A **stone wheel** is used to grind metal or to remove the mushroom from the top of punches or chisels. ● SEE FIGURE 9–10.

CAUTION: Always wear a face shield when using a wire wheel or a grinder. Also keep the part support ledge (table), also called a throat plate, within 1/16 inch (2 mm) of the stone.

Most **bench grinders** are equipped with a grinding wheel (stone) on one side and a wire brush wheel on the other side. A bench grinder is a very useful piece of shop equipment and the wire wheel end can be used for the following:

FIGURE 9–10 A typical pedestal grinder with a wire wheel on the left side and a stone wheel on the right side. Even though this machine is equipped with guards, safety glasses or a face shield should always be worn when using a grinder or wire wheel.

- Cleaning threads of bolts
- Cleaning gaskets from sheet metal parts, such as steel valve covers

CAUTION: Use a steel wire brush only on steel or iron components. If a steel wire brush is used on aluminum or copper-based metal parts, it can remove metal from the part.

The grinding stone end of the bench grinder can be used for the following:

- Sharpening blades and drill bits
- Grinding off the heads of rivets or parts
- Sharpening sheet metal parts for custom fitting

BENCH VISE

A **bench vise** is used to hold components so that work can be performed on the unit. The size of a vise is determined by the width of the jaws. Two common sizes of vises are 4 in. and 6 in. models. The jaws of most vises are serrated and can cause damage to some components unless protected. Many types of protection can be used, including aluminum or copper jaw covers or by simply placing wood between the vise jaws and the component being held. ● SEE FIGURE 9–11.

SAFE USE OF VISES. The jaws of vises can cause damage to the part or component being held. Use pieces of wood or other soft material between the steel jaws and the workpiece to help avoid causing damage. Many vises are sold with optional aluminum jaw covers. When finished using a vise, be sure to close the jaws and place the handle straight up and down to help avoid personal injury to anyone walking near the vise.

FIGURE 9–11 A typical vise mounted to a workbench.

FIGURE 9–12 A hydraulic press is usually used to press bearings on and off on rear axles and transmissions.

HYDRAULIC PRESSES

Hydraulic presses are hand-operated hydraulic cylinders mounted to a stand and designed to press bearings on or off of shafts, as well as other components. To press off a bearing, a unit called a **bearing splitter** is often required to apply force to the inner race of a bearing. Hydraulic presses use a pressure gauge to show the pressure being applied. Always follow the operating instructions supplied by the manufacturer of the hydraulic press. ● SEE FIGURE 9–12.

FIGURE 9–13 A typical portable crane used to lift and move heavy assemblies, such as engines and transmissions.

 TECH TIP

Cover Work While Pressing

Whenever pressing on a bearing or other component, use an old brake drum over the shaft and the bearing. In the event the bearing shatters during the pressing operation, the brake drum will prevent the parts of the bearing from flying outward where they could cause serious personal injury.

PORTABLE CRANE AND CHAIN HOIST

A **portable crane** is used to remove and install engines and other heavy vehicle components. Most portable cranes use a hand-operated hydraulic cylinder to raise and lower a boom that is equipped with a nylon strap or steel chain. At the end of the strap or chain is a steel hook that is used to attach around a bracket or auxiliary lifting device. ● SEE FIGURE 9–13.

SAFE USE OF PORTABLE CRANES. Always be sure to attach the hook(s) of the portable crane to a secure location on the unit being lifted. The hook should also be attached to the center of the weight of the object so it can be lifted straight up without tilting.

CAUTION: Always keep feet and other body parts out from underneath the engine or unit being lifted. Always work around a portable crane as if the chain or strap could break at any time.

ENGINE STANDS

An **engine stand** is designed to safely hold an engine and to allow it to be rotated. This allows the technician to easily remove, install, and perform service work to the engine. ● **SEE FIGURE 9–14.**

Most engine stands are constructed of steel and supported by four casters to allow easy movement. There are two basic places where an engine stand attaches to the engine depending on the size of the engine. For most engines and stands, the retaining bolts attach to the same location as the bell housing at the rear of the engine.

On larger engines, such as the 5.9 Cummins inline 6-cylinder diesel engine, the engine mounts to the stand using the engine mounting holes in the block. ● **SEE FIGURE 9–15.**

SAFE OPERATION OF AN ENGINE STAND. When mounting an engine to an engine stand, be sure that the engine is being supported by a portable crane. Be sure the attaching bolts are grade 5 or 8 and the same thread size as the threaded holes in the block. Check that there is at least 1/2 inch (13 mm) of bolt thread engaged in the threaded holes in the engine block. Be sure that all attaching bolts are securely tightened before releasing the weight of the engine from the crane. Use caution when loosening the rotation retaining bolts because the engine could rotate rapidly, causing personal injury.

CARE AND MAINTENANCE OF SHOP EQUIPMENT

All shop equipment should be maintained in safe working order. Maintenance of shop equipment usually includes the following operations or procedures.

- **Keep equipment clean.** Dirt and grime can attract and hold moisture, which can lead to rust and corrosion. Oil or grease can attract dirt.

- **Keep equipment lubricated.** While many bearings are sealed and do not require lubrication, always check the instructions for the use of the equipment for suggested lubrication and other service procedures.

FIGURE 9–14 Two engines on engine stands. The plastic bags help keep dirt from getting onto the engines.

FIGURE 9–15 An engine stand that attaches to the engine from the sides rather than the end.

CAUTION: Always follow the instructions from the equipment manufacturer regarding proper use and care of the equipment.

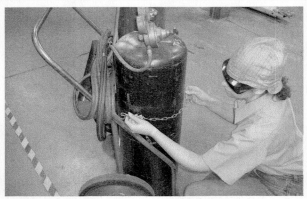

1 Inspect the cart and make sure the tanks are chained properly before moving it to the work location.

2 Start by attaching the appropriate work tip to the torch handle. The fitting should only be tightened hand tight. Make sure the valves on the torch handle are closed at this time.

3 Each tank has a regulator assembly with two gauges. The high pressure gauge shows tank pressure, and the low pressure gauge indicates working pressure.

4 Open the oxygen tank valve fully open, and open the acetylene tank valve 1/2 turn.

5 Open the oxygen valve on the torch handle 1/4 turn in preparation for adjusting oxygen gas pressure.

6 Turn the oxygen regulator valve clockwise and adjust oxygen gas pressure to 20 PSI. Close the oxygen valve on the torch handle.

7 Open the acetylene valve on the torch handle 1/4 turn and adjust acetylene gas pressure to 7 PSI. Close the acetylene valve on the torch handle.

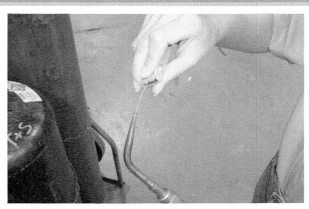

8 Open the oxygen valve on the torch handle 1/4 turn and use an appropriate size tip cleaner to clean the tip orifice. Finish by closing the oxygen valve.

9 Put on leather gloves and open the acetylene valve on the torch handle 1/4 turn. Use a flint striker to ignite the acetylene gas exiting the torch tip.

10 Adjust the acetylene valve until the base of the flame just touches the torch tip. Slowly open the oxygen valve on the torch handle and adjust for a neutral flame (blue cone is well-defined).

11 Once work is complete, extinguish the flame by quickly closing the acetylene valve on the torch handle. Be prepared to hear a loud "pop" when the flame goes out. Close the oxygen valve on the torch handle.

12 Close the valves on both tanks and turn the regulator handles CCW until they no longer contact the internal springs. Open the gas valves briefly on the torch handle to release gas pressure from the hoses. Close the gas valves on the torch handle and put away the torch assembly.

1 Heating attachments include ordinary heating tips, middle and right and a "rosebud" (left). Ordinary heating tips work fine for most purposes, but occasionally the rosebud is utilized when a great deal of heat is needed.

2 Note that while acetylene tank pressures are relatively low, the oxygen tank can be filled to over 2,000 PSI. This can represent a serious hazard if precautions are not taken. Be absolutely certain that the tanks are chained properly to the cart before attempting to move it!

3 Any time heating or cutting operations are being performed, be sure that any flammables have been removed from the immediate area. A fire blanket may be placed over floor drains or other objects to prevent fires. A fire extinguisher should be on hand in case of an emergency.

4 Be sure to wear appropriate personal protective equipment during heating and cutting operations.

5 Note that heating operations should be performed over steel or firebrick. Never heat or cut steel close to concrete, as it could cause the concrete to explode.

6 When heating steel, move the torch in a circular pattern to prevent melting of the metal. Don't hold the torch too close to the work as this will cause a "snapping" or "backfire" that can extinguish the flame.

1 Affix the cutting attachment to the torch handle. Note that the cutting attachment has a cutting handle and a separate oxygen valve.

2 Fully open the oxygen valve on the torch handle. Oxygen flow will now be controlled with the valve on the cutting attachment.

3 Oxygen gas pressure should be adjusted to 30 PSI whenever using the cutting attachment. Acetylene pressure is kept at 7 PSI.

4 Open the acetylene valve on the torch handle 1/4 turn and light the torch. Adjust the flame until its base just touches the cutting tip. Slowly open the oxygen valve on the cutting attachment and adjust the flame until the blue cone is well-defined.

5 Direct the flame onto a thin spot or sharp edge of the metal to be cut. This will build the heat quicker in order to get the cut started.

6 When the metal glows red, depress the cutting handle and move the torch to advance the cut. You will need to move the torch faster when cutting thinner pieces of steel. On thicker pieces, point the cutting tip into the direction of the cut.

1. Most shops are equipped with a large air compressor that supplies pressurized air to all stalls for use by the technician.

2. An air impact wrench is the most commonly used power tool in the shop. It is used mostly to remove fasteners.

3. Other air-operated tools include an air ratchet and a die grinder.

4. A bench or pedestal grinder usually has both a grinding stone and a wire brush wheel.

5. Trouble lights should be fluorescent or LED for maximum safety in the shop.

6. A hydraulic press is used to remove bearings from shafts and other similar operations.

7. A portable crane is used to remove and install engines or engine/transmission assemblies from vehicles.

8. Engine stands are designed to allow the technician to rotate the engine to get access to the various parts and components.

REVIEW QUESTIONS

1. List the tools used by service technicians that use compressed air?

2. Which trouble light design(s) is (are) the recommended type for maximum safety?

3. What safety precautions should be adhered to when working with a vise?

4. When using a blow gun, what precautions need to be taken?

CHAPTER QUIZ

1. When using compressed air and a blow gun, what is the maximum allowable air pressure?
   a. 10 PSI
   b. 20 PSI
   c. 30 PSI
   d. 40 PSI

2. Which air impact drive size is the most commonly used?
   a. 1/4 in.
   b. 3/8 in.
   c. 1/2 in.
   d. 3/4 in.

3. What type of socket should be used with an air impact wrench?
   a. Black
   b. Chrome
   c. 12 point
   d. Either a or b

4. What can be used to cover the jaws of a vise to help protect the object being held?
   a. Aluminum
   b. Wood
   c. Copper
   d. All of the above

5. Technician A says that impact sockets have thicker walls than conventional sockets. Technician B says that impact sockets have a black oxide finish. Which technician is correct?
   a. Technician A only
   b. Technician B only
   c. Both Technicians A and B
   d. Neither Technician A nor B

6. Two technicians are discussing the use of a typical bench/pedestal-mounted grinder. Technician A says that a wire brush wheel can be used to clean threads. Technician B says that the grinding stone can be used to clean threads. Which technician is correct?
   a. Technician A only
   b. Technician B only
   c. Both Technicians A and B
   d. Neither Technician A nor B

7. A hydraulic press is being used to separate a bearing from a shaft. What should be used to cover the bearing during the pressing operation?
   a. Shop cloth
   b. Brake drum
   c. Fender cover
   d. Paper towel

8. Which type of trouble light is recommended for use in the shop?
   a. Incandescent
   b. Fluorescent
   c. LED
   d. Either b or c

9. When mounting an engine to an engine stand, what grade of bolt should be used?
   a. 5 or 8
   b. 4 or 7
   c. 3 or 5
   d. 1 or 4

10. Proper care of shop equipment includes _____.
    a. Tuning up every six months
    b. Keeping equipment clean
    c. Keeping equipment lubricated
    d. Both b and c

chapter 10

MEASURING SYSTEMS AND TOOLS

OBJECTIVES: **After studying Chapter 10, the reader should be able to:** • Describe how to read a ruler. • Explain how to use a micrometer and vernier dial caliper. • Describe how to use a telescopic gauge and a micrometer to measure cylinder and lifter bores. • Discuss how to measure valve guides using a small-hole gauge.

KEY TERMS: • Feeler gauge 100 • Sleeve 96 • Small-hole gauge 99 • Spindle 96 • Split-ball gauge 99 • Straightedge 101 • Thickness gauge 100 • Thimble 96

ENGLISH CUSTOMARY MEASURING SYSTEM

The English customary measuring system was established about A.D. 1100 in England during the reign of Henry I. The foot was determined to be 12 inches and was taken from the length of a typical foot. The yard (36 inches) was determined to be the length from King Henry's nose to the end of his outstretched hand. The mile came from Roman days and was originally defined as the distance traveled by a soldier in 1,000 paces or steps. Other English units, such as the pound (weight) and volume (gallon), evolved over the years from Roman and English measurements.

The Fahrenheit temperature scale was created by Gabriel Fahrenheit (1686–1736) and he used 100°F as the temperature of the human body, which he missed by 1.4 degrees (98.6°F is considered now to be normal temperature). On the Fahrenheit scale, water freezes at 32°F and water boils at 212°F.

METRIC SYSTEM OF MEASURE

Most of the world uses the metric system of measure. The metric system was created in the late 1700s in France and used the physical world for the basis of the measurements. For example, the meter was defined as being 1/40,000,000 of the circumference of the earth (the distance around the earth at the poles). The Celsius temperature scale developed by Anders Celsius (1701–1744) used the freezing point of water as 0°C (32°F) and the boiling point of water as 100°C (212°F). Other units include a liter of water, which was then used as a standard of weight where 1 liter of water (about 1 quart) weighs 1 kilogram (1,000 grams). Units of measure are then divided or multiplied by 10,

100, or 1,000 to arrive at usable measurements. For example, a kilometer is 1,000 meters and is the most commonly used metric measurement for distance for travel. Other prefixes include:

  m = milli = 1/1,000
  k = kilo = 1,000
  M = mega = 1,000,000

LINEAR METRIC MEASUREMENTS

  1 kilometer = 0.62 mile
  1 meter = 39.37 inches
  1 centimeter (1/100 meter) = 0.39 inch
  1 millimeter (1/1,000 meter) = 0.039 inch

VOLUME MEASUREMENT

  1 cc (cubic centimeter) = 0.06 cubic inch
  1 liter = 0.26 U.S. gallon (about 1 quart)

WEIGHT MEASUREMENT

  1 gram = 0.035 ounce
  1 kilogram (1,000 grams) = 2.2 pounds

PRESSURE MEASUREMENTS

  1 kilopascal (kPa) = 0.14 pound per square inch
      (6.9 kPa = 1 PSI)
  1 bar = 14.5 pounds per square inch

DERIVED UNITS   All units of measure, except for the base units, are a combination of units that are referred to as derived units of measure. Some examples of derived units include:

  Torque
  Velocity
  Density
  Energy
  Power

What Weighs a Gram?

To better understand the metric system measurements, it is often helpful to visualize a certain object and relate it to a metric unit of measure. For example, the following objects weigh about 1 gram.

- A dollar bill
- A small paper clip

LINEAR MEASUREMENTS (TAPE MEASURE/RULE)

A tape measure or machinist rule divides inches into smaller units. Each smaller unit is drawn with a line shorter than the longer unit. The units of measure starting with the largest include:

1 inch
1/2 inch
1/4 inch
1/8 inch
1/16 inch

Some rules show 1/32 of an inch. ● **SEE FIGURE 10–1.**

A metric scale is also included on many tape measures and machinists rules. ● **SEE FIGURE 10–2.**

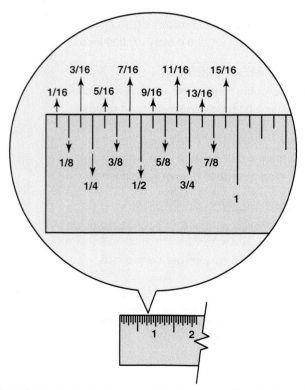

FIGURE 10–1 A rule showing that the larger the division, the longer the line.

FIGURE 10–2 A plastic rule that has both inches and centimeters. Each line between the numbers on the centimeters represents 1 millimeter because there are 10 millimeters in 1 centimeter.

MICROMETER

A micrometer is the most used measuring instrument in engine-service and repair. ● **SEE FIGURE 10–3.**

The **thimble** rotates over the **sleeve** on a screw that has 40 threads per inch. Every revolution of the thimble moves the **spindle** 0.025 in. The thimble is graduated into 25 equally spaced lines; therefore, each line represents 0.001 in. Every micrometer should be checked for calibration on a regular basis. ● **SEE FIGURES 10–4 THROUGH 10–6.**

FIGURE 10–3 A typical micrometer showing the names of the parts. The sleeve may also be called the *barrel* or *stock.*

FIGURE 10–4 All micrometers should be checked and calibrated as needed using a gauge rod.

FIGURE 10-5 The three micrometer readings are (a) 0.0212 in.; (b) 0.0775 in.; and (c) 0.5280 in. These measurements used the vernier scale on the sleeve to arrive at the ten-thousandth measurement. The number that is aligned represents the digit in the ten-thousandth place.

FIGURE 10-6 Metric micrometer readings that use the vernier scale on the sleeve to read to the nearest 0.001 millimeter. The arrows point to the final reading for each of the three examples.

CRANKSHAFT MEASUREMENT Even though the connecting rod journals and the main bearing journals are usually different sizes, they both can and should be measured for out-of-round and taper. ● **SEE FIGURE 10–7.**

OUT-OF-ROUND. A journal should be measured in at least two positions across the diameter and every 120 degrees around the journal, as shown in ● **FIGURE 10–8,** for an example of the six readings. Calculate the out-of-round measurement by subtracting the lowest reading from the highest reading for both A and B positions.

Position A: 2.0000 − 1.9995 = 0.0005 in.

Position B: 2.0000 − 1.9989 = 0.0011 in.

The maximum out-of-round measurement occurs in position B (0.0011 in.), which is the measurement that should be used to compare against factory specifications to determine if any machining will be necessary.

FIGURE 10–7 Using a micrometer to measure the connecting rod journal for out-of-round and taper.

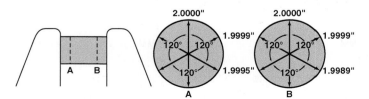

FIGURE 10–8 Crankshaft journal measurements. Each journal should be measured in at least six locations, but also in position A and position B and at 120-degree intervals around the journal.

TAPER. To determine the taper of the journal, compare the readings in the same place between A and B positions and subtract the lower reading from the higher reading.

For example:

Position A		Position B	
2.0000	−	2.0000	= 0.0000
1.9999	−	1.9999	= 0.0000
1.9995	−	1.9989	= 0.0006

Use 0.0006 in. as the taper for the journal and compare with factory specifications.

CAMSHAFT MEASUREMENT The journal of the camshaft(s) can also be measured using a micrometer and compared with factory specifications for taper and out-of-round. ● **SEE FIGURE 10–9.**

NOTE: On overhead valve (pushrod) engines, the camshaft journal diameter often decreases slightly toward the rear of the engine. Overhead camshaft engines usually have the same journal diameter.

The cam lift can also be measured with a micrometer and compared with factory specifications, as shown in ● **FIGURE 10–10.**

FIGURE 10–9 Camshaft journals should be measured in three locations, 120 degrees apart, to check for out-of-round.

FIGURE 10–10 Checking a camshaft for wear by measuring the lobe height with a micrometer.

TELESCOPIC GAUGE

A telescopic gauge is used with a micrometer to measure the inside diameter of a hole or bore.

The cylinder bore can be measured by inserting a telescopic gauge into the bore and rotating the handle lock to allow the arms of the gauge to contact the inside bore of the cylinder. Tighten the handle lock and remove the gauge from the cylinder. Use a micrometer to measure the telescopic gauge. ● **SEE FIGURE 10–11.**

A telescopic gauge can also be used to measure the following:

- Camshaft bearing (● **SEE FIGURE 10–12.**)
- Main bearing bore (housing bore) measurement
- Connecting rod bore measurement

(a)

(b)

FIGURE 10–12 (a) A telescopic gauge being used to measure the inside diameter (ID) of a camshaft bearing. (b) An outside micrometer used to measure the telescopic gauge.

(a)

(b)

FIGURE 10–11 When the head is first removed, the cylinder taper and out-of-round should be checked below the ridge (a) and above the piston when it is at the bottom of the stroke (b).

SMALL-HOLE GAUGE

A **small-hole gauge** (also called a **split-ball gauge**) is used with a micrometer to measure the inside diameter of small holes such as a valve guide in a cylinder head. ● **SEE FIGURES 10–13 AND 10–14.**

VERNIER DIAL CALIPER

A vernier dial caliper is normally used to measure length, inside and outside diameters, and depth. ● **SEE FIGURE 10–15.**

FIGURE 10–13 Cutaway of a valve guide with a hole gauge adjusted to the hole diameter.

FIGURE 10–14 The outside of a hole gauge being measured with a micrometer.

KNIFE EDGE JAWS TO MEASURE INSIDE DIAMETERS

DIAL

ROD USED TO MEASURE DEPTH OF RECESSES

BLADE

OUTSIDE JAWS USED TO MEASURE OUTSIDE DIAMETERS

(a)

EACH SMALL LINE IS EQUAL TO 0.002"

5"   0.5"

ADD READING ON BLADE (5.5")
TO READING ON DIAL (0.036") TO
GET FINAL TOTAL MEASUREMENT (5.536")

(b)

FIGURE 10–15 (a) A typical vernier dial caliper. This is a very useful measuring tool for automotive engine work because it is capable of measuring inside, outside, and depth measurements. (b) To read a vernier dial caliper, simply add the reading on the blade to the reading on the dial.

FEELER GAUGE

A **feeler gauge** (also known as a **thickness gauge**) is an accurately manufactured strip of metal that is used to determine the gap or clearance between two components. ● SEE **FIGURE 10–16.**

? **FREQUENTLY ASKED QUESTION**

What Is the Difference Between the Word *Gage* and *Gauge*?

The word *gauge* means "measurement or dimension to a standard of reference." The word *gauge* can also be spelled *gage*. Therefore, in most cases, the words mean the same.

INTERESTING NOTE: One vehicle manufacturing representative told me that *gage* was used rather than *gauge* because even though it is the second acceptable spelling of the word, it is correct and it saved the company a lot of money in printing costs because the word *gage* has one less letter! One letter multiplied by millions of vehicles with gauges on the dash and the word *gauge* used in service manuals adds up to a big savings to the manufacturer.

FIGURE 10-16 A group of feeler gauges (also known as thickness gauges), used to measure between two parts. The long gauges on the bottom are used to measure the piston-to-cylinder wall clearance.

FIGURE 10-17 A feeler gauge, also called a thickness gauge, is used to measure the small clearances such as the end gap of a piston ring.

A feeler gauge can be used to check the following:

- Piston ring end gap (● SEE FIGURE 10-17.)
- Piston ring side clearance
- Connecting rod side clearance
- Piston-to-wall clearance

STRAIGHTEDGE

A **straightedge** is a precision ground metal measuring gauge that is used to check the flatness of engine components when used with a feeler gauge. A straightedge is used to check the flatness of the following:

- Cylinder heads (● SEE FIGURE 10-18.)
- Cylinder block deck
- Straightness of the main bearing bores (saddles)

FIGURE 10-18 A straightedge is used with a feeler gauge to determine if a cylinder head is warped or twisted.

DIAL INDICATOR

A dial indicator is a precision measuring instrument used to measure crankshaft end play, crankshaft runout, and valve guide wear. A dial indicator can be mounted three ways, including:

- **Magnetic mount.** This is a very useful method because a dial indicator can be attached to any steel or cast iron part.
- **Clamp mount.** A clamp-mounted dial indicator is used in many places where a mount could be clamped.
- **Threaded rod.** Using a threaded rod allows the dial indicator to be securely mounted, such as shown in ● FIGURE 10-19.

FIGURE 10-19 A dial indicator is used to measure valve lift during flow testing of a high-performance cylinder head.

FIGURE 10–20 A dial bore gauge is used to measure cylinders and other engine parts for out-of-round and taper conditions.

DIAL BORE GAUGE

A dial bore gauge is an expensive, but important, gauge used to measure cylinder taper and out-of-round as well as main bearing (block housing) bore for taper and out-of-round.

● **SEE FIGURE 10–20.** A dial bore gauge has to be adjusted to a dimension, such as the factory specifications. The reading on the dial bore gauge then indicates plus (+) or minus (−) readings from the predetermined dimension. This is why a dial bore is best used to measure taper and out-of-round because it shows the difference in cylinder or bore rather than an actual measurement.

DEPTH MICROMETER

A depth micrometer is similar to a conventional micrometer except that it is designed to measure the depth from a flat surface. ● **SEE FIGURE 10–21.**

FIGURE 10–21 A depth micrometer being used to measure the height of the rotor of an oil pump from the surface of the housing.

SUMMARY

1. A tape measure or machinist rule can be used to measure linear distances.

2. A micrometer can measure 0.001 in. by using a thimble that has 40 threads per in. Each rotation of the thimble moves the thimble 0.025 in. The circumference of the thimble is graduated into 25 marks, each representing 0.001 in.

3. A micrometer is used to check the diameter of a crankshaft journal as well as the taper and out-of-round.

4. A camshaft bearing and lobe can be measured using a micrometer.

5. A telescopic gauge is used with a micrometer to measure the inside of a hole or bore, such as the big end of a connecting rod or a cylinder bore.

6. A small-hole gauge (also called a split-ball gauge) is used with a micrometer to measure small holes such as the inside diameter of a valve guide in a cylinder head.

7. A vernier dial caliper is used to measure the outside diameter of components such as pistons or crankshaft bearing journals as well as inside diameters and depth measurements.

8. A feeler gauge (also called a thickness gauge) is used to measure the gap or clearance between two components such as piston ring end gap, piston-ring side clearance, and connecting rod side clearance. A feeler gauge is also used with a precision straightedge to measure the flatness of blocks and cylinder heads.

9. A dial indicator and dial bore gauge are used to measure differences in a component such as crankshaft end play (dial indicator) or cylinder taper (dial bore gauge).

1. Explain how a micrometer is read.
2. Describe how to check a crankshaft journal for out-of-round and taper.
3. List engine components that can be measured with the help of a telescopic gauge.
4. List the gaps or clearances that can be measured using a feeler (thickness) gauge.
5. Explain why a dial bore gauge has to be set to a dimension before using.

CHAPTER QUIZ

1. The threaded movable part that rotates on a micrometer is called the _____.
   a. Sleeve
   b. Thimble
   c. Spindle
   d. Anvil

2. To check a crankshaft journal for taper, the journal should be measured in at least how many locations?
   a. One
   b. Two
   c. Four
   d. Six

3. To check a crankshaft journal for out-of-round, the journal should be measured in at least how many locations?
   a. Two
   b. Four
   c. Six
   d. Eight

4. A telescopic gauge can be used to measure a cylinder bore if what other measuring device is used to measure the telescopic gauge?
   a. Micrometer
   b. Feeler gauge
   c. Straightedge
   d. Dial indicator

5. To directly measure the diameter of a valve guide in a cylinder head, use a micrometer and a _____.
   a. Telescopic gauge
   c. Small-hole gauge
   b. Feeler gauge
   d. Dial indicator

6. Which of the following *cannot* be measured using a feeler gauge?
   a. Valve guide clearance
   b. Piston-ring end gap
   c. Piston-ring side clearance
   d. Connecting rod side clearance

7. Which of the following *cannot* be measured using a straightedge and a feeler gauge?
   a. Cylinder head flatness
   b. Block deck flatness
   c. Straightness of the main bearing bores
   d. Straightness of the cylinder bore

8. Which measuring gauge needs to be set up (adjusted) to a fixed dimension before use?
   a. Dial indicator
   b. Dial bore gauge
   c. Vernier dial gauge
   d. Micrometer

9. A feeler gauge is also called a _____.
   a. Dial gauge
   b. Flat gauge
   c. Straight gauge
   d. Thickness gauge

10. Which metric unit of measure is used for volume measurement?
    a. Meter
    b. cc
    c. Centimeter
    d. Millimeter

chapter 11

SERVICE INFORMATION

OBJECTIVES: **After studying Chapter 11, the reader should be able to:** • Discuss the importance of vehicle history. • Retrieve vehicle service information. • Read and interpret service manuals and electronic service information. • Describe the use of the vehicle owner's manual.

KEY TERMS: • Julian date 109 • Labor guides 107 • Service information 105 • Technical service bulletin (TSB) 108

VEHICLE SERVICE HISTORY RECORDS

Whenever service work is performed, a record of what was done is usually kept on file by the shop or service department for a number of years. The wise service technician will check the vehicle service history if working on a vehicle with an unusual problem. Often, a previous repair may indicate the reason for the current problem or it could be related to the same circuit or components. For example, a collision could have caused hidden damage that can affect the operation of the vehicle. Knowing that a collision had been recently repaired may be helpful to the technician.

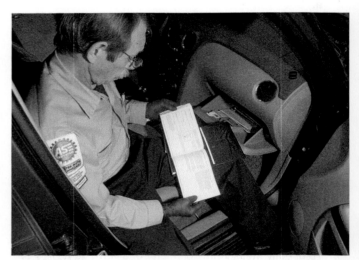

FIGURE 11–1 The owner's manual has a lot of information pertaining to the operation as well as the maintenance and resetting procedures that technicians often need.

OWNER'S MANUALS

It has been said by many professional automotive technicians and service advisors that the owner's manual is not read by many vehicle owners. Most owner's manuals contain all or most of the following information.

1. How to reset the maintenance reminder light
2. Specifications, including viscosity of oil needed and number of quarts (liters)
3. Tire pressures for standard as well as optional tire sizes
4. Maintenance schedule for all fluids, including coolant, brake fluid, automatic transmission fluid, and differential fluid

5. How to program the remote control as well as the power windows and door locks
6. How to reset the tire pressure monitoring system after a tire rotation

● **SEE FIGURE 11–1.**

LUBRICATION GUIDES

Lubrication guides, such as those published by Chek-Chart and Chilton, include all specifications for lubrication-related service, including:

- Hoisting location
- Lubrication points

Owner's Manual Is the Key to Proper Operation

A customer purchased a used Pontiac Vibe and complained to a shop that the cruise control would disengage and had to be reset if driven below 25 mph (40 km/h). The service technician was able to verify that in fact this occurred, but did not know if this feature was normal or not. The technician checked the owner's manual and discovered that this vehicle was designed to operate this way. Unlike other cruise control systems, those systems on Toyota-based vehicles are designed to shut off below 25 mph, requiring the driver to reset the desired speed. The customer was informed that nothing could be done to correct this concern and the technician also learned something. Vehicles that use the Toyota cruise control system include all Toyotas, plus Lexus, Pontiac Vibe, and Chevrolet Prism.

HINT: Some vehicle manufacturers offer owner's manuals on their website for a free download.

- Grease and oil specifications
- Capacities for engine oil, transmission fluid, coolant, and differential fluid

SERVICE MANUALS

Factory and aftermarket service manuals, also called shop manuals, contain specifications and service procedures. While factory service manuals cover just one year and one or more models of the same vehicle, most aftermarket service manuals cover multiple years and/or models in one manual.

Included in most service manuals are the following:

- Capacities and recommended specifications for all fluids
- Specifications, including engine and routine maintenance items
- Testing procedures
- Service procedures, including the use of special tools when needed
- Component location information

While some factory service manuals are printed in one volume, most factory **service information** is printed in several volumes due to the amount and depth of information presented. The typical factory service manual is divided into sections.

Exploded Views

Exploded views of components such as engines and transmissions are available in shop manuals and electronic service information, as well as in parts and labor time guides. These views, showing all of the parts as if the assembly was blown apart, give the service technician a clear view of the various parts and their relationship to other parts in the assembly.

GENERAL INFORMATION General information includes topics such as:

- Warnings and cautions
- Vehicle identification numbers on engine, transmission/transaxle, and body parts
- Lock cylinder coding
- Fastener information
- Decimal and metric equivalents
- Abbreviations and standard nomenclature used
- Service parts identification label and process code information

MAINTENANCE AND LUBRICATION INFORMATION

Maintenance and lubrication information includes topics such as:

- Schedule for "normal" as well as "severe" usage time and mileage charts
- Specified oil and other lubricant specifications
- Chassis lubrication points
- Tire rotation methods
- Periodic vehicle inspection services (items to check and time/mileage intervals)
- Maintenance item part numbers, such as oil and air filter numbers, and specifications, such as oil capacity and tire pressures

ENGINES

- Engine electrical diagnosis (battery, charging, cranking, ignition, and wiring)
- Engine mechanical diagnosis
- Specific engine information for each engine that may be used in the vehicle(s) covered by the service manual, including:
  - Engine identification
  - On-vehicle service procedures
  - Description of the engine and the operation of the lubrication system
  - Exploded views showing all parts of the engine
  - Disassembly procedures

- Inspection procedures and specifications of the parts and subsystems
- Assembly procedures
- Torque specifications for all fasteners, including the torque sequence

AUTOMATIC TRANSMISSION/TRANSAXLE

- General information (identification and specifications)
- Diagnosis procedures, including preliminary checks and fluid level procedures
- General service, including leak detection and correction
- Cooler flushing procedures
- Unit removal procedures
- Unit disassembly procedures and precautions
- Unit assembly procedures and torque specifications

ELECTRICAL SYSTEMS

- Symbols used
- Troubleshooting procedures
- Repair procedures (wire repair, connectors, and terminals)
- Power distribution
- Ground distribution
- Component location views
- Harness routing views
- Individual electrical circuits, including circuit operation and schematics

HEATING, VENTILATION, AND AIR CONDITIONING

- Heater system
  - General description
  - Heater control assembly
  - Diagnosis, including heater electrical wiring and vacuum system

TECH TIP

Print It Out

It is often a benefit to have the written instructions or schematics (wiring diagrams) at the vehicle while diagnosing or performing a repair. One advantage of a hard copy service manual is that it can be taken to the vehicle and used as needed. However, dirty hands can often cause pages to become unreadable. The advantage of electronic format service information is that the material can be printed out and taken to the vehicle for easy access. This also allows the service technician to write or draw on the printed copy, which can be a big help when performing tests such as electrical system measurements. These notes can then be used to document the test results on the work order.

TECH TIP

Look for Severe Service Times

Many time guides provide additional time for vehicles that may be excessively rusted due to climate conditions or have been subjected to abuse. Be sure to quote the higher rate if any of these conditions are present on the customer's vehicle.

- Blower motor and fan assembly diagnosis and servicing procedures
- Air distribution values
- Fastener torque specifications
- Air conditioning system
  - General description and system components
  - Air conditioning system diagnosis, including leak detection
  - Air conditioning and heater function tests
  - Air conditioning service procedures
  - Refrigerant recovery, recycling, adding oil, evacuating procedures, and charging procedures
  - Troubleshooting guide

ENGINE PERFORMANCE (DRIVEABILITY AND EMISSIONS)

- Vehicle emission control information (VECI) label, visual/physical underhood inspection
- On-board diagnostic system
- Scan tool values
- Wiring harness service
- Symptom charts
- Diagnostic trouble code (DTC) information

ADVANTAGES OF HARD COPY VERSUS ELECTRONIC SERVICE INFORMATION

All forms of service information have some advantages, including:

Hard Copy	Electronic Service Information
• Easy to use—no hardware or expensive computers needed	• Information can be printed out and taken to the vehicle
• Can be taken to the vehicle for reference	• Has a search function for information
• Can view several pages easily for reference	• Internet or network access allows use at several locations in the shop

DISADVANTGES OF HARD COPY VERSUS ELECTRONIC SERVICE INFORMATION

All forms of service information have some disadvantages, including:

Hard Copy	Electronic Service Information
• Can be lost or left in the vehicle	• Requires a computer and printer
• Cost is high for each manual	• Internet or network access can be a challenge
• Can get dirty and unreadable	• Cost can be high

LABOR GUIDE MANUALS

Labor guides, also called *flat-rate manuals*, list vehicle service procedures and the time it should take an average technician to complete the task. This flat-rate time is then the basis for estimates and pay for technicians. Some manuals also include a parts list, including the price of the part to help service advisors create complete estimates for both labor and parts. These manuals are usually called "parts and time guides." Some guides include labor time only. ● **SEE FIGURE 11–2.**

ELECTRONIC SERVICE INFORMATION

There are many programs available that will provide electronic service information for the automotive industry. Sometimes the vehicle makers make information available on CDs or DVDs, but mostly it is available online. Most electronic service information has technical service bulletins (TSBs), wiring diagrams, and a main menu that includes the major components of the vehicle as a starting point. ● **SEE FIGURE 11–3.** ALLDATA and Mitchell On-Demand are commonly used software programs that include service information for many vehicles.

Service information and testing procedures should be closely followed, including any symptom charts or flow charts. A sample of a symptom information chart is shown ● **CHART 11–1.**

HOME SCREEN The home screen is the first screen displayed when you start. It displays buttons that represent the major sections of the program. Access to the home screen is available from anywhere within the program by clicking the home button on the toolbar.

TOOLBARS A main toolbar is displayed on most screens, providing quick access to certain functions. This toolbar varies somewhat, depending upon what information is being accessed.

ELECTRONIC SERVICE INFORMATION Electronic service information is available mostly by subscription and provides access to an Internet site where service

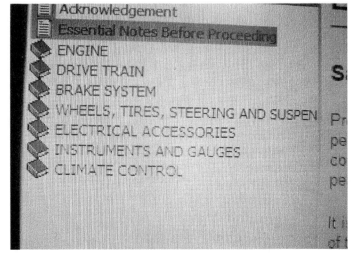

FIGURE 11–2 Some technical service bulletins also include the designated flat-rate time when specifying a repair procedure.

FIGURE 11–3 A main menu showing the major systems of the vehicle. Clicking on one of these major topics opens up another menu showing more detailed information.

POSSIBLE CAUSE	REASON
Throttle-position (TP) sensor	• The TP sensor should be within the specified range at idle. If too high or too low, the computer may not provide a strong enough extra pulse to prevent a hesitation. • An open or short in the TP sensor can result in hesitation because the computer would not be receiving correct information regarding the position of the throttle.
Throttle-plate deposit buildup	An airflow restriction at the throttle plates creates not only less air reaching the engine but also swirling air due to the deposits. This swirling or uneven airflow can cause an uneven air-fuel mixture being supplied to the engine, causing poor idle quality and a sag or hesitation during acceleration.
Manifold absolute pressure (MAP) sensor fault	The MAP sensor detects changes in engine load and signals to the computer to increase the amount of fuel needed for proper operation. Check the vacuum hose and the sensor itself for proper operation.
Check the throttle linkage for binding	A kinked throttle cable or cruise (speed) control cable can cause the accelerator pedal to bind.
Contaminated fuel	Fuel contaminated with excessive amounts of alcohol or water can cause a hesitation or sag during acceleration. HINT: To easily check for the presence of alcohol in gasoline, simply get a sample of the fuel and place it in a clean container. Add some water and shake. If no alcohol is in the gasoline, the water will settle to the bottom and be clear. If there is alcohol in the gasoline, the alcohol will absorb the water. The alcohol-water combination will settle to the bottom of the container, but will be cloudy rather than clear.
Clogged, shorted, or leaking fuel injectors	Any injector problem that results in less than an ideal amount of fuel being delivered to the cylinders can result in a hesitation, a sag, or stumble during acceleration.
Spark plugs or spark plug wires	Any fault in the ignition system such as a defective spark plug wire or cracked spark plug can cause hesitation, a sag, or stumble during acceleration. At higher engine speeds, a defective spark plug wire is not as noticeable as it is at lower speeds, especially in vehicles equipped with a V-8 engine.
EGR valve operation	Hesitation, a sag, or stumble can occur if the EGR valve opens too soon or is stuck partially open.
False air	A loose or cracked intake hose between the mass airflow (MAF) sensor and the throttle plate can be the cause of hesitation.

CHART 11–1

A chart showing symptoms for hesitation while accelerating. These charts help the technician diagnose faults that do not set a diagnostic trouble code (DTC).

manual–type information is available. Most vehicle manufacturers also offer electronic service information to their dealers and to most schools and colleges that offer corporate training programs.

TECHNICAL SERVICE BULLETINS
Technical service bulletins, often abbreviated TSBs, are issued by the vehicle manufacturer to notify service technicians of a problem and include the necessary corrective action. Technical service bulletins are designed for dealership technicians but are republished by aftermarket companies and made available along with other service information to shops and vehicle repair facilities.

INTERNET
The Internet has opened the field for information exchange and access to technical advice. One of the most useful websites is the International Automotive Technician's network at **www.iatn.net**. This is a free site but service technicians need to register to join. For a small monthly sponsor fee, the shop or service technician can gain access to the archives, which include thousands of successful repairs in the searchable database.

RECALLS AND CAMPAIGNS
A recall or campaign is issued by a vehicle manufacturer and a notice is sent to all owners in the event of a safety- or emission-related fault or concern. While these faults may be repaired by independent shops, it is generally handled by a local dealer. Items that have created recalls in the past have included potential fuel system leakage problems, exhaust leakage, or electrical malfunctions that could cause a possible fire or the engine to stall. Unlike technical service bulletins whose cost is only covered when the vehicle is within the warranty period, a recall or campaign is always done at no cost to the vehicle owner.

FREQUENTLY ASKED QUESTION

What Is the Julian Date?

The **Julian date** (abbreviated JD) is the number of the day of the year. January 1 is day 001. The Julian date is named for Julius Caesar, who developed the current calendar. The Julian date is often mentioned in technical service bulletin where changes need to be made to a certain component if the date of manufacture falls within the specified Julian dates.

HOTLINE SERVICES

A hotline service provider is a subscription-based helpline to assist service technicians solve technical problems. While services vary, most charge a monthly fee for a certain amount of time each month to talk to an experienced service technician who has a large amount of resource materials available for reference. Often, the technician hired by the hotline services specializes in one vehicle make and is familiar with many of the pattern failures that are seen by other technicians in the field. Hotline services are an efficient way to get information on an as-needed basis.

Some examples of hotline automotive service providers include:

- Identifix
- Autohotlineusa
- Taylor Automotive Tech-Line
- Aspire
  ● **SEE FIGURE 11–4.**

TECH TIP

Use a Bluetooth Hands-Free Telephone

When talking to a hotline service provider, it is wise to be looking at the vehicle during the call to be able to provide information about the vehicle and perform the suggested tests. This makes the job of troubleshooting easier and faster for both the technician and the service provider, resulting in shorter length calls. Using a Bluetooth hands-free telephone should help shorten the length of calls, which means the cost will be less for the help service.

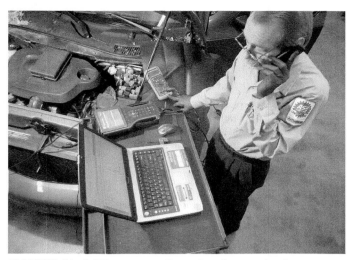

FIGURE 11–4 Whenever calling a hot line service be sure that you have all of the vehicle information ready and are prepared to give answers regarding voltage readings or scan tool data when talking to the vehicle specialist.

SPECIALITY REPAIR MANUALS

Examples of specialty repair manuals include unit repair for assembled components, such as automatic transmission/ transaxle, manual transmission/transaxle, differentials, and engines. Some specialty repair manuals cover older or antique vehicles, which may include unit repair sections.

AFTERMARKET SUPPLIES GUIDES AND CATALOGS

Aftermarket supplies guides and catalogs are usually free and often include expanded views of assembled parts along with helpful hints and advice. Sometimes the only place where this information is available is at trade shows associated with automotive training conferences and expos. Go to the following websites for examples of training conferences with trade shows.

- **www.CARSevent.com**
- **www.avtechexpo.com**
- **www.visionkc.com** (Vision Expo)

1. Vehicle history records are sometimes very helpful in determining problems that may be related to a previous fault or repair.

2. The vehicle owner's manual is very helpful to the service technician because it includes the procedures for resetting the maintenance reminder light (oil change light), as well as how to reset the tire pressure monitoring system after a tire rotation, and other important settings and specifications.

3. Lubrication guides provide information on the specified oil and lubricants needed along with the capacities and the location of lubrication points.

4. Factory service manuals or electronic service information include information that is vehicle and year specific and very detailed.

5. Other types of service information are labor and parts guides, wiring diagrams, component locator manuals, specialty manuals, and aftermarket supplies guides and catalogs.

6. Hotline services are subscription based and allow a technician to talk to an experienced technician who has many resources.

REVIEW QUESTIONS

1. What is included in the vehicle owner's manual that could be helpful for a service technician?

2. Lubrication service guides include what type of information?

3. Explain why factory service manuals or factory electronic service information are the most detailed of all service information.

4. Explain how flat-rate and parts guides are useful to customers.

5. List additional types of service manuals that are available.

6. Describe how hotline services and Internet sites assist service technicians.

CHAPTER QUIZ

1. What type of information is commonly included in the owner's manual that would be a benefit to service technicians?
   a. Maintenance reminder light reset procedures
   b. Tire pressure monitoring system reset procedures
   c. Maintenance items specifications
   d. All of the above

2. Two technicians are discussing the need for the history of the vehicle. Technician A says that an accident could cause faults due to hidden damage. Technician B says that some faults could be related to a previous repair. Which technician is correct?
   a. Technician A only
   b. Technician B only
   c. Both Technicians A and B
   d. Neither Technician A nor B

3. The viscosity of engine oil is found where?
   a. Owner's manual
   b. Factory service manual or service information
   c. Lubrication guide
   d. All of the above

4. Wiring diagrams are usually found where?
   a. Owner's manuals
   b. Factory service manuals
   c. Unit repair manuals
   d. Lubrication guides

5. What type of manual includes time needed to perform service procedures?
   a. Flat-rate manuals
   b. Owner's manuals
   c. Factory service manuals
   d. Parts guide

6. Component location can be found in _____.
   a. Factory service manuals
   b. Labor guide manuals
   c. Lubrication guides
   d. Both a and c

7. Aftermarket service information is available in what format?
   a. Manuals
   b. CDs or DVDs
   c. Internet
   d. All of the above

8. Hotline services are _____.
   a. Free
   b. Available for a service fee
   c. Available on CD or DVD format
   d. Accessed by the Internet

9. Aftermarket parts catalogs can be a useful source of infor-mation and they are usually _____.
   a. Free
   b. Available by paid subscription
   c. Available on CD or DVD
   d. Available for a fee on a secured Internet site

10. Which type of manual or service information includes the flat-rate time and the cost of parts?
   a. Parts and time guides
   b. Factory service manuals
   c. Component location guides
   d. Free Internet sites

OBJECTIVES: **After studying Chapter 12, the reader should be able to:** • Identify a vehicle. • Interpret vehicle identification numbers and placard information. • Interpret vehicle emissions and emission control information. • Read and interpret casting numbers. • Locate calibration codes.

KEY TERMS: • Bin number 114 • Calibration codes 116 • California Air Resources Board (CARB) 113 • Casting numbers 116 • Country of origin 112 • Environmental Protection Agency (EPA) 113 • Gross axle weight rating (GAWR) 113 • Gross vehicle weight rating (GVWR) 113 • Model year (MY) 112 • Tier 1 114 • Tier 2 114 • Vehicle emissions control information (VECI) 113 • Vehicle identification number (VIN) 112

PARTS OF A VEHICLE

The names of the parts of a vehicle are based on the location and purpose of the component.

LEFT SIDE OF THE VEHICLE—RIGHT SIDE OF THE VEHICLE Both of these terms refer to the left and right as if the driver is sitting behind the steering wheel. Therefore, the left side (including components under the hood) is on the driver's left.

FRONT AND REAR The proper term for the back portion of any vehicle is rear (for example, left rear tire).

FRONT-WHEEL DRIVE VERSUS REAR-WHEEL DRIVE

Front-wheel drive (FWD) means that the front wheels are being driven by the engine, as well as turned by the steering wheel. Rear-wheel drive (RWD) means that the rear wheels are driven by the engine. If the engine is in the front, it can be either front- or rear-wheel drive. In many cases, a front engine vehicle can also drive all four wheels called four-wheel drive (4WD) or all-wheel drive (AWD). If the engine is located at the rear of the vehicle, it can be rear-wheel drive or all-wheel-drive (AWD).

VEHICLE IDENTIFICATION

All service work requires that the vehicle, including the engine and accessories, be properly identified. The most common identification is the make, model, and year of the vehicle.

Make: e.g., Chevrolet

Model: e.g., Impala

Year: e.g., 2007

The year of the vehicle is often difficult to determine exactly. A model may be introduced as the next year's model as soon as January of the previous year. Typically, a new **model year** (abbreviated **MY**) starts in September or October of the year prior to the actual new year, but not always. This is why the **vehicle identification number**, usually abbreviated **VIN**, is so important. ● **SEE FIGURE 12–1**.

Since 1981, all vehicle manufacturers have used a VIN that is 17 characters long. Although every vehicle manufacturer assigns various letters or numbers within these 17 characters, there are some constants, including:

■ The first number or letter designates the **country of origin**. ● **SEE CHART 12–1**.

■ The model of the vehicle is commonly the fourth and/or fifth character.

■ The eighth character is often the engine code. (Some engines cannot be determined by the VIN number.)

■ The tenth character represents represents the model year and not the calendar year (CY) on all vehicles. ● **SEE CHART 12–2**.

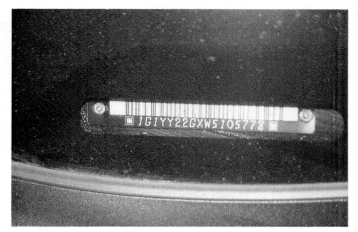

FIGURE 12–1 Typical vehicle identification number (VIN) as viewed through the windshield.

FIGURE 12–2 A VECI label on a 2008 Ford.

1 = United States	9 = Brazil	U = Romania
2 = Canada	J = Japan	V = France
3 = Mexico	K = Korea	W = Germany
4 = United States	L = China	X = Russia
5 = United States	R = Taiwan	Y = Sweden
6 = Australia	S = England	Z = Italy
8 = Argentina	T = Czechoslovakia	

A = 1980/2010	L = 1990/2020	Y = 2000/2030
B = 1981/2011	M = 1991/2021	1 = 2001/2031
C = 1982/2012	N = 1992/2022	2 = 2002/2032
D = 1983/2013	P = 1993/2023	3 = 2003/2033
E = 1984/2014	R = 1994/2024	4 = 2004/2034
F = 1985/2015	S = 1995/2025	5 = 2005/2035
G = 1986/2016	T = 1996/2026	6 = 2006/2036
H = 1987/2017	V = 1997/2027	7 = 2007/2037
J = 1988/2018	W = 1998/2028	8 = 2008/2038
K = 1989/2019	X = 1999/2029	9 = 2009/2039

CHART 12-2

VIN Year Chart *(The Pattern Repeats Every 30 Years)*

VEHICLE SAFETY CERTIFICATION LABEL

A vehicle safety certification label is attached to the left side pillar post on the rearward-facing section of the left front door. This label indicates the month and year of manufacture as well as the **gross vehicle weight rating (GVWR)**, the **gross axle weight rating (GAWR)**, and the vehicle identification number (VIN).

VECI LABEL

The **vehicle emissions control information (VECI)** label under the hood of the vehicle shows informative settings and emission hose routing information. ● **SEE FIGURE 12–2**.

The VECI label (sticker) can be located on the bottom side of the hood, the radiator fan shroud, the radiator core support, or the strut towers. The VECI label usually includes the following information.

- Engine identification
- Emissions standard that the vehicle meets
- Vacuum hose routing diagram
- Base ignition timing (if adjustable)
- Spark plug type and gap
- Valve lash
- Emission calibration code

EMISSION STANDARDS IN THE UNITED STATES

In the United States, emissions standards are managed by the **Environmental Protection Agency (EPA)** as well as some U.S. state governments. Some of the strictest standards in the world are formulated in California by the **California Air Resources Board (CARB)**.

TIER 1 AND TIER 2 Federal emission standards are set by the Clean Air Act Amendments (CAAA) of 1990 grouped by **tier**. All vehicles sold in the United States must meet

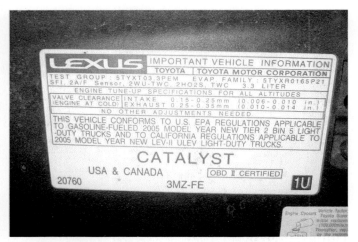

FIGURE 12–3 The underhood decal showing that this Lexus RX-330 meets both national (Tier 2; BIN 5) and California LEV-II (ULEV) regulation standards.

Tier 1 standards that went into effect in 1994 and are the least stringent. Additional **Tier 2** standards have been optional since 2001, and were completely adopted in 2009. The current Tier 1 standards are different between automobiles and light trucks (SUVs, pickup trucks, and minivans), but Tier 2 standards are the same for both types.

There are several ratings that can be given to vehicles, and a certain percentage of a manufacturer's vehicles must meet different levels in order for the company to sell its products in affected regions. Beyond Tier 1, and in order by stringency, are the following levels.

- **TLEV—Transitional Low-Emission Vehicle.** More stringent for HC than Tier 1.

- **LEV—(also known as LEV I)—Low-Emission Vehicle.** An intermediate California standard about twice as stringent as Tier 1 for HC and NO_X.

- **ULEV—(also known as ULEV I).** Ultra-Low-Emission Vehicle. A stronger California standard emphasizing very low HC emissions.

- **ULEV II—Ultra-Low-Emission Vehicle.** A cleaner-than-average vehicle certified under the Phase II LEV standard. Hydrocarbon and carbon monoxide emissions levels are nearly 50% lower than those of a LEV II-certified vehicle. ● **SEE FIGURE 12–3.**

- **SULEV—Super-Ultra-Low-Emission Vehicle.** A California standard even tighter than ULEV, including much lower HC and NO_X emissions; roughly equivalent to Tier 2 Bin 2 vehicles.

- **ZEV—Zero-Emission Vehicle.** A California standard prohibiting any tailpipe emissions. The ZEV category is largely restricted to electric vehicles and hydrogen-fueled vehicles. In these cases, any emissions that are created are produced at another site, such as a power plant or hydrogen reforming center, unless such sites run on renewable energy.

NOTE: A battery-powered electric vehicle charged from the power grid will still be up to 10 times cleaner than even the cleanest gasoline vehicles over their respective lifetimes.

The current California ZEV regulation allows manufacturers a choice of two options for meeting the ZEV requirements.

1. Vehicle manufacturers can meet the ZEV obligations by meeting standards that are similar to the ZEV rule as it existed in 2001. This means using a formula allowing a vehicle mix of 2% pure ZEVs, 2% AT-PZEVs (vehicles earning advanced technology partial ZEV credits), and 6% PZEVs (extremely clean conventional vehicles). The ZEV obligation is based on the number of passenger cars and small trucks a manufacturer sells in California.

2. Manufacturers may also choose a new alternative ZEV compliance strategy of meeting part of the ZEV requirement by producing the sales-weighted market share of approximately 250 fuel-cell vehicles. The remainder of the ZEV requirements could be achieved by producing 4% AT-PZEVs and 6% PZEVs. The required number of fuel-cell vehicles will increase to 2,500 from 2009 to 2011, 25,000 from 2012 through 2020, and 50,000 from 2015 through 2017. Manufacturers can substitute battery electric vehicles for up to 50% of the fuel-cell vehicle requirements.

   - **PZEV—Partial-Zero-Emission Vehicle.** Compliant with the SULEV standard; additionally has near-zero evaporative emissions and a 15-year/150,000-mile warranty on its emission control equipment.

Tier 2 standards are even more stringent. Tier 2 variations are appended with "II," such as LEV II or SULEV II. Other categories have also been created.

- **ILEV—Inherently Low-Emission Vehicle.**

- **AT-PZEV—Advanced Technology Partial-Zero-Emission Vehicle.** If a vehicle meets the PZEV standards and is using high-technology features, such as an electric motor or high-pressure gaseous fuel tanks for compressed natural gas, it qualifies as an AT-PZEV. Hybrid electric vehicles such as the Toyota Prius can qualify, as can internal combustion engine vehicles that run on natural gas (CNG), such as the Honda Civic GX. These vehicles are classified as "partial" ZEV because they receive partial credit for the number of ZEV vehicles that automakers would otherwise be required to sell in California.

- **NLEV—National Low-Emission Vehicle.** All vehicles nationwide must meet this standard, which started in 2001. ● **SEE CHARTS 12–3 AND 12–4.**

FEDERAL EPA BIN NUMBER The higher the tier number, the newer the regulation; the lower the **bin number**, the cleaner

		NMOG GRAMS (MILE)	CO GRAMS (MILE)	NO$_X$ GRAMS (MILE)
LEV I (Cars)	TLEV	0.125 (0.156)	3.4 (4.2)	0.4 (0.6)
	LEV	0.075 (0.090)	3.4 (4.2)	0.2 (0.3)
	ULEV	0.040 (0.055)	1.7 (2.1)	0.2 (0.3)
LEV II (Cars and Trucks less than 8,500 lbs)	LEV	0.075 (0.090)	3.4 (4.2)	0.05 (0.07)
	ULEV	0.040 (0.055)	1.7 (2.1)	0.05 (0.07)
	SULEV	— (0.010)	— (1.0)	— (0.02)

CHART 12–3

LEV Standard Categories

NOTE: Numbers in parentheses are 100,000-mile standards for LEV I, and 120,000-mile standards for LEV II. NMOG means non-methane organic gases, which includes alcohol. CO means carbon monoxide. NO$_X$ means oxides of nitrogen. Data compiled from California Environmental Protection Agency—Air Resource Board (CARB) documents.

CERTIFICATION LEVEL	NMOG (g/ml)	CO (g/ml)	NO$_X$ (g/ml)
LEV II	0.090	4.2	0.07
ULEV II	0.055	2.1	0.07
SULEV II	0.010	1.0	0.02

CHART 12–4

California LEV II 120,000-Mile Tailpipe Emissions Limits

NOTE: Numbers in parentheses are 100,000-mile standards for LEV I, and 120,000-mile standards for LEV II. NMOG means non-methane organic gases, which includes alcohol. CO means carbon monoxide. NO$_X$ means oxides of nitrogen. The specification is in grams per mile (g/ml). Data compiled from California Environmental Protection Agency—Air Resources Board (CARB) documents.

the vehicle. The 2004 Toyota Prius is a very clean Bin 3, while the Hummer H2 is a dirty Bin 11. Examples include:

- Tier 1: The former federal standard; carried over to model year 2004 for those vehicles not yet subject to the phase-in.
- Tier 2, Bin 1: The cleanest federal Tier 2 standard; a zero-emission vehicle (ZEV).
- Tier 2, Bins 4–2: Cleaner than the average standard.
- Tier 2, Bin 5: "Average" of new Tier 2 standards, roughly equivalent to a LEV II vehicle.
- Tier 2, Bins 6–9: Not as clean as the average requirement for a Tier 2 vehicle.
- Tier 2, Bin 10: Least-clean Tier 2 bin applicable to passenger vehicles. ● **SEE CHARTS 12–5 AND 12–6.**

CERTIFICATION LEVEL	NMOG (g/ml)	CO (g/ml)	NO$_X$ (g/ml)
Bin 1	0.0	0.0	0.0
Bin 2	0.010	2.1	0.02
Bin 3	0.055	2.1	0.03
Bin 4	0.070	2.1	0.04
Bin 5	0.090	4.2	0.07
Bin 6	0.090	4.2	0.10
Bin 7	0.090	4.2	0.15
Bin 8a	0.125	4.2	0.20
Bin 8b	0.156	4.2	0.20
Bin 9a	0.090	4.2	0.30
Bin 9b	0.130	4.2	0.30
Bin 9c	0.180	4.2	0.30
Bin 10a	0.156	4.2	0.60
Bin 10b	0.230	6.4	0.60
Bin 10c	0.230	6.4	0.60
Bin 11	0.230	7.3	0.90

CHART 12–5

EPA Tier 2—120,000-Mile Tailpipe Emission Limits

NOTE: The bin number is determined by the type and weight of the vehicle. The highest bin allowed for vehicles built after January 1, 2007 is Bin 8. Data compiled from the Environmental Protection Agency (EPA).

U.S. EPA VEHICLE INFORMATION PROGRAM (THE HIGHER THE SCORE, THE LOWER THE EMISSIONS)	
SELECTED EMISSIONS STANDARDS	SCORE
Bin 1 and ZEV	10
PZEV	9.5
Bin 2	9
Bin 3	8
Bin 4	7
Bin 5 and LEV II cars	6
Bin 6	5
Bin 7	4
Bin 8	3
Bin 9a and LEV I cars	2
Bin 9b	2
Bin 10a	1
Bin 10b and Tier 1 cars	1
Bin 11	0

CHART 12–6

Air Pollution Score

Courtesy of the Environmental Protection Agency (EPA).

FIGURE 12–4 A typical computer calibration sticker on the case of the controller. The information on the sticker is often needed when ordering parts or a replacement controller.

FIGURE 12–5 Engine block identification number cast into the block is used for identification.

CALIBRATION CODES

Calibration codes are usually located on powertrain control modules (PCMs) or other controllers. Some calibration codes are only accessible with a scan tool. Whenever diagnosing an engine operating fault, it is often necessary to know the calibration code to be sure that the vehicle is the subject of a technical service bulletin or other service procedure. ● **SEE FIGURE 12–4.**

CASTING NUMBERS

Whenever an engine part such as a block is cast, a number is put into the mold to identify the casting. ● **SEE FIGURE 12–5.** These **casting numbers** can be used to check dimensions such as the cubic inch displacement and other information. Sometimes changes are made to the mold, yet the casting number is not changed. Most often the casting number is the best piece of identifying information that the service technician can use for identifying an engine.

SUMMARY

1. The front, rear, left, and right side of a vehicle are as viewed from the driver's seat.
2. The vehicle identification number (VIN) is very important as it includes when the vehicle was built, as well as the engine code and many other details about the vehicle.
3. The VECI label under the hood often needs to be checked by the technician to properly service the vehicle.
4. Other vehicle information that the technician may need for a service or repair include calibration codes, casting numbers, and emissions rating.

REVIEW QUESTIONS

1. From what position are the terms left and right determined?
2. What are the major pieces of information that are included in the vehicle identification number (VIN)?
3. What information is included on the VECI label under the hood?
4. What does Tier 2 Bin 5 mean?

CHAPTER QUIZ

1. The passenger side in the United States is the _____.
   a. Right side
   b. Left side
   c. Either right or left side, depending on how the vehicle is viewed
   d. Both a and b

2. A vehicle with the engine in the front can be _____.
   a. Front-wheel drive
   b. Rear-wheel drive
   c. Four-wheel drive
   d. All of the above

3. The vehicle identification number (VIN) since 1981, is how many characters long?
   a. 10
   b. 12
   c. 17
   d. 21

4. The tenth character represents the year of the vehicle. If the tenth character is a "Y," what year is the vehicle?
   a. 1998
   b. 2000
   c. 2002
   d. 2004

5. The first character of the vehicle identification number is the country of origin. Where was the vehicle built that has a "5" as the first character?
   a. United States
   b. Canada
   c. Mexico
   d. Japan

6. The VECI label includes all *except* _____.
   a. Engine identification
   b. Horsepower and torque rating of the engine
   c. Spark plug type and gap
   d. Valve lash

7. The vehicle safety certification label includes all *except* _____.
   a. VIN
   b. GVWR
   c. Tire pressure recommendation
   d. GAWR

8. What are the characters called that are embedded in most engine blocks and are used for identification?
   a. VIN
   b. Calibration codes
   c. Bin number
   d. Casting number

9. If the first character of the VIN is an "S," where was the vehicle made?
   a. United States
   b. Mexico
   c. Canada
   d. England

10. Technician A says that the lower the bin number is, the less emissions the vehicle produces. Technician B says that SULEV has cleaner standards than ULEV. Which technician is correct?
    a. Technician A only
    b. Technician B only
    c. Both Technicians A and B
    d. Neither Technician A nor B

UNDER-HOOD VEHICLE INSPECTION

OBJECTIVES: **After studying Chapter 13, the reader should be able to:** • Prepare for ASE Engine Repair (A1) certification test content area "A" (General Engine Diagnosis) and content area "D" (Lubrication and Cooling Systems Diagnosis and Repair). • Perform routine fluid and service checks. • Discuss how to protect the vehicle during service. • List the items that should be checked during a safety inspection. • Discuss the items that require routine (preventative) maintenance. • Explain how to replace a cabin and engine air filter. • Explain how to check brake fluid. • Discuss the types of automatic transmission fluids. • Explain how to check engine coolant. • Describe how to check accessory drive belts. • Explain how to check power steering fluid level.

KEY TERMS: • Air filter 121 • Automatic transmission fluid (ATF) 123 • Brake fluid 121 • Cabin filter 120 • Dipstick 123 • DOT 3 121 • DOT 4 122 • DOT 5 122 • DOT 5.1 122 • Polyglycol 121 • Preventative maintenance (PM) 119 • Serpentine (Poly V) 127 • Silicone brake fluid 122 • Viscosity 123

VEHICLE INSPECTION

PRESERVICE INSPECTION Prior to any service work, it is wise to check the vehicle for damage and document the work order if any damage is found. In most dealerships and shops, this is the responsibility of the following personnel.

- Service adviser (service writer) or
- Shop foreman or
- Shop owner

The designated person should check the vehicle for the following:

1. Body damage
2. Missing components such as wheel covers, mirrors, and radio antennas
3. Glass damage such as a cracked windshield
4. Any faults or scratches in the paint or trim
5. Valid license plates

PROTECT THE VEHICLE Before most service work is done, protect the inside of the vehicle by using commercially available plastic or paper protective coverings for the following areas.

- Seats
- Floor
- Steering wheel

● **SEE FIGURE 13-1**

PROTECT THE TECHNICIAN Before starting routine preventative maintenance on a vehicle, be sure to perform the following:

1. Open the hood (engine compartment cover). Often the struts that hold a hood open are weak or defective. Therefore, before starting to work under the hood, always make sure that the hood is securely held open using a prop rod if needed.
2. Connect an exhaust system hose to the tailpipe(s) before work is started that will involve operating the engine. ● **SEE FIGURE 13–2.**
3. Wear personal protective equipment (PPE), including:
   - Safety glasses
   - Hearing protection if around air tools or other loud noises
   - Gloves if handling hot objects or chemicals such as used engine oil
4. In hybrid vehicles, make sure that the technician has possession of the key transmitter and that the vehicle is *not* in the ready mode before starting any inspection or service procedure.

SAFETY INSPECTION A safety inspection is usually recommended anytime the vehicle is in the shop for service or repair. These inspections should include all of the following:

1. Exterior lights, including:
   a. Headlights (high and low beam)
   b. Tail lights
   c. Turn signals
   d. License plate light
   e. Parking lights
   f. Hazard warning lights

FIGURE 13–1 Before service begins, be sure to cover the seats, floor, and steering wheel with protective coverings.

FIGURE 13–2 An exhaust system hose should be connected to the tailpipe(s) whenever the engine is being run indoors.

2. Horn

3. Windshield wiper operation

4. Mirrors

5. Defroster fan operation

6. Turn the steering wheel and check for excessive looseness

7. Shock absorbers that allow excessive body sway

8. Tire tread depth, and proper inflation pressure.

   NOTE: Checking, correcting, and indicating on the vehicle service invoice that a tire inflation service was completed and the tire pressure measurements after the service was performed is a law in some states.

9. Parking brake operation

10. Exhaust system for excessive noise or leaks

PREVENTATIVE MAINTENANCE

PURPOSE **Preventative maintenance (PM)** means periodic service work performed on a vehicle that will help keep it functioning correctly for a long time. All vehicle manufacturers publish a list of service work to be performed on a regular basis. Preventative maintenance is also called *routine maintenance*

because it is usually performed on a set scheduled routine. The interval specified for preventative maintenance is often expressed in time and miles (km), such as:

- Every six months (could be longer for many vehicles)
- Every 5,000 to 10,000 miles (8,000 to 16,000 km) depending on the vehicle and how it is being operated
- Either of the above, whichever occurs first

ITEMS REQUIRING MAINTENANCE The items or systems that require routine maintenance include:

1. Engine oil and oil filter replacement
2. Air and cabin filter replacement
3. Tire inflation pressure check, inspection, and rotation
4. Brake and suspension system inspection
5. Under-hood inspection and fluid checks
6. Under-vehicle inspection and fluid checks
7. Air conditioning system inspection and service
8. Routine cleaning of vehicle both inside and out

WINDSHIELD WIPER AND WASHER FLUID SERVICE

WINDSHIELD WIPERS Windshield wiper blades are constructed of rubber and tend to become brittle due to age. Wiper blades should be cleaned whenever the vehicle is cleaned using water and a soft cloth. Wiper blade or wiper blade insert replacement includes the following steps.

- Turn the key on, engine off (KOEO).
- Turn the wiper switch on and operate the wipers.

FIGURE 13–3 Installing a wiper blade insert into a wiper arm.

(a)

(b)

FIGURE 13–4 (a) The windshield wiper fluid reservoir cap is usually labeled with a symbol showing a windshield washer. (b) Use only the recommended washer fluid. Never use antifreeze in the windshield washer reservoir.

- When the wipers are located in an easy-to-reach location, turn the ignition switch off. The wipers should stop.
- Remove the insert or the entire blade as per service information and/or the instructions on the replacement windshield wiper blade package.
- After double-checking that the wiper is securely attached, turn the ignition switch on (run).
- Turn the wiper switch off and allow the wipers to reach the park position. Check for proper operation. ● **SEE FIGURE 13–3.**

WINDSHIELD WASHER FLUID Windshield washer fluid level should be checked regularly and refilled as necessary. Use only the fluid that is recommended for use in vehicle windshield washer systems. ● **SEE FIGURE 13–4.**

Most windshield washer fluid looks like blue water. It is actually water with an alcohol (methanol) additive to prevent freezing and to help clean the windshield by dissolving bugs. Be careful not to spill any washer fluid when filling the reservoir because the corrosiveness can harm wiring and electronic components.

CAUTION: Some mixed fluids are for summer-use only and do not contain antifreeze protection. Read the label carefully.

FILTER REPLACEMENT

CABIN FILTER A **cabin filter** is used in the heating, ventilation, and air conditioning (HVAC) system to filter the outside air drawn into the passenger compartment. Some filters contain activated charcoal to help eliminate odors. The cabin air filter should be replaced often—every year or every 12,000 miles (19,000 km). The cabin air filter can be accessed from:

- Under the hood at the cowl (bulkhead) or
- Under the dash, usually behind the glove (instrument panel) compartment. (Check service information for the exact location and servicing procedures for the vehicle being serviced.) ● **SEE FIGURE 13–5.**

UNDER HOOD

GLOVE COMPARTMENT

FIGURE 13–5 A cabin filter can be accessed either through the glove compartment or under the hood.

(a)

(b)

FIGURE 13–6 (a) A typical dirty air filter. (b) Always check the inlet passage leading to the air filter for debris that can reduce airflow to the engine.

ENGINE AIR FILTER An **air filter** filters dirt from the air before it enters the intake system of the engine. The air filter should be replaced according to the vehicle manufacturer's recommendations. Over time, the filter will start to get clogged and decrease the engine power. Many vehicle manufacturers recommend replacing the air filter every 30,000 miles (50,000 km), or more frequently under dusty conditions. Many service technicians recommend replacing the air filter every year. ● **SEE FIGURE 13–6.**

BRAKE FLUID

BRAKE FLUID LEVEL **Brake fluid** is used to transmit the force of the driver's foot on the brake pedal, called the service brake, to each individual wheel brake. The brake fluid should be checked at the same time the engine oil is changed, or every six months, whichever occurs first. It is normal for the brake fluid level to drop as the disc brake pads wear. Therefore, if the fluid level is low, check for two possible causes.

FIGURE 13–7 A master cylinder with a transparent reservoir. The brake fluid level should be between the MAX and the MIN levels as marked on the reservoir.

CAUSE 1 Normal disc brake pad wear. (Inspect the brakes if the fluid level is low.)

CAUSE 2 A leak somewhere in the hydraulic brake system. (Carefully inspect the entire brake system for leaks if the brakes are not worn and the brake fluid level is low.)

There are two types of brake master cylinder reservoirs.

- **Transparent reservoir.** This type of reservoir allows viewing of the brake fluid (and hydraulic clutch master cylinder if so equipped) without having to remove the cover of the reservoir. The proper level is between the MIN (minimum) and MAX (maximum) level indicated on the clear plastic reservoir. ● **SEE FIGURE 13–7.**

- **Metal or nontransparent plastic reservoir.** This type of reservoir used on older vehicles requires that the cover be removed to check the level of the brake fluid. The proper level of brake fluid should be 1/4 in. (6 mm) from the top.

CAUTION: Do not overfill a brake master cylinder. The brake fluid gets hotter as the brakes are used and there must be room in the master cylinder reservoir for the brake fluid to expand.

BRAKE FLUID TYPES Brake fluid is made from a combination of various types of glycol, a non-petroleum-based fluid. Brake fluid is a polyalkylene-glycol-ether mixture, called **polyglycol** for short. *All polyglycol brake fluids are clear to amber in color.*

CAUTION: DOT 3 brake fluid is a very strong solvent and can remove paint! Care is required when working with this type of brake fluid to avoid contact with the vehicle's painted surfaces. It also takes the color out of leather shoes.

All automotive brake fluids must meet Federal Motor Vehicle Safety Standard 116. The Society of Automotive Engineers (SAE) and the Department of Transportation (DOT) have established brake fluid specification standards.

- **DOT 3.** The **DOT 3** brake fluid is most often used. It absorbs moisture and, according to SAE, can absorb

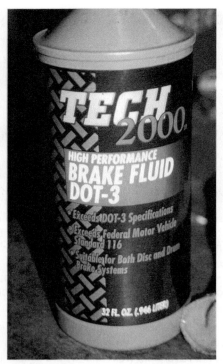

FIGURE 13–8 DOT 3 brake fluid. Always use fluid from a sealed container because brake fluid absorbs moisture from the air.

2% of its volume in water per year. Moisture is absorbed by the brake fluid through microscopic seams in the brake system and around seals. Over time, the water will corrode the system and thicken the brake fluid. Moisture can cause a spongy brake pedal because the increased concentration of water within the fluid boils at lower temperatures and can result in vapor lock. DOT 3 must be used from a sealed (capped) container. If allowed to remain open for any length of time, DOT 3 will absorb moisture from the surrounding air. ● SEE FIGURE 13–8.

- **DOT 4.** The **DOT 4** brake fluid is formulated for use by all vehicles, imported or domestic. It is commonly called low moisture absorption (LMA) because it does not absorb water as fast as DOT 3. It is still affected by moisture, however, and should be used only from a sealed container. The cost of DOT 4 is approximately double the cost of DOT 3.

- **DOT 5.** The **DOT 5** type is commonly called **silicone brake fluid.** Because it does not absorb water, it is called nonhygroscopic. DOT 5 brake fluid does not mix with and should not be used with DOT 3 or DOT 4 brake fluid. DOT 5 brake fluid is purple (violet), to distinguish it from DOT 3 or DOT 4 brake fluid.

- **DOT 5.1.** The **DOT 5.1** brake fluid is a non-silicone-based polyglycol fluid that is clear to amber in color. This severe-duty fluid has a boiling point of over 500°F (260°C), equal to the boiling point of silicone-based DOT 5 fluid. Unlike DOT 5, the DOT 5.1 fluid can be mixed with either DOT 3 or DOT 4 according to the brake fluid manufacturer's recommendations.

FIGURE 13–9 Brake fluid test strips are a convenient and easy-to-use method to determine if the brake fluid needs to be replaced.

CAUTION: Some vehicle manufacturers, such as Chrysler, do not recommend the use of or the mixing of other types of polyglycol brake fluids and specify the use of DOT 3 brake fluid only. Always follow the vehicle manufacturer's recommendation.

BRAKE FLUID INSPECTION

- **Visual inspection.** Check the color of the brake fluid. It should be clear or almost clear. If it is dark brown or black, it should be replaced.

- **Test strips.** A quick and easy way to check the condition of the brake fluid is to use test strips. Always follow the instructions that come with the test strips for accurate results. ● SEE FIGURE 13–9.

- **Boiling point.** The boiling point of brake fluid can be tested using a handheld tester. Follow the instructions that come with the tester.

 FREQUENTLY ASKED QUESTION

What Is Hydraulic Clutch Fluid?

The fluid used in hydraulic clutch master cylinders is DOT 3 brake fluid. It can be checked using the same procedures as those followed to check brake fluid. If the hydraulic clutch fluid is low, however, it has to be caused by a leak in the system. Therefore, do not fill the reservoir of the hydraulic clutch master cylinder without first finding and fixing the source of the leak. If the fluid gets too low, the clutch will not work and the transmission cannot be shifted. Always check service information for the exact procedure and fluid to use.

CAUTION: If any mineral oil such as engine oil, automatic transmission fluid (ATF), or power steering fluid gets into the brake fluid, the rubber seals will swell and cause damage to the entire braking system. Every part that includes a rubber seal will require replacement.

ENGINE OIL INSPECTION

OIL LEVEL The oil level should be checked when the vehicle is parked on level ground and after the engine has been off for at least several minutes. The *oil level indicator*, commonly called a **dipstick**, is clearly marked and is placed in a convenient location. ● **SEE FIGURE 13–10.**

To check the oil, remove the dipstick, wipe off the oil, and reinsert it all the way down. Once again remove the dipstick and check where the oil level touches the indicator. The "add" mark is usually at the 1 quart low point. ● **SEE FIGURE 13–11.**

If oil needs to be added, use the specified oil and add to the engine through the oil fill opening (not through the dipstick hole as is done with automatic transmission fluid).

FIGURE 13–10 A typical oil level indicator (dipstick).

FIGURE 13–11 The oil level should be between the MAX and the MIN marks when the vehicle is on level ground and the oil has had time to drain into the oil pan.

OIL CONDITION When checking the engine oil, perform the following steps:

- Rub the oil from the end of the dipstick between your fingers. The oil should feel slippery. If it feels gritty, then the oil definitely needs to be changed.
- If the oil is black in color then it likely needs to be changed. Normal oil, even when near the scheduled oil change, is usually dark brown.

   NOTE: Diesel engine oil can turn black well before a scheduled oil change. This is normal and does not indicate that an oil change is necessary.

- If the oil has a "milky" appearance, it indicates potential coolant in the system or some other malfunction.
- Check the oil life monitor on the dash to see if there is a percentage of oil life remaining or a lamp on indicating that an oil change is due or almost due.

AUTOMATIC TRANSMISSION FLUID

TYPES OF AUTOMATIC TRANSMISSION FLUID

Automatic transmission fluid (ATF) is high-quality oil that has additives that resist oxidation, inhibit rust formation, and allow the fluid to flow easily at all temperatures. The automatic transmission fluid is dyed red for identification. Various vehicle manufacturers recommend a particular type of ATF based mainly on its friction characteristics. Friction is needed between the bands, plates, and clutches inside an automatic transmission/transaxle to make the shifts occur.

While the additive packages and **viscosity** (thickness) vary, ATF is grouped in three basic types, including:

1. Nonfriction modified (used in older types of automatic transmissions)
2. Friction modified
3. Highly friction modified (most used in current-type electrically controlled automatic transmissions/transaxles).

TYPICAL ATF APPLICATIONS ● **SEE CHART 13–1** for examples of the types and application of selected vehicle and fluids. Using the wrong type of ATF can cause the transmission to shift too harshly or cause a vibration when the transmission shifts.

PROCEDURE The **automatic transmission fluid (ATF)** should be checked regularly. The recommended procedure is usually stamped on the transmission dipstick or written in the owner's manual and/or service manual. Most automatic transmission fluid levels should be checked under the following conditions.

GENERAL MOTORS	DESCRIPTION
Type A	1949
Type A, Suffice A	1957 (friction modified)
Dexron	1967 (lower viscosity)
Dexron II	1978 (lower viscosity)
Dexron II-E	1990 (improved low temperature fluidity)
Dexron III	1993–2005 (improved low temperature fluidity)
Dexron VI	2005 (improved viscosity stability)
FORD/JAGUAR	**DESCRIPTION**
Type F	1967 (Nonfriction modified. Designed for older band-type automatic transmissions)
Mercon	1987 (Friction modified)
Mercon V	1997 (Highly friction modified)
Mercon SP	Used in the Ford 6 speeds such as the 6R60 6HP 26 and also the 2003 and up Torque Shift
Idemitsu K-17	Jaguar X-type
CHRYSLER	**DESCRIPTION**
Chrysler 7176	Designed for front-wheel drive transaxles
ATF+2	1997 (improved cold temperature flow)
ATF+3	1997 (designed for four-speed automatics)
ATF+4	Used in most 2000 and newer Chrysler vehicles
HONDA/TOYOTA	**DESCRIPTION**
Honda Z-1	For use in all Honda automatic transaxles
Toyota Type III	Specific vehicles and years
Toyota Type IV	Specific vehicles and years
Toyota WS	Lower viscosity than Type IV. Used in specific vehicles and years
MAZDA/NISSAN/ SUBARU	**DESCRIPTION**
Mazda ATF-III	Specific vehicles and years
Mazda ATF-MV	Specific vehicles and years
Nissan Matic D	Specific vehicles and years
Nissan Matic J	Specific vehicles and years
Nissan Matic K	Specific vehicles and years
Subaru ATF	Specific vehicles and years
Subaru ATF-HP	Specific vehicles and years

AUDI/BMW/ MERCEDES/VOLVO	DESCRIPTION
Audi G-052-025-A2	Specific vehicles and years
Audi G-052-162-A1	Specific vehicles and years
BMW LA2634	Specific vehicles and years
BMW LT1141	Lifetime fill (BMW warns to not use any other type of fluid)
Mercedes 236.1	Specific vehicles and years
Mercedes 236.2	Specific vehicles and years
Mercedes 236.5	Specific vehicles and years
Mercedes 236.6	Specific vehicles and years
Mercedes 236.7	Specific vehicles and years
Mercedes 236.9	Specific vehicles and years
Mercedes 236.10	Specific vehicles and years
Volvo 97340	Specific vehicles and years
Volvo JWS 3309	Specific vehicles and years
MITSUBISHI/ HYUNDAI/KIA	**DESCRIPTION**
Diamond SP II	Specific vehicles and years
Diamond SP III	Specific vehicles and years

CHART 13–1

Selected samples of automatic transmission fluid and some applications. Always check service information before using the specified fluid when servicing any automatic transmissions or transaxles.

- The vehicle should be parked on a level surface.
- The transmission fluid should be at normal operating temperature. This may require the vehicle to be driven several miles before the level is checked.
- The engine should be running with the transmission in neutral or park, as specified by the vehicle manufacturer.

NOTE: Honda and Acura manufacturers usually specify that the transmission fluid be checked with the engine off. Always follow the recommended checking procedure.

To check the automatic transmission fluid, perform the following steps.

STEP 1   Start the engine and move the gear selector to all gear positions and return to park or neutral as specified by the vehicle manufacturer.

STEP 2   Remove the transmission/transaxle dipstick (fluid level indicator) and wipe it off using a clean cloth.

STEP 3   Reinsert the dipstick until fully seated. Remove the dipstick again and note the level. ● **SEE FIGURE 13–12.**

FIGURE 13–12 A typical automatic transmission dipstick.

NOTE: Some transmissions or transaxles do not use a dipstick. Check service information for the exact procedure to follow to check the fluid level. Some vehicles require the use of a scan tool to check the level of the fluid.

- **Do not overfill any automatic transmission/transaxle.** The "ADD" mark on most automatic transmissions indicates that it is down 1/2 quart (1/2 liter) instead of one quart as used when checking engine oil level. Even if just 1/2 quart too much was added by mistake, it could cause the fluid to foam. Foaming of the ATF is caused by the moving parts inside the transmission/transaxle, which stir up the fluid and introduce air into it. This foamy fluid cannot adequately lubricate or operate the hydraulic clutches that make the unit function correctly.

CAUTION: If the automatic transmission is overfilled, the extra fluid can be blown out through the vent tube at the top of the transmission/transaxle. This fluid could then be blown onto the exhaust system and catch fire.

- **Smell the ATF on the dipstick.** If it smells burned or rancid, further service of the automatic transmission/transaxle will be necessary.
- **Look at the color of the fluid.** It should be red or light brown. A dark brown or black color indicates severe oxidation usually caused by too high an operating temperature. Further service and diagnosis of the automatic transmission/transaxle will be required in that case.

NOTE: Chrysler warns that color and smell should not be used to determine the condition of ATF+4 used in most Chrysler-built vehicles since the 2000 model year. The dyes and additives can change during normal use and the change is not an indication of fluid contamination. This is true for most highly friction-modified ATF. Always follow the vehicle manufacturer's recommendation.

COOLING SYSTEM INSPECTION

STEPS INVOLVED Normal inspection/maintenance involves an occasional check of the following items.

1. Coolant level in the coolant recovery tank or in the surge tank. ● SEE FIGURE 13–13.
2. The front of the radiator should be carefully inspected and cleaned of bugs, dirt, or mud that can often restrict airflow.
3. Also included is a visual inspection for signs of coolant system leaks and for the condition of the coolant hoses and accessory drive belts.

FIGURE 13–13 Visually check the level and color of coolant in the coolant recovery or surge tank.

The exact type of coolant to be used is often specific for each make, model, and year of vehicle, so check service information for the exact coolant to be used.

COOLANT TESTING

- **Visual inspection.** Coolant should be clean and close to the color when it was new. If dark or muddy, it should be replaced. Milky colored coolant is an indication of oil in the system that might be caused by a defective engine gasket. If the coolant is dark or muddy looking, it should be replaced.
- **Test strips.** Coolant test strips are available to test the condition of the coolant. Check to see that the test strips are being used on the specified type of coolant, as some will work only on the old green inorganic additive technology (IAT) coolant.
- **Boiling/freezing points (refractometer and hydrometer).** A hydrometer can be used to check the freezing and boiling temperatures of the coolant. A refractometer can be used to check the freezing temperature of the coolant. ● SEE FIGURE 13–14.
- **Proper reading.** A proper 50–50 mix of antifreeze and water should result in a freezing temperature of −34°F (−37°C).

    1. If the freezing temperature is higher than −34°F (e.g., −20°F), there is too much water in the coolant.
    2. If the freezing temperature is lower than −34°F (e.g., −46°F), there is too much antifreeze in the coolant.

NOTE: Many hybrid electric vehicles use two separate cooling systems—one for the internal combustion engine (ICE) and the other to cool the electronics. Check service information for the exact procedures to follow.

(a)

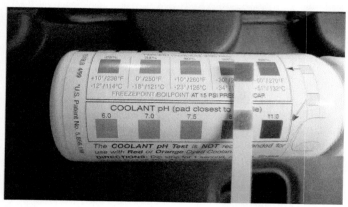

(b)

FIGURE 13–14 (a) A refractometer is used to measure the freezing point of coolant. A drop of coolant is added to a viewing screen, the lid is closed, and then held up to the light to view the display on the tool. (b) The use of test strips is a convenient and cost-effective method to check coolant condition and freezing temperature.

 TECH TIP

Ignore the Wind Chill Factor

The wind chill factor is a temperature that combines the actual temperature and the wind speed to determine the overall heat loss effect on open skin. Because it is the heat loss factor for open skin, the wind chill temperature is not to be considered when determining antifreeze protection levels. Although moving air makes it feel colder, the actual temperature is not changed by the wind, and the engine coolant will not be affected by the wind chill. If you are not convinced, try placing a thermometer in a room and wait until a stable reading is obtained. Now turn on a fan and have the air blow across the thermometer. The temperature will not change.

HOSE INSPECTION

RADIATOR AND HEATER HOSES Upper and lower radiator hoses must be pliable, yet not soft. The lower radiator hose will be reinforced or contain an inner spring to prevent the hose from being sucked closed, since the lower hose is attached to the suction side of the water pump. Heater hoses come in the following inside diameter sizes.

- 1/2 in.
- 5/8 in.
- 3/4 in.

The heater hoses connect the engine cooling system to the heater core. A heater core looks like a small radiator and is located inside the vehicle. All automotive hoses are made of rubber with reinforcing fabric weaving for strength. Sections of the coolant lines can be made from nylon-reinforced plastic or metal. All hoses should be inspected for leaks (especially near hose clamps), cracks, swollen areas indicating possible broken reinforcing material, and excessively brittle, soft, and swollen sections. Using a hand-operated pressure pump attached to the radiator opening is an excellent way to check for leaks. ● **SEE FIGURE 13–15.**

HOSE CLAMPS There are several types of hose clamps used depending on the make, model, and year of vehicle. The three basic types are as follows:

1. Worm drive (also called a screw band type)
2. Banded-type clamp
3. Wire clamp (spring type). **SEE FIGURE 13–16.**

FIGURE 13–15 Pressure testing the cooling system. A typical hand-operated pressure tester applies pressure equal to the radiator cap pressure. The pressure should hold; if it drops, this indicates a leak somewhere in the cooling system. An adapter is used to attach the pump to the cap to determine if the radiator can hold pressure, and release it when pressure rises above its maximum rated pressure setting.

FIGURE 13-16 Hose clamps come in a variety of shapes and designs.

ACCESSORY DRIVE BELT INSPECTION

TYPES OF BELTS Older V-belts (so-named because of their shape) are 34° at the V. The pulley they ride through is generally 36°. This 2° difference results in a wedging action and

FIGURE 13-17 A special tool is useful when installing a new accessory drive belt. The long-handled wrench fits in a hole of the belt tensioner.

FIGURE 13-18 A typical worn serpentine accessory drive belt. Newer belts made from ethylene propylene diene monomer (EPDM) do not crack like older belts that were made from neoprene rubber.

makes power transmission possible, but it is also the reason why V-belts must be closely inspected.

It is generally recommended that all belts, including the **serpentine** (or **Poly V**) belts be replaced every four to seven years. When a belt that turns the water pump breaks, the engine could rapidly overheat, causing serious engine damage, and if one belt breaks, it often causes the other belts to become tangled, causing them to break. ● **SEE FIGURES 13-17 AND 13-18.**

BELT INSPECTION Check the belt(s) for cracks or other signs of wear such as shiny areas that could indicate where the belt has been slipping. Replace any serpentine belt that has more than three cracks in any one rib that appears in a 3-in. span.

BELT TENSION MEASUREMENT There are four ways that vehicle manufacturers specify that the belt tension is within factory specifications.

1. **Belt tension gauge.** A belt tension gauge is needed to achieve the specified belt tension. Install the belt and operate the engine with all of the accessories turned on to "run-in" the belt for at least five minutes. Adjust the tension of the accessory drive belt to factory specifications. ● **SEE FIGURE 13-19.**

2. **Marks on a tensioner.** Many tensioners have marks that indicate the normal operating tension range for the accessory drive belt. Check service information for the preferred location of the tensioner mark. ● **SEE FIGURE 13-20.**

3. **Torque wrench reading.** Some vehicle manufacturers specify that a beam-type torque wrench be used to determine the torque needed to rotate the tensioner. If the torque reading is below specifications, the tensioner must be replaced.

4. **Deflection.** Depress the belt between the two pulleys that are the farthest apart, the flex or deflection should be 0.5 in.

FIGURE 13–19 A belt tension gauge displays the belt tension in pounds of force.

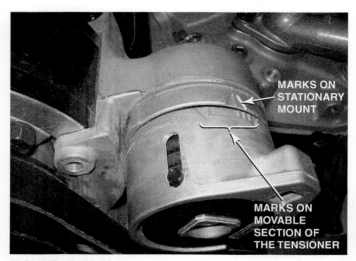

MARKS ON STATIONARY MOUNT

MARKS ON MOVABLE SECTION OF THE TENSIONER

FIGURE 13–20 Typical marks on an accessory drive belt tensioner.

BELT ROUTING GUIDE Always check the belt routing diagram located on the under-hood sticker or the service information for the proper routing when replacing an accessory drive belt. The belt routing can vary depending on engine size and accessories.

POWER STEERING FLUID

TYPES OF POWER STEERING FLUID The correct power steering fluid is *critical* to the operation and service life of the power steering system! The *exact* power steering fluid to use varies by vehicle manufacturer and sometimes

The Water Spray Trick

Lower-than-normal alternator output could be the result of a loose or slipping drive belt. All belts (V and serpentine multigroove) use an interference angle between the angle of the Vs of the belt and the angle of the Vs on the pulley. Over time, this interference angle is worn off the edges of the V of the belt. As a result, the belt may start to slip and make a squealing sound even if tensioned properly. A fast method to determine if the noise is from the belt is to spray water from a squirt bottle at the belt with the engine running. If the noise stops, the belt is the cause of the noise. The water quickly evaporates; therefore, water simply reveals the problem, but it does not provide a short-term fix.
● **SEE FIGURE 13–21.**

between models made by the same vehicle manufacturer because of differences among various steering component manufacturers. Always check service information for the specified fluid to use. The types of power steering fluid can include the following:

- Automatic transmission fluid (check for the exact type)
- Power steering fluid
- Unique fluid that is specially designed for the vehicle

FIGURE 13–21 A water spray bottle is an excellent diagnostic tool to help determine if the noise is due to an accessory drive belt. If the noise goes away when the belt is sprayed with a mist of water, then the belt is the cause.

CHECKING POWER STEERING FLUID Check power steering fluid level with the engine off. The cap for the power steering reservoir is marked with an icon of a steering wheel or the words "power steering." Remove the cap by twisting it counterclockwise and use the level indicator as part of the cap to determine the level.

Often the level marks are for cold and hot fluid.

- *If too low*, check for leaks especially at the high-pressure lines and fittings. Add the specified fluid to the correct level.

- *If too high*, use a fluid siphon pump or a "turkey baster" and remove the excess fluid until the level is correct.

CAUTION: Do not use fluid that is labeled "for all vehicles" as this type may not be compatible with the seals used in the power steering system or provide the specified friction additives needed to provide the proper steering feel to the driver. ● SEE FIGURE 13–22.

FIGURE 13–22 Most vehicles use a combination filler cap and level indicator (dipstick) that shows the level of power steering fluid in the reservoir.

SUMMARY

1. Prior to servicing a vehicle, protective coverings should be used on the steering wheel, seats, and floor.
2. Brake fluid should be checked regularly and not filled above 0.25 in. from the top of the reservoir or above the "maximum" line imprinted on the side of the master cylinder.
3. Most vehicle manufacturers specify DOT 3 brake fluid.
4. The engine oil should be checked when the vehicle is parked on level ground and after the engine has been off for at least several minutes.
5. Always use the specified automatic transmission fluid when topping off or when changing the fluid. Using the wrong type of ATF can cause the transmission to shift too harshly or cause a vibration when the transmission shifts.

REVIEW QUESTIONS

1. What are the items that should be used to protect the vehicle before service work is begun?
2. Why should brake fluid not be filled above the full or MAX level as indicated on the master cylinder reservoir?
3. Why should brake fluid be kept in an airtight container?
4. What is hydraulic clutch fluid?
5. What does color mean in relation to the type of coolant?
6. What are the three basic classifications of ATF?

CHAPTER QUIZ

1. When inspecting engine oil what should be checked?
   a. Proper Level
   b. Color
   c. Feels slippery and not gritty
   d. All of the above
2. Most vehicle manufacturers specify brake fluid that meets what specification?
   a. DOT 2
   b. DOT 3
   c. DOT 4
   d. DOT 5
3. The cabin filter can be accessed from _____.
   a. Under the hood in some vehicles
   b. Under the dash in some vehicles
   c. From under the vehicle in some vehicles
   d. Either a or b
4. Coolant can be checked using _____.
   a. Boiling/freezing points using a refractometer and hydrometer
   b. Visual inspection
   c. Test strips
   d. All of the above

5. Dexron VI and Mercon V are examples of _____?
   a. Automatic transmission fluid (ATF)
   b. Power steering fluid
   c. Brake fluid
   d. Engine oil

6. What should be done to protect the vehicle during inspections and service?
   a. Cover the steering wheel
   b. Protect the floor of the vehicle
   c. Protect the seats
   d. All of the above

7. Windshield washer fluid is designed to _____.
   a. Clean the windshield
   b. Help remove bugs
   c. Contains alcohol to keep it from freezing
   d. All of the above

8. The fluid used in power steering systems is _____.
   a. Automatic transmission fluid or special power steering fluid
   b. Brake fluid
   c. Antifreeze (coolant)
   d. Gear oil

9. Accessory drive belts should be checked for proper tension by _____.
   a. Deflection
   b. Tensioner marks
   c. A torque wrench reading on the tensioner
   d. Any of the above may be specified

10. Spraying accessory drive belts with a fine mist of water from a spray bottle is used to _____.
    a. Provides increased gripping power to the belt.
    b. Is used to check if a noise is due to the belt.
    c. Lubricates the belt
    d. Cools the belt

VEHICLE LIFTING AND HOISTING

OBJECTIVES: After studying Chapter 14, the reader should be able to: • Identify vehicle hoisting and lifting equipment. • Discuss safety procedures related to hoisting or lifting a vehicle. • Describe the proper methods to follow to safely hoist a vehicle.

KEY TERMS: • Creeper 131 • Floor jack 131 • Jack stands 131 • Safety stands 131

FLOOR JACK

A **floor jack** is a hand-operated hydraulic device that is used to lift vehicles or components, such as engines, transmissions, and rear axle assemblies. Most floor jacks use four casters, which allow the jack to be easily moved around the shop. ● **SEE FIGURE 14-1.**

SAFE USE OF FLOOR JACKS. Floor jacks are used to lift a vehicle or major vehicle component, but they are not designed to hold a load. Therefore, **safety stands,** also called **jack stands,** should always be used to support the vehicle. After the floor jack has lifted the vehicle, safety stands should be placed under the vehicle, and then, using the floor jack, lowered onto the safety stands. The floor jack can be

FIGURE 14-2 Safety stands are being used to support the rear of this vehicle. Notice a creeper also.

left in position as another safety device but the load should be removed from the floor jack. If a load is retained on the floor jack, hydraulic fluid can leak past seals in the hydraulic cylinders, which would lower the vehicle, possibly causing personal injury or death. ● **SEE FIGURE 14-2.**

CREEPERS

When working underneath a vehicle, most service technicians use a **creeper,** which consists of a flat or concaved surface equipped with low-profile casters. A creeper allows the technician to maneuver under the vehicle easily.

SAFE USE OF CREEPERS Creepers can create a fall hazard if left on the floor. When a creeper is not being used, it should be picked up and placed vertically against a wall or tool box to help prevent accidental falls.

FIGURE 14-1 A hydraulic hand-operated floor jack.

RAISE VEHICLE

HANDLE

OPEN RELEASE VALVE (LOWER JACK)

SADDLE

LIFTING ARM

CLOSE RELEASE VALVE

RELEASE VALVE

FRONT WHEELS

REAR CASTER

FIGURE 14-3 Most newer vehicles have a triangle symbol indicating the recommended hoisting lift points.

VEHICLE HOISTS

Vehicle hoists include older in ground pneumatic/hydraulic (air pressure over hydraulic) and above ground units. Most of the vehicle hoists used today use an electric motor to pressurize hydraulic fluid, which lifts the vehicle using hydraulic cylinders. Hoists are rated by the maximum weight that they can safely lift, such as 7,000 to 12,000 pounds (3200 to 5400 kg.) or more. Hoists can also have equal length arms or can be equipped with different length arms allowing the vehicle to be set so the doors can be opened and not hit the center support column. Many chassis and underbody service procedures require that the vehicle be hoisted or lifted off the ground. The simplest methods involve the use of drive-on ramps or a floor jack and safety (jack) stands, whereas in ground or surface-mounted lifts provide greater access.

SETTING THE PADS IS A CRITICAL PART OF THIS
PROCEDURE All automobile and light-truck service manuals include recommended locations to be used when hoisting (lifting) a vehicle. Some vehicles have a decal on the driver's door indicating the recommended lift points. The recommended standards for the lift points and lifting procedures are found in SAE Standard JRP-2184. ● **SEE FIGURE 14-3.**

These recommendations typically include the following points.

1. The vehicle should be centered on the lift or hoist so as not to overload one side or put too much force either forward or rearward. Use tall safety stands if a major component is going to be removed from the vehicle, such as the engine, to help support the vehicle. ● **SEE FIGURE 14-4.**

2. The pads of the lift should be spread as far apart as possible to provide a stable platform.

3. Each pad should be placed under a portion of the vehicle that is strong and capable of supporting the weight of the vehicle.
   a. Pinch welds at the bottom edge of the body are generally considered to be strong.

(a)

(b)

FIGURE 14-4 (a) Tall safety stands can be used to provide additional support for a vehicle while on a hoist. (b) A block of wood should be used to avoid the possibility of doing damage to components supported by the stand.

CAUTION: Even though pinch weld seams are the recommended location for hoisting many vehicles with unitized bodies (unit-body), care should be taken not to place the pad(s) too far forward or rearward. Incorrect placement of the vehicle on the lift could cause the vehicle to be imbalanced, and the vehicle could fall. This is exactly what happened to this vehicle. ● **SEE FIGURE 14-5.**

FIGURE 14-5 This training vehicle fell from the hoist when the pads were not set correctly. No one was hurt, but the vehicle was damaged.

(a)

(b)

FIGURE 14-6 (a) An assortment of hoist pad adapters that are often necessary to safely hoist many pickup trucks, vans, and sport utility vehicles. (b) A view from underneath a Chevrolet pickup truck showing how the pad extensions are used to attach the hoist lifting pad to contact the frame.

b. Boxed areas of the body are the best places to position the pads on a vehicle without a frame. Be careful to note whether the arms of the lift might come into contact with other parts of the vehicle before the pad touches the intended location. Commonly damaged areas include the following:

1. Rocker panel moldings
2. Exhaust system (including catalytic converter)
3. Tires or body panels. ● **SEE FIGURES 14-6 AND 14-7.**

4. As soon as the pads touch the vehicle, check for proper pad placement. The vehicle should be raised about 1 ft (30 cm) off the floor, then stopped and shaken to check for stability. If the vehicle seems to be stable when checked at a short distance from the floor, continue raising the vehicle and continue to view the vehicle until it has reached the desired height. The hoist should be lowered onto the mechanical locks, and then raised off of the locks before lowering.

(a)

(b)

FIGURE 14-7 (a) In this photo the pad arm is just contacting the rocker panel of the vehicle. (b) This photo shows what can occur if the technician places the pad too far inward underneath the vehicle. The arm of the hoist has dented the rocket panel.

CAUTION: Do not look away from the vehicle while it is being raised (or lowered) on a hoist. Often one side or one end of the hoist can stop or fail, resulting in the vehicle being slanted enough to slip or fall.

HINT: Most hoists can be safely placed at any desired height as long as it is high enough for the safety latches to engage. For ease while working, the area in which you are working should be at chest level. When working on brakes or suspension components, it is not necessary to work on them down near the floor or over your head. Raise the hoist so that the components are at chest level.

5. Before lowering the hoist, check that nothing is underneath the vehicle nor anyone near that may be injured when the vehicle is lowered. The safety latch(es) must be released and the direction of the controls reversed. The speed downward is often adjusted to be as slow as possible for additional safety.

DRIVE-ON RAMPS

Ramps are an inexpensive way to raise the front or rear of a vehicle. ● **SEE FIGURE 14–8.** Ramps are easy to store, but they can be dangerous because they can "kick out" when driving the vehicle onto the ramps.

DRIVE-ON
RAMPS

CHOCK

FIGURE 14–8 Drive-on-type ramps. The wheels on the ground level *must* be chocked (blocked) to prevent accidental movement down the ramp.

CAUTION: Professional repair shops do not use ramps because they are dangerous to use. Use only with extreme care.

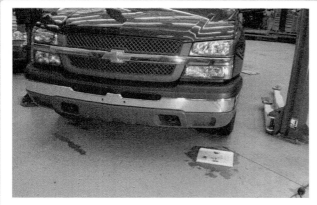

1 The first step in hoisting a vehicle is to properly align the vehicle in the center of the stall.

2 Most vehicles will be correctly positioned when the left front tire is centered on the tire pad.

3 The arms can be moved in and out and most pads can be rotated to allow for many different types of vehicle construction.

4 Most lifts are equipped with short pad extensions that are often necessary to use to allow the pad to contact the frame of a vehicle without causing the arm of the lift to hit and damage parts of the body.

5 Tall pad extensions can also be used to gain access to the frame of a vehicle. This position is needed to safely hoist many pickup trucks, vans, and sport utility vehicles.

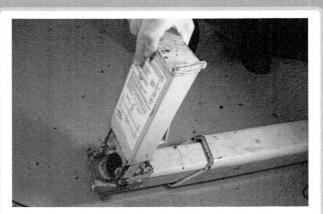

6 An additional extension may be necessary to hoist a truck or van equipped with running boards to give the necessary clearance.

CONTINUED ▶

7 Position the pads under the vehicle at the recommended locations.

8 After being sure all pads are correctly positioned, use the hoist controls to raise the vehicle.

9 With the vehicle raised one foot (30 cm) off the ground, push down on the vehicle to check to see if it is stable on the pads. If the vehicle rocks, lower the vehicle and reset the pads. The vehicle can be raised to any desired working level. Be sure the safety is engaged before working on or under the vehicle.

10 If raising a vehicle without a frame, place the flat pads under the pinch weld seam to spread the load. If additional clearance is necessary, the pads can be raised as shown.

11 When the service work is completed, the hoist should be raised slightly and the safety released before using the lever to lower the vehicle.

12 After lowering the vehicle, be sure all arms of the lift are moved out of the way before driving the vehicle out of the work stall.

SUMMARY

1. Whenever a vehicle is raised off the ground using a floor jack, it must be supported using safety stands.
2. Creepers should be stored vertically to prevent the possibility of stepping on it, which could cause a fall and personal injury.
3. Always adhere to the specified hoisting locations as found in service information.
4. Adapters or extensions are often needed when hoisting pickup trucks or vans.

REVIEW QUESTIONS

1. Why must safety stands be used after lifting a vehicle with a floor jack?
2. What precautions should be adhered to when storing a creeper?
3. What precautions should be adhered to when hoisting a vehicle?

CHAPTER QUIZ

1. A safety stand is also called a _____.
   a. Jack
   b. Jack stand
   c. Bottle jack
   d. Safety stool

2. Professional repair shops do not use ramps because _____.
   a. Can "kick out" and are dangerous to use
   b. Can be used to raise only the front of the vehicle
   c. Can be used to raise only the rear of the vehicle
   d. Can be used without having to block the wheels

3. The SAE standard for hoist location is _____.
   a. J-1980
   b. SAE-2009
   c. JRP-2184
   d. J-14302

4. Tall safety stands would be used to _____.
   a. Help support the vehicle when a major component is removed from the vehicle.
   b. Lift a vehicle
   c. Lift a component such as an engine high off the ground
   d. Both b and c

5. Commonly damaged areas of a vehicle during hoisting include _____.
   a. Rocker panels
   b. Exhaust systems
   c. Tires or body panels
   d. All of the above

6. Pad extensions may be needed when hoisting what type of vehicle?
   a. Small cars
   b. Pickup trucks
   c. Vans
   d. Either b or c

7. Technician A says that a hoist can be stopped at any level as long as the safety latch engages. Technician B says that the vehicle should be hoisted to the top of the hoist travel for safety. Which technician is correct?
   a. Technician A only
   b. Technician B only
   c. Both technicians A and B
   d. Neither technician A nor B

8. Before lowering the vehicle, what should the technician do?
   a. Be sure nothing is underneath the vehicle
   b. Raise the vehicle enough to release the safety latch
   c. Be sure no one will be walking under or near the vehicle
   d. All of the above

9. Technician A says that a creeper should be stored vertically. Technician B says that a creeper should be stored on its casters. Which technician is correct?
   a. Technician A only
   b. Technician B only
   c. Both technicians A and B
   d. Neither technician A nor B

10. When checking for stability, how high should the vehicle be raised?
    a. About 2 in. (5 cm)
    b. About 6 in. (15 cm)
    c. About 1 ft (30 cm)
    d. About 3 ft (91 cm)

SCIENTIFIC PRINCIPLES AND MATERIALS

OBJECTIVES: After studying Chapter 15, the reader will be able to: • Describe Newton's Laws of Motion. • Explain kinetic energy and why it is so important to brake design. • Discuss mechanical advantage and how it is used in a vehicle. • Define torque and horsepower. • Describe sound and acoustics. • Explain bases and acids. • Discuss the gas laws. • Explain the coefficient of friction. • Describe the difference between heat and temperature. • Describe the methods used to identify plastic, iron, steel, and aluminum.

KEY TERMS: Acid material 145 • Alkaline 145 • Brake 140 • Brake horsepower (bhp) 140 • BTU (British Thermal Unit) 143 • Caustic material 145 • Celsius (centigrade) 144 • Conduction 143 • Conductor 144 • Convection 144 • Dynamometer (dyno or dyn) 140 • Energy 139 • Fahrenheit 144 • First-class lever 142 • Force 139 • Fulcrum 142 • Horsepower 140 • Hypothesis 138 • Inertia 142 • Insulator 144 • Kinetic energy 139 • Leverage 142 • Mass 142 • Mechanical advantage 143 • Newton's laws of motion 141 • Pedal ratio 143 • PH 145 • Potential energy 139 • Power 140 • Propagation 145 • Radiation 144 • Root cause 138 • Scientific method 138 • Second-class lever 143 • Third-class lever 143 • Torque 139 • Weight 142 • Work 139 • Wrought alloys 147

SCIENTIFIC METHOD

The **scientific method** is a series of steps taken to solve a problem. These steps help eliminate errors and to achieve an accurate result. The scientific method is the foundation of automotive diagnosis. A scientific method involves the following steps:

STEP 1 Observe the conditions or problem and define or describe the problem.

STEP 2 Formulate an explanation that could be the cause of the problem.

STEP 3 Use the explanation (**hypothesis**) to test to see if it matches the existing problem. If not, then return to step 2 to formulate another explanation.

STEP 4 After the explanation has proved to be a possible solution to a problem, additional tests should be performed to verify that the method works all of the time.

USING THE SCIENTIFIC METHOD While a service technician will not perform research, using a scientific approach to problem solving is very important.

This means that every fault should be investigated to determine the root cause rather than solving what at first is thought to be the problem or fault. The **root cause** is the true cause of a failure, which may not be noticed at first. Many service technicians ask themselves "why" when they discover a fault. Often this leads to another possible prob-

lem and then the technician should ask another "why." This scientific method of finding the root cause of an automotive problem is often called the "five whys." By the time the technician has asked "why" five times, the root cause is usually discovered.

EXAMPLES OF THE FIVE WHYS As an example of using a scientific method approach to automotive faults, an owner may state that the vehicle does not start and the battery appears to be dead. Therefore, applying the five whys (scientific approach) first ask why:

- First why—What caused the battery to become discharged? To answer this question requires observation and the creating of a hypothesis, such as "is the battery defective" or "did the customer leave the lights on?" This requires questioning the owner and testing the battery.

- Second why—Assume that the battery was in good condition but discharged. Now the technician should ask the second why. "Why did the battery become discharged?" This means that a battery ignition off drain test needs to be performed as well as testing of the charging system. Assume the battery drain test was okay, but that the charging system was not working properly.

- Third why—The charging system was found to be not working correctly. A visual inspection found that the alternator drive belt was not tight enough to properly operate the alternator. The technician needs to ask

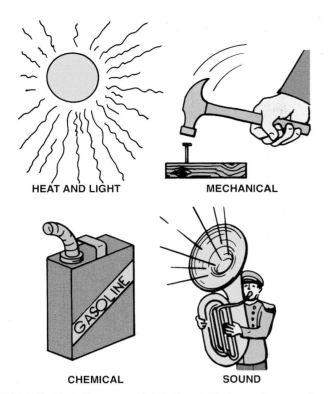

HEAT AND LIGHT   MECHANICAL

CHEMICAL   SOUND

FIGURE 15–1 Energy, which is the ability to perform work, exists in many forms.

1 FOOT

10 POUNDS

FIGURE 15–2 Torque is a twisting force equal to the distance from the pivot point times the force applied expressed in units called pound-feet (lb-ft) or Newton-meters (N-m).

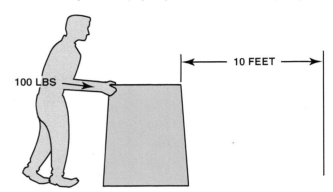

100 LBS

10 FEET

FIGURE 15–3 Work is calculated by multiplying force times distance. If you push 100 pounds 10 feet, you have done 1,000 foot-pounds of work.

the third why, "Why is the accessory drive belt still loose?"

- Fourth why—"Why was the accessory drive belt loose?" The cause could be a defective tensioner. If the tensioner itself was not a problem, then another "why" needs to be asked.

- Fifth why—If the accessory belt and belt tensioner were okay, then further investigation would be needed to find the root cause. For example, "Is one of the tensioner retaining bolts loose, maybe from a previous repair?" This could be the root cause.

ENERGY PRINCIPLES

Energy is the ability or the capacity to do work. There are many forms of energy, but chemical, mechanical, and electrical energy are the most familiar kinds involved in the operation of an automobile. ● **SEE FIGURE 15–1.** Energy in the form of a moving object is called **kinetic energy.** An example of kinetic energy is a moving vehicle. Energy is called **potential energy** if it is capable of being changed to useful energy, such as the potential energy stored in a battery or a vehicle at the top of a hill. In both of these cases, there is no energy being released but if the battery were connected to an electrical load, such as a light bulb, or the vehicle starts moving down the hill, the energy is being released.

TORQUE

Torque is the term used to describe a rotating force that may or may not result in motion. Torque is measured as the amount of **force** multiplied by the length of the lever through which it acts. If a one-foot-long wrench is used to apply 10 pounds of force to the end of the wrench to turn a bolt, then 10 pound-feet of torque is being applied. ● **SEE FIGURE 15–2.** The metric unit for torque is Newton-meters because Newton is the metric unit for force and the distance is expressed in meters.

    1 pound-foot = 1.3558 Newton-meters
    1 Newton-meter = 0.7376 pound-foot

WORK

Work is defined as actually accomplishing movement when force (torque) is applied to an object. A service technician can apply torque to a bolt in an attempt to loosen it, yet no work is done until the bolt actually moves. Work is calculated by multiplying the applied force (in pounds) by the distance the object moves (in feet). If you applied 100 pounds of force to move an object 10 feet, then you accomplished 1,000 foot-pounds of work (100 pounds × 10 feet = 1,000 foot pounds). ● **SEE FIGURE 15–3.**

N-m	Lb-ft	N-m	Lb-ft	N-m	Lb-ft	N-m	Lb-ft
				Newton-Meters to Pound-Feet Conversion Chart (1 N-m = 0.074 lb-ft)			
1	0.74	26	19.2	51	37.7	76	56.2
2	1.5	27	20.0	52	38.5	77	57.0
3	2.2	28	20.7	53	39.2	78	57.7
4	3.0	29	21.5	54	40.0	79	58.5
5	3.7	30	22.2	55	40.7	80	59.2
6	4.4	31	22.9	56	41.4	81	59.9
7	5.2	32	23.7	57	42.2	82	60.7
8	5.9	33	24.4	58	42.9	83	61.4
9	6.7	34	25.2	59	43.7	84	62.2
10	7.4	35	25.9	60	44.4	85	62.9
11	8.1	36	26.6	61	45.1	86	63.6
12	8.9	37	27.4	62	45.9	87	64.4
13	9.6	38	28.1	63	46.6	88	65.1
14	10.4	39	28.9	64	47.4	89	65.9
15	11.1	40	29.6	65	48.1	90	66.6
16	11.8	41	30.3	66	48.8	91	67.3
17	12.6	42	31.1	67	49.6	92	68.1
18	13.3	43	31.8	68	50.3	93	68.8
19	14.1	44	32.6	69	51.0	94	69.6
20	14.8	45	33.3	70	51.8	95	70.3
21	15.5	46	34.0	71	52.5	96	71.0
22	16.3	47	34.8	72	53.3	97	71.8
23	17.0	48	35.5	73	54.0	98	72.5
24	17.8	49	36.3	74	54.8	99	73.3
25	18.5	50	37.0	75	55.5	100	74.0

Newton-Meters to Pound-Feet Conversion Chart (1 N-m = 0.074 lb-ft)

Lb-ft	N-m	Lb-ft	N-m	Lb-ft	N-m	Lb-ft	N-m
1	1.4	26	36.4	51	71.4	76	106.4
2	2.8	27	37.8	52	72.8	77	107.8
3	4.2	28	39.2	53	74.2	78	109.2
4	5.6	29	40.6	54	75.6	79	110.6
5	7.0	30	42.0	55	77.0	80	112.0
6	8.4	31	43.4	56	78.4	81	113.4
7	9.8	32	44.8	57	79.8	82	114.8
8	11.2	33	46.2	58	81.2	83	116.2
9	12.6	34	47.6	59	82.6	84	117.6
10	14.0	35	49.0	60	84.0	85	119.0
11	15.4	36	50.4	61	85.4	86	120.4
12	16.8	37	51.8	62	86.8	87	121.8
13	18.2	38	53.2	63	88.2	88	123.2
14	19.6	39	54.6	64	89.6	89	124.6
15	21.0	40	56.0	65	91.0	90	126.0
16	22.4	41	57.4	66	92.4	91	127.4
17	23.8	42	58.8	67	93.8	92	128.8
18	25.2	43	60.2	68	95.2	93	130.2
19	26.6	44	61.6	69	96.6	94	131.6
20	28.0	45	63.0	70	98.0	95	133.0
21	29.4	46	64.4	71	99.4	96	134.4
22	30.8	47	65.8	72	100.8	97	135.8
23	32.2	48	67.2	73	102.2	98	137.2
24	33.6	49	68.6	74	103.6	99	138.6
25	35.0	50	70.0	75	105.0	100	140.0

Pound-Feet to Newton-Meters Conversion Chart (1 lb-ft = 1.4 N-m)

FREQUENTLY ASKED QUESTION

What Is the Difference between Torque and Work?

The designations for torque and work are often confusing. Torque is expressed in pound-feet because it represents a force exerted a certain distance from the object and acts as a lever. Work, however, is expressed in foot-pounds because work is the movement over a certain distance (feet) multiplied by the force applied (pounds). Engines produce torque and service technicians exert torque represented by the unit pound-feet.

POWER

The term **power** means the rate of doing work. Power equals work divided by time. Work is achieved when a certain amount of mass (weight) is moved a certain distance by a force. If the object is moved in 10 seconds or 10 minutes does not make a difference in the amount of work accomplished, but it does affect the amount of power needed. Power is expressed in units of foot-pounds per minute.

HORSEPOWER

The power an engine produces is called horsepower (hp). One **horsepower** is the power required to move 550 pounds one foot in one second, or 33,000 pounds one foot in one minute (550 lb × 60 sec = 33,000 lb). This is expressed as 500 foot-pounds (ft-lb) per second or 33,000 foot-pounds per minute. ● SEE FIGURE 15–4.

The actual horsepower produced by an engine is measured with a **dynamometer.** A dynamometer (often abbreviated as **dyno** or **dyn**) places a load on the engine and measures the amount of twisting force the engine crankshaft places against the load. The load holds the engine speed, so it is called a **brake.** The horsepower derived from a dynamometer is called **brake horsepower (bhp).** The dynamometer actually measures the torque output of the engine. Torque is a rotating force that

FIGURE 15–4 One horsepower is equal to 33,000 foot-pounds (200 lbs × 165 ft) of work per minute.

may or may not cause movement. The horsepower is calculated from the torque readings at various engine speeds (in revolutions per minute or RPM).

Horsepower is torque times RPM divided by 5252.

$$\text{Horsepower} = \frac{\text{Torque} \times \text{RPM}}{5252}$$

Torque is what the driver "feels" as the vehicle is being accelerated. A small engine operating at a high RPM may have the same horsepower as a large engine operating at a low RPM.

NOTE: As can be seen by the formula for horsepower, the higher the engine speed for a given amount of torque, the greater the horsepower.

NEWTON'S LAWS OF MOTION

Sir Isaac Newton (1643–1727) was an English physicist and mathematician who developed many theories of science, including three laws of motion.

1. **Newton's first law of motion** states that an object at rest tends to stay at rest and an object in motion tends to stay in motion unless acted on by an outside force. For example, it requires a large force to get a vehicle that is stopped into motion. It also requires that a force be applied to slow and stop a vehicle that is in motion.

2. **Newton's second law of motion** states that the force needed to move an object is proportional to the mass of the object multiplied by the acceleration rate of the object. This means that it requires a great deal more force to accelerate a heavy sport utility vehicle (SUV) than a small economy vehicle. The rate of acceleration also depends on the amount of force that is applied.

3. **Newton's third law of motion** states that for every action, there is an opposite and equal reaction. For example, when the air-fuel mixture is ignited in an engine, the force is exerted on the piston, which is forced downward, which causes the crankshaft of the engine to rotate. The opposite action is applied to the cylinder head of the engine and applies the same force although this part is designed not to move.

KINETIC ENERGY

Kinetic energy is a fundamental form of mechanical energy. It is the energy of mass in motion. Every moving object possesses kinetic energy, and the amount of that energy is determined by the object's mass and speed. The greater the mass of an object and the faster it moves, the more kinetic energy it possesses. Even at low speeds, a moving vehicle has enough kinetic energy to cause serious injury and damage. The job of the brake system is to dispose of that energy in a safe and controlled manner.

Engineers calculate kinetic energy using the following formula:

$$\frac{mv^2}{29.9} = E_k$$

where:
  m = mass or weight of the vehicle in pounds
  v = velocity of the vehicle in miles per hour
  E_k = kinetic energy in foot-pounds (ft-lb)

Another way to express this equation is as follows.

$$\frac{\text{weight} \times \text{speed}^2}{29.9} = \textbf{kinetic energy}$$

If a 3,000-pound vehicle traveling at 30 mph is compared to a 6,000-pound vehicle also traveling at 30 mph as shown in ● **FIGURE 15–5,** the equations for computing their respective kinetic energies look like this:

$$\frac{3,000 \text{ lb} \times 30^2 \text{ mph}}{29.9} = 90,301 \text{ ft-lb}$$

$$\frac{6,000 \text{ lb} \quad 30^2 \text{ mph}}{29.9} = 180,602 \text{ ft-lb}$$

The results show that when the weight of a vehicle is doubled from 3,000 to 6,000 pounds, its kinetic energy is also doubled from 90,301 foot-pounds to 180,602 foot-pounds. In mathematical terms, kinetic energy increases *proportionally* as weight increases. In other words, if the weight of a moving object

FIGURE 15–5 Kinetic energy increases in direct proportion to the weight of the vehicle.

What Is the Difference Between Mass and Weight?

Mass is the amount of matter in an object. One of the properties of mass is inertia. Inertia is the resistance to being put in motion and the tendency to remain in motion once it is set in motion.

The **weight** of an object is the force of gravity on the object and may be defined as the mass times the acceleration of gravity.

Therefore, mass means the property of an object and weight is a force.

 TECH TIP

Brakes Cannot Overcome the Laws of Physics

No vehicle can stop on a dime. The energy required to slow or stop a vehicle must be absorbed by the braking system. All drivers should be aware of this fact and drive at a reasonable speed for the road and traffic conditions.

doubles, its kinetic energy also doubles. If the weight quadruples, the kinetic energy becomes four times as great.

If a 3,000-pound vehicle traveling at 30 mph is compared to the same vehicle traveling at 60 mph (● **FIGURE 15–6**), the equations for computing their respective kinetic energies look like this:

$$\frac{3{,}000 \text{ lb} \times 30^2 \text{ mph}}{29.9} = 90{,}301 \text{ ft-lb}$$

$$\frac{3{,}000 \text{ lb} \times 60^2 \text{ mph}}{29.9} = 361{,}204 \text{ ft-lb}$$

The results show that the vehicle traveling at 30 mph has over 90,000 foot-pounds of kinetic energy, but at 60 mph the figure increases to over 350,000 foot-pounds. In fact, at twice the speed, the vehicle has exactly four times as much kinetic energy. If the speed were doubled again to 120 mph, the amount of kinetic energy would grow to almost 1,500,000 foot-pounds!

FIGURE 15–6 Kinetic energy increases as the square of any increase in vehicle speed.

In mathematical terms, kinetic energy increases as the *square of its speed.* In other words, if the speed of a moving object doubles (2), the kinetic energy becomes four times as great ($2^2 = 4$). And if the speed quadruples (4), say from 15 to 60 mph, the kinetic energy becomes 16 times as great ($4^2 = 16$). This is the reason speed has such an impact on kinetic energy.

KINETIC ENERGY AND BRAKE DESIGN The relationships between weight, speed, and kinetic energy have significant practical consequences for the brake system engineer. If vehicle A weighs twice as much as vehicle B, it needs a brake system that is twice as powerful. But if vehicle C has twice the speed potential of vehicle D, it needs brakes that are, not twice, but four times more powerful.

INERTIA

Although brake engineers take both weight and speed capability into account when designing a brake system, these are not the only factors involved. Another physical property, inertia, also affects the braking process and the selection of brake components. **Inertia** is defined by Isaac Newton's first law of motion, which states that a body at rest tends to remain at rest, and a body in motion tends to remain in motion in a straight line unless acted upon by an outside force.

MECHANICAL PRINCIPLES

The primary mechanical principle used to increase application force in every brake system is **leverage.** In the science of mechanics, a lever is a simple machine that consists of a rigid object, typically a metal bar that pivots about a fixed point called a **fulcrum.** There are three basic types of levers, but the job of all three is to change a quantity of energy into a more useful form.

A **first-class lever** increases the force applied to it and also changes the direction of the force. ● **SEE FIGURE 15–7.**

With a first-class lever, the weight is placed at one end while the lifting force is applied to the other. The fulcrum is positioned at some point in between. If the fulcrum is placed twice as far from the long end of the lever as from the short end, a 10-pound weight on the short end can be lifted by only

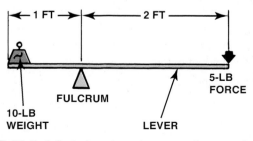

FIGURE 15–7 A first-class lever increases force and changes the direction of the force.

FIGURE 15–8 A second-class lever increases force in the same direction as it is applied.

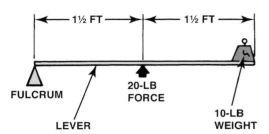

FIGURE 15–9 A third-class lever reduces force but increases the speed and travel of the resulting work.

FIGURE 15–10 This brake pedal assembly provides a 5:1 mechanical advantage because a 10-lb force input results in a 50-lb force into the master cylinder.

a 5-pound force at the long end. However, the short end of the lever will travel only half as far as the long end. Moving the fulcrum closer to the weight will further reduce the force required to lift it, but it will also decrease the distance the weight is moved.

A **second-class lever** increases the force applied to it and passes it along in the same direction. ● **SEE FIGURE 15–8.**

With a second-class lever, the fulcrum is located at one end while the lifting force is applied at the other. The weight is positioned at some point in between. If a 10-pound weight is placed at the center of the lever, it can be lifted by only a 5-pound force at the end of the lever. However, the weight will only travel half the distance the end of the lever does. As the weight is moved closer to the fulcrum, the force required to lift it, and the distance it travels, are both reduced.

A **third-class lever** actually reduces the force applied to it, but the resulting force moves farther and faster. ● **SEE FIGURE 15–9.**

With a third-class lever, the fulcrum is located at one end and the weight is placed at the other. The lifting force is applied at some point in between. If a 10-pound weight is placed at the end of the lever, it can be lifted by a 20-pound force applied at the middle of the lever. Although the force required to move the weight has doubled, the weight is moved twice as far and twice as fast as the point on the lever where the force was applied. The closer to the fulcrum the lifting force is applied, the greater the force required by the weight and the farther and faster the weight will move.

The levers in brake systems are used to increase force, so they are either first- or second-class. Second-class levers are the most common, and the service brake pedal is a good example. In a typical suspended brake pedal, the pedal arm is the lever, the pivot point is the fulcrum, and the force is applied at the foot pedal pad. ● **SEE FIGURE 15–10.** The force applied to the master cylinder by the pedal pushrod attached to the pivot

is much greater than the force applied at the pedal pad, but the pushrod does not travel nearly as far.

Leverage creates a **mechanical advantage** that, at the brake pedal, is called the **pedal ratio.** For example, a pedal ratio of 5 to 1 is common for manual brakes, which means that a force of 10 pounds at the brake pedal will result in a force of 50 pounds at the pedal pushrod. In practice, leverage is used at many points in both the service and parking brake systems to increase braking force while making it easier for the driver to control the amount of force applied.

HEAT AND TEMPERATURE

Heat and temperature are related but are not the same. Temperature is the intensity of the heat source, whereas heat is the quantity of heat. For example, the heat from a match and a large fire may measure the same temperature, but the amount of heat generated by the fire is far greater than the amount of heat generated by a single match.

HEAT Heat is measured in units called **British Thermal Units,** abbreviated **BTUs.** One BTU is the amount of heat needed to raise the temperature of one pound of water one degree Fahrenheit. For example, room heaters and air conditioners are rated in how many BTUs per hour can be added (heater) or removed (air conditioner) from a space in one hour.

Heat energy can be transferred by three ways, including:

- **Conduction**—Conduction is the process of the heat traveling from a hotter part to a colder part of the same object or by direct contact. For example, if one end of a steel bar is heated, then the heat will travel by conduction toward the colder areas of the bar. Also, if the metal were touched, heat

TECH TIP

Conductors and Insulators

If a material is a good conductor of heat, it is also a good conductor of electricity. Most **conductors** are metals, such as steel, copper, aluminum, and brass. Most insulators are nonmetals, such as plastic and rubber. Therefore, if a material does not conduct heat, it usually will not conduct electricity.

 FREQUENTLY ASKED QUESTION

How Does a Coat Keep You Warm?

A coat is worn in cold weather to keep warm. Does it keep the cold out or the heat in? Actually, both, but because heat travels from a warm object (human body) to a colder object (outside cold air), the primary purpose of a coat is to keep the body heat from escaping into the cold air.

FIGURE 15–11 A typical outdoor thermometer which is used to measure temperature, not heat.

 TECH TIP

Quick and Easy Temperature Conversion

Many service information and scan tool data are expressed in degrees Celsius, which is often confusing to those used to temperature expressed in Fahrenheit degrees. A quick and easy way to get an *approximate* conversion is to take the degrees in Celsius, double it, and add 25.

For example,

Celsius × 2 + 25 = approximate Fahrenheit degrees:

```
 0°C × 2 =   0 + 25 =  25°F (actual = 32°F)
10°C × 2 =  20 + 25 =  45°F (actual = 50°F)
15°C × 2 =  30 + 25 =  55°F (actual = 59°F)
20°C × 2 =  40 + 25 =  65°F (actual = 68°F)
25°C × 2 =  50 + 25 =  75°F (actual = 77°F)
30°C × 2 =  60 + 25 =  85°F (actual = 86°F)
35°C × 2 =  70 + 25 =  95°F (actual = 95°F)
40°C × 2 =  80 + 25 = 105°F (actual = 104°F)
45°C × 2 =  90 + 25 = 115°F (actual = 113°F)
50°C × 2 = 100 + 25 = 125°F (actual = 122°F)
```

would travel from the steel bar to the finger. Metals are good conductors of heat, whereas plastic, rubber, and ceramics are poor conductors of heat and are called **insulators.**

- **Convection**—Convection is the transfer of heat through a liquid or a gas, which causes it to rise while the cooler liquid or gas falls within a container. A hot air balloon is an example where hot gas in the balloon causes it to rise above the surrounding cooler air.

- **Radiation**—Radiation is a method of energy transfer where heat is transmitted through the air. Heat from the sun is transmitted through the atmosphere where it heats the ground. Heat can be felt above a hot stove.

TEMPERATURE   Temperature is the measurement of the ability to give up or absorb heat from another body. Heat always flows from a warmer object to a colder object.

Temperature is measured using two scales:

1. **Celsius** (also called **centigrade**). The Celsius scale was devised by taking the freezing point and the boiling point of water and dividing it into 100 equal parts.

2. **Fahrenheit.** The Fahrenheit scale was developed by Gabriel Fahrenheit (1686–1736), a German physicist who proposed the scale in 1724. He wanted to avoid using negative numbers, so the scale used had zero degrees representing the coldest outside air temperature he had ever measured and used his own body temperature to represent 100 degrees. Later, more accurate measurements indicate that average human body temperature to be 98.6 degrees so he was off by 1.4 degrees. Also, negative outside air temperatures can occur. ● **SEE FIGURE 15–11** and the comparison chart.

Temperature Symbol	Degree Celsius °C	Degree Fahrenheit °F
Boiling point of water	100.0	212.0
Average human body temperature	37.0	98.6
Average room temperature	20.0 to 25.0	68.0 to 77.0
Melting point of ice	0.0	32.0

FREQUENTLY ASKED QUESTION

What Is Thermodynamics?

Thermodynamics is the study of the relationship among temperature, pressure, and volume changes. The laws of thermodynamics help engineers design and develop engines with higher efficiency. Thermodynamics is therefore used in the design of the cooling system, as well as in the engine, because the more heat created by the burning of fuel in the engine, the more power the engine can develop using the same or less amount of fuel.

FREQUENTLY ASKED QUESTION

Can Water and Acid Be Mixed Together?

Acids have a very strong affinity for water and as a result, if water is poured into acid, the resulting reaction would be extremely violent and acid would be forced outward in all directions. Always pour acid into water, never water into acid.

Technicians seldom need to work with acids because even battery electrolytes from the water and acid are premixed to help prevent the possibility of a technician creating a harmful reaction.

ACIDS AND BASES

ACIDS   Acids are substances that can corrode metals and some can cause severe burns to the skin. Common household acids that are not harmful and taste sour include vinegar and lemon juice (citric acid). Stronger acids include:

- Hydrochloric acid
- Nitric acid
- Battery acid

BASES   A base is a substance that can also burn the skin if strong enough and is also referred to as **alkaline.** Common household bases are generally not harmful unless eaten and have a bitter taste, including baking soda, soap, and antacid, such as Milk of Magnesia®. Stronger bases, which can burn the skin include:

- Lye (sodium hydroxide)
- Bleach
- Drain cleaner

pH SCALE   Most chemical cleaners used for cleaning carbon-type deposits are a strong soap, or **caustic material.** A value called **pH,** measured on a scale from 1 to 14, is used to in-

dicate the amount of chemical activity. The term *pH* is from the French word *pouvoir hydrogine,* meaning "hydrogen power." Pure water is neutral. On the pH scale, water is pH 7. Caustic materials have pH numbers from 8 through 14. The higher the number, the stronger the caustic action will be. **Acid materials** have pH numbers from 6 through 1. The lower the number, the stronger the acid action will be. Caustic materials and acid materials neutralize each other, such as when baking soda (a caustic) is used to clean the outside of the battery (an acid surface). The caustic baking soda neutralizes any sulfuric acid that has been spilled or splashed on the outside of the battery.

CAUTION: Whenever working with chemicals, eye protection must be used.

GAS LAWS

Gas laws are a set of characteristics that describe how gases act and the relationship between their temperature, pressure, and volume. Gas laws have application in most systems of the vehicle, including tires, air-conditioning systems, and anywhere else gases are present.

BOYLE'S LAW   Boyle's law was first written in 1662 by Robert Boyle (1627–1691) and describes the relationship between volume and pressure of a gas in a closed container. Boyle's law states that the volume of a gas varies inversely (opposite) with the pressure exerted against it in a closed container. Therefore, if a closed container is compressed, the volume of the gas inside is reduced but the pressure is increased.

CHARLES'S LAW   Charles's Law was first formulated about 1787 by a French scientist, Jacque Charles (1746–1823). According to Charles's law when the temperature of a gas increases, the volume increases. When the temperature of a gas decreases, the volume decreases.

SOUND AND ACOUSTICS

Sound is the movement of air which the ear interprets as sound. Sound travels through the air, which is called **propagation.** Propagation of sound is normally thought to be only transmitted through air, but liquids can also transmit sound waves. Sound has two properties:

- **Frequency.** This is also called the pitch of the sound and is measured in Hertz or cycles per second. Normal hearing frequency ranges from as low as 20 Hertz to 20,000 Hertz. Very low frequencies, such as the heart beat, of one or two Hertz cannot be heard. High frequencies over 20,000 Hertz also cannot be detected by humans.

- **Intensity.** The intensity of sound, which is also called loudness, is measured in decibels (dB) named for Alexander Graham Bell (1847–1922), the inventor of the

Wear Hearing Protection

According to audiologists (hearing and speech doctors), a person should wear ear protection if the level of sound requires that your voice be raised in order to be heard. Any level that exceeds 90 dB requires the use of ear protection to avoid hearing loss. This means that ear protection should be worn when using a power mower or using an air tool, such as an air impact wrench or air ratchet.

FIGURE 15–12 This interior plastic part is labeled PE-HD, which means polyethylene-high density.

telephone. Relative intensity (loudness), using the decibel scale, includes the following examples:

- Whisper   10–20 dB
- Normal conversation   60 dB
- Thunder   110 dB
- Threshold of pain   120 dB

ACOUSTICS Acoustics is the study of sound and how it is generated and transmitted. Acoustic engineers are employed by vehicle manufacturers to help reduce noise and designing methods to reduce or stop the noise from being transmitted into the passenger compartment. For example, according to acoustic engineers, about 80% of the noise created by the movement of the tires on the road is transmitted through the chassis and body of the vehicle. Only about 20% of the sound is transferred to the passenger compartment through the air.

PLASTICS

There are two basic types of plastic.

THERMOSET PLASTIC This type of plastic is changed chemically when cured and shaped and cannot be reheated or reformed. Rubber is an example of a thermoset plastic material that cannot be remelted and reformed after curing. Other examples of thermoset plastics include:

- Bakelite (phenol formaldehyde resin)
- Polyester resin
- Epoxy resin

THERMOPLASTIC This type of plastic is flexible at room temperature. Thermoplastic can be recycled by grinding it into pieces and remolding it into another shape. Examples of thermoplastics include:

- Polyethylene (PE)
- Polyvinyl chloride (PVC)

- Polystyrene (PS)
- ABS (acrylonitrile butadiene styrene)
- PA nylon (polyamides)

PLASTIC IDENTIFICATION While it is not important for the average service technician to determine what kind of plastic is being used for what application, it is important to know when restoring a part or refinishing a plastic part. For example, interior plastic parts can be made from the following plastic material:

- Polypropylene plastic (PP)
- Polyethylene (PE) (● **SEE FIGURE 15–12**)
- ABS plastic
- ABS/PVC plastic
- Vinyl (PVC) plastic

Most large plastic pieces are labeled on the inside with letters, such as PP or PE. However, if no marking is visible, it is still possible to identify the type of plastic using a simple basic test. A painter will need to know the type of plastic if refinishing these parts. Often replacement plastic parts are available in only one color and must be painted to match the original when being replaced. A burn test is used to test if the plastic part is polypropylene or ABS plastic by performing the following steps:

STEP 1 Remove a small piece from a hidden back side of the plastic part being tested.

STEP 2 Hold the small piece of plastic with tweezers and ignite the plastic.

STEP 3 Observe the burning of the plastic:
- No visible smoke means that the plastic is polypropylene.
- Visible black smoke means that the plastic is ABS.

STEP 4 To determine if a part to be painted is polyvinyl chloride, a copper wire test needs to be performed by heating a copper wire and then touching the heated wire to a hidden back side surface of the part being tested. After melting some plastic onto the copper wire, return the wire to the flame and observe the color of the flame. If the color of the flame is green/blue or turquoise, then the plastic is polyvinyl chloride (vinyl).

After the type of plastic has been identified, then check with service information and paint literature to determine the proper paint and preparations needed to refinish the plastic part.

IRON AND STEEL

Iron is a chemical element with a symbol of Fe. It is one of the most commonly available elements on earth and is refined from iron ore. Steel is made from iron after further refining. The main difference between iron and steel is the amount of carbon. The amount of carbon is critical to the strength and characteristics of iron and steel.

CAST IRON Cast iron contains 2% to 4% carbon and this carbon is usually in the shape of flakes of graphite 0.001 to 0.004 inches long. Cast iron is used in many automotive applications, including engine blocks, rear axle assemblies, and some suspension components.

DUCTILE CAST IRON In ductile iron, the carbon in the alloy with silicon are small ball-shapes called spherloidols. Ductile iron is also called malleable iron and is used to make crankshafts.

GRAY CAST IRON Gray cast iron is cast iron that has another element, silicon, in the alloy giving the metal a gray color. Gray cast iron is used for engine blocks.

NOTE: Cast iron contains graphite, which acts as a lubricant when being machined. As a result, cooling oil or water is not needed when making cast iron brake rotors or brake drums.

SAE STEEL DESIGNATIONS

Steels are designed by a system established by the Society of Automotive Engineers and includes numbers to indicate the main element used in the alloy, plus the "points of carbon." One part of carbon is 0.01%. In other words, 100 points of carbon is equal to 1%. The percentage of carbon in steel has a huge input on the strength and characteristics of the steel. For example,

- **Mild (low carbon) steel** has less than 20 points of carbon (0.02%). Mild steel is soft and easily formed but is not very strong. Common usage of low carbon steel is in tables and chairs and vehicle body parts where strength is not an issue.
- **Medium carbon steel** usually has between 25 and 50 points of carbon (0.25% and 0.50%). This type of steel

can be heat treated to create steel that is ductile (flexible) and yet has good strength. This type of steel is usually used in forgings and machined components.

- **High carbon steel** usually has between 60 and 100 points (0.60% and 1.00%) of carbon and is very strong. It is commonly used in vehicle springs and can be hardened.

  CAUTION: Both medium carbon and high carbon steel can be hardened by heating and then cooling, using water or oil to rapidly cool the metal. Therefore, if heating any metal, always allow it to cool slowly to avoid changing the hardness of the steel.

The SAE numbering designation usually includes four numbers:

- The first two numbers indicate the type of alloy which could include several alloy elements.
- The last two numbers designate the points of carbon.

  1xxx = plain carbon steels
  2xxx = nickel steels
  3xxx = nickel-chromium steels
  4xxx = molybdenum steels
  5xxx = chromium steels
  6xxx = chromium-vanadium steels
  7xxx = tungsten-chromium steels
  9xxx = silicon-manganese steels

A commonly used alloy for forged crankshafts is SAE 4340. The analysis of this designation is: 4340 = An alloy that contains 1.82% nickel, 0.5% to 0.8% chromium, and 0.25% molybdenum with 40 points of carbon.

ALUMINUM AND ALUMINUM ALLOYS

Aluminum is a lightweight metal that is used in many automotive applications, including suspension components, engine blocks, and cylinder heads. Aluminum is almost always combined with small quantities of other metals to form an alloy, using copper, manganese, zinc, or silicon. Aluminum and aluminum alloys that are mechanical shaped are called **wrought alloys** and are labeled according to the International Alloy Designation system. The system uses a four-digit number, which identifies the alloying elements, followed by a dash (-) and then a letter identifying the type of heat treatment. This is followed by a number identifying the specific hardness or temper of the finished alloy. A typical example would be 6061-T6. The 6061 is a 6000 series alloy with magnesium and silicon. The "61" further identifies other elements and their percentages. The numbering system for cast aluminum alloy is similar but is designed by standards of the Aluminum Association (AA).

1. What is kinetic energy?
2. How is mechanical advantage used in the braking system?
3. What is the difference between torque and power?
4. How can a burn test help identify the type of plastic used?
5. What is the pH of acids and bases?

CHAPTER QUIZ

1. All of the following are correct statements about braking except:
   a. Kinetic energy must be absorbed by the braking system.
   b. Kinetic energy of a vehicle doubles when the speed doubles.
   c. The heavier the vehicle, the greater the kinetic energy when moving.
   d. If the vehicle weight is doubled, the kinetic energy of a moving vehicle is doubled.

2. The brake pedal assembly uses a mechanical lever to _____.
   a. Increase the driver's force on the brake pedal applied to the master cylinder.
   b. Decrease the distance the brake pedal needs to be depressed by the driver.
   c. Decrease the driver's force on the brake pedal applied to the master cylinder.
   d. Allow for clearance between the brake pedal and the floor when the brakes are applied.

3. Technician A says that work is being performed if a force is being applied, yet the object does not move. Technician B says that torque is a twisting force that may or may not result in motion. Which technician is correct?
   a. Technician A only
   b. Technician B only
   c. Both Technicians A and B
   d. Neither Technician A nor B

4. Two technicians are discussing engine horsepower and torque figures. Technician A says that torque is measured on a dynamometer. Technician B says that horsepower is measured on a dynamometer. Which technician is correct?
   a. Technician A only
   b. Technician B only
   c. Both Technicians A and B
   d. Neither Technician A nor B

5. An example of a lever and mechanical advantage used on a vehicle is the _____.
   a. Radio volume control
   b. Brake pedal
   c. Fuel tank
   d. Battery

6. Two technicians are discussing temperature and heat. Technician A says that temperature is the intensity of the heat source. Technician B says that heat is the amount of heat. Which technician is correct?
   a. Technician A only
   b. Technician B only
   c. Both Technicians A and B
   d. Neither Technician A nor B

7. Heat can move or travel by _____.
   a. Conduction
   b. Convection
   c. Radiation
   d. All of the above

8. Technician A says that zero degrees Celsius is the freezing temperature of water. Technician B says that 100 degrees Celsius is the boiling temperature of water. Which technician is correct?
   a. Technician A only
   b. Technician B only
   c. Both Technicians A and B
   d. Neither Technician A nor B

9. Technician A says that pure (distilled) water has a pH of 7. Technician B says that the pH of acids is less than 7. Which technician is correct?
   a. Technician A only
   b. Technician B only
   c. Both Technicians A and B
   d. Neither Technician A nor B

10. Technician A says that the kinetic energy of a vehicle is proportional to its weight. Technician B says that the kinetic energy of a moving vehicle is directly proportional to its speed. Which technician is correct?
    a. Technician A only
    b. Technician B only
    c. Both Technicians A and B
    d. Neither Technician A nor B

chapter 16

MATH, CHARTS, AND CALCULATIONS

OBJECTIVES: **After studying Chapter 16, the reader will be able to:** • Add and subtract decimal numbers. • Read a chart and graph. • Calculate percentages. • Explain how to work with fractions. • Demonstrate how to multiply and divide. • Discuss ratios. • Calculate fuel economy.

KEY TERMS: Chart 152 • Decimal point 149 • Diagram 153 • Direct drive 151 • Drive gear 151 • Driven gear 151 • Fractions 150 • Gear reduction 151 • Graph 152 • Overdrive 152 • Percentage 149 • Scientific notation 149 • Variable 152

DECIMALS

Decimals are commonly used by service technicians. The placement of the decimal point indicates the value of the number. The naming of decimals includes tenths, hundredths, thousandths, and higher. Decimals are used to represent fractions of a unit by using a dot called a **decimal point** to indicate that the number is a decimal.

TENTHS A decimal with one number to the right of the decimal point indicates an accuracy of 1/10 or 0.1. For example, 0.7 is the same as 7/10 and is pronounced "seven tenths" or "zero point seven." A decimal can also include numbers larger than zero, but has a resolution or accuracy measured in tenths, such as in 16.7.

HUNDREDTH Decimals with two numbers to the right of the decimal point indicate an accuracy to 1/100 or 0.01. For example, 0.47 is pronounced "forty-seven hundredth" or "zero point four seven."

THOUSANDTH A decimal with three numbers to the right of the decimal point indicates an accuracy to 1/1000 or 0.001. For example, 0.867 is pronounced "eight hundred sixty-seven thousandth" or "zero point eight six seven."

ADDING AND SUBTRACTING DECIMALS When adding or subtracting decimals, the decimal point has to be aligned. This ensures that the numbers are placed into the correct position of tenth, hundredth, and thousandth. For example:

$$
\begin{array}{r}
0.147 \\
+\ 0.02 \\
\hline
0.167
\end{array}
$$

Notice that the top number is expressed in thousandths and the lower number is expressed in hundredths. The final figure is also shown in thousandths.

NOTE: **If these numbers were measurements, the first result cannot be more accurate than the least accurate measurement. This means that the final result should be expressed in hundredths instead of thousandths.**

When subtracting or multiplying decimals, keep the decimal points aligned or use a calculator making certain to include the decimal point.

PERCENTAGE

Percentage is the relationship of a value or number out of 100. Using money as an example, three quarters (25 cents each) equals 75 cents ($0.75) or 75% of a dollar ($1.00). Many examples are not that easy, for example, 70 is what percentage of 120? To determine the percentage, divide the first number (70) by the second number (120).

$$70 \div 120 = 0.58$$

To convert this number to a percentage, multiply the number by 100 or move the decimal point two places to the right (58) and then add a percentage symbol to indicate that the number is a percentage (58%).

SCIENTIFIC NOTATION

Very large and very small decimal numbers are frequently expressed using scientific notation. **Scientific notation** is written as a number multiplied by the number of zeros to the right or left of the decimal point. For example, 68,000 could be written as 6.8×10^4, indicating that the number shown has 3 zeros plus the 8 to the right of the decimal point. Small numbers, such as 0.00068, would use a negative sign beside the number over the 10 to represent that the decimal point needs to be moved toward the left (6.8×10^{-4}).

ADDING AND SUBTRACTING

Technicians are often required to add or subtract measurements when working on vehicles. For example, adding and subtracting is needed to select shims (thin pieces of steel) for adjusting valve clearance or differential preload measurements.

For example, if the valve clearance specification is 0.012 in. and the clearance is actually 0.016 in., and the shim that is in place between the camshaft lobe and the valve bucket is 0.080 in. thick, what size (thickness) of shim needs to be installed to achieve the correct valve clearance?

Solution: The shim thickness of 0.080 in. results in a valve clearance of 0.016 in. The specification requires that the shim needs to be thicker to reduce the valve clearance. ● SEE FIGURE 16–1.

To determine the thickness of a shim, the amount of clearance needed to be corrected needs to be calculated. The original clearance is 0.016 in. and the specification is 0.012 in. The difference is determined by subtracting the actual clearance from the specified clearance:

$$0.016 - 0.012 = 0.004 \text{ in.}$$

The result (0.004 in.) then needs to be added to the thickness of the existing shim to determine the thickness of the replacement shim needed to achieve the correct valve clearance.

Existing shim thickness =	0.080 in.
Additional thickness needed =	+ 0.004 in.
Thickness of new shim =	0.084 in.

FIGURE 16–1 Valve clearance allows the metal parts to expand and maintain proper operation, both when the engine is cold or at normal operating temperature. Adjustment is achieved by changing the thickness of the adjusting shim.

FRACTIONS

Fractions, such as 1/2, 1/4, or 5/8 are commonly found in specifications for hose inside diameter measurements. A tape measure or machinists rule can be used to measure the fitting or the original part. Sometimes, fractions need to be converted to decimal units if the replacement parts are offered by that measurement method. When comparing fractions to decimal units, think about the number of cents in a dollar.

1/2 dollar = 50 cents
Quarter = 25 cents
1/10 (dime) = 10 cents
1/20 (nickel) = 5 cents

Other fractions, such as 3/8, 5/8, and 5/16 are harder to determine. If a chart is not available, divide the bottom number, called the denominator into the top number, called the numerator.

3/8 = 3 divided by 8 = 0.375
5/8 = 5 divided by 8 = 0.625
5/16 = 5 divided by 16 = 0.3125

MULTIPLYING AND DIVIDING

Multiplying by a service technician is usually done to determine gear ratios and to determine the total of many of the same items. For example, the final overall gear ratio is determined by multiplying the transmission gear ratio by the final drive ratio and is covered later in this chapter.

Dividing is commonly done when calculating total resistance of many resistances connected in parallel. In this situation, the value of the resistance is divided by the number of equal resistances. For example, if four bulbs with a resistance of 0.4 ohm were connected in parallel, the total resistance would be just 0.1 ohm ($0.4 \div 4 = 0.1$).

MATHEMATICAL FORMULAS

A formula uses letters to represent values or measurements and indicates how these numbers are to be multiplied, divided, added, or subtracted. To use a formula, the technician needs to replace the letters with the actual number and perform the indicated math functions.

For example, a formula used to determine engine speed in revolutions per minute (RPM) and is represented by the following formula:

$$\text{RPM} = \frac{\text{mph} \times \text{gear ratio} \times 336}{\text{tire diameter (inches)}}$$

How Is Metric Fuel Economy Measured?

In the United States fuel economy is expressed in miles per gallon. Outside of the United States, fuel economy is measured in the number of liters of fuel needed to travel 100 kilometers (62 miles), abbreviated L/100 km. This means that as the number increases, the fuel economy decreases. For example:

MPG	L/100 km
5	47.0
10	23.5
15	15.7
20	11.8
25	9.4
30	7.8
35	6.7
40	5.9
45	5.2
50	4.7

In the metric system, the fuel is measured; in the United States, the miles are measured.

This formula is used to determine the speed of the engine compared to the gear ratio and tire size. Sometimes, wheel and tire sizes are changed and knowing this is helpful.

To calculate the engine speed, the actual information needs to be placed into the formula.

Mph = 70 mph
Gear ratio = 2:41:1
Tire diameter = 26 inches

Replacing the terms with the actual numbers results in the following:

$$RPM = \frac{70 \times 2.41 \times 336}{26} = \frac{5668}{26} = 2180 \text{ RPM}$$

FUEL ECONOMY CALCULATOR

To calculate fuel economy in miles per gallons, two factors must be known:

1. How far was the vehicle driven.
2. How many gallons of fuel were needed.

This calculation requires that the fuel tank be filled two times; first at the start of the test and then at the end of the test distance. For example:

STEP 1 Fill the tank until the nozzle clicks off.

> **NOTE: Try to use the same station and pump, if possible, to achieve the most accurate results.**

STEP 2 Drive a reasonable distance. For the example, 220 miles were traveled.

STEP 3 Fill the fuel tank and record the number of gallons used. For this example, exactly 10.0 gallons were needed to refill the tank.

STEP 4 Calculate fuel economy: MPG = Miles driven divided by the number of gallons used.

MPG = 220 divided by 10.0 = 22.0 miles per gallon

GEAR RATIOS

When one gear turns another, the speed that the two gears turn in relation to each other is the gear ratio. Gear ratio is expressed as the number of rotations the **drive gear** must make in order to rotate the **driven gear** through one revolution. To obtain a gear ratio, simply divide the number of teeth on the driven gear by the number of teeth on the drive gear. Gear ratios, which are expressed relative to the number one, fall into three categories:

- Direct drive
- Gear reduction
- Overdrive

DIRECT DRIVE If two meshed gears are the same size and have the same number of teeth, they will turn at the same speed. Since the drive gear turns once for each revolution of the driven gear, the gear ratio is 1:1; this is called a **direct drive.** When a transmission is in direct drive, the engine and transmission turn at the same speed.

GEAR REDUCTION If one gear drives a second gear that has three times the number of teeth, the smaller drive gear must travel three complete revolutions in order to drive the larger gear through one rotation. ● **SEE FIGURE 16–2.** Divide the number of teeth on the driven gear by the number of teeth on the drive gear and you get a 3:1 gear ratio (pronounced three to one). This type of gear arrangement, where driven gear speed is slower than drive gear speed, provides **gear reduction.** Gear reduction may also be called underdrive as drive speed is less than, or under, driven speed. Both terms mean the same thing and use is a matter of preference.

Gear reduction is used for the lower gears in a transmission. First gear in a transmission is called "low" gear because output speed, not gear ratio, is low. Low gears have numerically

24 TEETH

8 TEETH

DRIVE GEAR

DRIVEN GEAR

FIGURE 16–2 The drive gear is attached or is closer to the power source and rotates or drives the driven gear.

24 TEETH

8 TEETH

DRIVEN GEAR

DRIVE GEAR

FIGURE 16–3 If the driven gear is rotating faster than the drive gear, it is called an overdrive ratio.

high gear ratios. That is, a 3:1 gear ratio is a lower gear than those with a 2:1 or 1:1 gear ratio. These three ratios taken in order represent a typical upshift pattern from low gear (3:1), to second gear (2:1), to third gear (1:1).

OVERDRIVE **Overdrive** is the opposite of a gear reduction condition and occurs when a driven gear turns faster than its drive gear. For the gears shown in **FIGURE 16–3,** the driven gear turns three times for each turn of the drive gear. The driven gear is said to overdrive the drive gear. For this example, the gear ratio is 0.33:1. Overdrive ratios of 0.65:1 and 0.70:1 are typical of those used in automotive applications.

NOTE: Ratios always end in 1 with a colon in between. Therefore, the first number is less than 1 if it is an overdrive ratio and greater than 1 if it is a gear reduction ratio.

MAX. POWER = 170.9   MAX TORQUE = 153.0

FIGURE 16–4 A graph showing horsepower and torque. Notice that the curves cross at 5252 RPM or a little bit to the right of the 50, which is expressed as the graph number multiplied by 100. Example is 52 multiplied by 100 equals 5200 RPM. The torque and horsepower curves cross at 5252 RPM because torque is measured by a dynamometer and then horsepower is calculated using a formula which causes both values to be the same at that one engine speed.

GRAPHS, CHARTS, AND DIAGRAMS

GRAPH READING A **graph** is a visual display of information. Graphs are commonly used in the automotive service industry to illustrate trends or specifications along with time or some other variable. A **variable** is a measurement of something that changes, such as engine speed or time. A graph has two variables displayed. One variable changes from left to right on the horizontal axis. This is called the X axis. The other variable is displayed on the vertical axis, called the Y axis.

A graph is created by making a series of dots at various locations and then connecting the dots with a line. ● **SEE FIGURE 16–4.**

INTERPRETING A GRAPH. To interpret a graph, select a point along the horizontal axis (X axis) and then look directly above the point where the line appears. Mark this spot and then look directly to the left along the vertical axis (Y axis) to see what value is represented by the points on the graph.

CHART READING A **chart** is used to represent data, such as numbers or specifications, along with another variable, such as model or year of vehicle. A chart is very useful for showing many different specifications or other facts in an easy-to-read format. ● **SEE FIGURE 16–5** for an example of

RANGE	GEAR	2–4 BAND	REVERSE INPUT CLUTCH	OVERRUN CLUTCH	FORWARD CLUTCH	FORWARD SPRAG CL. ASSEMBLY	3–4 CLUTCH	LO-ROLLER CLUTCH	LO-REV. CLUTCH
PARK-NEUTRAL									
OVERDRIVE	FIRST GEAR				APPLIED	HOLDING		HOLDING	
	SECOND GEAR	APPLIED			APPLIED	HOLDING			
	THIRD GEAR				APPLIED	HOLDING	APPLIED		
	FOURTH GEAR	APPLIED			APPLIED		APPLIED		
DRIVE	FIRST GEAR			APPLIED	APPLIED	HOLDING		HOLDING	
	SECOND GEAR	APPLIED		APPLIED	APPLIED	HOLDING			
	THIRD GEAR			APPLIED	APPLIED	HOLDING	APPLIED		
MANUAL 2ND	FIRST GEAR			APPLIED	APPLIED	HOLDING		HOLDING	
	SECOND GEAR	APPLIED		APPLIED	APPLIED	HOLDING			
MANUAL 1ST	FIRST GEAR			APPLIED		HOLDING		HOLDING	APPLIED
REVERSE	REVERSE		APPLIED						APPLIED

FIGURE 16–5 A typical chart showing what is applied in what gear in an automatic transmission.

a transmission specifications chart, which shows the transmission parts listed along the horizontal axis (X axis) and gear of the automatic transmission along the vertical or Y axis.

INTERPRETING A CHART. A chart can look complicated but if studied, it is easy to interpret. Start by looking along the horizontal or vertical axis for the information, such as the range of the transmission down the left column. Then look to the right to find which device is being used to achieve that transmission drive range.

DIAGRAM READING A **diagram** is a graphic design that explains or shows the arrangement of parts. Diagrams are commonly used in the automotive service industry to show how a component is assembled and in which order the parts are placed together. ● **SEE FIGURE 16–6** for an example.

INTERPRETING A DIAGRAM A diagram usually shows the relationship of many parts. Lines are used to show the centerline of the part and the identity of the part is often shown as a number or letter. A separate chart or area of the diagram needs to be looked at to determine the name of the part. Diagrams are most helpful when disassembling or assembling a component, such as a transmission. For best results, use electronic information and print out the diagram so it can be written on and can be thrown away when the repair has been completed. This process also helps prevent getting grease on the pages of a service manual.

FIGURE 16–6 An exploded view showing how the thermostat is placed in the engine.

REVIEW QUESTIONS

1. What is the formula for determining fuel economy?
2. Why are the torque and horsepower of an engine equal at 5252 RPM?
3. What service operation may require the technician to add and subtract?
4. What service operation may require the technician to multiply or divide?
5. How is fuel economy expressed in the metric system?
6. What math function is needed to calculate the overall gear ratio if the transmission and differential ratios are both known?

CHAPTER QUIZ

1. Ten of 30 vehicles checked during a safety inspection had at least one tire that was under inflated. This represents what percentage of the vehicles?
   a. 25%
   b. 33%
   c. 43%
   d. 67%

2. Which of the following shows the relationship of parts?
   a. Chart
   b. Graph
   c. Diagram
   d. Schematic

3. Add 0.102 in. and 0.080 inch. The answer is _____.
   a. 0.182 inch
   b. 0.1082 inch
   c. 0.0082 inch
   d. 0.8200 inch

4. Which is the largest?
   a. 1/10
   b. .25
   c. .375
   d. 1/50

5. What is 26 out of 87 in percentage?
   a. 33.5%
   b. 11.3%
   c. 29.89%
   d. 61.0%

6. What number is being represented by the scientific notation 6.28×10^3?
   a. 6.28
   b. 628
   c. 6,280
   d. 62,800

7. 3/16 is what number in decimal form?
   a. 0.1875
   b. 1.875
   c. 0.5333
   d. 5.333

8. How is 0.183 pronounced?
   a. One hundred eighty-three thousandth
   b. One thousand eighty-three
   c. Zero dot one hundred and eighty-three hundredths
   d. One tenth and 83 hundredths

9. Metric fuel economy is measured in what units?
   a. Miles per gallon
   b. Miles per kilometer
   c. Liters per 100 kilometers
   d. Kilometers per liter

10. Which is the smallest?
    a. 1/16
    b. .25
    c. 3/8
    d. .33

chapter 17

ELECTRICAL FUNDAMENTALS

OBJECTIVES: **After studying Chapter 17, the reader will be able to:** • Prepare for ASE Electrical/Electronic Systems (A6) certification test content area "A" (General Electrical/Electronic System Diagnosis). • Define electricity. • Explain the units of electrical measurement. • Discuss the relationship among volts, amperes, and ohms. • Explain how magnetism is used in automotive applications.

KEY TERMS: Ammeter 159 • Ampere 159 • Atom 155 • Bound electrons 157 • Conductors 157 • Conventional theory 159 • Coulomb 159 • Electrical potential 160 • Electricity 155 • Electrochemistry 162 • Electromotive force (EMF) 160 • Electron theory 159 • Free electrons 157 • Insulators 158 • Ion 156 • Neutral charge 155 • Ohmmeter 160 • Ohms 160 • Peltier effect 161 • Photoelectricity 161 • Piezoelectricity 162 • Positive temperature coefficient (PTC) 162 • Potentiometer 163 • Resistance 160 • Rheostat 164 • Semiconductor 158 • Static electricity 161 • Thermocouple 161 • Thermoelectricity 161 • Valence ring 157 • Volt 159 • Voltmeter 160 • Watt 161

INTRODUCTION

The electrical system is one of the most important systems in a vehicle today. Every year more and more components and systems use electricity. Those technicians who really know and understand automotive electrical and electronic systems will be in great demand.

Electricity may be difficult for some people to learn for the following reasons.

- It cannot be seen.
- Only the results of electricity can be seen.
- It has to be detected and measured.
- The test results have to be interpreted.

ELECTRICITY

BACKGROUND   Our universe is composed of matter, which is *anything* that has mass and occupies space. All matter is made from slightly over 100 individual components called *elements*. The smallest particle that an element can be broken into and still retain the properties of that element is known as an **atom.** ● **SEE FIGURE 17–1.**

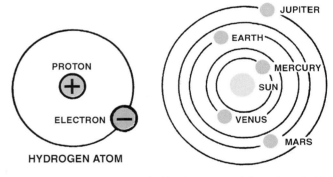

FIGURE 17–1 In an atom (left), electrons orbit protons in the nucleus just as planets orbit the sun in our solar system (right).

DEFINITION   **Electricity** is the movement of electrons from one atom to another. The dense center of each atom is called the nucleus. The nucleus contains:

- *Protons*, which have a positive charge
- *Neutrons*, which are electrically neutral (have no charge)

Electrons surround the nucleus in orbits. Each atom contains an equal number of electrons and protons. The physical aspect of all protons, electrons, and neutrons are the same for all atoms. It is the *number* of electrons and protons in the atom that determines the material and how electricity is conducted. Because the number of negative-charged electrons is balanced with the same number of positive-charged protons, an atom has a **neutral charge** (no charge).

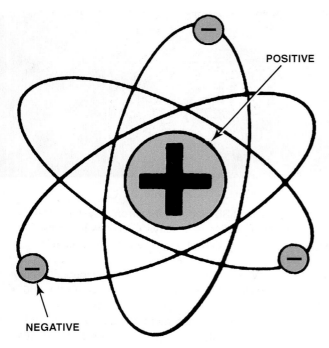

FIGURE 17–2 The nucleus of an atom has a positive (+) charge and the surrounding electrons have a negative (−) charge.

NOTE: As an example of the relative sizes of the parts of an atom, consider that if an atom were magnified so that the nucleus were the size of the period at the end of this sentence, the whole atom would be bigger than a house.

POSITIVE AND NEGATIVE CHARGES
The parts of the atom have different charges. The orbiting electrons are negatively charged, while the protons are positively charged. Positive charges are indicated by the "plus" sign (+), and negative charges by the "minus" sign (−), as shown in ● FIGURE 17–2.

These same + and − signs are used to identify parts of an electrical circuit. Neutrons have no charge at all. They are neutral. In a normal, or balanced, atom, the number of negative particles equals the number of positive particles. That is, there are as many electrons as there are protons. ● SEE FIGURE 17–3.

MAGNETS AND ELECTRICAL CHARGES
An ordinary magnet has two ends, or poles. One end is called the south pole, and the other is called the north pole. If two magnets are brought close to each other with like poles together (south to south or north to north), the magnets will push each other apart, because like poles repel each other. If the opposite poles of the magnets are brought close to each other, south to north, the magnets will snap together, because unlike poles attract each other.

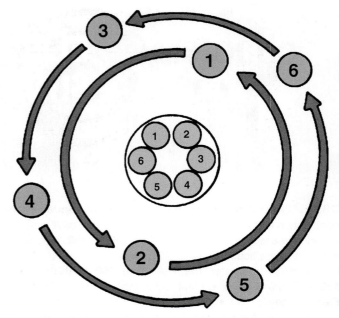

FIGURE 17–3 This figure shows a balanced atom. The number of electrons is the same as the number of protons in the nucleus.

FIGURE 17–4 Unlike charges attract and like charges repel.

The positive and negative charges within an atom are like the north and south poles of a magnet. Charges that are alike will repel each other, similar to the poles of a magnet. ● SEE FIGURE 17–4.

That is why the negative electrons continue to orbit around the positive protons. They are attracted and held by the opposite charge of the protons. The electrons keep moving in orbit because they repel each other.

IONS
When an atom loses any electrons, it becomes unbalanced. It will have more protons than electrons, and therefore will have a positive charge. If it gains more electrons than protons, the atom will be negatively charged. When an atom is not balanced, it becomes a charged particle called an **ion**. Ions try to regain their balance of equal protons and electrons by exchanging electrons with neighboring atoms. The flow of electrons during the "equalization" process is defined as the flow of electricity. ● SEE FIGURE 17–5.

ELECTRON SHELLS
Electrons orbit around the nucleus in definite paths. These paths form shells, like concentric rings, around the nucleus. Only a specific number of electrons can

FIGURE 17–5 An unbalanced, positively charged atom (ion) will attract electrons from neighboring atoms.

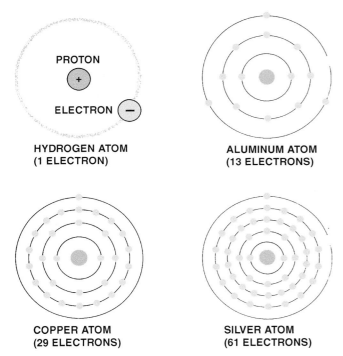

PROTON
(+)

ELECTRON (−)

HYDROGEN ATOM
(1 ELECTRON)

ALUMINUM ATOM
(13 ELECTRONS)

COPPER ATOM
(29 ELECTRONS)

SILVER ATOM
(61 ELECTRONS)

FIGURE 17–6 The hydrogen atom is the simplest atom, with only one proton, one neutron, and one electron. More complex elements contain higher numbers of protons, neutrons, and electrons.

orbit within each shell. If there are too many electrons for the first and closest shell to the nucleus, the others will orbit in additional shells until all electrons have an orbit within a shell. There can be as many as seven shells around a single nucleus. ● SEE FIGURE 17–6.

FREE AND BOUND ELECTRONS The outermost electron shell or ring, called the **valence ring**, is the most important part of understanding electricity. The number of electrons in this outer ring determines the valence of the atom, and indicates its capacity to combine with other atoms.

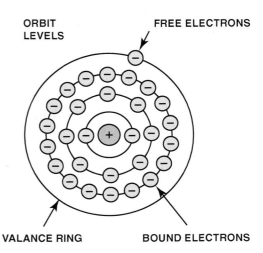

ORBIT LEVELS

FREE ELECTRONS

VALANCE RING

BOUND ELECTRONS

FIGURE 17–7 As the number of electrons increases, they occupy increasing energy levels that are farther from the center of the atom.

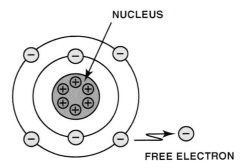

NUCLEUS

FREE ELECTRON

FIGURE 17–8 Electrons in the outer orbit, or shell, can often be drawn away from the atom and become free electrons.

If the valence ring of an atom has three or fewer electrons in it, the ring has room for more. The electrons there are held very loosely, and it is easy for a drifting electron to join the valence ring and push another electron away. These loosely held electrons are called **free electrons.** When the valence ring has five or more electrons in it, it is fairly full. The electrons are held tightly, and it is hard for a drifting electron to push its way into the valence ring. These tightly held electrons are called **bound electrons**. ● SEE FIGURES 17–7 AND 17–8.

The movement of these drifting electrons is called current. Current can be small, with only a few electrons moving, or it can be large, with a tremendous number of electrons moving. Electric current is the controlled, directed movement of electrons from atom to atom within a conductor.

CONDUCTORS **Conductors** are materials with fewer than four electrons in their atom's outer orbit. ● SEE FIGURE 17–9.

Copper is an excellent conductor because it has only one electron in its outer orbit. This orbit is far enough away from the

CONDUCTORS

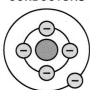

FIGURE 17-9 A conductor is any element that has one to three electrons in its outer orbit.

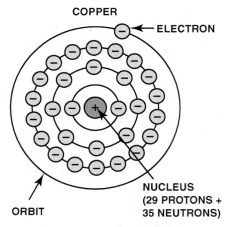

COPPER

← ELECTRON

NUCLEUS
(29 PROTONS +
35 NEUTRONS)

ORBIT

FIGURE 17-10 Copper is an excellent conductor of electricity because it has just one electron in its outer orbit, making it easy to be knocked out of its orbit and flow to other nearby atoms. This causes electron flow, which is the definition of electricity.

nucleus of the copper atom that the pull or force holding the outermost electron in orbit is relatively weak. ● **SEE FIGURE 17-10.**

Copper is the conductor most used in vehicles because the price of copper is reasonable compared to the relative cost of other conductors with similar properties. Examples of other commonly used conductors include:

- Gold
- Silver
- Aluminum
- Steel
- Cast iron

INSULATORS Some materials hold their electrons very tightly; therefore, electrons do not move through them very well. These materials are called insulators. **Insulators** are materials with more than four electrons in their atom's outer orbit. Because they have more than four electrons in their outer orbit, it becomes easier for these materials to acquire (gain) electrons than to release electrons. ● **SEE FIGURE 17-11.**

Examples of insulators include:

- Rubber
- Plastic
- Nylon

INSULATORS

FIGURE 17-11 Insulators are elements with five to eight electrons in the outer orbit.

SEMICONDUCTORS

FIGURE 17-12 Semiconductor elements contain exactly four electrons in the outer orbit.

? FREQUENTLY ASKED QUESTION

Is Water a Conductor?

Pure water is an insulator; however, if anything is in the water, such as salt or dirt, then the water becomes conductive. Because it is difficult to keep it from becoming contaminated, water is usually thought of as being capable of conducting electricity, especially high-voltage household 110 or 220 volt outlets.

- Porcelain
- Ceramic
- Fiberglass

Examples of insulators include plastics, wood, glass, rubber, ceramics (spark plugs), and varnish for covering (insulating) copper wires in alternators and starters.

SEMICONDUCTORS Materials with exactly four electrons in their outer orbit are neither conductors nor insulators, but are called **semiconductors.** Semiconductors can be either an insulator or a conductor in different design applications. ● **SEE FIGURE 17-12.**

Examples of semiconductors include:

- Silicon
- Germanium
- Carbon

Semiconductors are used mostly in transistors, computers, and other electronic devices.

HOW ELECTRONS MOVE THROUGH A CONDUCTOR

CURRENT FLOW The following events occur if a source of power, such as a battery, is connected to the ends of a conductor—a positive charge (lack of electrons) is placed on one end of the conductor and a negative charge is placed on the opposite end of the conductor. For current to flow, there *must* be an imbalance of excess electrons at one end of the circuit and a deficiency of electrons at the opposite end of the circuit.

- The negative charge will repel the free electrons from the atoms of the conductor, whereas the positive charge on the opposite end of the conductor will attract electrons.

- As a result of this attraction of opposite charges and repulsion of like charges, electrons will flow through the conductor. ● **SEE FIGURE 17–13.**

CONVENTIONAL THEORY VERSUS ELECTRON THEORY

- **Conventional theory.** It was once thought that electricity had only one charge and moved from positive to negative. This theory of the flow of electricity through a conductor is called the **conventional theory** of current flow. ● **SEE FIGURE 17–14.**

FIGURE 17–13 Current electricity is the movement of electrons through a conductor.

FIGURE 17–14 Conventional theory states that current flows through a circuit from positive (+) to negative (−). Automotive electricity uses the conventional theory in all electrical diagrams and schematics.

- **Electron theory.** The discovery of the electron and its negative charge led to the **electron theory,** which states that there is electron flow from negative to positive. Most automotive applications use the conventional theory. This book will use the conventional theory (positive to negative) unless stated otherwise.

UNITS OF ELECTRICITY

Electricity is measured using meters or other test equipment. The three fundamentals of electricity-related units include the ampere, volt, and ohm.

AMPERES The **ampere** is the unit used throughout the world to measure current flow. When 6.28 billion billion electrons (the name for this large number of electrons is a **coulomb**) move past a certain point in 1 second, this represents 1 ampere of current. ● **SEE FIGURE 17–15.**

The ampere is the electrical unit for the amount of electron flow, just as "gallons per minute" is the unit that can be used to measure the quantity of water flow. It is named for the French electrician, Andrè Marie Ampére (1775–1836). The conventional abbreviations and measurement for amperes are as follows:

1. The ampere is the unit of measurement for the amount of current flow.

2. A and amps are acceptable abbreviations for *amperes*.

3. The capital letter *I*, for *intensity*, is used in mathematical calculations to represent amperes.

4. Amperes do the actual work in the circuit. It is the actual movement of the electrons through a light bulb or motor that actually makes the electrical device work. Without amperage through a device it will not work at all.

5. Amperes are measured by an **ammeter** (not ampmeter). ● **SEE FIGURE 17–16.**

VOLTS The **volt** is the unit of measurement for electrical pressure. It is named for an Italian physicist, Alessandro Volta (1745–1827). The comparable unit using water pressure as an

FIGURE 17–15 One ampere is the movement of 1 coulomb (6.28 billion billion electrons) past a point in 1 second.

FIGURE 17–16 An ammeter is installed in the path of the electrons similar to a water meter used to measure the flow of water in gallons per minute. The ammeter displays current flow in amperes.

FIGURE 17–17 Voltage is the electrical pressure that causes the electrons to flow through a conductor.

example would be pounds per square inch (psi). It is possible to have very high pressures (volts) and low water flow (amperes). It is also possible to have high water flow (amperes) and low pressures (volts). Voltage is also called **electrical potential**, because if there is voltage present in a conductor, there is a potential (possibility) for current flow. This electrical pressure is a result of the following:

- Excess electrons remain at one end of the wire or circuit.

- There is a lack of electrons at the other end of the wire or circuit.

- The natural effect is to equalize this imbalance, creating a pressure to allow the movement of electrons through a conductor.

- It is possible to have pressure (volts) without any flow (amperes). For example, a fully charged 12 volt battery sitting on a workbench has 12 volts of pressure potential, but because there is not a conductor (circuit) connected between the positive and negative posts of the battery, there is no flow (amperes). Current will only flow when there is pressure and a circuit for the electrons to flow in order to "equalize" to a balanced state.

Voltage does *not* flow through conductors, but voltage does cause current (in amperes) to flow through conductors. ● **SEE FIGURE 17–17.**

The conventional abbreviations and measurement for voltage are as follows:

1. The volt is the unit of measurement for the amount of electrical pressure.

2. **Electromotive force**, abbreviated **EMF**, is another way of indicating voltage.

3. *V* is the generally accepted abbreviation for *volts*.

4. The symbol used in calculations is *E*, for *electromotive force*.

5. Volts are measured by a **voltmeter.** ● **SEE FIGURE 17–18.**

OHMS **Resistance** to the flow of current through a conductor is measured in units called **ohms**, named after the German physicist, George Simon Ohm (1787–1854). The resistance to the flow of free electrons through a conductor results from the countless collisions the electrons cause within the atoms of the conductor. ● **SEE FIGURE 17–19.**

The conventional abbreviations and measurement for resistance are as follows:

1. The ohm is the unit of measurement for electrical resistance.

2. The symbol for ohms is Ω (Greek capital letter omega), the last letter of the Greek alphabet.

3. The symbol used in calculations is *R*, for *resistance*.

4. Ohms are measured by an **ohmmeter**.

5. Resistance to electron flow depends on the material used as a conductor.

FIGURE 17–18 This digital multimeter set to read DC volts is being used to test the voltage of a vehicle battery. Most multimeters can also measure resistance (ohms) and current flow (amperes).

FIGURE 17–19 Resistance to the flow of electrons through a conductor is measured in ohms.

FIGURE 17–20 A display at the Henry Ford Museum in Dearborn, Michigan, which includes a hand-cranked generator and a series of light bulbs. This figure shows a young man attempting to light as many bulbs as possible. The crank gets harder to turn as more bulbs light because it requires more power to produce the necessary watts of electricity.

WATTS A **watt** is the electrical unit for *power,* the capacity to do work. It is named after a Scottish inventor, James Watt (1736–1819). The symbol for power is *P*. Electrical power is calculated as amperes times volts:

$$P \text{ (power)} = I \text{ (amperes)} \times E \text{ (volts)}$$

The formula can also be used to calculate the amperage if the wattage and the voltage are known. For example, a 100 watt light bulb powered by 120 volts AC in the shop requires how many amperes?

A (amperes) = P (watts) divided by E (volts)

A = 0.83 amperes

● **SEE FIGURE 17–20.**

SOURCES OF ELECTRICITY

FRICTION When certain different materials are rubbed together, the friction causes electrons to be transformed from one to the other. Both materials become electrically charged. These charges are not in motion, but stay on the surface where they were deposited. Because the charges are stationary, or static, this type of voltage is called **static electricity.** Walking across a carpeted floor creates a buildup of a static charge in your body which is an insulator and then the charge is discharged when you touch a metal conductor. Vehicle tires rolling on pavement often create static electricity that interferes with radio reception.

FIGURE 17–21 Electron flow is produced by heating the connection of two different metals.

HEAT When pieces of two different metals are joined together at both ends and one junction is heated, current passes through the metals. The current is very small, only millionths of an ampere, but this is enough to use in a temperature-measuring device called a **thermocouple.** ● **SEE FIGURE 17–21.**

Some engine temperature sensors operate in this manner. This form of voltage is called **thermoelectricity**.

Thermoelectricity was discovered and has been known for over a century. In 1823, a German physicist, Thomas Johann Seebeck, discovered that a voltage was developed in a loop containing two dissimilar metals, provided the two junctions were maintained at different temperatures. A decade later, a French scientist, Jean Charles Athanase Peltier, found that electrons moving through a solid can carry heat from one side of the material to the other side. This effect is called the **Peltier effect**. A Peltier effect device is often used in portable coolers to keep food items cool if the current flows in one direction and keep items warm if the current flows in reverse.

LIGHT In 1839, Edmond Becquerel noticed that by shining a beam of sunlight over two different liquids, he could develop an electric current. When certain metals are exposed to light, some of the light energy is transferred to the free electrons of the metal. This excess energy breaks the electrons loose from the surface of the metal. They can then be collected and made to flow in a conductor. ● **SEE FIGURE 17–22.**

This **photoelectricity** is widely used in light-measuring devices such as photographic exposure meters and automatic headlamp dimmers.

PRESSURE The first experimental demonstration of a connection between the generation of a voltage due to pressure applied to a crystal was published in 1880 by Pierre and Jacques Curie. Their experiment consisted of voltage being produced when prepared crystals, such as quartz, topaz, and Rochelle salt, had a force applied. ● **SEE FIGURE 17–23.**

FIGURE 17–22 Electron flow is produced by light striking a light-sensitive material.

FIGURE 17–23 Electron flow is produced by pressure on certain crystals.

This current is used in crystal microphones, underwater hydrophones, and certain stethoscopes. The voltage created is called **piezoelectricity**. A gas grille igniter uses the principle of piezoelectricity to produce a spark, and knock sensor (KS) use piezoelectricity to create a voltage signal for use as an input as an engine computer input signal.

CHEMICAL   Two different materials (usually metals) placed in a conducting and reactive chemical solution create a difference in potential, or voltage, between them. This principle is called **electrochemistry** and is the basis of the automotive battery.

MAGNETISM   Electricity can be produced if a conductor is moved through a magnetic field or a moving magnetic field is moved near a conductor. This is the principle of how many automotive devices work, including:

- Starter motor
- Alternator
- Ignition coils
- Solenoids and relays

1	Silver
2	Copper
3	Gold
4	Aluminum
5	Tungsten
6	Zinc
7	Brass (copper and zinc)
8	Platinum
9	Iron
10	Nickel
11	Tin
12	Steel
13	Lead

CHART 17–1

Conductor ratings (starting with the best).

CONDUCTORS AND RESISTANCE

All conductors have some resistance to current flow. The following are principles of conductors and their resistance.

- **If the conductor length is doubled, its resistance doubles.** This is the reason why battery cables are designed to be as short as possible.

- **If the conductor diameter is increased, its resistance is reduced.** This is the reason starter motor cables are larger in diameter than other wiring in the vehicle.

- **As the temperature increases, the resistance of the conductor also increases.** This is the reason for installing heat shields on some starter motors. The heat shield helps to protect the conductors (copper wiring inside the starter) from excessive engine heat and so reduces the resistance of starter circuits. Because a conductor increases in resistance with increased temperature, the conductor is called a **positive temperature coefficient (PTC)** resistor.

- **Materials used in the conductor have an impact on its resistance.** Silver has the lowest resistance of any conductor, but is expensive. Copper is the next lowest in resistance and is reasonably priced. ● **SEE CHART 17–1** for a comparison of materials.

FREQUENTLY ASKED QUESTION

Why Is Gold Used if Copper Has Lower Resistance?

Copper is used for most automotive electrical components and wiring because it has low resistance and is reasonably priced. Gold is used in airbag connections and sensors because it does not corrode. Gold can be buried for hundreds of years and when dug up it is just as shiny as ever.

RESISTORS

FIXED RESISTORS Resistance is the opposition to current flow. Resistors represent an electrical load, or resistance, to current flow. Most electrical and electronic devices use resistors of specific values to limit and control the flow of current. Resistors can be made from carbon or from other materials that restrict the flow of electricity and are available in various sizes and resistance values. Most resistors have a series of painted color bands around them. These color bands are coded to indicate the degree of resistance. ● **SEE FIGURES 17–24 AND 17–25.**

VARIABLE RESISTORS Two basic types of mechanically operated variable resistors are used in automotive applications.

- A **potentiometer** is a three-terminal variable resistor where a wiper contact provides a variable voltage output. ● **SEE FIGURE 17–26.** Potentiometers are most commonly used as throttle position (TP) sensors on computer-equipped engines. A potentiometer is also used to control audio volume, bass, treble, balance, and fade.

FIRST AND SECOND BAND COLORS REPRESENT NUMBERS

THIRD BAND COLOR MEANS NUMBER OF ZEROS

FOURTH BAND REPRESENTS TOLERANCE (ACCURACY)

BLACK = 0
BROWN = 1
RED = 2
ORANGE = 3
YELLOW = 4
GREEN = 5
BLUE = 6
VIOLET = 7
GRAY = 8
WHITE = 9

FOURTH BAND TOLERANCE CODE
NO FOURTH BAND = ±20%
SILVER = ±10%
* GOLD = ±5%
RED = ±2%
BROWN = ±1%

* GOLD IS THE MOST COMMONLY AVAILABLE RESISTOR TOLERANCE.

FIGURE 17–24 This figure shows a resistor color-code interpretation.

EXAMPLES:

470 Ω
GOLD (IF 5%)
YELLOW, VIOLET, BROWN (1 ZERO)
(4)   (7)

3900 Ω
GOLD (IF 5%)
ORANGE, WHITE, RED (2 ZEROS)
(3)   (9)

FIGURE 17–25 A typical carbon resistor.

B+ REFERENCE VOLTAGE

SIGNAL VOLTAGE (VARIABLE WITH POSITION OF MOVABLE CONTACT)

GROUND (0 VOLT)

MOVABLE CONTACT

FIGURE 17–26 A three-wire variable resistor is called a potentiometer.

■ Another type of mechanically operated variable resistor is the **rheostat.** A rheostat is a *two*-terminal unit in which all of the current flows through the movable arm. ● **SEE FIGURE 17-27.** A rheostat is commonly used for a dash light dimmer control.

B+

OUTPUT TERMINAL

MOVABLE CONTACT

FIGURE 17-27 A two-wire variable resistor is called a rheostat.

SUMMARY

1. Electricity is the movement of electrons from one atom to another.
2. In order for current to flow in a circuit or wire, there must be an excess of electrons at one end and a deficiency of electrons at the other end.
3. Automotive electricity uses the conventional theory that electricity flows from positive to negative.
4. The ampere is the measure of the amount of current flow.
5. Voltage is the unit of electrical pressure.
6. The ohm is the unit of electrical resistance.
7. Sources of electricity include friction, heat, light, pressure, and chemical.

REVIEW QUESTIONS

1. What is electricity?
2. What are the ampere, volt, and ohm?
3. What are three examples of conductors and three examples of insulators?
4. What are the four sources of electricity?

CHAPTER QUIZ

1. An electrical conductor is an element with _____ electrons in its outer orbit.
   a. Less than 2
   b. Less than 4
   c. Exactly 4
   d. More than 4

2. Like charges _____.
   a. Attract
   b. Repel
   c. Neutralize each other
   d. Add

3. Carbon and silicon are examples of _____.
   a. Semiconductors
   b. Insulators
   c. Conductors
   d. Photoelectric materials

4. Which unit of electricity does the work in a circuit?
   a. Volt
   b. Ampere
   c. Ohm
   d. Coulomb

5. As temperature increases, _____.
   a. The resistance of a conductor decreases
   b. The resistance of a conductor increases
   c. The resistance of a conductor remains the same
   d. The voltage of the conductor decreases

6. The _____ is a unit of electrical pressure.
   a. Coulomb
   b. Volt
   c. Ampere
   d. Ohm

7. Technician A says that a two-wire variable resistor is called a rheostat. Technician B says that a three-wire variable resistor is called a potentiometer. Which technician is correct?
   a. Technician A only
   b. Technician B only
   c. Both Technicians A and B
   d. Neither Technician A nor B

8. Creating electricity by exerting a force on a crystal is called _____.
   a. Electrochemistry
   b. Piezoelectricity
   c. Thermoelectricity
   d. Photoelectricity

9. The fact that a voltage can be created by exerting force on a crystal is used in which type of sensor?
   a. Throttle position (TP)
   b. Manifold absolute pressure (MAP)
   c. Barometric pressure (BARO)
   d. Knock sensor (KS)

10. A potentiometer, a three-wire variable resistance, is used in which type of sensor?
    a. Throttle position (TP)
    b. Manifold absolute pressure (MAP)
    c. Barometric pressure (BARO)
    d. Knock sensor (KS)Lifting and Hoisting

chapter 18
ELECTRICAL CIRCUITS AND OHM'S LAW

OBJECTIVES: After studying Chapter 18, the reader will be able to: • Prepare for ASE Electrical/Electronic Systems (A6) certification test content area "A" (General Electrical/Electronic Systems Diagnosis). • Explain Ohm's law. • Identify the parts of a complete circuit. • Explain Watt's law. • Describe the characteristics of an open, a short-to-ground, and a short-to-voltage.

KEY TERMS: • Circuit 165 • Complete circuit 165 • Continuity 165 • Electrical load 165 • Grounded 167 • High resistance 168 • Load 165 • Ohm's law 168 • Open circuit 166 • Power path 165 • Power source 165 • Protection 165 • Return path (ground) 165 • Shorted 166 • Short-to-ground 167 • Short-to-voltage 166 • Watt 169 • Watt's law 169

CIRCUITS

DEFINITION A **circuit** is a complete path that electrons travel from a power source (such as a battery) through a **load** such as a light bulb and back to the power source. It is called a *circuit* because the current must start and finish at the same place (power source).

For *any* electrical circuit to work at all, it must be continuous from the battery (power), through all the wires and components, and back to the battery (ground). A circuit that is continuous throughout is said to have **continuity.**

PARTS OF A COMPLETE CIRCUIT Every **complete circuit** contains the following parts. ● **SEE FIGURE 18–1.**

1. A **power source,** such as a vehicle's battery

2. **Protection** from harmful overloads (excessive current flow) (Fuses, circuit breakers, and fusible links are examples of electrical circuit protection devices.)

3. The **power path** for the current to flow through from the power source to the resistance (This path from a power source to the load—a light bulb in this example—is usually an insulated copper wire.)

4. The **electrical load** or resistance which converts electrical energy into heat, light, or motion

5. A **return path (ground)** for the electrical current from the load back to the power source so that there is a *complete* circuit (This return, or ground, path is usually the metal body, frame, ground wires, and engine block of the vehicle. ● **SEE FIGURE 18–2.**)

FIGURE 18–1 All complete circuits must have a power source, a power path, protection (fuse), an electrical load (light bulb in this case), and a return path back to the power source.

FIGURE 18–2 The return path back to the battery can be any electrical conductor, such as a copper wire or the metal frame or body of the vehicle.

FIGURE 18–3 An electrical switch opens the circuit and no current flows. The switch could also be on the return (ground) path wire.

FIGURE 18–4 Examples of common causes of open circuits. Some of these causes are often difficult to find.

6. Switches and controls that turn the circuit on and off (● **SEE FIGURE 18–3.**)

CIRCUIT FAULT TYPES

OPEN CIRCUITS An **open circuit** is any circuit that is *not* complete, or that lacks continuity, such as a broken wire. ● **SEE FIGURE 18–4.**

Open circuits have the following features.

1. *No current at all* will flow through an open circuit.
2. An open circuit may be created by a break in the circuit or by a switch that opens (turns off) the circuit and prevents the flow of current.

FIGURE 18–5 A short circuit permits electrical current to bypass some or all of the resistance in the circuit.

 TECH TIP

"Open" Is a Four-Letter Word

An open in a circuit breaks the path of current flow. The open can be any break in the power side, load, or ground side of a circuit. A switch is often used to close and open a circuit to turn it on and off. Just remember,

Open = no current flow
Closed = current flow

Trying to locate an open circuit in a vehicle is often difficult and may cause the technician to use other four-letter words, such as "HELP"!

3. In any circuit containing a power load and ground, an opening anywhere in the circuit will cause the circuit not to work.
4. A light switch in a home and the headlight switch in a vehicle are examples of devices that open a circuit to control its operation.
5. A blown (open) fuse occurs (caused by another fault in the circuit), but the fuse stopped (opened the circuit) to prevent any harm to the component or the wiring as a result of the fault.

SHORT-TO-VOLTAGE *If a wire (conductor) or component is shorted to voltage,* it is commonly referred to as being **shorted.** A **short-to-voltage** occurs when the power side of one circuit is electrically connected to the power side of another circuit. ● **SEE FIGURE 18–5.**

FIGURE 18–6 A fuse or circuit breaker opens the circuit to prevent possible overheating damage in the event of a short circuit.

 REAL WORLD FIX

The Short-to-Voltage Story

A technician was working on a Chevrolet pickup truck with the following unusual electrical problems.

1. When the brake pedal was depressed, the dash light and the side marker lights would light.
2. The turn signals caused all lights to blink and the fuel gauge needle to bounce up and down.
3. When the brake lights were on, the front parking lights also came on.

   The technician tested all fuses using a conventional test light and found them to be okay. All body-to-engine block ground wires were clean and tight. All bulbs were of the correct trade number as specified in the owner's manual.

NOTE: Using a single-filament bulb (such as a #1156) in the place of a dual-filament bulb (such as a #1157) could also cause many of these same problems.

Because most of the trouble occurred when the brake pedal was depressed, the technician decided to trace all the wires in the brake light circuit. The technician discovered the problem near the exhaust system. A small hole in the tailpipe (after the muffler) directed hot exhaust gases to the wiring harness containing all of the wires for circuits at the rear of the truck. The heat had melted the insulation and caused most of the wires to touch. Whenever one circuit was activated (such as when the brake pedal was applied), the current had a complete path to several other circuits. A fuse did not blow because there was enough resistance in the circuits being energized, so the current (in amperes) was too low to blow any fuses.

A short circuit has the following features.

1. It is a complete circuit in which the current usually bypasses *some* or *all* of the resistance in the circuit.
2. It involves the power side of the circuit.
3. It involves a copper-to-copper connection (two power-side wires touching together).
4. It is also called a *short-to-voltage*.
5. It usually affects more than one circuit. In this case if one circuit is electrically connected to another circuit, one of the circuits may operate when it is not supposed to because it is being supplied power from another circuit.
6. It *may* or *may not* blow a fuse. ● SEE FIGURE 18–6.

SHORT-TO-GROUND A **short-to-ground** is a type of short circuit that occurs when the current bypasses part of the normal circuit and flows directly to ground. A short-to-ground has the following features.

1. Because the ground return circuit is metal (vehicle frame, engine, or body), it is often identified as having current flowing from copper to steel.
2. It occurs any place where a power path wire accidentally touches a return path wire or conductor. ● SEE FIGURE 18–7.
3. A defective component or circuit that is shorted to ground is commonly called **grounded.**
4. A short-to-ground almost always results in a blown fuse, damaged connectors, or melted wires.

FIGURE 18–7 A short-to-ground affects the power side of the circuit. Current flows directly to the ground return, bypassing some or all of the electrical loads in the circuit. There is no current in the circuit past the short.

WATER HAS 12 FEET OF POTENTIAL ENERGY

WATER FLOW IS CONSTANT, WATER (AMPERES) DOES THE WORK WHILE THE PRESSURE (VOLTAGE) IS DROPPED TO ZERO

12 FEET

0 FEET

WATER HAS NO (0 FEET) POTENTIAL ENERGY

POND

FIGURE 18–8 Electrical flow through a circuit is similar to water flowing over a waterwheel. The more the water (amperes in electricity), the greater the amount of work (waterwheel). The amount of water remains constant, yet the pressure (voltage in electricity) drops as the current flows through the circuit.

 TECH TIP

Think of a Waterwheel

A beginner technician cleaned the positive terminal of the battery when the starter was cranking the engine slowly. When questioned by the shop foreman as to why only the positive post had been cleaned, the technician responded that the negative terminal was "only a ground." The foreman reminded the technician that the current, in amperes, is constant throughout a series circuit (such as the cranking motor circuit). If 200 amperes leave the positive post of the battery, then 200 amperes must return to the battery through the negative post.

The technician could not understand how electricity can do work (crank an engine), yet return the same amount of current, in amperes, as left the battery. The shop foreman explained that even though the current is constant throughout the circuit, the voltage (electrical pressure or potential) drops to zero in the circuit. To explain further, the shop foreman drew a waterwheel. ● **SEE FIGURE 18–8.**

As water drops from a higher level to a lower level, high potential energy (or voltage) is used to turn the waterwheel and results in low potential energy (or lower voltage). The same amount of water (or amperes) reaches the pond under the waterwheel as started the fall above the waterwheel. As current (amperes) flows through a conductor, it performs work in the circuit (turns the waterwheel) while its voltage (potential) drops.

HIGH RESISTANCE **High resistance** can be caused by any of the following:

- Corroded connections or sockets
- Loose terminals in a connector
- Loose ground connections

If there is high resistance anywhere in a circuit, it may cause the following problems.

1. Slow operation of a motor-driven unit, such as the windshield wipers or blower motor
2. Dim lights
3. "Clicking" of relays or solenoids
4. No operation of a circuit or electrical component

OHM'S LAW

DEFINITION The German physicist, George Simon Ohm, established that electric pressure (EMF) in volts, electrical resistance in ohms, and the amount of current in amperes flowing through any circuit are all related. **Ohm's law** states:

It requires 1 volt to push 1 ampere through 1 ohm of resistance.

This means that if the voltage is doubled, then the number of amperes of current flowing through a circuit will also double if the resistance of the circuit remains the same.

FORMULAS Ohm's law can also be stated as a simple formula used to calculate one value of an electrical circuit if the other two are known. ● **SEE FIGURE 18–9.**

$$I = \frac{E}{R}$$

where

I = Current in amperes (A)

E = Electromotive force (EMF) in volts (V)

R = Resistance in ohms (Ω)

1. Ohm's law can determine the resistance if the volts and amperes are known: $R = \dfrac{E}{I}$
2. Ohm's law can determine the *voltage* if the resistance (ohms) and amperes are known: $E = I \times R$
3. Ohm's law can determine the amperes if the resistance and voltage are known: $I = \dfrac{E}{R}$

NOTE: Before applying Ohm's law, be sure that each unit of electricity is converted into base units. For ex-

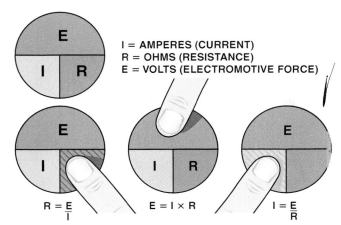

FIGURE 18–9 To calculate one unit of electricity when the other two are known, simply use your finger and cover the unit you do not know. For example, if both voltage (E) and resistance (R) are known, cover the letter *I* (amperes). Notice that the letter *E* is above the letter *R,* so divide the resistor's value into the voltage to determine the current in the circuit.

VOLTAGE	RESISTANCE	AMPERAGE
Up	Down	Up
Up	Same	Up
Up	Up	Same
Same	Down	Up
Same	Same	Same
Same	Up	Down
Down	Up	Down
Down	Same	Down

CHART 18-1

Ohm's law relationship with the three units of electricity.

ample, 10 KΩ should be converted to 10,000 ohms and 10 mA should be converted into 0.010 A.

● **SEE CHART 18-1.**

OHM'S LAW APPLIED TO SIMPLE CIRCUITS If a battery with 12 volts is connected to a resistor of 4 ohms, as shown in ● **FIGURE 18–10,** how many amperes will flow through the circuit?

Using Ohm's law, we can calculate the number of amperes that will flow through the wires and the resistor. Remember, if two factors are known (volts and ohms in this example), the remaining factor (amperes) can be calculated using Ohm's law.

$$I = \frac{E}{R} = \frac{12\,V}{4}\,A$$

FIGURE 18–10 This closed circuit includes a power source, power-side wire, circuit protection (fuse), resistance (bulb), and return path wire. In this circuit, if the battery has 12 volts and the electrical load has 4 ohms, then the current through the circuit is 3 amperes.

The values for the voltage (12) and the resistance (4) were substituted for the variables E and R, and I is thus 3 amperes

$$\left(\frac{12}{4} = 3\right)$$

If we want to connect a resistor to a 12 volt battery, we now know that this simple circuit requires 3 amperes to operate. This may help us for two reasons.

1. We can now determine the wire diameter that we will need based on the number of amperes flowing through the circuit.

2. The correct fuse rating can be selected to protect the circuit.

WATT'S LAW

BACKGROUND James Watt (1736–1819), a Scottish inventor, first determined the power of a typical horse while measuring the amount of coal being lifted out of a mine. The power of one horse was determined to be 33,000 foot-pounds per minute. Electricity can also be expressed in a unit of power called a watt and the relationship is known as **Watt's law,** which states:

A watt is a unit of electrical power represented by a current of 1 ampere through a circuit with a potential difference of 1 volt.

FORMULAS A **watt** is a unit of electrical power represented by a current of 1 ampere through a circuit with a potential difference of 1 volt.

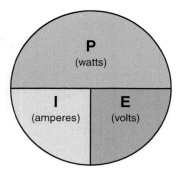

FIGURE 18–11 To calculate one unit when the other two are known, simply cover the unknown unit to see what unit needs to be divided or multiplied to arrive at the solution.

The symbol for a watt is the capital letter *W*. The formula for watts is:

$$W = I \times E$$

Another way to express this formula is to use the letter *P* to represent the unit of power. The formula then becomes:

$$P = I \times E$$

HINT: An easy way to remember this equation is that it spells "pie."

Engine power is commonly rated in watts or kilowatts (1,000 watts equal 1 kilowatt), because 1 horsepower is equal to 746 watts. For example, a 200 horsepower engine can be rated as having the power equal to 149,200 watts or 149.2 kilowatts (kW).

To calculate watts, both the current in amperes and the voltage in the circuit must be known. If any two of these factors are known, then the other remaining factor can be determined by the following equations:

$$P = I \times E \text{ (watts equal amperes times voltage)}$$

$$I = \frac{P}{E} \text{ (amperes equal watts divided by voltage)}$$

$$E = \frac{P}{I} \text{ (voltage equals watts divided by amperes)}$$

A Watt's circle can be drawn and used like the Ohm's law circle diagram. ● **SEE FIGURE 18–11.**

MAGIC CIRCLE The formulas for calculating any combination of electrical units are shown in ● **FIGURE 18–12.**

It is almost impossible to remember all of these formulas, so this one circle showing all of the formulas is nice to have available if needed.

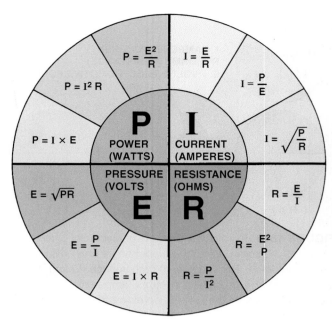

FIGURE 18–12 "Magic circle" of most formulas for problems involving Ohm's law. Each quarter of the "pie" has formulas used to solve for a particular unknown value: current (amperes), in the upper right segment; resistance (ohms), in the lower right; voltage (E), in the lower left; and power (watts), in the upper left.

TECH TIP

Wattage Increases by the Square of the Voltage

The brightness of a light bulb, such as an automotive headlight or courtesy light, depends on the number of watts available. The watt is the unit by which electrical power is measured. If the battery voltage drops, even slightly, the light becomes noticeably dimmer. The formula for calculating power (P) in watts is P = I × E. This can also be expressed as Watts = Amps × Volts.

According to Ohm's law, $I = \frac{E}{R}$. Therefore, $\frac{E}{R}$ can be substituted for I in the previous formula resulting in $P = \frac{E}{R} \times E$ or $P = \frac{E^2}{R}$.

E^2 means E multiplied by itself. A small change in the voltage (E) has a big effect on the total brightness of the bulb. (Remember, household light bulbs are sold according to their wattage.) Therefore, if the voltage to an automotive bulb is reduced, such as by a poor electrical connection, the brightness of the bulb is *greatly* affected. A poor electrical ground causes a voltage drop. The voltage at the bulb is reduced and the bulb's brightness is reduced.

1. All complete electrical circuits have a power source (such as a battery), a circuit protection device (such as a fuse), a power-side wire or path, an electrical load, a ground return path, and a switch or a control device.

2. A short-to-voltage involves a copper-to-copper connection and usually affects more than one circuit.

3. A short-to-ground usually involves a power path conductor coming in contact with a return (ground) path conductor and usually causes the fuse to blow.

4. An open is a break in the circuit resulting in absolutely no current flow through the circuit.

REVIEW QUESTIONS

1. What is included in a complete electrical circuit?

2. What is the difference between a short-to-voltage and a short-to-ground?

3. What is the difference between an electrical open and a short?

4. What is Ohm's law?

5. What occurs to current flow (amperes) and wattage if the resistance of a circuit is increased because of a corroded connection?

CHAPTER QUIZ

1. If an insulated wire rubbed through a part of the insulation and the wire conductor touched the steel body of a vehicle, the type of failure would be called a(n) _____.
   a. Short-to-voltage
   b. Short-to-ground
   c. Open
   d. Chassis ground

2. If two insulated wires were to melt together where the copper conductors touched each other, the type of failure would be called a(n) _____.
   a. Short-to-voltage
   b. Short-to-ground
   c. Open
   d. Floating ground

3. If 12 volts are being applied to a resistance of 3 ohms, _____ amperes will flow.
   a. 12
   b. 3
   c. 4
   d. 36

4. How many watts are consumed by a light bulb if 1.2 amperes are measured when 12 volts are applied?
   a. 14.4 watts
   b. 144 watts
   c. 10 watts
   d. 0.10 watt

5. How many watts are consumed by a starter motor if it draws 150 amperes at 10 volts?
   a. 15 watts
   b. 150 watts
   c. 1,500 watts
   d. 15,000 watts

6. High resistance in an electrical circuit can cause _____.
   a. Dim lights
   b. Slow motor operation
   c. Clicking of relays or solenoids
   d. All of the above

7. If the voltage increases in a circuit, what happens to the current (amperes) if the resistance remains the same?
   a. Increases
   b. Decreases
   c. Remains the same
   d. Cannot be determined

8. If 200 amperes flow from the positive terminal of a battery and operate the starter motor, how many amperes will flow back to the negative terminal of the battery?
   a. Cannot be determined
   b. Zero
   c. One half (about 100 amperes)
   d. 200 amperes

9. What is the symbol for voltage used in calculations?
   a. R
   b. E
   c. EMF
   d. I

10. Which circuit failure is most likely to cause the fuse to blow?
   a. Open
   b. Short-to-ground
   c. Short-to-voltage
   d. High resistance

SERIES CIRCUITS

OBJECTIVES: **After studying Chapter 19, the reader will be able to:** • Prepare for ASE Electrical/Electronic Systems (A6) certification test content area "A" (General Electrical/Electronic System Diagnosis). • Identify a series circuit. • Explain Kirchhoff's voltage law. • Calculate voltage drops in a series circuit. • Explain series circuit laws.
KEY TERMS: • Continuity 172 • Kirchhoff's voltage law 173 • Series circuit 172 • Series circuit laws 175 • Voltage drop 174

SERIES CIRCUITS

DEFINITION A **series circuit** is a complete circuit that has only one path for current to flow through all of the electrical loads. Electrical components such as fuses and switches are generally not considered to be included in the determination of a series circuit.

CONTINUITY The circuit must be continuous without any breaks. This is called **continuity.** Every circuit must have continuity in order for current to flow through the circuit. Because there is only one path for current to flow, the current is the same everywhere in a complete series circuit.

NOTE: Because an electrical load needs both a power and a ground to operate, a break (open) anywhere in a series circuit will cause the current in the circuit to stop.

FIGURE 19–1 A series circuit with three bulbs. All current flows through all resistances (bulbs). The total resistance of the circuit is the sum of the individual resistances of each bulb, and the bulbs will light dimly because of the increased resistance and the reduction of current flow (amperes) through the circuit.

OHM'S LAW AND SERIES CIRCUITS

SERIES CIRCUIT TOTAL RESISTANCE A series circuit is a circuit containing more than one resistance in which all current must flow through all resistances in the circuit. Ohm's law can be used to calculate the value of one unknown (voltage, resistance, or amperes) if the other two values are known.

Because *all* current flows through all resistances, the total resistance is the sum (addition) of all resistances. ● **SEE FIGURE 19–1.**

The total resistance of the circuit shown here is 6 ohms ($1\ \Omega + 2\ \Omega + 3\ \Omega$). The formula for total resistance (R_T) for a series circuit is:

$$R_T = R_1 + R_2 + R_3 + \ldots$$

Using Ohm's law to find the current flow, we have:

$$I = \frac{E}{R} = \frac{12\ V}{6\ \Omega} = 2\ A$$

Therefore, with a total resistance of 6 ohms using a 12 volt battery in the series circuit shown, 2 amperes of current will flow

FIGURE 19–2 A series circuit with two bulbs.

TECH TIP

Farsighted Quality of Electricity

Electricity almost seems to act as if it knows what resistances are ahead on the long trip through a circuit. If the trip through the circuit has many high-resistance components, very few electrons (amperes) will choose to attempt to make the trip. If a circuit has little or no resistance (for example, a short circuit), then as many electrons (amperes) as possible attempt to flow through the complete circuit. If another load, such as a light bulb, were added in series, the current flow would decrease and the bulbs would be dimmer than before the other bulb was added. If the flow exceeds the capacity of the fuse or the circuit breaker, then the circuit is opened and all current flow stops.

through the entire circuit. If the amount of resistance in a series circuit is reduced, more current will flow.

For example, in ● **FIGURE 19–2,** one resistance (3 ohm bulb) has been eliminated compared to Figure 19–1, and now the total resistance is 3 ohms (1 Ω + 2 Ω).

Using Ohm's law to calculate current flow yields 4 amperes.

$$I = \frac{E}{R} = \frac{12\ V}{3\ \Omega} = 4\ A$$

Notice that the current flow was doubled (4 amperes instead of 2 amperes) when the resistance was cut in half (from 6 ohms to 3 ohms). The current flow would also double if the applied voltage was doubled.

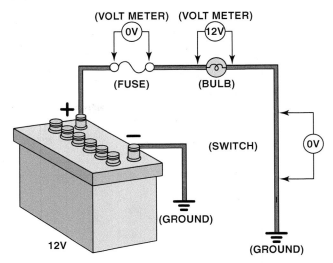

FIGURE 19–3 As current flows through a circuit, the voltage drops in proportion to the amount of resistance in the circuit. Most, if not all, of the resistance should occur across the load such as the bulb in this circuit. All of the other components and wiring should produce little, if any, voltage drop. If a wire or connection did cause a voltage drop, less voltage would be available to light the bulb and the bulb would be dimmer than normal.

KIRCHHOFF'S VOLTAGE LAW

DEFINITION A German physicist, Gustav Robert Kirchhoff (1824–1887), developed laws about electrical circuits. His second law, **Kirchhoff's voltage law,** concerns voltage drops. It states:

> The voltage around any closed circuit is equal to the sum (total) of the voltage drops across the resistances.

For example, the voltage that flows through a series circuit drops with each resistor in a manner similar to that in which the strength of an athlete drops each time a strenuous physical feat is performed. The greater the resistance is, the greater the drop in voltage.

APPLYING KIRCHHOFF'S VOLTAGE LAW Kirchhoff states in his second law that the voltage will drop in proportion to the resistance and that the total of all voltage drops will equal the applied voltage. ● **SEE FIGURE 19–3.**

Using ● **FIGURE 19–4,** the total resistance of the circuit can be determined by adding the individual resistances (2 Ω + 4 Ω + 6 Ω = 12 Ω).

The current through the circuit is determined by using Ohm's law, $I = \dfrac{E}{R} = \dfrac{12\ V}{12\ \Omega} = 1\ A.$

FIGURE 19–4 In a series circuit, the voltage is dropped or lowered by each resistance in the circuit. The higher the resistance is, the greater the drop in voltage.

Therefore, in the circuit shown, the following values are known.

 Resistance = 12 Ω

 Voltage = 12 V

 Current = 1 A

Everything is known *except* the voltage drop caused by each resistance. A **voltage drop** is the drop in voltage across a resistance when current flows through a complete circuit. In other words, a voltage drop is the amount of voltage (electrical pressure) required to push electrons through a resistance. The voltage drop can be determined by using Ohm's law and calculating for voltage (E) using the value of each resistance individually, as follows:

$$E = I \times R$$

where

 E = Voltage

 I = Current in the circuit (Remember, the current is constant in a series circuit; only the voltage varies.)

 R = Resistance of only one of the resistances

The voltage drops are as follows:

Voltage drop for bulb 1: $E = I \times R = 1\,A \times 2\,\Omega = 2\,V$

Voltage drop for bulb 2: $E = I \times R = 1\,A \times 4\,\Omega = 4\,V$

Voltage drop for bulb 3: $E = I \times R = 1\,A \times 6\,\Omega = 6\,V$

NOTE: Notice that the voltage drop is proportional to the resistance. In other words, the higher the resistance is, the greater the voltage drop. A 6 ohm resistance dropped the voltage three times as much as the voltage drop created by the 2 ohm resistance.

A. I = E/R (TOTAL "R" = 6 Ω)
  = 12/6 = 2A

B. E = I/R (VOLTAGE DROP)
  AT 2 Ω RESISTANCE =
  E = 2 x 2 = 4 V
  AT 4 Ω RESISTANCE =
  E = 2 x 4 = 8 V

C. 4 + 8 = 12 V
  SUM OF VOLTAGE DROP
  EQUALS APPLIED VOLTAGE

FIGURE 19–5 A voltmeter reads the differences of voltage between the test leads. The voltage read across a resistance is the voltage drop that occurs when current flows through a resistance. A voltage drop is also called an "IR" drop because it is calculated by multiplying the current (I) through the resistance (electrical load) by the value of the resistance (R).

According to Kirchhoff, the sum (addition) of the voltage drops should equal the applied voltage (battery voltage).

Total of voltage drops = 2 V + 4 V
+ 6 V = 12 V = Battery voltage

This proves Kirchhoff's second (voltage) law. Another example is illustrated in ● **FIGURE 19–5.**

VOLTAGE DROPS

VOLTAGE DROPS USED IN CIRCUITS A voltage drop indicates resistance in the circuit. Often a voltage drop is not wanted in a circuit because it causes the electrical load to not operate correctly. Some automotive electrical systems use voltage drops in cases such as the following:

1. **Dash lights.** Most vehicles are equipped with a method of dimming the brightness of the dash lights by turning a variable resistor. This type of resistor can be adjusted and therefore varies the voltage to the dash light bulbs. A high voltage to the bulbs causes them to be bright, and a low voltage results in a dim light.

2. **Blower motor** (heater or air-conditioning fan). Speeds can be controlled by a fan switch sending current through

Why Check the Voltage Drop Instead of Measuring the Resistance?

Imagine a wire with all strands cut except for one. An ohmmeter can be used to check the resistance of this wire and the resistance would be low, indicating that the wire was okay, but this one small strand cannot properly carry the current (amperes) in the circuit. A voltage drop test is therefore a better test to determine the resistance in components for two reasons:

- An ohmmeter can only test a wire or component that has been disconnected from the circuit and is not carrying current. The resistance can, and does, change when current flows.
- A voltage drop test is a dynamic test because as the current flows through a component, the conductor increases in temperature, which in turn increases resistance. This means that a voltage drop test is testing the circuit during normal operation and is therefore the most accurate way of determining circuit conditions.

A voltage drop test is also easier to perform because the resistance does not have to be known, only that the loss of voltage in a circuit should be less than 3%, or less than about 0.36 volt for any 12 volt circuit.

Light Bulbs and Ohm's Law

If the resistance of a typical automotive light bulb is measured at room temperature, the resistance will often be around 1 ohm. If 12 volts were to be applied to this bulb, a calculated current of 12 amperes would be expected ($I = \dfrac{E}{R} = 12 \div 1 = 12$ A). However, as current flows through the filament of the bulb, it increases in temperature and becomes incandescent, thereby giving off light. When the bulb is first connected to a power source and current starts to flow, a high amount of current, called surge current, flows through the filament. Then within a few thousandths of a second, the current flow is reduced to about 10% of the surge current due to the increasing resistance of the filament, resulting in an actual current flow of about 1.2 A or about 100 ohms of resistance when the bulb is working.

As a result, using Ohm's law to calculate current flow does not take into account the differences in temperature of the components during actual operation.

SERIES CIRCUIT LAWS

Electrical loads or resistance connected in series behave following **series circuit laws**.

LAW 1 The total resistance in a series circuit is the sum total of the individual resistances. The resistance values of each electrical load are simply added together.

LAW 2 The current is the same throughout the entire circuit.
● **SEE FIGURE 19–6.**

If 2 amperes of current leave the battery, 2 amperes of current return to the battery.

FIGURE 19–6 In this series circuit with a 2 ohm resistor and a 4 ohm resistor, current (2 amperes) is the same throughout, even though the voltage drops across each resistor are different.

high-, medium-, or low-resistance wire resistors. The highest resistance will drop the voltage the most, causing the motor to run at the lowest speed. The highest speed of the motor will occur when *no* resistance is in the circuit and full battery voltage is switched to the blower motor.

VOLTAGE DROPS AS A TESTING METHOD Any resistance in a circuit causes the voltage to drop in proportion to the amount of the resistance. Because a high resistance will drop the voltage more than a lower resistance, a voltmeter, as well as an ohmmeter, can be used to measure resistance. In fact, measuring the voltage drop is the preferred method recommended by most vehicle manufacturers to locate or test a circuit for excessive resistance. The formula for voltage drop is $E = I \times R$, where E is the voltage drop and I is the current in the circuit. Notice that as the value of the resistance (R) increases, the voltage drop increases.

LAW 3 Although the current (in amperes) is constant, the voltage drops across each resistance in the circuit can vary at each resistor. The voltage drop across each load is proportional to the value of the resistance compared to the total resistance. For example, if the resistance of each resistor in a two-resistor circuit is half of the total resistance, the voltage drop across that resistance will be half of the applied voltage. The sum total of all individual voltage drops equals the applied source voltage.

FIGURE 19–8 Example 2.

SERIES CIRCUIT EXAMPLES

Each of the four examples includes solving for the following:

- Total resistance in the circuit
- Current flow (amperes) through the circuit
- Voltage drop across each resistance

Example 1:

(● **SEE FIGURE 19–7.**)

The unknown in this problem is the value of R_2. Because the source voltage and the circuit current are known, the total circuit resistance, can be calculated using Ohm's law.

$$R_{Total} = \frac{E}{I} = 12 \text{ volts} \div 3 \text{ A} = 4 \ \Omega$$

Because R_1 is 3 ohms and the total resistance is 4 ohms, therefore the value of R_2 is 1 ohm.

Example 2:

(● **SEE FIGURE 19–8.**)

The unknown in this problem is the value of R_3. The total resistance, however, can be calculated using Ohm's law.

FIGURE 19–7 Example 1.

FIGURE 19–9 Example 3.

$$R_{Total} = \frac{E}{I} = 12 \text{ volts} \div 2 \text{ A} = 6 \ \Omega$$

The total resistance of R_1 (3 ohms) and R_2 (1 ohm) equals 4 ohms, so that the value of R_3 is the difference between the total resistance (6 ohms) and the value of the known resistance (4 ohms).

$$6 = 4 = 2 \text{ ohms} = R_3$$

Example 3:

(● **SEE FIGURE 19–9.**)

The unknown value in this problem is the voltage of the battery. To solve for voltage, use Ohm's law (E − I × R). The R in this problem refers to the total resistance (R_T). The total resistance of a series circuit is determined by adding the values of the individual resistors.

$$R_T = 1 \ \Omega + 1 \ \Omega + 1 \ \Omega$$

$$R_T = 3 \ \Omega$$

Placing the value for the total resistance (3 Ω) into the equation results in a battery voltage of 12 volts.

$$E = 4 \text{ A} \times 3 \Omega$$

$$E = 12 \text{ volts}$$

Example 4:

(● SEE FIGURE 19–10.)

The unknown in this example is the current (amperes) in the circuit. To solve for current, use Ohm's law.

$$I = \frac{E}{R} = 12 \text{ volts} \div 6 \text{ ohms} = 2 \text{ A}$$

Notice that the total resistance in the circuit (6 ohms) was used in this example, which is the total of the three individual resistors (2 Ω + 2 Ω + 2 Ω = 6 Ω). The current through the circuit is 2 amperes.

FIGURE 19–10 Example 4.

SUMMARY

1. In a simple series circuit, the current remains constant throughout, but the voltage drops as current flows through each of the resistances of the circuit.

2. The voltage drop across each resistance or load is directly proportional to the value of the resistance compared to the total resistance in the circuit.

3. The sum (total) of the voltage drops equals the applied voltage (Kirchhoff's voltage law).

4. An open or a break anywhere in a series circuit stops all current from flowing.

REVIEW QUESTIONS

1. What is Kirchhoff's voltage law?

2. What would current (amperes) do if the voltage were doubled in a circuit?

3. What would current (amperes) do if the resistance in the circuit were doubled?

4. What is the formula for voltage drop?

CHAPTER QUIZ

1. The amperage in a series circuit is _____.
   a. The same anywhere in the circuit
   b. Variable in the circuit due to the different resistances
   c. High at the beginning of the circuit and decreases as the current flows through the resistance
   d. Always less returning to the battery than leaving the battery

2. The sum of the voltage drops in a series circuit equals the _____.
   a. Amperage   c. Source voltage
   b. Resistance   d. Wattage

3. If the resistance and the voltage are known, what is the formula for finding the current (amperes)?
   a. $E = I \times R$ c. $R = E \times I$
   b. $I = E \times R$ d. $I = \frac{E}{R}$

4. A series circuit has three resistors of 6 ohms each. The voltage drop across each resistor is 4 volts. Technician A says that the source voltage is 12 volts. Technician B says that the total resistance is 18 ohms. Which technician is correct?
   a. Technician A only
   b. Technician B only
   c. Both Technicians A and B
   d. Neither Technician A nor B

5. If a 12 volt battery is connected to a series circuit with three resistors of 2 ohms, 4 ohms, and 6 ohms, how much current will flow through the circuit?
   a. 1 ampere
   b. 2 amperes
   c. 3 amperes
   d. 4 amperes

6. A series circuit has two 10 ohm bulbs. A third 10 ohm bulb is added in series. Technician A says that the three bulbs will be dimmer than when only two bulbs were in the circuit. Technician B says that the current in the circuit will increase. Which technician is correct?
   a. Technician A only
   b. Technician B only
   c. Both Technicians A and B
   d. Neither Technician A nor B

7. Technician A says that the sum of the voltage drops in a series circuit should equal the source voltage. Technician B says that the current (amperes) varies depending on the value of the resistance in a series circuit. Which technician is correct?
   a. Technician A only
   b. Technician B only
   c. Both Technicians A and B
   d. Neither Technician A nor B

8. Two light bulbs are wired in series and one bulb burns out (opens). Technician A says that the other bulb will work. Technician B says that the current will increase in the circuit because one electrical load (resistance) is no longer operating. Which technician is correct?
   a. Technician A only
   b. Technician B only
   c. Both Technicians A and B
   d. Neither Technician A nor B

9. Four resistors are connected to a 12 volt battery in series. The values of the resistors are 10 ohms, 100 ohms, 330 ohms, and 470 ohms. Technician A says that the greatest voltage drop will occur across the 10 ohm resistor. Technician B says that the greatest voltage drop will occur across the 470 ohm resistor. Which technician is correct?
   a. Technician A only
   b. Technician B only
   c. Both Technicians A and B
   d. Neither Technician A nor B

10. Three light bulbs are wired in series. A fourth bulb is connected to the circuit in series. Technician A says that the total voltage drop will increase. Technician B says that the current (amperes) will decrease. Which technician is correct?
    a. Technician A only
    b. Technician B only
    c. Both Technicians A and B
    d. Neither Technician A nor B

chapter 20

PARALLEL CIRCUITS

OBJECTIVES: After studying Chapter 20, the reader will be able to: • Prepare for ASE Electrical/Electronic Systems (A6) certification test content area "A" (General Electrical/Electronic Systems Diagnosis). • Identify a parallel circuit. • Explain parallel circuit laws. • Calculate voltage drops in a parallel circuit. • State Kirchhoff's current law.

KEY TERMS: Branches 179 • Kirchhoff's current law 179 • Legs 179 • Parallel circuit 179 • Shunts 179 • Total circuit resistance (R_T) 181

PARALLEL CIRCUITS

DEFINITION A **parallel circuit** is a complete circuit that has more than one path for the current to flow. The separate paths that split and meet at junction points are called **branches, legs,** or **shunts.** The current flow through each branch or leg varies depending on the resistance in that branch. A break or open in one leg or section of a parallel circuit does not stop the current flow through the remaining legs of the parallel circuit. Most circuits in vehicles are parallel circuits and each branch is connected to the 12 volt power supply. ● **SEE FIGURE 20–1.**

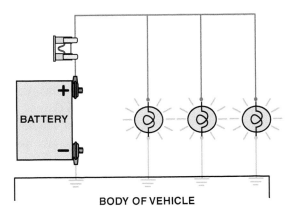

FIGURE 20–1 A typical parallel circuit used in vehicles includes many of the interior and exterior lights.

KIRCHHOFF'S CURRENT LAW

DEFINITION **Kirchhoff's current law** (his first law) states: The current flowing into any junction of an electrical circuit is equal to the current flowing out of that junction.

Kirchhoff's law states that the amount of current flowing into junction A will equal the current flowing out of junction A.

Example:

Because the 6 ohm leg requires 2 amperes and the 3 ohm resistance leg requires 4 amperes, it is necessary that the wire from the battery to junction A be capable of handling 6 amperes. Also notice that the sum of the current flowing *out* of a junction (2 + 4 = 6 A) is equal to the current flowing *into* the junction (6 A), proving Kirchhoff's current law. ● **SEE FIGURE 20–2.**

FIGURE 20–2 The amount of current flowing into junction point A equals the total amount of current flowing out of the junction.

? FREQUENTLY ASKED QUESTION

Why Are Parallel Circuits Used Instead of Series Circuits?

Parallel circuits are used for most automotive circuits for the following reasons.

1. In a series circuit, any circuit fault such as an open would stop the flow of electricity to all of the electrical components in the circuit.
2. In a parallel circuit if one device fails, the other units will continue to work because each device has its own power supply wire.

🔧 TECH TIP

The Path of Least Resistance

There is an old saying that electricity will always take the path of least resistance. This is true, especially if there is a fault such as in the secondary (high-voltage) section of the ignition system. If there is a path to ground that is lower resistance than the path to the spark plug, the high-voltage spark will take the path of least resistance. In a parallel circuit where there is more than one path for the current to flow, most of the current will flow through the branch with the lower resistance. This does not mean that all of the current will flow through the lowest resistance, because the other path provides a path to ground and the amount of current flow through the other branches is determined by the resistance and the applied voltage according to Ohm's law.

Therefore, the only place where electricity takes the path of least resistance is in a series circuit where there are not other paths for the current to flow.

PARALLEL CIRCUIT LAWS

LAW 1 The total resistance of a parallel circuit is always less than that of the smallest-resistance leg. This occurs because not all of the current flows through each leg or branch. With many branches, more current can flow from the battery just as more vehicles can travel on a road with five lanes compared to only one or two lanes.

LAW 2 The voltage is the same for each leg of a parallel circuit.

LAW 3 The sum of the individual currents in each leg will equal the total current. The amount of current flow through a parallel circuit may vary for each leg depending on the resistance of that leg. The current flowing through each leg results in the same voltage drop (from the power side to the ground side) as for every other leg of the circuit. ● **SEE FIGURE 20–3.**

NOTE: A parallel circuit drops the voltage from source voltage to zero (ground) across the resistance in each leg of the circuit.

DETERMINING TOTAL RESISTANCE IN A PARALLEL CIRCUIT

There are five methods commonly used to determine total resistance in a parallel circuit.

NOTE: Determining the total *resistance* of a parallel circuit is very important in automotive service. Electronic fuel injector and diesel engine glow plug circuits are two of the most commonly tested circuits where parallel circuit knowledge is required. Also, when installing extra lighting, the technician must determine the proper gauge wire and protection device.

METHOD 1 The total *current* (in amperes) can be calculated first by treating each leg of the parallel circuit as a simple circuit. ● **SEE FIGURE 20–4.**

Each leg has its own power (+) and ground (−) and, therefore, the current through each leg is independent of the current through any other leg.

Current through the 3 Ω resistance =

$$I = \frac{E}{R} = \frac{12V}{3\Omega} = 4\ A$$

FIGURE 20–3 The current in a parallel circuit splits (divides) according to the resistance in each branch. Each branch has 12 volts applied to the resistors.

SYMBOL FOR A BATTERY

3 Ω   4 Ω   6 Ω

SYMBOL FOR AN ELECTRICAL RESISTANCE

FIGURE 20–4 In a typical parallel circuit, each resistance has power and ground and each leg operates independently of the other legs of the circuit.

FIGURE 20–5 A schematic showing two resistors in parallel connected to a 12 volt battery.

FIGURE 20–6 A parallel circuit with three resistors connected to a 12 volt battery.

Current through the 4 Ω resistance =

$$I = \frac{E}{R} = \frac{12V}{4\Omega} = 3\ A$$

Current through the 4 Ω resistance =

$$I = \frac{E}{R} = \frac{12V}{6\Omega} = 2\ A$$

The total current flowing from the battery is the sum total of the individual currents for each leg. Total current from the battery is, therefore, 9 amperes (4 A + 3 A + 2 A = 9 A).

If **total circuit resistance** (R_T) is needed, Ohm's law can be used to calculate it because voltage (E) and current (I) are now known.

$$R_T = \frac{E}{I} = \frac{12\ V}{9\ A} = 1.33\ \Omega$$

Note that the total resistance (1.33 Ω) is smaller than that of the smallest-resistance leg of the parallel circuit. This characteristic of a parallel circuit holds true because not all of the total current flows through all resistances as in a series circuit.

Because the current has alternative paths to ground through the various legs of a parallel circuit, as additional resistances (legs) are added to a parallel circuit, the total current from the battery (power source) *increases*.

Additional current can flow when resistances are added in parallel, because each leg of a parallel circuit has its own power and ground and the current flowing through each leg is strictly dependent on the resistance of *that* leg.

METHOD 2 If only two resistors are connected in parallel, the total resistance (R_T) can be found using the formula $R_T = \left(\frac{R_1 \times R_2}{R_1 + R_2}\right)$. For example, using the circuit in

● **FIGURE 20–5** and substituting 3 ohms for R_1 and 4 ohms for R_2, $R_T = \frac{(3 \times 4)}{(3 + 4)} = \frac{12}{7} = 1.7\ \Omega$.

Note that the total resistance (1.7 Ω) is smaller than that of the smallest-resistance leg of the circuit.

NOTE: Which resistor is R_1 and which is R_2 is not important. The position in the formula makes no difference in the multiplication and addition of the resistor values.

This formula can be used for more than two resistances in parallel, but only two resistances can be calculated at a time. After solving for R_T for two resistors, use the value of R_T as R_1 and the additional resistance in parallel as R_2. Then solve for another R_T. Continue the process for all resistance legs of the parallel circuit. However, note that it might be easier to solve for R_T when there are more than two resistances in parallel by using either method 3 or method 4.

METHOD 3 A formula that can be used to find the total resistance for any number of resistances in parallel is

$$\frac{1}{R_T} = \frac{1}{R_1} + \frac{1}{R_2} + \frac{1}{R_3} + \ldots\ldots$$

To solve for R_T for the three resistance legs in ● **FIGURE 20–6,** substitute the values of the resistances for R_1, R_2, and R_3: $\frac{1}{R_T} = \frac{1}{3} + \frac{1}{4} + \frac{1}{6}$.

The fractions cannot be added together unless they all have the same denominator. The lowest common denominator in this example is 12.

TO SOLVE THIS PARALLEL CIRCUIT PROBLEM FOR R₁ (TOTAL RESISTANCE), PUSH THE EXACT BUTTONS ON AN ELECTRONIC CALCULATOR

NOTE: BE CERTAIN TO PUSH THE [=] BUTTON. FAILURE TO DO SO WILL RESULT IN INCORRECT ANSWERS WHEN USING MOST CALCULATORS.

(ANSWER = 1.3333)

FIGURE 20–7 Using an electronic calculator to determine the total resistance of a parallel circuit.

USE AN ELECTRONIC CALCULATOR TO SOLVE:

NOTE:

THE TOTAL RESISTANCE (R_T) MUST BE LESS THAN THE SMALLEST RESISTANCE (LESS THAN 20 Ω IN THIS EXAMPLE).

FIGURE 20–8 Another example of how to use an electronic calculator to determine the total resistance of a parallel circuit. The answer is 13.45 ohms. Notice that the effective resistance of this circuit is less than the resistance of the lowest branch (20 ohms).

Therefore, $\frac{1}{3}$ becomes $\frac{4}{12}$, $\frac{1}{4}$ becomes $\frac{3}{12}$, and $\frac{1}{6}$ becomes $\frac{2}{12}$.

$\frac{1}{R_T} = \frac{4}{12} + \frac{3}{12} + \frac{2}{12}$ or $\frac{9}{12}$. Cross multiplying

$R_T = \frac{12}{9} = 1.33\ \Omega$.

Note that the result (1.33 Ω) is the same regardless of the method used (see method 1). The most difficult part of using this method (besides using fractions) is determining the lowest common denominator, especially for circuits containing a wide range of ohmic values for the various legs. For an easier method using a calculator, see method 4.

METHOD 4 This method uses an electronic calculator, commonly available at very low cost. Instead of determining the lowest common denominator as in method 3, one can use the electronic calculator to convert the fractions to decimal equivalents. The memory buttons on most calculators can be used to keep a running total of the fractional values. Using ● **FIGURE 20–7**, calculate the total resistance (R_T) by pushing the indicated buttons on the calculator.

● Also **SEE FIGURE 20–8.**

FIGURE 20–9 A parallel circuit containing four 12 ohm resistors. When a circuit has more than one resistor of equal value, the total resistance can be determined by simply dividing the value of the resistance (12 ohms in this example) by the number of equal-value resistors (4 in this example) to get 3 ohms.

NOTE: This method can be used to find the total resistance of *any number* of resistances in parallel.

The memory recall (MRC) and equals (=) buttons invert the answer to give the correct value for total resistance (1.33 Ω). The inverse $\left(\frac{1}{X}\ \text{or}\ X^{-1}\right)$ button can be used with the sum (SUM) button on scientific calculators without using the memory button.

METHOD 5 This method can be easily used when two or more resistances connected in parallel are of the same value. ● **SEE FIGURE 20–9.**

To calculate the total resistance (R_T) of equal-value resistors, divide the number of equal resistors into the value of the resistance: R_T Value of equal resistance/Number of equal resistances

$$= \frac{12\,\Omega}{4} = 3\,\Omega.$$

NOTE: Because most automotive and light-truck electrical circuits involve multiple use of the same resistance, this method is the most useful. For example, if six additional 12 ohm lights were added to a vehicle, the additional lights would represent just 2 ohms of resistance $\left(\frac{12\,\Omega}{6}\text{ lights} = 2\right)$. Therefore, 6 amperes of additional current would be drawn by the additional lights $\left(I = \frac{E}{R} = \frac{12\,V}{2\,\Omega} = 6\,A\right)$.

PARALLEL CIRCUIT CALCULATION EXAMPLES

Each of the four examples includes solving for the following:

- Total resistance
- Current flow (amperes) through each branch as well as total current flow
- Voltage drop across each resistance

Example 1:

(● SEE FIGURE 20–10.)

In this example, the voltage of the battery is unknown and the equation to be used is $E = I \times R$, where R represents the total resistance of the circuit. Using the equation for two resistors in parallel, the total resistance is 6 ohms.

$$R_T = \frac{R_1 \times R_2}{R_1 + R_2} = \frac{12 \times 12}{12 + 12} = \frac{144}{24} = 6\,\Omega$$

Placing the value of the total resistors into the equation results in a value for the battery voltage of 12 volts.

$$E = I \times R$$

$$E = 2\,A \times 6\,\Omega$$

$$E = 12\text{ volts}$$

Example 2:

(● SEE FIGURE 20–11.)

In this example, the value of R_3 is unknown. Because the voltage (12 volts) and the current (12 A) are known, it is easier to solve for the unknown resistance by treating each branch or leg as a separate circuit. Using Kirchhoff's law, the total current equals the total current flow through each branch. The current flow through R_1 is 3 A $\left(I = \frac{E}{R} = \frac{12\,V}{4\,\Omega} = 3A\right)$ and the current flow through R_2 is 6 A $\left(I = \frac{E}{R} = \frac{12\,V}{2\,\Omega} = 6A\right)$. Therefore, the total current through the two known branches equals 9 A (3 A + 6 A = 9 A). Because there are 12 A leaving and returning to the battery, the current flow through R_3 must be 3 A (12 A − 9 A = 3 A). The resistance must therefore be 4 Ω $\left(I = \frac{E}{R} = \frac{12\,V}{4\,\Omega} = 3A\right)$.

Example 3:

(● SEE FIGURE 20–12.)

In this example, the voltage of the battery is unknown. The equation to solve for voltage according to Ohm's law is:

$$E = I \times R$$

FIGURE 20–10 Example 1.

FIGURE 20–11 Example 2.

FIGURE 20–12 Example 3.

FIGURE 20–13 Example 4.

The R in this equation refers to the total resistance. Because there are four resistors of equal value, the total can be determined by the following equation.

$$R_{Total} = \frac{\text{Value of resistors}}{\text{Number of equal resistors}} = \frac{12\ \Omega}{4} = 3\ \Omega$$

Inserting the value of the total resistors of the parallel circuit (3 Ω) into Ohm's law results in a battery voltage of 12 V.

$$E = 4\ A \times 3\ \Omega$$

$$E = 12\ V$$

Example 4:

(● SEE FIGURE 20–13.)

The unknown is the amount of current in the circuit. The Ohm's law equation for determining current is:

$$I = \frac{E}{R}$$

The R represents the total resistance. Because there are two equal resistances (8 Ω), these two can be replaced by one resistance of 4 Ω $\left(R_{Total} = \dfrac{\text{Value}}{\text{Number}} = \dfrac{8\ \Omega}{2} = 4\ \Omega \right)$.

The total resistance of this parallel circuit containing two 8 ohm resistors and one 4 ohm resistor is 2 ohms. The current flow from the battery is then calculated to be 6 A.

$$I = \frac{E}{R} = \frac{12\ V}{2\ \Omega} = 6\ A$$

SUMMARY

1. Parallel circuits are used in most automotive applications.
2. The total resistance of a parallel circuit is always lower than the smallest resistance in the leg of the circuit.
3. The separate paths which split and meet at junction points are called branches, legs, or shunts.
4. Kirchhoff's current law states: The current flowing into any junction of an electrical circuit is equal to the current flowing out of that junction.
5. There are five basic methods that can be used to calculate the total resistance in a parallel circuit.

REVIEW QUESTIONS

1. Why is the total resistance of a parallel circuit less than the smallest resistance?
2. Why are parallel circuits (instead of series circuits) used in most automotive applications?
3. What does Kirchhoff's current law state?
4. What are three of the five ways to calculate the total resistance of a parallel circuit?

1. Two bulbs are connected in parallel to a 12 volt battery. One bulb has a resistance of 6 ohms and the other bulb has a resistance of 2 ohms. Technician A says that only the 2 ohm bulb will light because all of the current will flow through the path with the least resistance and no current will flow through the 6 ohm bulb. Technician B says that the 6 ohm bulb will be dimmer than the 2 ohm bulb. Which technician is correct?
   a. Technician A only
   b. Technician B only
   c. Both Technicians A and B
   d. Neither Technician A nor B

2. Calculate the total resistance and current in a parallel circuit with three resistors of 4 Ω, 8 Ω, and 16 Ω, using any one of the five methods (calculator suggested). What are the values?
   a. 27 ohms (0.4 ampere)
   b. 14 ohms (0.8 ampere)
   c. 4 ohms (3 amperes)
   d. 2.3 ohms (5.3 amperes)

3. If an accessory such as an additional light is spliced into an existing circuit in parallel, what happens?
   a. The current increases in the circuit.
   b. The current decreases in the circuit.
   c. The voltage drops in the circuit.
   d. The resistance of the circuit increases.

4. A 6-cylinder engine uses six fuel injectors connected electrically in two groups of three injectors in parallel. What would be the resistance if the three 12 ohm injectors were connected in parallel?
   a. 36 ohms
   b. 12 ohms
   c. 4 ohms
   d. 3 ohms

5. A vehicle has four taillight bulbs all connected in parallel. If one bulb burns out (opens), the total current flow in the circuit _____.
   a. Increases and the other bulbs get brighter
   b. Decreases because only three bulbs are operating
   c. Remains the same because all the bulbs are wired in parallel
   d. Drops to zero and the other three bulbs go out

6. Two identical bulbs are connected to a 12 volt battery in parallel. The voltage drop across the first bulb is 12 volts as measured with a voltmeter. What is the voltage drop across the other bulb?
   a. 0 volt
   b. 1 volt
   c. 6 volts
   d. 12 volts

7. Three resistors are connected to a 12 volt battery in parallel. The current flow through each resistor is 4 amperes. What is the value of the resistors?
   a. 1 ohm
   b. 2 ohms
   c. 3 ohms
   d. 4 ohms

8. Two bulbs are connected to a 12 volt battery in parallel. Another bulb is added in parallel. Technician A says that the third bulb will be dimmer than the other two bulbs due to reduced current flow through the filament of the bulb. Technician B says that the amount of current flowing from the battery will decrease due to the extra load. Which technician is correct?
   a. Technician A only
   b. Technician B only
   c. Both Technicians A and B
   d. Neither Technician A nor B

9. A vehicle has four parking lights all connected in parallel and one of the bulbs burns out. Technician A says that this could cause the parking light circuit fuse to blow (open). Technician B says that it would decrease the total current in the circuit. Which technician is correct?
   a. Technician A only
   b. Technician B only
   c. Both Technicians A and B
   d. Neither Technician A nor B

10. Three resistors are connected in parallel to a 12 volt battery. The total current flow from the battery is 12 amperes. The first resistor is 3 ohms and the second resistor is 6 ohms. What is the value of the third resistor?
   a. 1 Ω
   b. 2 Ω
   c. 3 Ω
   d. 4 Ω

OBJECTIVES: **After studying Chapter 21, the reader will be able to:** • Prepare for ASE Electrical/Electronic Systems (A6) certification test content area "A" (General Electrical/Electronic System Diagnosis). • Identify a series-parallel circuit. • Calculate current flow and voltage drops in a series-parallel circuit. • Identify where faults in a series-parallel circuit can be detected or determined.

KEY TERMS: Combination circuit 186 • Compound circuit 186 • Series-parallel circuits 186

SERIES-PARALLEL CIRCUITS

DEFINITION **Series-parallel circuits** are a combination of series and parallel segments in one complex circuit. A series-parallel circuit is also called a **compound** or **combination circuit.** Many automotive circuits include sections that are in parallel and in series.

TYPES OF SERIES-PARALLEL CIRCUITS A series-parallel circuit includes both parallel loads or resistances, plus additional loads or resistances that are electrically connected in series. There are two basic types of series-parallel circuits.

- A circuit where the load is in series with other loads is parallel. ● **SEE FIGURE 21–1.**

  An example of this type of series-parallel circuit is a dash light dimming circuit. The variable resistor is used to limit current flow to the dash light bulbs, which are wired in parallel.

- A circuit where either a parallel circuit contains resistors or loads are in series in one or more branches. A headlight and starter circuit is an example of this type of series-parallel circuit. A headlight switch is usually connected in series with a dimmer switch and in parallel with the dash light dimmer resistors. The headlights are also connected in parallel along with the taillights and side marker lights. ● **SEE FIGURE 21–2.**

SERIES-PARALLEL CIRCUIT FAULTS If a conventional parallel circuit, such as a taillight circuit, had an electrical fault that increased the resistance in one branch of the circuit, then

FIGURE 21–1 A series-parallel circuit.

FIGURE 21–2 This complete headlight circuit with all bulbs and switches is a series-parallel circuit.

the amount of current flow through that one branch will be reduced. The added resistance, due to corrosion or other similar cause, would create a voltage drop. As a result of this drop in voltage, a lower voltage would be applied and the bulb in

FIGURE 21–3 Solving a series-parallel circuit problem.

FIGURE 21–4 Example 1.

the taillight would be dimmer than normal because the brightness of the bulb depends on the voltage and current applied. If, however, the added resistance occurred in a part of the circuit that fed both taillights, then both taillights would be dimmer than normal. In this case, the added resistance created a series-parallel circuit that was originally just a simple parallel circuit.

SOLVING SERIES-PARALLEL CIRCUIT CALCULATION PROBLEMS

The key to solving series-parallel circuit problems is to combine or simplify as much as possible. For example, if there are two loads or resistances in series within a parallel branch or leg, then the circuit can be made simpler if the two are first added together before attempting to solve the parallel section. ● **SEE FIGURE 21–3.**

SERIES-PARALLEL CIRCUIT CALCULATION EXAMPLES

Each of the four examples includes solving for the following:

- Total resistance
- Current flow (amperes) through each branch, as well as total current flow
- Voltage drop across each resistance

Example 1

(● **SEE FIGURE 21–4.**)

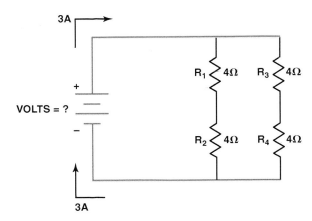

FIGURE 21–5 Example 2.

The unknown resistor is in series with the other two resistances, which are connected in parallel. The Ohm's law equation to determine resistance is:

$$R = \frac{E}{I} = \frac{12\ V}{3} = 4\ \Omega$$

The total resistance of the circuit is therefore 4 ohms and the value of the unknown can be determined by subtracting the value of the two resistors that are connected in parallel. The parallel branch resistance is 2 ohms.

$$R_T = \frac{4 \times 4}{4 + 4} = \frac{16}{8} = 2\ \Omega$$

The value of the unknown resistance is therefore 2 Ω. Total R = 4 Ω − 2 Ω = 2 Ω.

Example 2

(● **SEE FIGURE 21–5.**)

The unknown unit in this circuit is the voltage of the battery. The Ohm's law equation is:

$$E = I \times R$$

FIGURE 21-6 Example 3.

FIGURE 21-7 Example 4.

Before solving the problem, the total resistance must be determined. Because each branch contains two 4 ohm resistors in series, the value in each branch can be added to help simplify the circuit. By adding the resistors in each branch together, the parallel circuit now consists of two 8 ohm resistors.

$$R_T = \frac{R_1 \times R_2}{R_1 + R_2} = \frac{8 \times 8}{8 + 8} = \frac{64}{16} = 4 \; \Omega$$

Inserting the value for the total resistance into the Ohm's law equation results in a value of 12 volts for the battery voltage.

$$E = I \times R$$

$$E = 3 \, A \times 4 \; \Omega$$

$$E = 12 \; volts$$

Example 3

(● **SEE FIGURE 21-6.**)

In this example, the total current through the circuit is unknown. The Ohm's law equation to solve for is:

$$I = \frac{E}{R}$$

The total resistance of the parallel circuit must be determined before the equation can be used to solve for current (amperes). To solve for total resistance, the circuit can first be simplified by adding R_3 and R_4 together, because these two resistors are in series in the same branch of the parallel circuit. To simplify even more, the resulting parallel section of the circuit, now containing two 8 ohm resistors in parallel, can be replaced with one 4 ohm resistor.

$$R_T = \frac{R_1 \times R_2}{R_1 + R_2} = \frac{8 \times 8}{8 + 8} = \frac{64}{16} = 4 \; \Omega$$

With the parallel branches now reduced to just one 4 ohm resistor, this can be added to the 2 ohm (R_1) resistor because it is in series, creating a total circuit resistance of 6 ohms. Now the current flow can be determined from Ohm's law.

$$I = \frac{E}{R} = 12 \div 6 = 2 \, A$$

Example 4

(● **SEE FIGURE 21-7.**)

In this example, the value of resistor R_1 is unknown. Using Ohm's law, the total resistance of the circuit is 3 ohms.

$$R = \frac{E}{I} = \frac{12 \, V}{4A} = 3 \; \Omega$$

However, knowing the total resistance is not enough to determine the value of R_1. To simplify the circuit, R_2 and R_5 can combine to create a parallel branch resistance value of 8 ohms because they are in series. To simplify even further, the two 8 ohm branches can be reduced to one branch of 4 ohms.

$$R_T = \frac{R_1 \times R_2}{R_1 + R_2} = \frac{8 \times 8}{8 + 8} = \frac{64}{16} = 4 \; \Omega$$

Now the circuit has been simplified to one resistor in series (R_1) with two branches with 4 ohms in each branch. These two branches can be reduced to equal one 2 ohm resistor.

$$R_T = \frac{R_1 \times R_2}{R_1 + R_2} = \frac{4 \times 4}{4 + 4} = \frac{16}{8} = 2 \; \Omega$$

Now the circuit includes just one 2 ohm resistor plus the unknown R_1. Because the total resistance is 3 ohms, the value of R_1 must be 1 ohm.

$$3 \; \Omega - 2 \; \Omega = 1 \; \Omega$$

1. A series-parallel circuit is called a compound circuit or a combination circuit.

2. A series-parallel circuit is a combination of a series and a parallel circuit.

3. A fault in a series portion of a series-parallel circuit would affect the entire circuit operation if the series part was in the power or the ground side of the parallel portion of the circuit.

4. A fault in one leg of a series-parallel circuit will affect just the component(s) in that one leg.

REVIEW QUESTIONS

1. Explain why an increase in resistance in the series part of a series-parallel circuit will affect the current (amperes) through the parallel legs (branches).

2. What would be the effect of an open circuit in one leg of a parallel portion of a series-parallel circuit?

3. What would be the effect of an open circuit in a series portion of a series-parallel circuit?

CHAPTER QUIZ

1. Half of the dash is dark. Technician A says that a defective dash light dimmer can be the cause because it is in series with the bulbs that are in parallel. Technician B says that one or more bulbs could be defective. Which technician is correct?
   a. Technician A only
   b. Technician B only
   c. Both Technicians A and B
   d. Neither Technician A nor B

2. All brake lights are dimmer than normal. Technician A says that bad bulbs could be the cause. Technician B says that high resistance in the brake switch could be the cause. Which technician is correct?
   a. Technician A only
   b. Technician B only
   c. Both Technicians A and B
   d. Neither Technician A nor B

3. See ● FIGURE 21–8 to solve for total resistance (R_T) and total current (I_T).
   a. 10 ohms and 1.2 A
   b. 4 ohms and 3 A
   c. 6 ohms and 2 A
   d. 2 ohms and 6 A

Formulas:
$E = I \times R$
$I = E/R$
$R = E/I$

FIGURE 21–8 Chapter Quiz question 3.

E = 12V
R_1 = 2 Ohm
R_2 = 4 Ohm
R_3 = 4 Ohm
R_t = 4 Ohm
I =

FIGURE 21–9 Chapter Quiz question 4.

Formulas:
E = IxR
I = E/R
R = E/I

I

E
10V

.83A

R_1
6 Ohm

R_2
12 Ohm

R_3
? Ohm

E = 10V
R_1 =   6 Ohm
R_2 = 12 Ohm
R_3 =
R_t =
I   = .83

FIGURE 21–10 Chapter Quiz question 5.

Formulas:
E = IxR
I = E/R
R = E/I

I

E
?V

1.36A

R_1
2 Ohm

R_2
4 Ohm

R_3
6 Ohm

E =
R_1 = 2 Ohm
R_2 = 4 Ohm
R_3 = 6 Ohm
R_t =
I   = 1.36A

4. See ● **FIGURE 21–9** to solve for the value of R_3 *and* total resistance (R_T).
  a. 12 ohms and 12 ohms
  b. 1 ohm and 7 ohms
  c. 2 ohms and 8 ohms
  d. 6 ohms and 6 ohms

5. See ● **FIGURE 21–10** to solve for voltage (E) *and* total resistance (R_T).
  a. 16.3 volts and 12 ohms
  b. 3.3 volts and 2.4 ohms
  c. 1.36 volts and 1 ohm
  d. 6 volts and 4.4 ohms

6. See ● **FIGURE 21–11** to solve for R_1 *and* total resistance (R_T).
  a. 3 ohms and 15 ohms
  b. 1 ohm and 15 ohms
  c. 2 ohms and 5 ohms
  d. 5 ohms and 5 ohms

7. See ● **FIGURE 21–12** to solve for total resistance (R_T) *and* total current (I).
  a. 3.1 ohms and 7.7 amperes
  b. 5.1 ohms and 4.7 amperes
  c. 20 ohms and 1.2 amperes
  d. 6 ohms and 4 amperes

8. See ● **FIGURE 21–13** to solve for the value of E *and* total resistance (R_T).
  a. 13.2 volts and 40 ohms
  b. 11.2 volts and 34 ohms
  c. 8 volts and 24.2 ohms
  d. 8.6 volts and 26 ohms

FIGURE 21–11 Chapter Quiz question 6.

Formulas:
E = IxR
I = E/R
R = E/I

E   = 15V
R_1 =
R_2 =   6 Ohm
R_3 =   6 Ohm
R_t =
I   =   3A

FIGURE 21–12 Chapter Quiz question 7.

Formulas:
E = IxR
I = E/R
R = E/I

E   = 24V
R_1 =   2 Ohm
R_2 =   4 Ohm
R_3 =   6 Ohm
R_4 =   8 Ohm
R_t =
I   =

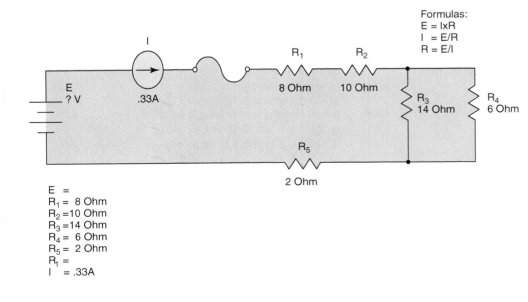

FIGURE 21–13 Chapter Quiz question 8.

Formulas:
E = IxR
I = E/R
R = E/I

E   =
R_1 =   8 Ohm
R_2 =10 Ohm
R_3 =14 Ohm
R_4 =   6 Ohm
R_5 =   2 Ohm
R_t =
I   = .33A

FIGURE 21-14 Chapter Quiz question 9.

Formulas:
E = IxR
I = E/R
R = E/I

I

E
12V

? A

R₁
2 Ohm

R₂
4 Ohm

R₃
12 Ohm

R₄
10 Ohm

E = 12V
R₁ =   2 Ohm
R₂ =   4 Ohm
R₃ = 12 Ohm
R₄ = 10 Ohm
Rₜ =
I =

FIGURE 21-15 Chapter
Quiz question 10.

Formulas:
E = IxR
I = E/R
R = E/I

I

E
20V

? A

R₁
14 Ohm

R₃
10 Ohm

R₅
8 Ohm

R₂
6 Ohm

R₄
8 Ohm

R₆
2 Ohm

E = 20V
R₁ = 14 Ohm
R₂ =   6 Ohm
R₃ = 10 Ohm
R₄ =   8 Ohm
R₅ =   8 Ohm
R₆ =   2 Ohm
Rₜ =
I =

9. See ● FIGURE 21-14 to solve for total resistance (Rₜ) *and* total current (I).
    a. 1.5 ohms and 8 amperes
    b. 18 ohms and 0.66 ampere
    c. 6 ohms and 2 amperes
    d. 5.5 ohms and 2.2 amperes

10. See ● FIGURE 21-15 to solve for total resistance (Rₜ) *and* total current (I).
    a. 48 ohms and 0.42 ampere
    b. 20 ohms and 1 ampere
    c. 30 ohms and 0.66 ampere
    d. 10.2 ohms and 1.96 amperes

CAPACITANCE AND CAPACITORS

OBJECTIVES: **After studying Chapter 22, the reader will be able to:** • Prepare for ASE Electrical/Electronic Systems (A6) certification test content area "A" (General Electrical/Electronic Systems). • Explain capacitance. • Describe how a capacitor can be used to filter electrical noise. • Describe how a capacitor can store an electrical charge. • Explain how a capacitor circuit can be used as a timer circuit.

KEY TERMS: Capacitance 193 • Condenser 193 • Dielectric 193 • Farads 196 • Leyden jar 193

CAPACITANCE

DEFINITION **Capacitance** is the ability of an object or surface to store an electrical charge. Around 1745, Ewald Christian von Kliest and Pieter van Musschenbroek independently discovered capacitance in an electric circuit. While engaged in separate studies of electrostatics, they discovered that an electric charge could be stored for a period of time. They used a device, now called a **Leyden jar,** for their experimentation, which consisted of a glass jar filled with water, with a nail piercing the stopper and dipping into the water.
● **SEE FIGURE 22-1.**

The two scientists connected the nail to an electrostatic charge. After disconnecting the nail from the source of the charge, they felt a shock by touching the nail, demonstrating that the device had stored the charge.

In 1747, John Bevis lined both the inside and outside of the jar with foil. This created a capacitor with two conductors (the inside and outside metal foil layers) equally separated by the insulating glass. The Leyden jar was also used by Benjamin Franklin to store the charge from lightning as well as in other experiments. The natural phenomenon of lightning includes capacitance, because huge electrical fields develop between cloud layers or between clouds and the earth prior to a lightning strike.

NOTE: Capacitors are also called condensers. This term developed because electric charges collect, or condense, on the plates of a capacitor much like water vapor collects and condenses on a cold bottle or glass.

FIGURE 22-1 A Leyden jar can be used to store an electrical charge.

CAPACITOR CONSTRUCTION AND OPERATION

CONSTRUCTION A capacitor (also called a condenser) consists of two conductive plates with an insulating material between them. The insulating material is commonly called a **dielectric.** This substance is a poor conductor of electricity and can include air, mica, ceramic, glass, paper, plastic, or any similar nonconductive material. The dielectric constant is the relative strength of a

FIGURE 22-2 This simple capacitor, made of two plates separated by an insulating material, is called a dielectric.

FIGURE 22-3 As the capacitor is charging, the battery forces electrons through the circuit.

FIGURE 22-4 When the capacitor is charged, there is equal voltage across the capacitor and the battery. An electrostatic field exists between the capacitor plates. No current flows in the circuit.

MATERIAL	DIELECTRIC CONSTANT
Vacuum	1
Air	1.00059
Polystyrene	2.5
Paper	3.5
Mica	5.4
Flint glass	9.9
Methyl alcohol	35
Glycerin	56.2
Pure water	81

CHART 22-1

The higher the dielectric constant is, the better the insulating properties between the plates of the capacitor.

material against the flow of electrical current. The higher the number is, the better the insulating properties. ● **SEE CHART 22-1.**

OPERATION When a capacitor is placed in a closed circuit, the voltage source (battery) forces electrons around the circuit. Because electrons cannot flow through the dielectric of the capacitor, excess electrons collect on what becomes the negatively charged plate. At the same time, the other plate loses electrons and, therefore, becomes positively charged. ● **SEE FIGURE 22-2.**

Current continues until the voltage charge across the capacitor plates becomes the same as the source voltage. At that time, the negative plate of the capacitor and the negative terminal of the battery are at the same negative potential. ● **SEE FIGURE 22-3.**

The positive plate of the capacitor and the positive terminal of the battery are also at equal positive potentials. There is then a voltage charge across the battery terminals and an equal voltage charge across the capacitor plates. The circuit is in balance, and there is no current. An electrostatic field now exists between the capacitor plates because of their opposite charges. It is this field that stores energy. In

FIGURE 22-5 The capacitor is charged through one circuit (top) and discharged through another (bottom).

other words, a charged capacitor is similar to a charged battery. ● **SEE FIGURE 22-4.**

If the circuit is opened, the capacitor will hold its charge until it is connected into an external circuit through which it can discharge. When the charged capacitor is connected to an external circuit, it discharges. After discharging, both plates of the capacitor are neutral because all the energy from a circuit stored in a capacitor is returned when it is discharged. ● **SEE FIGURE 22-5.**

FIXED CAPACITORS

VARIABLE CAPACITORS

FIGURE 22–6 Capacitor symbols are shown in electrical diagrams. The negative plate is often shown curved.

Theoretically, a capacitor holds its charge indefinitely. Actually, the charge slowly leaks off the capacitor through the dielectric. The better the dielectric, the longer the capacitor holds its charge. To avoid an electrical shock, any capacitor should be treated as if it were charged until it is proven to be discharged. To safely discharge a capacitor, use a test light with the clip attached to a good ground, and touch the pigtail or terminal with the point of the test light. ● **SEE FIGURE 22–6** for the symbol for capacitors as used in electrical schematics.

FACTORS OF CAPACITANCE

Capacitance is governed by three factors.

- The surface area of the plates
- The distance between the plates
- The dielectric material

 FREQUENTLY ASKED QUESTION

What Are "Points and Condenser"?

Points and condenser are used in point-type ignition systems.

Points. A set of points uses one stationary contact and a movable contact that is opened by a cam lobe inside the ignition distributor. When the points are closed, current flows through the primary windings of the ignition coil and creates a strong magnetic field. As the engine rotates, the distributor can open the contact points, which open the circuit to the coil. The stored magnetic field in the coil collapses and generates a high-voltage arc from the secondary winding of the coil. It is this spark that is sent to the spark plugs that ignites the air-fuel mixture inside the engine.

Condenser. The condenser (capacitor) is attached to the points and the case of the condenser is grounded. When the points start to open, the charge built up in the primary winding of the coil would likely start to arc across the opening points. To prevent the points from arcing and to increase how rapidly the current is turned off, the condenser stores the current temporarily. Points and condenser were used in vehicles and small gasoline engines until the mid-1970s. ● **SEE FIGURE 22–7.**

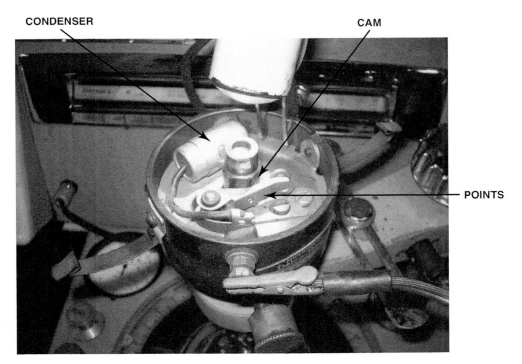

CONDENSER   CAM

POINTS

FIGURE 22–7 A point-type distributor shown with the condenser from an old vehicle being tested on a distributor machine.

The larger the surface area of the plates is, the greater the capacitance, because more electrons collect on a larger plate area than on a small one. The closer the plates are to each other, the greater the capacitance, because a stronger electrostatic field exists between charged bodies that are close together. The insulating qualities of the dielectric material also affect capacitance. The capacitance of a capacitor is higher if the dielectric is a very good insulator.

MEASUREMENT OF CAPACITANCE Capacitance is measured in **farads,** which is named after Michael Faraday (1791–1867), an English physicist. The symbol for farads is the letter F. If a charge of 1 coulomb is placed on the plates of a capacitor and the potential difference between them is 1 volt, then the capacitance is defined to be 1 farad, or 1 F. One coulomb is equal to the charge of 6.25×10^{18} electrons. One farad is an extremely large quantity of capacitance. Microfarads (0.000001 farad), or μF, are more commonly used.

The capacitance of a capacitor is proportional to the quantity of charge that can be stored in it for each volt difference in potential.

USES FOR CAPACITORS

SPIKE SUPPRESSION A capacitor can be used in parallel to a coil to reduce the resulting voltage spike that occurs when the circuit is opened. The energy stored to the magnet field of the coil is rapidly released at this time. The capacitor acts to absorb the high voltage produced and stop it from interfering with other electronic devices, such as automotive radio and video equipment.

NOISE FILTERING Interference in a sound system or radio is usually due to alternating current (AC) voltage created somewhere in the vehicle, such as in the alternator. A capacitor does the following:

- Blocks the flow of direct current (DC)
- Allows alternating current (AC) to pass

By connecting a capacitor (condenser) to the power lead of the radio or sound system amplifier, the AC voltage passes through the capacitor to the ground where the other end of the capacitor is connected. Therefore, the capacitor provides a path for the AC without affecting the DC power circuit. ● **SEE FIGURE 22–8.**

Because a capacitor stores a voltage charge, it opposes or slows any voltage change in a circuit. Therefore, capacitors are often used as voltage "shock absorbers." You sometimes find a capacitor attached to one terminal of an ignition coil. In this application, the capacitor absorbs and dampens changes in ignition voltage that interfere with radio reception.

SUPPLEMENTAL POWER SOURCE A capacitor can be used to supply electrical power for short bursts in an audio sys-

FIGURE 22–8 A capacitor blocks direct current (DC) but passes alternating current (AC). A capacitor makes a very good noise suppressor because most of the interference is AC and the capacitor will conduct this AC to ground before it can reach the radio or amplifier.

FIGURE 22–9 A 1 farad capacitor used to boost the power to large speakers.

tem to help drive the speakers. Woofers and subwoofers require a lot of electrical current that often cannot be delivered by the amplifier itself. ● **SEE FIGURE 22–9.**

TIMER CIRCUITS Capacitors are used in electronic circuits as part of a timer, to control window defoggers, interior lighting, pulse wipers, and automatic headlights. The capacitors store energy and then are allowed to discharge through a resistance load. The greater the capacity of the capacitor and the higher the resistance load, the longer the time it takes for the capacitor to discharge.

COMPUTER MEMORY In most cases, the main memory of a computer is a high-speed random-access memory (RAM). One type of main memory, called dynamic random-access memory (DRAM), is the most commonly used type of RAM. A single memory chip is made up of several million memory cells. In a DRAM chip, each memory cell consists of a capacitor. When a capacitor is electrically charged, it is said to store the binary digit 1, and when discharged, it represents 0.

CONDENSER MICROPHONES A microphone converts sound waves into an electric signal. All microphones have a diaphragm that vibrates as sound waves strike. The vibrating diaphragm in turn causes an electrical component to create an output flow of current at a frequency proportional to the sound waves. A condenser microphone uses a capacitor for this purpose.

In a condenser microphone, the diaphragm is the negatively charged plate of a charged capacitor. When a sound wave compresses the diaphragm, the diaphragm is moved closer to the positive plate. Decreasing the distance between the plates increases the electrostatic attraction between them, which results in a flow of current to the negative plate. As the diaphragm moves out in response to sound waves, it also moves further from the positive plate. Increasing the distance between the plates decreases the electrostatic attraction between them. This results in a flow of current back to the positive plate. These alternating flows of current provide weak electronic signals that travel to an amplifier and then to a loudspeaker.

CAPACITORS IN CIRCUITS

CAPACITORS IN PARALLEL CIRCUITS Capacitance can be increased in a circuit by connecting capacitors in parallel. For example, if a greater boost is needed for a sound system, then additional capacitors should be connected in parallel because their value adds together. ● **SEE FIGURE 22–10.**

We know that capacitance of a capacitor can be increased by increasing the size of its plates. Connecting two or more capacitors in parallel in effect increases plate size. Increasing plate area makes it possible to store more charge and therefore creates greater capacitance. To determine total capacitance of several parallel capacitors, simply add up their individual values. The following is the formula for calculating total capacitance in a circuit containing capacitors in parallel.

$$C_T = C_1 + C_2 + C_3 \ldots$$

For example, 220 µF + 220 µF = 440 µF when connected in parallel.

CAPACITORS IN SERIES CIRCUITS Capacitance can be decreased in a circuit by capacitors in series, as shown in ● **FIGURE 22–11.**

We know that capacitance of a capacitor can be decreased by placing the plates further apart. Connecting two or more capacitors in series in effect increases the distance between the plates and thickness of the dielectric, thereby decreasing the amount of capacitance.

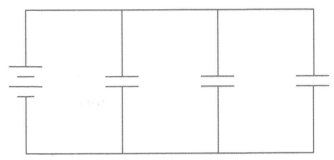

FIGURE 22–10 Capacitors in parallel effectively increase the capacitance.

FIGURE 22–11 Capacitors in series decrease the capacitance.

Following is the formula for calculating total capacitance in a circuit containing two capacitors in series.

$$C_T = \frac{C_1 \times C_2}{C_1 + C_2}$$

For example, $\dfrac{220 \, \mu F \times 220 \, \mu F}{220 \, \mu F + 220 \, \mu F} = \dfrac{48,400}{440} = 110 \, \mu F$

NOTE: Capacitors are often used to reduce radio interference or to improve the performance of a high-power sound system. Additional capacitance can, therefore, be added by attaching another capacitor in parallel.

SUPPRESSION CAPACITORS Capacitors are installed across many circuits and switching points to absorb voltage fluctuations. Among other applications, they are used across the following:

■ The primary circuit of some electronic ignition modules

■ The output terminal of most alternators

■ The armature circuit of some electric motors

Radio choke coils reduce current fluctuations resulting from self-induction. They are often combined with capacitors to act as electromagnetic interference EMI filter circuits for windshield wiper and electric fuel pump motors. Filters also may be incorporated in wiring connectors.

SUMMARY

1. Capacitors (condensers) are used in numerous automotive applications.
2. Capacitors can block direct current and pass alternating current.
3. Capacitors are used to control radio-frequency interference and are installed in various electronic circuits to control unwanted noise.
4. Capacitors connected in series reduce the capacitance, whereas if connected in parallel increase the capacitance.

REVIEW QUESTIONS

1. How does a capacitor store an electrical charge?
2. How should two capacitors be electrically connected if greater capacitance is needed?
3. Where can a capacitor be used as a power source?
4. How can a capacitor be used as a noise filter?

CHAPTER QUIZ

1. A capacitor _____.
   - a. Stores electrons
   - b. Passes AC
   - c. Blocks DC
   - d. All of the above

2. To increase the capacity, capacitors should be connected in _____.
   - a. Series
   - b. Parallel
   - c. With resistors connected between the leads
   - d. Series-parallel

3. Capacitors are commonly used as a _____.
   - a. Voltage supply
   - b. Timer
   - c. Noise filter
   - d. All of the above

4. A charged capacitor acts like a _____.
   - a. Switch
   - b. Battery
   - c. Resistor
   - d. Coil

5. The unit of measurement for capacitor rating is the _____.
   - a. Ohm
   - b. Volt
   - c. Farad
   - d. Ampere

6. Two technicians are discussing the operation of a capacitor. Technician A says that a capacitor can create electricity. Technician B says that a capacitor can store electricity. Which technician is correct?
   - a. Technician A only
   - b. Technician B only
   - c. Both Technicians A and B
   - d. Neither Technician A nor B

7. Capacitors block the flow of _____ current but allow _____ current to pass.
   - a. Strong; weak
   - b. AC; DC
   - c. DC; AC
   - d. Weak; strong

8. To increase the capacity, what could be done?
   - a. Connect another capacitor in series.
   - b. Connect another capacitor in parallel.
   - c. Add a resistor between two capacitors.
   - d. Both a and b

9. A capacitor can be used in what components?
   - a. Microphone
   - b. Radio
   - c. Speaker
   - d. All of the above

10. A capacitor used for spike protection will normally be placed in _____ to the load or circuit.
    - a. Series
    - b. Parallel
    - c. Either series or parallel
    - d. Parallel with a resistor in series

chapter 23

MAGNETISM AND ELECTROMAGNETISM

OBJECTIVES: **After studying Chapter 23, the reader will be able to:** • Prepare for ASE Electrical/Electronic Systems (A6) certification test content area "A" (General Electrical/Electronic Systems). • Explain magnetism. • Describe how magnetism and voltage are related. • Describe how an ignition coil works. • Explain how an electromagnet works.

KEY TERMS: Ampere-turns 203 • Counter electromotive force (CEMF) 207 • Electromagnet 203 • Electromagnetic induction 206 • Electromagnetic interference (EMI) 209 • Electromagnetism 201 • Flux density 200 • Flux lines 200 • Ignition control module (ICM) 209 • Left-hand rule 202 • Lenz's law 206 • Magnetic flux 200 • Magnetic induction 200 • Magnetism 199 • Mutual induction 207 • Permeability 201 • Pole 200 • Relay 204 • Reluctance 201 • Residual magnetism 200 • Right-hand rule 202 • Turns ratio 208

FUNDAMENTALS OF MAGNETISM

DEFINITION **Magnetism** is a form of energy that is caused by the motion of electrons in some materials. It is recognized by the attraction it exerts on other materials. Like electricity, magnetism cannot be seen. It can be explained in theory, however, because it is possible to see the results of magnetism and recognize the actions that it causes. Magnetite is the most naturally occurring magnet. Naturally magnetized pieces of magnetite, called *lodestone,* will attract and hold small pieces of iron. ● **SEE FIGURE 23–1.**

TECH TIP

A Cracked Magnet Becomes Two Magnets

Magnets are commonly used in vehicle crankshaft, camshaft, and wheel speed sensors. If a magnet is struck and cracks or breaks, the result is two smaller-strength magnets. Because the strength of the magnetic field is reduced, the sensor output voltage is also reduced. A typical problem occurs when a magnetic crankshaft sensor becomes cracked, resulting in a no-start condition. Sometimes the cracked sensor works well enough to start an engine that is cranking at normal speeds but will not work when the engine is cold. ● **SEE FIGURE 23–2.**

Many other materials can be artificially magnetized to some degree, depending on their atomic structure. Soft iron is very easy to magnetize, whereas some materials, such as aluminum, glass, wood, and plastic, cannot be magnetized at all.

FIGURE 23–1 A freely suspended natural magnet (lodestone) will point toward the magnetic north pole.

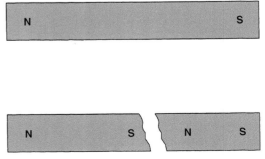

FIGURE 23–2 If a magnet breaks or is cracked, it becomes two weaker magnets.

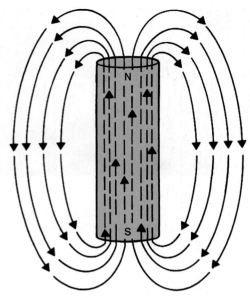

FIGURE 23–3 Magnetic lines of force leave the north pole and return to the south pole of a bar magnet.

FIGURE 23–4 Iron filings and a compass can be used to observe the magnetic lines of force.

FIGURE 23–5 Magnetic poles behave like electrically charged particles—unlike poles attract and like poles repel.

LINES OF FORCE The lines that create a field of force around a magnet are believed to be caused by the way groups of atoms are aligned in the magnetic material. In a bar magnet, the lines are concentrated at both ends of the bar and form closed, parallel loops in three dimensions around the magnet. Force does not flow along these lines the way electrical current flows, but the lines *do* have direction. They come out of the north end, or **pole**, of the magnet and enter at the other end. ● **SEE FIGURE 23–3.**

The opposite ends of a magnet are called its north and south poles. In reality, they should be called the "north seeking" and "south seeking" poles, because they seek the earth's North Pole and South Pole, respectively.

The more lines of force that are present, the stronger the magnet becomes. The magnetic lines of force, also called **magnetic flux** or **flux lines,** form a magnetic field. The terms *magnetic field, lines of force, flux,* and *flux lines* are used interchangeably.

Flux density refers to the number of flux lines per unit of area. A magnetic field can be measured using a Gauss gauge, named for German scientist Johann Carl Friedrick Gauss (1777–1855).

Magnetic lines of force can be seen by spreading fine iron filings or dust on a piece of paper laid on top of a magnet. A magnetic field can also be observed by using a compass. A compass is simply a thin magnet or magnetized iron needle balanced on a pivot. The needle will rotate to point toward the opposite pole of a magnet. The needle can be very sensitive to small magnetic fields. Because it is a small magnet, a compass usually has one north end (marked N) and one south end (marked S). ● **SEE FIGURE 23–4.**

MAGNETIC INDUCTION If a piece of iron or steel is placed in a magnetic field, it will also become magnetized. This process of creating a magnet by using a magnetic field is called **magnetic induction.**

If the metal is then removed from the magnetic field, and it retains some magnetism, this is called **residual magnetism.**

ATTRACTING OR REPELLING The poles of a magnet are called north (N) and south (S) because, when a magnet is suspended freely, the poles tend to point toward the earth's North Pole and South Pole. Magnetic flux lines exit from the north pole and bend around to enter the south pole. An equal number of lines exit and enter, so magnetic force is equal at both poles of a magnet. Flux lines are concentrated at the poles, and therefore magnetic force (flux density) is stronger at the ends.

Magnetic poles behave like positively and negatively charged particles. When unlike poles are placed close together, the lines exit from one magnet and enter the other. The two magnets are pulled together by flux lines. If like poles are placed close together, the curving flux lines meet head on, forcing the magnets apart. Therefore, like poles of a magnet repel and unlike poles attract. ● **SEE FIGURE 23–5.**

FIGURE 23–6 A crankshaft position sensor and reluctor (notched wheel).

 TECH TIP

Magnetize a Steel Needle

A piece of steel can be magnetized by rubbing a magnet in one direction along the steel. This causes the atoms to line up in the steel, so it acts like a magnet. The steel often will not remain magnetized, whereas the true magnet is permanently magnetized.

When soft iron or steel is used, such as a paper clip, it will lose its magnetism quickly. The atoms in a magnetized needle can be disturbed by heating it or by dropping the needle on a hard object, which would cause the needle to lose its magnetism. Soft iron is used inside ignition coils because it will not keep its magnetism.

PERMEABILITY Magnetic flux lines cannot be insulated. There is no known material through which magnetic force does not pass, if the force is strong enough. However, some materials allow the force to pass though more easily than others. This degree of passage is called **permeability.** Iron allows magnetic flux lines to pass through much more easily than air, so iron is highly permeable.

An example of this characteristic is the use of a reluctor wheel in magnetic-type camshaft position (CMP) and crankshaft position (CKP) sensors. The teeth on a reluctor cause the magnetic field to increase as each tooth gets closer to the sensor and decrease as the tooth moves away, thus creating an AC voltage signal. ● **SEE FIGURE 23–6.**

RELUCTANCE Although there is no absolute insulation for magnetism, certain materials resist the passage of magnetic force. This can be compared to resistance without an electrical circuit. Air does not allow easy passage, so air has a high **reluctance.** Magnetic flux lines tend to concentrate in permeable materials and avoid materials with high reluctance. As with electricity, magnetic force follows the path of least resistance.

ELECTROMAGNETISM

DEFINITION Scientists did not discover that current-carrying conductors also are surrounded by a magnetic field until 1820. These fields may be made many times stronger than those surrounding conventional magnets. Also, the magnetic field strength around a conductor may be controlled by changing the current.

- As current increases, more flux lines are created and the magnetic field expands.
- As current decreases, the magnetic field contracts. The magnetic field collapses when the current is shut off.
- The interaction and relationship between magnetism and electricity is known as **electromagnetism.**

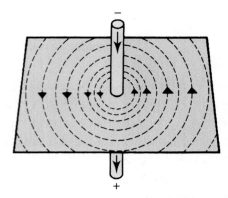

FIGURE 23–7 A magnetic field surrounds a straight, current-carrying conductor.

FIGURE 23–8 The left-hand rule for magnetic field direction is used with the electron flow theory.

FIGURE 23–9 The right-hand rule for magnetic field direction is used with the conventional theory of electron flow.

FIGURE 23–10 Conductors with opposing magnetic fields will move apart into weaker fields.

CREATING AN ELECTROMAGNET

An easy way to create an electromagnet is to wrap a nail with 20 turns of insulated wire and connect the ends to the terminals of a 1.5 volt dry cell battery. When energized, the nail will become a magnet and will be able to pick up tacks or other small steel objects.

STRAIGHT CONDUCTOR

The magnetic field surrounding a straight, current-carrying conductor consists of several concentric cylinders of flux that are the length of the wire. The amount of current flow (amperes) determines how many flux lines (cylinders) there will be and how far out they extend from the surface of the wire. ● SEE FIGURE 23–7.

LEFT-HAND AND RIGHT-HAND RULES

Magnetic flux cylinders have direction, just as the flux lines surrounding a bar magnet have direction. The **left-hand rule** is a simple way to determine this direction. When you grasp a conductor with your left hand so that your thumb points in the direction of electron flow (− to +) through the conductor, your fingers curl around the wire in the direction of the magnetic flux lines. ● SEE FIGURE 23–8.

Most automotive circuits use the conventional theory of current (+ to −) and, therefore, the **right-hand rule** is used to determine the direction of the magnetic flux lines. ● SEE FIGURE 23–9.

FIELD INTERACTION

The cylinders of flux surrounding current-carrying conductors interact with other magnetic fields. In the following illustrations, the cross symbol (+) indicates current moving inward, or away from you. It represents the tail of an arrow. The dot symbol (•) represents an arrowhead and indicates current moving outward. If two conductors carry current in opposite directions, their magnetic fields also carry current in opposite directions (according to the left-hand rule). If they are placed side by side, then the opposing flux lines between the conductors create a strong magnetic field. Current-carrying conductors tend to move out of a strong field into a weak field, so the conductors move away from each other. ● SEE FIGURE 23–10.

If the two conductors carry current in the same direction, then their fields are in the same direction. The flux lines between the two conductors cancel each other out, leaving a very weak field between them. The conductors are drawn into this weak field, and they tend to move toward each other.

MOTOR PRINCIPLE

Electric motors, such as vehicle starter motors, use this magnetic field interaction to convert electrical energy into mechanical energy. If two conductors carrying current in opposite directions are placed between strong north and south poles, the magnetic field of the conductor interacts with the magnetic fields of the poles. The counterclockwise field of the top conductor adds to the fields of the poles and creates a strong field beneath the conductor. The conductor then tries to move up to get out of this strong field. The clockwise field of the lower conductor adds to the field of the poles and creates a strong field above the conductor. The conductor then tries to move down to get out of this strong field. These forces cause the center of the motor, where the conductors are mounted, to turn clockwise. ● SEE FIGURE 23–11.

COIL CONDUCTOR

If several loops of wire are made into a coil, then the magnetic flux density is strengthened. Flux lines around a coil are the same as the flux lines around a bar magnet. ● SEE FIGURE 23–12.

FIGURE 23–11 Electric motors use the interaction of magnetic fields to produce mechanical energy.

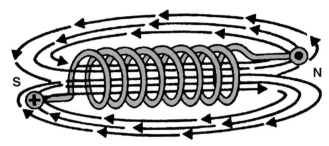

FIGURE 23–12 The magnetic lines of flux surrounding a coil look similar to those surrounding a bar magnet.

FIGURE 23–13 The left-hand rule for coils is shown.

They exit from the north pole and enter at the south pole. Use the left-hand thread rule to determine the north pole of a coil, as shown in ● **FIGURE 23–13.**

Grasp the coil with your left hand so that your fingers point in the direction of electron flow; your thumb will point toward the north pole of the coil.

ELECTROMAGNETIC STRENGTH The magnetic field surrounding a current-carrying conductor can be strengthened (increased) three ways.

- Place a soft iron core in the center of the coil.
- Increase the number of turns of wire in the coil.
- Increase the current flow through the coil windings.

 TECH TIP

Electricity and Magnetism

Electricity and magnetism are closely related because any electrical current flowing through a conductor creates a magnetic field. Any conductor moving through a magnetic field creates an electrical current. This relationship can be summarized as follows:

- Electricity creates magnetism.
- Magnetism creates electricity.

From a service technician's point of view, this relationship is important because wires carrying current should always be routed as the factory intended to avoid causing interference with another circuit or electronic component. This is especially important when installing or servicing spark plug wires, which carry high voltages and can cause high electromagnetic interference.

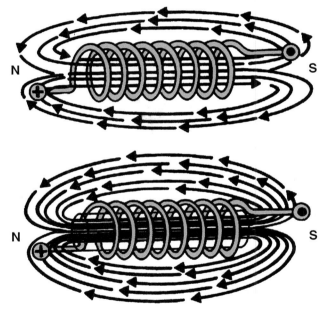

FIGURE 23–14 An iron core concentrates the magnetic lines of force surrounding a coil.

Because soft iron is highly permeable, magnetic flux lines pass through it easily. If a piece of soft iron is placed inside a coiled conductor, the flux lines concentrate in the iron core, rather than pass through the air, which is less permeable. The concentration of force greatly increases the strength of the magnetic field inside the coil. Increasing the number of turns in a coil and/or increasing the current flow through the coil results in greater field strength and is proportional to the number of turns. The magnetic field strength is often expressed in the units called **ampere-turns.** Coils with an iron core are called **electromagnets.** ● **SEE FIGURE 23–14.**

FIGURE 23–15 An electromagnetic switch that has a movable arm is referred to as a relay.

USES OF ELECTROMAGNETISM

RELAYS As mentioned in the previous chapter, a **relay** is a control device that allows a small amount of current to control a large amount of current in another circuit. A simple relay contains an electromagnetic coil in series with a battery and a switch. Near the electromagnet is a movable flat arm, called an *armature*, of some material that is attracted by a magnetic field. ● **SEE FIGURE 23–15.**

The armature pivots at one end and is held a small distance away from the electromagnet by a spring (or by the spring steel of the movable arm itself). A contact point, made

 FREQUENTLY ASKED QUESTION

Solenoid or Relay?

Often, either term is used to describe the same part in service information. ● **SEE CHART 23–1** for a summary of the differences.

of a good conductor, is attached to the free end of the armature. Another contact point is fixed a small distance away. The two contact points are wired in series with an electrical load and the battery.

When the switch is closed, the following occurs.

1. Current travels from the battery through a coil, creating an electromagnet.

2. The magnetic field created by the current attracts the armature, pulling it down until the contact points close.

3. Closing the contacts allows current in the heavy current circuit from the battery to the load.

When the switch is open, the following occurs.

1. The electromagnet loses its magnetism when the current is shut off.

2. Spring pressure lifts the arm back up.

3. The heavy current circuit is broken by the opening of the contact points.

Relays also may be designed with normally closed contacts that open when current passes through the electromagnetic coil.

SOLENOID A solenoid is an example of an electromagnetic switch. A solenoid uses a movable core rather than a movable arm and is generally used in higher-amperage applications. A solenoid can be a separate unit or attached to a starter such as a starter solenoid. ● **SEE FIGURE 23–16.**

	CONSTRUCTION	AMPERAGE RATING	USES	CALLED IN SERVICE INFORMATION
Relay	Uses a movable arm Coil: 60 to 100 ohms requiring 0.12 to 0.20 A to energize	1 to 30 A	Lower current switching, lower cost, more commonly used	Electromagnetic switch or relay
Solenoid	Uses a movable core Coil(s): 0.2 to 0.6 ohm requiring 20 to 60 A to energize	30 to 400 A	Higher cost, used in starter motor circuits and other high-amperage applications	Solenoid, relay or electromagnetic switch

CHART 23–1

Comparison between a relay and a solenoid.

HEAT SHIELD

"S" (START)
TERMINAL

SOLENOID

STARTER
MOTOR

"B" (BATTERY)
TERMINAL

"M" (MOTOR)
TERMINAL

(a)

MOVABLE ARM

NORMALLY CLOSED
(N.C.) CONTACT

NORMALLY OPEN
(N.O.) CONTACT

COIL
(60 TO 100 OHMS)

(b)

FIGURE 23–16 (a) A starter with attached solenoid. All of the current needed by the starter flows through the two large terminals of the solenoid and through the solenoid contacts inside. (b) A relay is designed to carry lower current compared to a solenoid and uses a movable arm.

FIGURE 23–17 Voltage can be induced by the relative motion between a conductor and magnetic lines of force.

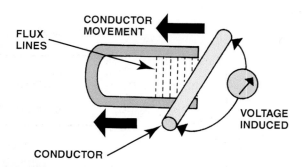

FIGURE 23–18 Maximum voltage is induced when conductors cut across the magnetic lines of force (flux lines) at a 90-degree angle.

ELECTROMAGNETIC INDUCTION

PRINCIPLES INVOLVED Electricity can be produced by using the relative movement of an electrical conductor and a magnetic field. There are three items necessary to produce electricity (voltage) from magnetism.

1. Electrical conductor (usually a coil of wire)
2. Magnetic field
3. Movement of either the conductor or the magnetic field

Therefore:

- Electricity creates magnetism.
- Magnetism can create electricity.

Magnetic flux lines create an electromotive force, or voltage, in a conductor if either the flux lines or the conductor is moving. This movement is called *relative motion*. This process is called induction, and the resulting electromotive force is called *induced voltage*. This creation of a voltage (electricity) in a conductor by a moving magnetic field is called **electromagnetic induction**. ● SEE FIGURE 23–17.

VOLTAGE INTENSITY Voltage is induced when a conductor cuts across magnetic flux lines. The amount of the voltage depends on the rate at which the flux lines are broken. The more flux lines that are broken per unit of time, the greater the induced voltage. If a single conductor breaks 1 million flux lines per second, 1 volt is induced.

There are four ways to increase induced voltage.

- Increase the strength of the magnetic field, so there are more flux lines.
- Increase the number of conductors that are breaking the flux lines.
- Increase the speed of the relative motion between the conductor and the flux lines so that more lines are broken per time unit.
- Increase the angle between the flux lines and the conductor to a maximum of 90 degrees. There is no voltage induced if the conductors move parallel to, and do not break, any flux lines.

Maximum voltage is induced if the conductors break flux lines at 90 degrees. Induced voltage varies proportionately at angles between 0 and 90 degrees. ● SEE FIGURE 23–18.

Voltage can be electromagnetically induced and can be measured. Induced voltage creates current. The direction of induced voltage (and the direction in which current moves) is called *polarity* and depends upon the direction of the flux lines, as well as the direction of relative motion.

LENZ'S LAW An induced current moves so that its magnetic field opposes the motion that induced the current. This principle is called **Lenz's law.** The relative motion of a conductor and a magnetic field is opposed by the magnetic field of the current it has induced.

SELF-INDUCTION When current begins to flow in a coil, the flux lines expand as the magnetic field forms and strengthens. As current increases, the flux lines continue to expand, cutting across the wires of the coil and actually inducing another voltage within the same coil. Following Lenz's law, this self-induced voltage tends to *oppose* the current that produces it. If the current continues to increase, the second voltage opposes the increase. When the current stabilizes, the countervoltage is no longer induced because there are no more expanding flux

FIGURE 23–19 Mutual induction occurs when the expansion or collapse of a magnetic field around one coil induces a voltage in a second coil.

lines (no relative motion). When current to the coil is shut off, the collapsing magnetic flux lines self-induce a voltage in the coil that tries to maintain the original current. The self-induced voltage *opposes* and *slows* the *decrease* in the original current. The self-induced voltage that opposes changes in current flow is an inductor called **counter electromotive force (CEMF).**

MUTUAL INDUCTION When two coils are close together, energy may be transferred from one to the other by magnetic coupling called mutual induction. **Mutual induction** means that the expansion or collapse of the magnetic field around one coil induces a voltage in the second coil.

IGNITION COILS

IGNITION COIL WINDINGS Ignition coils use two windings and are wound on the same iron core.

- One coil winding is connected to a battery through a switch and is called the *primary winding.*
- The other coil winding is connected to an external circuit and is called the *secondary winding.*

When the switch is open, there is no current in the primary winding. There is no magnetic field and, therefore, no voltage in the secondary winding. When the switch is closed, current is introduced and a magnetic field builds up around both windings.

The primary winding thus changes electrical energy from the battery into magnetic energy of the expanding field. As the field expands, it cuts across the secondary winding and induces a voltage in it. A meter connected to the secondary circuit shows current. ● **SEE FIGURE 23–19.**

When the magnetic field has expanded to its full strength, it remains steady as long as the same amount of current exists. The flux lines have stopped their cutting action. There is no relative motion and no voltage in the secondary winding, as shown on the meter.

When the switch is opened, primary current stops and the field collapses. As it does, flux lines cut across the secondary winding but in the opposite direction. This induces a secondary voltage with current in the opposite direction, as shown on the meter.

Mutual induction is used in ignition coils. In an ignition coil, low-voltage primary current induces a very high secondary voltage because of the different number of turns in the primary and secondary windings. Because the voltage is increased, an ignition coil is also called a *step-up transformer*.

- **Electrically connected windings.** Many ignition coils contain two separate but electrically connected windings of copper wire. This type of coil is called a "married" type and is used in older distributor-type ignition systems and in many coil-on-plug (COP) designs.
- **Electrically insulated windings.** Other coils are true transformers in which the primary and secondary windings are not electrically connected. This type of coil is

FIGURE 23–20 Some ignition coils are electrically connected, called married (top figure) whereas others use separated primary and secondary windings, called divorced (lower figure).

often called a "divorced" type and is used in all waste-spark-type ignition systems.

● **SEE FIGURE 23–20.**

IGNITION COIL CONSTRUCTION The center of an ignition coil contains a core of laminated soft iron (thin strips of soft iron). This core increases the magnetic strength of the coil. Surrounding the laminated core are approximately 20,000 turns of fine wire (approximately 42 gauge). These windings are called the secondary coil windings. Surrounding the secondary windings are approximately 150 turns of heavy wire (approximately 21 gauge). These windings are called the primary coil windings. The secondary winding has about 100 times the number of turns of the primary winding, referred to as the **turns ratio** (approximately 100:1). In many coils, these

windings are surrounded with a thin metal shield and insulating paper, and placed into a metal container. The metal container and shield help retain the magnetic field produced in the coil windings. The primary and secondary windings produce heat because of the electrical resistance in the turns of wire. Many coils contain oil to help cool the ignition coil. Other coil designs include the following:

- **Air-cooled, epoxy-sealed E coil.** The *E coil* is so named because the laminated, soft iron core is E shaped, with the coil wire turns wrapped around the center "finger" of the E and the primary winding wrapped inside the secondary winding. ● **SEE FIGURE 23–21.**

- **Spool design.** Used mostly for coil-on plug design, the coil windings are wrapped around a nylon or plastic spool or bobbin. ● **SEE FIGURE 23–22.**

FIGURE 23–21 A GM waste-spark ignition coil showing the section of laminations that is shaped like the letter *E*. These mild steel laminations improve the efficiency of the coil.

FIGURE 23–22 The coil-on-plug (COP) design typically uses a bobbin-type coil.

IGNITION COIL OPERATION The negative terminal is attached to an **ignition control module (ICM, or igniter)**, which opens and closes the primary ignition circuit by opening or closing the ground return path of the circuit. When the ignition switch is on, voltage should be available at *both* the positive terminal and the negative terminal of the coil if the primary windings of the coil have continuity.

A spark is created by the following sequence of events.

- A magnetic field is created in the primary winding of the coil when there is 12 volts applied to the primary coil winding and the ignition control module grounds the other end on the coil.

- When the ignition control module (or powertrain control module) opens the ground circuit, the stored magnetic field collapses and creates a high voltage (up to 40,000 volts or more) in the secondary winding.

- The high-voltage pulse then flows to the spark plug and creates a spark at the ground electrode inside the engine that ignites the air-fuel mixture inside the cylinder.

ELECTROMAGNETIC INTERFERENCE

DEFINITION Until the advent of the onboard computer, **electromagnetic interference (EMI)** was not a source of real concern to automotive engineers. The problem was mainly one of *radio-frequency interference (RFI)*, caused primarily by the use of secondary ignition cables. Using spark plug wires that contained a high-resistance, nonmetallic core made of carbon, linen, or fiberglass strands impregnated with graphite mostly solved RFI from the secondary ignition system. RFI is a part of electromagnetic interference, which deals with interference that affects radio reception. All electronic devices used in vehicles are affected by EMI/RFI.

HOW EMI IS CREATED Whenever there is current in a conductor, an electromagnetic field is created. When current stops and starts, as in a spark plug cable or a switch that opens and closes, the field strength changes. Each time this happens, it creates an electromagnetic signal wave. If it happens rapidly enough, the resulting high-frequency signal waves, or EMI, interfere with radio and television transmission or with other electronic systems such as those under the hood. This is an undesirable side effect of the phenomenon of electromagnetism.

Static electric charges caused by friction of the tires with the road, or the friction of engine drive belts contacting their pulleys, also produce EMI. Drive axles, driveshafts, and clutch or brake lining surfaces are other sources of static electric charges.

There are four ways of transmitting EMI, all of which can be found in a vehicle.

- Conductive coupling is actual physical contact through circuit conductors.
- Capacitive coupling is the transfer of energy from one circuit to another through an electrostatic field between two conductors.
- Inductive coupling is the transfer of energy from one circuit to another as the magnetic fields between two conductors form and collapse.
- Electromagnetic radiation is the transfer of energy by the use of radio waves from one circuit or component to another.

EMI SUPPRESSION DEVICES
There are four general ways in which EMI is reduced.

- **Resistance suppression.** Adding resistance to a circuit to suppress RFI works only for high-voltage systems. This has been done by the use of resistance spark plug cables, resistor spark plugs, and the silicone grease used on the distributor cap and rotor of some electronic ignitions.

- **Suppression capacitors and coils.** Capacitors are installed across many circuits and switching points to absorb voltage fluctuations. Among other applications, they are used across the following:
  - The primary circuit of some electronic ignition modules
  - The output terminal of most alternators
  - The armature circuit of some electric motors

Coils reduce current fluctuations resulting from self-induction. They are often combined with capacitors to act as EMI filter circuits for windshield wiper and electric fuel pump motors. Filters also may be incorporated in wiring connectors.

- **Shielding.** The circuits of onboard computers are protected to some degree from external electromagnetic waves by their metal housings.

- **Ground wires or straps.** Ground wires or braided straps between the engine and chassis of an automobile help suppress EMI conduction and radiation by providing a low-resistance circuit ground path. Such suppression ground straps are often installed between rubber-mounted components and body parts. On some models, ground straps are installed between body parts, such as between the hood and a fender panel, where no electrical circuit exists. The strap has no other job than to suppress EMI. Without it, the sheet-metal body and hood could function as a large capacitor. The space between the fender and hood could form an electrostatic field and couple with the computer circuits in the wiring harness routed near the fender panel. ● **SEE FIGURE 23-23.**

FIGURE 23-23 To help prevent underhood electromagnetic devices from interfering with the antenna input, it is important that all ground wires, including the one from this power antenna, be properly grounded.

Cell Phone Interference

A cellular phone emits a weak signal if it is turned on, even though it is not being used. This signal is picked up and tracked by cell phone towers. When the cell phone is called, it emits a stronger signal to notify the tower that it is on and capable of receiving a phone call. It is this "handshake" signal that can cause interference in the vehicle. Often this signal causes some static in the radio speakers even though the radio is off, but it can also cause a false antilock brake (ABS) trouble code to set. These signals from the cell phone create a voltage that is induced in the wires of the vehicle. Because the cell phone usually leaves with the customer, the service technician is often unable to verify the customer concern.

Remember, the interference occurs right *before* the cell phone rings. To fix the problem, connect an external antenna to the cell phone. This step will prevent the induction of a voltage in the wiring of the vehicle.

SUMMARY

1. Most automotive electrical components use magnetism, the strength of which depends on both the amount of current (amperes) and the number of turns of wire of each electromagnet.

2. The strength of electromagnets is increased by using a soft iron core.

3. Voltage can be induced from one circuit to another.

4. Electricity creates magnetism and magnetism creates electricity.

5. Radio-frequency interference (RFI) is a part of electromagnetic interference (EMI).

REVIEW QUESTIONS

1. What is the relationship between electricity and magnetism?

2. What is the difference between mutual induction and self-induction?

3. What is the result if a magnet cracks?

4. How can EMI be reduced or controlled?

CHAPTER QUIZ

1. Technician A says that magnetic lines of force can be seen by placing iron filings on a piece of paper and then holding them over a magnet. Technician B says that the effects of magnetic lines of force can be seen using a compass. Which technician is correct?
   a. Technician A only
   b. Technician B only
   c. Both Technicians A and B
   d. Neither Technician A nor B

2. Unlike magnetic poles _____, and like magnetic poles _____.
   a. Repel; attract
   b. Attract; repel
   c. Repel; repel
   d. Attract; attract

3. The conventional theory for current flow is being used to determine the direction of magnetic lines of force. Technician A says that the left-hand rule should be used. Technician B says that the right-hand rule should be used. Which technician is correct?
   a. Technician A only
   b. Technician B only
   c. Both Technicians A and B
   d. Neither Technician A nor B

4. Technician A says that a relay is an electromagnetic switch. Technician B says that a solenoid uses a movable core. Which technician is correct?
   a. Technician A only
   b. Technician B only
   c. Both Technicians A and B
   d. Neither Technician A nor B

5. Two technicians are discussing electromagnetic induction. Technician A says that the induced voltage can be increased if the speed is increased between the conductor and the magnetic lines of force. Technician B says that the induced voltage can be increased by increasing the strength of the magnetic field. Which technician is correct?
   a. Technician A only
   b. Technician B only
   c. Both Technicians A and B
   d. Neither Technician A nor B

6. An ignition coil operates using the principle(s) of _____.
   a. Electromagnetic induction
   b. Self-induction
   c. Mutual induction
   d. All of the above

7. Electromagnetic interference can be reduced by using a _____.
   a. Resistance
   b. Capacitor
   c. Coil
   d. All of the above

8. An ignition coil is an example of a _____.
   a. Solenoid
   b. Step-down transformer
   c. Step-up transformer
   d. Relay

9. Magnetic field strength is measured in _____.
   a. Ampere-turns
   b. Flux
   c. Density
   d. Coil strength

10. Two technicians are discussing ignition coils. Technician A says that some ignition coils have the primary and secondary windings electrically connected. Technician B says that some coils have totally separate primary and secondary windings that are not electrically connected. Which technician is correct?
    a. Technician A only
    b. Technician B only
    c. Both Technicians A and B
    d. Neither Technician A nor B

chapter 24

AUDIO SYSTEM OPERATION AND DIAGNOSIS

OBJECTIVES: After studying Chapter 24, the reader will be able to: • Prepare for ASE Electrical/Electronic Systems (A6) certification test content area "H" (Accessories Diagnosis and Repair). • Describe how AM and FM radio works. • Explain how to test speaker polarity. • Explain how to match speaker impedance. • Explain how crossovers work. • List causes and corrections of radio noise and interference. • Describe how satellite radio works. • Explain how Bluetooth systems work. • Discuss voice recognition systems.

KEY TERMS: Active crossover 220 • Alternator whine 225 • AM 214 • Bluetooth 223 • Crossover 220 • Decibels (dB) 220 • Floating ground system 219 • FM 214 • Frequency 214 • Ground plane 216 • Hertz 214 • High-pass filter 220 • Impedance 218 • Low-pass filter 220 • Modulation 214 • Powerline capacitor 221 • Radio choke 225 • Radio frequency (RF) 214 • RMS 222 • SDARS 224 • Skin effect 219 • Speakers 218 • Stiffening capacitor 221 • Subwoofer 219 • THD 222 • Tweeter 219 • Voice recognition 222 • Wavelength 213

AUDIO FUNDAMENTALS

INTRODUCTION   The audio system of today's vehicles is a complex combination of antenna system, receiver, amplifier, and speakers all designed to provide living room–type music reproduction while the vehicle is traveling in city traffic or at highway speed.

Audio systems produce audible sounds and include:

- Radio (AM, FM, and satellite)
- Antenna systems that are used to capture electronic energy broadcast to radios
- Speaker systems
- Aftermarket enhancement devices that increase the sound energy output of an audio system
- Diagnosis of audio-related problems

Many audio-related problems can be addressed and repaired by a service technician.

TYPES OF ENERGY   There are two types of energy that affect audio systems.

- **Electromagnetic energy or radio waves.** Antennas capture the radio waves which are then sent to the radio or receiver to be amplified.
- **Acoustical energy, usually called sound.** Radios and receivers amplify the radio wave signals and drive speak-

FIGURE 24–1 Audio systems use both electromagnetic radio waves and sound waves to reproduce sound inside the vehicle.

ers which reproduce the original sound as transmitted by radio waves.

● **SEE FIGURE 24–1.**

TERMINOLOGY   Radio waves travel at approximately the speed of light (186,282,000 miles per second) and are electromagnetic. Radio waves are measured in two ways, wavelength and frequency. A radio wave has a series of high points and low points. A **wavelength** is the time and distance between two consecutive points, either high or low. A wavelength is

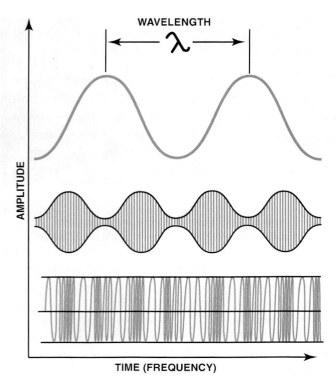

FIGURE 24–2 The relationship among wavelength, frequency, and amplitude.

AM WAVES

FIGURE 24–3 The amplitude changes in AM broadcasting.

FM WAVES

FIGURE 24–4 The frequency changes in FM broadcasting and the amplitude remains constant.

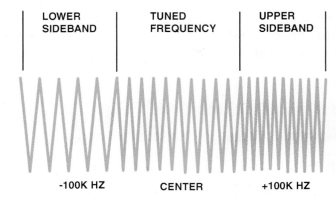

LOWER SIDEBAND	TUNED FREQUENCY	UPPER SIDEBAND
-100K HZ	CENTER	+100K HZ

FIGURE 24–5 Using upper and lower sidebands allows stereo to be broadcast. The receiver separates the signals to provide left and right channels.

measured in meters. **Frequency**, also known as **radio frequency (RF)**, is the number of times a particular waveform repeats itself in a given amount of time, and is measured in **hertz (Hz)**. A signal with a frequency of 1 Hz is one radio wavelength per second. Radio frequencies are measured in kilohertz (kHz), thousands of wavelengths per second, and megahertz (MHz), millions of wavelengths per second. ● **SEE FIGURE 24–2.**

- The higher the frequency, the shorter the wavelength.
- The lower the frequency, the longer the wavelength.

A longer wavelength can travel a further distance than a shorter wavelength. Therefore, lower frequencies provide better reception at further distances.

- AM radio frequencies range from 530 to 1,710 kHz.
- FM radio frequencies range from 87.9 to 107.9 MHz.

MODULATION **Modulation** is the term used to describe when information is added to a constant frequency. The base radio frequency used for RF is called the *carrier wave*. A carrier is a radio wave that is changed to carry information. The two types of modulation are:

- **Amplitude modulation (AM)**
- **Frequency modulation (FM)**

AM waves are radio waves that have amplitude that can be varied, transmitted, and detected by a receiver. Amplitude is the height of the wave as graphed on an oscilloscope. ● **SEE FIGURE 24–3.**

FM waves are also radio waves that have a frequency that can be varied, transmitted, and detected by a receiver. This type of modulation changes the number of cycles per second, or frequency, to carry the information. ● **SEE FIGURE 24–4.**

RADIO WAVE TRANSMISSION More than one signal can be carried by a radio wave. This process is called *sideband operation*. Sideband frequencies are measured in kilohertz. The amount of the signal above the assigned frequency is referred to as the upper sideband. The amount of the signal below the assigned frequency is called the lower sideband. This capability allows radio signals to carry stereo broadcasts. Stereo broadcasts use the upper sideband to carry one channel of the stereo signal, and the lower sideband to carry the other channel. When the signal is decoded by the radio, these two signals become the right and left channels. ● **SEE FIGURE 24–5.**

What Does a "Capture" Problem Mean?

A capture problem affects only FM reception and means that the receiver is playing more than one station if two stations are broadcasting at the same frequency. Most radios capture the stronger signal and block the weaker signal. However, if the stronger signal is weakened due to being blocked by buildings or mountains, the weaker signal will then be used. When this occurs, it will sound as if the radio is changing stations by itself. This is not a fault with the radio, but simply a rare occurrence with FM radio.

NOISE Because radio waves are a form of electromagnetic energy, other forms of energy can impact them. For example, a bolt of lightning generates broad radio-frequency bandwidths known as radio-frequency interference (RFI). RFI is one type of electromagnetic interference (EMI) and is the frequency that interferes with radio transmission.

AM CHARACTERISTICS AM radio reception can be achieved over long distances from the transmitter because the waves can bounce off the ionosphere, usually at night. Even during the day, the AM signals can be picked up some distance from the transmitter. AM radio reception depends on a good antenna. If there is a fault in the antenna circuit, AM reception is affected the most.

FM CHARACTERISTICS Because FM waves have a high RF and a short wavelength, they travel only a short distance. The waves cannot follow the shape of the earth but instead travel in a straight line from the transmitter to the receiver. FM waves will travel through the ionosphere and into space and do not reflect back to earth like AM waves.

MULTIPATH Multipath is caused by reflected, refracted, or line of sight signals reaching an antenna at different times. Multipath results from the radio receiving two signals to process on the same frequency. This causes an echo effect in the speakers. *Flutter,* or *picket fencing* as it is sometimes called, is caused by the blocking of part of the FM signal. This blocking causes a weakening of the signal resulting in only part of the signal getting to the antenna, causing an on-again off-again radio sound. Flutter also occurs when the transmitter and the receiving antenna are far apart.

RADIOS AND RECEIVERS

The antenna receives the radio wave where it is converted into very weak fluctuating electrical current. This current travels along the antenna lead-in to the radio that amplifies the signal and sends the new signal to the speakers where it is converted into acoustical energy.

Most late-model radios and receivers use five input/output circuits.

1. **Power.** Usually a constant 12 volt feed to keep the internal clock alive

2. **Ground.** This is the lowest voltage in the circuit and connects indirectly to the negative terminal of the battery.

3. **Serial data.** Used to turn the unit on and off and provide other functions such as steering wheel control operation

4. **Antenna input.** From one or more antennas

5. **Speaker outputs.** These wires connect the receiver to the speakers or as an input to an amplifier.

ANTENNAS

TYPES OF ANTENNAS The typical radio electromagnetic energy from the broadcast antenna induces a signal in the antenna that is very small, only about 25 microvolts AC (0.000025 VAC) in strength. The radio contains amplifier circuits that increase the received signal strength into usable information.

For example, the five types of antennas used on vehicles include:

- **Slot antenna.** The slot antenna is concealed in the roof of some plastic body vehicles such as older General Motors plastic body vans. This antenna is surrounded by metal on a Mylar sheet.

- **Rear window defogger grid.** This type of system uses the heating wires to receive the signals and special circuitry to separate the RF from the DC heater circuit.

- **Powered mast.** These antennas are controlled by the radio. When the radio is turned on, the antenna is raised; when the radio is shut off, the antenna is retracted. The antenna system consists of an antenna mast and a drive motor controlled by the radio "on" signal through a relay.

- **Fixed mast antenna.** This antenna offers the best overall performance currently available. The mast is simply a vertical rod. Mast antennas are typically located on the fender or rear quarter panel of the vehicle.

FOIL (SLOT) ANTENNA USED ON PLASTIC BODY VEHICLE BETWEEN HEADLINER AND ROOF

SLOT ANTENNA

REAR WINDOW DEFOGGER GRID

POWER MAST   INTEGRATED ANTENNA   FIXED MAST

FIGURE 24–6 The five types of antennas used on General Motors vehicles include the slot antenna, fixed mast antenna, rear window defogger grid antenna, a powered mast antenna, and an integrated antenna.

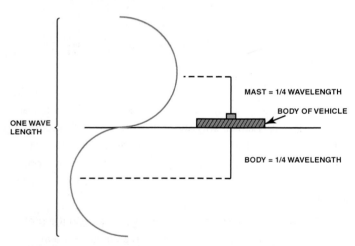

ONE WAVE LENGTH

MAST = 1/4 WAVELENGTH

BODY OF VEHICLE

BODY = 1/4 WAVELENGTH

FIGURE 24–7 The ground plane is actually one-half of the antenna.

■ **Integrated antenna.** This type of antenna is sandwiched in the windshield and an appliqué on the rear window glass. The antenna in the rear window is the primary antenna and receives both AM and FM signals. The secondary antenna is located in the front windshield typically on the passenger side of the vehicle. This antenna receives only FM signals. ● **SEE FIGURE 24–6.**

ANTENNA DIAGNOSIS

ANTENNA HEIGHT The antenna collects all radio-frequency signals. An AM radio operates best with as long an antenna as

What Is a Ground Plane?

Antennas designed to pick up the electromagnetic energy that is broadcast through the air to the transmitting antenna are usually one-half wavelength high, and the other half of the wavelength is the **ground plane**. This one-half wavelength in the ground plane is literally underground.

For ideal reception, the receiving antenna should also be the same as the wavelength of the signal. Because this length is not practical, a design compromise uses the length of the antenna as one-fourth of the wavelength; in addition, the body of the vehicle itself is one-fourth of the wavelength. The body of the vehicle, therefore, becomes the ground plane. ● **SEE FIGURE 24–7.**

Any faulty condition in the ground plane circuit will cause the ground plane to lose effectiveness, such as:

• Loose or corroded battery cable terminals
• Acid buildup on battery cables
• Engine grounds with high resistance
• Loss of antenna or audio system grounds
• Defective alternator, causing an AC ripple exceeding 50 mV (0.050 V)

possible, but FM reception is best when the antenna height is exactly 31 in. (79 cm). Most fixed-length antennas are, therefore, exactly this height. Even the horizontal section of a windshield antenna is 31 in. (79 cm) long.

A defective antenna will:

■ Greatly affect AM radio reception
■ May affect FM radio reception

ANTENNA TESTING If the antenna or lead-in cable is broken (open), FM reception will be heard but may be weak, and there will be *no* AM reception. An ohmmeter should read infinity between the center antenna lead and the antenna case. For proper reception and lack of noise, the case of the antenna must be properly grounded to the vehicle body. ● **SEE FIGURE 24–8.**

POWER ANTENNA TESTING AND SERVICE Most power antennas use a circuit breaker and a relay to power a reversible, permanent magnet (PM) electric motor that moves a nylon cord attached to the antenna mast. Some vehicles

FIGURE 24–8 If all ohmmeter readings are satisfactory, the antenna is good.

FIGURE 24–9 Cutting a small hole in a fender cover helps to protect the vehicle when replacing or servicing an antenna.

🔧 **TECH TIP**

The Hole in the Fender Cover Trick

A common repair is to replace the mast of a power antenna. To help prevent the possibility of causing damage to the body or paint of the vehicle, cut a hole in a fender cover and place it over the antenna.
● **SEE FIGURE 24–9.**

If a wrench or tool slips during the removal or installation process, the body of the vehicle will be protected.

FIGURE 24–10 A typical power antenna assembly. Note the braided ground wire used to ensure that the antenna has a good ground plane.

---

have a dash-mounted control that can regulate antenna mast height and/or operation, whereas many operate automatically when the radio is turned on and off. The power antenna assembly is usually mounted between the outer and inner front fender or in the rear quarter panel. The unit contains the motor, a spool for the cord, and upper- and lower-limit switches. The power antenna mast is tested in the same way as a fixed-mast antenna. (An infinity reading should be noted on an ohmmeter when the antenna is tested between the center antenna terminal and the housing or ground.) Except in the case of cleaning or mast replacement, most power antennas are ei-

ther replaced as a unit or repaired by specialty shops. ● **SEE FIGURE 24–10.**

Making certain that the drain holes in the motor housing are not plugged with undercoating, leaves, or dirt can prevent many power antenna problems. All power antennas should be kept clean by wiping the mast with a soft cloth and lightly oiling with light oil such as WD-40 or similar.

CONE MOVING IN

CONE MOVING OUT

FIGURE 24–11 Between 6 and 7 volts is applied to each speaker terminal, and the audio amplifier then increases the voltage on one terminal and at the same time decreases the voltage on the other terminal causing the speaker cone to move. The moving cone then moves the air, causing sound.

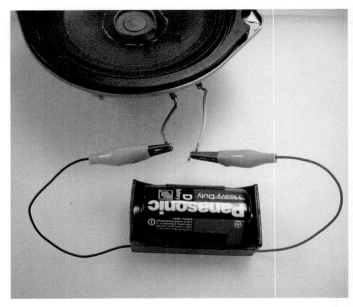

FIGURE 24–12 A typical automotive speaker with two terminals. The polarity of the speakers can be identified by looking at the wiring diagram in the service manual or by using a 1.5 volt battery to check. When the battery positive is applied to the positive terminal of the speaker, the cone will move outward. When the battery leads are reversed, the speaker cone will move inward.

SPEAKERS

PURPOSE AND FUNCTION The purpose of any **speaker** is to reproduce the original sound as accurately as possible. Speakers are also called *loudspeakers*. The human ear is capable of hearing sounds from a very low frequency of 20 Hz (cycles per seconds) to as high as 20,000 Hz. No one speaker is capable of reproducing sound over such a wide frequency range. ● **SEE FIGURE 24–11.**

Good-quality speakers are the key to a proper sounding radio or sound system. Replacement speakers should be securely mounted and wired according to the correct *polarity*. ● **SEE FIGURE 24–12.**

IMPEDANCE MATCHING All speakers used on the same radio or amplifier should have the same internal coil resistance, called **impedance**. If unequal-impedance speakers are used, sound quality may be reduced and serious damage to the radio may result. ● **SEE FIGURE 24–13.**

All speakers should have the same impedance. For example, if two 4 ohm speakers are being used for the rear and they are connected in parallel, the total impedance is 2 ohms.

$$R_T = \frac{4\Omega \,(\textbf{impedance of each speaker})}{2 \,(\textbf{number of speakers in parallel})} = 2\ \textbf{ohms}$$

The front speakers should also represent a 2 ohm load from the radio or amplifier. See the following example.

Two front speakers: each 2 ohms

Two rear speakers: each 8 ohms

Solution: Connect the front speakers in series (connect the positive [+] of one speaker to the negative [−] of the other) for a total impedance of 4 ohms ($2\ \Omega + 2\ \Omega = 4\ \Omega$). Connect the two rear speakers in parallel (connect the positive [+] of each speaker together and the negative [−] of each speaker together) for a total impedance of 4 ohms ($8\ \Omega \div 2 = 4\ \Omega$).

SPEAKER WIRING The wire used for speakers should be as large a wire (as low an AWG gauge number) as is practical in order to be assured that full power is reaching the speakers. Typical "speaker wire" is about 22 gauge (0.35 mm²), yet tests conducted by audio engineers have concluded that increasing the wire gauge—up to 4 gauge (19 mm²) or larger—greatly increases sound quality. All wiring connections should be soldered after making certain that all speaker connections have the correct polarity.

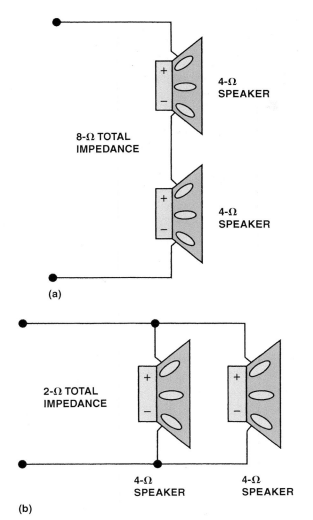

(a)

(b)

FIGURE 24–13 (a) Two 4 ohm speakers connected in series result in total impedance of 8 ohms. (b) Two 4 ohm speakers connected in parallel result in total impedance of 2 ohms.

CAUTION: Be careful when installing additional audio equipment on a General Motors vehicle system that uses a two-wire speaker connection called a floating ground system. Other systems run only one power (hot) lead to each speaker and ground the other speaker lead to the body of the vehicle.

This arrangement helps prevent interference and static that could occur if these components were connected to a chassis (vehicle) ground. If the components are chassis grounded, there may be a difference in the voltage potential (voltage); this condition is called a *ground loop.*

CAUTION: Regardless of radio speaker connections used, *never* operate any radio without the speakers connected, or the speaker driver section of the radio may be damaged as a result of the open speaker circuit.

 TECH TIP

Skin Effect

When a high-frequency signal (AC voltage) is transmitted through a wire, the majority of it travels on the outside surface of the wire. This characteristic is called **skin effect**. The higher the frequency is, the closer to the outer surface the signal moves. To increase audio system output, most experts recommend the use of wire that has many strands of very fine wire to increase the surface area or the skin area of the conductor. Therefore, most aftermarket speaker wire is stranded with many small-diameter copper strands.

SPEAKER TYPES

INTRODUCTION No one speaker is capable of reproducing sound over such a wide frequency range. Therefore, speakers are available in three basic types.

1. Tweeters are for high-frequency ranges.
2. Midrange are for mid-frequency ranges.
3. Woofers and subwoofers are for low-frequency ranges.

TWEETER A **tweeter** is a speaker designed to reproduce high-frequency sounds, usually between 4,000 and 20,000 Hz (4 and 20 kHz). Tweeters are very directional. This means that the human ear is most likely to be able to detect the location of the speaker while listening to music. This also means that a tweeter should be mounted in the vehicle where the sound can be directed in line of sight to the listener. Tweeters are usually mounted on the inside door near the top, windshield "A" pillar, or similar locations.

MIDRANGE A midrange speaker is designed and manufactured to be able to best reproduce sounds in the middle of the human hearing range, from 400 to 5,000 Hz. Most people are sensitive to the sound produced by these midrange speakers. These speakers are also directional in that the listener can usually locate the source of the sound.

SUBWOOFER A **subwoofer**, sometimes called a *woofer,* produces the lowest frequency of sounds, usually 125 Hz and lower. A *midbass* speaker may also be used to reproduce those frequencies between 100 and 500 Hz. Low-frequency sounds from these speakers are *not* directional. This means that the listener usually cannot detect the source of the sound from these speakers. The low-frequency sounds seem to be everywhere in the vehicle, so the location of the speakers is not as critical as with the higher frequency speakers.

The subwoofer can be placed almost anywhere in the vehicle. Most subwoofers are mounted in the rear of the vehicle where there is more room for the larger subwoofer speakers.

SPEAKER FREQUENCY RESPONSE Frequency response is how a speaker responds to a range of frequencies. A typical frequency response for a midrange speaker may be 500 to 4,000 Hz.

SOUND LEVELS

DECIBEL SCALE A **decibel (dB)** is a measure of sound power, and it is the faintest sound a human can hear in the midband frequencies. The dB scale is not linear (straight line) but logarithmic, meaning that a small change in the dB reading results in a large change in volume of noise. An increase of 10 dB in sound pressure is equal to doubling the perceived volume. Therefore, a small difference in dB rating means a big difference in the sound volume of the speaker.

EXAMPLES Some examples of decibel sound levels include:

- Quiet, faint
  - 30 dB: whisper, quiet library
  - 40 dB: quiet room
- Moderate
  - 50 dB: moderate range sound
  - 60 dB: normal conversation
- Loud
  - 70 dB: vacuum cleaner, city traffic
  - 80 dB: busy noisy traffic, vacuum cleaner
- Extremely loud
  - 90 dB: lawnmower, shop tools
  - 100 dB: chain saw, air drill
- Hearing loss possible
  - 110 dB: loud rock music

CROSSOVERS

DEFINITION A **crossover** is designed to separate the frequency of a sound and send a certain frequency range, such as low bass sounds, to a woofer designed to reproduce these low-frequency sounds. There are two types of crossovers: passive and active.

PASSIVE CROSSOVER A passive crossover does not use an external power source. Rather it uses a coil and a capacitor

WARNING

Hearing loss is possible if exposed to loud sounds. According to noise experts (audiologists), hearing protection should be used whenever the following occurs.
1. You must raise your voice to be heard by others next to you.
2. You cannot hear someone else speaking who is less than 3 ft (1 m) away.
3. You are operating power equipment, such as a lawnmower.

FREQUENTLY ASKED QUESTION

What Is a Bass Blocker?

A bass blocker is a capacitor and coil assembly that effectively blocks low frequencies. A bass blocker is normally used to block low frequencies being sent to the smaller front speakers. Using a bass blocker allows the smaller front speakers to more efficiently reproduce the midrange and high-range frequency sounds.

to block certain frequencies that a particular type of speaker cannot handle and allow just those frequencies that it can handle to be applied to the speaker. For example, a 6.6 millihenry coil and a 200 microfarad capacitor can effectively pass 100 Hz frequency sound to a large 10 in. subwoofer. This type of passive crossover is called a **low-pass filter**, because it passes (transfers) only the low-frequency sounds to the speaker and blocks all other frequencies. A **high-pass filter** is used to transfer higher frequency (over 100 Hz) to smaller speakers.

ACTIVE CROSSOVER **Active crossovers** use an external power source and produce superior performance. An active crossover is also called an *electronic crossover* or *crossover network*. These units include many powered filters and are considerably more expensive than passive crossovers. Two amplifiers are necessary to fully benefit from an active crossover. One amplifier is for the higher frequencies and midrange and the other amplifier is for the subwoofers. If you are on a budget and plan to use just one amplifier, then use passive crossover. If you can afford to use two or more amplifiers, then consider using the electronic (active) crossover. ● **SEE FIGURE 24–14** for an example of crossovers used in factory-installed systems.

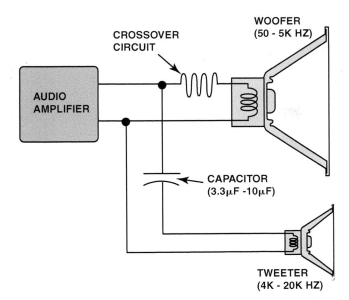

FIGURE 24-14 Crossovers are used in audio systems to send high-frequency sounds to the small (tweeter) speakers and low-frequency sounds to larger (woofer) speakers.

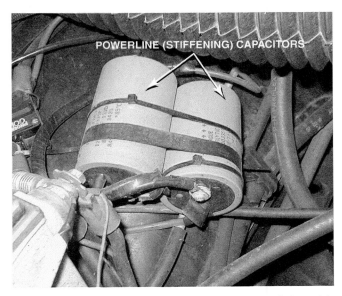

FIGURE 24-15 Two capacitors connected in parallel provide the necessary current flow to power large subwoofer speakers.

AFTERMARKET SOUND SYSTEM UPGRADE

POWER AND GROUND UPGRADES   If adding an amplifier and additional audio components, be sure to include the needed power and ground connections. These upgrades can include:

- A separate battery for the audio system
- An inline fuse near the battery to protect the wiring and the components
- Wiring that is properly sized to the amperage draw of the system and the length of wire (The higher the output wattage the greater the amperage required and the larger the wire gauge needed. The longer the distance between the battery and the components, the larger the wire gauge needed for best performance.)
- Ground wires at least the same gauge as the power side wiring (Some experts recommend using extra ground wires for best performance.)

Read, understand, and follow all instructions that come with audio system components.

POWERLINE CAPACITOR   A **powerline capacitor**, also called a **stiffening capacitor**, refers to a large capacitor (often abbreviated CAP) of 0.25 farad or larger connected to an amplifier power wire. The purpose and function of this capacitor is to provide the electrical reserve energy needed by the amplifier to provide deep bass notes. ● **SEE FIGURE 24-15.**

POWERLINE CAPACITOR USAGE GUIDE	
WATTS (AMPLIFIER)	**RECOMMENDED CAPACITOR IN FARADS (MICROFARADS)**
100 W	0.10 farad (100,000 µF)
200 W	0.20 farad (200,000 µF)
250 W	0.25 farad (250,000 µF)
500 W	0.50 farad (500,000 µF)
750 W	0.75 farad (750,000 µF)
1,000 W	1.00 farad (1,000,000 µF)

CHART 24-1

The rating of the capacitor needed to upgrade an audio system is directly related to the wattage of the system.

Battery power is often slow to respond; and when the amplifier attempts to draw a large amount of current, the capacitor will try to stabilize the voltage level at the amplifier by discharging stored current as needed.

A rule of thumb is to connect a capacitor with a capacity of 1 farad for each 1,000 watts of amplifier power. ● **SEE CHART 24-1.**

CAPACITOR INSTALLATION   A powerline capacitor connects to the power leads between the inline fuse and the amplifier. ● **SEE FIGURE 24-16.**

If the capacitor were connected to the circuit as shown without "precharging," the capacitor would draw so much current that it would blow the inline fuse. To safely connect a large capacitor, it must be *precharged*. To precharge the capacitor, follow these steps.

FIGURE 24–16 A powerline capacitor should be connected through the power wire to the amplifier as shown. When the amplifier requires more electrical power (watts) than the battery can supply, the capacitor will discharge into the amplifier and supply the necessary current for the fraction of a second it is needed by the amplifier. At other times when the capacitor is not needed, it draws current from the battery to keep it charged.

STEP 1 Connect the negative (−) terminal of the capacitor to a good chassis ground.

STEP 2 Insert an automotive 12 V light bulb, such as a headlight or parking light, between the positive (+) terminal of the capacitor and the positive terminal of the battery. The light will light as the capacitor is being charged and then go out when the capacitor is fully charged.

STEP 3 Disconnect the light from the capacitor, then connect the power lead to the capacitor. The capacitor is now fully charged and ready to provide the extra power necessary to supplement battery power to the amplifier.

VOICE RECOGNITION

PARTS AND OPERATION **Voice recognition** is an expanding technology. It allows the driver of a vehicle to perform tasks, such as locate an address in a navigation system by using voice commands rather than buttons. In the past, users had to say the exact words to make it work such as the following examples listed from an owner manual for a vehicle equipped with a voice-actuated navigation system.

"Go home"

"Repeat guidance"

"Nearest ATM"

The problem with these simple voice commands was that the exact wording had to be spoken. The voice recognition software would compare the voice command to a specific list of words or phrases stored in the system in order for a match to occur. Newer systems recognize speech patterns and take action based on learned patterns. Voice recognition can be used for the following functions.

1. Navigation system operation (● **SEE FIGURE 24–17.**)
2. Sound system operation
3. Climate control system operation

FIGURE 24–17 Voice commands can be used to control many functions, including navigation systems, climate control, telephone, and radio.

? **FREQUENTLY ASKED QUESTION**

What Do the Amplifier Specifications Mean?

RMS power	**RMS** means root-mean-square and is the rating that indicates how much power the amplifier is capable of producing continuously.
RMS power at 2 ohms	This specification in watts indicates how much power the amplifier delivers into a 2 ohm speaker load. This 2 ohm load is achieved by wiring two 4 ohm speakers in parallel or by using 2 ohm speakers.
Peak power	Peak power is the maximum wattage an amplifier can deliver in a short burst during a musical peak.
THD	**Total harmonic distortion (THD)** represents the amount of change of the signal as it is being amplified. The lower the number, the better the amplifier (e.g., a 0.01% rating is better than a 0.07% rating).
Signal-to-noise ratio	This specification is measured in decibels (dB) and compares the strength of the signal with the level of the background noise (hiss). A higher volume indicates less background noise (e.g., a 105 dB rating is better than a 100 dB rating).

4. Telephone dialing and other related functions (● **SEE FIGURE 24–18.**)

A microphone is usually placed in the driver's side sun visor or in the overhead console in the center top portion of the windshield area.

FIGURE 24-18 The voice command icon on the steering wheel of a Cadillac.

DIAGNOSIS AND SERVICE Voice recognition is usually incorporated into many functions of the vehicle. If a problem occurs with the system, perform the following steps.

1. Verify the customer complaint (concern). Check the owner manual or service information for the proper voice commands and verify that the system is not functioning correctly.

2. Check for any aftermarket accessories that may interfere or were converted to components used by the voice recognition system, such as remote start units, MP3 players, or any other electrical component.

3. Check for stored diagnostic trouble codes (DTCs) using a scan tool.

4. Follow the recommended troubleshooting procedures as stated in service information.

BLUETOOTH

OPERATION **Bluetooth** is a (radio frequency) standard for short-range communications. The range of a typical Bluetooth device is 33 ft (10 m) and it operates in the ISM (industrial, scientific, and medical) band between 2.4000 and 2.4835 MHz.

Bluetooth is a wireless standard that works on two levels.

- It provides physical communication using low power, requiring only about 1 milliwatt (1/1,000 of a watt) of electrical power, making it suitable for use with small handheld or portable devices, such as an ear-mounted speaker/microphone.

- It provides a standard protocol for how bits of data are sent and received.

The Bluetooth standard is an advantage because it is wireless, low cost, and automatic. The automotive use of Bluetooth technology is in the operation of a cellular telephone being tied

? FREQUENTLY ASKED QUESTION

Where Did Bluetooth Get Its Name?

The early adopters of the standard used the term Bluetooth, and they named it for Harold Bluetooth, the king of Denmark in the late 900s. The king was able to unite Denmark and part of Norway into a single kingdom.

? FREQUENTLY ASKED QUESTION

Can Two Bluetooth Telephones Be Used in a Vehicle?

Usually. In order to use two telephones, the second phone needs to be given a name. When both telephones enter the vehicle, check which one is recognized. Say "phone status" and the system will tell you to which telephone the system is responding. If it is not the one you want, simply say, "next phone" and it will move to the other one.

into the vehicle. The vehicle allows the use of hands-free telephone usage. A vehicle that is Bluetooth telephone equipped has the following components.

- A Bluetooth receiver can be built into the navigation or existing sound system.

- A microphone allows the driver to use voice commands as well as telephone conversations from the vehicle to the cell via Bluetooth wireless connections.

Many cell phones are equipped with Bluetooth which may allow the caller to use an ear-mounted microphone and speaker.
● **SEE FIGURE 24-19.**

FIGURE 24-19 Bluetooth earpiece that contains a microphone and speaker unit that is paired to a cellular phone. The telephone has to be within 33 ft (10 m) of the earpiece.

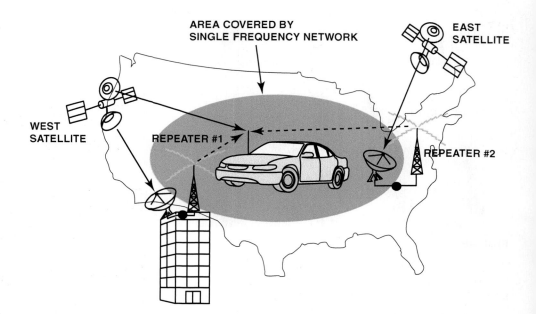

FIGURE 24–20 SDARS uses satellites and repeater stations to broadcast radio.

AREA COVERED BY SINGLE FREQUENCY NETWORK

EAST SATELLITE

WEST SATELLITE

REPEATER #1

REPEATER #2

If the vehicle and the cell phone are equipped with Bluetooth, the speaker and microphone can be used as a hands-free telephone when the phone is in the vehicle. The cell phone can be activated in the vehicle by using voice commands.

SATELLITE RADIO

PARTS AND OPERATION Satellite radio, also called **Satellite Digital Audio Radio Services** or **SDARS**, is a fee-based system that uses satellites to broadcast high-quality radio. SDARS broadcasts on the S-band of 2.1320 to 2.345 GHz.

SIRIUS/XM RADIO Sirius/XM radio is standard equipment or optional in most vehicles. XM radio uses two satellites launched in 2001 called Rock (XM-2) and Roll (XM-1) in a geosynchronous orbit above North America. Two replacement satellites, Rhythm (XM-3) and Blues (XM-4) were launched in 2006. Sirius and XM radio combined in 2008 and now share some programming. The two types of satellite radios use different protocols and, therefore, require separate radios unless a combination unit is purchased.

RECEPTION Reception from satellites can be affected by tall buildings and mountains. To help ensure consistent reception, both SDARS providers do the following:

- Include in the radio itself a buffer circuit that can store several seconds of broadcasts to provide service when traveling out of a service area
- Provide land-based repeater stations in most cities (● **SEE FIGURE 24–20.**)

FIGURE 24–21 An aftermarket XM radio antenna mounted on the rear deck lid. The deck lid acts as the ground plane for the antenna.

ANTENNA To be able to receive satellite radio, the antenna needs to be able to receive signals from both the satellite and the repeater stations located in many large cities. There are various types and shapes of antennas, including those shown in ● **FIGURES 24–21 AND 24–22.**

DIAGNOSIS AND SERVICE The first step in any diagnosis is to verify the customer complaint (concern). If no satellite service is being received, first check with the customer to verify that the monthly service fee has been paid and the account is up to date. If poor reception is the cause, carefully check the antenna for damage or faults with the lead-in wire. The antennas must be installed on a metal surface to provide the proper ground plane.

For all other satellite radio fault problems, check service information for the exact tests and procedures. Always follow the

FIGURE 24–22 A shark-fin-type factory antenna used for both XM and OnStar.

factory recommended procedures. Check the following websites for additional information.

- www.xmradio.com
- www.sirius.com
- www.siriusxm.com

RADIO INTERFERENCE

DEFINITION Radio interference is caused by variations in voltage in the powerline or picked up by the antenna. A "whine" that increases in frequency with increasing engine speed is usually referred to as an **alternator whine** and is eliminated by installing a radio choke or a filter capacitor in the power feed wire to the radio. ● **SEE FIGURE 24–23.**

CAPACITOR USAGE Ignition noise is usually a raspy sound that varies with the speed of the engine. This noise is usually eliminated by the installation of a capacitor on the positive side of the ignition coil. The capacitor should be connected to the power feed wire to either the radio or the amplifier, or both. The capacitor *has* to be grounded. A capacitor allows AC interference to pass through to ground while blocking the flow of DC current. Use a 470 μF, 50 volt electrolytic capacitor, which is readily available from most radio supply stores. A special coaxial capacitor can also be used in the powerline. ● **SEE FIGURE 24–24.**

RADIO CHOKE A **radio choke**, which is a coil of wire, can also be used to reduce or eliminate radio interference. Again, the radio choke is installed in the power feed wire to the radio equipment. Radio interference being picked up by the antenna can best be eliminated by stopping the source of the interference and making certain that all units containing a coil, such as electric motors, have a capacitor or diode attached to the power-side wire.

FIGURE 24–23 A radio choke and/or a capacitor can be installed in the power feed lead to any radio, amplifier, or equalizer.

FIGURE 24–24 Many automobile manufacturers install a co-axial capacitor, like this one, in the power feed wire to the blower motor to eliminate interference caused by the blower motor.

? FREQUENTLY ASKED QUESTION

What Does ESN Mean?

ESN means electronic serial number. This is necessary information to know when reviewing satellite radio subscriptions. Each radio has its own unique ESN, often found on a label at the back or bottom of the unit. It is also often shown on scan tools or test equipment designed to help diagnose faults in the units.

BRAIDED GROUND WIRE Using a braided ground wire is usually specified when electrical noise is a concern. The radio-frequency signals travel on the surface of a conductor rather than through the core of the wire. A braided ground strap is used because the overlapped wires short out any radio-frequency signals traveling on the surface.

AUDIO NOISE SUMMARY
In summary:

- Radio noise can be broadcast or caused by noise (voltage variations) in the power circuit to the radio.
- Most radio interference complaints come when someone installs an amplifier, power booster, equalizer, or other radio accessory.
- *A major cause of this interference is the variation in voltage through the ground circuit wires. To prevent or reduce this interference, make sure all ground connections are clean and tight.*
- Placing a capacitor in the ground circuit also may be beneficial.

CAUTION: Amplifiers sold to boost the range or power of an antenna often increase the level of interference and radio noise to a level that disturbs the driver.

Capacitor and/or radio chokes are the most commonly used components. Two or more capacitors can be connected in parallel to increase the capacity of the original capacitor. A "sniffer" can be used to locate the source of the radio noise. A sniffer is a length of antenna wire with a few inches of insulation removed from the antenna end. The sniffer is attached to the antenna input terminal of the radio, and the radio is turned on and set to a weak station. The other end of the sniffer is then moved around areas of the dash to locate where the source of the interference originates. The radio noise will greatly increase if the end of the sniffer comes close to where electromagnetic leakage is occurring.
● **SEE FIGURE 24–25.**
  ● **SEE CHART 24–2.**

TECH TIP

The Separate Battery Trick

Whenever diagnosing sound system interference, try running separate 14 gauge wire(s) from the sound system power lead and ground to a separate battery outside of the vehicle. If the noise is still heard, the interference is *not* due to an alternator diode or other source in the wiring of the vehicle.

FIGURE 24–25 A "sniffer" can be made from an old antenna lead-in cable by removing about 3 in. of the outer shielding from the end. Plug the lead-in cable into the antenna input of the radio and tune the radio to a weak station. Move the end of the antenna wire around the vehicle dash area. The sniffer is used to locate components that may not be properly shielded or grounded and can cause radio interference through the case (housing) of the radio itself.

AUDIO NOISE CONTROL SYMPTOM CHART		
NOISE SOURCE	**WHAT IT SOUNDS LIKE**	**WHAT TO TRY**
Alternator	A whine whose pitch changes with engine speed	Install a capacitor to a ground at the alternator output
Ignition	Ticking that changes with engine speed	Use a sniffer to further localize the source of the problem
Turn signals	Popping in time with the turn signals	Install a capacitor across the turn signal flasher
Brake lights	Popping whenever the brake pedal is depressed	Install a capacitor across the brake light switch contacts
Blower motor	Ticking in time with the blower motor	Install a capacitor to ground at the motor hot lead
Dash lamp dimmer	A buzzy whine whose pitch changes with the dimmer setting	Install a capacitor to ground at the dimmer hot lead
Horn switch	Popping when the horn is sounded	Install a capacitor between the hot lead and horn lead at the horn relay
Horn	Buzzing synchronized with the horn	Install a capacitor to ground at each horn hot lead
Amplifier power supply	A buzz, not affected by engine speed	Ground the amplifier chassis using a braided ground strap

CHART 24–2

Radio noise can have various causes, and knowing where or when the noise occurs helps pin down the location.

Lightning Damage

A radio failed to work in a vehicle that was outside during a thunderstorm. The technician checked the fuses and verified that power was reaching the radio. Then the technician noticed the antenna. It had been struck by lightning. Obviously, the high voltage from the lightning strike traveled to the radio receiver and damaged the circuits. Both the radio and the antenna were replaced to correct the problem.
● **SEE FIGURE 24–26.**

FIGURE 24–26 The tip of this antenna was struck by lightning.

The General Motors Security Radio Problem

A customer replaced the battery in a General Motors vehicle and now the radio display shows "LOC." This means that the radio is locked and there is a customer code stored in the radio.

Other displays and their meaning include:

"InOP" This display indicates that too many incorrect codes have been entered and the radio must be kept powered for one hour and the ignition turned on before any more attempts can be made.

"SEC" This display means there is a customer's code stored and the radio is unlocked, secured and operable.

"---" This means there is no customer code stored and the radio is unlocked.

"REP" This means the customer's code has been entered once and the radio now is asking that the code be repeated to verify it was entered correctly the first time.

To unlock the radio, the technician used the following steps (the code number being used is 4321).

STEP 1 Press the "HR" (hour) button: "000" is displayed.

STEP 2 Set the first two digits using the hour button: "4300" is displayed.

STEP 3 Set the last two digits of the code using the "MIN" (minutes) button: "4321" is displayed.

STEP 4 Press the AM-FM button to enter the code. The radio is unlocked and the clock displays "1:00."

Thankfully, the owner had the security code. If the owner had lost the code, the technician would have to secure a scrambled factory backup code from the radio and then call a toll-free number to obtain another code for the customer. The code will only be given to authorized dealers or repair facilities.

SUMMARY

1. Radios receive AM (amplitude modulation) and FM (frequency modulation) signals that are broadcast through the air.

2. The radio antenna is used to induce a very small voltage signal as an input into the radio from the electromagnetic energy via the broadcast station.

3. AM requires an antenna whereas FM may be heard from a radio without an antenna.

4. Speakers reproduce the original sound, and the impedance of all speakers should be equally matched.

5. Crossovers are used to block certain frequencies to allow each type of speaker to perform its job better. A low-pass filter is used to block high-frequency sounds being sent to large woofer speakers, and a high-pass filter blocks low-frequency sounds being sent to tweeters.

6. Radio interference can be caused by many different things, such as a defective alternator, a fault in the ignition system, a fault in a relay or solenoid, or a poor electrical ground connection.

1. Why do AM signals travel farther than FM signals?
2. What are the purpose and function of the ground plane?
3. How do you match the impedance of speakers?
4. What two items may need to be added to the wiring of a vehicle to control or reduce radio noise?

CHAPTER QUIZ

1. Technician A says that a radio can receive AM signals, but not FM signals, if the antenna is defective. Technician B says that a good antenna should give a reading of about 500 ohms when tested with an ohmmeter between the center antenna wire and ground. Which technician is correct?
   a. Technician A only
   b. Technician B only
   c. Both Technicians A and B
   d. Neither Technician A nor B

2. An antenna lead-in wire should have how many ohms of resistance between the center terminal and the grounded outer covering?
   a. Less than 5 ohms
   b. 5 to 50 ohms
   c. 300 to 500 ohms
   d. Infinity (OL)

3. Technician A says that a braided ground wire is best to use for audio equipment to help reduce interference. Technician B says to use insulated 14 gauge or larger ground wire to reduce interference. Which technician is correct?
   a. Technician A only
   b. Technician B only
   c. Both Technicians A and B
   d. Neither Technician A nor B

4. What maintenance should be performed to a power antenna to help keep it working correctly?
   a. Remove it from the vehicle and lubricate the gears and cable.
   b. Clean the mast with a soft cloth and lubricate with a light oil.
   c. Disassemble the mast and pack the mast with silicone grease (or equal).
   d. Loosen and then retighten the retaining nut.

5. If two 4 ohm speakers are connected in parallel, meaning positive (+) to positive (+) and negative (−) to negative (−), the total impedance will be _____.
   a. 8 ohms
   b. 4 ohms
   c. 2 ohms
   d. 1 ohm

6. If two 4 ohm speakers are connected in series, meaning the positive (+) of one speaker connected to the negative (−) of the other speaker, the total impedance will be _____.
   a. 8 ohms
   b. 4 ohms
   c. 5 ohms
   d. 1 ohm

7. An aftermarket satellite radio has poor reception. Technician A says that a lack of a proper ground plane on the antenna could be the cause. Technician B says that mountains or tall buildings can interfere with reception. Which technician is correct?
   a. Technician A only
   b. Technician B only
   c. Both Technicians A and B
   d. Neither Technician A nor B

8. 100,000 μF means _____.
   a. 0.10 farad
   b. 0.01 farad
   c. 0.001 farad
   d. 0.0001 farad

9. A radio choke is actually a _____.
   a. Resistor
   b. Capacitor
   c. Coil (inductor)
   d. Transistor

10. What device passes AC interference to ground and blocks DC voltage, and is used to control radio interference?
    a. Resistor
    b. Capacitor
    c. Coil (inductor)
    d. Transistor

chapter 25

CIRCUIT TESTERS AND DIGITAL METERS

OBJECTIVES: **After studying Chapter 25, the reader will be able to:** • Prepare for ASE Electrical/Electronic Systems (A6) certification test content area "A" (General Electrical/Electronic System Diagnosis). • Discuss how to safely use a fused jumper wire, a test light, and a logic probe. • Explain how to set up and use a digital meter to read voltage, resistance, and current. • Explain meter terms and readings. • Interpret meter readings and compare to factory specifications. • Discuss how to properly and safely use meters.

KEY TERMS: • AC/DC clamp-on DMM 236 • Continuity light 230 • DMM 231 • DVOM 231 • High-impedance test meter 231 • IEC 241 • Inductive ammeter 235 • Kilo (k) 237 • LED test light 230 • Logic probe 231 • Mega (M) 237 • Meter accuracy 240 • Meter resolution 239 • Milli (m) 237 • OL 233 • RMS 239 • Test light 230

FUSED JUMPER WIRE

DEFINITION A fused jumper wire is used to check a circuit by bypassing the switch or to provide a power or ground to a component. A fused jumper wire, also called a test lead, can be purchased or made by the service technician. ● **SEE FIGURE 25–1.**

FIGURE 25–1 A technician-made fused jumper lead, which is equipped with a red 10 ampere fuse. This fused jumper wire uses terminals for testing circuits at a connector instead of alligator clips.

It should include the following features:

- **Fused.** A typical fused jumper wire has a blade-type fuse that can be easily replaced. A 10 ampere fuse (red color) is often the value used.

- **Alligator clip ends.** Alligator clips on the ends allow the fused jumper wire to be clipped to a ground or power source while the other end is attached to the power side or ground side of the unit being tested.

- **Good-quality insulated wire.** Most purchased jumper wire is about 14 gauge stranded copper wire with a flexible rubberized insulation to allow it to move easily even in cold weather.

USES OF A FUSED JUMPER WIRE A fused jumper wire can be used to help diagnose a component or circuit by performing the following procedures.

- **Supply power or ground.** If a component, such as a horn, does not work, a fused jumper wire can be used to supply a temporary power and/or ground. Start by unplugging the electrical connector from the device and connect a fused jumper lead to the power terminal. Another fused jumper wire may be needed to provide the ground. If the unit works, the problem is in the power side or ground side circuit.

CAUTION: Never use a fused jumper wire to bypass any resistance or load in the circuit. The increased current flow could damage the wiring and could blow the fuse on the jumper lead.

NONPOWERED TEST LIGHT A 12-volt test light is one of the simplest testers that can be used to detect electricity. A **test light** is simply a light bulb with a probe and a ground wire attached. ● **SEE FIGURE 25–2.**

It is used to detect battery voltage potential at various test points. Battery voltage cannot be seen or felt, and can be detected only with test equipment.

The ground clip is connected to a clean ground on either the negative terminal of the battery or a clean metal part of the body and the probe touched to terminals or components. If the test light comes on, this indicates that voltage is available. ● **SEE FIGURE 25–3.**

A purchased test light could be labeled a "12 volt test light." Do not purchase a test light designed for household current (110 or 220 volts), as it will not light with 12 to 14 volts.

USES OF A 12-VOLT TEST LIGHT A 12-volt test light can be used to check the following:

■ **Electrical power.** If the test light lights, then there is power available. It will not, however, indicate the voltage level or if there is enough current available to operate an electrical load. This indicates only that there is enough voltage and current to light the test light (about 0.25 A).

■ **Grounds.** A test light can be used to check for grounds by attaching the clip of the test light to the positive terminal of the battery or any 12-volt electrical terminal. The tip of the test light can then be used to touch the ground wire. If there is a ground connection, the test light will light.

CONTINUITY TEST LIGHTS A **continuity light** is similar to a test light but includes a battery for self-power. A continuity

FIGURE 25–2 A 12-volt test light is attached to a good ground while probing for power.

12-VOLT TEST LIGHT

BODY GROUND POINT

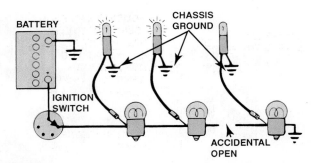

BATTERY

CHASSIS GROUND

IGNITION SWITCH

ACCIDENTAL OPEN

FIGURE 25–3 A test light can be used to locate an open in a circuit. Note that the test light is grounded at a different location than the circuit itself.

BATTERY IN HANDLE

LIGHT IN TIP

FIGURE 25–4 A continuity light should not be used on computer circuits because the applied voltage can damage delicate electronic components or circuits.

light illuminates whenever it is connected to both ends of a wire that has continuity or is not broken. ● **SEE FIGURE 25–4.**

CAUTION: The use of a self-powered (continuity) test light is not recommended on any electronic circuit, because a continuity light contains a battery and applies voltage; therefore, it may harm delicate electronic components.

HIGH-IMPEDANCE TEST LIGHT A high-impedance test light has a high internal resistance and therefore draws very low current in order to light. High-impedance test lights are safe to use on computer circuits because they will not affect the circuit current in the same way as conventional 12-volt test lights when connected to a circuit. There are two types of high-impedance test lights.

■ Some test lights use an electronic circuit to limit the current flow, to avoid causing damage to electronic devices.

■ An **LED test light** uses a light-emitting diode (LED) instead of a standard automotive bulb for a visual indication of voltage. An LED test light requires only about 25 milliamperes (0.025 ampere) to light; therefore, it can be used on electronic circuits as well as on standard circuits.

● **SEE FIGURE 25–5** for construction details for a homemade LED test light.

FIGURE 25-5 An LED test light can be easily made using low cost components and an old ink pen. With the 470-ohm resistor in series with the LED, this tester only draws 0.025 ampere (25 milliamperes) from the circuit being tested. This low current draw helps assure the technician that the circuit or component being tested will not be damaged by excessive current flow.

FIGURE 25-6 A logic probe connected to the vehicle battery. When the tip probe is connected to a circuit, it can check for power, ground, or a pulse.

LOGIC PROBE

PURPOSE AND FUNCTION A **logic probe** is an electronic device that lights up a red (usually) LED if the probe is touched to battery voltage. If the probe is touched to ground, a green (usually) LED lights. ● **SEE FIGURE 25-6.**

A logic probe can "sense" the difference between high- and low-voltage levels, which explains the name *logic.*

- A typical logic probe can also light another light (often amber color) when a change in voltage levels occurs.
- Some logic probes will flash the red light when a pulsing voltage signal is detected.
- Some will flash the green light when a pulsing ground signal is detected.

This feature is helpful when checking for a variable voltage output from a computer or ignition sensor.

USING A LOGIC PROBE A logic probe must first be connected to a power and ground source such as the vehicle battery. This connection powers the probe and gives it a reference low (ground).

Most logic probes also make a distinctive sound for each high- and low-voltage level. This makes troubleshooting easier when probing connectors or component terminals. A sound (usually a beep) is heard when the probe tip is touched to a changing voltage source. The changing voltage also usually lights the pulse light on the logic probe. Therefore, the probe can be used to check components such as:

- Pickup coils
- Hall-effect sensors
- Magnetic sensors

DIGITAL MULTIMETERS

TERMINOLOGY **Digital multimeter (DMM)** and **digital volt-ohm-meter (DVOM)** are terms commonly used for electronic **high-impedance test meters.** *High impedance* means that the electronic internal resistance of the meter is high enough to prevent excessive current draw from any circuit being tested. Most meters today have a minimum of 10 million ohms (10 megohms) of resistance. This high internal resistance between the meter leads is present only when measuring volts. The high resistance in the meter itself reduces the amount of current flowing through the meter when it is being used to measure voltage, leading to more accurate test results because the meter does not change the load on the circuit. High-impedance meters are required for measuring computer circuits.

CAUTION: Analog (needle-type) meters are almost always lower than 10 megohms and should not be used to measure any computer or electronic circuit. Connecting an analog meter to a computer circuit could damage the computer or other electronic modules.

MEGOHMS: 10 MΩ (10 MILLION OHMS) VOLT TEST

FIGURE 25–7 Typical digital multimeter. The black meter lead always is placed in the COM terminal. The red meter test lead should be in the volt-ohm terminal except when measuring current in amperes.

A high-impedance meter can be used to measure any automotive circuit within the ranges of the meter. ● **SEE FIGURE 25–7.**

The common abbreviations for the units that many meters can measure are often confusing. ● **SEE CHART 25–1** for the most commonly used symbols and their meanings.

MEASURING VOLTAGE A voltmeter measures the *pressure* or potential of electricity in units of volts. A voltmeter is connected to a circuit in parallel. Voltage can be measured by selecting either AC or DC volts.

- **DC volts (DCV).** This setting is the most common for automotive use. Use this setting to measure battery voltage and voltage to all lighting and accessory circuits.

- **AC volts (ACV).** This setting is used to check for unwanted AC voltage from alternators and some sensors.

- **Range.** The range is automatically set for most meters but can be manually ranged if needed. ● **SEE FIGURES 25–8 AND 25–9.**

SYMBOL	MEANING
AC	Alternating current or voltage
DC	Direct current or voltage
V	Volts
mV	Millivolts (1/1,000 volts)
A	Ampere (amps), current
mA	Milliampere (1/1,000 amps)
%	Percent (for duty cycle readings only)
Ω	Ohms, resistance
kΩ	Kilohm (1,000 ohms), resistance
MΩ	Megohm (1,000,000 ohms), resistance
Hz	Hertz (cycles per second), frequency
kHz	Kilohertz (1,000 cycles/sec.), frequency
Ms	Milliseconds (1/1,000 sec.) for pulse width measurements

CHART 25–1

Common symbols and abbreviations used on digital meters.

FIGURE 25–8 Typical digital multimeter (DMM) set to read DC volts.

BECAUSE THE SIGNAL READING IS BELOW 4 VOLTS, THE METER AUTORANGES TO THE 4-VOLT SCALE. IN THE 4-VOLT SCALE, THIS METER PROVIDES THREE DECIMAL PLACES.

(a)

WHEN THE VOLTAGE EXCEEDED 4 VOLTS, THE METER AUTORANGES INTO THE 40-VOLT SCALE. THE DECIMAL POINT MOVES ONE PLACE TO THE RIGHT LEAVING ONLY TWO DECIMAL PLACES.

(b)

FIGURE 25–9 A typical autoranging digital multimeter automatically selects the proper scale to read the voltage being tested. The scale selected is usually displayed on the meter face. (a) Note that the display indicates "4," meaning that this range can read up to 4 volts. (b) The range is now set to the 40-volt scale, meaning that the meter can read up to 40 volts on the scale. Any reading above this level will cause the meter to reset to a higher scale. If not set on autoranging, the meter display would indicate OL if a reading exceeds the limit of the scale selected.

MEASURING RESISTANCE An ohmmeter measures the resistance in ohms of a component or circuit section when no current is flowing through the circuit. An ohmmeter contains a battery (or other power source) and is connected in series with the component or wire being measured. When the leads are connected to a component, current flows through the test leads and the difference in voltage (voltage drop) between the leads is measured as resistance. Note the following facts about using an ohmmeter.

- Zero ohms on the scale means that there is no resistance between the test leads, thus indicating continuity or a continuous path for the current to flow in a closed circuit.
- Infinity means no connection, as in an open circuit.
- Ohmmeters have no required polarity even though red and black test leads are used for resistance measurement.

CAUTION: The circuit must be electrically open with no current flowing when using an ohmmeter. If current is flowing when an ohmmeter is connected, the reading will be incorrect and the meter can be destroyed.

Different meters have different ways of indicating infinity resistance, or a reading higher than the scale allows. Examples of an over limit display include:

- **OL,** meaning **over limit** or overload
- Flashing or solid number 1
- Flashing or solid number 3 on the left side of the display
- Flashing or solid number 4 on the display.

Check the meter instructions for the exact display used to indicate an open circuit or over range reading. ● **SEE FIGURES 25–10 AND 25–11.**

To summarize, open and zero readings are as follows:

0.00 Ω = Zero resistance (component or circuit has continuity)

OL = An open circuit or reading is higher than the scale selected (no current flows)

MEASURING AMPERES An ammeter measures the flow of *current* through a complete circuit in units of amperes. The ammeter has to be installed in the circuit (in series) so that

FIGURE 25–10 Using a digital multimeter set to read ohms (Ω) to test this light bulb. The meter reads the resistance of the filament.

FIGURE 25–11 Many digital multimeters can have the display indicate zero to compensate for test lead resistance. (1) Connect leads in the V Ω and COM meter terminals. (2) Select the Ω scale. (3) Touch the two meter leads together. (4) Push the "zero" or "relative" button on the meter. (5) The meter display will now indicate zero ohms of resistance.

it can measure all the current flow in that circuit, just as a water flow meter would measure the amount of water flow (cubic feet per minute, for example). **SEE FIGURE 25–12.**

How Much Voltage Does an Ohmmeter Apply?

Most digital meters that are set to measure ohms (resistance) apply 0.3 to 1 volt to the component being measured. The voltage comes from the meter itself to measure the resistance. Two things are important to remember about an ohmmeter.

1. The component or circuit must be disconnected from any electrical circuit while the resistance is being measured.
2. Because the meter itself applies a voltage (even though it is relatively low), a meter set to measure ohms can damage electronic circuits. Computer or electronic chips can be easily damaged if subjected to only a few milliamperes of current, similar to the amount an ohmmeter applies when a resistance measurement is being performed.

FIGURE 25–12 Measuring the current flow required by a horn requires that the ammeter be connected to the circuit in series and the horn button be depressed by an assistant.

Fuse Your Meter Leads!

Most digital meters include an ammeter capability. When reading amperes, the leads of the meter must be changed from volts or ohms (V or Ω) to amperes (A), milliamperes (mA), or microamperes (μA).

A common problem may then occur the next time voltage is measured. Although the technician may switch the selector to read volts, often the leads are not switched back to the volt or ohm position. Because the ammeter lead position results in zero ohms of resistance to current flow through the meter, the meter or the fuse inside the meter will be destroyed if the meter is connected to a battery. Many meter fuses are expensive and difficult to find.

To avoid this problem, simply solder an inline 10 ampere blade-fuse holder into one meter lead. ● **SEE FIGURE 25–13.**

Do not think that this technique is for beginners only. Experienced technicians often get in a hurry and forget to switch the lead. A blade fuse is faster, easier, and less expensive to replace than a meter fuse or the meter itself. Also, if the soldering is done properly, the addition of an inline fuse holder and fuse does not increase the resistance of the meter leads. All meter leads have some resistance. If the meter is measuring very low resistance, touch the two leads together and read the resistance (usually no more than 0.2 ohm). Simply subtract the resistance of the leads from the resistance of the component being measured.

What Does "CE" Mean on Many Meters?

The "CE" means that the meter meets the newest European Standards and the letters CE stands for a French term for "Conformite' Europeenne" meaning European Conformity in French.

CAUTION: An ammeter must be installed in series with the circuit to measure the current flow in the circuit. If a meter set to read amperes is connected in parallel, such as across a battery, the meter or the leads may be destroyed, or the fuse will blow, by the current available across the battery. Some digital multimeters (DMMs) beep if the unit selection does not match the test lead connection on the meter. However, in a noisy shop, this beep sound may be inaudible.

Digital meters require that the meter leads be moved to the ammeter terminals. Most digital meters have an ampere scale that can accommodate a maximum of 10 amperes. See the Tech Tip, "Fuse Your Meter Leads!"

INDUCTIVE AMMETERS

OPERATION **Inductive ammeters** do not make physical contact with the circuit. They measure the strength of the magnetic field surrounding the wire carrying the current, and use a Hall-effect sensor to measure current. The Hall-effect sensor detects the strength of the magnetic field that surrounds the wire carrying an electrical current. ● **SEE FIGURE 25–14.**

FIGURE 25–13 Note the blade-type fuse holder soldered in series with one of the meter leads. A 10-ampere fuse helps protect the internal meter fuse (if equipped) and the meter itself from damage that may result from excessive current flow if accidentally used incorrectly.

FIGURE 25–14 An inductive ammeter clamp is used with all starting and charging testers to measure the current flow through the battery cables.

FIGURE 25–15 A typical mini clamp-on-type digital multimeter. This meter is capable of measuring alternating current (AC) and direct current (DC) without requiring that the circuit be disconnected to install the meter in series. The jaws are simply placed over the wire and current flow through the circuit is displayed.

This means that the meter probe surrounds the wire(s) carrying the current and measures the strength of the magnetic field that surrounds any conductor carrying a current.

AC/DC CLAMP-ON DIGITAL MULTIMETERS An **AC/DC clamp-on digital multimeter (DMM)** is a useful meter for automotive diagnostic work. ● **SEE FIGURE 25–15.**

The major advantage of the clamp-on-type meter is that there is no need to break the circuit to measure current (amperes). Simply clamp the jaws of the meter around the power lead(s) or ground lead(s) of the component being measured and read the display. Most clamp-on meters can also measure alternating current, which is helpful in the diagnosis of an alternator problem. Volts, ohms, frequency, and temperature can also be measured with the typical clamp-on DMM, but use conventional meter leads. The inductive clamp is only used to measure amperes.

DIODE CHECK, PULSE WIDTH, AND FREQUENCY

DIODE CHECK Diode check is a meter function that can be used to check diodes including light-emitting diodes (LEDs). The meter is able to text diodes by way of the following:

- The meter applies roughly a 3 volt DC signal to the text leads.

- The voltage is high enough to cause a diode to work and the meter will display:

  1. 0.4 to 0.7 volt when testing silicon diodes such as found in alternators
  2. 1.5 to 2.3 volts when testing LEDs such as found in some lighting applications

TECH TIP

Over Limit Display Does Not Mean the Meter Is Reading "Nothing"

The meaning of the over limit display on a digital meter often confuses beginning technicians. When asked what the meter is reading when an over limit (OL) is displayed on the meter face, the response is often, "Nothing." Many meters indicate *over limit* or *over load,* which simply means that the reading is over the maximum that can be displayed for the selected range. For example, the meter will display OL if 12 volts are being measured but the meter has been set to read a maximum of 4 volts.

Autoranging meters adjust the range to match what is being measured. Here OL means a value higher than the meter can read (unlikely on the voltage scale for automobile usage), or infinity when measuring resistance (ohms). Therefore, OL means infinity when measuring resistance or an open circuit is being indicated. The meter will read 00.0 if the resistance is zero, so "nothing" in this case indicates continuity (zero resistance), whereas OL indicates infinity resistance. Therefore, when talking with another technician about a meter reading, make sure you know exactly what the reading on the face of the meter means. Also be sure that you are connecting the meter leads correctly. ● **SEE FIGURE 25–16.**

FIGURE 25–16 Typical digital multimeter showing OL (over limit) on the readout with the ohms (Ω) unit selected. This usually means that the unit being measured is open (infinity resistance) and has no continuity.

PULSE WIDTH Pulse width is the amount of time in a percentage that a signal is on compared to being off.

- 100% pulse width indicates that a device is being commanded on all of the time.
- 50% pulse width indicates that a device is being commanded on half of the time.
- 25% pulse width indicates that a device is being commanded on just 25% of the time.

Pulse width is used to measure the on time for fuel injectors and other computer-controlled solenoid and devices.

FREQUENCY Frequency is a measure of how many times per second a signal changes. Frequency is measured in a unit called hertz, formerly termed "cycles per second."

Frequency measurements are used when checking the following:

- Mass airflow (MAF) sensors for proper operation
- Ignition primary pulse signals when diagnosing a no-start condition
- Checking a wheel speed sensor

ELECTRICAL UNIT PREFIXES

DEFINITIONS Electrical units are measured in numbers such as 12 volts, 150 amperes, and 470 ohms. Large units over 1,000 may be expressed in kilo units. **Kilo (k)** means 1,000. ● **SEE FIGURE 25–17**.

4,700 ohms = 4.7 kilohms (kΩ)

If the value is over 1 million (1,000,000), then the prefix **mega (M)** is often used. For example:

1,100,000 volts = 1.1 megavolts (MV)

4,700,000 ohms = 4.7 megohms (MΩ)

Sometimes a circuit conducts so little current that a smaller unit of measure is required. Small units of measure expressed in 1/1,000 are prefixed by **milli (m)**. To summarize:

mega (M) = 1,000,000 (decimal point six places to the right = 1,000,000)

kilo (k) = 1,000 (decimal point three places to the right = 1,000)

milli (m) = 1/1,000 (decimal point three places to the left = 0.001)

HINT: Lowercase _m_ equals a small unit (milli), whereas a capital _M_ represents a large unit (mega).

● **SEE CHART 25–2.**

PREFIXES The prefixes can be confusing because most digital meters can express values in more than one unit, especially if the meter is autoranging. For example, an ammeter reading may show 36.7 mA on autoranging. When the scale is changed to amperes ("A" in the window of the display), the

THE SYMBOL ON THE RIGHT SIDE OF THE DISPLAY INDICATES WHAT RANGE THE METER HAS BEEN SET TO READ.

Ω = OHMS

IF THE ONLY SYMBOL ON THE DISPLAY IS THE OHMS SYMBOL, THE READING ON THE DISPLAY IS EXACTLY THE RESISTANCE IN OHMS.

KΩ = KILOHMS = OHMS TIMES 1000

A "K" IN FRONT OF THE OHMS SYMBOL MEANS "KILOHMS"; THE READING ON THE DISPLAY IS IN KILOHMS. YOU HAVE TO MULTIPLY THE READING ON THE DISPLAY BY 1,000 TO GET THE RESISTANCE IN OHMS.

MΩ = MEGOHMS = OHMS TIMES 1,000,000

A "M" IN FRONT OF THE OHMS SYMBOL MEANS "MEGOHMS"; THE READING ON THE DISPLAY IS IN MEGOHMS. YOU HAVE TO MULTIPLY THE READING ON THE DISPLAY BY 1,000,000 TO GET THE RESISTANCE IN OHMS.

FIGURE 25–17 Always look at the meter display when a measurement is being made, especially if using an autoranging meter.

TO/FROM	MEGA	KILO	BASE	MILLI
Mega	0 places	3 places to the right	6 places to the right	9 places to the right
Kilo	3 places to the left	0 places	3 places to the right	6 places to the right
Base	6 places to the left	3 places to the left	0 places	3 places to the right
Milli	9 places to the left	6 places to the left	3 places to the left	0 places

CHART 25–2

A conversion chart showing the decimal point location for the various prefixes.

number displayed will be 0.037 A. Note that the resolution of the value is reduced.

HINT: Always check the face of the meter display for the unit being measured. To best understand what is being displayed on the face of a digital meter, select a manual scale and move the selector until _whole units appear_, such as "A" for amperes instead of "mA" for milliamperes.

Think of Money

Digital meter displays can often be confusing. The display for a battery measured as 12 1/2 volts would be 12.50 V, just as $12.50 is 12 dollars and 50 cents. A 1/2-volt reading on a digital meter will be displayed as 0.50 V, just as $0.50 is half of a dollar.

It is more confusing when low values are displayed. For example, if a voltage reading is 0.063 volt, an autoranging meter will display 63 millivolts (63 mV), or 63/1,000 of a volt, or $63 of $1,000. (It takes 1,000 mV to equal 1 volt.) Think of millivolts as one-tenth of a cent, with 1 volt being $1.00. Therefore, 630 millivolts are equal to $0.63 of $1.00 (630 tenths of a cent, or 63 cents).

To avoid confusion, try to manually range the meter to read base units (whole volts). If the meter is ranged to base unit volts, 63 millivolts would be displayed as 0.063 or maybe just 0.06, depending on the display capabilities of the meter.

HOW TO READ DIGITAL METERS

STEPS TO FOLLOW Getting to know and use a digital meter takes time and practice. The first step is to read, understand, and follow all safety and operational instructions that come with the meter. Use of the meter usually involves the following steps.

STEP 1 **Select the proper unit of electricity for what is being measured.** This unit could be volts, ohms (resistance), or amperes (amount of current flow). If the meter is not autoranging, select the proper scale for the anticipated reading. For example, if a 12-volt battery is being measured, select a meter reading range that is higher than the voltage but not too high. A 20- or 30-volt range will accurately show the voltage of a 12-volt battery. If a 1,000-volt scale is selected, a 12-volt reading may not be accurate.

STEP 2 **Place the meter leads into the proper input terminals.**
- The black lead is inserted into the common (COM) terminal. This meter lead usually stays in this location for all meter functions.
- The red lead is inserted into the volt, ohm, or diode check terminal usually labeled "VΩ" when voltage, resistance, or diodes are being measured.
- When current flow in amperes is being measured, most digital meters require that the red test lead be inserted in the ammeter terminal, usually labeled "A" or "mA."

CAUTION: If the meter leads are inserted into ammeter terminals, even though the selector is set to volts, the meter may be damaged or an internal fuse may blow if the test leads touch both terminals of a battery.

STEP 3 **Measure the component being tested.** Carefully note the decimal point and the unit on the face of the meter.
- **Meter lead connections.** If the meter leads are connected to a battery backwards (red to the battery negative, for example), the display will still show the correct reading, but a negative sign (2) will be displayed in front of the number. The correct polarity is not important when measuring resistance (ohms) except where indicated, such as measuring a diode.
- **Autorange.** Many meters automatically default to the autorange position and the meter will display the value in the most readable scale. The meter can be manually ranged to select other levels or to lock in a scale for a value that is constantly changing.

  If a 12-volt battery is measured with an autoranging meter, the correct reading of 12.0 is given. "AUTO" and "V" should show on the face of the meter. For example, if a meter is manually set to the 2 kilohm scale, the highest that the meter will read is 2,000 ohms. If the reading is over 2,000 ohms, the meter will display OL. ● **SEE CHART 25–3.**

STEP 4 **Interpret the reading.** This is especially difficult on autoranging meters, where the meter itself selects the proper scale. The following are two examples of different readings:

Example 1: A voltage drop is being measured. The specifications indicate a maximum voltage drop of 0.2 volt. The meter reads "AUTO" and "43.6 mV." This reading means that the voltage drop is 0.0436 volt, or 43.6 mV, which is far lower than the 0.2 volt (200 millivolts). Because the number showing on the meter face is much larger than the specifications, many beginner technicians are led to believe that the voltage drop is excessive.

NOTE: Pay attention to the units displayed on the meter face and convert to whole units.

Example 2: A spark plug wire is being measured. The reading should be less than 10,000 ohms for each foot in length if the wire is okay. The wire being tested is 3 ft long (maximum allowable resistance is 30,000 ohms). The meter reads "AUTO" and "14.85 kΩ." This reading is equivalent to 14,850 ohms.

NOTE: When converting from kilohms to ohms, make the decimal point a comma.

Because this reading is well below the specified maximum allowable, the spark plug wire is okay.

VOLTAGE BEING MEASURED						
	0.01 V (10 MV)	0.150 V (150 MV)	1.5 V	10.0 V	2.0 V	120 V
Scale selected	Voltmeter will display:					
200 mV	10.0	150.0	OL	OL	OL	OL
2 V	0.100	0.150	1.500	OL	OL	OL
20 V	0.1	1.50	1.50	10.00	12.00	OL
200 V	00.0	01.5	01.5	10.0	12.0	120.0
2 kV	00.00	00.00	000.1	00.10	00.12	0.120
Autorange	10.0 mV	15.0 mV	1.50	10.0	12.0	120.0

RESISTANCE BEING MEASURED						
	10 OHMS	100 OHMS	470 OHMS	1 KILOHM	220 KILOHMS	1 MEGOHM
Scale selected	Ohmmeter will display:					
400 ohms	10.0	100.0	OL	OL	OL	OL
4 kilohms	010	100	0.470 k	1000	OL	OL
40 kilohms	00.0	0.10 k	0.47 k	1.00 k	OL	OL
400 kilohms	000.0	00.1 k	00.5 k	0.10 k	220.0 k	OL
4 megohms	00.00	0.01 M	0.05 M	00.1 M	0.22 M	1.0 M
Autorange	10.0	100.0	470.0	1.00 k	220 k	1.00 M

CURRENT BEING MEASURED						
	50 MA	150 MA	1.0 A	7.5 A	15.0 A	25.0 A
Scale selected	Ammeter will display:					
40 mA	OL	OL	OL	OL	OL	OL
400 mA	50.0	150	OL	OL	OL	OL
4 A	0.05	0.00	1.00	OL	OL	OL
40 A	0.00	0.000	01.0	7.5	15.0	25.0
Autorange	50.0 mA	150.0 mA	1.00	7.5	15.0	25.0

CHART 25–3

Sample meter readings using manually set and autoranging selection on the digital meter control.

RMS VERSUS AVERAGE Alternating current voltage waveforms can be true sinusoidal or nonsinusoidal. A true sine wave pattern measurement will be the same for both **root-mean-square (RMS)** and average reading meters. RMS and averaging are two methods used to measure the true effective rating of a signal that is constantly changing. ● **SEE FIGURE 25–18.**

Only true RMS meters are accurate when measuring nonsinusoidal AC waveforms, which are seldom used in automotive applications.

RESOLUTION, DIGITS, AND COUNTS Meter **resolution** refers to how small or fine a measurement the meter can make. By knowing the resolution of a DMM you can determine whether the meter could measure down to only 1 volt or down to 1 millivolt (1/1,000 of a volt).

You would not buy a ruler marked in 1 in. segments (or centimeters) if you had to measure down to 1/4 in. (or 1 mm). A thermometer that only measured in whole degrees is not of much use when your normal temperature is 98.6°F. You need a thermometer with 0.1° *resolution.*

The terms *digits* and *counts* are used to describe a meter's resolution. DMMs are grouped by the number of counts or digits they display.

- A 3 1/2-digit meter can display three full digits ranging from 0 to 9, and one "half" digit that displays only a 1 or is left blank. A 3 1/2-digit meter will display up to 1,999 counts of resolution.

- A 4 1/2-digit meter can display up to 19,000 counts of resolution. It is more precise to describe a meter by counts of resolution than by 3 1/2 or 4 1/2 digits. Some 3 1/2-digit meters have enhanced resolution of up to 3,200 or 4,000 counts.

FIGURE 25-18 When reading AC voltage signals, a true RMS meter (such as a Fluke 87) provides a different reading than an average responding meter (such as a Fluke 88). The only place this difference is important is when a reading is to be compared with a specification.

Meters with more counts offer better resolution for certain measurements. For example, a 1,999 count meter will not be able to measure down to a tenth of a volt when measuring 200 volts or more. ● **SEE FIGURE 25-19.**

However, a 3,200-count meter will display a tenth of a volt up to 320 volts. Digits displayed to the far right of the display may at times flicker or constantly change. This is called *digit rattle* and represents a changing voltage being measured on the ground (COM terminal of the meter lead). High-quality meters are designed to reject this unwanted voltage.

ACCURACY   **Meter accuracy** is the largest allowable error that will occur under specific operating conditions. In other words, it is an indication of how close the DMM's displayed measurement is to the actual value of the signal being measured.

Accuracy for a DMM is usually expressed as a percent of reading. An accuracy of ±1% of reading means that for a displayed reading of 100.0 V, the actual value of the voltage could be anywhere between 99.0 V and 101.0 V. Thus, the lower the percent of accuracy is, the better.

FIGURE 25-19 This meter display shows 052.2 AC volts. Notice that the zero beside the 5 indicates that the meter can read over 100 volts AC with a resolution of 0.1 volt.

- Unacceptable = 1.00%
- Okay = 0.50% (1/2%)
- Good = 0.25% (1/4%)
- Excellent = 0.10% (1/10%)

For example, if a battery had 12.6 volts, a meter could read between the following, based on its accuracy.

±0.10%	high =	12.61
	low =	12.59
±0.25%	high =	12.63
	low =	12.57
±0.50%	high =	12.66
	low =	12.54
±1.00%	high =	12.73
	low =	12.47

Before you purchase a meter, check the accuracy. Accuracy is usually indicated on the specifications sheet for the meter.

FIGURE 25–20 Be sure to only use a meter that is CAT III rated when taking electrical voltage measurements on a hybrid vehicle.

FIGURE 25–21 Always use meter leads that are CAT III rated on a meter that is also CAT III rated, to maintain the protection needed when working on hybrid vehicles.

SAFETY TIP

Meter Usage on Hybrid Electric Vehicles

Many hybrid electric vehicles use system voltage as high as 650 volts DC. Be sure to follow all vehicle manufacturer's testing procedures; and if a voltage measurement is needed, be sure to use a meter and test leads that are designed to insulate against high voltages. The **International Electrotechnical Commission (IEC)** has several categories of voltage standards for meter and meter leads. These categories are ratings for overvoltage protection and are rated CAT I, CAT II, CAT III, and CAT IV. The higher the category, the greater the protection against voltage spikes caused by high-energy circuits. Under each category there are various energy and voltage ratings.

CAT I	Typically a CAT I meter is used for low-energy voltage measurements such as at wall outlets in the home. Meters with a CAT I rating are usually rated at 300 to 800 volts.
CAT II	This higher rated meter would be typically used for checking higher energy level voltages at the fuse panel in the home. Meters with a CAT II rating are usually rated at 300 to 600 volts.
CAT III	This minimum rated meter should be used for hybrid vehicles. The CAT III category is designed for high-energy levels and voltage measurements at the service pole at the transformer. Meters with this rating are usually rated at 600 to 1,000 volts.
CAT IV	CAT IV meters are for clamp-on meters only. If a clamp-on meter also has meter leads for voltage measurements, that part of the meter will be rated as CAT III.

NOTE: Always use the highest CAT rating meter, especially when working with hybrid vehicles. A CAT III, 600 volt meter is safer than a CAT II, 1,000 volt meter because of the energy level of the CAT ratings.

Therefore, for best personal protection, use only meters and meter leads that are CAT III or CAT IV rated when measuring voltage on a hybrid vehicle. ● SEE FIGURES 25–20 AND 25–21.

1 For most electrical measurements, the black meter lead is inserted in the terminal labeled COM and the red meter lead is inserted into the terminal labeled V.

2 To use a digital meter, turn the power switch and select the unit of electricity to be measured. In this case, the rotary switch is turned to select DC volts. (V symbol with the straight line above)

3 For most automotive electrical use, such as for measuring battery voltage, select DC volts.

4 Connect the red meter lead to the positive (+) terminal of a battery and the black meter lead to the negative (−) terminal of a battery. The meter reads the voltage difference between the leads.

5 This jump start battery unit measures 13.151 volts with the meter set on autoranging on the DC voltage scale.

6 Another meter (Fluke 87 III) displays four digits when measuring the voltage of the battery jump start unit.

7 To measure resistance turn the rotary dial to the ohm (Ω) symbol. With the meter leads separated, the meter display reads OL (over limit).

8 The meter can read your own body resistance if you grasp the meter lead terminals with your fingers. The reading on the display indicates 196.35 kΩ.

9 When measuring anything; be sure to read the symbol on the meter face. In this case, the meter is reading 291.10 kΩ.

10 A meter set on ohms can be used to check the resistance of a light bulb filament. In this case, the meter reads 3.15 ohms. If the bulb were bad (filament open), the meter would display OL.

11 A digital meter set to read ohms should measure 0.00 as shown when the meter leads are touched together.

12 The large letter V means volts and the wavy symbol over the V means that the meter measures alternating current (AC) voltage if this position is selected.

CONTINUED ▶

DIGITAL METER USAGE (CONTINUED)

13 The next symbol is a V with a dotted and a straight line overhead. This symbol stands for direct current (DC) volts. This position is most used for automotive service.

14 The symbol mV indicates millivolts or 1/1,000 of a volt (0.001). The solid and dashed line above the mV means DC mV.

15 The rotary switch is turned to Ω (ohms) unit of resistance measure. The symbol to the left of the Ω symbol is the beeper or continuity indicator.

16 Notice that AUTO is in the upper left and the MΩ is in the lower right. This MΩ means megaohms or that the meter is set to read in millions of ohms.

17 The symbol shown is the symbol of a diode. In this position, the meter applies a voltage to a diode and the meter reads the voltage drop across the junction of a diode.

18 One of the most useful features of this meter is the MIN/MAX feature. By pushing the MIN/MAX button, the meter will be able to display the highest (MAX) and the lowest (MIN) reading.

19 Pushing the MIN/MAX button puts the meter into record mode. Note the 100 mS and "REC" on the display. In this position, the meter is capturing any voltage change that lasts 100 mS (0.1 sec) or longer.

20 To increase the range of the meter touch the range button. Now the meter is set to read voltage up to 40 volts DC.

21 Pushing the range button one more time changes the meter scale to the 400-voltage range. Notice that the decimal point has moved to the right.

22 Pushing the range button again changes the meter to the 4000-volt range. This range is not suitable to use in automotive applications.

23 By pushing and holding the range button, the meter will reset to autorange. Autorange is the preferred setting for most automotive measurements except when using MIN/MAX record mode.

1. Circuit testers include test lights and fused jumper leads.
2. Digital multimeter (DMM) and digital volt-ohm-meter (DVOM) are terms commonly used for electronic high-impedance test meters.
3. Use of a high-impedance digital meter is required on any computer-related circuit or component.
4. Ammeters measure current and must be connected in series in the circuit.
5. Voltmeters measure voltage and are connected in parallel.
6. Ohmmeters measure resistance of a component and must be connected in parallel, with the circuit or component disconnected from power.
7. Logic probes can indicate the presence of power, ground, or pulsed signals.

REVIEW QUESTIONS

1. Why should high-impedance meters be used when measuring voltage on computer-controlled circuits?
2. How is an ammeter connected to an electrical circuit?
3. Why must an ohmmeter be connected to a disconnected circuit or component?

CHAPTER QUIZ

1. Inductive ammeters work because of what principle?
   a. Magic
   b. Electrostatic electricity
   c. A magnetic field surrounds any wire carrying a current
   d. Voltage drop as it flows through a conductor

2. A meter used to measure amperes is called a(n) _____.
   a. Amp meter
   b. Ampmeter
   c. Ammeter
   d. Coulomb meter

3. A voltmeter should be connected to the circuit being tested _____.
   a. In series
   b. In parallel
   c. Only when no power is flowing
   d. Both a and c

4. An ohmmeter should be connected to the circuit or component being tested _____.
   a. With current flowing in the circuit or through the component
   b. When connected to the battery of the vehicle to power the meter
   c. Only when no power is flowing (electrically open circuit)
   d. Both b and c

5. A high-impedance meter _____.
   a. Measures a high amount of current flow
   b. Measures a high amount of resistance
   c. Can measure a high voltage
   d. Has a high internal resistance

6. A meter is set to read DC volts on the 4-volt scale. The meter leads are connected at a 12-volt battery. The display will read _____.
   a. 0.00
   b. OL
   c. 12 V
   d. 0.012 V

7. What could happen if the meter leads were connected to the positive and negative terminals of the battery while the meter and leads were set to read amperes?
   a. Could blow an internal fuse or damage the meter
   b. Would read volts instead of amperes
   c. Would display OL
   d. Would display 0.00

8. The highest amount of resistance that can be read by the meter set to the 2 kΩ scale is _____.
   a. 2,000 ohms
   b. 200 ohms
   c. 200 kΩ (200,000 ohms)
   d. 20,000,000 ohms

9. If a digital meter face shows 0.93 when set to read kΩ, the reading means _____.
   a. 93 ohms
   b. 930 ohms
   c. 9,300 ohms
   d. 93,000 ohms

10. A reading of 432 shows on the face of the meter set to the millivolt scale. The reading means _____.
    a. 0.432 volt
    b. 4.32 volts
    c. 43.2 volts
    d. 4,320 volts

chapter
26

OSCILLOSCOPES AND GRAPHING MULTIMETERS

OBJECTIVES: **After studying Chapter 26, the reader will be able to:** • Prepare for ASE Electrical/Electronic Systems (A6) certification test content area "A" (General Electrical/Electronic System Diagnosis). • Use a digital storage oscilloscope to measure voltage signals. • Interpret meter and scope readings and determine if the values are within factory specifications. • Explain time base and volts per division settings.

KEY TERMS: • AC coupling 249 • BNC connector 252 • Cathode ray tube (CRT) 247 • Channel 250 • DC coupling 249 • Digital storage oscilloscope (DSO) 247 • Division 248 • Duty cycle 250 • External trigger 251 • Frequency 250 • Graphing multimeter (GMM) 253 • Graticule 247 • Hertz 250 • Oscilloscope (scope) 247 • Pulse train 249 • Pulse width 250 • Pulse-width modulation (PWM) 250 • Time base 248 • Trigger level 251 • Trigger slope 251

TYPES OF OSCILLOSCOPES

TERMINOLOGY An **oscilloscope** (usually called a **scope**) is a visual voltmeter with a timer that shows when a voltage changes. Following are several types of oscilloscopes.

- An *analog scope* uses a **cathode ray tube (CRT)** similar to a television screen to display voltage patterns. The scope screen displays the electrical signal constantly.

- A *digital scope* commonly uses a liquid crystal display (LCD), but a CRT may also be used on some digital scopes. A digital scope takes samples of the signals that can be stopped or stored and is therefore called a **digital storage oscilloscope, or DSO.**

- A digital scope does not capture each change in voltage but instead captures voltage levels over time and stores them as dots. Each dot is a voltage level. Then the scope displays the waveforms using the thousands of dots (each representing a voltage level) and then electrically connects the dots to create a waveform.

- A DSO can be connected to a sensor output signal wire and can record over a long period of time the voltage signals. Then it can be replayed and a technician can see if any faults were detected. This feature makes a DSO the perfect tool to help diagnose intermittent problems.

- A digital storage scope, however, can sometimes miss faults called *glitches* that may occur between samples captured by the scope. This is why a DSO with a high "sampling rate" is preferred. Sampling rate means

that a scope is cable of capturing voltage changes that occur over a very short period of time. Some digital storage scopes have a capture rate of 25 million (25,000,000) samples per second. This means that the scope can capture a glitch (fault) that lasts just 40 nano (0.00000040) seconds long.

- A scope has been called "a voltmeter with a clock."

  - The voltmeter part means that a scope can capture and display changing voltage levels.

  - The clock part means that the scope can display these changes in voltage levels within a specific time period; and with a DSO it can be replayed so that any faults can be seen and studied.

OSCILLOSCOPE DISPLAY GRID A typical scope face usually has eight or ten grids vertically (up and down) and ten grids horizontally (left to right). The transparent scale (grid), used for reference measurements, is called a **graticule.** This arrangement is commonly 8 × 10 or 10 × 10 divisions. ● **SEE FIGURE 26–1.**

NOTE: These numbers originally referred to the metric dimensions of the graticule in centimeters. Therefore, an 8 × 10 display would be 8 cm (80 mm or 3.14 in.) high and 10 cm (100 mm or 3.90 in.) wide.

- Voltage is displayed on a scope starting with zero volts at the bottom and higher voltage being displayed vertically.

- The scope illustrates time left to right. The pattern starts on the left and sweeps across the screen from left to right.

8 VOLTS

1 VOLT

VOLTS/DIV SET
1 VOLT

500 ms OR (0.50 s) OR 1/2 OF 1 SECOND

TIME BASE SET TO "50 ms"

FIGURE 26–1 A scope display allows technicians to take measurements of voltage patterns. In this example, each vertical division is 1 volt and each horizontal division is set to represent 50 milliseconds.

SCOPE SETUP AND ADJUSTMENTS

SETTING THE TIME BASE Most scopes use 10 graticules from left to right on the display. Setting the **time base** means setting how much time will be displayed in each block called a **division**. For example, if the scope is set to read 2 seconds per division (referred to as *s/div*), then the total displayed would be 20 seconds (2 × 10 divisions = 20 sec.). The time base should be set to an amount of time that allows two to four events to be displayed. Milliseconds (0.001 sec.) are commonly used in scopes when adjusting the time base. Sample time is milliseconds per division (indicated as *ms/div*) and total time. ● **SEE CHART 26–1.**

NOTE: Increasing the time base reduces the number of samples per second.

The horizontal scale is divided into 10 divisions (sometimes called *grats*). If each division represents 1 second of time, then the total time period displayed on the screen will be 10 seconds. The time per division is selected so that several events of the waveform are displayed. Time per division settings can vary greatly in automotive use, including:

MILLISECONDS PER DIVISION (MS/DIV)	TOTAL TIME DISPLAYED
1	10 ms (0.010 sec.)
10	100 ms (0.100 sec.)
50	500 ms (0.500 sec.)
100	1 sec. (1.000 sec.)
500	5 sec. (5.0 sec.)
1,000	10 sec. (10.0 sec.)

CHART 26–1

The time base is milliseconds (ms) and total time of an event that can be displayed.

- MAP/MAF sensors: 2 ms/div (20 ms total)
- Network (CAN) communications network: 2 ms/div (20 ms total)
- Throttle position (TP) sensor: 100 ms per division (1 sec. total)
- Fuel injector: 2 ms/div (20 ms total)
- Oxygen sensor: 1 sec. per division (10 sec. total)
- Primary ignition: 10 ms/div (100 ms total)
- Secondary ignition: 10 ms/div (100 ms total)
- Voltage measurements: 5 ms/div (50 ms total)

FIGURE 26-2 The display on a digital storage oscilloscope (DSO) displays the entire waveform of a throttle position (TP) sensor from idle to wide-open throttle and then returns to idle. The display also indicates the maximum reading (4.72 V) and the minimum (680 mV or 0.68 V). The display does not show anything until the throttle is opened, because the scope has been set up to only start displaying a waveform after a certain voltage level has been reached. This voltage is called the trigger or trigger point.

The total time displayed on the screen allows comparisons to see if the waveform is consistent or is changing. Multiple waveforms shown on the display at the same time also allow for measurements to be seen more easily. ● **SEE FIGURE 26-2** for an example of a throttle position sensor waveform created by measuring the voltage output as the throttle was depressed and then released.

VOLTS PER DIVISION

The volts per division, abbreviated *V/div*, should be set so that the entire anticipated waveform can be viewed. Examples include:

Throttle position (TP) sensor: 1 V/div (8 V total)

Battery, starting and charging: 2 V/div (16 V total)

Oxygen sensor: 200 mV/div (1.6 V total)

Notice from the examples that the total voltage to be displayed exceeds the voltage range of the component being tested. This ensures that all the waveform will be displayed. It also allows for some unexpected voltage readings. For example, an oxygen sensor should read between 0 V and 1 V (1,000 mV). By setting the V/div to 200 mV, up to 1.6 V (1,600 mV) will be displayed.

DC AND AC COUPLING

DC COUPLING DC coupling is the most used position on a scope because it allows the scope to display both alternating current (AC) voltage signals and direct current (DC) voltage signals present in the circuit. The AC part of the signal will ride on top of the DC component. For example, if the engine is running and the charging voltage is 14.4 volts DC, this will be displayed as a horizontal line on the screen. Any AC ripple voltage leaking past the alternator diodes will be displayed as an AC signal on

FIGURE 26-3 Ripple voltage is created from the AC voltage from an alternator. Some AC ripple voltage is normal but if the AC portion exceeds 0.5 volt, then a bad diode is the most likely cause. Excessive AC ripple can cause many electrical and electronic devices to work incorrectly.

top of the horizontal DC voltage line. Therefore, both components of the signal can be observed at the same time.

AC COUPLING When the **AC coupling** position is selected, a capacitor is placed into the meter lead circuit, which effectively blocks all DC voltage signals but allows the AC portion of the signal to pass and be displayed. AC coupling can be used to show output signal waveforms from sensors such as:

- Distributor pickup coils
- Magnetic wheel speed sensors
- Magnetic crankshaft position sensors
- Magnetic camshaft position sensors
- Magnetic vehicle speed sensors
- The AC ripple from an alternator. ● **SEE FIGURE 26-3.**

NOTE: Check the instructions from the scope manufacturer for the recommended settings to use. Sometimes it is necessary to switch from DC coupling to AC coupling or from AC coupling to DC coupling to properly see some waveforms.

PULSE TRAINS

DEFINITION Scopes can show all voltage signals. Among the most commonly found in automotive applications is a DC voltage that varies up and down and does not go below zero like an AC voltage. A DC voltage that turns on and off in a series of pulses is called a **pulse train.** Pulse trains differ from an AC signal in that they do not go below zero. An alternating voltage goes above and below zero voltage. Pulse train signals can vary in several ways. ● **SEE FIGURE 26-4.**

1. FREQUENCY—FREQUENCY IS THE NUMBER OF CYCLES THAT TAKE PLACE PER SECOND. THE MORE CYCLES THAT TAKE PLACE IN ONE SECOND, THE HIGHER THE FREQUENCY READING. FREQUENCIES ARE MEASURED IN HERTZ, WHICH IS THE NUMBER OF CYCLES PER SECOND. AN 8 HERTZ SIGNAL CYCLES EIGHT TIMES PER SECOND.

THIS IS WHAT AN 8 HERTZ WOULD LOOK LIKE—8 HERTZ MEANS "8 CYCLES PER SECOND."

2. DUTY CYCLE—DUTY CYCLE IS A MEASUREMENT COMPARING THE SIGNAL ON-TIME TO THE LENGTH OF ONE COMPLETE CYCLE. AS ON-TIME INCREASES, OFF-TIME DECREASES. DUTY CYCLE IS MEASURED IN PERCENTAGE OF ON-TIME. A 60% DUTY CYCLE IS A SIGNAL THAT'S ON 60% OF THE TIME, AND OFF 40% OF THE TIME. ANOTHER WAY TO MEASURE DUTY CYCLE IS DWELL, WHICH IS MEASURED IN DEGREES INSTEAD OF PERCENT.

DUTY CYCLE IS THE RELATIONSHIP BETWEEN ONE COMPLETE CYCLE, AND THE SIGNAL'S ON-TIME. A SIGNAL CAN VARY IN DUTY CYCLE WITHOUT AFFECTING THE FREQUENCY.

3. PULSE WIDTH—PULSE WIDTH IS THE ACTUAL ON-TIME OF A SIGNAL, MEASURED IN MILLISECONDS. WITH PULSE WIDTH MEASUREMENTS, OFF-TIME DOESN'T REALLY MATTER—THE ONLY REAL CONCERN IS HOW LONG THE SIGNAL'S ON. THIS IS A USEFUL TEST FOR MEASURING CONVENTIONAL INJECTOR ON-TIME, TO SEE THAT THE SIGNAL VARIES WITH LOAD CHANGE.

PULSE WIDTH IS THE ACTUAL TIME A SIGNAL'S ON, MEASURED IN MILLISECONDS. THE ONLY THING BEING MEASURED IS HOW LONG THE SIGNAL IS ON.

FIGURE 26–4 A pulse train is any electrical signal that turns on and off, or goes high and low in a series of pulses. Ignition module and fuel-injector pulses are examples of a pulse train signal.

FREQUENCY

Frequency is the number of cycles per second measured in **hertz.** The engine revolutions per minute (RPM) signal is an example of a signal that can occur at various frequencies. At low engine speed, the ignition pulses occur fewer times per second (lower frequency) than when the engine is operated at higher engine speeds (RPM).

DUTY CYCLE

Duty cycle refers to the percentage of on-time of the signal during one complete cycle. As on-time increases, the amount of time the signal is off decreases and is usually measured in percentage. Duty cycle is also called **pulse-width modulation (PWM)** and can be measured in degrees. ● **SEE FIGURE 26–5.**

PULSE WIDTH

The **pulse width** is a measure of the actual on-time measured in milliseconds. Fuel injectors are usually controlled by varying the pulse width. ● **SEE FIGURE 26–6.**

NUMBER OF CHANNELS

DEFINITION Scopes are available that allow the viewing of more than one sensor or event at the same time on the display. The number of events, which require leads for each, is called a **channel.** A channel is an input to a scope. Commonly available scopes include:

- **Single channel.** A single channel scope is capable of displaying only one sensor signal waveform at a time.
- **Two channel.** A two-channel scope can display the waveform from two separate sensors or components at the same time. This feature is very helpful when

(a)

DIGITAL MULTIMETER

AUTO

082.4 %

TRIG 40

THE % SIGN IN THE UPPER RIGHT CORNER OF THE DISPLAY INDICATES THAT THE METER IS READING A DUTY CYCLE SIGNAL.

(b)

FIGURE 26–5 (a) A scope representation of a complete cycle showing both on-time and off-time. (b) A meter display indicating the on-time duty cycle in a percentage (%). Note the trigger and negative (2) symbol. This indicates that the meter started to record the percentage of on-time when the voltage dropped (start of on-time).

testing the camshaft and crankshaft position sensors on an engine to see if they are properly timed. ● **SEE FIGURE 26–7.**

- **Four channel.** A four-channel scope allows the technician to view up to four different sensors or actuators on one display.

NOTE: Often the capture speed of the signals is slowed when using more than one channel.

TRIGGERS

EXTERNAL TRIGGER   An **external trigger** is when the waveform starts when a signal is received from another external source rather than from the signal pickup lead. A common example of an external trigger comes from the probe clamp around the cylinder #1 spark plug wire to trigger the start of an ignition pattern.

TRIGGER LEVEL   **Trigger level** is the voltage that must be detected by the scope before the pattern will be displayed. A scope will only start displaying a voltage signal when it is

ON A GROUND-CONTROLLED CIRCUIT, THE ON-TIME PULSE IS THE LOWER HORIZONTAL PULSE.

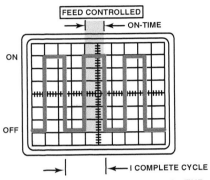

ON A FEED-CONTROLLED CIRCUIT, THE ON-TIME PULSE IS THE UPPER HORIZONTAL PULSE.

FIGURE 26–6 Most automotive computer systems control the device by opening and closing the ground to the component.

triggered or is told to start. The trigger level must be set to start the display. If the pattern starts at 1 volt, then the trace will begin displaying on the left side of the screen *after* the trace has reached 1 volt.

TRIGGER SLOPE   The **trigger slope** is the voltage direction that a waveform must have in order to start the display. Most often, the trigger to start a waveform display is taken from the signal itself. Besides trigger voltage level, most scopes can be adjusted to trigger only when the voltage rises past the trigger-level voltage. This is called a *positive slope*. When the voltage falling past the higher level activates the trigger, this is called a *negative slope*.

The scope display indicates both a positive and a negative slope symbol. For example, if a waveform such as a magnetic sensor used for crankshaft position or wheel speed starts moving upward, a positive slope should be selected. If a negative slope is selected, the waveform will not start showing until the voltage reaches the trigger level in a downward direction. A negative slope should be used when a fuel-injector circuit is being analyzed. In this circuit, the computer provides the ground and the voltage level drops when the computer commands the injector on. Sometimes the technician needs to change from negative to positive or positive to negative trigger if a waveform is not being shown correctly. ● **SEE FIGURE 26–8.**

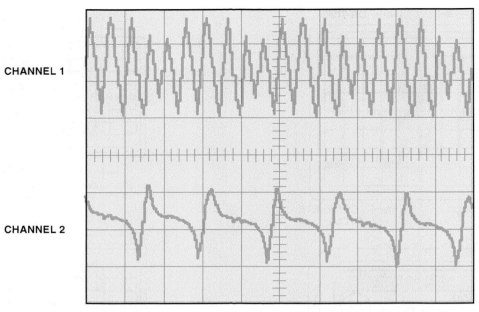

CHANNEL 1

CHANNEL 2

10 ms/Div 5 V/Div

FIGURE 26–7 A two-channel scope being used to compare two signals on the same vehicle.

(a)   (b)

FIGURE 26–8 (a) A symbol for a positive trigger—a trigger occurs at a rising (positive) edge of the signal (waveform). (b) A symbol for a negative trigger— a trigger occurs at a falling (negative) edge of the signal (waveform).

USING A SCOPE

USING SCOPE LEADS   Most scopes, both analog and digital, normally use the same test leads. These leads usually attach to the scope through a **BNC connector,** a miniature standard coaxial cable connector. BNC is an international standard that is used in the electronics industry. If using a BNC connector, be sure to connect one lead to a good clean, metal engine ground. The probe of the scope lead attaches to the circuit or component being tested. Many scopes use one ground lead and then each channel has it own signal pickup lead.

MEASURING BATTERY VOLTAGE WITH A SCOPE

One of the easiest things to measure and observe on a scope is battery voltage. A lower voltage can be observed on the scope

FIGURE 26–9 Constant battery voltage is represented by a flat horizontal line. In this example, the engine was started and the battery voltage dropped to about 10 V as shown on the left side of the scope display. When the engine started, the alternator started to charge the battery and the voltage is shown as climbing.

display as the engine is started and a higher voltage should be displayed after the engine starts. ● **SEE FIGURE 26–9.**

FIGURE 26–10 A typical graphing multimeter that can be used as a digital meter, plus it can display the voltage levels on the display screen.

An analog scope displays rapidly and cannot be set to show or freeze a display. Therefore, even though an analog scope shows all voltage signals, it is easy to miss a momentary glitch on an analog scope.

CAUTION: Check the instructions for the scope being used before attempting to scope household AC circuits. Some scopes, such as the Snap-On MODIS, are not designed to measure high-voltage AC circuits.

GRAPHING MULTIMETER

A **graphing multimeter,** abbreviated **GMM,** is a cross between a digital meter and a digital storage oscilloscope. A graphing multimeter displays the voltage levels at two places:

- On a display screen
- In a digital readout

It is usually not capable of capturing very short duration faults or glitches that would likely be captured with a digital storage oscilloscope. ● **SEE FIGURE 26–10.**

GRAPHING SCAN TOOLS

Many scan tools are capable of displaying the voltage levels captured by the scan tool through the data link connector (DLC) on a screen. This feature is helpful where seeing changes in voltage levels is difficult to detect by looking at numbers that are constantly changing. Read and follow the instructions for the scan tool being used.

SUMMARY

1. Analog oscilloscopes use a cathode ray tube to display voltage patterns.
2. The waveforms shown on an analog oscilloscope cannot be stored for later viewing.
3. A digital storage oscilloscope (DSO) creates an image or waveform on the display by connecting thousands of dots captured by the scope leads.
4. An oscilloscope display grid is called a graticule. Each of the 8 × 10 or 10 × 10 dividing boxes is called a division.
5. Setting the time base means establishing the amount of time each division represents.
6. Setting the volts per division allows the technician to view either the entire waveform or just part of it.
7. DC coupling and AC coupling are two selections that can be made to observe different types of waveforms.
8. A graphing multimeter is not capable of capturing short duration faults but can display usable waveforms.
9. Oscilloscopes display voltage over time. A DSO can capture and store a waveform for viewing later.

REVIEW QUESTIONS

1. What are the differences between an analog and a digital oscilloscope?
2. What is the difference between DC coupling and AC coupling?
3. Why are DC signals that change called pulse trains?
4. What is the difference between an oscilloscope and a graphing multimeter?

1. Technician A says an analog scope can store the waveform for viewing later. Technician B says that the trigger level has to be set on most scopes to be able to view a changing waveform. Which technician is correct?
   a. Technician A only
   b. Technician B only
   c. Both Technicians A and B
   d. Neither Technician A nor B

2. An oscilloscope display is called a _____.
   a. Grid
   b. Graticule
   c. Division
   d. Box

3. A signal showing the voltage of a battery displayed on a digital storage oscilloscope (DSO) is being discussed. Technician A says that the display will show one horizontal line above the zero line. Technician B says that the display will show a line sloping upward from zero to the battery voltage level. Which technician is correct?
   a. Technician A only
   b. Technician B only
   c. Both Technicians A and B
   d. Neither Technician A nor B

4. Setting the time base to 50 ms per division will allow the technician to view a waveform how long in duration?
   a. 50 ms
   b. 200 ms
   c. 400 ms
   d. 500 ms

5. A throttle position sensor waveform is going to be observed. At what setting should the volts per division be set to see the entire waveform from 0 to 5 volts?
   a. 0.5 V/div
   b. 1.0 V/div
   c. 2.0 V/div
   d. 5.0 V/div

6. Two technicians are discussing the DC coupling setting on a DSO. Technician A says that the position allows both the DC and AC signals of the waveform to be displayed. Technician B says that this setting allows just the DC part of the waveform to be displayed. Which technician is correct?
   a. Technician A only
   b. Technician B only
   c. Both Technicians A and B
   d. Neither Technician A nor B

7. Voltage signals (waveforms) that do not go below zero are called _____.
   a. AC signals
   b. Pulse trains
   c. Pulse width
   d. DC coupled signals

8. Cycles per second are expressed in _____.
   a. Hertz
   b. Duty cycle
   c. Pulse width
   d. Slope

9. Oscilloscopes use what type of lead connector?
   a. Banana plugs
   b. Double banana plugs
   c. Single conductor plugs
   d. BNC

10. A digital meter that can show waveforms is called a _____.
   a. DVOM
   b. DMM
   c. GMM
   d. DSO

chapter 27

AUTOMOTIVE WIRING AND WIRE REPAIR

OBJECTIVES: **After studying Chapter 27, the reader will be able to:** • Prepare for ASE Electrical/Electronic Systems (A6) certification test content area "A" (General Electrical/Electronic Systems Diagnosis). • Explain the wire gauge number system. • Describe how fusible links and fuses protect circuits and wiring. • Discuss electrical terminals and connectors. • Describe how to solder. • Discuss circuit breakers and PTC electronic circuit protection devices. • Explain the types of electrical conduit • List the steps for performing a proper wire repair.

KEY TERMS: • Adhesive-lined heat shrink tubing 265 • American wire gauge (AWG) 255 • Auto link 259 • Battery cables 257 • Braided ground straps 257 • Circuit breakers 260 • Cold solder joint 265 • Connector 263 • Connector position assurance (CPA) 263 • Crimp-and-seal connectors 265 • Fuse link 259 • Fuses 258 • Fusible link 261 • Heat shrink tubing 265 • Jumper cables 257 • Lock tang 263 • Metric wire gauge 256 • Pacific fuse element 259 • Primary wire 256 • PTC circuit protectors 261 • Rosin-core solder 264 • Skin effect 257 • Terminal 263 • Twisted pair 257

AUTOMOTIVE WIRING

DEFINITION AND TERMINOLOGY Most automotive wire is made from strands of copper covered by plastic insulation. Copper is an excellent conductor of electricity that is reasonably priced and very flexible. However, solid copper wire can break when moved repeatedly; therefore, most copper wiring is constructed of multiple small strands that allow for repeated bending and moving without breaking. Solid copper wire is generally used for components such as starter armature and alternator stator windings that do not bend or move during normal operation. Copper is the best electrical conductor besides silver, which is a great deal more expensive. The conductivity of various metals is rated. ● **SEE CHART 27–1.**

AMERICAN WIRE GAUGE Wiring is sized and purchased according to gauge size as assigned by the **American wire gauge (AWG)** system. AWG numbers can be confusing because as the gauge number *increases,* the size of the conductor wire *decreases.* Therefore, a 14 gauge wire is smaller than a 10 gauge wire. The *greater* the amount of current (in amperes) that is flowing through a wire, the *larger the diameter (smaller gauge number)* that will be required. ● **SEE CHART 27–2,** which compares the AWG number to the actual wire diameter in inches. The diameter refers to the diameter of the metal conductor and does not include the insulation.

Following are general applications for the most commonly used wire gauge sizes. Always check the installation instructions or the manufacturer's specifications for wire gauge size before replacing any automotive wiring.

1.	Silver
2.	Copper
3.	Gold
4.	Aluminum
5.	Tungsten
6.	Zinc
7.	Brass (copper and zinc)
8.	Platinum
9.	Iron
10.	Nickel
11.	Tin
12.	Steel
13.	Lead

CHART 27–1

The list of relative conductivity of metals, showing silver to be the best.

- 20 to 22 gauge: radio speaker wires
- 18 gauge: small bulbs and short leads
- 16 gauge: taillights, gas gauge, turn signals, windshield wipers
- 14 gauge: horn, radio power lead, headlights, cigarette lighter, brake lights
- 12 gauge: headlight switch-to-fuse box, rear window defogger, power windows and locks
- 10 gauge: alternator-to-battery
- 4, 2, or 0 (1/0) gauge: battery cables

WIRE GAUGE DIAMETER TABLE	
AMERICAN WIRE GAUGE (AWG)	**WIRE DIAMETER IN INCHES**
20	0.03196118
18	0.040303
16	0.0508214
14	0.064084
12	0.08080810
10	0.10189
8	0.128496
6	0.16202
5	0.18194
4	0.20431
3	0.22942
2	0.25763
1	0.2893
0	0.32486
00	0.3648

CHART 27–2

American wire gauge (AWG) number and the actual conductor diameter in inches.

 FREQUENTLY ASKED QUESTION

Do They Make 13 Gauge Wire?

Yes. AWG sizing of wire includes all gauge numbers, including 13, even though the most commonly used sizes are even numbered, such as 12, 14, or 16.

Because the sizes are so close, wire in every size is not commonly stocked, but can be ordered for a higher price. Therefore, if a larger wire size is needed, it is common practice to select the next lower, even-numbered gauge.

METRIC WIRE GAUGE Most manufacturers indicate on the wiring diagrams the **metric wire gauge** sizes measured in square millimeters (mm²) of cross-sectional area. The following chart gives conversions or comparisons between metric gauge and AWG sizes. Notice that the metric wire size increases with size (area), whereas the AWG size gets smaller with larger size wire. ● **SEE CHART 27–3.**

The AWG number should be decreased (wire size increased) with increased lengths of wire. ● **SEE CHART 27–4.**

For example, a trailer may require 14 gauge wire to light all the trailer lights, but if the wire required is over 25 ft long,

METRIC SIZE (mm²)	**AWG SIZE**
0.5	20
0.8	18
1.0	16
2.0	14
3.0	12
5.0	10
8.0	8
13.0	6
19.0	4
32.0	2
52.0	0

CHART 27–3

Metric wire size in squared millimeters (mm²) conversion chart to American wire gauge (AWG).

12 V	RECOMMENDED WIRE GAUGE (AWG) (FOR LENGTH IN FEET)*						
AMPS	**3`**	**5`**	**7`**	**10`**	**15`**	**20`**	**25`**
5	18	18	18	18	18	18	18
7	18	18	18	18	18	18	16
10	18	18	18	18	16	16	16
12	18	18	18	18	16	16	14
15	18	18	18	18	14	14	12
18	18	18	16	16	14	14	12
20	18	18	16	16	14	12	10
22	18	18	16	16	12	12	10
24	18	18	16	16	12	12	10
30	18	16	16	14	10	10	10
40	18	16	14	12	10	10	8
50	16	14	12	12	10	10	8
100	12	12	10	10	6	6	4
150	10	10	8	8	4	4	2
200	10	8	8	6	4	4	2

* When mechanical strength is a factor, use the next larger wire gauge.

CHART 27–4

Recommended AWG wire size increases as the length increases because all wire has internal resistance. The longer the wire is, the greater the resistance. The larger the diameter is, the lower the resistance.

12 gauge wire should be used. Most automotive wire, except for spark plug wire, is often called **primary wire** (named for the voltage range used in the primary ignition circuit) because it is designed to operate at or near battery voltage.

GROUND WIRES

PURPOSE AND FUNCTION All vehicles use ground wires between the engine and body and/or between the body and the negative terminal of the battery. The two types of ground wires are:

- Insulated copper wire
- Braided ground straps

Braided grounds straps are uninsulated. It is not necessary to insulate a ground strap because it does not matter if it touches metal, as it already attaches to ground. Braided ground straps are more flexible than stranded wire. Because the engine will move slightly on its mounts, the braided ground strap must be able to flex without breaking. ● SEE FIGURE 27–1.

SKIN EFFECT The braided strap also dampens out some radio-frequency interference that otherwise might be transmitted through standard stranded wiring due to the skin effect.

The **skin effect** is the term used to describe how high-frequency AC electricity flows through a conductor. Direct current flows through a conductor, but alternating current tends to travel through the outside (skin) of the conductor. Because of the skin effect, most audio (speaker) cable is constructed of many small-diameter copper wires instead of fewer larger strands, because the smaller wire has a greater surface area and therefore results in less resistance to the flow of AC voltage.

NOTE: Body ground wires are necessary to provide a circuit path for the lights and accessories that ground to the body and flow to the negative battery terminal.

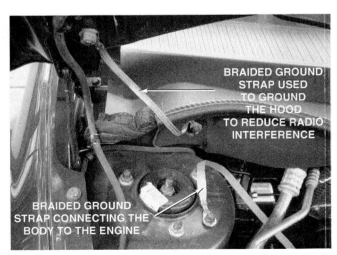

FIGURE 27–1 All lights and accessories ground to the body of the vehicle. Body ground wires such as this one are needed to conduct all of the current from these components back to the negative terminal of the battery. The body ground wire connects the body to the engine. Most battery negative cables attach to the engine.

FIGURE 27–2 Battery cables are designed to carry heavy starter current and are therefore usually 4 gauge or larger wire. Note that this battery has a thermal blanket covering to help protect the battery from high underhood temperatures. The wiring is also covered with plastic conduit called split-loom tubing.

BATTERY CABLES

Battery cables are the largest wires used in the automotive electrical system. The cables are usually 4 gauge, 2 gauge, or 1 gauge wires (19 mm^2 or larger). ● SEE FIGURE 27–2.

Wires larger than 1 gauge are called 0 gauge (pronounced "ought"). Larger cables are labeled 2/0 or 00 (2 ought) and 3/0 or 000 (3 ought). Electrical systems that are 6 volts require battery cables two sizes larger than those used for 12 volt electrical systems, because the lower voltage used in antique vehicles resulted in twice the amount of current (amperes) to supply the same electrical power.

JUMPER CABLES

Jumper cables are 4 to 2/0 gauge electrical cables with large clamps attached and are used to connect a vehicle that has a discharged battery to a vehicle that has a good battery.

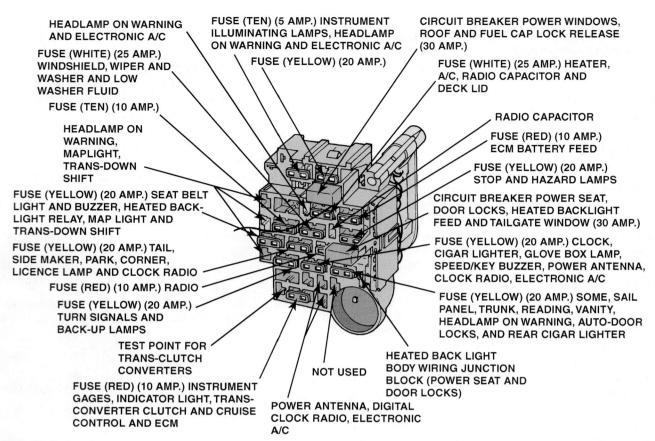

HEADLAMP ON WARNING AND ELECTRONIC A/C

FUSE (WHITE) (25 AMP.) WINDSHIELD, WIPER AND WASHER AND LOW WASHER FLUID

FUSE (TEN) (10 AMP.)

HEADLAMP ON WARNING, MAPLIGHT, TRANS-DOWN SHIFT

FUSE (YELLOW) (20 AMP.) SEAT BELT LIGHT AND BUZZER, HEATED BACK-LIGHT RELAY, MAP LIGHT AND TRANS-DOWN SHIFT

FUSE (YELLOW) (20 AMP.) TAIL, SIDE MAKER, PARK, CORNER, LICENCE LAMP AND CLOCK RADIO

FUSE (RED) (10 AMP.) RADIO

FUSE (YELLOW) (20 AMP.) TURN SIGNALS AND BACK-UP LAMPS

TEST POINT FOR TRANS-CLUTCH CONVERTERS

FUSE (RED) (10 AMP.) INSTRUMENT GAGES, INDICATOR LIGHT, TRANS-CONVERTER CLUTCH AND CRUISE CONTROL AND ECM

FUSE (TEN) (5 AMP.) INSTRUMENT ILLUMINATING LAMPS, HEADLAMP ON WARNING AND ELECTRONIC A/C

FUSE (YELLOW) (20 AMP.)

NOT USED

POWER ANTENNA, DIGITAL CLOCK RADIO, ELECTRONIC A/C

CIRCUIT BREAKER POWER WINDOWS, ROOF AND FUEL CAP LOCK RELEASE (30 AMP.)

FUSE (WHITE) (25 AMP.) HEATER, A/C, RADIO CAPACITOR AND DECK LID

RADIO CAPACITOR

FUSE (RED) (10 AMP.) ECM BATTERY FEED

FUSE (YELLOW) (20 AMP.) STOP AND HAZARD LAMPS

CIRCUIT BREAKER POWER SEAT, DOOR LOCKS, HEATED BACKLIGHT FEED AND TAILGATE WINDOW (30 AMP.)

FUSE (YELLOW) (20 AMP.) CLOCK, CIGAR LIGHTER, GLOVE BOX LAMP, SPEED/KEY BUZZER, POWER ANTENNA, CLOCK RADIO, ELECTRONIC A/C

FUSE (YELLOW) (20 AMP.) SOME, SAIL PANEL, TRUNK, READING, VANITY, HEADLAMP ON WARNING, AUTO-DOOR LOCKS, AND REAR CIGAR LIGHTER

HEATED BACK LIGHT BODY WIRING JUNCTION BLOCK (POWER SEAT AND DOOR LOCKS)

FIGURE 27–3 A typical automotive fuse panel.

Good-quality jumper cables are necessary to prevent excessive voltage drops caused by cable resistance. Aluminum wire jumper cables should not be used, because even though aluminum is a good electrical conductor (although not as good as copper), it is less flexible and can crack and break when bent or moved repeatedly. The size should be 6 gauge or larger.

1/0 AWG welding cable can be used to construct an excellent set of jumper cables using welding clamps on both ends. Welding cable is usually constructed of many very fine strands of wire, which allow for easier bending of the cable as the strands of fine wire slide against each other inside the cable.

NOTE: Always check the wire gauge of any battery cables or jumper cables and do not rely on the outside diameter of the wire. Many lower cost jumper cables use smaller gauge wire, but may use thick insulation to make the cable look as if it is the correct size wire.

FUSES AND CIRCUIT PROTECTION DEVICES

CONSTRUCTION **Fuses** should be used in every circuit to protect the wiring from overheating and damage caused by excessive current flow as a result of a short circuit or other malfunction. The symbol for a fuse is a wavy line between two points:

A fuse is constructed of a fine tin conductor inside a glass, plastic, or ceramic housing. The tin is designed to melt and open the circuit if excessive current flows through the fuse. Each fuse is rated according to its maximum current-carrying capacity.

Many fuses are used to protect more than one circuit of the automobile. ● **SEE FIGURE 27–3.**

A typical example is the fuse for the cigarette lighter that also protects many other circuits, such as those for the courtesy lights, clock, and other circuits. A fault in one of these circuits can cause this fuse to melt, which will prevent the operation of all other circuits that are protected by the fuse.

NOTE: The SAE term for a cigarette lighter is cigar lighter because the diameter of the heating element is large enough for a cigar. The term cigarette lighter will be used throughout this book because it is the most common usage.

FUSE RATINGS Fuses are used to protect the wiring and components in the circuit from damage if an excessive amount of current flows. The fuse rating is normally about 20% higher than the normal current in the circuit. ● **SEE CHART 27–5** for a typical fuse rating based on the normal current in the circuit. In other words, the normal current flow should be about 80% of the fuse rating.

NORMAL CURRENT IN THE CIRCUIT (AMPERES)	FUSE RATING (AMPERES)
7.5	10
16	20
24	30

CHART 27–5

The fuse rating should be 20% higher than the maximum current in the circuit to provide the best protection for the wiring and the component being protected.

BLADE FUSES   Colored blade-type fuses are also referred to as ATO fuses and have been used since 1977. The color of the plastic of blade fuses indicates the maximum current flow, measured in amperes.

● **SEE CHART 27–6** for the color and the amperage rating of blade fuses.

Each fuse has an opening in the top of its plastic portion to allow access to its metal contacts for testing purposes. ● **SEE FIGURE 27–4.**

MINI FUSES   To save space, many vehicles use mini (small) blade fuses. Not only do they save space but they also allow the vehicle design engineer to fuse individual circuits instead of grouping many different components on one fuse. This improves customer satisfaction because if one component fails, it only affects that one circuit without stopping electrical power to several other circuits as well. This makes troubleshooting

AMPERAGE RATING	COLOR
1	Dark green
2	Gray
2.5	Purple
3	Violet
4	Pink
5	Tan
6	Gold
7.5	Brown
9	Orange
10	Red
14	Black
15	Blue
20	Yellow
25	White
30	Green

CHART 27–6

The amperage rating and the color of the blade fuse are standardized.

FIGURE 27–4 Blade-type fuses can be tested through openings in the plastic at the top of the fuse.

AMPERAGE RATING	COLOR
5	Tan
7.5	Brown
10	Red
15	Blue
20	Yellow
25	Natural
30	Green

CHART 27–7

Mini fuse amperage rating and colors.

AMPERAGE RATING	COLOR
20	Yellow
30	Green
40	Amber
50	Red
60	Blue
70	Brown
80	Natural

CHART 27–8

Maxi fuse amperage rating and colors.

a lot easier too, because each circuit is separate. ● **SEE CHART 27–7** for the amperage rating and corresponding fuse color for mini fuses.

MAXI FUSES   Maxi fuses are a large version of blade fuses and are used to replace fusible links in many vehicles. Maxi fuses are rated up to 80 amperes or more. ● **SEE CHART 27–8** for the amperage rating and corresponding color for maxi fuses.

● **SEE FIGURE 27–5** for a comparison of the various sizes of blade-type fuses.

PACIFIC FUSE ELEMENT   First used in the late 1980s, **Pacific fuse elements** (also called a **fuse link** or **auto link**) are used to protect wiring from a direct short-to-ground.

FIGURE 27–5 Three sizes of blade-type fuses: mini on the left, standard or ATO type in the center, and maxi on the right.

TOP

SIDE

FUSE ELEMENT (PACIFIC FUSE)

MAXIFUSE

ATO FUSE

MINIFUSE

FIGURE 27–6 A comparison of the various types of protective devices used in most vehicles.

The housing contains a short link of wire sized for the rated current load. The transparent top allows inspection of the link inside. ● **SEE FIGURE 27–6.**

TESTING FUSES

It is important to test the condition of a fuse if the circuit being protected by the fuse does not operate. Most blown fuses can be detected quickly because the center conductor is melted. Fuses can also fail and open the circuit because of a poor connection in the fuse itself or in the fuse holder. Therefore, just because a fuse "looks okay" does not mean that it *is* okay. All fuses should be tested with a test light. The test light should be connected to first one side of the fuse and then the other. A test light should light on both sides. If the test light only lights on one side, the fuse is blown or open. If the test light does not light on either side of the fuse, then that circuit is not being supplied power. ● **SEE FIGURE 27–7.** An ohmmeter can be used to test fuses.

CIRCUIT BREAKERS

Circuit breakers are used to prevent harmful overload (excessive current flow) in a circuit by opening

FIGURE 27–7 To test a fuse, use a test light to check for power at the power side of the fuse. The ignition switch and lights may have to be on before some fuses receive power. If the fuse is good, the test light should light on both sides (power side and load side) of the fuse.

FUSE BLOCK

30 AMP CIRCUIT BREAKER

6 AMP CIRCUIT BREAKER

BIMETALLIC STRIP

CONTACTS CLOSED

CURRENT FLOW

FIGURE 27–8 Typical blade circuit breaker fits into the same space as a blade fuse. If excessive current flows through the bimetallic strip, the strip bends and opens the contacts and stops current flow. When the circuit breaker cools, the contacts close again, completing the electrical circuit.

the circuit and stopping the current flow to prevent overheating and possible fire caused by hot wires or electrical components. **Circuit breakers** are mechanical units made of two different metals (bimetallic) that deform when heated and open a set of contact points that work in the same manner as an "off" switch. ● **SEE FIGURE 27–8.**

Cycling-type circuit breakers, therefore, are reset when the current stops flowing, which causes the bimetallic strip to cool and the circuit to close again. A circuit breaker is used in circuits that could affect the safety of passengers if a

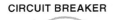

FIGURE 27–9 Electrical symbols used to represent circuit breakers.

conventional nonresetting fuse were used. The headlight circuit is an excellent example of the use of a circuit breaker rather than a fuse. A short or grounded circuit anywhere in the headlight circuit could cause excessive current flow and, therefore, the opening of the circuit. Obviously, a sudden loss of headlights at night could have disastrous results. A circuit breaker opens and closes the circuit rapidly, thereby protecting the circuit from overheating and also providing sufficient current flow to maintain at least partial headlight operation.

Circuit breakers are also used in other circuits where conventional fuses could not provide for the surges of high current commonly found in those circuits. ● **SEE FIGURE 27–9** for the electrical symbols used to represent a circuit breaker.

Examples are the circuits for the following accessories.

1. Power seats
2. Power door locks
3. Power windows

PTC CIRCUIT PROTECTORS **Positive temperature coefficient (PTC) circuit protectors** are solid state (without moving parts). Like all other circuit protection devices, PTCs are installed in series in the circuit being protected. If excessive current flows, the temperature and resistance of the PTC increase.

This increased resistance reduces current flow (amperes) in the circuit and may cause the electrical component in the circuit not to function correctly. For example, when a PTC circuit protector is used in a power window circuit, the increased resistance causes the operation of the power window to be much slower than normal.

Unlike circuit breakers or fuses, PTC circuit protection devices do *not* open the circuit, but rather provide a very high resistance between the protector and the component. ● **SEE FIGURE 27–10.**

In other words, voltage will be available to the component. This fact has led to a lot of misunderstanding about how these circuit protection devices actually work. It is even more confusing when the circuit is opened and the PTC circuit protector cools down. When the circuit is turned back on, the component may operate normally for a short time; however, the PTC circuit protector will again get hot because of too much current flow. Its resistance again increases to limit current flow.

The electronic control unit (computer) used in most vehicles today incorporates thermal overload protection devices. ● **SEE FIGURE 27–11.**

Therefore, when a component fails to operate, do not blame the computer. The current control device is controlling current flow to protect the computer. Components that do not operate correctly should be checked for proper resistance and current draw.

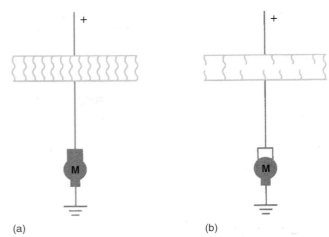

(a)   (b)

FIGURE 27–10 (a) The normal operation of a PTC circuit protector such as in a power window motor circuit showing the many conducting paths. With normal current flow, the temperature of the PTC circuit protector remains normal. (b) When current exceeds the amperage rating of the PTC circuit protector, the polymer material that makes up the electronic circuit protector increases in resistance. As shown, a high-resistance electrical path still exists even though the motor will stop operating as a result of the very low current flow through the very high resistance. The circuit protector will not reset or cool down until voltage is removed from the circuit.

FIGURE 27–11 PTC circuit protectors are used extensively in the power distribution center of this Chrysler vehicle.

FUSIBLE LINKS A **fusible link** is a type of fuse that consists of a short length (6–9 in. long) of standard copper-strand wire covered with a special nonflammable insulation. This wire is usually four wire numbers smaller than the wire of the circuits it protects. For example, a 12 gauge circuit is protected by a 16 gauge fusible link. The special thick insulation over the wire may make it look larger than other wires of the same gauge number. ● **SEE FIGURE 27–12.**

FIGURE 27–12 Fusible links are usually located close to the battery and are usually attached to a junction block. Notice that they are only 6–9 in. long and feed more than one fuse from each fusible link.

FIGURE 27–13 A 125 ampere rated mega fuse used to protect the alternator output circuit.

If excessive current flow (caused by a short-to-ground or a defective component) occurs, the fusible link will melt in half and open the circuit to prevent a fire hazard. Some fusible links are identified with "fusible link" tags at the junction between the fusible link and the standard chassis wiring, which represent only the junction. Fusible links are the backup system for circuit protection. All current except the current used by the starter motor flows through fusible links and then through individual circuit fuses. It is possible that a fusible link will melt and not blow a fuse. Fusible links are installed as close to the battery as possible so that they can protect the wiring and circuits coming directly from the battery.

MEGA FUSES   Many newer vehicles are equipped with mega fuses instead of fusible links to protect high-amperage circuits. Circuits often controlled by mega fuses include:

- Charging circuit
- HID headlights
- Heated front or rear glass
- Multiple circuits usually protected by mega fuses
- Mega fuse rating for vehicles, including 80, 100, 125, 150, 175, 200, 225, and 250 amperes
- **SEE FIGURE 27–13.**

CHECKING FUSIBLE LINKS AND MEGA FUSES
Fusible links and mega fuses are usually located near where electrical power is sent to other fuses or circuits, such as:

- Starter solenoid battery terminals
- Power distribution centers
- Output terminals of alternators
- Positive terminals of the battery

TECH TIP

Find the Root Cause

If a mega fuse or fusible link fails, find the root cause before replacing it. A mega fuse can fail due to vibration or physical damage as a result of a collision or corrosion. Check to see if the fuse itself is loose and can be moved by hand. If loose, then simply replace the mega fuse. If a fusible link or mega fuse has failed due to excessive current, check for evidence of a collision or any other reason that could cause an excessive amount of current to flow. This inspection should include each electrical component being supplied current from the fusible link. After being sure that the root cause has been found and corrected, then replace the fusible link or mega fuse.

Fusible links can melt and not show any external evidence of damage. To check a fusible link, gently pull on each end to see if it stretches. If the insulation stretches, then the wire inside has melted and the fusible link must be replaced after determining what caused the link to fail.

Another way to check a fusible link is to use a test light or a voltmeter and check for available voltage at both ends of the fusible link. If voltage is available at only one end, then the link is electrically open and should be replaced.

REPLACING A FUSIBLE LINK   If a fusible link is found to be melted, perform the following steps.

STEP 1   Determine why the fusible link failed and repair the fault.

STEP 2   Check service information for the exact length, gauge, and type of fusible link required.

STEP 3   Replace the fusible link with the specified fusible link wire and according to the instructions found in the service information.

CAUTION: Always use the exact length of fusible link wire required because if it is too short, it will not have enough resistance to generate the heat needed to melt the wire and protect the circuits or components. If the wire is too long, it could melt during normal operation of the circuits it is protecting. Fusible link wires are usually longer than 6 in. and shorter than 9 in.

TERMINALS AND CONNECTORS

A **terminal** is a metal fastener attached to the end of a wire, which makes the electrical connection. The term **connector** usually refers to the plastic portion that snaps or connects together, thereby making the mechanical connection. Wire terminal ends usually snap into and are held by a connector. Male and female connectors can then be snapped together, thereby completing an electrical connection. Connectors exposed to the environment are also equipped with a weather-tight seal. ● **SEE FIGURE 27–14.**

Terminals are retained in connectors by the use of a **lock tang.** Removing a terminal from a connector includes the following steps.

STEP 1 Release the **connector position assurance (CPA),** if equipped, that keeps the latch of the connector from releasing accidentally.

STEP 2 Separate the male and female connector by opening the lock. ● **SEE FIGURE 27–15.**

STEP 3 Release the secondary lock, if equipped. ● **SEE FIGURE 27–16.**

STEP 4 Using a pick, look for the slot in the plastic connector where the lock tang is located, depress the lock tang, and gently remove the terminal from the connector. ● **SEE FIGURE 27–17.**

FIGURE 27–14 Some terminals have seals attached to help seal the electrical connections.

FIGURE 27–15 Separate a connector by opening the lock and pulling the two apart.

FIGURE 27–16 The secondary locks help retain the terminals in the connector.

FIGURE 27–17 Use a small removal tool, sometimes called a pick, to release terminals from the connector.

Look for the "Green Crud"

Corroded connections are a major cause of intermittent electrical problems and open circuits. The usual sequence of conditions is as follows:

1. **Heat causes expansion.** This heat can be from external sources such as connectors being too close to the exhaust system. Another possible source of heat is a poor connection at the terminal, causing a voltage drop and heat due to the electrical resistance.
2. **Condensation occurs when a connector cools.** The moisture in the condensation causes rust and corrosion.
3. **Water gets into the connector.** If corroded connectors are noticed, the terminal should be cleaned and the condition of the electrical connection to the wire terminal end(s) confirmed. Many vehicle manufacturers recommend using a dielectric silicone or lithium-based grease inside connectors to prevent moisture from getting into and attacking the connector.

FIGURE 27–18 Always use rosin-core solder for electrical or electronic soldering. Also, use small-diameter solder for small soldering irons. Use large-diameter solder only for large-diameter (large-gauge) wire and higher-wattage soldering irons (guns).

WIRE REPAIR

FIGURE 27–19 A butane-powered soldering tool. The cap has a built-in striker to light a converter in the tip of the tool. This handy soldering tool produces the equivalent of 60 watts of heat. It operates for about 1/2 hour on one charge from a commonly available butane refill dispenser.

SOLDER Many manufacturers recommend that all wiring repairs be soldered. Solder is an alloy of tin and lead used to make a good electrical contact between two wires or connections in an electrical circuit. However, a flux must be used to help clean the area and to help make the solder flow. Therefore, solder is made with a resin (rosin) contained in the center, called **rosin-core solder.** ● **SEE FIGURE 27–18.**

CAUTION: Never use acid-core solder to repair electrical wiring as the acid will cause corrosion.

An acid-core solder is also available but should only be used for soldering sheet metal. Solder is available with various percentages of tin and lead in the alloy. Ratios are used to identify these various types of solder, with the first number denoting the percentage of tin in the alloy and the second number giving the percentage of lead. The most commonly used solder is 50/50, which means that 50% of the solder is tin and the other 50% is lead. The percentages of each alloy primarily determine the melting point of the solder.

- 60/40 solder (60% tin/40% lead) melts at 361°F (183°C).
- 50/50 solder (50% tin/50% lead) melts at 421°F (216°C).
- 40/60 solder (40% tin/60% lead) melts at 460°F (238°C).

NOTE: The melting points stated here can vary depending on the purity of the metals used.

Because of the lower melting point, 60/40 solder is the most highly recommended solder to use, followed by 50/50.

SOLDERING GUNS When soldering wires, be sure to heat the wires (not the solder) using:

- An electric soldering gun or soldering pencil (60 to 150 watt rating)
- Butane-powered tool that uses a flame to heat the tip (about 60 watt rating) ● **SEE FIGURE 27–19.**

SOLDERING PROCEDURE Soldering a wiring splice includes the following steps.

STEP 1 While touching the soldering gun to the splice, apply solder to the junction of the gun and the wire.

STEP 2 The solder will start to flow. Do not move the soldering gun.

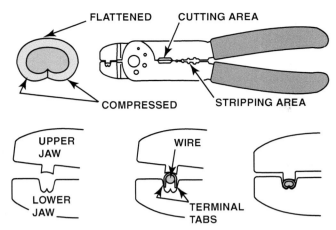

FIGURE 27-20 Notice that to create a good crimp the open part of the terminal is placed in the jaws of the crimping tool toward the anvil or the W-shape part.

FIGURE 27-21 All hand-crimped splices or terminals should be soldered to be assured of a good electrical connection.

STEP 3 Just keep feeding more solder into the splice as it flows into and around the strands of the wire.

STEP 4 After the solder has flowed throughout the splice, remove the soldering gun and the solder from the splice and allow the solder to cool slowly.

The solder should have a shiny appearance. Dull-looking solder may be caused by not reaching a high enough temperature, which results in a **cold solder joint.** Reheating the splice and allowing it to cool often restores the shiny appearance.

CRIMPING TERMINALS Terminals can be crimped to create a good electrical connection if the proper type of crimping tool is used. Most vehicle manufacturers recommend that a W-shaped crimp be used to force the strands of the wire into a tight space. ● **SEE FIGURE 27-20.**

Most vehicle manufacturers also specify that all hand-crimped terminals or splices be soldered. ● **SEE FIGURE 27-21.**

HEAT SHRINK TUBING **Heat shrink tubing** is usually made from polyvinyl chloride (PVC) or polyolefin and shrinks to about half of its original diameter when heated; this is usually called a 2:1 shrink ratio. Heat shrink by itself does not provide protection against corrosion, because the ends of the tubing are not sealed against moisture. DaimlerChrysler Corporation recommends that all wire repairs that may be exposed to the elements be repaired and sealed using **adhesive-lined heat shrink tubing.** The tubing is usually made from flame-retardant flexible polyolefin with an internal layer of special thermoplastic adhesive. When heated, this tubing shrinks to one-third of its original diameter (3:1 shrink ratio) and the adhesive melts and seals the ends of the tubing. ● **SEE FIGURE 27-22.**

CRIMP-AND-SEAL CONNECTORS General Motors Corporation recommends the use of crimp-and-seal connectors as the method for wire repair. **Crimp-and-seal connectors**

FIGURE 27-22 A butane torch especially designed for use on heat shrink applies heat without an open flame, which could cause damage.

contain a sealant and shrink tubing in one piece and are not simply butt connectors. ● **SEE FIGURE 27-23.**

The usual procedure specified for making a wire repair using a crimp-and-seal connector is as follows:

STEP 1 Strip the insulation from the ends of the wire (about 5/16 in., or 8 mm).

STEP 2 Select the proper size of crimp-and-seal connector for the gauge of wire being repaired. Insert the wires into the splice sleeve and crimp.

NOTE: Only use the specified crimping tool to help prevent the pliers from creating a hole in the cover.

STEP 3 Apply heat to the connector until the sleeve shrinks down around the wire and a small amount of sealant is observed around the ends of the sleeve, as shown in ● **FIGURE 27-24.**

FIGURE 27-23 A typical crimp-and-seal connector. This type of connector is first lightly crimped to retain the ends of the wires and then it is heated. The tubing shrinks around the wire splice, and thermoplastic glue melts on the inside to provide an effective weather-resistant seal.

FIGURE 27-24 Heating the crimp-and-seal connector melts the glue and forms an effective seal against moisture.

ALUMINUM WIRE REPAIR Some vehicle manufacturers used plastic-coated solid aluminum wire for some body wiring. Because aluminum wire is brittle and can break as a result of vibration, it is only used where there is no possible movement of the wire, such as along the floor or sill area. This section of wire is stationary, and the wire changes back to copper at a junction terminal after the trunk or rear section of the vehicle, where movement of the wiring may be possible.

If any aluminum wire must be repaired or replaced, the following procedure should be used to be assured of a proper repair. The aluminum wire is usually found protected in a plastic conduit. This conduit is then normally slit, after which the wires can easily be removed for repair.

STEP 1 Carefully strip only about 1/4 in. (6 mm) of insulation from the aluminum wire, being careful not to nick or damage the aluminum wire case.

FREQUENTLY ASKED QUESTION

What Method of Wire Repair Should I Use?

Good question. Vehicle manufacturers recommend all wire repairs performed under the hood, or where the repair could be exposed to the elements, be weatherproof. The most commonly recommended methods include:

- **Crimp and seal connector.** These connectors are special and are not like low cost insulated-type crimp connectors. This type of connector is recommended by General Motors and others and is sealed using heat after the mechanical crimp has secured the wire ends together.
- **Solder and adhesive-lined heat shrink tubing.** This method is recommended by Chrysler and it uses the special heat shrink that has glue inside that melts when heated to form a sealed connection. Regular heat shrink tubing can be used inside a vehicle, but should not be used where it can be exposed to the elements.
- **Solder and electrical tape.** This is acceptable to use inside the vehicle where the splice will not be exposed to the outside elements. It is best to use a crimp and seal even on the inside of the vehicle for best results.

FREQUENTLY ASKED QUESTION

What Is in Lead-Free Solder?

Lead is an environmental and a health concern and all vehicle manufacturers are switching to lead-free solder. Lead free solder does not contain lead but usually a very high percentage of tin. Several formulations of lead-free solder include:

- 95% Tin; 5% Antimony (melting temperature 450°F (245°C)
- 97% Tin; 3% Copper (melting temperature 441°F (227°C)
- 96% Tin; 4% Silver (melting temperature 443°F (228°C)

STEP 2 Use a crimp connector to join two wires together. Do not solder an aluminum wire repair. Solder will not readily adhere to aluminum because the heat causes an oxide coating on the surface of the aluminum.

STEP 3 The spliced, crimped connection must be coated with petroleum jelly to prevent corrosion.

STEP 4 The coated connection should be covered with shrinkable plastic tubing or wrapped with electrical tape to seal out moisture.

FIGURE 27–25 Conduit that has a paint strip is constructed of plastic that can withstand high underhood temperatures.

ELECTRICAL CONDUIT

Electrical conduit covers and protects wiring. The color used on electrical convoluted conduit tells the technician a lot if some information is known, such as the following:

- **Black conduit with a green or blue stripe.** This conduit is designed for high temperatures and is used under the hood and near hot engine parts. Do not replace high-temperature conduit with low-temperature conduit that does not have a strip when performing wire repairs. ● SEE FIGURE 27–25.

- **Blue or yellow conduit.** This color conduit is used to cover wires that have voltages ranging from 12 to 42 volts. Circuits that use this high voltage usually are for the electric power steering. While 42 volts does not represent a shock hazard, an arc will be maintained if a line circuit is disconnected. Use caution around these circuits. ● SEE FIGURE 27–26.

- **Orange conduit.** This color conduit is used to cover wiring that carries high-voltage current from 144 to 650 volts. These circuits are found in hybrid electric vehicles (HEVs). An electric shock from these wires can be fatal, so extreme caution has to be taken when working on or near the components that have orange conduit. Follow the vehicle manufacturer's instruction for de-powering the high-voltage circuits before work begins on any of the high-voltage components. ● SEE FIGURE 27–27.

(a)

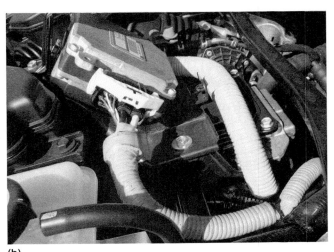

(b)

FIGURE 27–26 (a) Blue conduit is used to cover circuits that carry up to 42 volts. (b) Yellow conduit can also be used to cover 42–volt wiring.

FIGURE 27–27 Always follow the vehicle manufacturer's instructions which include the use of linesman's (high-voltage) gloves if working on circuits that are covered in orange conduit.

SUMMARY

1. The higher the AWG size number, the smaller the wire diameter.
2. Metric wire is sized in square millimeters (mm^2) and the higher the number, the larger the wire.
3. All circuits should be protected by a fuse, fusible link, or circuit breaker. The current in the circuit should be about 80% of the fuse rating.
4. A terminal is the metal end of a wire, whereas a connector is the plastic housing for the terminal.
5. All wire repair should use either soldering or a crimp-and-seal connector.

REVIEW QUESTIONS

1. What is the difference between the American wire gauge (AWG) system and the metric system?
2. What is the difference between a wire and a cable?
3. What is the difference between a terminal and a connector?
4. How do fuses, PTC circuit protectors, circuit breakers, and fusible links protect a circuit?
5. How should a wire repair be done if the repair is under the hood where it is exposed to the outside?

CHAPTER QUIZ

1. The higher the AWG number, _____.
   a. The smaller the wire diameter
   b. The larger the wire diameter
   c. The thicker the insulation
   d. The more strands in the conductor core

2. Metric wire size is measured in units of _____.
   a. Meters
   b. Cubic centimeters
   c. Square millimeters
   d. Cubic millimeters

3. Which statement is true about fuse ratings?
   a. The fuse rating should be less than the maximum current for the circuit.
   b. The fuse rating should be higher than the normal current for the circuit.
   c. Of the fuse rating, 80% should equal the current in the circuit.
   d. Both b and c

4. Which statements are true about wire, terminals, and connectors?
   a. Wire is called a lead, and the metal end is a connector.
   b. A connector is usually a plastic piece where terminals lock in.
   c. A lead and a terminal are the same thing.
   d. Both a and c

5. The type of solder that should be used for electrical work is _____.
   a. Rosin core
   b. Acid core
   c. 60/40 with no flux
   d. 50/50 with acid paste flux

6. A technician is performing a wire repair on a circuit under the hood of the vehicle. Technician A says to use solder and adhesive-lined heat shrink tubing or a crimp and seal connector. Technician B says to solder and use electrical tape. Which technician is correct?
   a. Technician A only
   b. Technician B only
   c. Both Technicians A and B
   d. Neither Technician A nor B

7. Two technicians are discussing fuse testing. Technician A says that a test light should light on both test points of the fuse if it is okay. Technician B says the fuse is defective if a test light only lights on one side of the fuse. Which technician is correct?
   a. Technician A only
   b. Technician B only
   c. Both Technicians A and B
   d. Neither Technician A nor B

8. What is true about the plastic conduit covering the wiring?
   a. The color stripe is used to identify the temperature rating of the conduit.
   b. The color identifies the voltage level of the circuits being protected.
   c. Protects the wiring.
   d. All of the above

9. Many ground straps are uninsulated and braided because _____.
   a. They are more flexible to allow movement of the engine without breaking the wire.
   b. They are less expensive than conventional wire.
   c. They help dampen radio-frequency interference (RFI).
   d. Both a and c

10. What causes a fuse to blow?
    a. A decrease in circuit resistance
    b. An increase in the current flow through the circuit
    c. A sudden decrease in current flow through the circuit
    d. Both a and b

chapter 28

WIRING SCHEMATICS AND CIRCUIT TESTING

OBJECTIVES: • **After studying Chapter 28, the reader will be able to:** • Prepare for ASE Electrical/Electronic Systems (A6) certification test content area "A" (General Electrical/Electronics System Diagnosis). • Interpret wiring schematics. • Explain how relays work. • Discuss the various methods that can be used to locate a short circuit. • List the electrical troubleshooting diagnosis steps.

KEY TERMS: • Coil 275 • DPDT 274 • DPST 274 • Gauss gauge 281 • Momentary switch 275 • N.C. 274 • N.O. 274 • Poles 274 • Relay 275 • Short circuit 280 • SPDT 274 • SPST 274 • Terminal 270 • Throws 274 • Tone generator tester 282 • Wiring schematic 269

WIRING SCHEMATICS AND SYMBOLS

TERMINOLOGY The service manuals of automotive manufacturers include wiring schematics of every electrical circuit in a vehicle. A **wiring schematic,** sometimes called a *diagram,* shows electrical components and wiring using symbols and lines to represent components and wires. A typical wiring schematic may include all of the circuits combined on several large foldout sheets, or they may be broken down to show individual circuits. All circuit schematics or diagrams include:

- Power-side wiring of the circuit
- All splices
- Connectors
- Wire size
- Wire color
- Trace color (if any)
- Circuit number
- Electrical components
- Ground return paths
- Fuses and switches

CIRCUIT INFORMATION Many wiring schematics include numbers and letters near components and wires that may confuse readers of the schematic. Most letters used near or on a wire identify the color or colors of the wire.

- The first color or color abbreviation is the color of the wire insulation.

FIGURE 28–1 The center wire is a solid color wire, meaning that the wire has no other identifying tracer or stripe color. The two end wires could be labeled "BRN/WHT," indicating a brown wire with a white tracer or stripe.

FIGURE 28–2 Typical section of a wiring diagram. Notice that the wire color changes at connection C210. The ".8" represents the metric wire size in square millimeters.

- The second color (if mentioned) is the color of the stripe or tracer on the base color. ● **SEE FIGURE 28–1.**

Wires with different color tracers are indicated by both colors with a slash (/) between them. For example, BRN/WHT means a brown wire with a white stripe or tracer. ● **SEE CHART 28–1.**

WIRE SIZE Wire size is shown on all schematics. ● **FIGURE 28–2** illustrates a rear side-marker bulb circuit diagram where ".8" indicates the metric wire gauge size in square millimeters (mm^2) and "PPL" indicates a solid purple wire.

The wire diagram also shows that the color of the wire changes at the number C210. This stands for "connector #210" and is used for reference purposes. The symbol for the connection can vary depending on the manufacturer. The color change from purple (PPL) to purple with a white tracer (PPL/WHT) is not important except for knowing where the wire changes color in the circuit. The wire gauge has remained the same on both sides of the connection (0.8 mm² or 18 gauge). The ground circuit is the ".8 BLK" wire. ● **FIGURE 28–3** shows many of the electrical and electronic symbols that are used in wiring and circuit diagrams.

ABBREVIATION	COLOR
BRN	Brown
BLK	Black
GRN	Green
WHT	White
PPL	Purple
PNK	Pink
TAN	Tan
BLU	Blue
YEL	Yellow
ORN	Orange
DK BLU	Dark blue
LT BLU	Light blue
DK GRN	Dark green
LT GRN	Light green
RED	Red
GRY	Gray
VIO	Violet

CHART 28–1

Typical abbreviations used on schematics to show wire color. Some vehicle manufacturers use two letters to represent a wire color. Check service information for the color abbreviations used.

TECH TIP

Read the Arrows

Wiring diagrams indicate connections by symbols that look like arrows. ● **SEE FIGURE 28–4** on page 272.

Do *not* read these "arrows" as pointers showing the direction of current flow. Also observe that the power side (positive side) of the circuit is usually the female end of the connector. If a connector becomes disconnected, it will be difficult for the circuit to become shorted to ground or to another circuit because the wire is recessed inside the connector.

SCHEMATIC SYMBOLS

In a schematic drawing, photos or line drawings of actual components are replaced with a symbol that represents the actual component. The following discussion centers on these symbols and their meanings.

BATTERY   The plates of a battery are represented by long and short lines. ● **SEE FIGURE 28–5** on page 266.

The longer line represents the positive plate of a battery and the shorter line represents the negative plate of the battery. Therefore, each pair of short and long lines represents one cell of a battery. Because each cell of a typical automotive lead-acid battery has 2.1 volts, a battery symbol showing a 12-volt battery should have six pairs of lines. However, most battery symbols simply use two or three pairs of long and short lines and then list the voltage of the battery next to the symbol. As a result, the battery symbols are shorter and yet clear, because the voltage is stated. The positive terminal of the battery is often indicated with a plus sign (+), representing the positive post of the battery, and is placed next to the long line of the end cell. The negative terminal of the battery is represented by a negative sign (−) and is placed next to the shorter cell line. The negative battery terminal is connected to ground. ● **SEE FIGURE 28–6.**

WIRING   Electrical wiring is shown as straight lines and with a few numbers and/or letters to indicate the following:

- **Wire size.** This can be either AWG, such as 18 gauge, or in square millimeters, such as 0.8 mm².

- **Circuit numbers.** Each wire in part of a circuit is labeled with the circuit number to help the service technician trace the wiring and to provide an explanation of how the circuit should work.

- **Wire color.** Most schematics also indicate an abbreviation for the color of the wire and place it next to the wire. Many wires have two colors: a solid color and a stripe color. In this case, the solid color is listed, followed by a dark slash (/) and the color of the stripe. For example, Red/Wht would indicate a red wire with a white tracer. ● **SEE FIGURE 28–7.**

- **Terminals.** The metal part attached at the end of a wire is called a **terminal**. A symbol for a terminal is shown in ● **FIGURE 28–8.**

- **Splices.** When two wires are electrically connected, the junction is shown with a black dot. The identification of the splice is an "S" followed by three numbers, such as S103. ● **SEE FIGURE 28–9.** When two wires cross in a schematic that are not electrically connected, one of the wires is shown as going over the other wire and does not connect. ● **SEE FIGURE 28–10.**

- **Connectors.** An electrical connector is a plastic part that contains one or more terminals. Although the terminals provide the electrical connection in a circuit, it is the

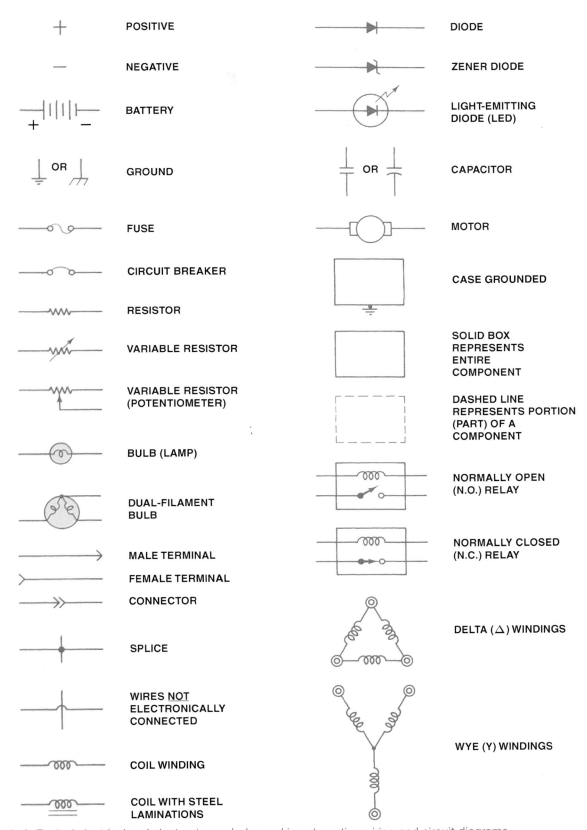

FIGURE 28–3 Typical electrical and electronic symbols used in automotive wiring and circuit diagrams.

TO BATTERY ————————————<< ————— TO ELECTRICAL COMPONENT

FIGURE 28–4 In this typical connector, note that the positive terminal is usually a female connector.

FIGURE 28–5 The symbol for a battery. The positive plate of a battery is represented by the longer line and the negative plate by the shorter line. The voltage of the battery is usually stated next to the symbol.

OR

FIGURE 28–6 The ground symbol on the left represents earth ground. The ground symbol on the right represents a chassis ground.

FIGURE 28–7 Starting at the top, the wire from the ignition switch is attached to terminal B of connector C2, the wire is 0.5 mm^2 (20 gauge AWG), and is yellow. The circuit number is 5. The wire enters connector C202 at terminal B3.

FIGURE 28–8 The electrical terminals are usually labeled with a letter or number.

———————•——————— SPLICE

FIGURE 28–9 Two wires that cross at the dot indicate that the two are electrically connected.

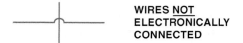
WIRES <u>NOT</u> ELECTRONICALLY CONNECTED

FIGURE 28–10 Wires that cross, but do not electrically contact each other, are shown with one wire bridging over the other.

plastic connector that keeps the terminals together mechanically.

- **Location.** Connections are usually labeled "C" and then three numbers. The three numbers indicate the general location of the connector. Normally, the connector number represents the general area of the vehicle, including:

100 to 199	Under the hood
200 to 299	Under the dash
300 to 399	Passenger compartment
400 to 499	Rear package or trunk area
500 to 599	Left-front door
600 to 699	Right-front door
700 to 799	Left-rear door
800 to 899	Right-rear door

Even-numbered connectors are on the right (passenger side) of the vehicle and odd-numbered connectors are on the left (driver's side) of the vehicle. For example, C102 is a connector located under the hood (between 100 and 199) on the right side of the vehicle (even number 102). ● **SEE FIGURE 28–11.**

- **Grounds and splices.** These are also labeled using the same general format as connectors. Therefore, a ground located under the dash on the driver's side could be labeled G305 (G means "ground" and the "305" means that it is located in the passenger compartment). ● **SEE FIGURE 28–12.**

FIGURE 28–11 Connectors (C), grounds (G), and splices (S) are followed by a number, generally indicating the location in the vehicle. For example, G209 is a ground connection located under the dash.

FIGURE 28–12 The ground for the battery is labeled G305 indicating the ground connector is located in the passenger compartment of the vehicle. The ground wire is black (BLK), the circuit number is 50, and the wire is 32 mm² (2 gauge AWG).

FIGURE 28–13 The symbol for light bulbs shows the filament inside a circle, which represents the glass ampoule of the bulb.

ELECTRICAL COMPONENTS
Most electrical components have their own unique symbol that shows the basic function or parts.

■ **Bulbs.** Light bulbs often use a filament, which heats and then gives off light when electrical current flows. The symbol used for a light bulb is a circle with a filament inside. A dual-filament bulb, such as is used for taillights and brake light/turn signals, is shown with two filaments. ● **SEE FIGURE 28–13.**

ELECTRIC MOTORS
An electric motor symbol shows a circle with the letter *M* in the center and two electrical connections, one to the top and one at the bottom. ● **SEE FIGURE 28–14** for an example of a cooling fan motor.

RESISTORS
Although resistors are usually part of another component, the symbol appears on many schematics and wiring diagrams. A resistor symbol is a jagged line representing resistance to current flow. If the resistor is variable, such as a thermistor, an arrow is shown running through the symbol of a fixed resistor. A potentiometer is a three-wire variable resistor,

shown with an arrow pointing toward the resistance part of a fixed resistor. ● **SEE FIGURE 28–15.**

A two-wire rheostat is usually shown as part of another unit, such as a fuel level sending unit. ● **SEE FIGURE 28–16.**

CAPACITORS
Capacitors are usually part of an electronic component, but not a replaceable component unless the vehicle is an older model. Many older vehicles used capacitors to reduce radio interference and were installed inside alternators or attached to wiring connectors. ● **SEE FIGURE 28–17.**

ELECTRIC HEATED UNIT
Electric grid-type rear window defoggers and cigarette lighters are shown with a square box-type symbol. ● **SEE FIGURE 28–18.**

FIGURE 28–14 An electric motor symbol shows a circle with the letter *M* in the center and two black sections that represent the brushes of the motor. This symbol is used even though the motor is a brushless design.

FIGURE 28–15 Resistor symbols vary depending on the type of resistor.

FIGURE 28–16 A rheostat uses only two wires—one is connected to a voltage source and the other is attached to the movable arm.

FIGURE 28–17 Symbols used to represent capacitors. If one of the lines is curved, this indicates that the capacitor being used has a polarity, while the one without a curved line can be installed in the circuit without concern about polarity.

BOXED COMPONENTS If a component is shown in a box using a solid line, the box is the entire component. If a box uses dashed lines, it represents part of a component. A commonly used dashed-line box is a fuse panel. Often, just one or two fuses are shown in a dashed-line box. This means that a fuse panel has more fuses than shown. ● **SEE FIGURES 28–19 AND 28–20.**

SEPARATE REPLACEABLE PART Often components are shown on a schematic that cannot be replaced, but are part of a complete assembly. When looking at a schematic of General Motors vehicles, the following is shown.

- If a part name is underlined, it is a replaceable part.
- If a part is not underlined, it is not available as a replaceable part, but is included with other components shown and sold as an assembly.
- If the case itself is grounded, the ground symbol is attached to the component as shown in ● **FIGURE 28–21.**

SWITCHES Electrical switches are drawn on a wiring diagram in their normal position. This can be one of two possible positions.

- **Normally open.** The switch is not connected to its internal contacts and no current will flow. This type of switch is labeled **N.O.**
- **Normally closed.** The switch is electrically connected to its internal contacts and current will flow through the switch. This type of switch is labeled **N.C.**

FIGURE 28–18 The gridlike symbol represents an electrically heated element.

FIGURE 28–19 A dashed outline represents a portion (part) of a component.

FIGURE 28–20 A solid box represents an entire component.

FIGURE 28–21 This symbol represents a component that is case grounded.

Other switches can use more than two contacts.

The **poles** refer to the number of circuits completed by the switch and the **throws** refer to the number of output circuits. A **single-pole, single-throw (SPST)** switch has only two positions, on or off. A **single-pole, double-throw (SPDT)** switch has three terminals, one wire in and two wires out. A headlight dimmer switch is an example of a typical SPDT switch. In one position, the current flows to the low-filament headlight; in the other, the current flows to the high-filament headlight.

NOTE: A SPDT switch is not an on or off type of switch but instead directs power from the source to either the high-beam lamps or the low-beam lamps.

There are also **double-pole, single-throw (DPST)** switches and **double-pole, double-throw (DPDT)** switches. ● **SEE FIGURE 28–22.**

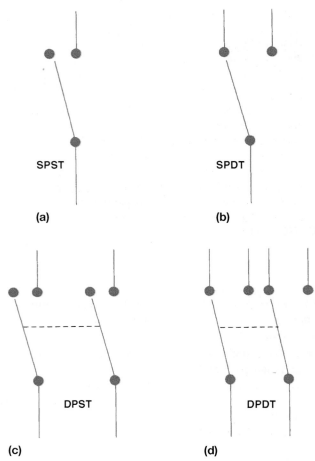

FIGURE 28–22 (a) A symbol for a single-pole, single-throw (SPST) switch. This type of switch is normally open (N.O.) because nothing is connected to the terminal that the switch is contacting in its normal position. (b) A single-pole, double-throw (SPDT) switch has three terminals. (c) A double-pole, single-throw (DPST) switch has two positions (off and on) and can control two separate circuits. (d) A double-pole, double-throw (DPDT) switch has six terminals—three for each pole. Note: Both (c) and (d) also show a dotted line between the two arms indicating that they are mechanically connected, called a "ganged switch."

NOTE: All switches are shown on schematics in their normal position. This means that the headlight switch will be shown normally off, as are most other switches and controls.

MOMENTARY SWITCH

A **momentary switch** is a switch primarily used to send a voltage signal to a module or controller to request that a device be turned on or off. The switch makes momentary contact and then returns to the open position. A horn switch is a commonly used momentary switch. The symbol that represents a momentary switch uses two dots for the contact with a switch above them. A momentary switch can be either normally open or normally closed. ● **SEE FIGURE 28–23.**

TECH TIP

Color-Coding Is Key to Understanding

Whenever diagnosing an electrical problem, it is common practice to print out the schematic of the circuit and then take it to the vehicle. A meter is then used to check for voltage at various parts of the circuit to help determine where there is a fault. The diagnosis can be made easier if the parts of the circuit are first color coded using markers or color pencils. A color-coding system that has been widely used is one developed by Jorge Menchu (**www.aeswave.com**).

The colors represent voltage conditions in various parts of a circuit. Once the circuit has been color coded, then the circuit can be tested using the factory wire colors as a guide. ● **SEE FIGURE 28–24.**

(a)   **(b)**

FIGURE 28–23 (a) A symbol for a normally open (N.O.) momentary switch. (b) A symbol for a normally closed (N.C.) momentary switch.

A momentary switch, for example, can be used to lock or unlock a door or to turn the air conditioning on or off. If the device is currently operating, the signal from the momentary switch will turn it off, and if it is off, the switch will signal the module to turn it on. The major advantage of momentary switches is that they can be lightweight and small, because the switch does not carry any heavy electrical current, just a small voltage signal. Most momentary switches use a membrane constructed of foil and plastic.

RELAY TERMINAL IDENTIFICATION

DEFINITION A **relay** is a magnetic switch that uses a movable armature to control a high-amperage circuit by using a low-amperage electrical switch.

ISO RELAY TERMINAL IDENTIFICATION Most automotive relays adhere to common terminal identification. The primary source for this common identification comes from the standards established by the International Standards Organization (ISO). Knowing this terminal information will help in the correct diagnosis and troubleshooting of any circuit containing a relay. ● **SEE FIGURES 28–25 AND 28–26.**

Relays are found in many circuits because they are capable of being controlled by computers, yet are able to handle enough current to power motors and accessories. Relays include the following components and terminals.

RELAY OPERATION

1. **Coil** (terminals 85 and 86)
   - A coil provides the magnetic pull to a movable armature (arm).
   - The resistance of most relay coils ranges from 50 to 150 ohms, but is usually between 60 and 100 ohms.

FIGURE 28–24 Using a marker and color-coding the various parts of the circuit makes the circuit easier to understand and helps diagnosing electrical problems easier. *(Courtesy of Jorge Menchu.)*

86　87　87a

85　　30

86 - POWER SIDE OF THE COIL
85 - GROUND SIDE OF THE COIL

(MOSTLY RELAY COILS
HAVE BETWEEN
50 and 150 OHMS
OF RESISTANCE)

30 - COMMON POWER FOR RELAY CONTACTS
87 - NORMALLY OPEN OUTPUT (N.O.)
87a - NORMALLY CLOSED OUTPUT (N.C.)

FIGURE 28–25 A relay uses a movable arm to complete a circuit whenever there is a power at terminal 86 and a ground at terminal 85. A typical relay only requires about 1/10 ampere through the relay coil. The movable arm then closes the contacts (#30 to #87) and can relay 30 amperes or more.

FIGURE 28–26 A cross-sectional view of a typical four-terminal relay. Current flowing through the coil (terminals 86 and 85) causes the movable arm (called the armature) to be drawn toward the coil magnet. The contact points complete the electrical circuit connected to terminals 30 and 87.

- The ISO identification of the coil terminals are 86 and 85. The terminal number 86 represents the power to the relay coil and the terminal labeled 85 represents the ground side of the relay coil.
- The relay coil can be controlled by supplying either power or ground to the relay coil winding.
- The coil winding represents the control circuit which uses low current to control the higher current through the other terminals of the relay. ● SEE FIGURE 28–27.

FIGURE 28–27 A typical relay showing the schematic of the wiring in the relay.

2. Other terminals used to control the load current
   - The higher amperage current flow through a relay flows through terminals 30 and 87, and often 87a.
   - Terminal 30 is usually where power is applied to a relay. Check service information for the exact operation of the relay being tested.
   - When the relay is at rest without power and ground to the coil, the armature inside the relay electrically connects terminals 30 and 87a if the relay has five terminals. When there is power at terminal 85 and a ground at terminal 86 of the relay, a magnetic field is created in the coil winding, which draws the armature of the relay toward the coil. The armature, when energized electrically, connects terminals 30 and 87.

The maximum current through the relay is determined by the resistance of the circuit, and relays are designed to safely handle the designed current flow. ● **SEE FIGURES 28–28 AND 28–29.**

RELAY VOLTAGE SPIKE CONTROL Relays contain a coil and when power is removed, the magnetic field surrounding the coil collapses, creating a voltage to be induced in the coil winding. This induced voltage can be as high as 100 volts or more and can cause problems with other electronic devices in the vehicle. For example, the short high-voltage surge can be heard as a "pop" in the radio. To reduce the induced voltage, some relays contain a diode connected across the coil. ● **SEE FIGURE 28–30.**

NORMALLY OPEN (N.O.) RELAY

NORMALLY CLOSED (N.C.) RELAY

FIGURE 28-28 All schematics are shown in their normal, nonenergized position.

FIGURE 28-29 A typical horn circuit. Note that the relay contacts supply the heavy current to operate the horn when the horn switch simply completes a low-current circuit to ground, causing the relay contacts to close.

FIGURE 28-30 When the relay or solenoid coil current is turned off, the stored energy in the coil flows through the clamping diode and effectively reduces voltage spike.

When the current flows through the coil, the diode is not part of the circuit because it is installed to block current. However, when the voltage is removed from the coil, the resulting voltage induced in the coil windings has a reversed polarity to the applied voltage. Therefore, the voltage in the coil is applied to the coil in a forward direction through the diode, which conducts the current back into the winding. As a result, the induced voltage spike is eliminated.

Divide the Circuit in Half

When diagnosing any circuit that has a relay, start testing at the relay and divide the circuit in half.

- **High current portion:** Remove the relay and check that there are 12 volts at the terminal 30 socket. If there is, then the power side is okay. Use an ohmmeter and check between terminal 87 socket and ground. If the load circuit has continuity, there should be some resistance. If OL, the circuit is electrically open.
- **Control circuit (low current):** With the relay removed from the socket, check that there is 12 volts to terminal 86 with the ignition on and the control switch on. If not, check service information to see if power should be applied to terminal 86, then continue troubleshooting the switch power and related circuit.
- **Check the relay itself:** Use an ohmmeter and measure for continuity and resistance.
  - Between terminals 85 and 86 (coil), there should be 60 to 100 ohms. If not, replace the relay.
  - Between terminals 30 and 87 (high-amperage switch controls), there should be continuity (low ohms) when there is power applied to terminal 85 and a ground applied to terminal 86 that operates the relay. If OL is displayed on the meter set to read ohms, the circuit is open which requires that the reply be replaced.
  - Between terminals 30 and 87a (if equipped), with the relay turned off, there should be low resistance (less than 5 ohms).

Most relays use a resistor connected in parallel with the coil winding. The use of a resistor, typically about 400 to 600 ohms, reduces the voltage spike by providing a path for the voltage created in the coil to flow back through the coil windings when the coil circuit is opened. ● **SEE FIGURE 28-31.**

FIGURE 28-31 A resistor used in parallel with the coil windings is a common spike reduction method used in many relays.

What Is the Difference Between a Relay and a Solenoid?

Often, these terms are used differently among vehicle manufacturers, which can lead to some confusion.

Relay: A relay is an electromagnetic switch that uses a movable arm. Because a relay uses a movable arm, it is generally limited to current flow not exceeding 30 amperes.

Solenoid: A solenoid is an electromagnetic switch that uses a movable core. Because of this type of design, a solenoid is capable of handling 200 amperes or more and is used in the starter motor circuit and other high-amperage applications, such as in the glow plug circuit of diesel engines.

The Electric Mirror Fault Story

Often, a customer will notice just one fault even though other lights or systems may not be working correctly. For example, a customer noticed that the electric mirrors stopped working. The service technician checked all electrical components in the vehicle and discovered that the interior lights were also not working.

The interior lights were not mentioned by the customer as being a problem most likely because the driver only used the vehicle in daylight hours.

The service technician found the interior light and power accessory fuse blown. Replacing the fuse restored the proper operation of the electric outside mirror and the interior lights. However, what caused the fuse to blow? A visual inspection of the dome light, next to the electric sunroof, showed an area where a wire was bare. Evidence showed the bare wire had touched the metal roof, which could cause the fuse to blow. The technician covered the bare wire with a section of vacuum hose and then taped the hose with electrical tape to complete the repair.

LOCATING AN OPEN CIRCUIT

TERMINOLOGY An open circuit is a break in the electrical circuit that prevents current from flowing and operating an electrical device. Examples of open circuits include:

- Blown (open) light bulbs
- Cut or broken wires
- Disconnected or partially disconnected electrical connectors
- Electrically open switches
- Loose or broken ground connections or wires
- Blown fuse

PROCEDURE TO LOCATE AN OPEN CIRCUIT The typical procedure for locating an open circuit involves the following steps.

STEP 1 **Perform a thorough visual inspection.** Check the following:
- Look for evidence of a previous repair. Often, an electrical connector or ground connection can be accidentally left disconnected.
- Look for evidence of recent body damage or body repairs. Movement due to a collision can cause metal to move, which can cut wires or damage connectors or components.

STEP 2 **Print out the schematic.** Trace the circuit and check for voltage at certain places. This will help pinpoint the location of the open circuit.

STEP 3 **Check everything that does and does not work.** Often, an open circuit will affect more than one component. Check the part of the circuit that is common to the other components that do not work.

STEP 4 **Check for voltage.** Voltage is present up to the location of the open circuit fault. For example, if there is battery voltage at the positive terminal and the negative (ground) terminal of a two-wire light bulb socket with the bulb plugged in, then the ground circuit is open.

COMMON POWER OR GROUND

When diagnosing an electrical problem that affects more than one component or system, check the electrical schematic for a common power source or a common ground. ● **SEE FIGURE 28–32** for an example of lights being powered by one fuse (power source).

Underhood light
- Inside lighted mirrors
- Dome light
- Left-side courtesy light
- Right-side courtesy light

Therefore, if a customer complains about one or more of the items listed, check the fuse and the common part of the circuit that feeds all of the affected lights. Check for a common ground if several components that seem unrelated are not functioning correctly.

FIGURE 28–32 A typical wiring diagram showing multiple switches and bulbs powered by one fuse.

CIRCUIT TROUBLE-SHOOTING PROCEDURE

Follow these steps when troubleshooting wiring problems.

STEP 1 Verify the malfunction. If, for example, the backup lights do not operate, make certain that the ignition is on (key on, engine off), with the gear selector in reverse, and check for operation of the backup lights.

 TECH TIP

Do It Right—Install a Relay

Often the owners of vehicles, especially owners of pickup trucks and sport utility vehicles (SUVs), want to add additional electrical accessories or lighting. It is tempting in these cases to simply splice into an existing circuit. However, when another circuit or component is added, the current that flows through the newly added component is also added to the current for the original component. This additional current can easily overload the fuse and wiring. Do not simply install a larger amperage fuse; the wire gauge size was not engineered for the additional current and could overheat.

The solution is to install a relay, which uses a small coil to create a magnetic field that causes a movable arm to switch on a higher current circuit. The typical relay coil has from 50 to 150 ohms (usually 60 to 100 ohms) of resistance and requires just 0.24 to 0.08 ampere when connected to a 12-volt source. This small additional current will not be enough to overload the existing circuit. ● **SEE FIGURE 28–33** for an example of how additional lighting can be added.

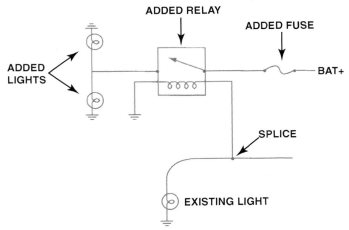

FIGURE 28–33 To add additional lighting, simply tap into an existing light wire and connect a relay. Whenever the existing light is turned on, the coil of the relay is energized. The arm of the relay then connects power from another circuit (fuse) to the auxiliary lights without overloading the existing light circuit.

STEP 2 Check everything else that does or does not operate correctly. For example, if the taillights are also not working, the problem could be a loose or broken ground connection in the trunk area that is shared by both the backup lights and the taillights.

STEP 3 Check the fuse for the backup lights. ● **SEE FIGURE 28–34**.

FIGURE 28–34 Always check the simple things first. Check the fuse for the circuit you are testing. Maybe a fault in another circuit controlled by the same fuse could have caused the fuse to blow. Use a test light to check that both sides of the fuse have voltage.

STEP 4   Check for voltage at the backup light socket. This can be done using a test light or a voltmeter.

If voltage is available at the socket, the problem is either a defective bulb or a poor ground at the socket or a ground wire connection to the body or frame. If no voltage is available at the socket, consult a wiring diagram for the type of vehicle being tested. The wiring diagram should show all of the wiring and components included in the circuit. For example, the backup light current must flow through the fuse and ignition switch to the gear selector switch before traveling to the rear backup light socket. As stated in the second step, the fuse used for the backup lights may also be used for other vehicle circuits.

The wiring diagram can be used to determine all other components that share the same fuse. If the fuse is blown (open circuit), the cause can be a short in any of the circuits sharing the same fuse. Because the backup light circuit current must be switched on and off by the gear selector switch, an open in the switch can also prevent the backup lights from functioning.

LOCATING A SHORT CIRCUIT

TERMINOLOGY   A short circuit usually blows a fuse, and a replacement fuse often also blows in the attempt to locate the source of the short circuit. A **short circuit** is an electrical connection to another wire or to ground before the current flows

through some or all of the resistance in the circuit. A short-to-ground will always blow a fuse and usually involves a wire on the power side of the circuit coming in contact with metal. Therefore, a thorough visual inspection should be performed around areas involving heat or movement, especially if there is evidence of a previous collision or previous repair that may not have been properly completed.

?   FREQUENTLY ASKED QUESTION

Where to Start?

The common question is, where does a technician start the troubleshooting when using a wiring diagram (schematic)?

HINT 1   If the circuit contains a relay, start your diagnosis at the relay. The entire circuit can be tested at the terminals of the relay.

HINT 2   The easiest first step is to locate the unit on the schematic that is not working at all or not working correctly.
   a. Trace where the unit gets its ground connection.
   b. Trace where the unit gets its power connection.
   Often a ground is used by more than one component. Therefore, ensure that everything else is working correctly. If not, then the fault may lie at the common ground (or power) connection.

HINT 3   Divide the circuit in half by locating a connector or a part of the circuit that can be accessed easily. Then check for power and ground at this midpoint. This step could save you much time.

HINT 4   Use a fused jumper wire to substitute a ground or a power source to replace a suspected switch or section of wire.

A short-to-voltage may or may not cause the fuse to blow and usually affects another circuit. Look for areas of heat or movement where two power wires could come in contact with each other. Several methods can be used to locate the short.

FUSE REPLACEMENT METHOD   Disconnect one component at a time and then replace the fuse. If the new fuse blows, continue the process until you determine the location of the short. This method uses many fuses and is *not* a preferred method for finding a short circuit.

CIRCUIT BREAKER METHOD   Another method is to connect an automotive circuit breaker to the contacts of the fuse holder with alligator clips. Circuit breakers are available that plug directly into the fuse panel, replacing a blade-type fuse. The circuit breaker will alternately open and close the circuit, protecting the wiring from possible overheating damage while still providing current flow through the circuit.

NOTE: A heavy-duty (HD) flasher can also be used in place of a circuit breaker to open and close the circuit. Wires and terminals must be made to connect the flasher unit where the fuse normally plugs in.

All components included in the defective circuit should be disconnected one at a time until the circuit breaker stops clicking. The unit that was disconnected and stopped the circuit breaker clicking is the unit causing the short circuit. If the circuit breaker continues to click with all circuit components unplugged, the problem is in the wiring *from* the fuse panel *to* any one of the units in the circuit. Visual inspection of all the wiring or further disconnecting will be necessary to locate the problem.

TEST LIGHT METHOD

To use the test light method, simply remove the blown fuse and connect a test light to the terminals of the fuse holder (polarity does not matter). If there is a short circuit, current will flow from the power side of the fuse holder through the test light and on to ground through the short circuit, and the test light will then light. Unplug the connectors or components protected by the fuse until the test light goes out. The circuit that was disconnected, which caused the test light to go out, is the circuit that is shorted.

BUZZER METHOD

The buzzer method is similar to the test light method, but uses a buzzer to replace a fuse and act as an electrical load. The buzzer will sound if the circuit is shorted and will stop when the part of the circuit that is grounded is unplugged.

OHMMETER METHOD

The fourth method uses an ohmmeter connected to the fuse holder and ground. This is the recommended method of finding a short circuit, as an ohmmeter will indicate low ohms when connected to a short circuit. However, an ohmmeter should never be connected to an operating circuit. The correct procedure for locating a short using an ohmmeter is as follows:

1. Connect one lead of an ohmmeter (set to a low scale) to a good clean metal ground and the other lead to the circuit (load) side of the fuse holder.

   CAUTION: Connecting the lead to the power side of the fuse holder will cause current flow through and damage to the ohmmeter.

2. The ohmmeter will read zero or almost zero ohms if the circuit or a component in the circuit is shorted.

3. Disconnect one component in the circuit at a time and watch the ohmmeter. If the ohmmeter reading goes to high ohms or infinity, the component just unplugged was the source of the short circuit.

4. If all of the components have been disconnected and the ohmmeter still reads low ohms, then disconnect electrical connectors until the ohmmeter reads high ohms. The location of the short-to-ground is then between the ohmmeter and the disconnected connector.

NOTE: Some meters, such as the Fluke 87, can be set to beep (alert) when the circuit closes or when the circuit opens—a very useful feature.

GAUSS GAUGE METHOD

If a short circuit blows a fuse, a special pulsing circuit breaker (similar to a flasher unit) can be installed in the circuit in place of the fuse. Current will flow through the circuit until the circuit breaker opens the circuit. As soon as the circuit breaker opens the circuit, it closes again. This on-and-off current flow creates a pulsing magnetic field around the wire carrying the current. A **Gauss gauge** is a handheld meter that responds to weak magnetic fields. It is used to observe this pulsing magnetic field, which is indicated on the gauge as needle movement. This pulsing magnetic field will register on the Gauss gauge even through the metal body of the vehicle. A needle-type compass can also be used to observe the pulsing magnetic field. ● SEE FIGURES 28–35 AND 28–36.

(a)

(b)

FIGURE 28–35 (a) After removing the blown fuse, a pulsing circuit breaker is connected to the terminals of the fuse. (b) The circuit breaker causes current to flow, then stop, then flow again, through the circuit up to the point of the short-to-ground. By observing the Gauss gauge, the location of the short is indicated near where the needle stops moving due to the magnetic field created by the flow of current through the wire.

FUSE

CIRCUIT BREAKER CAUSING PULSING CURRENT FLOW IN AFFECTED CIRCUIT

GAUSS GAUGE OSCILLATING BACK AND FORTH UNTIL GAUGE REACHES POINT OF SHORT CIRCUIT

FIGURE 28–36 A Gauss gauge can be used to determine the location of a short circuit even behind a metal panel.

FIGURE 28–37 A tone generator-type tester used to locate open circuits and circuits that are shorted-to-ground. Included with this tester is a transmitter (tone generator), receiver probe, and headphones for use in noisy shops.

TECH TIP

Heat or Movement

Electrical shorts are commonly caused either by movement, which causes the insulation around the wiring to be worn away, or by heat melting the insulation. When checking for a short circuit, first check the wiring that is susceptible to heat, movement, and damage.

1. **Heat.** Wiring near heat sources, such as the exhaust system, cigarette lighter, or alternator
2. **Wire movement.** Wiring that moves, such as in areas near the doors, trunk, or hood
3. **Damage.** Wiring subject to mechanical injury, such as in the trunk, where heavy objects can move around and smash or damage wiring; can also occur as a result of an accident or a previous repair

TECH TIP

Wiggle Test

Intermittent electrical problems are common yet difficult to locate. To help locate these hard-to-find problems, try operating the circuit and then start wiggling the wires and connections that control the circuit. If in doubt where the wiring goes, try moving all the wiring starting at the battery. Pay particular attention to wiring running near the battery or the windshield washer container. Corrosion can cause wiring to fail, and battery acid fumes and alcohol-based windshield washer fluid can start or contribute to the problem. If you notice any change in the operation of the device being tested while wiggling the wiring, look closer in the area you were wiggling until you locate and correct the actual problem.

ELECTRICAL TROUBLESHOOTING GUIDE

ELECTRONIC TONE GENERATOR TESTER An electronic tone generator tester can be used to locate a short-to-ground or an open circuit. Similar to test equipment used to test telephone and cable television lines, a **tone generator tester** generates a tone that can be heard through a receiver (probe). ● **SEE FIGURE 28–37.**

The tone will be generated as long as there is a continuous electrical path along the circuit. The signal will stop if there is a short-to-ground or an open in the circuit. ● **SEE FIGURE 28–38.**

The windings in the solenoids and relays will increase the strength of the signal in these locations.

When troubleshooting any electrical component, remember the following hints to find the problem faster and more easily.

1. For a device to work, it must have two things: power and ground.
2. If there is no power to a device, an open power side (blown fuse, etc.) is indicated.
3. If there is power on both sides of a device, an open ground is indicated.
4. If a fuse blows immediately, a grounded power-side wire is indicated.

FIGURE 28–38 To check for a short-to-ground using a tone generator, connect the black transmitter lead to a good chassis ground and the red lead to the load side of the fuse terminal. Turn the transmitter on and check for tone signal with the receiver. Using a wiring diagram, follow the strongest signal to the location of the short-to-ground. There will be no signal beyond the fault, either a short-to-ground as shown or an open circuit.

5. Most electrical faults result from heat or movement.

6. Most noncomputer-controlled devices operate by opening and closing the power side of the circuit (power-side switch).

7. Most computer-controlled devices operate by opening and closing the ground side of the circuit (ground-side switch).

STEP-BY-STEP TROUBLESHOOTING PROCEDURE

Knowing what should be done and when it should be done is a major concern for many technicians trying to repair an electrical problem. The following field-tested procedure provides a step-by-step guide for troubleshooting an electrical fault.

STEP 1 Determine the customer concern (complaint) and get as much information as possible from the customer or service advisor.
a. When did the problem start?
b. Under what conditions does the problem occur?
c. Have there been any recent previous repairs to the vehicle which could have created the problem?

STEP 2 Verify the customer's concern by actually observing the fault.

STEP 3 Perform a thorough visual inspection and be sure to check everything that does and does not work.

STEP 4 Check for technical service bulletins (TSBs).

STEP 5 Locate the wiring schematic for the circuit being diagnosed.

STEP 6 Check the factory service information and follow the troubleshooting procedure.
a. Determine how the circuit works.
b. Determine which part of the circuit is good, based on what works and what does not work.
c. Isolate the problem area.

NOTE: Split the circuit in half to help isolate the problem and start at the relay (if the circuit has a relay).

STEP 7 Determine the root cause and repair the vehicle.

STEP 8 Verify the repair and complete the work order by listing the three Cs (complaint, cause, and correction).

Shocking Experience

A customer complained that after driving for a while, he got a static shock whenever he grabbed the door handle when exiting the vehicle. The customer thought that there must be an electrical fault and that the shock was coming from the vehicle itself. In a way, the shock was caused by the vehicle, but it was not a fault. The service technician sprayed the cloth seats with an antistatic spray and the problem did not reoccur. Obviously, a static charge was being created by the movement of the driver's clothing on the seats and then discharged when the driver touched the metal door handle.
● SEE FIGURE 28–39.

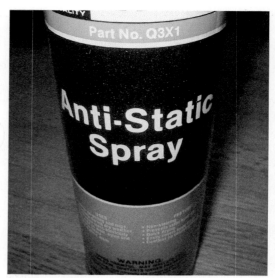

FIGURE 28–39 Antistatic spray can be used by customers to prevent being shocked when they touch a metal object like the door handle.

SUMMARY

1. Most wiring diagrams include the wire color, circuit number, and wire gauge.
2. The number used to identify connectors, grounds, and splices usually indicates where they are located in the vehicle.
3. All switches and relays on a schematic are shown in their normal position either normally closed (N.C.) or normally open (N.O.).
4. A typical relay uses a small current through a coil (terminals 85 and 86) to operate the higher current part (terminals 30 and 87).
5. A short-to-voltage affects the power side of the circuit and usually involves more than one circuit.
6. A short-to-ground usually causes the fuse to blow and usually affects only one circuit.
7. Most electrical faults are a result of heat or movement.

REVIEW QUESTIONS

1. List the numbers used on schematics to indicate grounds, splices, and connectors and where they are used in the vehicle.
2. List and identify the terminals of a typical ISO type relay.
3. List three methods that can be used to help locate a short circuit.
4. How can a tone generator be used to locate a short circuit?

CHAPTER QUIZ

1. On a wiring diagram, S110 with a ".8 BRN/BLK" means
   _____.
   a. Circuit #8, spliced under the hood
   b. A connector with 0.8 mm^2 wire
   c. A splice of a brown with black stripe, wire size being 0.8 mm^2 (18 gauge AWG)
   d. Both a and b
2. Where is connector C250?
   a. Under the hood
   b. Under the dash
   c. In the passenger compartment
   d. In the trunk

3. All switches illustrated in schematics are _____.
   a. Shown in their normal position
   b. Always shown in their on position
   c. Always shown in their off position
   d. Shown in their on position except for lighting switches

4. When testing a relay using an ohmmeter, which two terminals should be touched to measure the coil resistance?
   a. 87 and 30   b. 86 and 85
   c. 87a and 87   d. 86 and 87

5. Technician A says that a good relay should measure between 60 and 100 ohms across the coil terminals. Technician B says that OL should be displayed on an ohmmeter when touching terminals 30 and 87. Which technician is correct?
   a. Technician A only
   b. Technician B only
   c. Both Technicians A and B
   d. Neither Technician A nor B

6. Which relay terminal is the normally closed (N.C.) terminal?
   a. 30   b. 85
   c. 87   d. 87a

7. Technician A says that there is often more than one circuit being protected by each fuse. Technician B says that more than one circuit often shares a single ground connector. Which technician is correct?
   a. Technician A only
   b. Technician B only
   c. Both Technicians A and B
   d. Neither Technician A nor B

8. Two technicians are discussing finding a short-to-ground using a test light. Technician A says that the test light, connected in place of the fuse, will light when the circuit that has the short is disconnected. Technician B says that the test light should be connected to the positive (+) and negative (−) terminals of the battery during this test. Which technician is correct?
   a. Technician A only
   b. Technician B only
   c. Both Technicians A and B
   d. Neither Technician A nor B

9. A short circuit can be located using a _____.
   a. Test light   b. Gauss gauge
   c. Tone generator   d. All of the above

10. For an electrical device to operate, it must have _____.
    a. Power and a ground
    b. A switch and a fuse
    c. A ground and fusible link
    d. A relay to transfer the current to the device

OBJECTIVES: After studying Chapter 29, the reader will be able to: • Prepare for ASE Electrical/Electronic Systems (A6) certification test content area "B" (Battery Diagnosis and Service). • Describe how a battery works. • List battery ratings. • Describe deep cycling. • List the safety precautions necessary when working with batteries. • Explain how to safely charge a battery. • Discuss how to perform a battery drain test. • Describe how to perform a battery load test. • Explain how to perform a conductance test. • Discuss how to jump start a vehicle safely. • Discuss hybrid electric vehicle auxiliary batteries. • Explain the types of high-voltage battery used in most hybrid electric vehicles.

KEY TERMS: • AGM 289 • Alkaline 299 • Ampere hour 291 • Battery electrical drain test 294 • CA 290 • Cathode 298 • CCA 290 • Cells 288 • Deep cycling 290 • Electrolyte 288 • Element 288 • Flooded cell batteries 289 • Gassing 287 • Gel battery 290 • Grid 287 • IOD 294 • Lithium-polymer (Li-poly) 300 • Load test 292 • Low-water-loss batteries 286 • Maintenance-free battery 286 • MCA 290 • Parasitic load test 294 • Partitions 288 • Porous lead 287 • Recombinant battery 290 • Reserve capacity 290 • Sediment chamber 286 • SLA 289 • SLI 287 • Sponge lead 287 • SVR 289 • VRLA 289 • Zinc–air 300

INTRODUCTION

PURPOSE AND FUNCTION Every electrical component in a vehicle is supplied current from the battery. The battery is one of the most important parts of a vehicle because it is the heart or foundation of the electrical system. The primary purpose of an automotive battery is to provide a source of electrical power for all of the vehicle's electrical needs.

WHY BATTERIES ARE IMPORTANT The battery also acts as a stabilizer to the voltage for the entire electrical system. The battery is a voltage stabilizer because it acts as a reservoir where large amounts of current (amperes) can be removed quickly during starting and replaced gradually by the alternator during charging.

- The battery *must* be in good (serviceable) condition before the charging system and the cranking system can be tested. For example, if a battery is discharged, the cranking circuit (starter motor) could test as being defective because the battery voltage might drop below specifications.

- The battery must be confirmed to be in serviceable condition before performing any starting or charging system testing.

- The charging circuit could also test as being defective because of a weak or discharged battery. It is important to test the vehicle battery before further testing of the cranking or charging system.

BATTERY CONSTRUCTION

CASE Most automotive battery cases (container or covers) are constructed of polypropylene, a thin (approximately 0.08 in., or 0.02 mm, thick), strong, and lightweight plastic. In contrast, containers for industrial batteries and some truck batteries are constructed of a hard, thick rubber material. Inside the case are six cells (for a 12-volt battery). ● **SEE FIGURE 29–1.**

Each cell has positive and negative plates. Built into the bottom of many batteries are ribs that support the lead-alloy plates and provide a space for sediment to settle, called the **sediment chamber.** This space prevents spent active material from causing a short circuit between the plates at the bottom of the battery. A **maintenance-free battery** uses little water during normal service because of the alloy material used to construct the battery plate grids. Maintenance-free batteries are also called **low-water-loss batteries.**

FIGURE 29–1 Batteries are constructed of plates grouped into cells and installed in a plastic case.

PLASTIC CASE

NEGATIVE PLATES

POSITIVE PLATES

SEPARATORS

FIGURE 29–2 A grid from a battery used in both positive and negative plates.

? **FREQUENTLY ASKED QUESTION**

What Is an SLI Battery?

Sometimes the term *SLI* is used to describe a type of battery. **SLI** means starting, lighting, and ignition, and describes the use of a typical automotive battery. Other types of batteries used in industry are usually batteries designed to be deep cycled and are usually not as suitable for automotive needs.

GRIDS Each positive and negative plate in a battery is constructed on a framework, or **grid,** made primarily of lead. Lead is a soft material and must be strengthened for use in an automotive battery grid. Adding antimony or calcium to the pure lead adds strength to the lead grids. ● **SEE FIGURE 29–2.**

Battery grids hold the active material and provide the electrical pathways for the current created in the plate. Maintenance-free batteries use calcium instead of antimony, because 0.2% calcium has the same strength as 6% antimony. A typical lead-calcium grid uses only 0.09% to 0.12% calcium. Using low amounts of calcium instead of higher amounts of antimony reduces **gassing.** Gassing is the release of hydrogen and oxygen from the battery that occurs during charging and results in water usage. Low-maintenance batteries use a low percentage of antimony (about 2% to 3%), or use antimony only in the positive grids and calcium for the negative grids. *The percentages that make up the alloy of the plate grids constitute the major difference between standard and maintenance-free batteries.* The chemical reactions that occur inside each battery are identical regardless of the type of material used to construct the grid plates.

POSITIVE PLATES The positive plates have *lead dioxide (peroxides),* in paste form, placed onto the grid framework. This process is called *pasting.* This active material can react with the sulfuric acid of the battery and is dark brown in color.

NEGATIVE PLATES The negative plates are pasted to the grid with a pure **porous lead,** called **sponge lead,** and are gray in color.

SEPARATORS The positive and the negative plates must be installed alternately next to each other without touching. Nonconducting *separators* are used, which allow room for the reaction of the acid with both plate materials, yet insulate the plates to prevent shorts. These separators are porous (with many small holes) and have ribs facing the positive plate. Separators can be made from resin-coated paper, porous rubber, fiberglass, or expanded plastic. Many batteries use envelope-type separators that encase the entire plate and help prevent any material that may shed from the plates causing a short circuit between plates at the bottom of the battery.

CELLS

Cells are constructed of positive and negative plates with insulating separators between each plate. Most batteries use one more negative plate than positive plate in each cell; however, many newer batteries use the same number of positive and negative plates. A cell is also called an **element.** Each cell is actually a 2.1-volt battery, regardless of the number of positive or negative plates used. The greater the number of plates used in each cell, the greater the amount of current (amperes) that can be produced. Typical batteries contain four positive plates and five negative plates per cell. A 12-volt battery contains six cells connected in series, which produce 12.6 volts ($6 \times 2.1 = 12.6$) and contain 54 plates (9 plates per cell $\times$ 6 cells). If the same 12-volt battery had 5 positive plates and 6 negative plates, for a total of 11 plates per cell (5×6), or 66 plates (11 plates $\times$ 6 cells), then it would have the same voltage, but the amount of current that the battery could produce would be increased. ● **SEE FIGURE 29-3.**

The amperage capacity of a battery is determined by the amount of active plate material in the battery and the area of the plate material exposed to the electrolyte in the battery.

PARTITIONS

Each cell is separated from the other cells by **partitions,** which are made of the same material as that used for the outside case of the battery. Electrical connections between cells are provided by lead connectors that loop over the top of the partition and connect the plates of the cells together. Many batteries connect the cells directly through the partition connectors, which provide the shortest path for the current and the lowest resistance. ● **SEE FIGURE 29-4.**

FIGURE 29-4 A cutaway battery showing the connection of the cells to each other through the partition.

ELECTROLYTE

Electrolyte is the term used to describe the acid solution in a battery. The electrolyte used in automotive batteries is a solution (liquid combination) of 36% sulfuric acid and 64% water. This electrolyte is used for both lead-antimony and lead calcium (maintenance-free) batteries. The chemical formula for this sulfuric acid solution is H_2SO_4.

- H_2 = Symbol for hydrogen (the subscript 2 means that there are two atoms of hydrogen)
- S = Symbol for sulfur
- O_4 = Symbol for oxygen (the subscript 4 indicates that there are four atoms of oxygen)

Electrolyte is sold premixed in the proper proportion and is factory installed or added to the battery when the battery is sold. Additional electrolyte must *never* be added to any battery after the original electrolyte fill. It is normal for some water (H_2O) in the form of hydrogen and oxygen gases to escape during charging as a result of the chemical reactions. The escape of gases from a battery during charging or discharging is called gassing. Only pure distilled water should be added to a battery. If distilled water is not available, clean drinking water can be used.

FIGURE 29-3 Two groups of plates are combined to form a battery element.

SEPARATORS

SET OF POSITIVE PLATES

SET OF NEGATIVE PLATES

HOW A BATTERY WORKS

PRINCIPLE INVOLVED How a battery works is based on a scientific principle discovered years ago that states:

- When two dissimilar metals are placed in an acid, electrons flow between the metals if a circuit is connected between them.

- This can be demonstrated by pushing a steel nail and a piece of solid copper wire into a lemon. Connect a voltmeter to the ends of the copper wire and the nail, and voltage will be displayed.

A fully charged lead-acid battery has a positive plate of lead dioxide (peroxide) and a negative plate of lead surrounded by a sulfuric acid solution (electrolyte). The difference in potential (voltage) between lead peroxide and lead in acid is approximately 2.1 volts.

DURING DISCHARGING The positive plate lead dioxide (PbO_2) combines with the SO_4, forming $PbSO_4$ from the electrolyte and releases its O_2 into the electrolyte, forming H_2O. The negative plate also combines with the SO_4 from the electrolyte and becomes lead sulfate ($PbSO_4$). ●**SEE FIGURE 29–5.**

FULLY DISCHARGED STATE When the battery is fully discharged, both the positive and the negative plates are $PbSO_4$ (lead sulfate) and the electrolyte has become water (H_2O). As the battery is being discharged, the plates and electrolyte approach the completely discharged state. When a battery is completely discharged, there are no longer dissimilar metals submerged in an acid. The plates have become the same material ($PbSO_4$) and the electrolyte becomes water (H_2O). This is a chemical reaction and that can be reversed during charging.

CAUTION: Never charge or jump start a frozen battery because the hydrogen gas can get trapped in the ice and ignite if a spark is caused during the charging process. The result can be an explosion.

FIGURE 29–5 Chemical reaction for a lead-acid battery that is fully charged being discharged by the attached electrical load.

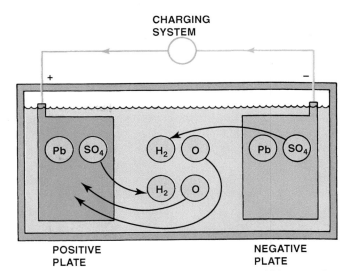

FIGURE 29–6 Chemical reaction for a lead-acid battery that is fully discharged being charged by the attached alternator.

DURING CHARGING During charging, the sulfate that was deposited on the positive and negative plates returns to the electrolyte, where it becomes normal-strength sulfuric acid solution. The positive plate returns to lead dioxide (PbO_2), the negative plate is again pure lead (Pb), and the electrolyte becomes H_2SO_4. ●**SEE FIGURE 29–6.**

VALVE-REGULATED LEAD-ACID BATTERIES

TERMINOLOGY There are two basic types of **valve regulated lead-acid (VRLA),** also called **sealed valve-regulated (SVR)** or **sealed lead-acid (SLA),** batteries. These batteries use a low-pressure venting system that releases excess gas and automatically reseals if a buildup of gas is created due to overcharging. The two types include the following:

- **Absorbed glass mat.** The acid used in an **absorbed glass mat (AGM)** battery is totally absorbed into the separator, making the battery leak-proof and spill-proof. The battery is assembled by compressing the cell about 20%, then inserting it into the container. The compressed cell helps reduce damage caused by vibration and helps keep the acid tightly against the plates. The sealed maintenance-free design uses a pressure release valve in each cell. Unlike conventional batteries that use a liquid electrolyte, called **flooded cell batteries,** most of the hydrogen and oxygen given off during charging remains inside the battery. The separator or mat is only 90% to 95% saturated with electrolyte, thereby allowing a portion of the mat to be filled with gas. The gas spaces provide channels to allow the hydrogen and oxygen gases to recombine rapidly and safely. Because the acid

FIGURE 29–7 An absorbed glass mat battery is totally sealed and is more vibration resistant than conventional lead-acid batteries.

is totally absorbed into the glass mat separator, an AGM battery can be mounted in any direction. AGM batteries also have a longer service life, often lasting 7 to 10 years. Absorbed glass mat batteries are used as standard equipment in some vehicles such as the Chevrolet Corvette and in most Toyota hybrid electric vehicles. ● SEE FIGURE 29–7.

■ **Gelled electrolyte batteries.** In a gelled electrolyte battery, silica is added to the electrolyte, which turns the electrolyte into a substance similar to gelatin. This type of battery is also called a **gel battery.** Both types of valve-regulated, lead-acid batteries are also called **recombinant battery** design. A recombinant-type battery means that the oxygen gas generated at the positive plate travels through the dense electrolyte to the negative plate. When the oxygen reaches the negative plate, it reacts with the lead, which consumes the oxygen gas and prevents the formation of hydrogen gas. It is because of this oxygen recombination that VRLA batteries do not use water.

BATTERY RATINGS

Batteries are rated according to the amount of current they can produce under specific conditions.

COLD-CRANKING AMPERES Every automotive battery must be able to supply electrical power to crank the engine in cold weather and still provide battery voltage high enough to operate the ignition system for starting. The cold-cranking ampere rating of a battery is the number of amperes that can be supplied by a battery at 0°F (−18°C) for 30 seconds while the battery still maintains a voltage of 1.2 volts per cell or higher. This means that the battery voltage would be 7.2 volts for a 12-volt battery and 3.6 volts for a 6-volt battery. The cold-cranking performance rating is called **cold-cranking amperes**

(CCA). Try to purchase a battery with the highest CCA for the money. See the vehicle manufacturer's specifications for recommended battery capacity.

CRANKING AMPERES The designation **CA** refers to the number of amperes that can be supplied by a battery at 32°F (0°C). This rating results in a higher number than the more stringent CCA rating. ● SEE FIGURE 29–8.

MARINE CRANKING AMPERES Marine cranking amperes (MCA) is similar to the cranking amperes (CA) rating and is tested at 32°F (0°C).

RESERVE CAPACITY The **reserve capacity** rating for batteries is *the number of minutes* for which the battery can produce 25 amperes and still have a battery voltage of 1.75 volts per cell (10.5 volts for a 12-volt battery). This rating is actually a measurement of the time for which a vehicle can be driven in the event of a charging system failure.

FIGURE 29–8 This battery has a rating of 1,000 amperes using the cold cranking rating and 900 amperes using the CCA (cold-cranking method).

AMPERE HOUR

Ampere hour is an older battery rating system that measures how many amperes of current the battery can produce over a period of time. For example, a battery that has a 50 ampere-hour (A-H) rating can deliver 50 amperes for 1 hour or 1 ampere for 50 hours or any combination that equals 50 ampere-hours.

BATTERY SERVICE SAFETY PRECAUTIONS

HAZARDS Batteries contain acid and release explosive gases (hydrogen and oxygen) during normal charging and discharging cycles.

SAFETY PROCEDURES To help prevent physical injury or damage to the vehicle, always adhere to the following safety procedures:

1. When working on any electrical component on a vehicle, disconnect the negative battery cable from the battery. When the negative cable is disconnected, all electrical circuits in the vehicle will be open, which will prevent accidental electrical contact between an electrical component and ground. Any electrical spark has the potential to cause explosion and personal injury.

2. Wear eye protection (goggles preferred) when working around any battery.

3. Wear protective clothing to avoid skin contact with battery acid.

4. Always adhere to all safety precautions as stated in the service procedures for the equipment used for battery service and testing.

5. Never smoke or use an open flame around any battery.

6. Never stand near a battery that is being jump-started, especially in cold weather because the battery could explode.

BATTERY VOLTAGE TEST

STATE-OF-CHARGE Testing the battery voltage with a voltmeter is a simple method for determining the state-of-charge (SOC) of any battery. ● **SEE FIGURE 29–9.**

The voltage of a battery does not necessarily indicate whether the battery can perform satisfactorily, but it does indicate to the technician more about the battery's condition than a simple visual inspection. A battery that "looks good" may not be good. This test is commonly called an *open circuit battery voltage test* because it is conducted with an open circuit, no current flowing, and no load applied to the battery.

(a)

(b)

FIGURE 29–9 (a) A voltage reading of 12.28 volts indicates that the battery is not fully charged and should be charged before testing. (b) A battery that measures 12.6 volts or higher after the surface charge has been removed is 100% charged.

STATE-OF-CHARGE (SOC)	BATTERY VOLTAGE
Fully charged	12.6 volts or higher
75% charged	12.4 volts
50%	12.2 volts
25%	12.0 volts
Discharged	11.9 volts or lower

CHART 29–1

A comparison showing the relationship between battery voltage and state-of-charge.

1. If the battery has just been charged or the vehicle has recently been driven, it is necessary to remove the surface charge from the battery before testing. A surface charge is a charge of higher-than-normal voltage that is just on the surface of the battery plates. The surface charge is quickly removed when the battery is loaded and therefore does not accurately represent the true state-of-charge of the battery.

2. To remove the surface charge, turn the headlights on high beam (brights) for one minute, then turn the headlights off and wait two minutes. With the engine and all electrical accessories off, and the doors shut (to turn off the interior lights), connect a voltmeter to the battery posts. Connect the red positive lead to the positive post and the black negative lead to the negative post.

   NOTE: If the meter reads negative (–), the battery has been reverse charged (has reversed polarity) and should be replaced, or the meter has been connected incorrectly.

3. Read the voltmeter and compare the results with the state-of-charge (SOC). The voltages shown are for a battery at or near room temperature (70°F to 80°F, or 21°C to 27°C). ● SEE CHART 29–1.

BATTERY LOAD TESTING

TERMINOLOGY One test to determine the condition of any battery is the **load test.** Most automotive starting and charging testers use a carbon pile to create an electrical load on the battery. The amount of the load is determined by the original CCA rating of the battery, which should be at least 75% charged before performing a load test. The capacity is measured in cold-cranking amperes, which is the number of amperes that a battery can supply at 0°F (–18°C) for 30 seconds.

TEST PROCEDURE To perform a battery load test, take the following steps:

STEP 1 **Determine the CCA rating of the battery.** The proper electrical load used to test a battery is one-half of the CCA rating or three times the ampere-hour rating, with a minimum 150 ampere load. ● SEE FIGURE 29–10.

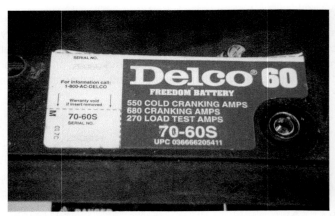

FIGURE 29–10 This battery has cold-cranking amperes (CCA) of 550 A, cranking amperes (CA) of 680 A, and load test amperes of 270 A listed on the top label. Not all batteries have this complete information.

STEP 2 **Connect the load tester to the battery.** Follow the instructions for the tester being used.

STEP 3 **Apply the load for a full 15 seconds.** Observe the voltmeter during the load testing and check the voltage at the end of the 15-second period while the battery is still under load. A good battery should indicate above 9.6 volts.

STEP 4 **Repeat the test.** Many battery manufacturers recommend performing the load test twice, using the first load period to remove the surface charge on the battery and the second test to provide a truer indication of the condition of the battery. Wait 30 seconds between tests to allow time for the battery to recover.

Results: If the battery fails the load test, recharge the battery and retest. If the load test is failed again, the battery needs to be replaced. ● SEE FIGURE 29–11.

FIGURE 29–11 An alternator regulator battery starter tester (ARBST) automatically loads the battery with a fixed load for 15 seconds to remove the surface charge, then removes the load for 30 seconds to allow the battery to recover, and then reapplies the load for another 15 seconds. The results of the test are then displayed.

ELECTRONIC CONDUCTANCE TESTING

TERMINOLOGY General Motors Corporation, Chrysler, Honda, and Ford specify that an electronic conductance tester be used to test batteries in vehicles still under factory warranty. Conductance is a measure of how well a battery can create current. This tester sends a small signal through the battery and then measures a part of the AC response. As a battery ages, the plates can become sulfated and shed active materials from the grids, reducing the battery capacity. Conductance testers can be used to test flooded or AGM-type batteries. The unit can determine the following information about a battery:

- CCA
- State-of-charge
- Voltage of the battery
- Defects such as shorts and opens
- Most conductance testers also display an internal resistance value

However, a conductance tester is not designed to accurately determine the state-of-charge or CCA rating of a new battery. Unlike a battery load test, a conductance tester can be used on a battery that is discharged. This type of tester should only be used to test batteries that have been in service. ● **SEE FIGURE 29–12.**

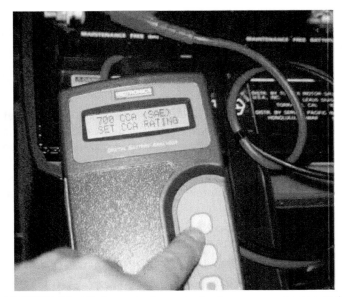

FIGURE 29–12 A conductance tester is very easy to use and has proved to accurately determine battery condition if the connections are properly made. Follow the instructions on the display exactly for best results.

TEST PROCEDURE To test a battery using an electronic conductance tester perform the following steps:

STEP 1 Connect the unit to the positive and negative terminals of the battery. If testing a side post battery, always use the lead adapters and *never.* use steel bolts as these can cause an incorrect reading.

> **NOTE: Test results can be incorrectly reported on the display if proper, clean connections to the battery are not made. Also be sure that all accessories and the ignition switch are in the off position.**

STEP 2 Enter the CCA rating (if known).

STEP 3 The tester determines and displays the measured CCA of the battery as well as state-of-charge and the voltage plus one of the following:
- **Good battery.** The battery can return to service.
- **Charge and retest.** Fully recharge the battery and return it to service.
- **Replace the battery.** The battery is not serviceable and should be replaced.
- **Bad cell—replace.** The battery is not serviceable and should be replaced.

Some conductance testers can check the charging and cranking circuits, too.

BATTERY CHARGING

CHARGING PROCEDURE If the state-of-charge of a battery is low, it must be recharged. It is best to slow charge any battery to prevent possible overheating damage to the battery. Perform the following steps:

STEP 1 **Determine the charge rate.** The charge rate is based on the current state-of-charge (SOC) and charging rate. ● **SEE CHART 29–2** for the recommended charging rate.

STEP 2 **Connect a battery charger to the battery.** Be sure the charger is not plugged in when connecting to a battery. Always follow the battery charger's instructions for proper use.

STEP 3 **Set the charging rate.** The initial charge rate should be about 35 A for 30 minutes to help start the charging process. Fast charging a battery increases the temperature of the battery and can cause warping of the plates inside the battery. Fast charging also increases the amount of gassing (release of hydrogen and oxygen), which can create a health and fire hazard. The battery temperature should not exceed 125°F (hot to the touch).
- Fast charge: 15 A maximum
- Slow charge: 5 A maximum
● **SEE FIGURE 29–13.**

OPEN CIRCUIT VOLTAGE	STATE-OF-CHARGE (SOC) (%)	@60 A	@50 A	@40 A	@30 A	@20 A	@20 A
12.6	100	N.A. (Fully charged)	N.A. (Fully charged)	N.A. (Fully charged)	N.A. (Fully charged)	N.A. (Fully charged)	N.A. (Fully charged)
12.4	75	15 min.	20 min.	27 min.	35 min.	48 min.	90 min.
12.2	50	35 min.	45 min.	55 min.	75 min.	95 min.	180 min.
12.0	25	50 min.	65 min.	85 min.	115 min.	145 min.	260 min.
11.8	0	65 min.	85 min.	110 min.	150 min.	195 min.	370 min.

CHART 29–2

Battery charging guidelines based on the state-of-charge of the battery and the charging rate.

FIGURE 29–13 A typical industrial battery charger. Be sure that the ignition switch is in the off position before connecting any battery charger. Connect the cables of the charger to the battery before plugging the charger into the outlet. This helps prevent a voltage spike and spark that could occur if the charger happened to be accidentally left on. Always follow the battery charger manufacturer's instructions.

CHARGING AGM BATTERIES Charging an absorbed glass mat (AGM) battery requires a different charger than is used to recharge a flooded-type battery. The differences include:

- The AGM can be charged with high current, up to 75% of the ampere-hour rating due to lower internal resistance.
- The charging voltage has to be kept at or below 14.4 volts to prevent damage.

Because most conventional battery chargers use a charging voltage of 16 volts or higher, a charger specifically designed to charge AGM batteries must be used. Absorbed glass mat batteries are often used as auxiliary batteries in hybrid electric vehicles when the battery is located inside the vehicle.

BATTERY CHARGE TIME The time needed to charge a completely discharged battery can be estimated by using the reserve capacity rating of the battery in minutes divided by the charging rate.

Hours needed to charge the battery = Reserve capacity/ Charge current

For example, if a 10-A charge rate is applied to a discharged battery that has a 90-minute reserve capacity, the time needed to charge the battery will be 9 hours.

90 minutes/10 A = 9 hours

BATTERY ELECTRICAL DRAIN TESTING

TERMINOLOGY The **battery electrical drain test** determines if any component or circuit in a vehicle is causing a drain on the battery when everything is off. This test is also called the **ignition off draw (IOD)** or **parasitic load test.** Many electronic components draw a continuous, slight amount of current from the battery when the ignition is off. These components include:

1. Electronically tuned radios for station memory and clock circuits
2. Computers and controllers, through slight diode leakage
3. The alternator, through slight diode leakage

These components may cause a voltmeter to read full battery voltage if it is connected between the negative battery terminal and the removed end of the negative battery cable. Because of this fact, voltmeters should not be used for battery drain testing. This test should be performed when one of the following conditions exists:

1. When a battery is being charged or replaced (a battery drain could have been the cause for charging or replacing the battery).

2. When the battery is suspected of being drained.

PROCEDURE FOR BATTERY ELECTRICAL DRAIN TEST
There are many different testers that can be used for battery electrical drain testing, but using an inductive ammeter is one of the most commonly used.

- **Inductive DC ammeter.** The fastest and easiest method to measure battery electrical drain is to connect an inductive DC ammeter that is capable of measuring low current (10 mA) around either battery cable. ● **SEE FIGURE 29–14.**

- **DMM set to read milliamperes.** The following is the procedure for performing the battery electrical drain test using a DMM set to read DC amperes.

STEP 1 Make certain that all lights, accessories, and ignition are off.

STEP 2 Check all vehicle doors to be certain that the interior courtesy (dome) lights are off.

STEP 3 Disconnect the *negative* (−) battery cable and install a parasitic load tool, as shown in ● **FIGURE 29–15.**

STEP 4 Start the engine and drive the vehicle about 10 minutes, being sure to turn on all the lights and accessories, including the radio.

STEP 5 Turn the engine and all accessories off, including the under-hood light.

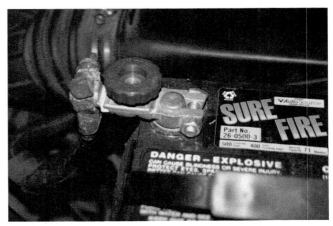

FIGURE 29–15 After connecting the shut-off tool, start the engine and operate all accessories. Stop the engine and turn off everything. Connect the ammeter across the shut-off switch in parallel. Wait 20 minutes. This time allows all electronic circuits to "time out" or shut down. Open the switch—all current now will flow through the ammeter. A reading greater than specified (usually greater than 50 mA, or 0.05 A) indicates a problem that should be corrected.

STEP 6 Connect an ammeter across the parasitic load tool switch and wait 20 minutes for all computers and circuits to shut down.

STEP 7 Open the switch on the load tool and read the battery electrical drain on the meter display.

NOTE: Using a voltmeter or test light to measure battery drain is *not.* recommended by most vehicle manufacturers. The high internal resistance of the voltmeter results in an irrelevant reading that does not provide the technician with adequate information about a problem.

Results:
- Normal = 20 to 30 mA (0.02 to 0.03 A)
- Maximum allowable = 50 mA (0.05 A)

RESET ALL MEMORY FUNCTIONS
Be sure to reset the clock, "auto up" windows, and antitheft radio if equipped. ● **SEE FIGURE 29–16.**

BATTERY DRAIN AND RESERVE CAPACITY
It is normal for a battery to self-discharge even if there is not an electrical load such as computer memory to drain the battery. According to General Motors, this self-discharge is about 13 mA (0.013 A). Some vehicle manufacturers specify that a maximum allowable parasitic draw or battery drain be based on the reserve capacity of the battery. The calculation used is the reserve capacity of the battery divided by 4; this equals the maximum allowable battery drain. For example, a battery rated at 120 minutes reserve capacity should have a maximum battery drain of 30 mA.

$$120\text{ minutes reserve capacity}/4 = 30\text{ mA}$$

FIGURE 29–14 This mini clamp-on digital multimeter is being used to measure the amount of battery electrical drain that is present. In this case, a reading of 20 mA (displayed on the meter as 00.02 A) is within the normal range of 20 to 30 mA. Be sure to clamp around all of the positive battery cable or all of the negative battery cable, whichever is easiest to get the clamp around.

FIGURE 29–16 The battery was replaced in this Acura and the radio displayed "code" when the replacement battery was installed. Thankfully, the owner had the five-digit code required to unlock the radio.

RESCUE VEHICLE

FIGURE 29–17 Jump starting a 2001–2003 Toyota Prius using a 12-volt supply to boost the 12-volt auxiliary battery in the trunk.

FINDING THE SOURCE OF THE DRAIN If there is a drain, check and temporarily disconnect the following components:

1. Under-hood light
2. Glove compartment light
3. Trunk light

If after disconnecting these three components the battery drain draws more than 50 mA (0.05 A), disconnect one fuse at a time from the fuse box until the excessive drain drops to normal.

NOTE: Do not reinsert fuses after they have been removed as this action can cause modules to "wake up," leading to an inconclusive test.

If the excessive battery drain stops after one fuse is disconnected, the source of the drain is located in that particular circuit, as labeled on the fuse box. Continue to disconnect the *power-side* wire connectors from each component included in that particular circuit until the test light goes off. The source of the battery drain can then be traced to an individual component or part of one circuit. If all fuses have been removed and the drain is still in excess of 50mA, disconnect fusible links one at a time while observing the ammeter.

HYBRID AUXILIARY BATTERIES

Absorbed glass mat batteries are often used as auxiliary batteries in hybrid electric vehicles when the battery is located inside the vehicle. ● **SEE CHART 29–3** for a summary of the locations of the 12-volt auxiliary battery and high-voltage battery and safety switch/plug.

JUMP STARTING

To jump start another vehicle with a dead battery, connect good-quality copper jumper cables or a jump box to the good battery and the dead battery. ● **SEE FIGURE 29–17.**

When using jumper cables or a battery jump box, the last connection made should always be on the engine block or an engine bracket on the dead vehicle as far from the battery as possible. It is normal for a spark to be created when the jumper cables finally complete the jumping circuit, and this spark could cause an explosion of the gases around the battery. Many newer vehicles have special ground and/or positive power connections built away from the battery just for the purpose of jump starting. Check the owner's manual or service information for the exact location.

HYBRID AND ELECTRIC VEHICLE BATTERIES

NICKEL-METAL HYDRIDE All current production hybrid electric vehicle use nickel-metal hydride batteries for their high-voltage battery packs.

■ **Construction.** Nickel-Metal Hydride (NiMH) uses a positive electrode made of nickel hydroxide and potassium hydroxide electrolyte. The nominal voltage of an NiMH battery cell is 1.2 volts.

■ **Advantages.** Nickel-based alkaline batteries have a number of advantages over other battery designs. These include the following:

■ High specific energy.

MAKE, MODEL (YEAR)	AUXILIARY 12-V BATTERY LOCATION	HV BATTERY PACK LOCATION (VOLTAGE)	TYPE OF 12-V BATTERY
Cadillac Escalade (2008+) (two mode)	Under the hood; driver's side	Under second row seat (300 volts)	Flooded lead-acid
Chevrolet Malibu (2008+)	Under the hood; driver's side	Mounted behind rear seat under vehicle floor (36 volts)	Flooded lead-acid
Chevrolet Silverado (2004–2008) (PHT)	Under the hood; driver's side	Under second row seat (42 volts)	Flooded lead-acid
Chevrolet Tahoe (2008+) (two mode)	Under the hood; driver's side	Under second row seat (300 volts)	Flooded lead-acid
Chrysler Aspen (2009)	Under driver's side door, under vehicle	Under rear seat; driver's side (288 volts)	Flooded lead-acid
Dodge Durango (2009)	Under driver's side door, under vehicle	Under rear seat; driver's side (288 volts)	Flooded lead-acid
Ford Escape (2005+)	Under the hood; driver's side	Cargo area in the rear under carpet (300 volts)	Flooded lead-acid
GMC Sierra (2004–2008) (PHT)	Under the hood; driver's side	Under second row seat (42 volts)	Flooded lead-acid
GMC Yukon (2008+) (two mode)	Under the hood; driver's side	Under second row seat (300 volts)	Flooded lead-acid
Honda Accord (2005–2007)	Under the hood; driver's side	Behind rear seat (144 volts)	Flooded lead-acid
Honda Civic (2003+)	Under the hood; driver's side	Behind rear seat (144 to 158 volts, 2006+)	Flooded lead-acid
Honda Insight (1999–2005)	Under the hood; center under windshield	144 volts; under hatch floor in the rear	Flooded lead-acid
Honda Insight (2010+)	Under the hood; driver's side	144 volts; under floor behind rear seat	Flooded lead-acid
Lexus GS450h (2007+)	In the trunk; driver's side, behind interior panel	Trunk behind rear seat (288 volts)	Absorbed glass mat (AGM)
Lexus LS 600h (2006+)	In the trunk; driver's side, behind interior panel	Trunk behind rear seat (288 volts)	Absorbed glass mat (AGM)
Lexus RX400h (2006–2009)	Under the hood; passenger side	Under the second row seat (288 volts)	Flooded lead-acid
Mercury Mariner (2005–2011)	Under the hood; driver's side	Cargo area in the rear under carpet (300 volts)	Flooded lead-acid
Nissan Altima (2007–2011)	In the trunk; driver's side	Behind rear seat (245 volts)	Absorbed glass mat (AGM)
Saturn AURA Hybrid (2007–2010)	Under the hood; driver's side	Behind the rear seat; under the vehicle floor (36 volts)	Flooded lead-acid
Saturn VUE Hybrid (2007–2010)	Under the hood; driver's side	Behind the rear seat; under the vehicle floor (36 volts)	Flooded lead-acid
Toyota Camry Hybrid (2007+)	In the trunk; passenger side	Behind the rear seat; under the vehicle floor (245 volts)	Absorbed glass mat (AGM)

CHART 29–3

CONTINUED

A summary chart showing where the 12-volt and high-voltage batteries and shut-off switch/plugs are located. Only the auxiliary 12-volt batteries can be serviced or charged.

MAKE, MODEL (YEAR)	AUXILIARY 12-V BATTERY LOCATION	HV BATTERY PACK LOCATION (VOLTAGE)	TYPE OF 12-V BATTERY
Toyota Highlander Hybrid (2006–2009)	Under the hood; passenger side	Under the second row seat (288 volts)	Flooded lead-acid
Toyota Prius (2001–2003)	In the trunk; driver's side	Behind rear seat (274 volts)	Absorbed glass mat (AGM)
Toyota Prius (2004–2009)	In the trunk; driver's side	Behind rear seat (201 volts)	Absorbed glass mat (AGM)
Toyota Prius (2010+)	In the trunk; driver's side	Behind rear seat (201.6 volts)	Absorbed glass mat (AGM)

CHART 29–3 (CONTINUED)

- The nickel electrode can be manufactured with large surface areas, which increase the overall battery capacity.
- The electrolyte does not react with steel, so NiMH batteries can be housed in sealed steel containers that transfer heat reasonably well.
- The materials used in NiMH batteries are environment friendly and can be recycled.
- Excellent cycle life.
- Durable and safe.

● **SEE FIGURE 29–18.**

- **Disadvantages.** Disadvantages of the NiMH battery include:

  - High rate of self-discharge, especially at elevated temperatures.
  - Moderate levels of memory effect, although this seems to be less prominent in newer designs.
  - Moderate to high cost. This will almost certainly lessen with increased market acceptance.

FIGURE 29–18 An NiMH cell. The unique element in a nickel-metal hydride cell is the negative electrode. Note that the electrolyte does not enter into the chemical reaction and is able to maintain a constant conductivity regardless of the state-of-charge of the cell.

 FREQUENTLY ASKED QUESTIONS

How Many Types of Lithium-Ion Batteries Are There?

There are numerous types of lithium-ion batteries, and the list is growing. While every component of the battery is under development, the primary difference between the various designs is the materials used for the positive electrode or **cathode.** The original Li-ion cell design used lithium cobalt oxide for its cathode, which has good energy storage characteristics but suffers chemical breakdown at relatively low temperatures. This failure results in the release of heat and oxygen, which often leads to a fire or explosion as the electrolyte ignites.

In order to make lithium-ion batteries safer and more durable, a number of alternative cathode materials have been formulated. One of the more promising cathode designs for automotive applications is lithium iron phosphate ($LiFePO_4$), which is stable at higher temperatures and releases less energy when it does suffer breakdown. Other lithium-ion cathode designs include:

- Lithium nickel cobalt oxide (LNCO)
- Lithium metal oxide (LMO)
- Nickel cobalt manganese (NCM)
- Nickel cobalt aluminum (NCA)
- Manganese oxide spinel (MnO)

Research and development continues on not only cathode design, but also anodes, separator materials, and electrolyte chemistry.

LITHIUM-ION A battery design that shows a great deal of promise for electric vehicles (EV) and hybrid electric vehicles (HEV) applications is *lithium-ion (Li-ion)* technology. Lithium-ion batteries have been used extensively in consumer electronics since 1991 and are currently used in the Chevrolet VOLT, Nissan Leaf, and Tesla. A lithium-ion cell is so named because during battery cycling, lithium ions move back and forth between the positive and negative electrodes. Lithium-ion has approximately twice the specific energy of nickel-metal hydride (NiMH).

- **Construction.** The positive electrode in a conventional lithium-ion battery has lithium cobalt oxide as its main ingredient, with the negative electrode being made from a specialty carbon. The electrolyte is an organic solvent, and this is held in a separator layer between the two electrode plates. To prevent battery rupture and ensure safety, a pressure release valve is built into the battery's housing that will release gas if the internal pressure rises above a preset point.

- **Operation.** The lithium-ion cell is designed so that lithium ions can pass back and forth between the electrodes when the battery is in operation.

  - During battery discharge, lithium ions leave the anode (negative electrode) and enter the cathode (positive electrode).

  - The reverse takes place when the battery is charging.

- **Advantages.** Lithium-ion batteries have the following advantages:

  - High specific energy

  - Good high temperature performance

  - Low self-discharge

  - Minimal memory effect

  - High nominal cell voltage. The nominal voltage of a lithium-ion cell is 3.6 volts, which is three times that of nickel-based alkaline batteries. This allows for fewer battery cells being required to produce high voltage from an HV battery.

  ● **SEE FIGURE 29–19**

- **Disadvantages.** Disadvantages of the lithium-ion battery include:

  - High cost

  - Issues related to battery overheating

NOTE: **Early lithium-ion battery designs have experienced problems with thermal runaway, which has led to fire and even explosions. Li-ion battery packs in** automotive applications must be designed with cooling and safety systems that will prevent overheating and isolate cell failures.

 FREQUENTLY ASKED QUESTION

What Were the Causes of Lithium-Ion Battery Failure?

Three major factors are responsible for failure of lithium-ion batteries:

- Operating the cells outside their required voltage range (2 to 4 volts)
- Operating the cells outside their required temperature range (0°C to 80°C)
- Short circuits (internal or external)

  For these reasons, lithium-ion battery packs in automotive applications require precise battery management using specialized cooling and safety systems.

OTHER HIGH-VOLTAGE BATTERY TYPES

There are many different types of batteries that are not being used in electric or hybrid electric vehicles but may find other applications. These types of batteries include the following:

NICKEL-CADMIUM The nickel-cadmium design is known as an **alkaline** battery, because of the alkaline nature of its *electrolyte*. Alkaline batteries generate electrical energy through the chemical reaction of a metal with oxygen in an alkaline electrolyte. A nickel-cadmium battery uses the following materials:

- Nickel hydroxide for the positive electrode
- Metallic cadmium for the negative electrode
- Potassium hydroxide (an alkaline solution) for the electrolyte

The nominal voltage of a Ni-Cd battery cell is 1.2 volts.

- **Advantages of Ni-Cd batteries** include:

  - Good low temperature performance

  - Long life

  - Excellent reliability

  - Low maintenance requirements

- **Disadvantages of Ni-Cd batteries** include:

  - Ni-Cd batteries have a specific energy that is only slightly better than lead-acid technology

  - Suffers from toxicity related to its cadmium content.

FIGURE 29–19 One advantage of a lithium-ion cell is that it produces 3.6 volts, whereas an NiMH or Ni-Cd cell only produces 1.2 volts.

FREQUENTLY ASKED QUESTIONS

How Is an Alkaline Battery Different from a Lead-Acid Battery?

Lead-acid batteries use sulfuric acid as the electrolyte that acts as the medium between the battery's positive and negative electrodes. Acids have a pH that is below 7, where pure water has a pH of exactly 7. If electrolyte from a lead-acid battery is spilled, it can be neutralized using a solution of baking soda and water (an alkaline solution).

Alkaline batteries use an electrolyte such as potassium hydroxide, which has a pH greater than 7. This means that the electrolyte solution is basic, which is the opposite of acidic. If an alkaline battery's electrolyte is spilled, it can be neutralized using a solution of vinegar and water (vinegar is acidic). Both nickel-cadmium (Ni-Cd) and nickel-metal hydride (NiMH) batteries are alkaline battery designs.

FIGURE 29–20 Zinc-air batteries are recharged by replacing the zinc anodes. These batteries are also considered to be a type of fuel cell, because the positive electrode is oxygen taken from atmospheric air.

LITHIUM POLYMER The **lithium-polymer (Li-poly)** battery design came out of the development of solid-state electrolytes in the 1970s. Solid-state electrolytes are solids that can conduct ions but do not allow electrons to move through them. Since lithium-polymer batteries use solid electrolytes, they are known as *solid-state.* batteries. Solid polymer is much less flammable than liquid electrolytes and is able to conduct ions at temperatures above 140°F (60°C).

- **Advantages.** Li-poly batteries show good promise for EV and HEV applications for a number of reasons, including:
  - The lithium in the battery is in ionic form, making the battery safer because it is much less reactive than pure lithium metal.
  - The Li-poly battery cell can be made in many different shapes and forms, so they can be made to fit into the available space in the vehicle chassis.
  - Li-Poly batteries have good cycle and calendar life, and have the potential to have the highest specific energy and power of any battery technology.
- **Disadvantages.** The major disadvantage with the Li-poly battery is that it is a high temperature design and must be operated between 176°F and 248°F (80°C and 120°C).

ZINC-AIR The **Zinc-air** design is a mechanically rechargeable battery. This is because it uses a positive electrode of gaseous oxygen and a sacrificial negative electrode made of zinc. The negative electrode is spent during the discharge cycle, and the battery is recharged by replacing the zinc electrodes. Zinc-air is one of several metal–air battery designs (others include aluminum-air and iron-air) that must be recharged by replacement of the negative electrode (anode). ● **SEE FIGURE 29–20.**

- **Advantages.** Zinc-air has a very high specific energy and efficiency, and the potential range of an EV vehicle equipped with zinc-air batteries is up to 600 km. Zinc-air batteries can be recharged very quickly, since a full recharge is achieved through replacement of the zinc electrodes.
- **Disadvantages.** The primary disadvantage with this design is the level of infrastructure required to make recharging practical.

ZEBRA BATTERY

- **Construction.** The ZEBRA battery is a sodium-metal-chloride battery. This battery was invented in 1985 by the Zeolite Battery Research Africa (ZEBRA) project. This type of battery utilizes two different electrolytes; first the beta alumina similar to the sodium-sulfur design, then another layer of electrolyte between the beta alumina and the positive electrode. ● **SEE FIGURE 29–21.**

FIGURE 29–21 Sodium-metal-chloride batteries are also known as ZEBRA batteries. These batteries are lightweight (40% of the weight of lead-acid) and have a high energy density.

- **Disadvantages.** A disadvantage of the sodium-metal-chloride design is high operating temperatures. However, this design has been used successfully in various applications and has proven to be safe under all operating conditions. Sodium-metal-chloride technology is considered to have very good potential for EV and HEV applications.

BATTERY COMPARISON

SEE CHART 29–4 shows a comparison of specific energy and nominal voltage for the various battery technologies.

SECONDARY BATTERIES COMPARISON

BATTERY TYPE	NOMINAL VOLTAGE (V) PER CELL	THEORETICAL SPECIFIC ENERGY (WH/KG*)	PRACTICAL SPECIFIC ENERGY (WH/KG*)	MAJOR ISSUES
Lead-Acid	2.1	252	35	Heavy, low cycle life, toxic materials
Nickel-Cadmium	1.2	244	50	Toxic materials, cost
Nickel-Metal Hydride	1.2	278–800	80	Cost, high self-discharge rate, memory effect
Lithium-Ion	3.6	766	120	Safety issues, calendar life, cost
Zinc-Air	1.1	1,320	110	Low power, limited cycle life, bulky
Sodium-Sulfur	2.0	792	100	High temperature battery, safety, low power electrolyte
Sodium-Nickel-Chloride	2.5	787	90	High temperature operation, low power

*Specific energy is measured in Watt-hours/kilogram

CHART 29–4

Secondary-type battery comparison showing specifications and limitations.

SUMMARY

1. When a battery is being discharged, the acid (SO_4) is leaving the electrolyte and being deposited on the plates. When the battery is being charged, the acid (SO_4) is forced off the plates and back into the electrolyte.

2. All batteries give off hydrogen and oxygen when being charged.

3. Batteries are rated according to CCA and reserve capacity.

4. Batteries can be tested with a voltmeter to determine the state-of-charge. A battery load test loads the battery to one-half of its CCA rating.

5. A good battery should be able to maintain higher than 9.6 volts for the entire 15-second test period.

6. Batteries can be tested with a conductance tester even if discharged.

7. A battery drain test should be performed if the battery runs down.

8. Be sure that a battery charger is unplugged from a power outlet when making connections to a battery.

9. NiMH batteries are the type most used in hybrid electric vehicles.

10. Lithium-ion (Li-ion) type batteries are used in some electric and plug-in electric vehicles.

REVIEW QUESTIONS

1. Why can discharged batteries freeze?
2. What are the battery-rating methods?
3. What are the results of a voltmeter test of a battery and its state-of-charge?
4. What are the steps for performing a battery load test?
5. What battery types are most used in electric and hybrid electric vehicles?

1. When a battery becomes completely discharged, both positive and negative plates become _____ and the electrolyte becomes _____.
   a. H$_2$SO4/Pb
   b. PbSO$_4$/H$_2$O
   c. PbO$_2$/H$_2$SO$_4$
   d. PbSO$_4$/H$_2$SO$_4$

2. Deep cycling means _____.
   a. Overcharging the battery
   b. Overfilling or underfilling the battery with water
   c. The battery is fully discharged and then recharged
   d. The battery is overfilled with acid (H$_2$SO$_4$)

3. Which battery rating is tested at 0°F (–18°C)?
   a. Cold-cranking amperes (CCA)
   b. Cranking amperes (CA)
   c. Reserve capacity
   d. Battery voltage test

4. Which battery rating is expressed in minutes?
   a. Cold-cranking amperes (CCA)
   b. Cranking amperes (CA)
   c. Reserve capacity
   d. Battery voltage test

5. What battery rating is tested at 32°F (0°C)?
   a. Cold-cranking amperes (CCA)
   b. Cranking amperes (CA)
   c. Reserve capacity
   d. Battery voltage test

6. When load testing a battery, which battery rating is often used to determine how much load to apply to the battery?
   a. CA
   b. RC
   c. MCA
   d. CCA

7. A battery high-rate discharge (load capacity) test is being performed on a 12-volt battery. Technician A says that a good battery should have a voltage reading of higher than 9.6 volts while under load at the end of the 15-second test. Technician B says that the battery should be discharged (loaded) to twice its CCA rating. Which technician is correct?
   a. Technician A only
   b. Technician B only
   c. Both technicians A and B
   d. Neither technician A nor B

8. When charging a lead-acid (flooded-type) battery, _____.
   a. The initial charging rate should be about 35 amperes for 30 minutes
   b. The battery may not accept a charge for several hours, yet may still be a good (serviceable) battery
   c. The battery temperature should not exceed 125°F (hot to the touch)
   d. All of the above

9. Normal battery drain (parasitic drain) in a vehicle with many computer and electronic circuits is _____.
   a. 20 to 30 milliamperes
   b. 2 to 3 amperes
   c. 150 to 300 milliamperes
   d. None of the above CCA

10. Which type of battery is most used in hybrid electric vehicles?
    a. Nickel-Metal Hydride
    b. Lithium-Ion
    c. Nickel-Cadmium
    d. Sodium-Nickel-Chloride

chapter 30

CRANKING SYSTEM

OBJECTIVES: After studying Chapter 30, the reader will be able to: • Prepare for ASE Electrical/Electronic Systems (A6) certification test content area "C" (Starting System Diagnosis and Repair). • Describe how the cranking circuit works. • Discuss how a starter motor converts electrical power into mechanical power. • Describe the hold-in and pull-in windings of a starter solenoid.

KEY TERMS: • Armature 307 • Brush-end housing 307 • Brushes 308 • CEMF 306 • Commutator-end housing 307 • Commutator segments 308 • Compression spring 311 • Drive-end housing 307 • Field coils 307 • Field housing 307 • Field poles 307 • Ground brushes 308 • Hold-in winding 312 • Insulated brushes 308 • Mesh spring 311 • Neutral safety switch 304 • Overrunning clutch 310 • PM starter 307 • Pole shoes 307 • Pull-in winding 312 • RVS 305 • Starter drive 310 • Starter solenoid 312 • Through bolts 307

CRANKING CIRCUIT

PARTS INVOLVED For any engine to start, it must first be rotated using an external power source. It is the purpose and function of the cranking circuit to create the necessary power and transfer it from the battery to the starter motor, which rotates the engine.

The cranking circuit includes those mechanical and electrical components required to crank the engine for starting. The cranking force in the early 1900s was the driver's arm, because the driver had to physically crank the engine until it started. Modern cranking circuits include the following:

1. **Starter motor.** The starter is normally a 0.5 to 2.6 horsepower (0.4 to 2 kilowatts) electric motor that can develop nearly 8 horsepower (6 kilowatts) for a very short time when first cranking a cold engine. ● SEE FIGURE 30–1.

2. **Battery.** The battery must be of the correct capacity and be at least 75% charged to provide the necessary current and voltage for correct starter operation.

3. **Starter solenoid or relay.** The high current required by the starter must be able to be turned on and off. A large switch would be required if the current were controlled by the driver directly. Instead, a small current switch (ignition switch) operates a solenoid or relay that controls the high current to the starter.

FIGURE 30–1 A typical solenoid-operated starter.

4. **Starter drive.** The starter drive uses a small pinion gear that contacts the engine flywheel gear teeth and transmits starter motor power to rotate the engine.

5. **Ignition switch.** The ignition switch and safety control switches control the starter motor operation. ● SEE FIGURE 30–2.

CONTROL CIRCUIT PARTS AND OPERATION The engine is cranked by an electric motor that is controlled by a key-operated ignition switch. The ignition switch will not operate the starter unless the automatic transmission is in neutral or park, or the clutch pedal is depressed on manual transmission/transaxle vehicles. This is to prevent an accident that might result from the vehicle moving forward or rearward when the engine is started.

FIGURE 30–2 Some column-mounted ignition switches act directly on the electrical ignition switch itself, whereas others use a link from the lock cylinder to the ignition switch.

The types of controls that are used to be sure that the vehicle will not move when being cranked include the following:

- Many automobile manufacturers use an electric switch called a **neutral safety switch,** which opens the circuit between the ignition switch and the starter to prevent starter motor operation, unless the gear selector is in neutral or park. The safety switch can be attached either to the steering column inside the vehicle near the floor or on the side of the transmission.

- Many manufacturers use a mechanical blocking device in the steering column to prevent the driver from turning the key switch to the start position unless the gear selector is in neutral or park.

- Many manual transmission vehicles also use a safety switch to permit cranking only if the clutch is depressed. This switch is commonly called the *clutch safety switch.* ● **SEE FIGURE 30–3.**

COMPUTER-CONTROLLED STARTING

OPERATION Some key-operated ignition systems and most push-button-to-start systems use the computer to crank the engine. The ignition switch start position on the push-to-start button is used as an input signal to the powertrain control module (PCM). Before the PCM cranks the engine, the following conditions must be met.

- The brake pedal is depressed.
- The gear selector is in park or neutral.
- The correct key fob (code) is present in the vehicle.

FIGURE 30–3 To prevent the engine from cranking, an electrical switch is usually installed to open the circuit between the ignition switch and the starter solenoid.

A typical push-button start system includes the following sequence.

- The ignition key can be turned to the start position, released, and the PCM cranks the engine until it senses that the engine has started.

- The PCM can detect that the engine has started by looking at the engine speed signal.

- Normal cranking speed can vary between 100 and 250 RPM. If the engine speed exceeds 400 RPM, the PCM determines that the engine started and opens the circuit to the "S" (start) terminal of the starter solenoid that stops the starter motor.

Computer-controlled starting is almost always part of the system if a push-button start is used. ● **SEE FIGURE 30–4.**

FIGURE 30–4 Instead of using an ignition key to start the engine, some vehicles are using a start button which is also used to stop the engine, as shown on this Jaguar.

FIGURE 30-5 The top button on this key fob is the remote start button.

REMOTE STARTING

REMOTE STARTING Remote starting, sometimes called **remote vehicle start (RVS),** is a system that allows the driver to start the engine of the vehicle from inside the house or a building at a distance of about 200 ft (65 m). The doors remain locked to reduce the possibility of theft. This feature allows the heating or air-conditioning system to start before the driver arrives. ● **SEE FIGURE 30-5.**

NOTE: Most remote start systems will turn off the engine after 10 minutes of run time unless reset by using the remote.

STARTER MOTOR OPERATION

PRINCIPLES A starter motor uses electromagnetic principles to convert electrical energy from the battery (up to 300 amperes) to mechanical power (up to 8 horsepower [6 kilowatts]) to crank the engine. Current for the starter motor or power circuit is controlled by a solenoid or relay, which is itself controlled by the driver-operated ignition switch.

The current travels through the brushes and into the armature windings, where other magnetic fields are created around each copper wire loop in the armature. The two strong magnetic fields created inside the starter housing create the force that rotates the armature.

Inside the starter housing is a strong magnetic field created by the field coil magnets. The armature, a conductor, is installed inside this strong magnetic field, with little clearance between the armature and the field coils.

The two magnetic fields act together, and their lines of force "bunch up" or are strong on one side of the armature loop wire and become weak on the other side of the conductor. This causes the conductor (armature) to move from the area of strong magnetic field strength toward the area of weak magnetic field strength. ● **SEE FIGURES 30-6 AND 30-7.**

The difference in magnetic field strength causes the armature to rotate. This rotation force (torque) is increased as the current flowing through the starter motor increases. The torque of a starter is determined by the strength of the magnetic fields inside the starter. Magnetic field strength is measured in

FIGURE 30-6 This series-wound electric motor shows the basic operation with only two brushes: one hot brush and one ground brush. The current flows through both field coils, then through the hot brush and the loop winding of the armature, before reaching ground through the ground brush.

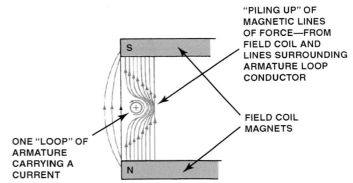

FIGURE 30-7 The interaction of the magnetic fields of the armature loops and field coils creates a stronger magnetic field on the right side of the conductor, causing the armature loop to move toward the left.

ampere-turns. If the current or the number of turns of wire is increased, the magnetic field strength is increased.

The magnetic field of the starter motor is provided by two or more pole shoes and field windings. The pole shoes are made of iron and are attached to the frame with large screws. ● **SEE FIGURE 30-8.**

● **FIGURE 30-9** shows the paths of magnetic flux lines within a four pole motor.

The field windings are usually made of a heavy copper ribbon to increase their current-carrying capacity and electromagnetic field strength. ● **SEE FIGURE 30-10.**

Automotive starter motors usually have four pole shoes and two to four field windings to provide a strong magnetic field within the motor. Pole shoes that do not have field windings are magnetized by flux lines from the wound poles.

(a)

(b)

↙ ROTATION

(c)

POLE SHOE   POLE SHOE

S   N

ROTATION

(d)

FIGURE 30-8 The armature loops rotate due to the difference in the strength of the magnetic field. The loops move from a strong magnetic field strength toward a weaker magnetic field strength.

SERIES MOTORS

A series motor develops its maximum torque at the initial start (0 RPM) and develops less torque as the speed increases.

- A series motor is commonly used for an automotive starter motor because of its high starting power characteristics.

- A series starter motor develops less torque at high RPM, because a current is produced in the starter itself that acts against the current from the battery. Because

AIR GAP   WINDINGS

ARMATURE   POLE SHOE

N

S   S

N

FIGURE 30-9 Magnetic lines of force in a four-pole motor.

FIELD WINDINGS

POLE SHOE

FIGURE 30-10 A pole shoe and field winding.

this current works against battery voltage, it is called counterelectromotive force, or **CEMF.** This CEMF is produced by electromagnetic induction in the armature conductors, which are cutting across the magnetic lines of force formed by the field coils. This induced voltage operates against the applied voltage supplied by the battery, which reduces the strength of the magnetic field in the starter.

- Because the power (torque) of the starter depends on the strength of the magnetic fields, the torque of the starter decreases as the starter speed increases. A series-wound starter also draws less current at higher speeds and will keep increasing in speed under light loads. This could lead to the destruction of the starter motor unless controlled or prevented. ● **SEE FIGURE 30-11.**

SHUNT MOTORS

Shunt-type electric motors have the field coils in parallel (or shunt) across the armature.

A shunt-type motor has the following features.

- A shunt motor does not decrease in torque at higher motor RPM, because the CEMF produced in the armature does not decrease the field coil strength.

FIGURE 30-11 This wiring diagram illustrates the construction of a series-wound electric motor. Notice that all current flows through the field coils, then through the armature (in series) before reaching ground.

FIGURE 30-12 This wiring diagram illustrates the construction of a shunt-type electric motor, and shows the field coils in parallel (or shunt) across the armature.

FIGURE 30-13 A compound motor is a combination of series and shunt types, using part of the field coils connected electrically in series with the armature and some in parallel (shunt).

- A shunt motor, however, does not produce as high a starting torque as that of a series-wound motor, and is not used for starters. Some small electric motors, such as used for windshield wiper motors, use a shunt motor but most use permanent magnets rather than electromagnets. ● **SEE FIGURE 30–12.**

PERMANENT MAGNET MOTORS A **permanent magnet (PM) starter** uses permanent magnets that maintain constant field strength, the same as a shunt-type motor, so they have similar operating characteristics. To compensate for the lack of torque, all PM starters use gear reduction to multiply starter motor torque. The permanent magnets used are an alloy of neodymium, iron, and boron, and are almost 10 times more powerful than previously used permanent magnets.

COMPOUND MOTORS A compound-wound, or compound, motor has the operating characteristics of a series motor *and* a shunt-type motor, because some of the field coils are connected to the armature in series and some (usually only one) are connected directly to the battery in parallel (shunt) with the armature.

Compound-wound starter motors are commonly used in Ford, Chrysler, and some GM starters. The shunt-wound field coil is called a shunt coil and is used to limit the maximum speed of the starter. Because the shunt coil is energized as soon as the battery current is sent to the starter, it is used to engage the starter drive on older Ford positive engagement–type starters. ● **SEE FIGURE 30–13.**

FIGURE 30-14 A typical starter motor showing the drive-end housing.

HOW THE STARTER MOTOR WORKS

PARTS INVOLVED A starter consists of the main structural support of a starter called the main **field housing,** one end of which is called a **commutator-end** or (**brush-end**) **housing** and the other end a **drive-end housing.** The drive-end housing contains the drive pinion gear, which meshes with the engine flywheel gear teeth to start the engine. The commutator-end plate supports the end containing the starter brushes. **Through bolts** hold the three components together. ● **SEE FIGURE 30–14.**

- **Field coils.** The steel housing of the starter motor contains permanent magnets or four electromagnets that are connected directly to the positive post of the battery to provide a strong magnetic field inside the starter. The four electromagnets use heavy copper or aluminum wire wrapped around a soft-iron core, which is contoured to fit against the rounded internal surface of the starter frame. The soft-iron cores are called **pole shoes.** Two of the four pole shoes are wrapped with copper wire in one direction to create a north pole magnet, and the other two pole shoes are wrapped in the opposite direction to create a south pole magnet. These magnets, when energized, create strong magnetic fields inside the starter housing and, therefore, are called **field coils.** The soft-iron cores (pole shoes) are often called **field poles.** ● **SEE FIGURE 30–15.**

- **Armature.** Inside the field coils is an **armature** that is supported with either bushings or ball bearings at both ends, which permit it to rotate. The armature is constructed of thin, circular disks of steel laminated together and wound lengthwise with heavy-gauge insulated copper wire. The laminated iron core supports the copper loops of wire and helps concentrate the magnetic field produced by the coils. ● **SEE FIGURE 30–16.**

FIGURE 30–15 Pole shoes and field windings installed in the housing.

FIGURE 30–17 An armature showing how its copper wire loops are connected to the commutator.

FIGURE 30–16 A typical starter motor armature. The armature core is made from thin sheet metal sections assembled on the armature shaft, which is used to increase the magnetic field strength.

Insulation between the laminations helps to increase the magnetic efficiency in the core. For reduced resistance, the armature conductors are made of a thick copper wire. The two ends of each conductor are attached to two adjacent commutator bars.

The commutator is made of copper bars insulated from each other by mica or some other insulating material. ● **SEE FIGURE 30–17.**

The armature core, windings, and commutator are assembled on a long armature shaft. This shaft also carries the pinion gear that meshes with the engine flywheel ring gear.

STARTER BRUSHES To supply the proper current to the armature, a four-pole motor must have four brushes riding on the commutator. Most automotive starters have two grounded and two insulated brushes, which are held against the commutator by spring force.

The ends of the copper armature windings are soldered to **commutator segments.** The electrical current that passes through the field coils is then connected to the commutator of the armature by brushes that can move over the segments of the rotating armature. These **brushes** are made of a combination of copper and carbon.

- The copper is a good conductor material.
- The carbon added to the starter brushes helps provide the graphite-type lubrication needed to reduce wear of the brushes and the commutator segments.

The starter uses four brushes—two brushes to transfer the current from the field coils to the armature, and two brushes to provide the ground return path for the current that flows through the armature.

The two sets of brushes include:

1. Two **insulated brushes**, which are in holders and are insulated from the housing.
2. Two **ground brushes**, which use bare, stranded copper wire connections to the brushes. The ground brush holders are not insulated and attach directly to the field housing or brush-end housing.

● **SEE FIGURE 30–18.**

PERMANENT MAGNET FIELDS Permanent magnets are used in place of the electromagnetic field coils and pole shoes in many starters today. This eliminates the motor field circuit, which in turn eliminates the potential for field coil faults and other electrical problems. The motor has only an armature circuit.

FIGURE 30–18 A cutaway of a typical starter motor showing the commutator, brushes, and brush spring.

GEAR-REDUCTION STARTERS

PURPOSE AND FUNCTION Gear-reduction starters are used by many automotive manufacturers. The purpose of the gear reduction (typically 2:1 to 4:1) is to increase starter motor speed and provide the torque multiplication necessary to crank an engine.

 TECH TIP

Don't Hit That Starter!

In the past, it was common to see service technicians hitting a starter in their effort to diagnose a no-crank condition. Often the shock of the blow to the starter aligned or moved the brushes, armature, and bushings. Many times, the starter functioned after being hit, even if only for a short time.

However, most starters today use permanent magnet fields, and the magnets can be easily broken if hit. A magnet that is broken becomes two weaker magnets. Some early PM starters used magnets that were glued or bonded to the field housing. If struck with a heavy tool, the magnets could be broken with parts of the magnet falling onto the armature and into the bearing pockets, making the starter impossible to repair or rebuild. ● SEE FIGURE 30–19.

FIGURE 30–19 This starter permanent magnet field housing was ruined when someone used a hammer on the field housing in an attempt to "fix" a starter that would not work. A total replacement is the only solution in this case.

As a series-wound motor increases in rotational speed, the starter produces less power, and less current is drawn from the battery because the armature generates greater CEMF as the starter speed increases. However, a starter motor's maximum torque occurs at 0 RPM and torque decreases with increasing RPM. A smaller starter using a gear-reduction design can produce the necessary cranking power with reduced starter amperage requirements. Lower current requirements mean that smaller battery cables can be used. Many permanent magnet starters use a planetary gear set (a type of gear reduction) to provide the necessary torque for starting. ● SEE FIGURE 30–20.

FIGURE 30–20 A typical gear-reduction starter.

STARTER DRIVES

PURPOSE AND FUNCTION A **starter drive** includes small pinion gears that mesh with and rotate the larger gear on the engine flywheel or flex plate for starting. The pinion gear must engage with the engine gear slightly *before* the starter motor rotates, to prevent serious damage to either the starter gear or the engine, but must be disengaged after the engine starts. The ends of the starter pinion gear are tapered to help the teeth mesh more easily without damaging the flywheel ring gear teeth. ● **SEE FIGURE 30–21.**

STARTER DRIVE GEAR RATIO The ratio of the number of teeth on the engine ring gear to the number on the starter pinion is between 15:1 and 20:1. A typical small starter pinion

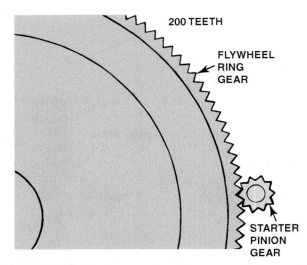

FIGURE 30–22 The ring gear to pinion gear ratio is usually 15:1 to 20:1.

gear has 9 teeth that turn an engine ring gear with 166 teeth. This provides an 18:1 gear reduction; thus, the starter motor is rotating approximately 18 times faster than the engine. Normal cranking speed for the engine is 200 RPM (varies from 70 to 250 RPM). This means that the starter motor speed is 18 times faster, or 3,600 starter RPM (200 × 18 = 3,600). If the engine starts and is accelerated to 2,000 RPM (normal cold engine speed), the starter will be destroyed by the high speed (36,000 RPM) if the starter was not disengaged from the engine. ● **SEE FIGURE 30–22.**

STARTER DRIVE OPERATION All starter drive mechanisms use a type of one-way clutch that allows the starter to rotate the engine, but then turns freely if the engine speed is greater than the starter motor speed. This clutch, called an **overrunning clutch,** protects the starter motor from damage if the ignition switch is held in the start position after the engine starts. The overrunning clutch, which is built in as a part of the starter drive unit, uses steel balls or rollers installed in tapered notches. ● **SEE FIGURE 30–23.**

FIGURE 30–21 A cutaway of a typical starter drive showing all of the internal parts.

(a)   (b)

FIGURE 30–23 Operation of the overrunning clutch. (a) Starter motor is driving the starter pinion and cranking the engine. The rollers are wedged against spring force into their slots. (b) The engine has started and is rotating faster than the starter armature. Spring force pushes the rollers so they can rotate freely.

This taper forces the balls or rollers tightly into the notch, when rotating in the direction necessary to start the engine. When the engine rotates faster than the starter pinion, the balls or rollers are forced out of the narrow tapered notch, allowing the pinion gear to turn freely (overrun).

The spring between the drive tang or pulley and the overrunning clutch and pinion is called a **mesh spring.** It helps to cushion and control the engagement of the starter drive pinion with the engine flywheel gear. This spring is also called a **compression spring,** because the starter solenoid or starter yoke compresses the spring and the spring tension causes the starter pinion to engage the engine flywheel.

FAILURE MODE A starter drive is generally a dependable unit and does not require replacement unless defective or worn. The major wear occurs in the overrunning clutch section of the starter drive unit. The steel balls or rollers wear and often do not wedge tightly into the tapered notches as is necessary for engine cranking. A worn starter drive can cause the starter motor to operate and then stop cranking the engine and creating a "whining" noise. The whine indicates that the starter motor is operating and that the starter drive is not rotating the engine flywheel. The entire starter drive is replaced as a unit. The overrunning clutch section of the starter drive cannot be serviced or repaired separately because the drive is a sealed unit. Starter drives are most likely to fail intermittently at first and then more frequently, until replacement becomes necessary to start the engine. Intermittent starter drive failure (starter whine) is often most noticeable during cold weather.

POSITIVE ENGAGEMENT STARTERS

OPERATION Positive engagement starters (direct drive) were used on Ford engines from 1973 to 1990. These starters use the shunt coil winding and a movable pole shoe to engage the starter drive. The high starting current is controlled by an ignition switch-operated starter solenoid, usually mounted near the positive post of the battery. When this control circuit is closed, current flows through a hollow coil (called a drive coil) that attracts a movable pole shoe.

As soon as the starter drive has engaged the engine flywheel, a tang on the movable pole shoe "opens" a set of contact points. The contact points provide the ground return path for the drive coil operation. After these grounding contacts are opened, all of the starter current can flow through the remaining three field coils and through the brushes to the armature, causing the starter to operate.

The movable pole shoe is held down (which keeps the starter drive engaged) by a smaller coil on the inside of the main drive coil. This coil, called the *holding coil*, is strong enough to hold the starter drive engaged while permitting the flow of the maximum possible current to operate the starter. ● **SEE FIGURE 30–24.**

ADVANTAGES The movable metal pole shoe is attached to and engages the starter drive with a lever (called the plunger lever). As a result, this type of starter does not use a solenoid to engage the starter drive.

FIGURE 30–24 A Ford movable pole shoe starter.

DISADVANTAGES If the grounding contact points are severely pitted, the starter may not operate the starter drive or the starter motor because of the resulting poor ground for the drive coil. If the contact points are bent or damaged enough to prevent them from opening, the starter will "clunk" the starter drive into engagement but will not allow the starter motor to operate.

SOLENOID-OPERATED STARTERS

SOLENOID OPERATION A **starter solenoid** is an electromagnetic switch containing two separate, but connected, electromagnetic windings. This switch is used to engage the starter drive and control the current from the battery to the starter motor.

SOLENOID WINDINGS The two internal windings contain approximately the same number of turns but are made from different-gauge wire. Both windings together produce a strong magnetic field that pulls a metal plunger into the solenoid. The plunger is attached to the starter drive through a shift fork lever. When the ignition switch is turned to the start position, the motion of the plunger into the solenoid causes the starter drive to move into mesh with the flywheel ring gear.

1. The heavier-gauge winding (called the **pull-in winding**) is needed to draw the plunger into the solenoid and is grounded through the starter motor.

2. The lighter-gauge winding (called the **hold-in winding**), which is grounded through the starter frame, produces enough magnetic force to keep the plunger in position. The main purpose of using two separate windings is to permit as much current as possible to operate the starter and yet provide the strong magnetic field required to move the starter drive into engagement. ● **SEE FIGURE 30–25.**

OPERATION

1. The solenoid operates as soon as the ignition or computer- controlled relay energizes the "S" (start) terminals. At that instant, the plunger is drawn into the solenoid enough to engage the starter drive.

2. The plunger makes contact with a metal disk that connects the battery terminal post of the solenoid to the motor terminal. This permits full battery current to flow through the solenoid to operate the starter motor.

3. The contact disk also electrically disconnects the pull-in winding. The solenoid *has* to work to supply current to the starter. Therefore, if the starter motor operates at all, the solenoid is working, even though it may have high external resistance that could cause slow starter motor operation.

FIGURE 30–25 Wiring diagram of a typical starter solenoid. Notice that both the pull-in winding and the hold-in winding are energized when the ignition switch is first turned to the "start" position. As soon as the solenoid contact disk makes electrical contact with both the B and M terminals, the battery current is conducted to the starter motor and electrically neutralizes the pull-in winding.

? FREQUENTLY ASKED QUESTION

How Are Starters Made So Small?

Starters and most components in a vehicle are being made as small and as light in weight as possible to help increase vehicle performance and fuel economy. A starter can be constructed smaller due to the use of gear reduction and permanent magnets to achieve the same cranking torque as a straight drive starter, but using much smaller components. ● **SEE FIGURE 30–26** for an example of an automotive starter armature that is palm size.

FIGURE 30–26 A palm-size starter armature.

SUMMARY

1. All starter motors use the principle of magnetic interaction between the field coils attached to the housing and the magnetic field of the armature.
2. The control circuit includes the ignition switch, neutral safety (clutch) switch, and solenoid.
3. The power circuit includes the battery, battery cables, solenoid, and starter motor.
4. The parts of a typical starter include the main field housing, commutator-end (or brush-end) housing, drive-end housing, brushes, armature, and starter drive.

REVIEW QUESTIONS

1. What is the difference between the control circuit and the power (motor) circuit sections of a typical cranking circuit?
2. What are the parts of a typical starter?
3. Why does a gear-reduction unit reduce the amount of current required by the starter motor?
4. What are the symptoms of a defective starter drive?

CHAPTER QUIZ

1. Starter motors operate on the principle that _____.
   a. The field coils rotate in the opposite direction from the armature
   b. Opposite magnetic poles repel
   c. Like magnetic poles repel
   d. The armature rotates from a strong magnetic field toward a weaker magnetic field
2. Series-wound electric motors _____.
   a. Produce electrical power
   b. Produce maximum power at 0 RPM
   c. Produce maximum power at high RPM
   d. Use a shunt coil
3. Technician A says that a defective solenoid can cause a starter whine. Technician B says that a defective starter drive can cause a starter whining noise. Which technician is correct?
   a. Technician A only
   b. Technician B only
   c. Both Technicians A and B
   d. Neither Technician A nor B
4. The neutral safety switch is located _____.
   a. Between the starter solenoid and the starter motor
   b. Inside the ignition switch itself
   c. Between the ignition switch and the starter solenoid
   d. In the battery cable between the battery and the starter solenoid

5. The brushes are used to transfer electrical power between _____.
   a. Field coils and the armature
   b. The commutator segments
   c. The solenoid and the field coils
   d. The armature and the solenoid
6. The faster a starter motor rotates, _____.
   a. The more current it draws from the battery
   b. The less CEMF is generated
   c. The less current it draws from the battery
   d. The greater the amount of torque produced
7. Normal cranking speed of the engine is about _____.
   a. 2,000 RPM   b. 1,500 RPM
   c. 1,000 RPM   d. 200 RPM
8. A starter motor rotates about _____ times faster than the engine.
   a. 18   b. 10
   c. 5   d. 2
9. Permanent magnets are commonly used for what part of the starter?
   a. Armature   b. Solenoid
   c. Field coils   d. Commutator
10. What unit contains a hold-in winding and a pull-in winding?
   a. Field coil   b. Starter solenoid
   c. Armature   d. Ignition switch

chapter 31

CRANKING SYSTEM DIAGNOSIS AND SERVICE

OBJECTIVES: **After studying Chapter 31, the reader will be able to:** • Prepare for ASE Electrical/Electronic Systems (A6) certification test content area "C" (Starting System Diagnosis and Repair). • Explain how to disassemble and reassemble a starter motor and solenoid. • Discuss how to perform a voltage drop test on the cranking circuit. • Describe how to perform cranking system repair procedures. • Describe testing and repair procedures of the cranking circuit and components.

KEY TERMS: • Bench testing 320 • Growler 318 • Shims 320 • Voltage drop 315

STARTING SYSTEM TROUBLESHOOTING PROCEDURE

OVERVIEW The proper operation of the starting system depends on a good battery, good cables and connections, and a good starter motor. Because a starting problem can be caused by a defective component anywhere in the starting circuit, it is important to check for the proper operation of each part of the circuit to diagnose and repair the problem quickly.

STEPS INVOLVED Following are the steps involved in the diagnosis of a fault in the cranking circuit.

STEP 1 **Verify the customer concern.** Sometimes the customer is not aware of how the cranking system is supposed to work, especially if it is computer controlled.

STEP 2 **Visually inspect the battery and battery connections.** The starter is the highest amperage draw device used in a vehicle and any faults, such as corrosion on battery terminals, can cause cranking system problems.

STEP 3 **Test battery condition.** Perform a battery load or conductance test on the battery to be sure that the battery is capable of supplying the necessary current for the starter.

STEP 4 **Check the control circuit.** An open or high resistance anywhere in the control circuit can cause the starter motor to not engage. Items to check include:
- "S" terminal of the starter solenoid
- Neutral safety or clutch switch

THEFT DETERRENT
INDICATOR LAMP

FIGURE 31–1 A theft deterrent indicator lamp on the dash. A flashing lamp usually indicates a fault in the system, and the engine may not start.

- Starter enable relay (if equipped)
- Antitheft system fault (If the engine does not crank or start and the theft indicator light is on or flashing, there is likely a fault in the theft deterrent system. Check service information for the exact procedures to follow before attempting to service the cranking circuit. ● **SEE FIGURE 31–1.**)

STEP 5 **Check voltage drop of the starter circuit.** Any high resistance in either the power side or ground side of the starter circuit will cause the starter to rotate slowly or not at all.

VOLTAGE DROP TESTING

PURPOSE **Voltage drop** is the drop in voltage that occurs when current is flowing through a resistance. For example, a voltage drop is the difference between voltage at the source and voltage at the electrical device to which it is flowing. The higher the voltage drop is, the greater the resistance in the circuit. Even though voltage drop testing can be performed on any electrical circuit, the most common areas of testing include the cranking circuit and the charging circuit wiring and connections. Voltage drop testing should be performed on both the power side and ground side of the circuit.

A high-voltage drop (high resistance) in the cranking circuit wiring can cause slow engine cranking with less than normal starter amperage drain as a result of the excessive circuit resistance. If the voltage drop is high enough, such as that caused by dirty battery terminals, the starter may not operate. A typical symptom of high resistance in the cranking circuit is a "clicking" of the starter solenoid.

TECH TIP

Voltage Drop Is Resistance

Many technicians have asked, "Why measure voltage drop when the resistance can be easily measured using an ohmmeter?" Think of a battery cable with all the strands of the cable broken, except for one strand. If an ohmmeter were used to measure the resistance of the cable, the reading would be very low, probably less than 1 ohm. However, the cable is not capable of conducting the amount of current necessary to crank the engine. In less severe cases, several strands can be broken, thereby affecting the operation of the starter motor. Although the resistance of the battery cable will not indicate an increase, the restriction to current flow will cause heat and a drop of voltage available at the starter. Because resistance is not effective until current flows, measuring the voltage drop (differences in voltage between two points) is the most accurate method of determining the true resistance in a circuit.

How much is too much? According to Bosch Corporation, all electrical circuits should have a maximum of 3% loss of the circuit voltage to resistance. Therefore, in a 12-volt circuit, the maximum loss of voltage in cables and connections should be 0.36 volt ($12 \times 0.03 = 0.36$ volt). The remaining 97% of the circuit voltage (11.64 volts) is available to operate the electrical device (load). Just remember:

- Low-voltage drop = Low resistance
- High-voltage drop = High resistance

TEST PROCEDURE Voltage drop testing of the wire involves connecting a voltmeter set to read DC volts to the suspected high-resistance cable ends and cranking the engine. ● **SEE FIGURES 31–2 THROUGH 31–4.**

TECH TIP

A Warm Cable Equals High Resistance

If a cable or connection is warm to the touch, there is electrical resistance in the cable or connection. The resistance changes electrical energy into heat energy. Therefore, if a voltmeter is not available, touch the battery cables and connections while cranking the engine. If any cable or connection is hot to the touch, it should be cleaned or replaced.

NOTE: Before a difference in voltage (voltage drop) can be measured between the ends of a battery cable, current must be flowing through the cable. *Resistance is not effective unless current is flowing.* If the engine is not being cranked, current is not flowing through the battery cables and the voltage drop cannot be measured.

STEP 1 Disable the ignition or fuel injection as follows:
- Disconnect the primary (low-voltage) electrical connection(s) from the ignition module or ignition coils.
- Remove the fuel-injection fuse or relay, or the electrical connection leading to all of the fuel injectors.

CAUTION: Never disconnect the high-voltage ignition wires unless they are connected to ground. The high voltage that could occur when cranking can cause the ignition coil to fail (arc internally).

STEP 2 Connect one lead of the voltmeter to the starter motor battery terminal and the other end to the positive battery terminal.

STEP 3 Crank the engine and observe the reading while cranking. (Disregard the first higher reading.) The reading should be less than 0.20 volt (200 mV).

STEP 4 If accessible, test the voltage drop across the "B" and "M" terminals of the starter solenoid with the engine cranking. The voltage drop should be less than 0.20 volt (200 mV).

STEP 5 Repeat the voltage drop on the ground side of the cranking circuit by connecting one voltmeter lead to the negative battery terminal and the other at the starter housing. Crank the engine and observe the voltmeter display. The voltage drop should be less than 0.2 volt (200 mV).

FIGURE 31–2 Voltmeter hookups for voltage drop testing of a solenoid-type cranking circuit.

FIGURE 31–3 Voltmeter hookups for voltage drop testing of a Ford cranking circuit.

FIGURE 31-4 To test the voltage drop of the battery cable connection, place one voltmeter lead on the battery terminal and the other voltmeter lead on the cable end and crank the engine. The voltmeter will read the difference in voltage between the two leads, which should not exceed 0.20 volt (200 mV).

CONTROL CIRCUIT TESTING

PARTS INVOLVED The control circuit for the starting circuit includes the battery, ignition switch, neutral or clutch safety switch, theft deterrent system, and starter solenoid. When the ignition switch is rotated to the start position, current flows through the ignition switch and neutral safety switch to activate the solenoid. High current then flows directly from the battery through the solenoid and to the starter motor. Therefore, an open or break anywhere in the control circuit will prevent the operation of the starter motor.

 TECH TIP

Watch the Dome Light

When diagnosing any starter-related problem, open the door of the vehicle and observe the brightness of the dome or interior light(s).

The brightness of any electrical lamp is proportional to the voltage of the battery.

Normal operation of the starter results in a slight dimming of the dome light.

If the light remains bright, the problem is usually an open in the control circuit.

If the light goes out or almost goes out, there could be a problem with the following:

■ A shorted or grounded armature of field coils inside the starter
■ Loose or corroded battery connections or cables
■ Weak or discharged battery

If a starter is inoperative, first check for voltage at the "S" (start) terminal of the starter solenoid. Check for faults with the following:

■ Neutral safety or clutch switch
■ Blown crank fuse
■ Open at the ignition switch in the crank position

Some models with antitheft controls use a relay to open this control circuit to prevent starter operation.

STARTER AMPERAGE TEST

REASON FOR A STARTER AMPERAGE TEST A starter should be tested to see if the reason for slow or no cranking is due to a fault with the starter motor or another problem. A voltage drop test is used to find out if the battery cables and connections are okay. A starter amperage draw test determines if the starter motor is the cause of a no or slow cranking concern.

TEST PREPARATION Before performing a starter amperage test, be certain that the battery is sufficiently charged (75% or more) and capable of supplying adequate starting current. Connect a starter amperage tester following the tester's instructions. ● **SEE FIGURE 31-5.**

A starter amperage test should be performed when the starter fails to operate normally (is slow in cranking) or as part of a routine electrical system inspection.

SPECIFICATIONS Some service manuals specify normal starter amperage for starter motors being tested on the vehicle; however, most service manuals only give the specifications for bench testing a starter without a load applied. These specifications are helpful in making certain that a repaired starter meets exact specifications, but they do not apply to starter testing on the vehicle. If exact specifications are not available,

FIGURE 31-5 A starter amperage tester uses an amp probe around the positive or negative battery cables.

the following can be used as general *maximum* amperage draw specifications for testing a starter on the vehicle.

- **4-cylinder engines** = 150 to 185 amperes (normally less than 100 A) at room temperature

- **6-cylinder engines** = 160 to 200 amperes (normally less than 125 A) at room temperature

- **8-cylinder engines** = 185 to 250 amperes (normally less than 150 A) at room temperature

Excessive current draw may indicate one or more of the following:

1. Binding of starter armature as a result of worn bushings

2. Oil too thick (viscosity too high) for weather conditions

3. Shorted or grounded starter windings or cables

4. Tight or seized engine

5. Shorted starter motor (usually caused by fault with the field coils or armature)
   - High mechanical resistance = High starter amperage draw
   - High electrical resistance = Low starter amperage draw

Lower amperage draw and slow or no cranking may indicate one or more of the following:

- Dirty or corroded battery connections
- High internal resistance in the battery cable(s)
- High internal starter motor resistance
- Poor ground connection between the starter motor and the engine block

FIGURE 31–6 The starter is located under the intake manifold on this Cadillac Northstar engine.

STARTER REMOVAL

PROCEDURE After testing has confirmed that a starter motor may need to be replaced, most vehicle manufacturers recommend the following general steps and procedures.

STEP 1 Disconnect the negative battery cable.

STEP 2 Hoist the vehicle safely.

> NOTE: This step may not be necessary. Check service information for the specified procedure for the vehicle being serviced. Some starters are located under the intake manifold. ● SEE FIGURE 31–6.

STEP 3 Remove the starter retaining bolts and lower the starter to gain access to the wire(s) connection(s) on the starter.

STEP 4 Disconnect and label the wire(s) from the starter and remove the starter.

STEP 5 Inspect the flywheel (flexplate) for ring gear damage. Also check that the mounting holes are clean and the mounting flange is clean and smooth. Service as needed.

STARTER MOTOR SERVICE

PURPOSE Most starter motors are replaced as an assembly or not easily disassembled or serviced. However, some starters, especially on classic muscle or collector vehicles, can be serviced.

DISASSEMBLY PROCEDURE Disassembly of a starter motor usually includes the following steps.

STEP 1 Remove the starter solenoid assembly.

STEP 2 Mark the location of the through bolts on the field housing to help align them during reassembly.

STEP 3 Remove the drive-end housing and then the armature assembly.
   ● **SEE FIGURE 31–7.**

INSPECTION AND TESTING The various parts should be inspected and tested to see if the components can be used to restore the starter to serviceable condition.

- **Solenoid.** Check the resistance of the solenoid winding. The solenoid can be tested using an ohmmeter to check for the proper resistance in the hold-in and pull-in windings. ● **SEE FIGURE 31–8.**

Most technicians replace the solenoid whenever the starter is replaced and is usually included with a replacement starter.

- **Starter armature.** After the starter drive has been removed from the armature, it can be checked for runout using a dial indicator and V-blocks, as shown in
   ● **FIGURE 31–9.**

- **Growler.** Because the loops of copper wire are interconnected in the armature of a starter, an armature can be accurately tested only by use of a **growler**. A growler is a 110-volt AC test unit that generates an alternating

FIGURE 31–7 An exploded view of a typical solenoid-operated starter.

FIGURE 31–8 GM solenoid ohmmeter check. The reading between 1 and 3 (S terminal and ground) should be 0.4 to 0.6 ohm (hold-in winding). The reading between 1 and 2 (S terminal and M terminal) should be 0.2 to 0.4 ohm (pull-in winding).

(60 hertz) magnetic field around an armature. A starter armature is placed into the V-shaped top portion of a laminated soft-iron core surrounded by a coil of copper wire. Plug the growler into a 110-volt outlet and then follow the instructions for testing the armature.

FIGURE 31–9 Measuring an armature shaft for runout using a dial indicator and V-blocks.

- **Starter motor field coils.** With the armature removed from the starter motor, the field coils should be tested for opens and grounds using a powered test light or an ohmmeter. To test for a grounded field coil, touch one lead of the tester to a field brush (insulated or hot) and the other end to the starter field housing. The ohmmeter should indicate infinity (no continuity), and the test light should *not* light. If there is continuity, replace the field coil housing assembly. The ground brushes should show continuity to the starter housing.

NOTE: Many starters use removable field coils. These coils must be rewound using the proper equipment and insulating materials. Usually, the cost involved in replacing defective field coils exceeds the cost of a replacement starter.

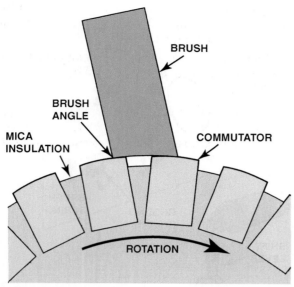

FIGURE 31–10 Replacement starter brushes should be installed so the beveled edge matches the rotation of the commutator.

- **Starter brush inspection.** Starter brushes should be replaced if the brush length is less than half of its original length (less than 0.5 in. [13 mm]). On some models of starter motors, the field brushes are serviced with the field coil assembly and the ground brushes with the brush holder. Many starters use brushes that are held in with screws and are easily replaced, whereas other starters may require soldering to remove and replace the brushes. ● **SEE FIGURE 31–10.**

BENCH TESTING

Every starter should be tested before installation in a vehicle. **Bench testing** is the usual method and involves clamping the starter in a vise to prevent rotation during operation and connecting heavy-gauge jumper wires (minimum 4 gauge) to both a battery known to be good and the starter. The starter motor should rotate as fast as specifications indicate and not draw more than the free-spinning amperage permitted. A typical amperage specification for a starter being tested on a bench (not installed in a vehicle) usually ranges from 60 to 100 amperes.

STARTER INSTALLATION

After verifying that the starter assembly is functioning correctly, verify that the negative battery cable has been disconnected. Then safely hoist the vehicle, if necessary. Following are the usual steps to install a starter. Be sure to check service information for the exact procedures to follow for the vehicle being serviced.

STEP 1 Check service information for the exact wiring connections to the starter and/or solenoid.

STEP 2 Verify that all electrical connections on the starter motor and/or solenoid are correct for the vehicle and that they are in good condition.

NOTE: Be sure that the locking nuts for the studs are tight. Often, the retaining nut that holds the wire to the stud will be properly tightened, but if the stud itself is loose, cranking problems can occur.

STEP 3 Attach the power and control wires.

STEP 4 Install the starter, and torque all the fasteners to factory specifications and tighten evenly.

STEP 5 Perform a starter amperage draw test and check for proper engine cranking.

CAUTION: Be sure to install all factory heat shields to help ensure problem starter operation under all weather and driving conditions.

STARTER DRIVE-TO-FLYWHEEL CLEARANCE

NEED FOR SHIMS For the proper operation of the starter and absence of abnormal starter noise, there must be a slight clearance between the starter pinion and the engine flywheel ring gear. Many starters use **shims,** which are thin metal strips between the flywheel and the engine block mounting pad to provide the proper clearance. ● **SEE FIGURE 31–11.**

Some manufacturers use shims under the starter drive-end housings during production. Other manufacturers *grind* the mounting pads at the factory for proper starter pinion gear clearance. If a GM starter is replaced, the starter pinion should be checked and corrected as necessary to prevent starter damage and excessive noise.

SYMPTOMS OF CLEARANCE PROBLEMS

- If the clearance is too great, the starter will produce a high-pitched whine *during* cranking.

- If the clearance is too small, the starter may bind, crank slowly, or produce a high-pitched whine *after* the engine starts, just as the ignition key is released.

PROCEDURE FOR PROPER CLEARANCE To be sure that the starter is shimmed correctly, use the following procedure.

STEP 1 Place the starter in position and finger-tighten the mounting bolts.

STEP 2 Use a 1/8 in. diameter drill bit (or gauge tool) and insert between the armature shaft and a tooth of the engine flywheel.

SHIM

1/2 SHIM

OUTSIDE MOUNTING PAD

FLYWHEEL

GAUGE TOOL   (1/8" DIAMETER DRILL BIT OR EQUAL)

ARMATURE SHAFT

FIGURE 31–11 A shim (or half shim) may be needed to provide the proper clearance between the flywheel teeth of the engine and the pinion teeth of the starter.

TECH TIP

Reuse Drive-End Housing to Be Sure

Most GM starter motors use a pad mount and attach to the engine with bolts through the drive-end (nose) housing. Many times when a starter is replaced on a GM vehicle, the starter makes noise because of improper starter pinion-to-engine flywheel ring gear clearance. Instead of spending a lot of time shimming the new starter, simply remove the drive-end housing from the original starter and install it on the replacement starter. Service the bushing in the drive-end housing if needed. Because the original starter did not produce excessive gear engagement noise, the replacement starter will also be okay. Reuse any shims that were used with the original starter. This is preferable to removing and reinstalling the replacement starter several times until the proper clearance is determined.

STEP 3 If the gauge tool cannot be inserted, use a full-length shim across both mounting holes to move the starter away from the flywheel.

STEP 4 Remove a shim (or shims) if the gauge tool is loose between the shaft and the tooth of the engine flywheel.

STEP 5 If no shims have been used and the fit of the gauge tool is too loose, add a half shim to the outside pad only. This moves the starter closer to the teeth of the engine flywheel.

STARTING SYSTEM SYMPTOM GUIDE

The following list will assist technicians in troubleshooting starting systems.

Problem	Possible Causes
1. Starter motor whines	1. Possible defective starter drive; worn starter drive engagement yoke; defective flywheel; improper starter drive to flywheel clearance
2. Starter rotates slowly	2. Possible high resistance in the battery cables or connections; possible defective or discharged battery; possible worn starter bushings, causing the starter armature to drag on the field coils; possible worn starter brushes or weak brush springs; possible defective (open or shorted) field coil
3. Starter fails to rotate	3. Possible defective ignition switch or neutral safety switch, or open in the starter motor control circuit; theft deterrent system fault; possible defective starter solenoid
4. Starter produces grinding noise	4. Possible defective starter drive unit; possible defective flywheel; possible incorrect distance between the starter pinion and the flywheel; possible cracked or broken starter drive-end housing; worn or damaged flywheel or ring gear teeth
5. Starter clicks when engaged	5. Low battery voltage; loose or corroded battery connections

STARTER OVERHAUL

1 This dirty and greasy starter can be restored to useful service.

2 The connecting wire between the solenoid and the starter is removed.

3 An old starter field housing is being used to support the drive-end housing of the starter as it is being disassembled. This rebuilder is using an electric impact wrench to remove the solenoid fasteners.

4 A Torx driver is used to remove the solenoid attaching screws.

5 After the retaining screws have been removed, the solenoid can be separated from the starter motor. This rebuilder always replaces the solenoid.

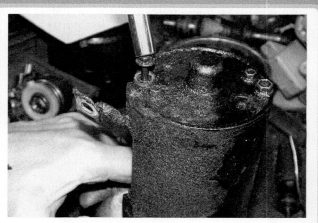

6 The through-bolts are being removed.

7 The brush end plate is removed.

8 The armature assembly is removed from the field frame.

9 Notice that the length of a direct-drive starter armature (top) is the same length as the overall length of a gear-reduction armature except smaller in diameter.

10 A light tap with a hammer dislodges the armature thrust ball (in the palm of the hand) from the center of the gear reduction assembly.

11 This figure shows the planetary ring gear and pinion gears.

12 A close-up of one of the planetary gears, which shows the small needle bearings on the inside.

CONTINUED ▶

13 The clip is removed from the shaft so the planetary gear assembly can be separated and inspected.

14 The shaft assembly is being separated from the stationary gear assembly.

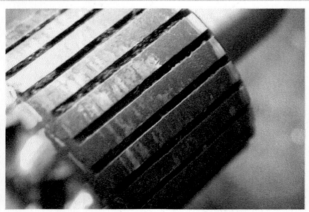

15 The commutator on the armature is discolored and the brushes may not have been making good contact with the segments.

16 All of the starter components are placed in a tumbler with water-based cleaner. The armature is installed in a lathe and the commutator is resurfaced using emery cloth.

17 The finished commutator looks like new.

18 Starter reassembly begins by installing a new starter drive on the shaft assembly. The stop ring and stop ring retainer are then installed.

19 The gear-reduction assembly is positioned along with the shift fork (drive lever) into the cleaned drive-end housing.

20 After gear retainer has been installed over the gear reduction assembly, the armature is installed.

21 New brushes are being installed into the brush holder assembly.

22 The brush end plate and the through-bolts are installed, being sure that the ground connection for the brushes is clean and tight.

23 This starter was restored to useful service by replacing the solenoid, the brushes, and the starter drive assembly plus a thorough cleaning and attention to detail in the reassembly.

SUMMARY

1. Proper operation and testing of the starter motor depends on the battery being at least 75% charged and the battery cables being of the correct size (gauge) and having no more than a 0.2-volt drop.

2. Voltage drop testing includes cranking the engine, measuring the drop in voltage from the battery to the starter, and measuring the drop in voltage from the negative terminal of the battery to the engine block.

3. The cranking circuit should be tested for proper amperage draw.

4. An open in the control circuit can prevent starter motor operation.

REVIEW QUESTIONS

1. What are the parts of the cranking circuit?

2. What are the steps taken to perform a voltage drop test of the cranking circuit?

3. What are the steps necessary to replace a starter?

CHAPTER QUIZ

1. A growler is used to test what starter component?
   a. Field coils
   b. Armatures
   c. Commutator
   d. Solenoid

2. Two technicians are discussing what could be the cause of slow cranking and excessive current draw. Technician A says that an engine mechanical fault could be the cause. Technician B says that the starter motor could be binding or defective. Which technician is correct?
   a. Technician A only
   b. Technician B only
   c. Both Technicians A and B
   d. Neither Technician A nor B

3. A V-6 is being checked for starter amperage draw. The initial surge current was about 210 amperes and about 160 amperes during cranking. Technician A says the starter is defective and should be replaced because the current flow exceeds 200 amperes. Technician B says this is normal current draw for a starter motor on a V-6 engine. Which technician is correct?
   a. Technician A only
   b. Technician B only
   c. Both Technicians A and B
   d. Neither Technician A nor B

4. What component or circuit can keep the engine from cranking?
   a. Antitheft
   b. Solenoid
   c. Ignition switch
   d. All of the above

5. Technician A says that a discharged battery (lower than normal battery voltage) can cause solenoid clicking. Technician B says that a discharged battery or dirty (corroded) battery cables can cause solenoid clicking. Which technician is correct?
   a. Technician A only
   b. Technician B only
   c. Both Technicians A and B
   d. Neither Technician A nor B

6. Slow cranking by the starter can be caused by all *except* _____.
   a. A low or discharged battery
   b. Corroded or dirty battery cables
   c. Engine mechanical problems
   d. An open neutral safety switch

7. Bench testing of a starter should be done _____.
   a. After reassembling an old starter
   b. Before installing a new starter
   c. After removing the old starter
   d. Both a and b

8. If the clearance between the starter pinion and the engine flywheel is too great, _____.
   a. The starter will produce a high-pitched whine during cranking
   b. The starter will produce a high-pitched whine after the engine starts
   c. The starter drive will not rotate at all
   d. The solenoid will not engage the starter drive unit

9. A technician connects one lead of a digital voltmeter to the positive (1) terminal of the battery and the other meter lead to the battery terminal (B) of the starter solenoid and then cranks the engine. During cranking, the voltmeter displays a reading of 878 mV. Technician A says that this reading indicates that the positive battery cable has too high resistance. Technician B says that this reading indicates that the starter is defective. Which technician is correct?
   a. Technician A only
   b. Technician B only
   c. Both Technicians A and B
   d. Neither Technician A nor B

10. A vehicle equipped with a V-8 engine does not crank fast enough to start. Technician A says the battery could be discharged or defective. Technician B says that the negative cable could be loose at the battery. Which technician is correct?
    a. Technician A only
    b. Technician B only
    c. Both Technicians A and B
    d. Neither Technician A nor B

chapter
32

CHARGING SYSTEM

OBJECTIVES: **After studying Chapter 32, the reader will be able to:** • Prepare for ASE Electrical/Electronic Systems (A6) certification test content area "D" (Charging System Diagnosis and Repair). • List the parts of a typical alternator. • Describe how an alternator works. • Explain how the powertrain control module (PCM) controls the charging circuit.

KEY TERMS: • Alternator 327 • Claw poles 329 • Delta winding 333 • Diodes 330 • Drive-end (DE) housing 327 • Duty cycle 336 • EPM 336 • IDP 328 • OAD 328 • OAP 327 • Rectifier 330 • Rotor 329 • Slip-ring-end (SRE) housing 327 • Stator 330 • Thermistor 335

PRINCIPLES OF ALTERNATOR OPERATION

TERMINOLOGY It is the purpose and function of the charging system to keep the battery fully charged. The Society of Automotive Engineers (SAE) term for the unit that generates electricity is *generator.* The term **alternator** is most commonly used in the trade and will be used in this title.

PRINCIPLES All electrical alternators use the principle of electromagnetic induction to generate electrical power from mechanical power. Electromagnetic induction involves the generation of an electrical current in a conductor when the conductor is moved through a magnetic field. The amount of current generated can be increased by the following factors.

1. Increasing the *speed* of the conductors through the magnetic field
2. Increasing the *number* of conductors passing through the magnetic field
3. Increasing the *strength* of the magnetic field

CHANGING AC TO DC An alternator generates an alternating current (AC) because the current changes polarity during the alternator's rotation. However, a battery cannot "store" alternating current; therefore, this alternating current is changed to direct current (DC) by diodes inside the alternator. Diodes are one-way electrical check valves that permit current to flow in only one direction.

ALTERNATOR CONSTRUCTION

HOUSING An alternator is constructed using a two-piece cast aluminum housing. Aluminum is used because of its lightweight, nonmagnetic properties and heat transfer properties needed to help keep the alternator cool. A front ball bearing is pressed into the front housing, called the **drive-end (DE) housing,** to provide the support and friction reduction necessary for the belt-driven rotor assembly. The rear housing, or the **slip-ring-end (SRE) housing,** usually contains either a roller bearing or ball bearing support for the rotor and mounting for the brushes, diodes, and internal voltage regulator (if so equipped). ● **SEE FIGURES 32–1 AND 32–2.**

ALTERNATOR OVERRUNNING PULLEYS

PURPOSE AND FUNCTION Many alternators are equipped with an **overrunning alternator pulley (OAP),** also called an *overrunning clutch pulley* or an *alternator clutch pulley.* The purpose of this pulley is to help eliminate noise and vibration in the accessory drive belt system, especially when the engine is at idle speed. At idle, engine impulses are transmitted to the alternator through the accessory drive belt. The mass of the rotor of the alternator tends to want to keep spinning, but the engine crankshaft speeds up and slows down

FIGURE 32–1 A typical alternator on a Chevrolet V-8 engine.

FIGURE 32–3 An OAP on a Chevrolet Corvette alternator.

SLIP-RING-END HOUSING

DRIVE-END HOUSING

STATOR

FIGURE 32–2 The end frame toward the drive belt is called the drive-end housing and the rear section is called the slip-ring-end housing.

BEARINGS

CLUTCH

CENTER HUB

OUTER HUB

OVERUNNING ALTERNATOR PULLEY (OAP)

FIGURE 32–4 An exploded view of an overrunning alternator pulley showing all of the internal parts.

slightly due to the power impulses. Using a one-way clutch in the alternator pulley allows the belt to apply power to the alternator in only one direction, thereby reducing fluctuations in the belt. ● SEE FIGURES 32–3 AND 32–4.

A conventional drive pulley attaches to the alternator (rotor) shaft with a nut and lock washer. In the overrunning clutch pulley, the inner race of the clutch acts as the nut as it screws on to the shaft. Special tools are required to remove and install this type of pulley.

Another type of alternator pulley uses a dampener spring inside, plus a one-way clutch. These units have the following names.

- **Isolating Decoupler Pulley (IDP)**
- Active Alternator Pulley (AAP)
- Alternator Decoupler Pulley (ADP)
- Alternator Overrunning Decoupler Pulley
- **Overrunning Alternator Dampener (OAD)** (most common term)

OAP or OAD pulleys are primarily used on vehicles equipped with diesel engines or on luxury vehicles where noise and vibration need to be kept at a minimum. Both are designed to:

- Reduce accessory drive belt noise
- Improve the life of the accessory drive belt
- Improve fuel economy by allowing the engine to be operated at a low idle speed

ALTERNATOR COMPONENTS AND OPERATION

ROTOR CONSTRUCTION The **rotor** is the rotating part of the alternator and is driven by the accessory drive belt. The rotor creates the magnetic field of the alternator and produces a current by electromagnetic induction in the stationary stator windings. The rotor is constructed of many turns of copper wire coated with a varnish insulation wound over an iron core. The iron core is attached to the rotor shaft.

 TECH TIP

Alternator Horsepower and Engine Operation

Many technicians are asked how much power certain accessories require. A 100 ampere alternator requires about 2 horsepower from the engine. One horsepower is equal to 746 watts. Watts are calculated by multiplying amperes times volts.

Power in watts = 100 A × 14.5 V = 1,450 W
hp = 746 W

Therefore, 1,450 watts is about 2 horsepower.

Allowing about 20% for mechanical and electrical losses adds another 0.4 horsepower. Therefore, when someone asks how much power it takes to produce 100 amperes from an alternator, the answer is 2.4 horsepower.

Many alternators delay the electrical load to prevent the engine from stumbling when a heavy electrical load is applied. The voltage regulator or vehicle computer is capable of gradually increasing the output of the alternator over a period of several minutes. Even though 2 horsepower does not sound like much, a sudden demand for 2 horsepower from an idling engine can cause the engine to run rough or stall. The difference in part numbers of various alternators is often an indication of the time interval over which the load is applied. Therefore, using the wrong replacement alternator could cause the engine to stall!

? **FREQUENTLY ASKED QUESTION**

Can I Install an OAP or an OAD to My Alternator?

Usually, no. An alternator needs to be equipped with the proper shaft to allow the installation of an OAP or OAD. This also means that a conventional pulley often cannot be used to replace a defective overrunning alternator pulley or dampener with a conventional pulley. Check service information for the exact procedure to follow.

 TECH TIP

Always Check the OAP or OAD First

Overrunning alternator pulleys and overrunning alternator dampeners can fail. The most common factor is the one-way clutch. If it fails, it can freewheel and not power the alternator or it can lock up and not provide the dampening as designed. If the charging system is not working, the OAP or OAD could be the cause, rather than a fault in the alternator itself.

In most cases, the entire alternator assembly will be replaced because each OAP or OAD is unique for each application and both require special tools to remove and replace.
● **SEE FIGURE 32–5.**

At both ends of the rotor windings are heavy-gauge metal plates bent over the windings with triangular fingers called **claw poles.** These pole fingers do not touch, but alternate or interlace, as shown in ● **FIGURE 32–6.**

HOW ROTORS CREATE MAGNETIC FIELDS The two ends of the rotor winding are connected to the rotor's slip rings. Current for the rotor flows from the battery into one brush that rides on one of the slip rings, then flows through the rotor winding, then exits the rotor through the other slip ring and brush. One alternator brush is considered to be the "positive" brush and one is considered to be the "negative" or "ground" brush. The voltage regulator is connected to either the positive or the negative brush and controls the field current through the rotor that controls the output of the alternator.

FIGURE 32–5 A special tool is needed to remove and install overrunning alternator pulleys or dampeners.

INTERNAL COOLING FAN   ROTOR POLES   FRONT BEARING   DRIVE PULLEY

FIGURE 32–6 A cutaway of an alternator, showing the rotor and cooling fan that is used to force air through the unit to remove the heat created when it is charging the battery and supplying electrical power for the vehicle.

If current flows through the rotor windings, the metal pole pieces at each end of the rotor become electromagnets. Whether a north or a south pole magnet is created depends on the *direction* in which the wire coil is wound. Because the pole pieces are attached to each end of the rotor, one pole piece will be a north pole magnet. The other pole piece is on the opposite end of the rotor and therefore is viewed as being wound in the opposite direction, creating a south pole. Therefore, the rotor fingers are alternating north and south magnetic poles. The magnetic fields are created between the alternating pole piece fingers. These individual magnetic fields produce a current by electromagnetic induction in the stationary stator windings. ● **SEE FIGURE 32–7.**

ROTOR CURRENT The current necessary for the field (rotor) windings is conducted through slip rings with carbon brushes. The maximum rated alternator output in amperes depends on the number and gauge of the rotor windings. Substituting rotors from one alternator to another can greatly affect maximum output. Many commercially rebuilt alternators are tested and then display a sticker to indicate their tested output. The original rating stamped on the housing is then ground off.

The current for the field is controlled by the voltage regulator and is conducted to the slip rings through carbon brushes. The brushes conduct only the field current which is usually between 2 and 5 amperes.

STATOR CONSTRUCTION The **stator** consists of the stationary coil windings inside the alternator. The stator is supported between the two halves of the alternator housing, with three copper wire windings that are wound on a laminated metal core.

As the rotor revolves, its moving magnetic field induces a current in the stator windings. ● **SEE FIGURE 32–8.**

MAGNETIC LINES OF FORCE

SLIP RINGS

ROTOR ASSEMBLY

ROTOR WINDINGS (ALTERNATOR FIELD)

FIGURE 32–7 Rotor assembly of a typical alternator. Current through the slip rings causes the "fingers" of the rotor to become alternating north and south magnetic poles. As the rotor revolves, these magnetic lines of force induce a current in the stator windings.

DIODES **Diodes** are constructed of a semiconductor material (usually silicon) and operate as a one-way electrical check valve that permits the current to flow in only one direction. Alternators often use six diodes (one positive and one negative set for each of the three stator windings) to convert alternating current to direct current.

Diodes used in alternators are included in a single part called a **rectifier,** or *rectifier bridge*. A rectifier not only includes the diodes (usually six), but also the cooling fins and connections for the stator windings and the voltage regulator. ● **SEE FIGURE 32–9.**

DIODE TRIO Some alternators are equipped with a diode trio that supplies current to the brushes from the stator windings. A diode trio uses three diodes, in one housing, with one diode for each of the three stator windings and then one output terminal.

HOW AN ALTERNATOR WORKS

FIELD CURRENT IS PRODUCED A rotor inside an alternator is turned by a belt and drive pulley which are turned by the engine. The magnetic field of the rotor generates a current in the stator windings by electromagnetic induction. ● **SEE FIGURE 32–10.**

FIGURE 32–8 An exploded view of a typical alternator showing all of its internal parts including the stator windings.

FIGURE 32–9 A rectifier usually includes six diodes in one assembly and is used to rectify AC voltage from the stator windings into DC voltage suitable for use by the battery and electrical devices in the vehicle.

FIGURE 32–10 Magnetic lines of force cutting across a conductor induce a voltage and current in the conductor.

Field current flowing through the slip rings to the rotor creates an alternating north and south pole on the rotor, with a magnetic field between each finger of the rotor.

CURRENT IS INDUCED IN THE STATOR The induced current in the stator windings is an alternating current because of the alternating magnetic field of the rotor. The induced current starts to increase as the magnetic field starts to induce current in each winding of the stator. The current then peaks

FIGURE 32–11 A sine wave (shaped like the letter *S* on its side) voltage curve is created by one revolution of a winding as it rotates in a magnetic field.

when the magnetic field is the strongest and starts to decrease as the magnetic field moves away from the stator winding. Therefore, the current generated is described as being of a sine wave or alternating current pattern. ● **SEE FIGURE 32–11.**

As the rotor continues to rotate, this sine wave current is induced in each of the three windings of the stator.

Because each of the three windings generates a sine wave current, as shown in ● **FIGURE 32–12,** the resulting currents combine to form a three-phase voltage output.

The current induced in the stator windings connects to diodes (one-way electrical check valves) that permit the alternator output current to flow in only one direction. All alternators contain six diodes, one pair (a positive and a negative diode) for each of the three stator windings. Some

alternators contain eight diodes with another pair connected to the center connection of a wye-type stator.

WYE-CONNECTED STATORS The Y (pronounced "wye" and generally so written) type or star pattern is the most commonly used alternator stator winding connection. ● **SEE FIGURE 32–13.**

The output current with a wye-type stator connection is constant over a broad alternator speed range.

Current is induced in each winding by electromagnetic induction from the rotating magnetic fields of the rotor. In a wye-type stator connection, the currents must combine because two windings are always connected in series. ● **SEE FIGURE 32–14.**

FIGURE 32–12 When three windings (A, B, and C) are present in a stator, the resulting current generation is represented by the three sine waves. The voltages are 120 degrees out of phase. The connection of the individual phases produces a three-phase alternating voltage.

FIGURE 32–13 Wye-connected stator winding.

FIGURE 32–14 As the magnetic field, created in the rotor, cuts across the windings of the stator, a current is induced. Notice that the current path includes passing through one positive (+) diode on the way to the battery and one negative (−) diode as a complete circuit is completed through the rectifier and stator.

The current produced in each winding is added to the other windings' current and then flows through the diodes to the alternator output terminal. One-half of the current produced is available at the neutral junction (usually labeled "STA" for stator). The voltage at this center point is used by some alternator manufacturers (especially Ford) to control the charge indicator light or is used by the voltage regulator to control the rotor field current.

DELTA-CONNECTED STATORS The **delta winding** is connected in a triangular shape. Delta is a Greek letter shaped like a triangle. ● **SEE FIGURE 32–15.**

FIGURE 32–15 Delta-connected stator winding.

Current induced in each winding flows to the diodes in a parallel circuit. More current can flow through two parallel circuits than can flow through a series circuit (as in a wye-type stator connection).

Delta-connected stators are used on alternators where high output at high-alternator RPM is required. The delta-connected alternator can produce 73% more current than the same alternator with wye-type stator connections. For example, if an alternator with a wye-connected stator can produce 55 A, the *same* alternator with delta-connected stator windings can produce 73% more current, or 95 A (55 × 1.73 = 95). The delta-connected alternator, however, produces lower current at low speed and must be operated at high speed to produce its maximum output.

ALTERNATOR OUTPUT FACTORS

The output voltage and current of an alternator depend on the following factors.

1. **Speed of rotation.** Alternator output is increased with alternator rotational speed up to the alternator's maximum possible ampere output. Alternators normally rotate at a speed two to three times faster than engine speed, depending on the relative pulley sizes used for the belt drive. For example, if an engine is operating at 5000 RPM, the alternator will be rotating at about 15,000 RPM.

2. **Number of conductors.** A high-output alternator contains more turns of wire in the stator windings. Stator winding connections (whether wye or delta) also affect the maximum alternator output. ● **SEE FIGURE 32–16** for an example of a stator that has six rather than three windings, which greatly increases the amperage output of the alternator.

3. **Strength of the magnetic field.** If the magnetic field is strong, a high output is possible because the current generated by electromagnetic induction is dependent on the number of magnetic lines of force that are cut.

FIGURE 32–16 A stator assembly with six, rather than the normal three, windings.

a. The strength of the magnetic field can be increased by increasing the number of turns of conductor wire wound on the rotor. A higher output alternator rotor has more turns of wire than an alternator rotor with a low rated output.

b. The strength of the magnetic field also depends on the current through the field coil (rotor). Because magnetic field strength is measured in ampere-turns, the greater the amperage or the number of turns, or both, the greater the alternator output.

ALTERNATOR VOLTAGE REGULATION

PRINCIPLES
An automotive alternator must be able to produce electrical pressure (voltage) higher than battery voltage to charge the battery. Excessively high voltage can damage the battery, electrical components, and the lights of a vehicle. Basic principles include the following:

- If no (zero) amperes of current existed throughout the field coil of the alternator (rotor), alternator output would be zero because without field current a magnetic field does not exist.

- The field current required by most automotive alternators is less than 3 amperes. It is the *control* of the *field* current that controls the output of the alternator.

- Current for the rotor flows from the battery positive post, through the rotor positive brush, into the rotor field winding, and exits the rotor winding through the rotor ground brush. Most voltage regulators control field current by controlling the amount of field current through the ground brush.

- The voltage regulator simply opens the field circuit if the voltage reaches a predetermined level, then closes the field circuit again as necessary to maintain the correct charging voltage. ● **SEE FIGURE 32–17.**

- The electronic circuit of the voltage regulator cycles between 10 and 7,000 times per *second* as needed to accurately control the field current through the rotor, and therefore control the alternator output.

REGULATOR OPERATION

- The control of the field current is accomplished by opening and closing the *ground* side of the field circuit through the rotor on most alternators.

- The zener diode is a major electronic component that makes voltage regulation possible. A zener diode blocks current flow until a specific voltage is reached, then it permits current to flow. Alternator voltage from the stator and diodes is first sent through a thermistor, which changes resistance with temperature, and then to a zener diode. When the upper-limit voltage is reached, the zener diode conducts current to a transistor, which then opens the field (rotor) circuit. The electronics are usually housed in a separate part inside the alternator. ● **SEE FIGURES 32–18 AND 32–19.**

BATTERY CONDITION AND CHARGING VOLTAGE
If the automotive battery is discharged, its voltage will be lower than the voltage of a fully charged battery. The alternator will supply charging current, but it may not reach the maximum charging voltage. For example, if a vehicle is jump started and run at a fast idle (2,000 RPM), the charging voltage may be only 12 volts. In this case, the following may occur.

- As the battery becomes charged and the battery voltage increases, the charging voltage will also increase, until the voltage regulator limit is reached.

- Then the voltage regulator will start to control the charging voltage. A good, but discharged, battery should be able to convert into chemical energy all the current the alternator can produce. As long as alternator voltage is higher than battery voltage, current will flow from the alternator (high voltage) to the battery (lower voltage).

- Therefore, if a voltmeter is connected to a discharged battery with the engine running, it may indicate charging voltage that is lower than normally acceptable.

In other words, the condition and voltage of the battery *do* determine the charging rate of the alternator. It is often stated that the battery is the true "voltage regulator" and that the voltage regulator simply acts as the upper-limit voltage control. This is the reason why all charging system testing *must*

FIGURE 32–17 Typical voltage regulator range.

FIGURE 32–18 A typical electronic voltage regulator with the cover removed showing the circuits inside.

FIGURE 32–19 Typical General Motors SI-style alternator with an integral voltage regulator. Voltage present at terminal 2 is used to reverse bias the zener diode (D2) that controls TR2. The positive brush is fed by the ignition current (terminal I) plus current from the diode trio.

be performed with a reliable and known to be good battery, at least 75% charged, to be assured of accurate test results. If a discharged battery is used during charging system testing, tests could mistakenly indicate a defective alternator and/or voltage regulator and could cause the stator windings to overheat.

TEMPERATURE COMPENSATION All voltage regulators (mechanical or electronic) provide a method for increasing the charging voltage slightly at low temperatures and for lowering the charging voltage at high temperatures. A battery requires a higher charging voltage at low temperatures because of the resistance to chemical reaction changes. However, the battery would be overcharged if the charging voltage were not reduced during warm weather. Electronic voltage regulators use a temperature-sensitive resistor in the regulator circuit. This resistor, called a **thermistor,** provides lower resistance as the

FIGURE 32–20 A coolant-cooled alternator showing the hose connections where coolant from the engine flows through the rear frame of the alternator.

temperature increases. A thermistor is used in the electronic circuits of the voltage regulator to control charging voltage over a wide range of underhood temperatures.

NOTE: Voltmeter test results may vary according to temperature. Charging voltage tested at 32°F (0°C) will be higher than for the same vehicle tested at 80°F (27°C) because of the temperature-compensation factors built into voltage regulators.

ALTERNATOR COOLING

Alternators create heat during normal operation and this heat must be removed to protect the components inside, especially the diodes and voltage regulator. The types of cooling include:

- External fan
- Internal fan(s)
- Both an external fan and an internal fan
- Coolant cooled (● **SEE FIGURE 32–20.**)

COMPUTER-CONTROLLED ALTERNATORS

TYPES OF SYSTEMS Computers can interface with the charging system in three ways.

1. The computer can *activate* the charging system by turning on and off the field current to the rotor. In other words, the computer, usually the powertrain control module (PCM), controls the field current to the rotor.

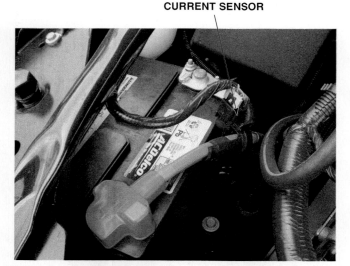

CURRENT SENSOR

FIGURE 32–21 A Hall-effect current sensor attached to the positive battery cable is used as part of the EPM system.

2. The computer can *monitor* the operation of the alternator and increase engine speed if needed during conditions when a heavy load is demanded by the alternator.

3. The computer can *control* the alternator by controlling alternator output to match the needs of the electrical system. This system detects the electrical needs of the vehicle and commands the alternator to charge only when needed to improve fuel economy.

GM ELECTRICAL POWER MANAGEMENT SYSTEM

A typical system used on some General Motors vehicles is called **electrical power management (EPM).** It uses a Hall-effect sensor attached to the negative or positive battery cable to measure the current leaving and entering the battery. ● **SEE FIGURE 32–21.**

COMMAND DUTY CYCLE (%)	ALTERNATOR OUTPUT VOLTAGE (V)
10	11.0
20	11.6
30	12.1
40	12.7
50	13.3
60	13.8
70	14.4
80	14.9
90	15.5

CHART 32–1

The output voltage is controlled by varying the duty cycle as controlled by the PCM.

The engine control module (ECM) controls the alternator by changing the on-time of the current through the rotor. ● **SEE FIGURE 32–22.**

The on-time, called **duty cycle,** varies from 5% to 95%. ● **SEE CHART 32–1.**

This system has six modes of operation.

1. **Charge mode.** The charge mode is activated when any of the following occurs.
   - Electric cooling fans are on high speed.
   - Rear window defogger is on.
   - Battery state of charge (SOC) is less than 80%.
   - Outside (ambient) temperature is less than 32°F (0°C).

2. **Fuel economy mode.** This mode reduces the load on the engine from the alternator for maximum fuel economy. This mode is activated when the following conditions are met.

FIELD CURRENT

HIGH-AVERAGE FIELD CURRENT → OFF 10% ON 90% TIME

LOW-AVERAGE FIELD CURRENT → ON 10% OFF 90% TIME

FIGURE 32–22 The amount of time current is flowing through the field (rotor) determines the alternator output.

- Ambient temperature is above 32°F (0°C).
- The state of charge of the battery is 80% or higher.
- The cooling fans and rear defogger are off.

The target voltage is 13 volts and will return to the charge mode, if needed.

3. **Voltage reduction mode.** This mode is commanded to reduce the stress on the battery during low-load conditions. This mode is activated when the following conditions are met.
   - Ambient temperature is above 32°F (0°C).
   - Battery discharge rate is less than 7 amperes.
   - Rear defogger is off.
   - Cooling fans are on low or off.
   - Target voltage is limited to 12.7 volts.

4. **Start-up mode.** This mode is selected after engine start and commands a charging voltage of 14.5 volts for 30 seconds. After 30 seconds, the mode is changed depending on conditions.

5. **Battery sulfation mode.** This mode is commanded if the output voltage is less than 13.2 volts for 45 minutes, which can indicate that sulfated plates could be the cause. The target voltage is 13.9 to 15.5 volts for three minutes. After three minutes, the system returns to another mode based on conditions.

6. **Headlight mode.** This mode is selected when the headlights are on and the target voltage is 14.5 volts.

COMPUTER-CONTROLLED CHARGING SYSTEMS

Computer control of the charging system has the following advantages.

1. The computer controls the field of the alternator, which can pulse it on or off as needed for maximum efficiency, thereby saving fuel.

   NOTE: Some vehicle manufacturers, such as Honda/Acura, use an *electronic load control (ELC)*, which turns on the alternator when decelerating, where the additional load on the engine is simply used to help slow the vehicle. This allows the battery to be charged without placing a load on the engine, helping to increase fuel economy.

TECH TIP

The Voltage Display Can Be a Customer Concern

A customer may complain that the voltmeter reading on the dash fluctuates up and down. This may be normal as the computer-controlled charging system commands various modes of operation based on the operating conditions. Follow the vehicle manufacturer's recommended procedures to verify proper operation.

2. Engine idle can also be improved by turning on the alternator slowly, rather than all at once, if an electrical load is switched on, such as the air-conditioning system.

3. Most computers can also reduce the load on the electrical system if the demand exceeds the capacity of the charging system by reducing fan speed, shutting off rear window defoggers, or increasing engine speed to cause the alternator to increase the amperage output.

   NOTE: A commanded higher-than-normal idle speed may be the result of the computer compensating for an abnormal electrical load. This higher idle speed could indicate a defective battery or other electrical system faults.

4. The computer can monitor the charging system and set diagnostic trouble codes (DTCs) if a fault is detected. Many systems allow the service technician to control the charging of the alternator using a scan tool.

5. Because the charging system is computer controlled, it can be checked using a scan tool. Some vehicle systems allow the scan tool to activate the alternator field and then monitor the output to help detect fault locations. Always follow the vehicle manufacturer's diagnostic procedure.

SUMMARY

1. Alternator output is increased if the speed of the alternator is increased.

2. The parts of a typical alternator include the drive-end (DE) housing, slip-ring-end (SRE) housing, rotor assembly, stator, rectifier bridge, brushes, and voltage regulator.

3. The magnetic field is created in the rotor.

4. The alternator output current is created in the stator windings.

5. The voltage regulator controls the current flow through the rotor winding.

1. How can a small electronic voltage regulator control the output of a typical 100 ampere alternator?

2. What are the component parts of a typical alternator?

3. How is the computer used to control an alternator?

4. Why do voltage regulators include temperature compensation?

5. How is AC voltage inside the alternator changed to DC voltage at the output terminal?

6. What is the purpose of an OAP or OAD?

CHAPTER QUIZ

1. Technician A says that the diodes regulate the alternator output voltage. Technician B says that the field current can be computer controlled. Which technician is correct?
   a. Technician A only
   b. Technician B only
   c. Both Technicians A and B
   d. Neither Technician A nor B

2. A magnetic field is created in the _____ in an alternator (AC alternator).
   a. Stator
   b. Diodes
   c. Rotor
   d. Drive-end frame

3. The voltage regulator controls current through the _____.
   a. Alternator brushes
   b. Rotor
   c. Alternator field
   d. All of the above

4. Technician A says that two diodes are required for each stator winding lead. Technician B says that diodes change alternating current into direct current. Which technician is correct?
   a. Technician A only
   b. Technician B only
   c. Both Technicians A and B
   d. Neither Technician A nor B

5. The alternator output current is produced in the _____.
   a. Stator
   b. Rotor
   c. Brushes
   d. Diodes (rectifier bridge)

6. Alternator brushes are constructed from _____.
   a. Copper
   b. Aluminum
   c. Carbon
   d. Silver-copper alloy

7. How much current flows through the alternator brushes?
   a. All of the alternator output flows through the brushes
   b. 25 to 35 A, depending on the vehicle
   c. 10 to 15 A
   d. 2 to 5 A

8. Technician A says that an alternator overrunning pulley is used to reduce vibration and noise. Technician B says that an overrunning alternator pulley or dampener uses a one-way clutch. Which technician is correct?
   a. Technician A only
   b. Technician B only
   c. Both Technicians A and B
   d. Neither Technician A nor B

9. Operating an alternator in a vehicle with a defective battery can harm the _____.
   a. Diodes (rectifier bridge)
   b. Stator
   c. Voltage regulator
   d. Brushes

10. Technician A says that a wye-wound stator produces more maximum output than the same alternator equipped with a delta-wound stator. Technician B says that an alternator equipped with a delta-wound stator produces more maximum output than a wye-wound stator. Which technician is correct?
    a. Technician A only
    b. Technician B only
    c. Both Technicians A and B
    d. Neither Technician A nor B

chapter 33

CHARGING SYSTEM DIAGNOSIS AND SERVICE

OBJECTIVES: • **After studying Chapter 33, the reader will be able to:** • Prepare for ASE Electrical/Electronic Systems (A6) certification test content area "D" (Charging System Diagnosis and Repair). • Describe how to perform a charging voltage test. • Discuss how to perform an AC ripple voltage test. • Explain how to perform an alternator output test. • Explain how to disassemble an alternator and test its component parts. • Discuss how to check the wiring from the alternator to the battery. • Describe how to test the operation of a computer-controlled charging system.

KEY TERMS: • AC ripple voltage 342 • Alternator output test 344 • Charging voltage test 339 • Cores 350

CHARGING SYSTEM TESTING AND SERVICE

BATTERY STATE OF CHARGE The charging system can be tested as part of a routine vehicle inspection or to determine the reason for a no-charge or reduced charging circuit performance. The battery *must* be at least 75% charged before testing the alternator and the charging system. A weak or defective battery will cause inaccurate test results. If in doubt, replace the battery with a known good shop battery for testing.

CHARGING VOLTAGE TEST The **charging voltage test** is the easiest way to check the charging system voltage at the battery. Use a digital multimeter to check the voltage, as follows:

STEP 1 Select DC volts.

STEP 2 Connect the red meter lead to the positive (+) terminal of the battery and the black meter lead to the negative (−) terminal of the battery.

> **NOTE: The polarity of the meter leads is not too important when using a digital multimeter. If the meter leads are connected backward on the battery, the resulting readout will simply have a negative (−) sign in front of the voltage reading.**

STEP 3 Start the engine and increase the engine speed to about 2000 RPM (fast idle) and record the charging voltage. ● **SEE FIGURE 33–1.**

Specifications for charging voltage = 13.5 to 15 V

- If the voltage is too high, check that the alternator is properly grounded.

FIGURE 33–1 The digital multimeter should be set to read DC volts, with the red lead connected to the positive (+) battery terminal and the black meter lead connected to the negative (−) battery terminal.

- If the voltage is lower than specifications, then there is a fault with the wiring or the alternator.
- If the wiring and the connections are okay, then additional testing is required to help pinpoint the root cause. Replacement of the alternator and/or battery is often required if the charging voltage is not within factory specifications.

SCAN TESTING THE CHARGING CIRCUIT Most vehicles that use a computer-controlled charging system can be diagnosed using a scan tool. Not only can the charging voltage be monitored, but also in many vehicles, the field circuit can be controlled and the output voltage monitored to check that the system is operating correctly. ● **SEE FIGURE 33–2.**

FIGURE 33–2 A scan tool can be used to diagnose charging system problems.

FIGURE 33–3 Before replacing an alternator, the wise technician checks that battery voltage is present at the output and battery voltage sense terminals. If not, then there is a fault in the wiring.

 FREQUENTLY ASKED QUESTION

What Is a Full-Fielding Test?

Full fielding is a procedure used on older noncomputerized vehicles for bypassing the voltage regulator that could be used to determine if the alternator is capable of producing its designed output. This test is no longer performed for the following reasons.

- The voltage regulator is built into the alternator, therefore requiring that the entire assembly be replaced even if just the regulator is defective.
- When the regulator is bypassed, the alternator can produce a high voltage (over 100 volts in some cases) which could damage all of the electronic circuits in the vehicle.

   Always follow the vehicle manufacturer's recommended testing procedures.

 TECH TIP

Use a Test Light to Check for a Defective Fusible Link

Most alternators use a fusible link or mega fuse between the output terminal and the positive (+) terminal of the battery. If this fusible link or fuse is defective (blown), then the charging system will not operate at all. Many alternators have been replaced repeatedly because of a blown fusible link that was not discovered until later. A quick and easy test to check if the fusible link is okay is to touch a test light to the output terminal. With the other end of the test light attached to a good ground, the fusible link or mega fuse is okay if the light lights. This test confirms that the circuit between the alternator and the battery has continuity. ● **SEE FIGURE 33–3.**

DRIVE BELT INSPECTION AND ADJUSTMENT

BELT VISUAL INSPECTION   It is generally recommended that all belts be inspected regularly and replaced as needed. Replace any serpentine belt that has more than three cracks in any one rib that appears in a 3 in. span. Check service information for the specified procedure and recommended replacement interval. ● **SEE FIGURE 33–4.**

BELT TENSION MEASUREMENT   If the vehicle does not use a belt tensioner, then a belt tension gauge is needed to achieve the specified belt tension. Install the belt and operate the engine with all of the accessories turned on to "run-in" the belt for at least five minutes. Adjust the tension of the accessory drive belt to factory specifications or use the following table for an example of the proper tension based on the size of the belt.

NOTE: Some charging systems, such as those on many Honda/Acura vehicles, use an electronic load detection circuit that energizes the field circuit only when an electrical load is detected. For example, if the engine is running and there are no accessories on, the voltage read at the battery may be 12.6 V, which could indicate that the charging system is not operating. In this situation, turning on the head-lights or an accessory should cause the computer to activate the field circuit, and the alternator should produce normal charging voltage.

FIGURE 33–4 This accessory drive belt is worn and requires replacement. Newer belts are made from ethylene propylene diene monomer (EPDM). This rubber does not crack like older belts and may not show wear even though the ribs do wear and can cause slippage.

There are four ways that vehicle manufacturers specify that the belt tension is within factory specifications.

1. **Belt tension gauge.** A belt tension gauge is needed to determine if it is at the specified belt tension. Install the belt and operate the engine with all of the accessories turned on to "run-in" the belt for at least five minutes. Adjust the tension of the accessory drive belt to factory specifications, or see ● **CHART 33–1** foran example of the proper tension based on the size of the belt.

 TECH TIP

The Hand Cleaner Trick

Lower-than-normal alternator output could be the result of a loose or slipping drive belt. All belts (V and serpentine multigroove) use an interference angle between the angle of the Vs of the belt and the angle of the Vs on the pulley. As the belt wears, the interference angles are worn off of both edges of the belt. As a result, the belt may start to slip and make a squealing sound even if tensioned properly.

A common trick used to determine if the noise is belt related is to use grit-type hand cleaner or scouring powder. With the engine off, sprinkle some powder onto the pulley side of the belt. Start the engine. The excess powder will fly into the air, so get away from under the hood when the engine starts. If the belts are now quieter, you know that it was the glazed belt that made the noise.

The noise can sound exactly like a noisy bearing. Therefore, before you start removing and replacing parts, try the hand cleaner trick.

Often, the grit from the hand cleaner will remove the glaze from the belt and the noise will not return. However, if the belt is worn or loose, the noise will return and the belt should be replaced. A fast, alternative method to see if the noise is from the belt is to spray water from a squirt bottle at the belt with the engine running. If the noise stops, the belt is the cause of the noise. The water quickly evaporates and, therefore, unlike the gritty hand cleaner, water simply finds the problem—it does not provide a short-term fix.

2. **Marks on a tensioner.** Many tensioners have marks that indicate the normal operating tension range for the accessory drive belt. Check service information for the preferred location of the tensioner mark. ● **SEE FIGURE 33–5.**

SERPENTINE BELTS	
NUMBER OF RIBS USED	TENSION RANGE (LB)
3	45–60
4	60–80
5	75–100
6	90–125
7	105–145
V-BELTS	
V-BELT TOP WIDTH (IN.)	TENSION RANGE (LB)
1/4	45–65
5/16	60–85
25/64	85–115
31/64	105–145

CHART 33–1

Typical belt tension for various widths of belts. Tension is the force needed to depress the belt as displayed on a belt tension gauge.

FIGURE 33–5 Check service information for the exact marks where the tensioner should be located for proper belt tension.

3. **Torque wrench reading.** Some vehicle manufacturers specify that a beam-type torque wrench be used to determine the torque needed to rotate the tensioner. If the torque reading is below specifications, the tensioner must be replaced.

4. **Deflection.** Depress the belt between the two pulleys that are the farthest apart; the flex or deflection should be 1/2 in. (13 mm).

TESTING AN ALTERNATOR USING A SCOPE

Defective diodes and open or shorted stators can be detected on an ignition scope. Connect the scope leads as usual, except for the coil negative connection, which attaches to the alternator output ("BAT") terminal. With the pattern selection set to "raster" (stacked), start the engine and run to approximately 1000 RPM (slightly higher-than-normal idle speed). The scope should show an even ripple pattern reflecting the slight alternating up-and-down level of the alternator output voltage.

If the alternator is controlled by an electronic voltage regulator, the rapid on-and-off cycling of the field current can create vertical spikes evenly throughout the pattern. These spikes are normal. If the ripple pattern is jagged or uneven, a defective diode (open or shorted) or a defective stator is indicated. ● **SEE FIGURES 33–6 THROUGH 33–8.** If the alternator scope pattern does not show even ripples, the alternator should be replaced.

AC RIPPLE VOLTAGE CHECK

PRINCIPLES A good alternator should produce very little AC voltage or current output. It is the purpose of the diodes in the alternator to rectify or convert most AC voltage into DC voltage. While it is normal to measure some AC voltage

FIGURE 33–6 Normal alternator scope pattern. This AC ripple is on top of a DC voltage line. The ripple should be less than 0.50 V high.

FIGURE 33–7 Alternator pattern indicating a shorted diode.

FIGURE 33–8 Alternator pattern indicating an open diode.

FIGURE 33–9 This overrunning alternator dampener (OAD) is longer than an overrunning alternator pulley (OAP) because it contains a dampener spring as well as a one way clutch. Be sure to check that it locks in one direction.

 TECH TIP

Check the Overrunning Clutch

If low or no alternator output is found, remove the alternator drive belt and check the overrunning alternator pulley (OAP) or overrunning alternator dampener (OAD) for proper operation. Both types of overrunning clutches use a one-way clutch. Therefore, the pulley should freewheel in one direction and rotate the alternator rotor when rotated in the opposite direction. ● **SEE FIGURE 33–9.**

from an alternator, excessive AC voltage, called AC ripple, is undesirable and indicates a fault with the rectifier diodes or stator windings inside the alternator.

TESTING AC RIPPLE VOLTAGE The procedure to check for **AC ripple voltage** includes the following steps.

STEP 1 Set the digital meter to read AC volts.

STEP 2 Start the engine and operate it at 2000 RPM (fast idle).

STEP 3 Connect the voltmeter leads to the positive and negative battery terminals.

STEP 4 Turn on the headlights to provide an electrical load on the alternator.

NOTE: A more accurate reading can be obtained by touching the meter lead to the output or "battery" terminal of the alternator. ● **SEE FIGURE 33–10.**

The results should be interpreted as follows: If the rectifier diodes are good, the voltmeter should read *less* than 400 mV (0.4 volt) AC. If the reading is over 500 mV (0.5 volt) AC, the rectifier diodes are defective.

NOTE: Many conductance testers, such as Midtronic and Snap-On, automatically test for AC ripple.

MEASURING THE AC RIPPLE FROM THE ALTERNATOR TELLS A LOT ABOUT ITS CONDITION. IF THE AC RIPPLE IS ABOVE 500 MILLIVOLTS, OR 0.5 VOLTS, LOOK FOR A PROBLEM IN THE DIODES OR STATOR. IF THE RIPPLE IS BELOW 500 MILLIVOLTS, CHECK THE ALTERNATOR OUTPUT TO DETERMINE ITS CONDITION.

FIGURE 33–10 Testing AC ripple at the output terminal of the alternator is more accurate than testing at the battery due to the resistance of the wiring between the alternator and the battery. The reading shown on the meter, set to AC volts, is only 78 mV (0.078 V), far below what the reading would be if a diode were defective.

TESTING AC RIPPLE CURRENT

All alternators should create direct current (DC) if the diodes and stator windings are functioning correctly. A mini clamp-on meter capable of measuring AC amperes can be used to check the alternator. A good alternator should produce less than 10% of its rated amperage output in AC ripple amperes. For example, an alternator rated at 100 amperes should not produce more than 10 amperes AC ripple (100 × 10% = 10). It is normal for a good alternator to produce 3 or 4 A of AC ripple current to the battery. Only if the AC ripple current exceeds 10% of the rating of the alternator should the alternator be repaired or replaced.

🔧 TECH TIP

The Lighter Plug Trick

Battery voltage measurements can be read through the lighter socket. Simply construct a test tool using a lighter plug at one end of a length of two-conductor wire and the other end connected to a double banana plug. The double banana plug will fit most meters in the common (COM) terminal and the volt terminal of the meter. This is handy to use while road testing the vehicle under real-life conditions. Both DC voltage and AC ripple voltage can be measured. ● SEE FIGURE 33–11.

FIGURE 33–11 Charging system voltage can be easily checked at the lighter plug by connecting a lighter plug to the voltmeter through a double banana plug.

TEST PROCEDURE   To measure the AC current to the battery, perform the following steps.

STEP 1   Start the engine and turn on the lights to create an electrical load on the alternator.

STEP 2   Using a mini clamp-on digital multimeter, place the clamp around either all of the positive (+) battery cables or all of the negative (−) battery cables.

An AC/DC current clamp adapter can also be used with a conventional digital multimeter set on the DC millivolts scale.

STEP 3   To check for AC current ripple, switch the meter to read AC amperes and record the reading. Read the meter display.

STEP 4   The results should be within 10% of the specified alternator rating. A reading of greater than 10 amperes AC indicates defective alternator diodes. ● SEE FIGURE 33–12.

FIGURE 33–12 A mini clamp-on meter can be used to measure alternator output as shown here (105.2 Amp). Then the meter can be used to check AC current ripple by selecting AC Amps on the rotary dial. AC ripple current should be less than 10% of the DC current output.

CHARGING SYSTEM VOLTAGE DROP TESTING

ALTERNATOR WIRING
For the proper operation of any charging system, there must be good electrical connections between the battery positive terminal and the alternator output terminal. The alternator must also be properly grounded to the engine block.

Many manufacturers of vehicles run the lead from the output terminal of the alternator to other connectors or junction blocks that are electrically connected to the positive terminal of the battery. If there is high resistance (a high-voltage drop) in these connections or in the wiring itself, the battery will not be properly charged.

VOLTAGE DROP TEST PROCEDURE
When there is a suspected charging system problem (with or without a charge indicator light on), simply follow these steps to measure the voltage drop of the insulated (power-side) charging circuit.

STEP 1 Start the engine and run it at a fast idle (about 2000 engine RPM).

STEP 2 Turn on the headlights to ensure an electrical load on the charging system.

STEP 3 Using any voltmeter set to read DC volts, connect the positive test lead (red) to the output terminal of the alternator. Attach the negative test lead (black) to the positive post of the battery.

The results should be interpreted as follows:

1. If there is less than a 0.4 volt (400 mV) reading, then all wiring and connections are satisfactory.
2. If the voltmeter reads higher than 0.4 volt, there is excessive resistance (voltage drop) between the alternator output terminal and the positive terminal of the battery.
3. If the voltmeter reads battery voltage (or close to battery voltage), there is an open circuit between the battery and the alternator output terminal.

To determine whether the alternator is correctly grounded, maintain the engine speed at 2000 RPM with the headlights on. Connect the positive voltmeter lead to the case of the alternator and the negative voltmeter lead to the negative terminal of the battery. The voltmeter should read less than 0.2 volt (200 mV) if the alternator is properly grounded. If the reading is over 0.2 volt, connect one end of an auxiliary ground wire to the case of the alternator and the other end to a good engine ground. ● SEE FIGURE 33–13.

ALTERNATOR OUTPUT TEST

PRELIMINARY CHECKS
An **alternator output test** measures the current (amperes) of the alternator. A charging circuit may be able to produce correct charging circuit voltage, but not be able to produce adequate amperage output. If in doubt about charging system output, first check the condition

BATTERY (OUTPUT)

TYPICAL MAXIMUM READING 0.4 V

VOLTAGE DROP-INSULATED CHARGING CIRCUIT

ENGINE AT 2,000 RPM. CHARGING SYSTEM LOADED TO 20A

TYPICAL MAXIMUM READING 0.2 V

VOLTAGE DROP-CHARGING GROUND CIRCUIT

FIGURE 33–13 Voltmeter hookup to test the voltage drop of the charging circuit.

FIGURE 33-14 A typical tester used to test batteries as well as the cranking and charging system. Always follow the operating instructions.

of the alternator drive belt. With the engine off, attempt to rotate the fan of the alternator by hand. Replace or tighten the drive belt if the alternator fan can be rotated this way.

CARBON PILE TEST PROCEDURE   A carbon pile tester uses plates of carbon to create an electrical load. A carbon pile test is used to load test a battery and/or an alternator. ●SEE FIGURE 33-14.
 The testing procedure for alternator output is as follows:

STEP 1   Connect the starting and charging test leads according to the manufacturer's instructions, which usually include installing the amp clamp around the output wire near the alternator.

STEP 2   Turn off all electrical accessories to be sure that the tester is measuring the true output of the alternator.

STEP 3   Start the engine and operate it at 2000 RPM (fast idle). Turn the load increase control slowly to obtain the highest reading on the ammeter scale. Do not allow the voltage to drop below 12.6 volts. Note the ampere reading.

STEP 4   Add 5 to 7 amperes to the reading because this amount of current is used by the ignition system to operate the engine.

STEP 5   Compare the output reading to factory specifications. The rated output may be stamped on the alternator or can be found in service information.

CAUTION: *NEVER* disconnect a battery cable with the engine running. All vehicle manufacturers warn not to do this, because this was an old test, before alternators, to see if a generator could supply current to operate the ignition system without a battery. When a battery cable is removed, the alternator (or PCM) will lose the battery voltage sense signal. Without a battery voltage sense circuit, the alternator will do one of two things, depending on the make and model of vehicle.

- The alternator output can exceed 100 volts. This high voltage may not only damage the alternator but also electrical components in the vehicle, including the PCM and all electronic devices.
- The alternator stops charging as a fail safe measure to protect the alternator and all of the electronics in the vehicle from being damaged due to excessively high voltage.

MINIMUM REQUIRED ALTERNATOR OUTPUT

PURPOSE   All charging systems must be able to supply the electrical demands of the electrical system. If lights and accessories are used constantly and the alternator cannot supply the necessary ampere output, the battery will be drained. To determine the minimum electrical load requirements, connect an inductive ammeter probe around either battery cable or the alternator output cable. ●SEE FIGURE 33-15.

NOTE: If using an inductive pickup ammeter, be certain that the pickup is over *all* the wires leaving the battery terminal.
 Failure to include the small body ground wire from the negative battery terminal to the body or the small positive wire (if testing from the positive side) will greatly decrease the current flow readings.

PROCEDURE   After connecting an ammeter correctly in the battery circuit, continue as follows:

1. Start the engine and operate to about 2000 RPM (fast idle).

2. Turn the heat selector to air conditioning (if the vehicle is so equipped).

FIGURE 33-15 The best place to install a charging system tester amp probe is around the alternator output terminal wire, as shown.

3. Turn the blower motor to high speed.

4. Turn the headlights on bright.

5. Turn on the rear defogger.

6. Turn on the windshield wipers.

7. Turn on any other accessories that may be used continuously (do not operate the horn, power door locks, or other units that are not used for more than a few seconds).

8. Observe the ammeter. The current indicated is the electrical load that the alternator is able to exceed to keep the battery fully charged.

TEST RESULTS The minimum acceptable alternator output is 5 amperes greater than the accessory load. A negative (discharge) reading indicates that the alternator is not capable of supplying the current (amperes) that may be needed.

TECH TIP

Use a Fused Jumper Wire as a Diagnostic Tool

When diagnosing an alternator charging problem, try using a fused jumper wire to connect the positive and negative terminals of the alternator directly to the positive and negative terminals of the battery. If a definite improvement is noticed, the problem is in the wiring of the vehicle. High resistance, due to corroded connections or loose grounds, can cause low alternator output, repeated regulator failures, slow cranking, and discharged batteries. A voltage drop test of the charging system can also be used to locate excessive resistance (high-voltage drop) in the charging circuit, but using a fused jumper wire is often faster and easier.

TECH TIP

Bigger Is Not Always Better

Many technicians are asked to install a higher output alternator to allow the use of emergency equipment or other high-amperage equipment such as a high-wattage sound system.

Although many higher output units can be physically installed, it is important not to forget to upgrade the wiring and the fusible link(s) in the alternator circuit. Failure to upgrade the wiring could lead to overheating. The usual failure locations are at junctions or electrical connectors.

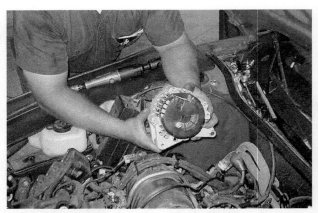

FIGURE 33–16 Replacing an alternator is not always as easy as it is from a Buick with a 3800 V-6, where the alternator is easy to access. Many alternators are difficult to access, and require the removal of other components.

ALTERNATOR REMOVAL

After diagnosis of the charging system has determined that there is a fault with the alternator, it must be removed safely from the vehicle. Always check service information for the exact procedure to follow on the vehicle being serviced. A typical removal procedure includes the following steps.

STEP 1 Before disconnecting the negative battery cable, use a test light or a voltmeter and check for battery voltage at the output terminal of the alternator. A complete circuit must exist between the alternator and the battery. If there is no voltage at the alternator output terminal, check for a blown fusible link or other electrical circuit fault.

STEP 2 Disconnect the negative (−) terminal from the battery. (Use a memory saver to maintain radio, memory seats, and other functions.)

STEP 3 Remove the accessory drive belt that drives the alternator.

STEP 4 Remove electrical wiring, fasteners, spacers, and brackets, as necessary, and remove the alternator from the vehicle.

● **SEE FIGURE 33–16.**

ALTERNATOR DISASSEMBLY

DISASSEMBLY PROCEDURE

STEP 1 Mark the case with a scratch or with chalk to ensure proper reassembly of the alternator case. ● **SEE FIGURE 33–17.**

STEP 2 After the through bolts have been removed, carefully separate the two halves. The stator windings must stay with the rear case. When this happens, the brushes and springs will fall out.

STEP 3 Remove the rectifier assembly and voltage regulator.

FIGURE 33–17 Always mark the case of the alternator before disassembly to be assured of correct reassembly.

TECH TIP

The Sniff Test

When checking for the root cause of an alternator failure, one test that a technician could do is to sniff (smell) the alternator. If the alternator smells like a dead rat (rancid smell), the stator windings have been overheated by trying to charge a discharged or defective battery. If the battery voltage is continuously low, the voltage regulator will continue supplying full-field current to the alternator. The voltage regulator is designed to cycle on and off to maintain a narrow charging system voltage range.

If the battery voltage is continually below the cutoff point of the voltage regulator, the alternator is continually producing current in the stator windings. This constant charging can often overheat the stator and burn the insulating varnish covering the stator windings. If the alternator fails the sniff test, the technician should replace the stator and other alternator components that are found to be defective *and* replace or recharge and test the battery.

ROTOR TESTING The slip rings on the rotor should be smooth and round (within 0.002 in. of being perfectly round).

- If grooved, the slip rings can be machined to provide a suitable surface for the brushes. Do not machine beyond the minimum slip-ring dimension as specified by the manufacturer.
- If the slip rings are discolored or dirty, they can be cleaned with 400-grit or fine emery (polishing) cloth. The rotor must be turned while being cleaned to prevent flat spots on the slip rings.

What Is a "Clock Position"?

Most alternators of a particular manufacturer can be used on a variety of vehicles, which may require wiring connections placed in various locations. For example, a Chevrolet and a Buick alternator may be identical except for the position of the rear section containing the electrical connections. The four through bolts that hold the two halves together are equally spaced; therefore, the rear alternator housing *can* be installed in any one of four positions to match the wiring needs of various models. Always check the clock position of the original and be sure that it matches the replacement unit. ● SEE FIGURE 33–18.

- Measure the resistance between the slip rings using an ohmmeter. Typical resistance values and results include the following:

  1. The resistance measured between either slip ring and the steel rotor shaft should be infinity (OL). If there is continuity, then the rotor is shorted-to-ground.
  2. Rotor resistance range is normally between 2.4 and 6 ohms.

FIGURE 33–18 Explanation of clock positions. Because the four through bolts are equally spaced, it is possible for an alternator to be installed in one of four different clock positions. The connector position is determined by viewing the alternator from the diode end with the threaded adjusting lug in the up or 12 o'clock position. Select the 3 o'clock, 6 o'clock, 9 o'clock, or 12 o'clock position to match the unit being replaced.

**CHECKING FOR GROUNDS
(SHOULD READ INFINITY IF
ROTOR IS <u>NOT</u> GROUNDED)**

FIGURE 33-19 Testing an alternator rotor using an ohmmeter.

3. If the resistance is below specification, the rotor is shorted.
4. If the resistance is above specification, the rotor connections are corroded or open.

If the rotor is found to be bad, it must be replaced or repaired at a specialized shop. ● **SEE FIGURE 33–19.**

NOTE: The cost of a replacement rotor may exceed the cost of an entire rebuilt alternator. Be certain, however, that the rebuilt alternator is rated at the same output as the original or higher.

STATOR TESTING The stator must be disconnected from the diodes (rectifiers) before testing. Because all three windings of the stator are electrically connected (either wye or delta), an ohmmeter can be used to check a stator.

- There should be low resistance at all three stator leads (continuity).
- There should *not* be continuity (in other words, there should be a meter reading of infinity ohms) when the stator is tested between any stator lead and the metal stator core.
- If there is continuity, the stator is shorted-to-ground and must be repaired or replaced. ● **SEE FIGURE 33–20.**

NOTE: Because the resistance is very low for a normal stator, it is generally *not* possible to test for a *shorted* (copper-to-copper) stator. A shorted stator will, however, greatly reduce alternator output. An ohmmeter cannot detect an open stator if the stator is delta wound. The

**(CHECK FOR OPENS)
OHMMETER**

**STATOR IS OPEN
IF METER READS
INFINITY (OL)**   **IF OHMMETER READS
ANY RESISTANCE
EXCEPT INFINITY (OL),
STATOR IS GROUNDED**

FIGURE 33-20 If the ohmmeter reads infinity between any two of the three stator windings, the stator is open and, therefore, defective. The ohmmeter should read infinity between any stator lead and the steel laminations. If the reading is less than infinity, the stator is grounded. Stator windings cannot be tested if shorted because the normal resistance is very low.

ohmmeter will still indicate low resistance because all three windings are electrically connected.

TESTING THE DIODE TRIO Many alternators are equipped with a diode trio. A diode is an electrical one-way check valve that permits current to flow in only one direction. Because *trio* means "three," a diode trio is three diodes connected together. ● **SEE FIGURE 33–21.**

FIGURE 33-21 Typical diode trio. If one leg of a diode trio is open, the alternator may produce close to normal output, but the charge indicator light on the dash will be on dimly.

The diode trio is connected to all three stator windings. The current generated in the stator flows through the diode trio to the internal voltage regulator. The diode trio is designed to supply current for the field (rotor) and turns off the charge indicator light when the alternator voltage equals or exceeds the battery voltage. If one of the three diodes in the diode trio is defective (usually open), the alternator may produce close-to-normal output; however, the charge indicator light will be on dimly.

A diode trio should be tested with a digital multimeter. The meter should be set to the diode-check position. The multimeter should indicate 0.5 to 0.7 V (500 to 700 mV) one way and OL (overlimit) after reversing the test leads and touching all three connectors of the diode trio.

TESTING THE RECTIFIER

TERMINOLOGY The rectifier assembly usually is equipped with six diodes including three positive diodes and three negative diodes (one positive and one negative for each winding of the stator).

METER SETUP The rectifier(s) (diodes) should be tested using a multimeter that is set to "diode check" position on the digital multimeter (DMM).

Because a diode (rectifier) should allow current to flow in only one direction, each diode should be tested to determine if the diode allows current flow in one direction and blocks current flow in the opposite direction. To test some alternator diodes, it may be necessary to unsolder the stator connections. ● **SEE FIGURE 33–22.**

Accurate testing is not possible unless the diodes are separated electrically from other alternator components.

TESTING PROCEDURE Connect the leads to the leads of the diode (pigtail and housing of the rectifier bridge). Read the meter. Reverse the test leads. A good diode should have high resistance (OL) one way (reverse bias) and low voltage drop of 0.5 to 0.7 V (500 to 700 mV) the other way (forward bias).

RESULTS Open or shorted diodes must be replaced. Most alternators group or combine all positive and all negative diodes in the one replaceable rectifier component.

FIGURE 33–22 A typical rectifier bridge that contains all six diodes in one replaceable assembly.

REASSEMBLING THE ALTERNATOR

BRUSH HOLDER REPLACEMENT Alternator carbon brushes often last for many years and require no scheduled maintenance. The life of the alternator brushes is extended because they conduct only the field (rotor) current, which is normally only 2 to 5 amperes. The alternator brushes should be inspected when the alternator is disassembled and should be replaced when worn to less than 1/2 in. long. Brushes are commonly purchased assembled together in a brush holder. After the brushes are installed (usually retained by two or three screws) and the rotor is installed in the alternator housing, a brush retainer pin can be pulled out through an access hole in the rear of the alternator, allowing the brushes to be pressed against the slip rings by the brush springs.
● **SEE FIGURE 33–23.**

BEARING SERVICE AND REPLACEMENT The bearings of an alternator must be able to support the rotor and reduce friction. An alternator must be able to rotate at up to 15,000 RPM and withstand the forces created by the drive belt. The front bearing is usually a ball bearing type and the rear can be either a smaller roller or ball bearing.

The old or defective bearing can sometimes be pushed out of the front housing and the replacement pushed in by applying pressure with a socket or pipe against the outer edge of the bearing (outer race). Replacement bearings are usually prelubricated and sealed. Many alternator front bearings must be removed from the rotor using a special puller.

FIGURE 33–23 A brush holder assembly with new brushes installed. The holes in the brushes are used to hold the brushes up in the holder when it is installed in the alternator. After the rotor has been installed, the retaining pin is removed which allows the brushes to contact the slip rings of the rotor.

The Two-Minute Alternator Repair

A Chevrolet pickup truck was brought to a shop for routine service. The customer stated that the battery required a jump start after a weekend of sitting. The technician tested the battery and charging system voltage using a small handheld digital multimeter. The battery voltage was 12.4 volts (about 75% charged), but the charging voltage was also 12.4 volts at 2000 RPM. Because normal charging voltage should be 13.5 to 15 volts, it was obvious that the charging system was not operating correctly.

The technician checked the dash and found that the "charge" light was *not* on. Before removing the alternator for service, the technician checked the wiring connection on the alternator. When the connector was removed, it was discovered to be rusty. After the contacts were cleaned, the charging system was restored to normal operation. The technician had learned that the simple things should always be checked first before tearing into a big (or expensive) repair.

ALTERNATOR ASSEMBLY   After testing or servicing, the alternator rectifier(s), regulator, stator, and brush holder must be reassembled using the following steps.

STEP 1   If the brushes are internally mounted, insert a wire through the holes in the brush holder to hold the brushes against the springs.

STEP 2   Install the rotor and front-end frame in proper alignment with the mark made on the outside of the alternator housing. Install the through bolts. Before removing the wire pin holding the brushes, spin the alternator pulley. If the alternator is noisy or not rotating freely, the alternator can easily be disassembled again to check for the cause. After making certain the alternator is free to rotate, remove the brush holder pin and spin the alternator again by hand. The noise level may be slightly higher with the brushes released onto the slip rings.

STEP 3   Alternators should be tested on a bench tester, if available, before they are reinstalled on a vehicle. When installing the alternator on the vehicle, be certain that all mounting bolts and nuts are tight. The battery terminal should be covered with a plastic or rubber protective cap to help prevent accidental shorting to ground, which could seriously damage the alternator.

REMANUFACTURED ALTERNATORS

Remanufactured or rebuilt alternators are totally disassembled and rebuilt. Even though there are many smaller rebuilders who may not replace all worn parts, the major national remanufacturers *totally* remanufacture the alternator. Old alternators (called **cores**) are totally disassembled and cleaned. Both bearings are replaced and all components are tested. Rotors are rewound to original specifications if required. The rotor windings are not counted but are rewound on the rotor "spool," using the correct-gauge copper wire, to the *weight* specified by the original manufacturer. New slip rings are replaced as required, soldered to the rotor spool windings, and machined. The rotors are also balanced and measured to ensure that the outside diameter of the rotor meets specifications. An undersized rotor will produce less alternator output because the field must be close to the stator windings for maximum output. Bridge rectifiers are replaced, if required. Every alternator is then assembled and tested for proper output, boxed, and shipped to a warehouse. Individual parts stores (called jobbers) purchase parts from various regional or local warehouses.

ALTERNATOR INSTALLATION

Before installing a replacement alternator, check service information for the exact procedure to follow for the vehicle being serviced. A typical installation procedure includes the following steps.

STEP 1   Verify that the replacement alternator is the correct unit for the vehicle.

STEP 2   Install the alternator wiring on the alternator and install the alternator.

STEP 3   Check the condition of the drive belt and replace, if necessary. Install the drive belt over the drive pulley.

STEP 4   Properly tension the drive belt.

STEP 5   Tighten all fasteners to factory specifications.

STEP 6   Double-check that all fasteners are correctly tightened and remove all tools from the engine compartment area.

STEP 7   Reconnect the negative battery cable.

STEP 8   Start the engine and verify proper charging circuit operation.

1 Before the alternator is disassembled, it is spin tested and connected to a scope to check for possible defective components.

2 The scope pattern shows that the voltage output is far from being a normal pattern. This pattern indicates serious faults in the rectifier diodes.

3 The first step is to remove the drive pulley. This rebuilder is using an electric impact wrench to accomplish the task.

4 Carefully inspect the drive galley for damage of embedded rubber from the drive belt. The slightest fault can cause a vibration, noise, or possible damage to the alternator.

5 Remove the external fan (if equipped) and then the spacers as shown.

6 Next pop off the plastic cover (shield) covering the stator/rectifier connection.

CONTINUED ▶

7 After the cover has been removed, the stator connections to the rectifier can be seen.

8 Using a diagonal cutter, cut the weld to separate the stator from the rectifier.

9 Before separating the halves of the case, this technician uses a punch to mark both halves.

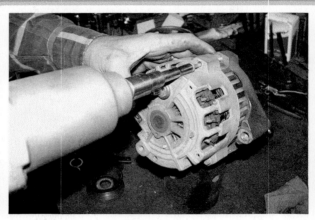

10 After the case has been marked, the through bolts are removed.

11 The drive-end housing and the stator are being separated from the rear (slip-ring-end) housing.

12 The stator is checked by visual inspection for discoloration or other physical damage, and then checked with an ohmmeter to see if the windings are shorted-to-ground.

13 The front bearing is removed from the drive-end housing using a press.

14 A view of the slip-ring-end (SRE) housing showing the black plastic shield, which helps direct air flow across the rectifier.

15 A punch is used to dislodge the plastic shield retaining clips.

16 After the shield has been removed, the rectifier, regulator, and brush holder assembly can be removed by removing the retaining screws.

17 The hear transfer grease is visible when the rectifier assembly is lifted out of the rear housing.

18 The parts are placed into a tumbler where ceramic stones and a water-based solvent are used to clean the parts.

CONTINUED ▶

19 This rebuilder is painting the housing using a high-quality industrial grade spray paint to make the rebuilt alternator look like new.

20 The slip rings on the rotor are being machined on a lathe.

21 The rotor is being tested using an ohmmeter. The specifications for the resistance between the slip rings on the CS-130 are 2.2 to 3.5 ohms.

22 The rotor is also tested between the slip ring and the rotor shaft. This reading should be infinity.

23 A new rectifier. This replacement unit is significantly different than the original but is designed to replace the original unit and meets the original factory specifications.

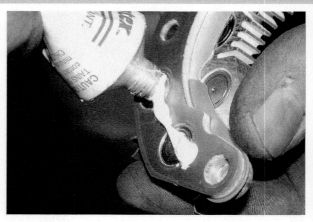

24 Silicone heat transfer compound is applied to the heat sink of the new rectifier.

25 Replacement brushes and springs are assembled into the brush holder.

26 The brushes are pushed into the brush holder and retained by a straight wire, which extends through the rear housing of the alternator. This wire is then pulled out when the unit is assembled.

27 Here is what the CS alternator looks like after installing the new brush holder assembly, rectifier bridge, and voltage regulator.

28 The junction between the rectifier bridge and the voltage regulator is soldered.

29 The plastic deflector shield is snapped back into location using a blunt chisel and a hammer. This shield directs the airflow from the fan over the rectifier bridge and voltage regulator.

30 Before the stator windings can be soldered to the rectifier bridge, the varnish insulation is removed from the ends of the leads.

CONTINUED ▶

31 After the stator has been inserted into the rear housing the stator leads are soldered to the copper lugs of the rectifier bridge.

32 New bearings are installed. A spacer is placed between the bearing and the slip rings to help prevent the possibility that the bearing could move on the shaft and short against the slip ring.

33 The slip-ring-end (SRE) housing is aligned with the marks made during disassembly and is pressed into the drive-end (DE) housing.

34 The retaining bolts, which are threaded into the drive-end housing from the back of the alternator are installed.

35 The external fan and drive pulley are installed and the retaining nut is tightened on the rotor shaft.

36 The scope pattern shows that the diodes and stator are functioning correctly and voltage check indicates that the voltage regulator is also functioning correctly.

1. Charging system testing requires that the battery be at least 75% charged to be assured of accurate test results. The charge indicator light should be on with the ignition switch on, but should go out when the engine is running. Normal charging voltage (at 2000 engine RPM) is 13.5 to 15 volts.

2. To check for excessive resistance in the wiring between the alternator and the battery, a voltage drop test should be performed.

3. Alternators do not produce their maximum rated output unless required by circuit demands. Therefore, to test for maximum alternator output, the battery must be loaded to force the alternator to produce its maximum output.

4. Each alternator should be marked across its case before disassembly to ensure proper clock position during reassembly. After disassembly, all alternator internal components should be tested using a continuity light or an ohmmeter. The following components should be tested.

   a. Stator
   b. Rotor
   c. Diodes
   d. Diode trio (if the alternator is so equipped)
   e. Bearings
   f. Brushes (should be more than 1/2 in. long)

REVIEW QUESTIONS

1. How does a technician test the voltage drop of the charging circuit?

2. How does a technician measure the amperage output of an alternator?

3. What tests can be performed to determine whether a diode or stator is defective before removing the alternator from the vehicle?

CHAPTER QUIZ

1. To check the charging voltage, connect a digital multimeter (DMM) to the positive (+) and the negative (−) terminals of the battery and select _____.
   a. DC volts
   b. AC volts
   c. DC amps
   d. AC amps

2. To check for ripple voltage from the alternator, connect a digital multimeter (DMM) and select _____.
   a. DC volts
   b. AC volts
   c. DC amps
   d. AC amps

3. The maximum allowable alternating current (AC) in amperes that is being sent to the battery from the alternator is _____.
   a. 0.4 A
   b. 1 to 3 A
   c. 3 to 4 A
   d. 10% of the rated output of the alternator

4. Why should the lights be turned on when checking for ripple voltage or alternating current from the alternator?
   a. To warm the battery
   b. To check that the battery is fully charged
   c. To create an electrical load for the alternator
   d. To test the battery before conducting other tests

5. An acceptable charging circuit voltage on a 12 volt system is _____.
   a. 13.5 to 15 volts
   b. 12.6 to 15.6 volts
   c. 12 to 14 volts
   d. 14.9 to 16.1 volts

6. Technician A says that the voltage drop between the output terminal of the alternator and the positive terminal of the battery should be less than 0.4 volt. Technician B says that the voltage drop between the case of the alternator and the negative terminal of the battery should be less than 0.2 volt. Which technician is correct?
   a. Technician A only
   b. Technician B only
   c. Both Technicians A and B
   d. Neither Technician A nor B

7. Technician A says that a voltage drop test of the charging circuit should only be performed when current is flowing through the circuit. Technician B says to connect the leads of a voltmeter to the positive and negative terminals of the battery to measure the voltage drop of the charging system. Which technician is correct?
   a. Technician A only
   b. Technician B only
   c. Both Technicians A and B
   d. Neither Technician A nor B

8. When testing an alternator rotor, if an ohmmeter shows zero ohms with one meter lead attached to the slip rings and the other meter lead touching the rotor shaft, the rotor is _____.
   a. Okay (normal)
   b. Defective (shorted-to-ground)
   c. Defective (shorted-to-voltage)
   d. Okay (rotor windings are open)

9. An alternator diode is being tested using a digital multimeter set to the diode-check position. A good diode will read _____ if the leads are connected one way across the diode and _____ if the leads are reversed.
   a. 300/300   b. 0.475/0.475
   c. OL/OL   d. 0.551/OL

10. An alternator could test as producing lower-than-normal output, yet be okay, if the _____.
    a. Battery is weak or defective
    b. Engine speed is not high enough during testing
    c. Drive belt is loose or slipping
    d. All of the above

chapter 34

ELECTRONIC FUNDAMENTALS

OBJECTIVES: **After studying Chapter 34, the reader will be able to:** • Prepare for ASE Electrical/Electronic Systems (A6) certification test content area "A" (General Electrical/Electronic Systems Diagnosis). • Identify semiconductor components. • Explain precautions necessary when working with semiconductor circuits. • Discuss where various electronic and semiconductor devices are used in vehicles. • Explain how diodes and transistors work. • Describe how to test diodes and transistors. • List the precautions that a service technician should follow to avoid damage to electronic components from electrostatic discharge.

KEY TERMS: • Anode 361 • Base 367 • Bipolar transistor 367 • Burn in 362 • Cathode 361 • CHMSL 366 • Clamping diode 362 • Collector 367 • Control current 367 • Darlington pair 368 • Despiking diode 362 • Diode 360 • Doping 359 • Dual inline pins (DIP) 369 • Emitter 367 • ESD 374 • FET 368 • Forward bias 361 • Gate 370 • Germanium 359 • Heat sink 369 • Holes 360 • Hole theory 360 • Impurities 359 • Integrated circuit (IC) 369 • Inverter 373 • Junction 361 • Light emitting diode (LED) 364 • MOSFET 368 • NPN transistor 367 • NTC 366 • N-type material 359 • Op-amps 370 • Photodiodes 365 • Photons 365 • Photoresistor 365 • Phototransistor 369 • Peak inverse voltage (PIV) 364 • Peak reverse voltage (PRV) 364 • PNP transistor 367 • P-type material 360 • PWM 372 • Rectifier bridge 366 • Reverse bias 361 • SCR 365 • Semiconductors 359 • Silicon 359 • Spike protection resistor 363 • Suppression diode 362 • Thermistor 366 • Threshold voltage 367 • Transistor 366 • Zener diode 362

Electronic components are the heart of computers. Knowing how electronic components work helps take the mystery out of automotive electronics.

SEMICONDUCTORS

DEFINITION Semiconductors are neither conductors nor insulators. The flow of electrical current is caused by the movement of electrons in materials, known as conductors having *fewer* than four electrons in their atom's outer orbit. Insulators contain *more* than four electrons in their outer orbit and cannot conduct electricity because their atomic structure is stable (no free electrons).

Semiconductors are materials that contain exactly four electrons in the outer orbit of their atom structure and are, therefore, neither good conductors nor good insulators.

EXAMPLES OF SEMICONDUCTORS Two examples of semiconductor materials are **germanium** and **silicon,** which have exactly four electrons in their valance ring and no free electrons to provide current flow. However, both of these semiconductor materials can be made to conduct current if another material is added to provide the necessary conditions for electron movement.

CONSTRUCTION When another material is added to a semiconductor material in very small amounts, it is called **doping.** The doping elements are called **impurities;** therefore, after their addition, the germanium and silicon are no longer considered *pure* elements. The material added to pure silicon or germanium to make it electrically conductive represents only one atom of impurity for every *100 million* atoms of the pure semiconductor material. The resulting atoms are still electrically *neutral,* because the number of electrons still equals the number of protons of the combined materials. These combined materials are classified into two groups depending on the number of electrons in the bonding between the two materials.

- N-type materials
- P-type materials

N-TYPE MATERIAL **N-type material** is silicon or germanium that is doped with an element such as *phosphorus*, *arsenic*, or *antimony*, each having five electrons in its outer orbit. These five electrons are combined with the four electrons of the silicon or germanium to total nine electrons. There is room for only eight electrons in the bonding between the semiconductor material and the doping material. This leaves extra electrons, and even though the material is still electrically neutral, these extra electrons tend to repel other electrons outside the material. ● **SEE FIGURE 34–1.**

FIGURE 34–1 N-type material. Silicon (Si) doped with a material (such as phosphorus) with five electrons in the outer orbit results in an extra free electron.

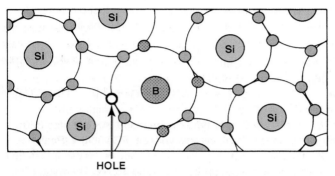

FIGURE 34–2 P-type material. Silicon (Si) doped with a material, such as boron (B), with three electrons in the outer orbit results in a hole capable of attracting an electron.

P-TYPE MATERIAL **P-type material** is produced by doping silicon or germanium with the element *boron* or the element *indium*. These impurities have only three electrons in their outer shell and, when combined with the semiconductor material, result in a material with seven electrons, one electron *less* than is required for atom bonding. This lack of one electron makes the material able to attract electrons, even though the material still has a neutral charge. This material tends to attract electrons to fill the **holes** for the missing eighth electron in the bonding of the materials. ● **SEE FIGURE 34–2.**

SUMMARY OF SEMICONDUCTORS

The following is a summary of semiconductor fundamentals.

1. The two types of semiconductor materials are P type and N type. N-type material contains extra electrons; P-type material contains holes due to missing electrons. The number of excess electrons in an N-type material must remain constant, and the number of holes in the P-type material must also remain constant. Because electrons are interchangeable, movement of electrons in or out of the material is possible to maintain a balanced material.

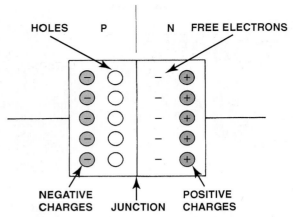

FIGURE 34–3 Unlike charges attract and the current carriers (electrons and holes) move toward the junction.

? FREQUENTLY ASKED QUESTION

What Is the Hole Theory?

Current flow is expressed as the movement of electrons from one atom to another. In semiconductor and electronic terms, the movement of electrons fills the holes of the P-type material. Therefore, as the holes are filled with electrons, the unfilled holes move opposite to the flow of the electrons. This concept of hole movement is called the hole theory of current flow. The holes move in the direction opposite that of electron flow. For example, think of an egg carton, where if an egg is moved in one direction, the holes created move in the opposite direction. ● **SEE FIGURE 34–3.**

2. In P-type semiconductors, electrical conduction occurs mainly as the result of holes (absence of electrons). In N-type semiconductors, electrical conduction occurs mainly as the result of electrons (excess of electrons).

3. Hole movement results from the jumping of electrons into new positions.

4. Under the effect of a voltage applied to the semiconductor, electrons travel toward the positive terminal and holes move toward the negative terminal. The direction of hole current agrees with the conventional direction of current flow.

DIODES

CONSTRUCTION A **diode** is an electrical one-way check valve made by combining a P-type material and an N-type material. The word *diode* means "having two electrodes." Electrodes are electrical connections: The positive electrode is

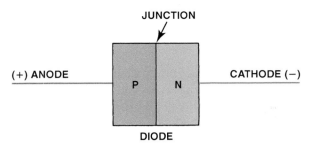

FIGURE 34–4 A diode is a component with P-type and N-type materials together. The negative electrode is called the cathode and the positive electrode is called the anode.

called the **anode;** the negative electrode is called the **cathode.** The point where the two types of materials join is called the **junction.** ● SEE FIGURE 34–4.

OPERATION The N-type material has one extra electron, which can flow into the P-type material. The P type has a need for electrons to fill its holes. If a battery were connected to the diode positive (+) to P-type material and negative (−) to N-type material, then the electrons that left the N-type material and flowed into the P-type material to fill the holes would be quickly replaced by the electron flow from the battery. Current flows through a forward-bias diode for the following reasons.

- Electrons move toward the holes (P-type material).
- Holes move toward the electrons (N-type material).
  ● **SEE FIGURE 34–5.**

As a result, current would flow through the diode with low resistance. This condition is called **forward bias.**

If the battery connections were reversed and the positive side of the battery was connected to the N-type material, the electrons would be pulled toward the battery and away from the junction of the N-type and P-type materials. (Remember, unlike charges attract, whereas like charges repel.) Because electrical conduction requires the flow of electrons across the

FIGURE 34–6 Diode connected with reversed polarity. No current flows across the junction between the P-type and N-type materials. This connection is called reverse bias.

junction of the N-type and P-type materials and because the battery connections are actually reversed, the diode offers very high resistance to current flow. This condition is called **reverse bias.** ● SEE FIGURE 34–6.

Therefore, diodes allow current flow only when current of the correct polarity is connected to the circuit.

- Diodes are used in alternators to control current flow in one direction, which changes the AC voltage generated into DC voltage.
- Diodes are also used in computer controls, relays, air-conditioning circuits, and many other circuits to prevent possible damage due to reverse current flows that may be generated within the circuit. ● SEE FIGURE 34–7.

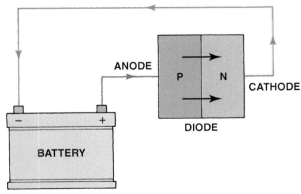

FIGURE 34–5 Diode connected to a battery with correct polarity (battery positive to P type and battery negative to N-type). Current flows through the diode. This condition is called forward bias.

? FREQUENTLY ASKED QUESTION

What Is the Difference Between Electricity and Electronics?

Electronics usually means that solid-state devices are used in the electrical circuits. Electricity as used in automotive applications usually means electrical current flow through resistance and loads without the use of diodes, transistors, or other electronic devices.

FIGURE 34–7 Diode symbol and electrode names. The arrow always points toward the N-type material. The stripe on one end of a diode represents the cathode end of the diode.

TECH TIP

"Burn In" to Be Sure

A common term heard in the electronic and computer industry is **burn in,** which means to operate an electronic device, such as a computer, for a period from several hours to several days.

Most electronic devices fail in infancy, or during the first few hours of operation. This early failure occurs if there is a manufacturing defect, especially at the P-N junction of any semiconductor device. The junction will usually fail after only a few operating cycles.

What does this information mean to the average person? When purchasing a personal or business computer, have the computer burned in before delivery. This step helps ensure that all of the circuits have survived infancy and that the chances of chip failure are greatly reduced. Purchasing sound or television equipment that has been on display may be a good value, because during its operation as a display model, the burn-in process has been completed. The automotive service technician should be aware that if a replacement electronic device fails shortly after installation, the problem may be a case of early electronic failure.

NOTE: Whenever there is a failure of a replacement part, the technician should always check for excessive voltage or heat to and around the problem component.

ZENER DIODE SYMBOL

FIGURE 34–8 A zener diode blocks current flow until a certain voltage is reached, then it permits current to flow.

HIGH-VOLTAGE SPIKE PROTECTION

CLAMPING DIODES   Diodes can be used as a high-voltage clamping device when the power (+) is connected to the cathode (−) of the diode. If a coil is pulsed on and off, a high-voltage spike is produced whenever the coil is turned off. To control and direct this possibly damaging high-voltage spike, a diode can be installed across the leads to the coil to redirect the high-voltage spike back through the coil windings to prevent possible damage to the rest of the vehicle's electrical or electronic circuits. A diode connected across the terminals of a coil to control voltage spikes is called a **clamping diode.** Clamping diodes can also be called **despiking** or **suppression diodes.** ● **SEE FIGURE 34–9.**

CLAMPING DIODE APPLICATION   Diodes were first used on A/C compressor clutch coils at the same time electronic devices were first used. The diode was used to help prevent

ZENER DIODES

CONSTRUCTION   A **zener diode** is a specially constructed diode designed to operate with a reverse-bias current. Zener diodes were named in 1934 for their inventor, Clarence Melvin Zener, an American professor of physics.

OPERATION   A zener diode acts as any diode in that it blocks reverse-bias current, but only up to a certain voltage. Above this certain voltage (called the *breakdown voltage* or the zener region), a zener diode will conduct current in the opposite direction without damage to the diode. A zener diode is heavily doped, and the reverse-bias voltage does not harm the material. The voltage drop across a zener diode remains practically the same before and after the breakdown voltage, and this factor makes a zener diode perfect for voltage regulation. Zener diodes can be constructed for various breakdown voltages and can be used in a variety of automotive and electronic applications, especially for electronic voltage regulators used in the charging system. ● **SEE FIGURE 34–8.**

(a)

(b)

FIGURE 34–9 (a) Notice that when the coil is being energized, the diode is reverse biased and the current is blocked from passing through the diode. The current flows through the coil in the normal direction. (b) When the switch is opened, the magnetic field surrounding the coil collapses, producing a high-voltage surge in the reverse polarity of the applied voltage. This voltage surge forward biases the diode, and the surge is dissipated harmlessly back through the windings of the coil.

FIGURE 34–10 A diode connected to both terminals of the air-conditioning compressor clutch used to reduce the high-voltage spike that results when a coil (compressor clutch coil) is de-energized.

the high voltage spike generated inside the A/C clutch coil from damaging delicate to delicate electronic circuits anywhere in the vehicle's electrical system. ● **SEE FIGURE 34–10.**

Because most automotive circuits eventually are electrically connected to each other in parallel, a high-voltage surge anywhere in the vehicle could damage electronic components in other circuits.

The circuits most likely to be affected by the high-voltage surge, if the diode fails, are the circuits controlling the operation of the A/C compressor clutch and any component that uses a coil, such as those of the blower motor and climate control units.

Many relays are equipped with a diode to prevent a voltage spike when the contact points open and the magnetic field in the coil winding collapses. ● **SEE FIGURE 34–11.**

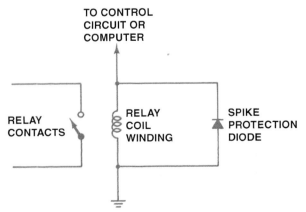

FIGURE 34–11 Spike protection diodes are commonly used in computer-controlled circuits to prevent damaging high-voltage surges that occur any time current flowing through a coil is stopped.

FIGURE 34–12 A zener diode is commonly used inside automotive computers to protect delicate electronic circuits from high-voltage spikes. A 35-volt zener diode will conduct any voltage spike higher than 35 voltage resulting from the discharge of the fuel injector coil safely to ground through a current-limiting resistor in series with the zener diode.

DESPIKING ZENER DIODES Zener diodes can also be used to control high-voltage spikes and keep them from damaging delicate electronic circuits. Zener diodes are most commonly used in electronic fuel-injection circuits that control the firing of the injectors. If clamping diodes were used in parallel with the injection coil, the resulting clamping action would tend to delay the closing of the fuel injector nozzle. A zener diode is commonly used to clamp only the higher voltage portion of the resulting voltage spike without affecting the operation of the injector. ● **SEE FIGURE 34–12.**

DESPIKING RESISTORS All coils must use some protection against high-voltage spikes that occur when the voltage is removed from any coil. Instead of a diode installed in parallel with the coil windings, a resistor can be used, called a **spike protection resistor.** ● **SEE FIGURE 34–13.**

FIGURE 34–13 A despiking resistor is used in many automotive applications to help prevent harmful high-voltage surges from being created when the magnetic field surrounding a coil collapses when the coil circuit is opened.

Resistors are often preferred for two reasons.

| Reason 1 | Coils will usually fail when shorted rather than open, as this shorted condition results in greater current flow in the circuit. A diode installed in the reverse-bias direction cannot control this extra current, whereas a resistor in parallel can help reduce potentially damaging current flow if the coil becomes shorted. |
| Reason 2 | The protective diode can also fail, and diodes usually fail by shorting before they blow open. If a diode becomes shorted, excessive current can flow through the coil circuit, perhaps causing damage. A resistor usually fails open and, therefore, even in failure could not in itself cause a problem. |

Resistors on coils are often used in relays and in climate-control circuit solenoids to control vacuum to the various air management system doors as well as other electronically controlled applications.

DIODE RATINGS

SPECIFICATIONS Most diodes are rated according to the following:

- Maximum current flow in the forward-bias direction. Diodes are sized and rated according to the amount of current they are designed to handle in the forward-bias direction. This rating is normally from 1 to 5 amperes for most automotive applications.
- This rating of resistance to reverse-bias voltage is called the **peak inverse voltage (PIV)** rating, or the **peak reverse voltage (PRV)** rating. It is important that the service technician specifies and uses only a replacement diode that has the same or a higher rating than specified by the vehicle manufacturer for both amperage and PIV rating. Typical 1 A diodes use an industry numbering code that indicates the PIV rating. For example:

  1N 4001-50 V PIV

  1N 4002-100 V PIV

  1N 4003-200 V PIV (most commonly used)

  1N 4004-400 V PIV

  1N 4005-600 V PIV

- The "1N" means that the diode has one P-N junction. A higher rating diode can be used with no problems (except for slightly higher cost, even though the highest rated diode generally costs less than $1). Never substitute a *lower* rated diode than is specified.

DIODE VOLTAGE DROP The voltage drop across a diode is about the same voltage as that required to forward bias the diode. If the diode is made from germanium, the forward voltage is 0.3 to 0.5 volt. If the diode is made from silicon, the forward voltage is 0.5 to 0.7 volt.

NOTE: When diodes are tested using a digital multimeter, the meter will display the voltage drop across the P-N junction (about 0.5 to 0.7 volt) when the meter is set to the *diode-check* position.

LIGHT-EMITTING DIODES

OPERATION All diodes radiate some energy during normal operation. Most diodes radiate heat because of the junction barrier voltage drop (typically 0.6 volt for silicon diodes). **Light emitting diode (LED)** radiate light when current flows through the diode in the forward-bias direction. ● **SEE FIGURE 34–14.**

The forward-bias voltage required for an LED ranges between 1.5 and 2.2 volts.

An LED will only light if the voltage at the anode (positive electrode) is at least 1.5 to 2.2 volts higher than the voltage at the cathode (negative electrode).

NEED FOR CURRENT LIMITING If an LED were connected across a 12-volt automotive battery, the LED would light brightly, but only for a second or two. Excessive current (amperes) that flows across the P-N junction of any electronic device can destroy the junction. A resistor *must* be connected in series with every diode (including LEDs) to control current flow across the P-N junction. This protection should include the following:

1. The value of the resistor should be from 300 to 500 ohms for each P-N junction. Commonly available resistors in this range include 470, 390, and 330 ohm resistors.

2. The resistors can be connected to either the anode or the cathode end. (Polarity of the resistor does not matter.) Current flows through the LED in series with the resistor, and the resistor will control the current flow through the LED regardless of its position in the circuit.

FIGURE 34–14 A typical light-emitting diode (LED). This particular LED is designed with a built-in resistor so that 12 volts DC may be applied directly to the leads without an external resistor. Normally a 300 to 500 ohm, 0.5-watt resistor is required to be attached in series with the LED, to control current flow to about 0.020 A (20 mA) or damage to the P-N junction may occur.

How Does an LED Emit Light?

An LED contains a chip that houses P-type and N-type materials. The junction between these regions acts as a barrier to the flow of electrons between the two materials. When a voltage of 1.5 to 2.2 volts of the correct polarity is applied, current will flow across the junction. As the electrons enter the P-type material, it combines with the holes in the material and releases energy in the form of light (called **photons**). The amount and color the light produces depends on materials used in the creation of the semiconductor material.

LEDs are very efficient compared to conventional incandescent bulbs, which depend on heat to create light. LEDs generate very little heat, with most of the energy consumed converted directly to light. LEDs are reliable and are being used for taillights, brake lights, daytime running lights, and headlights in some vehicles.

3. Resistors protecting diodes can be actual resistors or other current-limiting loads such as lamps or coils. With the current-limiting devices to control the current, the average LED will require about 20 to 30 milliamperes (mA), or 0.020 to 0.030 ampere.

PHOTODIODES

PURPOSE AND FUNCTION All semiconductor P-N junctions emit energy, mostly in the form of heat or light such as with an LED. In fact, if an LED is exposed to bright light, a voltage potential is established between the anode and the cathode. **Photodiodes** are specially constructed to respond to various wavelengths of light with a "window" built into the housing. ● SEE FIGURE 34–15.

Photodiodes are frequently used in steering wheel controls for transmitting tuning, volume, and other information

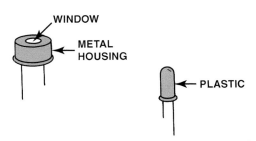

FIGURE 34–15 Typical photodiodes. They are usually built into a plastic housing so that the photodiode itself may not be visible.

FIGURE 34–16 Symbol for a photodiode. The arrows represent light striking the P-N junction of the photodiode.

from the steering wheel to the data link and the unit being controlled. If several photodiodes are placed on the steering column end and LEDs or phototransistors are placed on the steering wheel side, then data can be transmitted between the two moving points without the interference that could be caused by physical contact types of units.

CONSTRUCTION A photodiode is sensitive to light. When light energy strikes the diode, electrons are released and the diode will conduct in the forward-bias direction. (The light energy is used to overcome the barrier voltage.)

The resistance across the photodiode decreases as the intensity of the light increases. This characteristic makes the photodiode a useful electronic device for controlling some automotive lighting systems such as automatic headlights. The symbol for a photodiode is shown in ● FIGURE 34–16.

PHOTORESISTORS

A **photoresistor** is a semiconductor material (usually cadmium sulfide) that changes resistance with the presence or absence of light.

Dark = High resistance

Light = Low resistance

Because resistance is reduced when the photoresistor is exposed to light, the photoresistor can be used to control headlight dimmer relays and for automotive headlights. ● SEE FIGURE 34–17.

SILICON-CONTROLLED RECTIFIERS

CONSTRUCTION A **silicon-controlled rectifier (SCR)** is commonly used in the electronic circuits of various automotive

FIGURE 34–17 Either symbol may be used to represent a photoresistor.

FIGURE 34–18 Symbol and terminal identification of an SCR.

FIGURE 34–19 Wiring diagram for a center high-mounted stoplight (CHMSL) using SCRs.

FIGURE 34–20 Symbols used to represent a thermistor.

	COPPER WIRE	NTC THERMISTOR
Cold	Lower resistance	Higher resistance
Hot	Higher resistance	Lower resistance

CHART 34–1

The resistance changes opposite that of a copper wire with changes in temperature.

applications. An SCR is a semiconductor device that looks like two diodes connected end to end. ● SEE FIGURE 34–18.

If the anode is connected to a higher voltage source than the cathode in a circuit, no current will flow as would occur with a diode. If, however, a positive voltage source is connected to the gate of the SCR, then current can flow from anode to cathode with a typical voltage drop of 1.2 volts (double the voltage drop of a typical diode, at 0.6 volt).

Voltage applied to the gate is used to turn the SCR on. However, if the voltage source at the gate is shut off, the current will still continue to flow through the SCR until the source current is stopped.

USES OF AN SCR
SCRs can be used to construct a circuit for a **center high-mounted stoplight (CHMSL).** If this third stoplight were wired into either the left- or the right-side brake light circuit, the CHMSL would also flash whenever the turn signals were used for the side that was connected to the CHMSL. When two SCRs are used, both brake lights must be activated to supply current to the CHMSL. The current to the CHMSL is shut off when both SCRs lose their power source (when the brake pedal is released, which stops the current flow to the brake lights). ● SEE FIGURE 34–19.

THERMISTORS

CONSTRUCTION
A **thermistor** is a semiconductor material such as silicon that has been doped to provide a

given resistance. When the thermistor is heated, the electrons within the crystal gain energy and electrons are released. This means that a thermistor actually produces a small voltage when heated. If voltage is applied to a thermistor, its resistance decreases because the thermistor itself is acting as a current carrier rather than as a resistor at higher temperatures.

USES OF THERMISTORS
A thermistor is commonly used as a temperature-sensing device for coolant temperature and intake manifold air temperature. Because thermistors operate in a manner opposite to that of a typical conductor, they are called **negative temperature coefficient (NTC)** thermistors; their resistance decreases as the temperature increases. ● SEE CHART 34–1.

Thermistor symbols are shown in ● FIGURE 34–20.

RECTIFIER BRIDGES

DEFINITION
The word *rectify* means "to set straight"; therefore, a rectifier is an electronic device (such as a diode) used to convert a changing voltage into a straight or constant voltage. A **rectifier bridge** is a group of diodes that is used to change alternating current (AC) into direct current (DC). A rectifier bridge is used in alternators to rectify the AC voltage produced in the stator (stationary windings) of the alternator into DC voltage. These rectifier bridges contain six diodes: one pair of diodes (one positive and one negative) for each of the three stator windings. ● SEE FIGURE 34–21.

TRANSISTORS

PURPOSE AND FUNCTION
A **transistor** is a semiconductor device that can perform the following electrical functions.

FIGURE 34–21 This rectifier bridge contains six diodes; the three on each side are mounted in an aluminum-finned unit to help keep the diode cool during alternator operation.

1. Act as an electrical switch in a circuit
2. Act as an amplifier of current in a circuit
3. Regulate the current in a circuit

The word *transistor,* derived from the words *transfer* and *resistor,* is used to describe the transfer of current across a resistor. A transistor is made of three alternating sections or layers of P-type and N-type materials. This type of transistor is usually called a **bipolar transistor.**

CONSTRUCTION   A transistor that has P-type material on each end, with N-type material in the center, is called a **PNP transistor.** Another type, with the exact opposite arrangement, is called an **NPN transistor.**

The material at one end of a transistor is called the **emitter** and the material at the other end is called the **collector.** The **base** is in the center and the voltage applied to the base is used to control current through a transistor.

TRANSISTOR SYMBOLS   All transistor symbols contain an arrow indicating the emitter part of the transistor. The arrow points in the direction of current flow (conventional theory).

When an arrowhead appears in any semiconductor symbol, it stands for a P-N junction and it points from the P-type material toward the N-type material. The arrow on a transistor is always attached to the *emitter* side of the transistor. ● **SEE FIGURE 34–22.**

 FREQUENTLY ASKED QUESTION

Is a Transistor Similar to a Relay?

Yes, in many cases a transistor is similar to a relay.
Both use a low current to control a higher current circuit. ● **SEE CHART 34–2.**
A relay can only be on or off. A transistor can provide a variable output if the base is supplied a variable current input.

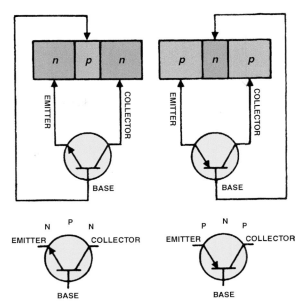

FIGURE 34–22 Basic transistor operation. A small current flowing through the base and emitter of the transistor turns on the transistor and permits a higher amperage current to flow from the collector and the emitter.

	RELAY	TRANSISTOR
Low-current circuit	Coil (terminals 85 and 86)	Base and emitter
High-current circuit	Contacts terminals 30 and 87	Collector and emitter

CHART 34–2

Comparison between the control (low-current) and high-current circuits of a transistor compared to a mechanical relay.

HOW A TRANSISTOR WORKS   A transistor is similar to two back-to-back diodes that can conduct current in only one direction. As in a diode, N-type material can conduct electricity by means of its supply of free electrons, and P-type material conducts by means of its supply of positive holes.

A transistor will allow current flow if the electrical conditions allow it to switch on, in a manner similar to the working of an electromagnetic relay. The electrical conditions are determined, or switched, by means of the base, or *B*. The base will carry current only when the proper voltage and polarity are applied. The main circuit current flow travels through the other two parts of the transistor: the emitter *E* and the collector *C*. ● **SEE FIGURE 34–23.**

If the base current is turned off or on, the current flow from collector to emitter is turned off or on. The current controlling the base is called the **control current.** The control current must be high enough to switch the transistor on or off. (This control voltage, called the **threshold voltage,** must be above approximately 0.3 volt for germanium and 0.6 volt for silicon transistors.) This control current can also "throttle" or regulate the main circuit, in a manner similar to the operation of a water faucet.

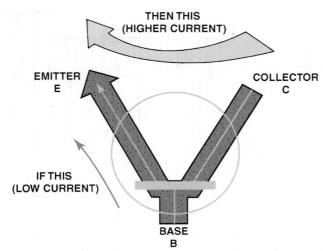

FIGURE 34–23 Basic transistor operation. A small current flowing through the base and emitter of the transistor turns on the transistor and permits a higher amperage current to flow from the collector and the emitter.

FIGURE 34–24 The three terminals of a field-effect transistor (FET) are called the source, gate, and drain.

 FREQUENTLY ASKED QUESTION

What Does the Arrow Mean on a Transistor Symbol?

The arrow on a transistor symbol is always on the emitter and points toward the N-type material. The arrow on a diode also points toward the N-type material. To know which type of transistor is being shown, note which direction the arrow points.

- PNP: pointing in
- NPN: not pointing in

HOW A TRANSISTOR AMPLIFIES A transistor can amplify a signal if the signal is strong enough to trigger the base of a transistor on and off. The resulting on-off current flow through the transistor can be connected to a higher powered electrical circuit. This results in a higher powered circuit being controlled by a lower powered circuit. This low-powered circuit's cycling is exactly duplicated in the higher powered circuit, and therefore any transistor can be used to amplify a signal. However, because some transistors are better than others for amplification, specialized types of transistors are used for each specialized circuit function.

FIELD-EFFECT TRANSISTORS

Field-effect transistors (FETs) have been used in most automotive applications since the mid-1980s. They use less electrical current and rely mostly on the strength of a small voltage signal to control the output. The parts of a typical FET include the *source, gate,* and *drain.* ● **SEE FIGURE 34–24.**

Many field-effect transistors are constructed of metal oxide semiconductor (MOS) materials, called **MOSFETs.** MOSFETs are highly sensitive to static electricity and can be easily damaged if exposed to excessive current or high-voltage surges (spikes). Most automotive electronic circuits use MOSFETs, which explains why it is vital for the

 FREQUENTLY ASKED QUESTION

What Is a Darlington Pair?

A **Darlington pair** consists of two transistors wired together. This arrangement permits a very small current flow to control a large current flow. The Darlington pair is named for Sidney Darlington, an American physicist for Bell Laboratories from 1929 to 1971. Darlington amplifier circuits are commonly used in electronic ignition systems, computer engine control circuits, and many other electronic applications. ● **SEE FIGURE 34–25.**

FIGURE 34–25 A Darlington pair consists of two transistors wired together, allowing for a very small current to control a larger current flow circuit.

(a)   (b)

FIGURE 34–26 Symbols for a phototransistor. (a) This symbol uses the line for the base; (b) this symbol does not.

service technician to use caution to avoid doing anything that could result in a high-voltage spike, and perhaps destroy an expensive computer module. Some vehicle manufacturers recommend that technicians wear an antistatic wristband when working with modules that contain MOSFETs. Always follow the vehicle manufacturer's instructions found in service information to avoid damaging electronic modules or circuits.

PHOTOTRANSISTORS

Similar in operation to a photodiode, a **phototransistor** uses light energy to turn on the base of a transistor. A phototransistor is an NPN transistor that has a large exposed base area to permit light to act as the control for the transistor. Therefore, a phototransistor may or may not have a base lead. If not, then it has only a collector and emitter lead. When the phototransistor is connected to a powered circuit, the light intensity is amplified by the gain of the transistor. Phototransistors, along with photo diodes, are frequently used in steering wheel controls. ● **SEE FIGURE 34–26.**

INTEGRATED CIRCUITS

PURPOSE AND FUNCTION Solid-state components are used in many electronic semiconductors and/or circuits. They are called "solid state" because they have no moving parts, just higher or lower voltage levels within the circuit. Discrete (individual) diodes, transistors, and other semiconductor devices were often used to construct early electronic ignition and electronic voltage regulators. Newer style electronic devices use the same components, but they are now combined (integrated) into one group of circuits, and are thus called an **integrated circuit (IC).**

CONSTRUCTION Integrated circuits are usually encased in a plastic housing called a CHIP with two rows of inline pins. This arrangement is called the **dual inline pins (DIP)** chips. ● **SEE FIGURE 34–27.**

Therefore, most computer circuits are housed as an integrated circuit in a DIP chip.

HEAT SINK **Heat sink** is a term used to describe any area around an electronic component that, because of its shape

FIGURE 34–27 A typical automotive computer with the case removed to show all of the various electronic devices and integrated circuits (ICs). The CPU is an example of a DIP chip and the large red and orange devices are ceramic capacitors.

or design, can conduct damaging heat away from electronic parts. Examples of heat sinks include the following:

1. Ribbed electronic ignition control units
2. Cooling slits and cooling fan attached to an alternator
3. Special heat-conducting grease under the electronic ignition module in General Motors HEI distributor ignition systems and other electronic systems

Heat sinks are necessary to prevent damage to diodes, transistors, and other electronic components due to heat buildup. Excessive heat can damage the junction between the N-type and P-type materials used in diodes and transistors.

? FREQUENTLY ASKED QUESTION

What Causes a Transistor or Diode to Blow?

Every automotive diode and transistor is designed to operate within certain voltage and amperage ranges for individual applications. For example, transistors used for switching are designed and constructed differently from transistors used for amplifying signals.

Because each electronic component is designed to operate satisfactorily for its particular application, any severe change in operating current (amperes), voltage, or heat can destroy the *junction.* This failure can cause either an open circuit (no current flows) or a short (current flows through the component all the time when the component should be blocking the current flow).

TRANSISTOR GATES

PURPOSE AND FUNCTION An understanding of the basic operation of electronic gates is important to understanding how computers work. A **gate** is an electronic circuit whose output depends on the location and voltage of two inputs.

CONSTRUCTION Whether a transistor is on or off depends on the voltage at the base of the transistor. If the voltage is at least a 0.6 volt difference from that of the emitter, the transistor is turned on. Most electronic and computer circuits use 5 volts as a power source. If two transistors are wired together, several different outputs can be received depending on how the two transistors are wired. ● **SEE FIGURE 34–28.**

OPERATION If the voltage at *A* is higher than that of the emitter, the top transistor is turned on; however, the bottom transistor is off unless the voltage at *B* is also higher. If both transistors are turned on, the output signal voltage will be high. If only one of the two transistors is on, the output will be zero (off or no voltage). Because it requires both *A* and *B* to be on to result in a voltage output, this circuit is called an *AND gate*. In other words, both transistors have to be on before the gate opens and allows a voltage output. Other types of gates can be constructed using various connections to the two transistors. For example:

AND gate. Requires both transistors to be on to get an output.

OR gate. Requires either transistor to be on to get an output.

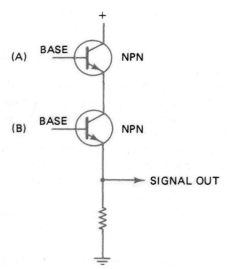

FIGURE 34–28 Typical transistor AND gate circuit using two transistors. The emitter is always the line with the arrow. Notice that both transistors must be turned on before there will be voltage present at the point labeled "signal out."

? FREQUENTLY ASKED QUESTION

What Are Logic Highs and Lows?

All computer circuits and most electronic circuits (such as gates) use various combinations of high and low voltages. High decreases as the temperature increases is generally considered zero (ground). However, high voltages do not *have* to begin at 5 volts. *High, or the number 1, to a computer is the presence of voltage above a certain level.* For example, a circuit could be constructed where any voltage higher than 3.8 volts would be considered high. *Low, or the number 0, to a computer is the absence of voltage or a voltage lower than a certain value.* For example, a voltage of 0.62 may be considered low. Various associated names and terms can be summarized.

- Logic low = Low voltage = Number 0 = Reference low
- Logic high = Higher voltage = Number 1 = Reference high

NAND (NOT-AND) gate. Output is on unless both transistors are on.

NOR (NOT-OR) gate. Output is on only when both transistors are off.

Gates represent logic circuits that can be constructed so that the output depends on the voltage (on or off; high or low) of the inputs to the bases of transistors. Their inputs can come from sensors or other circuits that monitor sensors, and their outputs can be used to operate an output device if amplified and controlled by other circuits. For example, the blower motor will be commanded on when the following events occur, to cause the control module to turn it on.

1. The ignition must be on (input).
2. The air conditioning is commanded on.
3. The engine coolant temperature is within a predetermined limit.

If all of these conditions are met, then the control module will command the blower motor on. If any of the input signals are incorrect, the control module will not be able to perform the correct command.

OPERATIONAL AMPLIFIERS

Operational amplifiers (op-amps) are used in circuits to control and amplify digital signals. Op-amps are frequently used for motor control in climate control systems (heating and

FIGURE 34-29 Symbol for an operational amplifier (op-amp).

air conditioning) airflow control door operation. Op-amps can provide the proper voltage polarity and current (amperes) to control the direction of permanent magnetic (PM) motors. The symbol for an op-amp is shown in ● **FIGURE 34-29.**

ELECTRONIC COMPONENT FAILURE CAUSES

Electronic components such as electronic ignition modules, electronic voltage regulators, onboard computers, and any other electronic circuit are generally quite reliable; however, failure can occur. Frequent causes of premature failure include the following:

- **Poor connections.** It has been estimated that most engine computers returned as defective have simply had poor connections at the wiring harness terminal ends. These faults are often intermittent and hard to find.

    NOTE: When cleaning electronic contacts, use a pencil eraser. This cleans the contacts without harming the thin, protective coating used on most electronic terminals.

- **Heat.** The operation and resistance of electronic components and circuits are affected by heat. Electronic components should be kept as cool as possible and never hotter than 260°F (127°C).

- **Voltage spikes.** A high-voltage spike can literally burn a hole through semiconductor material. The source of these high-voltage spikes is often the discharge of a coil without proper (or with defective) despiking protection. A poor electrical connection at the battery or other major electrical connection can cause high-voltage spikes to occur, because the *entire wiring harness creates its own magnetic field*, similar to that formed around a coil. If the connection is loose and momentary loss of contact occurs, a high-voltage surge can occur through the entire electrical system. To help prevent this type of damage, ensure that all electrical connections, including grounds, are properly clean and tight.

    CAUTION: One of the major causes of electronic failure occurs during jump starting a vehicle. Always check that the ignition switch is off on both vehicles when making the connection. Always double check that the correct battery polarity (+ to + and − to −) is being performed.

FIGURE 34-30 Schematic for a blinking LED theft deterrent.

 TECH TIP

Blinking LED Theft Deterrent

A blinking (flashing) LED consumes only about 5 milliamperes (5/1,000 of 1 ampere or 0.005 A). Most alarm systems use a blinking red LED to indicate that the system is armed. A fake alarm indicator is easy to make and install.

A 470 ohm, 0.5-watt resistor limits current flow to prevent battery drain. The positive terminal (anode) of the diode is connected to a fuse that is hot at all times, such as the cigarette lighter. The negative terminal (cathode) of the LED is connected to any ignition-controlled fuse. ● SEE **FIGURE 34-30.**

When the ignition is turned off, the power flows through the LED to ground and the LED flashes. To prevent distraction during driving, the LED goes out when the ignition is on. Therefore, this fake theft deterrent is "auto setting" and no other action is required to activate it when you leave your vehicle except to turn off the ignition and remove the key as usual.

- **Excessive current.** All electronic circuits are designed to operate within a designated range of current (amperes). If a solenoid or relay is controlled by a computer circuit, the resistance of that solenoid or relay becomes part of that control circuit. If a coil winding inside the solenoid or relay becomes shorted, the resulting lower resistance will increase the current through the circuit. Even though individual components are used with current-limiting resistors in series, the coil winding resistance is also used as a current-control component in the circuit. If a computer fails, always measure the resistance across all computer-controlled relays and solenoids. The resistance should be within specifications (generally *over* 20 ohms) for each component that is computer controlled.

NOTE: Some computer-controlled solenoids are pulsed on and off rapidly. This type of solenoid is used in many electronically shifted transmissions. Their resistance is usually about half of the resistance of a simple on-off solenoid—usually between 10 and 15 ohms. Because the computer controls the on-time of the solenoid, the solenoid and its circuit control are called pulse-width modulated (PWM).

HOW TO TEST DIODES AND TRANSISTORS

TESTERS   Diodes and transistors can be tested with an ohmmeter. The diode or transistor being tested must be disconnected from the circuit for the results to be meaningful.

- Use the *diode-check* position on a digital multimeter.
- In the diode-check position on a digital multimeter, the meter applies a higher voltage than when the ohms test function is selected.
- This slightly higher voltage (about 2 to 3 volts) is enough to forward bias a diode or the P-N junction of transistors.

DIODES   Using the diode test position, the meter applies a voltage. The display will show the voltage drop across the diode P-N junction. A good diode should give an over limit (OL) reading with the test leads attached to each lead of the diode in one way, and a voltage reading of 0.400 to 0.600 V when the leads are reversed. This reading is the voltage drop or the barrier voltage across the P-N junction of the diode.

1. A low-voltage reading with the meter leads attached both ways across a diode means that the diode is *shorted* and must be replaced.

2. An OL reading with the meter leads attached both ways across a diode means that the diode is *open* and must be replaced. ● **SEE FIGURE 34–31.**

TRANSISTORS   Using a digital meter set to the diode-check position, a good transistor should show a voltage drop of 0.400 to 0.600 volt between the following:

- The emitter (*E*) and the base (*B*) and between the base (*B*) and the collector (*C*) with a meter connected one way, and OL when the meter test leads are reversed.

FIGURE 34–31 To check a diode, select "diode check" on a digital multimeter. The display will indicate the voltage drop (difference) between the meter leads. The meter itself applies a low-voltage signal (usually about 3 volts) and displays the difference on the display. (a) When the diode is forward biased, the meter should display a voltage between 0.500 and 0.700 V (500 to 700 mV). (b) When the meter leads are reversed, the meter should read OL (over limit) because the diode is reverse biased and blocking current flow.

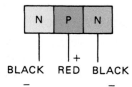

FIGURE 34–32 If the red (positive) lead of the ohmmeter (or a multimeter set to diode check) is touched to the center and the black (negative lead) touched to either end of the electrode, the meter should forward bias the P-N junction and indicate on the meter as low resistance. If the meter reads high resistance, reverse the meter leads, putting the black on the center lead and the red on either end lead. If the meter indicates low resistance, the transistor is a good PNP type. Check all P-N junctions in the same way.

- An OL reading (no continuity) in both directions when a transistor is tested between the emitter (*E*) and the collector (*C*). (A transistor tester can also be used if available.)

● **SEE FIGURE 34–32.**

CONVERTERS AND INVERTERS

CONVERTERS DC to DC converters (usually written as DC-DC converter) are electronic devices used to transform DC voltage from one level of DC voltage to another higher or lower level. They are used to distribute various levels of DC voltage throughout a vehicle from a single power bus (or voltage source).

EXAMPLES OF USE One example of a DC-DC converter circuit is the circuit the PCM uses to convert 14 V to 5 V. The 5 volts is called the reference voltage, abbreviated V-ref, and is used to power many sensors in a computer-controlled engine management system. The schematic of a typical 5 volt V-ref interfacing with the TP sensor circuit is shown in ● **FIGURE 34–33.**

The PCM operates on 14 volts, using the principle of DC conversion to provide a constant 5 volts of sensor reference voltage to the TP sensor and others. The TP sensor demands little current, so the V-ref circuit is a low-power DC voltage converter in the range of 1 watt. The PCM uses a DC-DC converter, which is a small semiconductor device called a voltage regulator, and is designed to convert battery voltage to a constant 5 volts regardless of changes in the charging voltage.

Hybrid electric vehicles use DC-DC converters to provide higher or lower DC voltage levels and current requirements.

A high-power DC-DC converter schematic is shown in ● **FIGURE 34–34** and represents how a nonelectronic DC-DC converter works.

The central component of a converter is a transformer that physically isolates the input (42 V) from the output (14 V). The power transistor pulses the high-voltage coil of the transformer, and the resulting changing magnetic field induces a voltage in the coil windings of the lower voltage side of the transformer. The diodes and capacitors help control and limit the voltage and frequency of the circuit.

FIGURE 34–33 A DC to DC converter is built into most powertrain control modules (PCMs) and is used to supply the 5-volt reference called V-ref to many sensors used to control the internal combustion engine.

FIGURE 34–34 This DC-DC converter is designed to convert 42 volts to 14 volts, to provide 14 V power to accessories on a hybrid electric vehicle operating with a 42-volt electrical system.

DC-DC CONVERTER CIRCUIT TESTING Usually a DC control voltage is used, which is supplied by a digital logic circuit to shift the voltage level to control the converter. A voltage test can indicate if the correct voltages are present when the converter is on and off.

> ☠ **WARNING**
>
> Always follow the manufacturer's safety precautions for discharging capacitors in DC-DC converter circuits.

Voltage measurements are usually specified to diagnose a DC-DC converter system. A digital multimeter (DMM) that is CAT III rated should be used.

1. Always follow the manufacturer's safety precautions when working with high-voltage circuits. These circuits are usually indicated by orange wiring.
2. Never tap into wires in a DC-DC converter circuit to access power for another circuit.
3. Never tap into wires in a DC-DC converter circuit to access a ground for another circuit.
4. Never block airflow to a DC-DC converter heat sink.
5. Never use a heat sink for a ground connection for a meter, scope, or accessory connection.
6. Never connect or disconnect a DC-DC converter while the converter is powered up.
7. Never connect a DC-DC converter to a larger voltage source than specified.

INVERTERS An **inverter** is an electronic circuit that changes direct current (DC) into alternating current (AC). In most DC-AC inverters, the switching transistors, which are usually MOSFETs, are turned on alternately for short pulses. As a result, the transformer produces a modified sine wave output, rather than a true sine wave. ● **SEE FIGURE 34–35.**

The waveform produced by an inverter is not the perfect sine wave of household AC, but is rather more like a pulsing

FIGURE 34–35 A typical circuit for an inverter designed to change direct current from a battery to alternating current for use by the electric motors used in a hybrid electric vehicle.

PEAK TO PEAK VOLTAGE

FIGURE 34–36 The switching (pulsing) MOSFETs create a waveform called a modified sine wave (solid lines) compared to a true sine wave (dotted lines).

DC that reacts similar to sine wave AC in transformers and in induction motors. ● SEE FIGURE 34–36.

Inverters power AC motors. An inverter converts DC power to AC power at the required frequency and amplitude. The inverter consists of three half-bridge units, and the output voltage is mostly created by a pulse-width modulation (PWM) technique. The three-phase voltage waves are shifted 120 degrees to each other, to power each of the three phases.

WARNING

Do not touch the terminals of a battery that are being used to power an inverter. There is always a risk that those battery terminals could deliver a much greater shock than from batteries alone, if a motor or inverter should develop a fault.

ELECTROSTATIC DISCHARGE

DEFINITION Electrostatic discharge (ESD) is created when static charges build up on the human body when movement occurs. The friction of the clothing and the movement of shoes against carpet or vinyl floors cause a high voltage to build. Then when we touch a conductive material, such as a doorknob, the static charge is rapidly discharged. These charges, although just slightly painful to us, can cause severe damage to delicate electronic components. The following are typical static voltages.

- If you can feel it, it is at least 3,000 volts.
- If you can hear it, it is at least 5,000 volts.
- If you can see it, it is at least 10,000 volts.

Although these voltages seem high, the current, in amperes, is extremely low. However, sensitive electronic components such as vehicle computers, radios, and instrument panel clusters can be ruined if exposed to as little as 30 volts. This is a problem, because harm can occur to components at voltages lower than we can feel.

AVOIDING ESD To help prevent damage to components, follow these easy steps.

1. Keep the replacement electronic component in the protective wrapping until just before installation.
2. Before handling any electronic component, ground yourself by touching a metal surface to drain away any static charge.

3. Do not touch the terminals of electronic components.

4. If working in an area where touching terminals may occur, wear a static electrically grounding wrist strap available at most electronic parts stores, such as Radio Shack.

If these precautions are observed, ESD damage can be eliminated or reduced. Remember, just because the component works after being touched does not mean that damage has not occurred. Often, a section of the electronic component may be damaged, yet will not fail until several days or weeks later.

SUMMARY

1. Semiconductors are constructed by doping semiconductor materials such as silicon.

2. N-type and P-type materials can be combined to form diodes, transistors, SCRs, and computer chips.

3. Diodes can be used to direct and control current flow in circuits and to provide despiking protection.

4. Transistors are electronic relays that can also amplify signals.

5. All semiconductors can be damaged if subjected to excessive voltage, current, or heat.

6. Never touch the terminals of a computer or electronic device; static electricity can damage electronic components.

REVIEW QUESTIONS

1. What is the difference between P-type material and N-type material?

2. How can a diode be used to suppress high-voltage surges in automotive components or circuits containing a coil?

3. How does a transistor work?

4. To what precautions should all service technicians adhere, to avoid damage to electronic and computer circuits?

CHAPTER QUIZ

1. A semiconductor is a material _____.
   a. With fewer than four electrons in the outer orbit of its atoms
   b. With more than four electrons in the outer orbit of its atoms
   c. With exactly four electrons in the outer orbit of its atoms
   d. Determined by other factors besides the number of electrons

2. The arrow in a symbol for a semiconductor device _____.
   a. Points toward the negative
   b. Points away from the negative
   c. Is attached to the emitter on a transistor
   d. Both a and c

3. A diode installed across a coil with the cathode toward the battery positive is called a(n) _____.
   a. Clamping diode   b. Forward-bias diode
   c. SCR   d. Transistor

4. A transistor is controlled by the polarity and current at the _____.
   a. Collector   b. Emitter
   c. Base   d. Both a and b

5. A transistor can _____.
   a. Switch on and off b. Amplify
   c. Throttle   d. All of the above

6. Clamping diodes _____.
   a. Are connected into a circuit with the positive (+) voltage source to the cathode and the negative (−) voltage to the anode
   b. Are also called despiking diodes
   c. Can suppress transient voltages
   d. All of the above

7. A zener diode is normally used for voltage regulation. A zener diode, however, can also be used for high-voltage spike protection if connected _____.
   a. Positive to anode, negative to cathode
   b. Positive to cathode, ground to anode
   c. Negative to anode, cathode to a resistor then to a lower voltage terminal
   d. Both a and c

8. The forward-bias voltage required for an LED is _____.
   a. 0.3 to 0.5 volt   b. 0.5 to 0.7 volt
   c. 1.5 to 2.2 volts   d. 4.5 to 5.1 volts

9. An LED can be used in a _____.
   a. Headlight   b. Taillight
   c. Brake light   d. All of the above

10. Another name for a ground is _____.
    a. Logic low   b. Zero
    c. Reference low   d. All of the above

chapter 35
COMPUTER FUNDAMENTALS

OBJECTIVES: **After studying Chapter 35, the reader will be able to:** • Prepare for ASE Electrical/Electronic Systems (A6) certification test content area "A" (General Electrical/Electronic Systems Diagnosis). • Explain the purpose and function of onboard computers. • List the various parts of an automotive computer. • List input sensors. • List output devices (actuators) controlled by the computer.

KEY TERMS: • Actuator 378 • Analog-to-digital (AD) converter 377 • Baud rate 379 • Binary system 380 • Clock generator 379 • Controller 376 • CPU 378 • Digital computer 378 • Duty cycle 382 • E²PROM 377 • ECA 376 • ECM 376 • ECU 376 • EEPROM 377 • Engine mapping 378 • Input 376 • Input conditioning 377 • KAM 377 • Nonvolatile RAM 377 • Output drivers 381 • Powertrain control module (PCM) 376 • PROM 377 • PWM 381 • RAM 377 • ROM 377 • SAE 376

COMPUTER FUNDAMENTALS

PURPOSE AND FUNCTION Modern automotive control systems consist of a network of electronic sensors, actuators, and computer modules designed to regulate the powertrain and vehicle support systems. The onboard automotive computer has many names. It may be called an **electronic control unit (ECU), electronic control module (ECM), electronic control assembly (ECA),** or a **controller,** depending on the manufacturer and the computer application. The **Society of Automotive Engineers (SAE)** bulletin J1930 standardizes the name as a **powertrain control module (PCM).** The PCM coordinates engine and transmission operation, processes data, maintains communications, and makes the control decisions needed to keep the vehicle operating. Not only is it capable of operating the engine and transmission, but it is also able to perform the following:

- Undergo self-tests (40% of the computing power is devoted to diagnosis)
- Set and store diagnostic trouble codes (DTCs)
- Communicate with the technician using a scan tool

VOLTAGE SIGNALS Automotive computers use voltage to send and receive information. Voltage is electrical pressure and does not flow through circuits, but voltage can be used as a signal. A computer converts input information or data into voltage signal combinations that represent number

FIGURE 35–1 All computer systems perform four basic functions: input, processing, storage, and output.

combinations. A computer processes the input voltage signals it receives by computing what they represent, and then delivering the data in computed or processed form.

COMPUTER FUNCTIONS

BASIC FUNCTIONS The operation of every computer can be divided into four basic functions. ● **SEE FIGURE 35–1.**

- **Input.** Receives voltage signals from sensors
- **Processing.** Performs mathematical calculations
- **Storage.** Includes short-term and long-term memory
- **Output.** Controls an output device by either turning it on or off

INPUT FUNCTIONS First, the computer receives a voltage signal (input) from an input device. **Input** is a signal from a device that can be as simple as a button or a switch on an

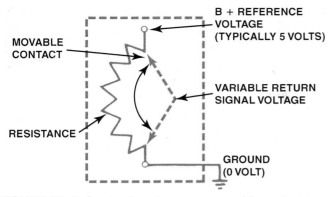

FIGURE 35–2 A potentiometer uses a movable contact to vary resistance and send an analog voltage right to the PCM.

FIGURE 35–3 An AD converter changes analog (variable) voltage signals into digital signals that the PCM can process.

instrument panel, or a sensor on an automotive engine. ● **SEE FIGURE 35–2** for a typical type of automotive sensor.

Vehicles use various mechanical, electrical, and magnetic sensors to measure factors such as vehicle speed, throttle position, engine RPM, air pressure, oxygen content of exhaust gas, airflow, engine coolant temperature, and status of electrical circuits (on-off). Each sensor transmits its information in the form of voltage signals. The computer receives these voltage signals, but before it can use them, the signals must undergo a process called **input conditioning.** This process includes amplifying voltage signals that are too small for the computer circuitry to handle. Input conditioners generally are located inside the computer, but a few sensors have their own input conditioning circuitry.

A digital computer changes the analog input signals (voltage) to digital bits (*binary digits*) of information through an **analog-to-digital (AD) converter** circuit. The binary digital number is used by the computer in its calculations or logic networks. ● **SEE FIGURE 35–3.**

PROCESSING The term *processing* is used to describe how input voltage signals received by a computer are handled through a series of electronic logic circuits maintained in its programmed instructions. These logic circuits change the input voltage signals, or data, into output voltage signals or commands.

STORAGE Storage is the place where the program instructions for a computer are stored in electronic memory. Some programs may require that certain input data be stored for later reference or future processing. In others, output commands may be delayed or stored before they are transmitted to devices elsewhere in the system.

Computers have two types of memory.

1. Permanent memory is called **read-only memory (ROM)** because the computer can only read the contents; it cannot change the data stored in it. This data is retained even when power to the computer is shut off. Part of the ROM is built into the computer, and the rest is located

in an integrated circuit (IC) chip called a **programmable read-only memory (PROM)** or calibration assembly. Many chips are erasable, meaning that the program can be changed. These chips are called erasable programmable read-only memory, or EPROM. Since the early 1990s, most programmable memory has been electronically erasable, meaning that the program in the chip can be reprogrammed by using a scan tool and the proper software. This computer reprogramming is usually called *reflashing*. These chips are electrically erasable programmable read-only memory, abbreviated **EEPROM** or **E²PROM**.

All vehicles equipped with onboard diagnosis second generation, called OBD-II, are equipped with EEPROMs.

2. Temporary memory is called **random-access memory (RAM)**, because the computer can write or store new data into it as directed by the computer program, as well as read the data already in it. Automotive computers use two types of RAM memory.

   ■ Volatile RAM memory is lost whenever the ignition is turned off. However, a type of volatile RAM called **keep-alive memory (KAM)** can be wired directly to battery power. This prevents its data from being erased when the ignition is turned off. One example of RAM and KAM is the loss of station settings in a programmable radio when the battery is disconnected. Because all the settings are stored in RAM, they have to be reset when the battery is reconnected. System trouble codes are commonly stored in RAM and can be erased by disconnecting the battery.

   ■ **Nonvolatile RAM** memory can retain its information even when the battery is disconnected. One use for this type of RAM is the storage of odometer information in an electronic speedometer. The memory chip retains the mileage accumulated by the vehicle. When speedometer replacement is necessary, the odometer chip is removed and installed in the new speedometer unit. KAM is used primarily in conjunction with adaptive strategies.

OUTPUT FUNCTIONS After the computer has processed the input signals, it sends voltage signals or commands to other devices in the system, such as system actuators. An **actuator** is an electrical or mechanical output device that converts electrical energy into a mechanical action, such as:

- Adjusting engine idle speed
- Operating fuel injectors
- Ignition timing control
- Altering suspension height

COMPUTER COMMUNICATION A typical vehicle can have many computers, also called modules or controllers. Computers also can communicate with, and control, each other through their output and input functions. This means that the output signal from one computer system can be the input signal for another computer system through a data network. See Chapter 15 for details on network communications.

FIGURE 35–4 Many electronic components are used to construct a typical vehicle computer including chips, resistors, and capacitors.

DIGITAL COMPUTERS

PARTS OF A COMPUTER The software consists of the programs and logic functions stored in the computer's circuitry. The hardware is the mechanical and electronic parts of a computer.

- **Central processing unit.** The microprocessor is the **central processing unit (CPU)** of a computer. Because it performs the essential mathematical operations and logic decisions that make up its processing function, the CPU can be considered the brain of a computer. Some computers use more than one microprocessor, called a coprocessor. The digital computer can process thousands of digital signals per second because its circuits are able to switch voltage signals on and off in billionths of a second. It is called a **digital computer** because it processes zeros and ones (digits) and needs to have any variable input signals, called analog inputs, converted to digital form before it can function. ● **SEE FIGURE 35–4.**

- **Computer memory.** Other integrated circuit (IC) devices store the computer operating program, system sensor input data, and system actuator output data—information that is necessary for CPU operation.

- **Computer programs.** By operating a vehicle on a dynamometer and manually adjusting the variable factors such as speed, load, and spark timing, it is possible to determine the optimum output settings for the best driveability, economy, and emission control. This is called engine mapping. ● **SEE FIGURE 35–5.**

Engine mapping creates a three-dimensional performance graph that applies to a given vehicle and powertrain combination. Each combination is mapped in this manner to

FIGURE 35–5 Typical engine map developed from testing and used by the vehicle computer to provide the optimum ignition timing for all engine speeds and load combinations.

produce a PROM or EEPROM calibration. This allows an automaker to use one basic computer for all models.

Many older-vehicle computers used a single PROM that plugged into the computer.

NOTE: If the computer needs to be replaced, the PROM or calibration module must be removed from the defective unit and installed in the replacement computer. Since the mid-1990s, PCMs do not have removable calibration PROMs, and must be programmed or *flashed* using a scan tool before being put into service.

CLOCK RATES AND TIMING The microprocessor receives sensor input voltage signals, processes them by using information from other memory units, and then sends voltage signals to the appropriate actuators. The microprocessor communicates by transmitting long strings of 0s and 1s in a language called binary

FIGURE 35–6 The clock generator produces a series of pulses that are used by the microprocessor and other components to stay in step with each other at a steady rate.

FIGURE 35–7 This powertrain control module (PCM) is located under the hood on this Chevrolet pickup truck.

code; but the microprocessor must have some way of knowing when one signal ends and another begins. That is the job of a crystal oscillator called a **clock generator**. ● SEE FIGURE 35–6.

The computer's crystal oscillator generates a steady stream of one-bit-long voltage pulses. Both the microprocessor and the memories monitor the clock pulses while they are communicating. Because they know how long each voltage pulse should be, they can distinguish between a 01 and a 0011. To complete the process, the input and output circuits also watch the clock pulses.

COMPUTER SPEEDS   Not all computers operate at the same speed; some are faster than others. The speed at which a computer operates is specified by the cycle time, or clock speed, required to perform certain measurements. Cycle time or clock speed is measured in megahertz (4.7 MHz, 8 MHz, 15 MHz, 18 MHz, and 32 Hz, which is the clock speed of most vehicle computers today).

BAUD RATE   The computer transmits bits of a serial datastream at precise intervals. The computer's speed is called the **baud rate,** or bits per second. The term *baud* was named after J. M. Emile Baudot (1845–1903), a French telegraph operator who developed a five-bit-per-character code of telegraph. Just as mph helps in estimating the length of time required to travel a certain distance, the baud rate is useful in estimating how long a given computer will need to transmit a specified amount of data to another computer.

Automotive computers have evolved from a baud rate of 160 used in the early 1980s to a baud rate as high as 500,000 for some networks. The speed of data transmission is an important factor both in system operation and in system troubleshooting.

CONTROL MODULE LOCATIONS   The computer hardware is all mounted on one or more circuit boards and installed in a metal case to help shield it from electromagnetic interference

FIGURE 35–8 This PCM on a Chrysler vehicle can only be seen by hoisting the vehicle, because it is located next to the radiator and in the airflow to help keep it cool.

(EMI). The wiring harnesses that link the computer to sensors and actuators connect to multipin connectors or edge connectors on the circuit boards.

Onboard computers range from single-function units that control a single operation to multifunction units that manage all of the separate (but linked) electronic systems in the vehicle. They vary in size from a small module to a notebook-size box. Most other engine computers are installed in the passenger compartment either under the instrument panel or in a side kick panel where they can be shielded from physical damage caused by temperature extremes, dirt, and vibration, or interference by the high currents and voltages of various underhood systems. ● SEE FIGURES 35–7 AND 35–8.

What Is a Binary System?

In a digital computer the signals are simple high-low, yes-no, on-off signals. The digital signal voltage is limited to two voltage levels: high voltage and low voltage. Since there is no stepped range of voltage or current in between, a digital binary signal is a "square wave." The signal is called "digital" because the on and off signals are processed by the computer as the digits or numbers 0 and 1. The number system containing only these two digits is called the **binary system.** Any number or letter from any number system or language alphabet can be translated into a combination of binary 0s and 1s for the digital computer. A digital computer changes the analog input signals (voltage) to digital bits (*binary digits*) of information through an analog-to-digital (AD) converter circuit. The binary digital number is used by the computer in its calculations or logic networks. Output signals usually are digital signals that turn system actuators on and off.

COMPUTER INPUT SENSORS

The vehicle computer uses signals (voltage levels) from the following sensors.

- **Engine speed (revolutions per minute, or RPM) sensor.** This signal comes from the primary ignition signal in the ignition control module (ICM) or directly from the crankshaft position (CKP) sensor.

- **Switches or buttons for accessory operation.** Many accessories use control buttons that signal the body computer to turn on or off an accessory such as the windshield wiper or heated seats.

- **Manifold absolute pressure (MAP) sensor.** This sensor detects engine load by using a signal from a sensor that measures the vacuum in the intake manifold.

- **Mass airflow (MAF) sensor.** This sensor measures the mass (weight and density) of the air flowing through the sensor and entering the engine.

- **Engine coolant temperature (ECT) sensor.** This sensor measures the temperature of the engine coolant. This is a sensor used for engine controls and for automatic air-conditioning control operation.

- **Oxygen sensor (O2S).** This sensor measures the oxygen in the exhaust stream. There are as many as four oxygen sensors in some vehicles.

- **Throttle position (TP) sensor.** This sensor measures the throttle opening and is used by the computer for engine control and the shift points of the automotive transmission/transaxle.

- **Vehicle speed (VS) sensor.** This sensor measures the vehicle speed using a sensor located at the output of the transmission/transaxle or by monitoring sensors at the wheel speed sensors. This sensor is used by the speedometer, cruise control, and airbag systems.

COMPUTER OUTPUTS

OUTPUT CONTROLS After the computer has processed the input signals, it sends voltage signals or commands to other devices in the system, as follows:

- **Operate actuators.** An actuator is an electrical or mechanical device that converts electrical energy into heat, light, or motion to control engine idle speed, suspension height, ignition timing, and other output devices.

- **Network communication.** Computers also can communicate with another computer system through a network.

  A vehicle computer can do only two things.

  1. Turn a device on.
  2. Turn a device off.

  Typical output devices include the following:

- **Fuel injectors.** The computer can vary the amount of time in milliseconds the injectors are held open, thereby controlling the amount of fuel supplied to the engine.

- **Blower motor control.** Many blower motors are controlled by the body computer by pulsing the current on and off to maintain the desired speed.

- **Transmission shifting.** The computer provides a ground to the shift solenoids and torque converter clutch (TCC) solenoid. The operation of the automatic transmission/transaxle is optimized based on vehicle sensor information.

- **Idle speed control.** The computer can control the idle air control (IAC) or electronic throttle control (ETC) to maintain engine idle speed and to provide an increased idle speed as needed.

- **Evaporative emission control solenoids.** The computer can control the flow of gasoline fumes from the charcoal canister to the engine and seal off the system to perform a fuel system leak detection test as part of the OBD-II system requirements.

  Most outputs work electrically in one of three ways:

  1. Digital
  2. Pulse-width modulated
  3. Switched

FIGURE 35–9 A typical output driver. In this case, the PCM applies voltage to the fuel pump relay coil to energize the fuel pump.

Digital control is mostly used for computer communications and involves voltage signals that are transmitted and received in packets.

Pulse-width control allows a device, such as a blower motor, to be operated at variable speed by changing the amount of time electrical power is supplied to the device.

A switched output is an output that is either on or off. In many circuits, the PCM uses a relay to switch a device on or off, because the relay is a low-current device that can switch to a higher current device. Most computer circuits cannot handle high amounts of current. By using a relay circuit, the PCM provides the output control to the relay, which in turn provides the output control to the device.

The relay coil, which the PCM controls, typically draws less than 0.5 ampere. The device that the relay controls may draw 30 amperes or more. The PCM switches are actually transistors, and are often called **output drivers.** ● SEE **FIGURE 35–9.**

OUTPUT DRIVERS   There are two basic types of output drivers.

1. **Low-side drivers.** The low-side drivers (LSDs) are transistors inside the computer that complete the ground path of relay coil. Ignition (key-on) voltage and battery voltage are supplied to the relay. The ground side of the relay coil is connected to the transistor inside the computer. In the example of a fuel pump relay, when the transistor turns "on," it will complete the ground for the relay coil, and the relay will then complete the power circuit between the battery power and the fuel pump. A relatively low current flows through the relay coil and transistor that is inside the computer. This causes the relay to switch and provides the fuel pump with battery voltage. The majority of switched outputs have typically been low-side drivers. ● **SEE FIGURE 35–10.**

FIGURE 35–10 A typical low-side driver (LSD) which uses a control module to control the ground side of the relay coil.

Low-side drivers can often perform a diagnostic circuit check by monitoring the voltage from the relay to check that the control circuit for the relay is complete. A low-side driver, however, cannot detect a short-to-ground.

2. **High-side drivers.** The high-side drivers (HSDs) control the power side of the circuit. In these applications when the transistor is switched on, voltage is applied to the device. A ground has been provided to the device so when the high-side driver switches, the device will be energized. In some applications, high-side drivers are used instead of low-side drivers to provide better circuit protection. General Motors vehicles have used a high-side driver to control the fuel pump relay instead of a low-side driver. In the event of an accident, should the circuit to the fuel pump relay become grounded, a high-side driver would cause a short circuit, which would cause the fuel pump relay to de-energize. High-side drivers inside modules can detect electrical faults such as a lack of continuity when the circuit is not energized. ● **SEE FIGURE 35–11.**

PULSE-WIDTH MODULATION   Pulse-width modulation **(PWM)** is a method of controlling an output using a digital signal. Instead of just turning devices on or off, the computer can control the amount of on-time. For example, a solenoid could be a PWM device. If, for example, a vacuum solenoid is controlled by a switched driver, switching either on or off would mean that either full vacuum would flow through the solenoid or no vacuum would flow through the solenoid. However, to control the amount of vacuum that flows through the solenoid, pulse-width modulation could be used.

FIGURE 35–11 A typical module-controlled high-side driver (HSD) where the module itself supplies the electrical power to the device. The logic circuit inside the module can detect circuit faults including continuity of the circuit and if there is a short-to-ground in the circuit being controlled.

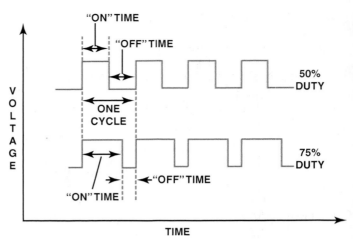

FIGURE 35–12 Both the top and bottom pattern have the same frequency. However, the amount of on-time varies. Duty cycle is the percentage of the time during a cycle that the signal is turned on.

A PWM signal is a digital signal, usually 0 volt and 12 volts, which is cycling at a fixed frequency. Varying the length of time that the signal is on provides a signal that can vary the on- and off-time of an output. The ratio of on-time relative to the period of the cycle is referred to as **duty cycle.** ● SEE FIGURE 35–12.

Depending on the frequency of the signal, which is usually fixed, this signal would turn the device on and off a fixed number of times per second. When, for example, the voltage is high (12 volts) 90% of the time and low (0 volt) the other 10% of the time, the signal has a 90% duty cycle. In other words, if this signal were applied to the vacuum solenoid, the solenoid would

be on 90% of the time. This would allow more vacuum to flow through the solenoid. The computer has the ability to vary this on- and off-time or pulse-width modulation at any rate between 0% and 100%. A good example of pulse-width modulation is the cooling fan speed control. The speed of the cooling fan is controlled by varying the amount of on-time that the battery voltage is applied to the cooling fan motor.

- 100% duty cycle: fan runs at full speed
- 75% duty cycle: fan runs at 3/4 speed
- 50% duty cycle: fan runs at 1/2 speed
- 25% duty cycle: fan runs at 1/4 speed

The use of PWM, therefore, results in precise control of an output device to achieve the amount of cooling needed and conserve electrical energy compared to simply timing the cooling fan on high when needed. PWM may be used to control vacuum through a solenoid, the amount of purge of the evaporative purge solenoid, the speed of a fuel pump motor, control of a linear motor, or even the intensity of a light bulb.

SUMMARY

1. The Society of Automotive Engineers (SAE) standard J1930 specifies that the term powertrain control module (PCM) be used for the computer that controls the engine and transmission in a vehicle.

2. The four basic computer functions are input, processing, storage, and output.

3. Types of memory include read-only memory (ROM) which can be programmable (PROM), erasable (EPROM), or electrically erasable (EEPROM); RAM; and KAM.

4. Computer input sensors include engine speed (RPM), MAP, MAF, ECT, O2S, TP, and VS.

5. A computer can only turn a device on or turn a device off, but it can do either operation rapidly.

REVIEW QUESTIONS

1. What part of the vehicle computer is considered to be the brain?
2. What is the difference between volatile and nonvolatile RAM?
3. What are the four input sensors?
4. What are the four output devices?

CHAPTER QUIZ

1. What unit of electricity is used as a signal for a computer?
   a. Volt
   b. Ohm
   c. Ampere
   d. Watt

2. The four basic computer functions include _____.
   a. Writing, processing, printing, and remembering
   b. Input, processing, storage, and output
   c. Data gathering, processing, output, and evaluation
   d. Sensing, calculating, actuating, and processing

3. All OBD-II vehicles use what type of read-only memory?
   a. ROM
   b. PROM
   c. EPROM
   d. EEPROM

4. The "brain" of the computer is the _____.
   a. PROM
   b. RAM
   c. CPU
   d. AD converter

5. Computer speed is measured in _____.
   a. Baud rate
   b. Clock speed (Hz)
   c. Voltage
   d. Bytes

6. Which item is a computer input sensor?
   a. RPM
   b. Throttle position
   c. Engine coolant temperature
   d. All of the above

7. Which item is a computer output device?
   a. Fuel injector
   b. Transmission shift solenoid
   c. Evaporative emission control solenoid
   d. All of the above

8. The SAE term for the vehicle computer is _____.
   a. PCM
   b. ECM
   c. ECA
   d. Controller

9. What two things can a vehicle computer actually perform (output)?
   a. Store and process information
   b. Turn something on or turn something off
   c. Calculate and vary temperature
   d. Control fuel and timing only

10. Analog signals from sensors are changed to digital signals for processing by the computer through which type of circuit?
   a. Digital
   b. Analog
   c. Analog-to-digital converter
   d. PROM

chapter 36

CAN AND NETWORK COMMUNICATIONS

OBJECTIVES: **After studying Chapter 36, the reader will be able to:** • Prepare for ASE Electrical/Electronic Systems (A6) certification test content area "A" (General Electrical/Electronic Systems Diagnosis). • Describe the types of networks and serial communications used on vehicles. • Discuss how the networks connect to the data link connector and to other modules. • Explain how to diagnose module communication faults.

KEY TERMS: • Breakout box (BOB) 395 • BUS 387 • CAN 387 • Chrysler collision detection (CCD) 391 • Class 2 387 • E & C 387 • GMLAN 388 • Keyword 387 • Multiplexing 384 • Network 384 • Node 384 • Plastic optical fiber (POF) 395 • Programmable controller interface (PCI) 392 • Protocol 387 • Serial communications interface (SCI) 392 • Serial data 384 • Splice pack 386 • Standard corporate protocol (SCP) 390 • State of health (SOH) 396 • SWCAN 388 • Terminating resistors 396 • Twisted pair 384 • UART 387 • UART-based protocol (UBP) 390

MODULE COMMUNICATIONS AND NETWORKS

NEED FOR NETWORK Since the 1990s, vehicles have used modules to control the operation of most electrical components. A typical vehicle will have 10 or more modules and they communicate with each other over data lines or hard wiring, depending on the application.

ADVANTAGES Most modules are connected together in a network because of the following advantages.

- A decreased number of wires are needed, thereby saving weight and cost, as well as helping with installation at the factory and decreased complexity, making servicing easier.
- Common sensor data can be shared with those modules that may need the information, such as vehicle speed, outside air temperature, and engine coolant temperature.

● **SEE FIGURE 36–1.**

NETWORK FUNDAMENTALS

MODULES AND NODES Each module, also called a **node,** must communicate to other modules. For example, if the driver depresses the window-down switch, the power window switch

sends a window-down message to the body control module. The body control module then sends the request to the driver's side window module. This module is responsible for actually performing the task by supplying power and ground to the window lift motor in the current polarity to cause the window to go down. The module also contains a circuit that monitors the current flow through the motor and will stop and/or reverse the window motor if an obstruction causes the window motor to draw more than the normal amount of current.

TYPES OF COMMUNICATION The types of communications include the following:

- **Differential.** In the differential form of module communication, a difference in voltage is applied to two wires, which are twisted to help reduce electromagnetic interference (EMI). These transfer wires are called a **twisted pair.**
- **Parallel.** In the parallel type of module communication, the send and receive signals are on different wires.
- **Serial data.** The **serial data** is data transmitted over one wire by a series of rapidly changing voltage signals pulsed from low to high or from high to low.
- **Multiplexing.** The process of **multiplexing** involves the sending of multiple signals of information at the same time over a signal wire and then separating the signals at the receiving end.

This system of intercommunication of computers or processors is referred to as a **network.** ● **SEE FIGURE 36–2.**

By connecting the computers together on a communications network, they can easily share information back and forth. This multiplexing has the following advantages.

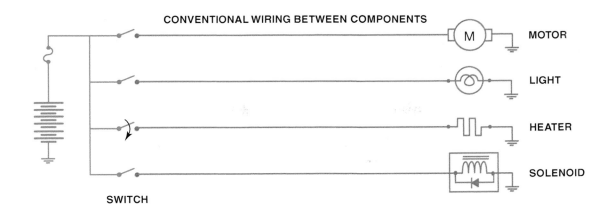

CONVENTIONAL WIRING BETWEEN COMPONENTS

MOTOR

LIGHT

HEATER

SOLENOID

SWITCH

ECU

ECU

DISCRETE
SIGNALS

M L H S

MPX
COMMUNICATION
LINE

MOTOR

LIGHT

HEATER

SOLENOID

SWITCH

FIGURE 36–1 Module communications makes controlling multiple electrical devices and accessories easier by utilizing simple low-current switches to signal another module, which does the actual switching of the current to the device.

PROGRAMMED TO USE
VEHICLE SPEED SIGNAL

POWERTRAIN
CONTROL
MODULE (PCM)

CRUISE
CONTROL
MODULE

DRIVER'S DOOR
MODULE (DDM)

ANTI-LOCK BRAKE
CONTROL MODULE

PROGRAMMED TO USE
VEHICLE SPEED SIGNAL

FIGURE 36–2 A network allows all modules to communicate with other modules.

- Elimination of redundant sensors and dedicated wiring for these multiple sensors
- Reduction of the number of wires, connectors, and circuits
- Addition of more features and option content to new vehicles
- Weight reduction due to fewer components, wires, and connectors, thereby increasing fuel economy
- Changeable features with software upgrades versus component replacement

MODULE COMMUNICATIONS CONFIGURATION

The three most common types of networks used on vehicles include:

1. **Ring link networks.** In a ring-type network, all modules are connected to each other by a serial data line (in a line) until all are connected in a ring. ● **SEE FIGURE 36–3.**

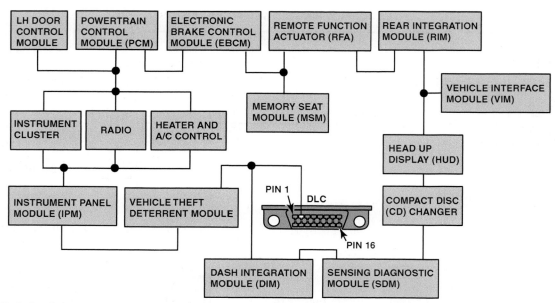

FIGURE 36–3 A ring link network reduces the number of wires it takes to interconnect all of the modules.

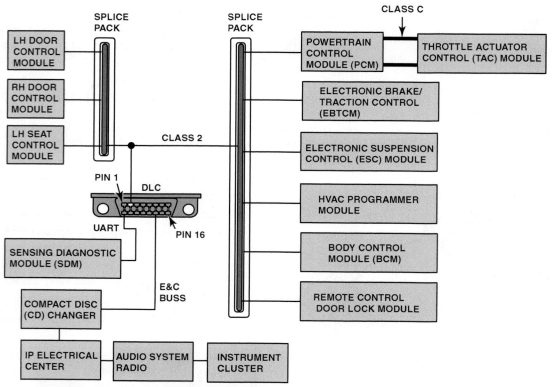

FIGURE 36–4 In a star link network, all of the modules are connected using splice packs.

2. **Star link networks.** In a star link network, a serial data line attaches to each module and then each is connected to a central point. This central point is called a **splice pack,** abbreviated SP such as in "SP 306." The splice pack uses a bar to splice all of the serial lines together. Some GM vehicles use two or more splice packs to tie the modules together. When more than one splice pack is used, a serial data line connects one splice pack to the others. In most applications, the BUS bar used in each splice pack can be removed. When the BUS bar is removed, a special tool (J 42236) can be installed in place of the removed BUS bar. Using this tool, the serial data line for each module can be isolated and tested for a possible problem. Using the special tool at the splice pack makes diagnosing this type of network easier than many others. ● **SEE FIGURE 36–4.**

3. **Ring/star hybrid.** In a ring/star network, the modules are connected using both types of network configurations. Check service information (SI) for details on how this network is connected on the vehicle being diagnosed and always follow the recommended diagnostic steps.

NETWORK COMMUNICATIONS CLASSIFICATIONS

The Society of Automotive Engineers (SAE) standards include the following three categories of in-vehicle network communications.

CLASS A Low-speed networks, meaning less than 10,000 bits per second (bps, or 10 Kbs), are generally used for trip computers, entertainment, and other convenience features.

CLASS B Medium-speed networks, meaning 10,000 to 125,000 bps (10 to 125 Kbs), are generally used for information transfer among modules, such as instrument clusters, temperature sensor data, and other general uses.

CLASS C High-speed networks, meaning 125,000 to 1,000,000 bps, are generally used for real-time powertrain and vehicle dynamic control. High-speed BUS communication systems now use a **controller area network (CAN).** ● SEE FIGURE 36–5.

GENERAL MOTORS COMMUNICATIONS PROTOCOLS

UART General Motors and others use UART communications for some electronic modules or systems. **UART** is a serial data communications protocol that stands for **universal asynchronous receive and transmit.** UART uses a master control module connected to one or more remote modules.

The master control module is used to control message traffic on the data line by poling all of the other UART modules. The remote modules send a response message back to the master module.

UART uses a fixed pulse-width switching between 0 and 5 V. The UART data BUS operates at a baud rate of 8,192 bps. ● SEE FIGURE 36–6.

ENTERTAINMENT AND COMFORT COMMUNICATION

The GM **entertainment and comfort (E & C)** serial data is similar to UART, but uses a 0 to 12 V toggle. Like UART, the E & C serial data uses a master control module connected to other remote modules, which could include the following:

- Compact disc (CD) player
- Instrument panel (IP) electrical center
- Audio system (radio)
- Heating, ventilation, and air-conditioning (HVAC) programmer and control head
- Steering wheel controls

● SEE FIGURE 36–7.

CLASS 2 COMMUNICATIONS Class 2 is a serial communications system that operates by toggling between 0 and 7 V at a transfer rate of 10.4 Kbs. Class 2 is used for most high-speed communications between the powertrain control module (PCM) and other control modules, plus to the scan tool. Class 2 is the primary high-speed serial communications system used by GMCAN (CAN). ● SEE FIGURE 36–8 on page 389.

KEYWORD COMMUNICATION Keyword 81, 82, and 2000 serial data are also used for some module-to-module communication on GM vehicles. Keyword data BUS signals are toggled from 0 to 12 V when communicating. The voltage or the datastream is zero volts when not communicating. Keyword serial communication is used by the seat heater module and others, but is not connected to the data link connector (DLC). ● SEE FIGURE 36–9. on page 389.

GMLAN General Motors, like all vehicle manufacturers, must use high-speed serial data to communicate with scan tools on all vehicles effective with the 2008 model year. As mentioned, the standard is called controller area network

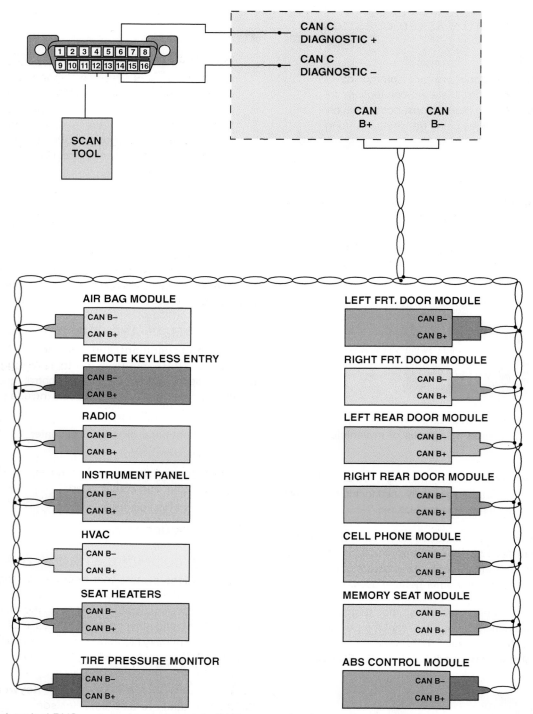

FIGURE 36–5 A typical BUS system showing module CAN communications and twisted pairs of wire.

(CAN), which General Motors calls **GMLAN,** which stands for **GM local area network.**

General Motors uses two versions of GMLAN.

- **Low-speed GMLAN.** The low-speed version is used for driver-controlled functions such as power windows and door locks. The baud rate for low-speed GMLAN is 33,300 bps. The GMLAN low-speed serial data is not connected directly to the data link connector and uses one wire. The voltage toggles between 0 and 5 V after an initial 12 V spike, which indicates to the modules to turn on or wake up and listen for data on the line. Low-speed GMLAN is also known as **single-wire CAN,** or **SWCAN** and is located at pin 1 of the DLC.

- **High-speed GMLAN.** The baud rate is almost real time at 500 Kbs. This serial data method uses a two-twisted-wire circuit which is connected to the data link connector on pins 6 and 14. ● **SEE FIGURE 36–10.**

FIGURE 36–6 UART serial data master control module is connected to the data link connector at pin 9.

FIGURE 36–7 The E & C serial data is connected to the data link connector (DLC) at pin 14.

FIGURE 36–8 Class 2 serial data communication is accessible at the data link connector (DLC) at pin 2.

KEYWORD 81, 82, AND 2000

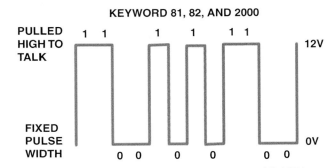

FIGURE 36–9 Keyword 82 operates at a rate of 8,192 bps, similar to UART, and keyword 2000 operates at a baud rate of 10,400 bps (the same as a Class 2 communicator).

FIGURE 36–10 GMLAN uses pins at terminals 6 and 14. Pin 1 is used for low speed GMLAN on 2006 and newer GM vehicles.

? FREQUENTLY ASKED QUESTION

Why Is a Twisted Pair Used?

A twisted pair is where two wires are twisted to prevent electromagnetic radiation from affecting the signals passing through the wires. By twisting the two wires about once every inch (9 to 16 times per foot), the interference is canceled by the adjacent wire. ● SEE FIGURE 36–11.

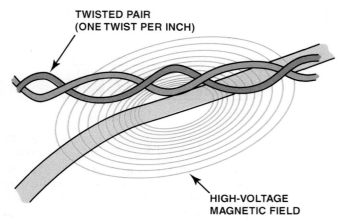

FIGURE 36–11 A twisted pair is used by several different network communications protocols to reduce interference that can be induced in the wiring from nearby electromagnetic sources.

FIGURE 36–12 A CANDi module will flash the green LED rapidly if communication is detected.

A CANDi (CAN diagnostic interface) module is required to be used with the Tech 2 to be able to connect a GM vehicle equipped with GMLAN. ● **SEE FIGURE 36–12.**

FORD NETWORK COMMUNICATIONS PROTOCOLS

STANDARD CORPORATE PROTOCOL Only a few Fords had scan tool data accessible through the OBD-I data link connector. To identify an OBD-I (1988–1995) on a Ford vehicle that is equipped with **standard corporate protocol (SCP)** and be able to communicate through a

FIGURE 36–13 A Ford OBD-I diagnostic link connector showing that SCP communication uses terminals in cavities 1 (upper left) and 3 (lower left).

scan tool, look for terminals in cavities 1 and 3 of the DLC. ● **SEE FIGURE 36–13.**

SCP uses the J-1850 protocol and is active with the key on. The SCP signal is from 4 V negative to 4.3 V positive, and a scan tool does not have to be connected for the signal to be detected on the terminals. OBD-II (EECV) Ford vehicles use terminals 2 (positive) and 10 (negative) of the 16 pin data link connector (DLC) for network communication, using the SCP module communications.

UART-BASED PROTOCOL Newer Fords use the CAN for scan tool diagnosis, but still retain SCP and **UART-based protocol (UBP)** for some modules. ● **SEE FIGURES 36–14 AND 36–15.**

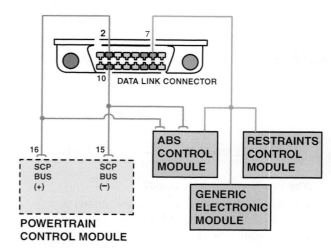

FIGURE 36–14 A scan tool can be used to check communications with the SCP BUS through terminals 2 and 10 and to the other modules connected to terminal 7 of the data link connector (DLC).

FREQUENTLY ASKED QUESTION

What Are U Codes?

The U diagnostic trouble codes were at first "undefined" but are now network-related codes. Use the network codes to help pinpoint the circuit or module that is not working correctly.

FIGURE 36-15 Many Fords use UBP module communications along with CAN.

CHRYSLER COMMUNICATIONS PROTOCOLS

CCD Since the late 1980s, the **Chrysler Collision Detection (CCD)** multiplex network is used for scan tool and module communications. It is a differential-type communication and uses a twisted pair of wires. The modules connected to the network apply a bias voltage on each wire. CCD signals are divided into plus and minus (CCD+ and CCD−) and the voltage difference does not exceed 0.02 V. The baud rate is 7,812.5 bps.

NOTE: The "collision" in the Chrysler Collision detection BUS communications refers to the program that avoids conflicts of information exchange within the BUS, and does not refer to airbags or other accident-related circuits of the vehicle.

The circuit is active without a scan tool command. ● **SEE FIGURE 36–16.**

The modules on the CCD BUS apply a bias voltage on each wire by using termination resistors. ● **SEE FIGURE 36–17.**

The difference in voltage between CCD+ and CCD− is less than 20 mV. For example, using a digital meter with the black

FIGURE 36–16 CCD signals are labeled plus and minus and use a twisted pair of wires. Notice that terminals 3 and 11 of the data link connector are used to access the CCD BUS from a scan tool. Pin 16 is used to supply 12 volts to the scan tool.

FIGURE 36–17 The differential voltage for the CCD BUS is created by using resistors in a module.

FIGURE 36–18 Many Chrysler vehicles use both SCI and CCD for module communication.

meter lead attached to ground and the red meter lead attached at the data link connector (DLC), a normal reading could include:

- Terminal 3 = 2.45 volts
- Terminal 11 = 2.47 volts

This is an acceptable reading because the readings are 20 mV (0.020 volt) of each other. If both had been exactly 2.5 volts, then this could indicate that the two data lines are shorted together. The module providing the bias voltage is usually the body control module on passenger cars and the front control module on Jeeps and trucks.

PROGRAMMABLE CONTROLLER INTERFACE The Chrysler **programmable controller interface (PCI)** is a one-wire communication protocol that connects at the OBD-II DLC at terminal 2. The PCI BUS is connected to all modules on the BUS in a star configuration and operates at a baud rate of 10,200 bps. The voltage signal toggles between 7.5 and 0 V. If this voltage is checked at terminal 2 of the OBD-II DLC, a voltage of about 1 V indicates the average voltage and means that the BUS is functioning and is not shorted-to-ground. PCI and CCD are often used in the same vehicle. ● **SEE FIGURE 36–18.**

SERIAL COMMUNICATIONS INTERFACE Chrysler used **serial communications interface (SCI)** for most scan tool and flash reprogramming functions until it was replaced with CAN. SCI is connected at the OBD-II diagnostic link connector (DLC) at terminals 6 (SCI receive) and 7 (SCI transmit). A scan tool must be connected to test the circuit.

CONTROLLER AREA NETWORK

BACKGROUND Robert Bosch Corporation developed the CAN protocol, which was called CAN 1.2, in 1993. The CAN protocol was approved by the Environmental Protection Agency (EPA) for 2003 and newer vehicle diagnostics, and a legal requirement for all vehicles by 2008. The CAN diagnostic systems use pins 6 and 14 in the standard 16 pin OBD-II (J-1962) connector. Before CAN, the scan tool protocol had been manufacturer specific.

CAN FEATURES The CAN protocol offers the following features.

- Faster than other BUS communication protocols
- Cost effective because it is an easier system than others to use
- Less effected by electromagnetic interference (Data is transferred on two wires that are twisted together, called twisted pair, to help reduce EMI interference.)
- Message based rather than address based which makes it easier to expand
- No wakeup needed because it is a two-wire system
- Supports up to15 modules plus a scan tool
- Uses a 120-ohm resistor at the ends of each pair to reduce electrical noise
- Applies 2.5 volts on both wires:

  H (high) goes to 3.5 volts when active

  L (low) goes to 1.5 volts when active

  ● **SEE FIGURE 36–19.**

CAN CLASS A, B, AND C There are three classes of CAN and they operate at different speeds. The CAN A, B, and C networks can all be linked using a gateway within the same vehicle. The gateway is usually one of the many modules in the vehicle.

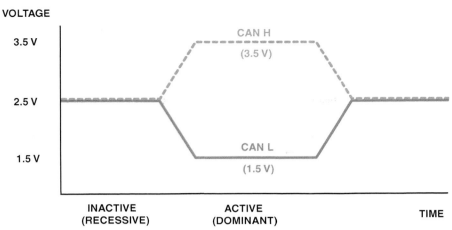

FIGURE 36–19 CAN uses a differential type of module communication where the voltage on one wire is the equal but opposite voltage on the other wire. When no communication is occurring, both wires have 2.5 volts applied. When communication is occurring, CAN H (high) goes up 1 volt to 3.5 volts and CAN L (low) goes down 1 volt to 1.5 volts.

- **CAN A.** This class operates on only one wire at slow speeds and is therefore less expensive to build. CAN A operates a data transfer rate of 33.33 Kbs in normal mode and up to 83.33 Kbs during reprogramming mode. CAN A uses the vehicle ground as the signal return circuit.

- **CAN B.** This class operates on a two-wire network and does not use the vehicle ground as the signal return circuit. CAN B uses a data transfer rate of 95.2 Kbs. Instead, CAN B (and CAN C) uses two network wires for differential signaling. This means that the two data signal voltages are opposite to each other and used for error detection by constantly being compared. In this case, when the signal voltage at one of the CAN data

wires goes high (CAN H), the other one goes low (CAN L), hence the name *differential signaling.* Differential signaling is also used for redundancy, in case one of the signal wires shorts out.

- **CAN C.** This class is the highest speed CAN protocol with speeds up to 500 Kbs. Beginning with 2008 models, all vehicles sold in the United States must use CAN BUS for scan tool communications. Most vehicle manufacturers started using CAN in older models; and it is easy to determine if a vehicle is equipped with CAN. The CAN BUS communicates to the scan tool through terminals 6 and 14 of the DLC indicating that the vehicle is equipped with CAN. ● **SEE FIGURE 36–20.**

FIGURE 36–20 A typical (generic) system showing how the CAN BUS is connected to various electrical accessories and systems in the vehicle.

The total voltage remains constant at all times and the electromagnetic field effects of the two data BUS lines cancel each other out. The data BUS line is protected against received radiation and is virtually neutral in sending radiation.

HONDA/TOYOTA COMMUNICATIONS

The primary BUS communications on pre-CAN-equipped vehicles is ISO 9141-2 using terminals 7 and 15 at the OBD-II DLC. ● SEE FIGURE 36-21.

A factory scan tool or an aftermarket scan tool equipped with enhanced original equipment (OE) software is needed to access many of the BUS messages. ● SEE FIGURE 36-22.

FIGURE 36-21 A DLC from a pre-CAN Acura. It shows terminals in cavities 4, 5 (grounds), 7, 10, 14, and 16 (B+).

FIGURE 36-22 A Honda scan display showing a B and two U codes, all indicating a BUS-related problem(s).

EUROPEAN BUS COMMUNICATIONS

UNIQUE DIAGNOSTIC CONNECTOR Many different types of module communications protocols are used on European vehicles such as Mercedes and BMW.

Most of these communication BUS messages cannot be accessed through the data link connector (DLC). To check the operation of the individual modules, a scan tool equipped with factory-type software will be needed to communicate with the module through the gateway module. ● SEE FIGURE 36-23 for an alternative access method to the modules.

MEDIA ORIENTED SYSTEM TRANSPORT BUS The media oriented system transport (MOST) BUS uses fiber optics for module-to-module communications in a ring or star configuration. This BUS system is currently being used for entertainment equipment data communications for videos, CDs, and other media systems in the vehicle.

MOTOROLA INTERCONNECT BUS Motorola interconnect (MI) is a single-wire serial communications protocol, using one master control module and many slave modules. Typical application of the MI BUS protocol is with power and memory mirrors, seats, windows, and headlight levelers.

DISTRIBUTED SYSTEM INTERFACE BUS Distributed system interface (DSI) BUS protocol was developed by Motorola and uses a two-wire serial BUS. This BUS protocol is currently being used for safety-related sensors and components.

FIGURE 36-23 A typical 38-cavity diagnostic connector as found on many BMW and Mercedes vehicles under the hood. The use of a breakout box (BOB) connected to this connector can often be used to gain access to module BUS information.

BOSCH-SIEMANS-TEMIC BUS The Bosch-Siemans-Temic (BST) BUS is another system that is used for safety-related components and sensors in a vehicle, such as airbags. The BST BUS is a two-wire system and operates up to 250,000 bps.

> **? FREQUENTLY ASKED QUESTION**
>
> **How Do You Know What System Is Used?**
>
> Use service information to determine which network communication protocol is used. However, due to the various systems on some vehicles, it may be easier to look at the data link connection to determine the system. All OBD-II vehicles have terminals in the following cavities.
>
> Terminal 4: chassis ground
>
> Terminal 5: computer (signal) ground
>
> Terminal 16: 12 V positive
>
> The terminals in cavities 6 and 14 mean that this vehicle is equipped with CAN as the only module communication protocol available at the DLC. To perform a test of the BUS, use a **breakout box (BOB)** to gain access to the terminals while connecting to the vehicle, using a scan tool. ● **SEE FIGURE 36-24** or a typical OBD-II connector breakout box.

BYTEFLIGHT BUS The byteflight BUS is used in safety critical systems, such as airbags, and uses the time division multiple access (TDMA) protocol, which operates at 10 million bps using a **plastic optical fiber (POF).**

FLEXRAY BUS FlexRay BUS is a version of byteflight, and is a high-speed serial communication system for in-vehicle networks. FlexRay is commonly used for steer-by-wire and brake-by-wire systems.

DOMESTIC DIGITAL BUS The domestic digital BUS, commonly designated D2B, is an optical BUS system connecting audio, video, computer, and telephone components in a single-ring structure with a speed of up to 5,600,000 bps.

LOCAL INTERCONNECT NETWORK BUS Local interconnect network (LIN) is a BUS protocol used between intelligent sensors and actuators, and has a BUS speed of 19,200 bps.

NETWORK COMMUNICATIONS DIAGNOSIS

STEPS TO FINDING A FAULT When a network communications fault is suspected, perform the following steps.

STEP 1 **Check everything that does and does not work.** Often accessories that do not seem to be connected can help identify which module or BUS circuit is at fault.

STEP 2 **Perform module status test.** Use a factory level scan tool or an aftermarket scan tool equipped with enhanced software that allows OE-like functions. Check if the components or systems can be operated through the scan tool. ● **SEE FIGURE 36-25.**

FIGURE 36-24 A breakout box (BOB) used to access the BUS terminals while using a scan tool to activate the modules. This breakout box is equipped with LEDs that light when circuits are active.

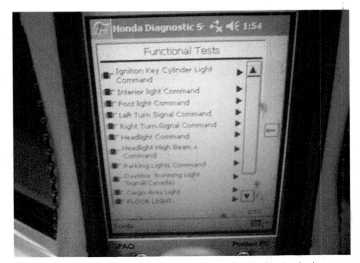

FIGURE 36-25 This Honda scan tool allows the technician to turn on individual lights and operate individual power windows and other accessories that are connected to the BUS system.

No Communication? Try Bypass Mode.

If a Tech 2 scan tool shows "no communication," try using the bypass mode to see what should be on the data display. To enter bypass mode, perform the following steps.

STEP 1   Select tool option (F3).

STEP 2   Set communications to bypass (F5).

STEP 3   Select enable.

STEP 4   Input make/model and year of vehicle.

STEP 5   Note all parameters that should be included, as shown. The values will not be shown.

■ **Ping modules.** Start the Class 2 diagnosis by using a scan tool and select *diagnostic circuit check*. If no diagnostic trouble codes (DTCs) are shown, there could be a communication problem. Select *message monitor,* which will display the status of all of the modules on the Class 2 BUS circuit. The modules that are awake will be shown as active and the scan tool can be used to ping individual modules or command all modules. The ping command should change the status from "active" to "inactive." ● **SEE FIGURE 36–26.**

NOTE: If an excessive parasitic draw is being diagnosed, use a scan tool to ping the modules in one way to determine if one of the modules is not going to sleep and causing the excessive battery drain.

■ **Check state of health.** All modules on the Class 2 BUS circuit have at least one other module responsible for reporting **state of health (SOH).**

Class 2 Message Monitor		
Modules	Status	
BCM/BFC/DIM/SBM/TBC	Active	1
PCM/VCM	Active	1
ABS/TCS	Active	1
IPC	Active	1
SIR	Active	1
Radio	Active	1
ACM/HCM	Active	1
	00:00:03 1 / 9	
BCM/BFC/DIM/SBM/TBC		
Sleep Mode	Ping Module	Ping All Modules

FIGURE 36–26 Modules used in a General Motors vehicle can be "pinged" using a Tech 2 scan tool.

If a module fails to send a state of health message within five seconds, the companion module will set a diagnostic trouble code for the module that did not respond. The defective module is not capable of sending this message.

STEP 3   **Check the resistance of the terminating resistors.** Most high-speed BUS systems use resistors at each end, called **terminating resistors.** These resistors are used to help reduce interference into other systems in the vehicle. Usually two 120-ohm resistors are installed at each end and are therefore connected electrically in parallel. Two 120-ohm resistors connected in parallel would measure 60 ohms if being tested using an ohmmeter. ● **SEE FIGURE 36–27.**

STEP 4   **Check data BUS for voltages.** Use a digital multimeter set to DC volts, to monitor communications and check the BUS for proper operation. Some BUS conditions and possible causes include:

■ **Signal is zero volt all of the time.** Check for short-to-ground by unplugging modules one at a time to check if one module is causing the problem.

■ **Signal is high or 12 volts all of the time.** The BUS circuit could be shorted to 12 V. Check with the customer to see if any service or body repair work was done recently. Try unplugging each module one at a time to pin down which module is causing the communications problem.

FIGURE 36–27 Checking the terminating resistors using an ohmmeter at the DLC.

- **A variable voltage usually indicates that messages are being sent and received.** CAN and Class 2 can be identified by looking at the data link connector (DLC) for a terminal in cavity number 2. Class 2 is active all of the time the ignition is on, and therefore voltage variation between 0 and 7 V can be measured using a DMM set to read DC volts. ● **SEE FIGURE 36–28.**

STEP 5 **Use a digital storage oscilloscope to monitor the waveforms of the BUS circuit.** Using a scope on the data line terminals can show if communication is being transmitted. Typical faults and their causes include:

- **Normal operation.** Normal operation shows variable voltage signals on the data lines. It is impossible to know what information is being transmitted, but if there is activity with short sections of inactivity, this indicates normal data line transmission activity. ● **SEE FIGURE 36–29.**

FIGURE 36–28 Use front-probe terminals to access the data link connector. Always follow the specified back-probe and front-probe procedures as found in service information.

CAN BUS LOOKS GOOD

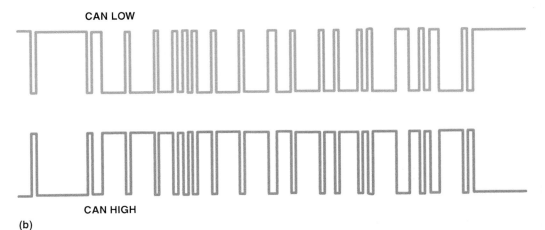

FIGURE 36–29 (a) Data is sent in packets, so it is normal to see activity then a flat line between messages. (b) A CAN BUS should show voltages that are opposite when there is normal communications. CAN H (high) circuit should go from 2.5 volts at rest to 3.5 volts when active. The CAN L (low) circuit goes from 2.5 volts at rest to 1.5 volts when active.

- **High voltage.** If there is a constant high-voltage signal without any change, this indicates that the data line is shorted to voltage.
- **Zero or low voltage.** If the data line voltage is zero or almost zero and not showing any higher voltage signals, then the data line is short-to-ground.

STEP 6 **Follow factory service information instructions to isolate the cause of the fault.** This step often involves disconnecting one module at a time to see if it is the cause of a short-to-ground or an open in the BUS circuit.

 FREQUENTLY ASKED QUESTION

Which Module Is the Gateway Module?

The gateway module is responsible for communicating with other modules and acts as the main communications module for scan tool data. Most General Motors vehicles use the body control module (BCM) or the instrument panel control (IPC) module as the gateway. To verify which module is the gateway, check the schematic and look for one that has voltage applied during all of the following conditions.

- Key on, engine off
- Engine cranking
- Engine running

 REAL WORLD FIX

The Radio Caused No-Start Story

A 2005 Chevrolet Cobalt did not start. A technician checked with a subscription-based helpline service and discovered that a fault with the Class 2 data circuit could prevent the engine from starting. The advisor suggested that a module should be disconnected one at a time to see if one of them was taking the data line to ground. The two most common components on the Class 2 serial data line that have been known to cause a lack of communication and become shorted-to-ground are the radio and electronic brake control module (EBCM). The first one the technician disconnected was the radio. The engine started and ran. Apparently the Class 2 serial data line was shorted-to-ground inside the radio, which took the entire BUS down. When BUS communication is lost, the PCM is not able to energize the fuel pump, ignition, or fuel injectors so the engine would not start. The radio was replaced to solve the no-start condition.

 OBD-II DATA LINK CONNECTOR

All OBD-II vehicles use a 16 pin connector that includes:

Pin 4 = chassis ground

Pin 5 = signal ground

Pin 16 = battery power (4 A max)

● **SEE FIGURE 36–30.**

GENERAL MOTORS VEHICLES

- SAE J-1850 (VPW, Class 2, 10.4 Kbs) standard, which uses pins 2, 4, 5, and 16, but not 10
- GM Domestic OBD-II

Pin 1 and 9: CCM (comprehensive component monitor) slow baud rate, 8,192 UART (prior to 2006)

Pin 1 (2006+): low speed GMLAN

Pins 2 and 10: OEM enhanced, fast rate, 40,500 baud rate

Pins 7 and 15: generic OBD-II, ISO 9141, 10,400 baud rate

Pins 6 and 14: GMLAN

 TECH TIP

Check Computer Data Line Circuit Schematic

Many General Motors vehicles use more than one type of BUS communications protocol. Check service information (SI) and look at the schematic for computer data line circuits which should show all of the data BUSes and their connectors to the diagnostic link connector (DLC). ● **SEE FIGURE 36–31.**

PIN
NO. ASSIGNMENTS

1. MANUFACTURER'S DISCRETION
2. BUS + LINE, SAE J1850
3. MANUFACTURER'S DISCRETION
4. CHASSIS GROUND
5. SIGNAL GROUND
6. MANUFACTURER'S DISCRETION
7. K LINE, ISO 9141
8. MANUFACTURER'S DISCRETION
9. MANUFACTURER'S DISCRETION
10. BUS – LINE' SAE J1850
11. MANUFACTURER'S DISCRETION
12. MANUFACTURER'S DISCRETION
13. MANUFACTURER'S DISCRETION
14. MANUFACTURER'S DISCRETION
15. L LINE, ISO 9141
16. VEHICLE BATTERY POSITIVE (4A MAX)

OBD-II DLC

FIGURE 36–30 A 16 pin OBD-II DLC with terminals identified. Scan tools use the power pin (16) and ground pin (4) for power so that a separate cigarette lighter plug is not necessary on OBD-II vehicles.

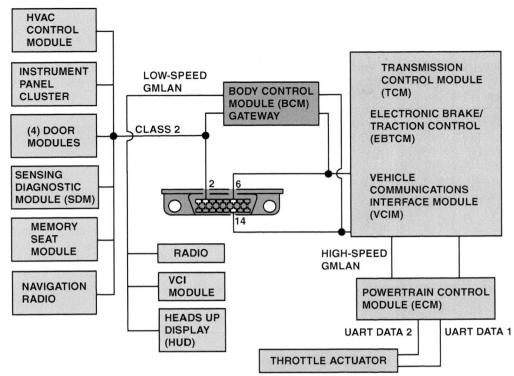

FIGURE 36–31 This schematic of a Chevrolet Equinox shows that the vehicle uses a GMLAN BUS (DLC pins 6 and 14), plus a Class 2 (pin 2) and UART.

ASIAN, CHRYSLER, AND EUROPEAN VEHICLES

- ISO 9141-2 standard, which uses pins 4, 5, 7, 15, and 16
- Chrysler Domestic Group OBD-II

  Pins 2 and 10: CCM

  Pins 3 and 14: OEM enhanced, 60,500 baud rate

  Pins 7 and 15: generic OBD-II, ISO 9141, 10,400 baud rate

FORD VEHICLES

- SAE J-1850 (PWM, 41.6 Kbs) standard, which uses pins 2, 4, 5, 10, and 16
- Ford Domestic OBD-II

  Pins 2 and 10: CCM

  Pins 6 and 14: OEM enhanced, Class C, 40,500 baud rate

  Pins 7 and 15: generic OBD-II, ISO 9141, 10,400 baud rate

SUMMARY

1. The use of a network for module communications reduces the number of wires and connections needed.
2. Module communication configurations include ring link, star link, and ring/star hybrid systems.
3. The SAE communication classifications for vehicle communications systems include Class A (low speed), Class B (medium speed), and Class C (high speed).
4. Various module communications used on General Motors vehicles include UART, E & C, Class 2, keyword communications, and GMLAN (CAN).
5. Types of module communications used on Ford vehicles include SCP, UBP, and CAN.
6. Chrysler brand vehicles use SCI, CCD, PCI, and CAN communications protocols.
7. Many European vehicles use an underhood electrical connector that can be used to access electrical components and modules using a breakout box (BOB) or special tester.
8. Diagnosis of network communications includes checking the terminating resistors and checking for changing voltage signals at the DLC.

REVIEW QUESTIONS

1. Why is a communication network used?
2. Why are the two wires twisted if used for network communications?
3. Why is a gateway module used?
4. What are U codes?

1. Technician A says that module communications networks are used to reduce the number of wires in a vehicle. Technician B says that a communications network is used to share data from sensors, which can be used by many different modules. Which technician is correct?
   a. Technician A only
   b. Technician B only
   c. Both Technicians A and B
   d. Neither Technician A nor B

2. A module is also known as a _____.
   a. BUS
   b. Node
   c. Terminator
   d. Resistor pack

3. A high-speed CAN BUS communicates with a scan tool through which terminal(s)?
   a. 6 and 14   b. 2
   c. 7 and 15   d. 4 and 16

4. UART uses a _____ signal that toggles 0 V.
   a. 5 V   b. 7 V
   c. 8 V   d. 12 V

5. GM Class 2 communication toggles between _____.
   a. 5 and 7 V   b. 0 and 12 V
   c. 7 and 12 V   d. 0 and 7 V

6. Which terminal of the data link connector does General Motors use for Class 2 communication?
   a. 1   b. 2
   c. 3   d. 4

7. GMLAN is the General Motors term for which type of module communication?
   a. UART
   b. Class 2
   c. High-speed CAN
   d. Keyword 2000

8. CAN H and CAN L operate how?
   a. CAN H is at 2.5 volts when not transmitting.
   b. CAN L is at 2.5 volts when not transmitting.
   c. CAN H goes to 3.5 volts when transmitting.
   d. All of the above

9. Which terminal of the OBD-II data link connector is the signal ground for all vehicles?
   a. 1   b. 3
   c. 4   d. 5

10. Terminal 16 of the OBD-II data link connector is used for what?
    a. Chassis ground
    b. 12 V positive
    c. Module (signal ground)
    d. Manufacturer's discretion

chapter 37

LIGHTING AND SIGNALING CIRCUITS

OBJECTIVES: **After studying Chapter 37, the reader will be able to:** • Prepare for ASE Electrical/Electronic Systems (A6) certification test content area "E" (Lighting System Diagnosis and Repair). • Read and interpret a bulb chart. • Describe how interior and exterior lighting systems work. • Read and interpret a bulb chart. • Discuss troubleshooting procedures for lighting and signaling circuits.

KEY TERMS: • AFS 413 • Brake lights 406 • Candlepower 402 • CHMSL 406 • Color shift 413 • Composite headlight 411 • Courtesy lights 415 • DOT 408 • DRL 415 • Feedback 418 • Fiber optics 417 • Hazard warning 409 • HID 411 • Hybrid flasher 408 • Kelvin (K) 412 • LED 406 • Rheostat 409 • Trade number 402 • Troxler effect 418 • Xenon headlights 412

INTRODUCTION

The vehicle has many different lighting and signaling systems, each with its own specific components and operating characteristics. The major light-related circuits and systems covered include:

- Exterior lighting
- Headlights (halogen, HID, and LED)
- Bulb trade numbers
- Brake lights
- Turn signals and flasher units
- Courtesy lights
- Light-dimming rearview mirrors

EXTERIOR LIGHTING

HEADLIGHT SWITCH CONTROL Exterior lighting is controlled by the headlight switch, which is connected directly to the battery on most vehicles. Therefore, if the light switch is left on manually, the lights could drain the battery. Older headlight switches contained a built-in circuit breaker. If excessive current flows through the headlight circuit, the circuit breaker will momentarily open the circuit, then close it again. The result is headlights that flicker on and off rapidly. This feature allows the headlights to function, as a safety measure, in spite of current overload.

The headlight switch controls the following lights on most vehicles, usually through a module.

1. Headlights
2. Taillights
3. Side-marker lights
4. Front parking lights
5. Dash lights
6. Interior (dome) light(s)

COMPUTER-CONTROLLED LIGHTS Because these lights can easily drain the battery if accidentally left on, many newer vehicles control these lights through computer modules. The computer module keeps track of the time the lights are on and can turn them off if the time is excessive. The computer can control either the power side or the ground side of the circuit.

For example, a typical computer-controlled lighting system usually includes the following steps.

STEP 1 The driver depresses or rotates the headlight switch.

STEP 2 The signal from the headlight switch is sent to the nearest control module.

STEP 3 The control module then sends a request to the headlight control module to turn on the headlights as well as the front park and side-marker lights.

Through the data BUS, the rear control module receives the lights on signal and turns on the lights at the rear of the vehicle.

STEP 4 All modules monitor current flow through the circuit and will turn on a bulb failure warning light if it detects an open bulb or a fault in the circuit.

STEP 5 After the ignition has been turned off, the modules will turn off the lights after a time delay to prevent the battery from being drained.

BULB NUMBERS

TRADE NUMBER The number used on automotive bulbs is called the bulb **trade number,** as recorded with the American National Standards Institute (ANSI). The number is the same regardless of the manufacturer. ● **SEE FIGURE 37–1.**

CANDLEPOWER The trade number also identifies the size, shape, number of filaments, and amount of light produced, measured in **candlepower.** For example, the 1156 bulb, commonly used for backup lights, is 32 candlepower. A 194 bulb, commonly used for dash or side-marker lights, is rated at only 2 candlepower. The amount of light produced by a bulb is determined by the resistance of the filament wire, which also affects the amount of current (in amperes) required by the bulb.

It is important that the correct trade number of bulb always be used for replacement to prevent circuit or component damage. The correct replacement bulb for a vehicle is usually listed in the owner or service manual. ● **REFER TO CHART 37–1** for a listing of common bulbs and their specifications used in most vehicles.

BULB NUMBER SUFFIXES Many bulbs have suffixes that indicate some feature of the bulb, while keeping the same size and light output specifications.

**DOUBLE CONTACT
1157/2057 BULB**

**SINGLE CONTACT
1156 BULB**

**WEDGE
194 BULB**

FIGURE 37–1 Dual-filament (double-contact) bulbs contain both a low-intensity filament for taillights or parking lights and a high-intensity filament for brake lights and turn signals. Bulbs come in a variety of shapes and sizes. The numbers shown are the trade numbers.

BULB NUMBER	FILAMENTS	AMPERAGE LOW/HIGH	WATTAGE LOW/HIGH	CANDLEPOWER LOW/HIGH
Headlights				
1255/H1	1	4.58	55.00	129.00
1255/H3	1	4.58	55.00	121.00
6024	2	2.73/4.69	35.00/60.00	27,000/35,000
6054	2	2.73/5.08	35.00/65.00	35,000/40,000
9003	2	4.58/5.00	55.00/60.00	72.00/120.00
9004	2	3.52/5.08	45.00/65.00	56.00/95.00
9005	1	5.08	65.00	136.00
9006	1	4.30	55.00	80.00
9007	2	4.30/5.08	55.00/65.00	80.00/107.00
9008	2	4.30/5.08	55.00/65.00	80.00/107.00
9011	1	5.08	65.00	163.50
Headlights (HID—Xenon)				
D2R	Air Gap	0.41	35.00	222.75
D2S	Air Gap	0.41	35.00	254.57
Taillights, Stop, and Turn Lamps				
1156	1	2.10	26.88	32.00
1157	2	0.59/2.10	8.26/26.88	3.00/32.00
2057	2	0.49/2.10	6.86/26.88	2.00/32.00
3057	2	6.72/26.88	0.48/2.10	1.50/24.00
3155	1	1.60	20.48	21.00
3157	2	0.59/2.10	8.26/26.88	2.20/24.00
4157	2	0.59/2.10	8.26/26.88	3.00/32.00
7440	1	1.75	21.00	36.60
7443	2	0.42/1.75	5.00/21.00	2.80/36.60
17131	1	0.33	4.00	2.80
17635	1	1.75	21.00	37.00
17916	2	0.42/1.75	5.00/21.00	1.20/35.00
Parking, Daytime Running Lamps				
24	1	0.24	3.36	2.00
67	1	0.59	7.97	4.00
168	1	0.35	4.90	3.00
194	1	0.27	3.78	2.00
889	1	3.90	49.92	43.00
912	1	1.00	12.80	12.00
916	1	0.54	7.29	2.00
1034	2	0.59/1.80	8.26/23.04	3.00/32.00
1156	1	2.10	26.88	32.00

CHART 37–1

Bulb chart sorted by typical applications. Check the owner's manual, service information, or a bulb manufacturer's application chart for the exact bulb to use.

BULB NUMBER	FILAMENTS	AMPERAGE LOW/HIGH	WATTAGE LOW/HIGH	CANDLEPOWER LOW/HIGH
1157	2	0.59/2.10	8.26/26.88	3.00/32.00
2040	1	0.63	8.00	10.50
2057	2	0.49/2.10	6.86/26.88	1.50/24.00
2357	2	0.59/2.23	8.26/28.54	3.00/40.00
3157	2	0.59/2.10	8.26/26.88	3.00/32.00
3357	2	0.59/2.23	8.26/28.54	3.00/40.00
3457	2	0.59/2.23	8.26/28.51	3.00/40.00
3496	2	0.66/2.24	8.00/27.00	3.00/45.00
3652	1	0.42	5.00	6.00
4114	2	0.59/2 23	8.26/31.20	3.00/32.00
4157	2	0.59/2.10	8.26/26/88	3.00/32.00
7443	2	0.42/1.75	5.00/21.00	2.80/36.60
17131	1	0.33	4.00	2.80
17171	1	0.42	5.00	4.00
17177	1	0.42	5.00	4.00
17311	1	0.83	10.00	10.00
17916	2	0.42/1.75	5.00/21.00	1.20/35.00
68161	1	0.50	6.00	10.00

Center High-Mounted Stop Lamp (CHMSL)

BULB NUMBER	FILAMENTS	AMPERAGE LOW/HIGH	WATTAGE LOW/HIGH	CANDLEPOWER LOW/HIGH
70	1	0.15	2.10	1.50
168	1	0.35	4.90	3.00
175	1	0.58	8.12	5.00
211-2	1	0.97	12.42	12.00
577	1	1.40	17.92	21.00
579	1	0.80	10.20	9.00
889	1	3.90	49.92	43.00
891	1	0.63	8.00	11.00
906	1	0.69	8.97	6.00
912	1	1.00	12.80	12.00
921	1	1.40	17.92	21.00
922	1	0.98	12.54	15.00
1141	1	1.44	18.43	21.00
1156	1	2.10	26.88	32.00
2723	1	0.20	2.40	1.50
3155	1	1.60	20.48	21.00
3156	1	2.10	26.88	32.00
3497	1	2.24	27.00	45.00
7440	1	1.75	21.00	36.60
17177	1	0.42	5.00	4.00
17635	1	1.75	21.00	37.00

CONTINUED

BULB NUMBER	FILAMENTS	AMPERAGE LOW/HIGH	WATTAGE LOW/HIGH	CANDLEPOWER LOW/HIGH
License Plate, Glove Box, Dome, Side Marker, Trunk, Map, Ashtray, Step/Courtesy, Underhood				
37	1	0.09	1.26	0.50
67	1	0.59	7.97	4.00
74	1	0.10	1.40	.070
98	1	0.62	8.06	6.00
105	1	1.00	12.80	12.00
124	1	0.27	3.78	1.50
161	1	0.19	2.66	1.00
168	1	0.35	4.90	3.00
192	1	0.33	4.29	3.00
194	1	0.27	3.78	2.00
211-1	1	0.968	12.40	12.00
212-2	1	0.74	9.99	6.00
214-2	1	0.52	7.02	4.00
293	1	0.33	4.62	2.00
561	1	0.97	12.42	12.00
562	1	0.74	9.99	6.00
578	1	0.78	9.98	9.00
579	1	0.80	10.20	9.00
PC579	1	0.80	10.20	9.00
906	1	0.69	8.97	6.00
912	1	1.00	12.80	12.00
917	1	1.20	14.40	10.00
921	1	1.40	17.92	21.00
1003	1	0.94	12.03	15.00
1155	1	0.59	7.97	4.00
1210/H2	1	8.33	100.00	239.00
1210/H3	1	8.33	100.00	192.00
1445	1	0.14	2.02	0.70
1891	1	0.24	3.36	2.00
1895	1	0.27	3.78	2.00
3652	1	0.42	5.00	6.00
11005	1	0.39	5.07	4.00
11006	1	0.24	3.36	2.00
12100	1	0.77	10.01	9.55
13050	1	0.38	4.94	3.00
17036	1	0.10	1.20	0.48
17097	1	0.25	3.00	1.76
17131	1	0.33	4.00	2.80
17177	1	0.42	5.00	4.00
17314	1	0.83	10.00	8.00
17916	2	0.42/1.75	5.00/21.00	1.20/35.00
47830	1	0.39	5.00	6.70

CONTINUED

BULB NUMBER	FILAMENTS	AMPERAGE LOW/HIGH	WATTAGE LOW/HIGH	CANDLEPOWER LOW/HIGH
Instrument Panel				
37	1	0.09	1.26	0.50
73	1	0.08	1.12	0.30
74	1	0.10	1.40	0.70
PC74	1	0.10	1.40	0.70
PC118	1	0.12	1.68	0.70
124	1	0.27	3.78	1.50
158	1	0.24	3.36	2.00
161	1	0.19	2.66	1.00
192	1	0.33	4.29	3.00
194	1	0.27	3.78	2.00
PC194	1	0.27	3.78	2.00
PC195	1	0.27	3.78	1.80
1210/H1	1	8.33	100.00	217.00
1210/H3	1	8.33	100.00	192.00
17037	1	0.10	1.20	0.48
17097	1	0.25	3.00	1.76
17314	1	0.83	10.00	8.00
Backup, Cornering, Fog/Driving Lamps				
67	1	0.59	7.97	4.00
579	1	0.80	10.20	9.00
880	1	2.10	26.88	43.00
881	1	2.10	26.88	43.00
885	1	3.90	49.92	100.00
886	1	3.90	49.92	100.00
893	1	2.93	37.50	75.00
896	1	2.93	37.50	75.00
898	1	2.93	37.50	60.00
899	1	2.93	37.50	60.00
921	1	1.40	17.92	21.00
1073	1	1.80	23.04	32.00
1156	1	2.10	26.88	32.00
1157	2	0.59/2.10	8.26/26.88	3.00/32.00
1210/H1	1	8.33	100.00	217.00
1255/H1	1	4.58	55.00	129.00
1255/H3	1	4.58	55.00	121.00
1255/H11	1	4.17	55.00	107.00
2057	2	0.49/2.10	6.86/26.88	1.50/24.00
3057	2	0.48/2.10	6.72/26.88	2.00/32.00
3155	1	1.60	20.48	21.00

BULB NUMBER	FILAMENTS	AMPERAGE LOW/HIGH	WATTAGE LOW/HIGH	CANDLEPOWER LOW/HIGH
3156	1	2.10	26.88	32.00
3157	2	0.59/2.10	8.26/26.88	3.00/32.00
4157	2	0.59/2.10	8.26/26/88	3.00/32.00
7440	1	1.75	21.00	36.00
9003	2	4.58/5.00	55.00/60.00	72.00/120.00
9006	1	4.30	55.00	80.00
9145	1	3.52	45.00	65.00
17635	1	1.75	21.00	37.00

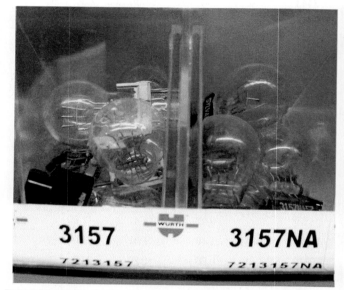

FIGURE 37–2 Bulbs that have the same trade number have the same operating voltage and wattage. The NA means that the bulb uses a natural amber glass ampoule which are used on vehicles with clear turn signal lenses.

Typical bulb suffixes include:

- NA: natural amber (amber glass)
- A: amber (painted glass)
- HD: heavy duty
- LL: long life
- IF: inside frosted
- R: red
- B: blue
- G: green

● **SEE FIGURE 37–2.**

CONTINUED

REAL WORLD FIX

Weird Problem—Easy Solution

A General Motors minivan had the following electrical problems.

- The turn signals flashed rapidly on the left side.
- With the ignition key off, the lights-on warning chime sounded if the brake pedal was depressed.
- When the brake pedal was depressed, the dome light came on.

All of these problems were caused by *one* defective 2057 dual-filament bulb, as shown in ●**FIGURE 37–3.**

Apparently, the two filaments were electrically connected when one filament broke and then welded to the other filament. This caused the electrical current to feed back from the brake light filament into the taillight circuit, causing all the problems.

TESTING BULBS Bulbs can be tested using two basic tests.

1. Perform a visual inspection of any bulb. Many faults, such as a shorted filament, corroded connector, or water, can cause weird problems that are often thought to be wiring issues. ●**SEE FIGURES 37–4 AND 37–5.**

2. Bulbs can be tested using an ohmmeter and checking the resistance of the filaments(s). Most bulbs will read low resistance at room temperature between 0.5 and 20 ohms depending on the bulb. Test results include:

   - **Normal resistance.** The bulb is good. Check both filaments if it is a two-filament bulb. ●**SEE FIGURE 37–6.**
   - **Zero ohms.** It is unlikely but possible for the bulb filament to be shorted.
   - **OL (electrically open).** The reading indicates that the bulb filament is broken.

FIGURE 37–3 Close-up a 2057 dual-filament (double-contact) bulb that failed. Notice that the top filament broke from its mounting and melted onto the lower filament. This bulb caused the dash lights to come on whenever the brakes were applied.

FIGURE 37–4 Corrosion caused the two terminals of this dual-filament bulb to be electrically connected.

FIGURE 37–5 Often the best diagnosis is a thorough visual inspection. This bulb was found to be filled with water, which caused weird problems.

FIGURE 37–6 This single-filament bulb is being tested with a digital multimeter set to read resistance in ohms. The reading of 1.1 ohms is the resistance of the bulb when cold. As soon as current flows through the filament, the resistance increases about 10 times. It is the initial surge of current flowing through the filament when the bulb is cool that causes many bulbs to fail in cold weather as a result of the reduced resistance. As the temperature increases, the resistance increases.

BRAKE LIGHTS

OPERATION **Brake lights,** also called stop lights, use the high-intensity filament of a double-filament bulb. (The low-intensity filament is for the taillights.) When the brakes are applied, the brake switch is closed and the brake lamps light. The brake switch receives current from a fuse that is hot all the time. The brake light switch is a normally open (N.O.) switch, but is closed when the driver depresses the brake pedal. Since 1986, all vehicles sold in the United States have a third brake light commonly referred to as the **center high-mounted stop light (CHMSL).** ● SEE FIGURE 37–7.

The brake switch is also used as an input switch (signal) for the following:

1. Cruise control (deactivates when the brake pedal is depressed)

2. Antilock brakes (ABS)

3. Brake shift interlock (prevents shifting from park position unless the brake pedal is depressed)

FIGURE 37–7 Typical brake light and taillight circuit showing the brake switch and all of the related circuit components.

FIGURE 37-8 A replacement LED taillight bulb is constructed of many small, individual light-emitting diodes.

TURN SIGNALS

OPERATION   The turn signal circuit is supplied power from the ignition switch and operated by a lever and switch. ● **SEE FIGURE 37-9.**

When the turn signal switch is moved in either direction, the corresponding turn signal lamps receive current through the flasher unit. The flasher unit causes the current to start

FIGURE 37-9 The typical turn signal switch includes various springs and cams to control the switch and to cause the switch to cancel after a turn has been completed.

FIGURE 37-10 When the stop lamps and turn signals share a common bulb filament, stop light current flows through the turn signal switch.

and stop as the turn signal lamp flashes on and off with the interrupted current.

ONE-FILAMENT STOP/TURN BULBS   In many vehicles, the stop and turn signals are both provided by one filament. When the turn signal switch is turned on (closed), the filament receives interrupted current through the flasher unit. When the brakes are applied, the current first flows to the turn signal switch, except for the high-mounted stop, which is fed directly from the brake switch. If neither turn signal is on, then current through the turn signal switch flows to both rear brake lights. If the turn signal switch is operated (turned to either left or right), current flows through the flasher unit on the side that was selected and directly to the brake lamp on the opposite side. If the brake pedal is not depressed, then current flows through the flasher and only to one side. ● **SEE FIGURE 37-10.**

Moving the lever up or down completes the circuit through the flasher unit and to the appropriate turn signal lamps. A turn signal switch includes cams and springs that cancel the signal after the turn has been completed. As the steering wheel is turned in the signaled direction and then returns to its normal position, the cams and springs cause the turn signal switch contacts to open and break the circuit.

TWO-FILAMENT STOP/TURN BULBS   In systems using separate filaments for the stop and turn lamps, the brake and turn signal switches are not connected. If the vehicle uses the same filament for both purposes, then brake switch current is routed through contacts within the turn signal switch. By linking certain contacts, the bulbs can receive either brake switch current or flasher current, depending upon which direction is being signaled. For example, ● **FIGURE 37-11** shows current flow through the switch when the brake switch is closed and a right turn is signaled.

FIGURE 37–11 When a right turn in signaled, the turn signal switch contacts send flasher current to the right-hand filament and brake switch current to the left-hand filament.

FIGURE 37–12 Two styles of two-prong flasher units.

Steady current through the brake switch is sent to the left brake lamp. Interrupted current from the turn signal is sent to the right turn lamps.

FLASHER UNITS
A turn signal flasher unit is a metal or plastic can containing a switch that opens and closes the turn signal circuit. Vehicles can be equipped with many different types of flasher units. ● SEE FIGURE 37–12.

- **DOT flashers.** This turn signal flasher unit is often installed in a metal clip attached to the dash panel to allow the "clicking" noise of the flasher to be heard by the driver. The turn signal flasher is designed to transmit the current to light the front and rear bulbs on only one side at a time. The U.S. **Department of Transportation (DOT)** regulation requires that the driver be alerted when a turn signal bulb is not working. This is achieved by using a series-type flasher unit. The flasher unit requires current flow through two bulbs (one in the front and one in the rear) in order to flash. If one bulb burns out, the current flow through only one bulb is not sufficient to make the

unit flash; it will be a steady light. These turn signal units are often called DOT flashers.

- **Bimetal flashers.** The bimetal flashers have a lower cost and shorter life expectancy than hybrid or solid-state flashers. The operation of this flasher is current sensitive, which means that the flasher will stop flashing when one of the light bulbs is out and that it will flash at a faster rate when adding additional load, such as a trailer. The bimetal element is a sandwich of two different metals that distorts with temperature changes similar to a circuit breaker. The turn signal lamp current is passed through the bimetal element and causes heating. When the element is hot enough, the bimetal distorts, opening the contacts and turning off the lamps. After the bimetal cools, it returns to the original shape, closing the contacts and turning on the lamps again. This sequence is repeated until the load is removed. If one bulb burns out, the turn signal indicator lamp on the dash will remain lighted. The flasher will not flash because there is not enough current flow through the one remaining bulb to cause the flasher to become heated enough to open.

- **Hybrid flashers.** The **hybrid flashers** have an electronic flasher control circuit to operate the internal electro-mechanical relay and are commonly called a *flasher relay*. This type of flasher has a stable electronic timing circuitry that enables a wide operating voltage and temperature range with a reasonable cost. The life expectancy is considerably longer compared to bimetal units and is dependent on the load and relay used internally for switching the load. The hybrid flasher has a lamp current-sensing circuit which will cause the flash rate to double when a bulb is burned out.

- **Solid-state flashers.** The solid-state flashers have an internal electronic circuit for timing and solid-state power output devices for load switching. Life expectancy is longer than other flashers because there are no moving parts for mechanical breakdown. The biggest disadvantage of solid state is the higher cost. Solid-state units cause the turn indicator to flash rapidly if a bulb is burned out.

ELECTRONIC FLASHER REPLACEMENT UNITS Older vehicles (and a few newer ones) use thermal (bimetal) flashers that use heat to switch on and off. Most turn signal flasher units are mounted in a metal clip that is attached to the dash. The dash panel acts as a sounding board, increasing the sound of the flasher unit. Most four-way hazard flasher units are plugged into the fuse panel. Some turn signal flasher units are plugged into the fuse panel. How do you know for sure where the flasher unit is located? With both the turn signal and the ignition on, listen and/or feel for the clicking of the flasher unit. Some service manuals also give general locations for the placement of flasher units.

Newer vehicles have electronic flashers that use micro-chips to control the on/off function. Electronic flashers are compatible with older systems and are wise to use for the following reasons.

FIGURE 37-13 A hazard warning flasher uses a parallel resistor across the contacts to provide a constant flashing rate regardless of the number of bulbs used in the circuit.

1. Electronic flashers do not burn out, and they provide a faster "flash" of the turn signals.
2. If upgrading to LED tail lamps, or lights, the LED bulbs only work with electronic flashers unless a resistor is added in the circuit.

HAZARD WARNING FLASHER The **hazard warning** flasher is a device installed in a vehicle lighting system with the primary function of causing both the left and right turn signal lamps to flash when the hazard warning switch is activated. Secondary functions may include visible dash indicators for the hazard system and an audible signal to indicate when the flasher is operating. A typical hazard warning flasher is also called a *parallel* or *variable-load* flasher because there is a resistor in parallel with the contacts to provide a control load and, therefore, a constant flash rate, regardless of the number of bulbs being flashed. ● **SEE FIGURE 37-13.**

 FREQUENTLY ASKED QUESTION

Where is the flasher unit?

Many newer vehicles do not use a flasher unit. On many vehicles, such as on many 2006+ General Motors vehicles, the turn signal switch is an input to the body control module (BCM). The BCM sends a signal through the data lines to the lighting module(s) to flash the lights. The BCM also sends a signal to the radio which sends a clicking sound to the driver's side speaker even if the radio is off.

FREQUENTLY ASKED QUESTION

Why Does the Side-Marker Light Alternately Flash?

A question that service technicians are asked frequently is why the side-marker light alternately goes out when the turn signal is on, and is on when the turn signal is off. Some vehicle owners think that there is a fault with the vehicle, but this is normal operation. The side-marker light goes out when the lights are on and the turn signal is flashing because there are 12 volts on both sides of the bulb (see points X and Y in ● **FIGURE 37-14**).

Normally, the side-marker light gets its ground through the turn signal bulb.

COMBINATION TURN SIGNAL AND HAZARD WARNING FLASHER The combination flasher is a device that combines the functions of a turn signal flasher and a hazard warning flasher into one package, which often uses three electrical terminals.

HEADLIGHTS

HEADLIGHT SWITCHES The headlight switch operates the exterior and interior lights of most vehicles. On noncomputer-controlled lighting systems, the headlight switch is connected directly to the battery through a fusible link, and has continuous power or is "hot" all the time. A circuit breaker is built into most older model headlight switches to protect the headlight circuit. ● **SEE FIGURE 37-15.**

The headlight switch may include the following:

- The interior dash lights can often be dimmed manually by rotating the headlight switch knob or by another rotary knob that controls a variable resistor (called a **rheostat**). The rheostat drops the voltage sent to the dash lights. Whenever there is a voltage drop (increased resistance), there is heat. A coiled resistance wire is built into a ceramic housing that is designed to insulate the rest of the switch from the heat and allow heat to escape.

- The headlight switch also contains a built-in circuit breaker that will rapidly turn the headlights on and off in the event of a short circuit. This prevents a total loss of headlights. If the headlights are rapidly flashing on and off, check the entire headlight circuit for possible shorts. The circuit breaker controls only the headlights. The other lights controlled by the headlight switch (taillights, dash lights, and parking lights) are fused separately. Flashing headlights also may be caused by a failure in the built-in circuit breaker, requiring replacement of the switch assembly.

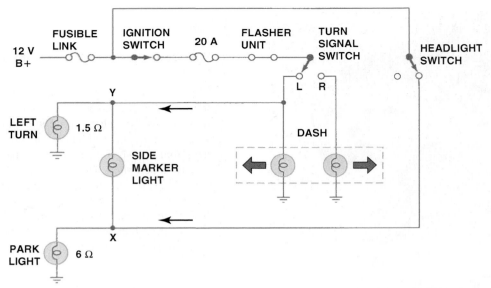

FIGURE 37–14 The side-marker light goes out whenever there is voltage at both points X and Y. These opposing voltages stop current flow through the side-marker light. The left turn light and left park light are actually the same bulb (usually 2057) and are shown separately to help explain how the side-marker light works on many vehicles.

FIGURE 37–15 Typical headlight circuit diagram. Note that the headlight switch is represented by a dotted outline indicating that other circuits (such as dash lights) also operate from the switch.

AUTOMATIC HEADLIGHTS Computer-controlled lights use a light sensor that signals when to have the computer turn on the headlights. The sensor is mounted on the dashboard or mirror. Often these systems have a driver-adjusted sensitivity control that allows for the lights to be turned on at various levels of light. Most systems also have a computer module control over the time that the lights remain on after the ignition has been turned off and the last door has been closed. A scan tool is often needed to change this time delay.

SEALED BEAM HEADLIGHTS A sealed beam headlight consists of a sealed glass or plastic assembly containing the bulb, reflective surface, and prism lenses to properly focus the light beam. Low-beam headlights contain two filaments and three electrical terminals.

- One for low beam
- One for high beam
- Common ground

High-beam headlights contain only one filament and two terminals. Because low-beam headlights also contain a high-beam filament, the entire headlight assembly must be replaced if either filament is defective. ● **SEE FIGURE 37–16.**

A sealed beam headlight can be tested with an ohmmeter. A good bulb should indicate low ohms between the ground terminal and both power-side (hot) terminals. If either the high-beam or the low-beam filament is burned out, the ohmmeter will indicate infinity (OL).

HALOGEN SEALED BEAM HEADLIGHTS Halogen sealed beam headlights are brighter and more expensive than normal headlights. Because of their extra brightness, it is common practice to have only two headlights on at any

FIGURE 37–16 A typical four-headlight system using sealed beam headlights.

FIGURE 37–18 Handle a halogen bulb by the base to prevent the skin's oil from getting on the glass.

one time, because the candlepower output would exceed the maximum U.S. federal standards if all four halogen headlights were on. Therefore, before trying to repair the problem that only two of the four lamps are on, check the owner or shop manual for proper operation.

CAUTION: Do not attempt to wire all headlights together. The extra current flow could overheat the wiring from the headlight switch through the dimmer switch and to the headlights. The overloaded circuit could cause a fire.

COMPOSITE HEADLIGHTS **Composite headlights** are constructed using a replaceable bulb and a fixed lens cover that is part of the vehicle. Composite headlights are the result of changes in the aerodynamic styling of vehicles where sealed beam lamps could no longer be used. ● SEE FIGURE 37–17.

The replaceable bulbs are usually bright halogen bulbs. Halogen bulbs get very hot during operation, between 500°F and 1,300°F (260°C and 700°C). It is important never to touch

 TECH TIP

Diagnose Bulb Failure

Halogen bulbs can fail for various reasons. Some causes for halogen bulb failure and their indications are as follows:

- **Gray color.** Low voltage to bulb (check for corroded socket or connector)
- **White (cloudy) color.** Indication of an air leak
- **Broken filament.** Usually caused by excessive vibration
- **Blistered glass.** Indication that someone has touched the glass

NOTE: *Never touch the glass (called the ampoule) of any halogen bulb.* **The oils from your fingers can cause unequal heating of the glass during operation, leading to a shorter-than-normal service life.** ● SEE FIGURE 37–18.

FIGURE 37–17 A typical composite headlamp assembly. The lens, housing, and bulb sockets are usually included as a complete assembly.

the glass of any halogen bulb with bare fingers because the natural oils of the skin on the glass bulb can cause the bulb to break when it heats during normal operation.

HIGH-INTENSITY DISCHARGE HEADLIGHTS

PARTS AND OPERATION **High-intensity discharge (HID)** headlights produce a distinctive blue-white light that is crisper, clearer, and brighter than light produced by a halogen headlight.

FIGURE 37–19 The igniter contains the ballast and transformer needed to provide high-voltage pulses to the arc tube bulb.

FIGURE 37–20 HID (xenon) headlights emit a whiter light than halogen headlights and usually look blue compared to halogen bulbs.

 FREQUENTLY ASKED QUESTION

What Is the Difference Between the Temperature of the Light and the Brightness of the Light?

The temperature of the light indicates the color of the light. The brightness of the light is measured in lumens. A standard 100 watt incandescent light bulb emits about 1,700 lumens. A typical halogen headlight bulb produces about 2,000 lumens, and a typical HID bulb produces about 2,800 lumens.

High-intensity discharge lamps do not use a filament like conventional electrical bulbs, but contain two electrodes about 0.2 in. (5 mm) apart. A high-voltage pulse is sent to the bulb which arcs across the tips of electrodes producing light.

It creates light from an electrical discharge between two electrodes in a gas-filled arc tube. It produces twice the light with less electrical input than conventional halogen bulbs.

The HID lighting system consists of the discharge arc source, igniter, ballast, and headlight assembly. ● **SEE FIGURE 37–19.**

The two electrodes are contained in a tiny quartz capsule filled with xenon gas, mercury, and metal halide salts. HID headlights are also called **xenon headlights.** The lights and support electronics are expensive, but they should last the life of the vehicle unless physically damaged.

HID headlights produce a white light giving the lamp a blue-white color. The color of light is expressed in temperature using the Kelvin scale. **Kelvin (K)** temperature is the Celsius temperature plus 273 degrees. Typical color temperatures include:

- Daylight: 5,400°K
- HID: 4,100°K
- Halogen: 3,200°K
- Incandescent (tungsten): 2,800°K
  ● **SEE FIGURE 37–20.**

The HID ballast is powered by 12 volts from the headlight switch on the body control module. The HID headlights operate in three stages or states.

1. Start-up or stroke state
2. Run-up state
3. Steady state

START-UP OR STROKE STATE When the headlight switch is turned to the on position, the ballast may draw up to 20 amperes at 12 volts. The ballast sends multiple high-voltage pulses to the arc tube to start the arc inside the bulb. The voltage provided by the ballast during the start-up state ranges from −600 volts to +600 volts, which is increased by a transformer to about 25,000 volts. The increased voltage is used to create an arc between the electrodes in the bulb.

RUN-UP STATE After the arc is established, the ballast provides a higher than steady state voltage to the arc tube to keep the bulb illuminated. On a cold bulb, this state could last as long as 40 seconds. On a hot bulb, the run-up state may last only 15 seconds. The current requirements during the run-up state are about 360 volts from the ballast and a power level of about 75 watts.

STEADY STATE The steady state phase begins when the power requirement of the bulb drops to 35 watts. The ballast provides a minimum of 55 volts to the bulb during steady state operation.

BI-XENON HEADLIGHTS Some vehicles are equipped with bi-xenon headlights, which use a shutter to block some of the light during low-beam operation and then mechanically move to expose more of the light from the bulb for high-beam operation. Because xenon lights are relatively slow to start working, vehicles equipped with bi-xenon headlights use two halogen lights for the "flash-to-pass" feature.

FAILURE SYMPTOMS The following symptoms indicate bulb failure.

- A light flickers
- Lights go out (caused when the ballast assembly detects repeated bulb restrikes)
- Color changes to a dim pink glow

Bulb failures are often intermittent and difficult to repeat. However, bulb failure is likely if the symptoms get worse over time. Always follow the vehicle manufacturer's recommended testing and service procedures.

DIAGNOSIS AND SERVICE High-intensity discharge headlights will change slightly in color with age. This **color shift** is usually not noticeable unless one headlight arc tube assembly has been replaced due to a collision repair, and then the difference in color may be noticeable. The difference in color will gradually change as the arc tube ages and should not be too noticeable by most customers. If the arc tube assembly is near the end of its life, it may not light immediately if it is turned off and then back on immediately. This test is called a "hot restrike" and if it fails, a replacement arc tube assembly may be needed or there is another fault, such as a poor electrical connection, that should be checked.

☠ **WARNING**

Always adhere to all warnings because the high-voltage output of the ballast assembly can cause personal injury or death.

LED HEADLIGHTS

Some vehicles, including several Lexus models, use LED headlights either as standard equipment (Lexus LS600h) or optional. ● **SEE FIGURE 37–21.**

Advantages include:

- Long service life
- Reduced electrical power required

FIGURE 37–21 LED headlights usually require multiple units to provide the needed light as seen on this Lexus LS600h.

Disadvantages include:

- High cost
- Many small LEDs required to create the necessary light output

HEADLIGHT AIMING

According to U.S. federal law, all headlights, regardless of shape, must be able to be aimed using headlight aiming equipment. Older vehicles equipped with sealed beam headlights used a headlight aiming system that attached to the headlight itself. ● **SEE FIGURES 37–22 AND 37–23.** Also see the photo sequence on headlight aiming at the end of the chapter.

ADAPTIVE FRONT LIGHTING SYSTEM

PARTS AND OPERATION A system that mechanically moves the headlights to follow the direction of the front wheels is called **adaptive (or advanced) front light system, or AFS**. The AFS provides a wide range of visibility during cornering. The headlights are usually capable of rotating 15 degrees to the left and 5 degrees to the right (some systems rotate 14 degrees and 9 degrees, respectively). Vehicles that use AFS include Lexus, Mercedes, and certain domestic models, usually as an extra cost option. ● **SEE FIGURE 37–24.**

NOTE: These angles are reversed on vehicles sold in countries that drive on the left side of the road, such as Great Britain, Japan, Australia, and New Zealand.

The vehicle has to be moving above a predetermined speed, usually above 20 mph (30 km/h) and the lights stop moving when the speed drops below about 3 mph (5 km/h).

AFS is often used in addition to self-leveling motors so that the headlights remain properly aimed regardless of how the vehicle is loaded. Without self-leveling, headlights would shine higher than normal if the rear of the vehicle is heavily loaded. ● **SEE FIGURE 37–25.**

When a vehicle is equipped with an adaptive front lighting system, the lights are moved by the headlight controller outward, and then inward as well as up and down as a test of the system. This action is quite noticeable to the driver, and is normal operation of the system.

DIAGNOSIS AND SERVICE The first step when diagnosing an AFS fault is to perform the following visual inspection.

- Start by checking that the AFS is switched on. Most AFS headlights are equipped with a switch that allows the driver to turn the system on and off. ● **SEE FIGURE 37–26.**
- Check that the system performs a self-test during start-up.

FIGURE 37-22 Typical headlight aiming diagram as found in service information.

ADJUSTING PATTERN FOR LOW BEAM

ADJUSTING PATTERN FOR HIGH BEAM

FIGURE 37-23 Many composite headlights have a built-in bubble level to make aiming easy and accurate.

- Verify that both low-beam and high-beam lights function correctly. The system may be disabled if a fault with one of the headlights is detected.

FIGURE 37-24 Adaptive front lighting systems rotate the low-beam headlight in the direction of travel.

- Use a scan tool to test for any AFS-related diagnostic trouble codes. Some systems allow the AFS to be checked and operated using a scan tool.

FIGURE 37–25 A typical adaptive front lighting system uses two motors: one for the up and down movement and the other for rotating the low-beam headlight to the left and right.

FIGURE 37–26 Typical dash-mounted switch that allows the driver to disable the front lighting system.

Always follow the recommended testing and service procedures as specified by the vehicle manufacturer in service information.

DAYTIME RUNNING LIGHTS

PURPOSE AND FUNCTION Daytime running lights (DRLs) involve operation of the following:

- Front parking lights
- Separate DRL lamps
- Headlights (usually at reduced current and voltage) when the vehicle is running

Canada has required daytime running lights on all new vehicles since 1990. Studies have shown that DRLs have reduced accidents where used.

Daytime running lights primarily use a control module that turns on either the low- or high-beam headlights or separate daytime running lights. The lights on some vehicles come on when the engine starts. Other vehicles will turn on the lamps when the engine is running but delay their operation until a signal from the vehicle speed sensor indicates that the vehicle is moving.

Checking a Dome Light Can Be Confusing

If a technician checks a dome light with a test light, both sides of the bulb will "turn on the light" if the bulb is good. This will be true if the system's "ground switched" doors are closed and the bulb is good. This confuses many technicians because they do not realize that the ground will not be sensed unless the door is open.

To avoid having the lights on during servicing, some systems will turn off the headlights when the parking brake is applied and the ignition switch is cycled off then back on. Others will only light the headlights when the vehicle is in a drive gear. ● SEE FIGURE 37–27.

CAUTION: Most factory daytime running lights operate the headlights at reduced intensity. These are *not* designed to be used at night. Normal intensity of the headlights (and operation of the other external lamps) is actuated by turning on the headlights as usual.

DIMMER SWITCHES

The headlight switch controls the power or hot side of the headlight circuit. The current is then sent to the dimmer switch, which allows current to flow to either the high-beam or the low-beam filament of the headlight bulb, as shown in ● FIGURE 37–28 on page 417.

An indicator light illuminates on the dash when the high beams are selected.

The dimmer switch is usually hand operated by a lever on the steering column. Some steering column switches are actually attached to the *outside* of the steering column and are spring loaded. To replace these types of dimmer switches, the steering column needs to be lowered slightly to gain access to the switch itself.

COURTESY LIGHTS

Courtesy light is a generic term primarily used for interior lights, including overhead (dome) and under-the-dash (courtesy) lights. These interior lights are controlled by operating switches located in the doorjambs of the vehicle doors or by a switch on the dash. ● SEE FIGURE 37–29 on page 417.

Many Ford vehicles use the door switches to open and close the power side of the circuit. Many newer vehicles operate the interior lights through the vehicle computer or through an electronic module. Because the exact wiring and operation of these units differ, consult the service information for the exact model of the vehicle being serviced.

FIGURE 37–27 Typical daytime running light (DRL) circuit. Follow the arrows from the DRL module through both headlights. Notice that the left and right headlights are connected in series, resulting in increased resistance, less current flow, and dimmer than normal lighting. When the normal headlights are turned on, both headlights receive full battery voltage, with the left headlight grounding through the DRL module.

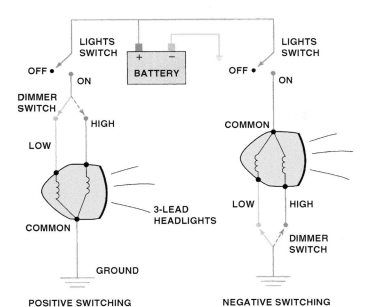

FIGURE 37–28 Most vehicles use positive switching of the high- and low-beam headlights. Notice that both filaments share the same ground connection. Some vehicles use negative switching and place the dimmer switch between the filaments and the ground.

FIGURE 37–29 A typical courtesy light doorjamb switch. Newer vehicles use the door switch as an input to the vehicle computer and the computer turns the interior lights on or off. By placing the lights under the control of the computer, the vehicle engineers have the opportunity to delay the lights after the door is closed and to shut them off after a period of time to avoid draining the battery.

ILLUMINATED ENTRY

Some vehicles are equipped with illuminated entry, meaning the interior lights are turned on for a given amount of time when the outside door handle is operated while the doors are locked.

Most vehicles equipped with illuminated entry also light the exterior door keyhole. Vehicles equipped with body computers use the input from the key fob remote to "wake up" the power supply for the body computer.

FIBER OPTICS

Fiber optics is the transmission of light through special plastic (polymethyl methacrylate) that keeps the light rays parallel even if the plastic is tied in a knot. These strands of plastic are commonly used in automotive applications as indicators for the driver that certain lights are functioning. For example, some vehicles are equipped with fender-mounted units that light when the lights or turn signals are operating. Plastic fiber-optic strands, which often look like standard electrical wire, transmit the light at the bulb to the indicator on top of the fender so that the driver can determine if a certain light is operating. Fiber-optic strands also can be run like wires to indicate the operation of all lights on the dash or console. Fiber-optic strands are also commonly used to light ashtrays, outside door locks, and other areas where a small amount of light is required. The source of the light can be any normally operating light bulb, which means that one bulb can be used to illuminate many areas. A special bulb clip is normally used to retain the fiber-optic plastic tube near the bulb.

AUTOMATIC DIMMING MIRRORS

PARTS AND OPERATION   Automatic dimming mirrors use electrochromic technology to dim the mirror in proportion to the amount of headlight glare from other vehicles at the rear. The electrochromic technology developed by Gentex Corporation uses a gel that changes with light between two pieces of glass. One piece of glass acts as a reflector and the other has a transparent (clear) electrically conductive coating. The inside rearview mirror also has a forward-facing light sensor that is used to detect darkness and signal the rearward-facing sensor to begin to check for excessive glare from headlights behind the vehicle. The rearward-facing sensor sends a voltage to the electrochromic gel in the mirror that is in proportion to the amount of glare detected. The mirror dims in proportion to the glare and then becomes like a standard rearview mirror when the glare is no longer detected. If automatic dimming mirrors are used on the exterior, the sensors in the interior mirror and electronics are used to control both the interior and exterior mirrors. ● SEE FIGURE 37–30.

DIAGNOSIS AND SERVICE   If a customer concern states that the mirrors do not dim when exposed to bright headlights from the vehicle behind, the cause could be sensors

FIGURE 37–30 An automatic dimming mirror compares the amount of light toward the front of the vehicle to the rear of the vehicle and allies a voltage to cause the gel to darken the mirror.

or the mirror itself. Be sure that the mirror is getting electrical power. Most automotive dimming mirrors have a green light to indicate the presence of electrical power. If no voltage is found at the mirror, follow standard troubleshooting procedures to find the cause. If the mirror is getting voltage, start the diagnosis by placing a strip of tape over the forward-facing light sensor. Turn the ignition key on, engine off (KOEO), and observe the operation of the mirror when a flashlight or trouble light is directed onto the mirror. If the mirror reacts and dims, the forward-facing sensor is defective. Most often, the entire mirror assembly has to be replaced if any sensor or mirror faults are found.

One typical fault with automatic dimming mirrors is a crack can occur in the mirror assembly, allowing the gel to escape from between the two layers of glass. This gel can drip onto

the dash or center console and harm these surfaces. The mirror should be replaced at the first sign of any gel leakage.

FEEDBACK

DEFINITION When current that lacks a good ground goes backward along the power side of the circuit in search of a return path (ground) to the battery, this reverse flow is called **feedback,** or *reverse-bias* current flow. Feedback can cause other lights or gauges that should not be working to actually turn on.

FEEDBACK EXAMPLE A customer complained that when the headlights were on, the left turn signal indicator light on the dash remained on. The cause was found to be a poor ground connection for the left front parking light socket. The front parking light bulb is a dual filament: one filament for the parking light (dim) and one filament for the turn signal operation (bright). A corroded socket did not provide a good enough ground to conduct all current required to light the dim filament of the bulb.

The two filaments of the bulb share the same ground connection and are electrically connected. When all the current could not flow through the bulb's ground in the socket, it caused a feedback or reversed its flow through the other filament, looking for ground. The turn signal filament is electrically connected to the dash indicator light; therefore, the reversed current on its path toward ground could light the turn signal indicator light. Cleaning or replacing the socket usually solves the problem if the ground wire for the socket is making a secure chassis ground connection.

LIGHTING SYSTEM DIAGNOSIS

Diagnosing any faults in the lighting and signaling systems usually includes the following steps.

STEP 1   Verify the customer concern.

STEP 2   Perform a visual inspection, checking for collision damage or other possible causes that would affect the operation of the lighting circuit.

STEP 3   Connect a factory or enhanced scan tool with bidirectional control of the computer modules to check for proper operation of the affected lighting circuit.

STEP 4   Follow the diagnostic procedure as found in service information to determine the root cause of the problem.

LIGHTING SYSTEM SYMPTOM GUIDE

The following list will assist technicians in troubleshooting lighting systems.

Problem	Possible Causes and/or Solutions
One headlight dim	1. Poor ground connection on body 2. Corroded connector
One headlight out (low or high beam)	1. Burned out headlight filament (Check the headlight with an ohmmeter. There should be a low-ohm reading between the power-side connection and the ground terminal of the bulb.) 2. Open circuit (no 12 volts to the bulb)
Both high- and low-beam headlights out	1. Burned out bulbs (Check for voltage at the wiring connector to the headlights for a possible open circuit to the headlights or open [defective] dimmer switch.) 2. Open circuit (no 12 volts to the bulb)

Problem	Possible Causes and/or Solutions
All headlights inoperative	1. Burned out filaments in all headlights (Check for excessive charging system voltage.) 2. Defective dimmer switch 3. Defective headlight switch
Slow turn signal operation	1. Defective flasher unit 2. High resistance in sockets or ground wire connections 3. Incorrect bulb numbers
Turn signals operating on one side only	1. Burned out bulb on affected side 2. Poor ground connection or defective socket on affected side 3. Incorrect bulb number on affected side 4. Defective turn signal switch
Interior light(s) inoperative	1. Burned out bulb(s) 2. Open in the power-side circuit (blown fuse) 3. Open in doorjamb switch(es)
Interior lights on all the time	1. Shorted doorjamb switch 2. Shorted control switch
Brake lights inoperative	1. Defective brake switch 2. Defective turn signal switch 3. Burned out brake light bulbs 4. Open circuit or poor ground connection 5. Blown fuse
Hazard warning lights inoperative	1. Defective hazard flasher unit 2. Open in hazard circuit 3. Blown fuse 4. Defective hazard switch
Hazard warning lights blinking too rapidly	1. Incorrect flasher unit 2. Shorted wiring to front or rear lights 3. Incorrect bulb numbers

TAILLIGHT BULB REPLACEMENT

1 The driver noticed that the taillight fault indicator (icon) on the dash was on any time the lights were on.

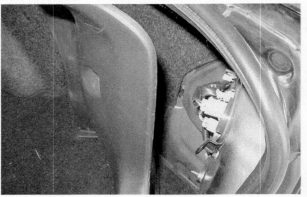

2 A visual inspection at the rear of the vehicle indicated that the right rear taillight bulb did not light. Removing a few screws from the plastic cover revealed the taillight assembly.

3 The bulb socket is removed from the taillight assembly by gently twisting the base of the bulb counterclockwise.

4 The bulb is removed from the socket by gently grasping the bulb and pulling the bulb straight out of the socket. Many bulbs required that you rotate the bulb 90° (1/4 turn) to release the retaining bulbs.

5 The new 7443 replacement bulb is being checked with an ohmmeter to be sure that it is okay before it is installed in the vehicle.

6 The replacement bulb in inserted into the taillight socket and the lights are turned on to verify proper operation before putting the components back together.

OPTICAL HEADLIGHT AIMING

1 Before checking the vehicle for headlight aim, be sure that all the tires are at the correct inflation pressure, and that the suspension is in good working condition.

2 The headlight aim equipment will have to be adjusted for the slope of the floor in the service bay. Start the process by turning on the laser light generator on the side of the aimer body.

3 Place a yardstick or measuring tape vertically in front of the center of the front wheel, noting the height of the laser beam.

4 Move the yardstick to the center of the rear wheel and measure the height of the laser beam at this point. The height at the front and rear wheels should be the same.

5 If the laser beam height measurements are not the same, the floor slope of the aiming equipment must be adjusted. Turn the floor slope knob until the measurements are equal.

6 Place the aimer in front of the headlight to be checked, at a distance of 10 to 14 inches (25 to 35 cm). Use the aiming pointer to adjust the height of the aimer to the middle of the headlight.

CONTINUED ▶

7 Align the aimer horizontally, using the pointer to place the aimer at the center of the headlight.

8 Lateral alignment (aligning the body of the aimer with the body of the vehicle) is done by looking through the upper visor. The line in the upper visor is aligned with symmetrical points on the vehicle body.

9 Turn on the vehicle headlights, being sure to select the correct beam position for the headlight to be aimed.

10 View the light beam through the aimer window. The position of the light pattern will be different for high and low beams.

11 If the first headlight is aimed adequately, move the aimer to the headlight on the opposite side of the vehicle. Follow the previous steps to position the aimer accurately.

12 If adjustment is required, move the headlight adjusting screws using a special tool or a 1/4-in. drive ratchet/socket combination. Watch the light beam through the aimer window to verify the adjustment.

1. Automotive bulbs are identified by trade numbers.
2. The trade number is the same regardless of manufacturer for the exact same bulb specification.
3. Daytime running lights (DRLs) are used on many vehicles.
4. High-intensity discharge (HID) headlights are brighter and have a blue tint.
5. Turn signal flashers come in many different types and construction.

REVIEW QUESTIONS

1. Why should the exact same trade number of bulb be used as a replacement?
2. Why is it important to avoid touching a halogen bulb with your fingers?
3. How do you diagnose a turn signal operating problem?
4. How do you aim headlights on a vehicle equipped with aerodynamic-style headlights?

CHAPTER QUIZ

1. Technician A says that the bulb trade number is the same for all bulbs of the same size. Technician B says that a dual-filament bulb has different candlepower ratings for each filament. Which technician is correct?
   a. Technician A only
   b. Technician B only
   c. Both Technicians A and B
   d. Neither Technician A nor B

2. Two technicians are discussing flasher units. Technician A says that only a DOT-approved flasher unit should be used for turn signals. Technician B says that a parallel (variable-load) flasher will function for turn signal usage, although it will not warn the driver if a bulb burns out. Which technician is correct?
   a. Technician A only
   b. Technician B only
   c. Both Technicians A and B
   d. Neither Technician A nor B

3. Interior overhead lights (dome lights) are operated by doorjamb switches that _____.
   a. Complete the power side of the circuit
   b. Complete the ground side of the circuit
   c. Move the bulb(s) into contact with the power and ground
   d. Either a or b depending on application

4. Electrical feedback is usually a result of _____.
   a. Too high a voltage in a circuit
   b. Too much current (in amperes) in a circuit
   c. Lack of a proper ground
   d. Both a and b

5. According to Chart 37-1, which bulb is brightest?
   a. 194
   b. 168
   c. 194NA
   d. 1157

6. If a 1157 bulb were to be installed in a left front parking light socket instead of a 2057 bulb, what would be the most likely result?
   a. The left turn signal would flash faster.
   b. The left turn signal would flash slower.
   c. The left parking light would be slightly brighter.
   d. The left parking light would be slightly dimmer.

7. A technician replaced a 1157NA with a 1157A bulb. Which is the most likely result?
   a. The bulb is brighter because the 1157A candlepower is higher.
   b. The amber color of the bulb is a different shade.
   c. The bulb is dimmer because the 1157A candlepower is lower.
   d. Both b and c

8. A customer complained that every time he turned on his vehicle's lights, the left-side turn signal indicator light on the dash remained on. The most likely cause is a _____.
   a. Poor ground to the parking light (or taillight) bulb on the *left* side
   b. Poor ground to the parking light (or taillight) bulb on the *right* side, causing current to flow to the left-side lights
   c. Defective (open) parking light (or taillight) bulb on the left side
   d. Both a and c

9. A defective taillight or front park light bulb could cause the _____.
   a. Turn signal indicator on the dash to light when the lights are turned on
   b. Dash lights to come on when the brake lights are on
   c. Lights-on warning chime to sound if the brake pedal is depressed
   d. All of the above

10. A defective brake switch could prevent proper operation of the _____.
    a. Cruise control
    b. ABS brakes
    c. Shift interlock
    d. All of the above

OBJECTIVES: **After studying Chapter 38, the reader will be able to:** • Prepare for ASE Electrical/Electronic Systems (A6) certification test content area "F" (Gauges, Warning Devices, and Driver Information System Diagnosis and Repair). • Be able to identify the meaning of dash warning symbols. • Discuss how a fuel gauge works. • Explain how to use a service manual to troubleshoot a malfunctioning dash instrument. • Describe how a navigation system works. • List the various types of dash instrument displays.

KEY TERMS: • Backup camera 441 • CFL 434 • Combination valve 428 • CRT 434 • EEPROM 437 • GPS 438 • HUD 432 • IP 430 • LCD 433 • LDWS 443 • LED 433 • NVRAM 437 • Phosphor 434 • PM generator 435 • Pressure differential switch 428 • RPA 442 • Stepper motor 430 • VTF 434 • WOW display 434

DASH WARNING SYMBOLS

PURPOSE AND FUNCTION   All vehicles are equipped with warning lights that are often confusing to drivers. Because many vehicles are sold throughout the world, symbols instead of words are being used as warning lights. The dash warning lights are often called *telltale* lights as they are used to notify the driver of a situation or fault.

BULB TEST   When the ignition is first turned on, all of the warning lights come on as part of a self-test and to help the driver or technician spot any warning light that may be burned out. Technicians or drivers who are familiar with what lights should light may be able to determine if one or more warning lights are not on when the ignition is first turned on. Most factory scan tools can be used to command all of the warning lights on to help determine if one is not working.

ENGINE FAULT WARNING   Engine fault warning lights include the following:

■ **Engine coolant temperature.** This warning lamp should come on when the ignition is first turned on as a bulb check and if the coolant temperature reaches 248°F to 258°F (120°C to 126°C), depending on the make and model of the vehicle. ● **SEE FIGURE 38–1.**

If the engine coolant temperature warning lamp comes on while driving, perform the following in an attempt to reduce the temperature.

1.   Turn off the air conditioning.

2.   Turn on the heater.

 OR [HOT]

FIGURE 38–1 Engine coolant temperature is too high.

 OR [OIL]

FIGURE 38–2 Engine oil pressure too low.

3.   If the hot light remains on, drive to a safe location and shut off the engine and allow it to cool to help avoid serious engine damage.

■ **Engine oil pressure.** This warning lamp should light when the ignition is first turned on as a bulb check; or if the engine oil pressure light comes on when driving, perform the following:

1.   Pull off the road as soon as possible.

2.   Shut off the engine.

3.   Check the oil level.

4.   Do not drive the vehicle with the engine oil light on or severe engine damage can occur.

● **SEE FIGURE 38–2.**

■ **Water in diesel fuel warning.** This warning lamp will light when the ignition is first turned on as a bulb check and if water is detected in the diesel fuel. This lamp is only used or operational in vehicles equipped with a diesel engine. If the water in diesel fuel warning lamp comes on, do the following:

1.   Remove the water using the built-in drain, usually part of the fuel filter.

2.   Check service information for the exact procedure to follow.

● **SEE FIGURE 38–3.**

- **Maintenance required warning.** The maintenance required lamp comes on when the ignition is first turned on as a bulb check and if the vehicle requires service. The service required could include:
  1. Oil and oil filter change
  2. Tire rotation
  3. Inspection

  Check service information for the exact service required. ● **SEE FIGURE 38–4.**

- **Malfunction indicator lamp (MIL), also called a check engine or service engine soon (SES) light.** This warning lamp comes on when the ignition is first turned on as a bulb test and then only if a fault in the powertrain control module (PCM) has been detected. If the MIL comes on when driving, it is not necessary to stop the vehicle, but the cause for why the warning lamp came on should be determined as soon as possible to avoid harming the engine or engine control systems. The MIL could come on if any of the following has been detected.
  1. A sensor or actuator is electrically open or shorted.
  2. A sensor is out of range for expected values.
  3. An emission control system failure occurs, such as a loose gas cap.

  If the MIL is on, a diagnostic trouble code has been set Use a scan tool to retrieve the code(s) and follow service information for the exact procedure to follow. ● **SEE FIGURE 38–5.**

FIGURE 38–3 Water detected in fuel. Notice to drain the water from the fuel filter assembly on a vehicle equipped with a diesel engine.

FIGURE 38–4 Maintenance required. This usually means that the engine oil is scheduled to be changed or other routine service items replaced or checked.

FIGURE 38–5 Malfunction indicator lamp (MIL), also called a check engine light. The light means the engine control computer has detected a fault.

ELECTRICAL SYSTEM–RELATED WARNING LIGHTS

- **Charging system fault.** This warning lamp will come on when the ignition is first turned on as a bulb check and if a fault in the charging system has been detected. The lamp could include a fault with any of the following:
  1. Battery state of charge (SOC), electrical connections, or the battery itself
  2. Alternator or related wiring
  ● **SEE FIGURE 38–6.**

  If the charge system warning lamp comes on, continue to drive until it is safe to pull over. The vehicle can usually be driven for several miles using battery power alone.

  Check the following by visible inspection.
  1. Alternator drive belt
  2. Loose or corroded electrical connections at the battery
  3. Loose or corroded wiring to the alternator
  4. Defective alternator

SAFETY-RELATED WARNING LAMPS   Safety-related warning lamps include the following

- **Safety belt warning lamp.** The safety belt warning lamp will light and sound an alarm to notify the driver if the driver's side or passenger's side safety belt is not fastened. It is also used to indicate a fault in the safety belt circuit. Check service information for the exact procedure to follow if the safety belt warning light remains on even when the belts are fastened. ● **SEE FIGURE 38–7.**

- **Airbag warning lamp.** The airbag warning lamp comes on and flashes when the ignition is first turned on as part of a self-test of the system. If the airbag warning lamp remains on after the self-test, then the airbag controller has detected a fault. Check service information for the exact procedure to follow if the airbag warning lamp is on. ● **SEE FIGURE 38–8.**

FIGURE 38–6 Charging system fault detected.

FIGURE 38–7 Fasten safety belt warning light.

FIGURE 38–8 Fault detected in the supplemental restraint (airbag) system.

NOTE: The passenger side airbag light may indicate that it is on or off, depending if there is a passenger or an object heavy enough to trigger the seat sensor.

■ **Red brake fault warning light.** All vehicles are equipped with a red brake warning (RBW) lamp that lights if a fault in the base (hydraulic) brake system is detected. Three types of sensors are used to light this warning light.

1. A brake fluid level sensor located in the master cylinder brake fluid reservoir

2. A pressure switch located in the pressure differential switch, which detects a difference in pressure between the front and rear or diagonal brake systems

3. The parking brake could be applied. ● **SEE FIGURE 38–9.**

If the red brake warning light comes on, do not drive the vehicle until the cause is determined and corrected.

■ **Brake light bulb failure.** Some vehicles are able to detect if a brake light is burned out. The warning lamp will warn the driver when a situation like this occurs. ● **SEE FIGURE 38–10.**

■ **Exterior light bulb failure.** Many vehicles use the body control module (BCM) to monitor current flow through all of the exterior lights and therefore can detect if a bulb is not working. ● **SEE FIGURE 38–11.**

■ **Worn brake pads.** Some vehicles are equipped with sensors built into the disc brake pads that are used to trigger a dash warning light. The warning light often comes on when the ignition is first turned on as a bulb check and then goes out. If the brake pad warning lamp is on, check service information for the exact service procedure to follow. ● **SEE FIGURE 38–12.**

 OR

FIGURE 38–9 Fault detected in base brake system.

FIGURE 38–10 Brake light bulb failure detected.

FIGURE 38–11 Exterior light bulb failure detected.

FIGURE 38–12 Worn brake pads or linings detected.

FIGURE 38–13 Fault detected in antilock brake system.

FIGURE 38–14 Low tire pressure detected.

FIGURE 38–15 Door open or ajar.

 TECH TIP

Check the Spare

Some vehicles that are equipped with a full-size spare tire also have a sensor in the spare. If the warning lamp is on and all four tires are properly inflated, check the spare.

■ **Antilock brake system (ABS) fault.** The amber antilock brake system warning light comes on if the ABS controller detects a fault in the antilock braking system. Examples of what could trigger the warning light include:

1. Defective wheel speed sensor

2. Low brake fluid level in the hydraulic control unit assembly

3. Electrical fault detected anywhere in the system
● **SEE FIGURE 38–13.**

If the amber ABS warning lamp is on, it is safe to drive the vehicle, but the antilock portion may not function.

■ **Low tire pressure warning.** A tire pressure monitoring system (TPMS) warns if the inflation pressure of a tire has decreased by 25% (about 8 psi). If the warning lamp or message of a low tire is displayed, check the tire pressures before driving. If the inflation pressure is low, repair or replace the tire. ● **SEE FIGURE 38–14.**

DRIVER INFORMATION SYSTEM

■ **Door open or ajar warning light.** If a door is open or ajar, a warning light is used to notify the driver. Check and close all doors and tailgates before driving. ● **SEE FIGURE 38–15.**

■ **Windshield washer fluid low.** A sensor in the windshield washer fluid reservoir is used to turn on the low washer fluid warning lamp. ● **SEE FIGURE 38–16.**

■ **Low fuel warning.** A low fuel indicator light is used to warn the driver that the fuel level is low. In most vehicles,

OR

FIGURE 38–16 Windshield washer fluid low.

 OR

FIGURE 38–17 Low fuel level.

FIGURE 38–18 Headlights on.

 OR

FIGURE 38–19 Low traction detected. Traction control system is functioning to restore traction (usually flashes when actively working to restore traction).

VSC

FIGURE 38–20 Vehicle stability control system either off or working if flashing.

the light comes on when there is between 1 and 3 gallons (3.8 and 11 liters) of fuel remaining. ● **SEE FIGURE 38–17.**

- **Headlights on light.** This dash indicator lights whenever the headlights are on. ● **SEE FIGURE 38–18.**

  NOTE: This light may or may not indicate that the headlights are on if the headlight switch is set to the automatic position.

- **Low traction detected.** On a vehicle equipped with a traction control system (TCS), a dash indicator light is flashed whenever the system is working to restore traction. If the low traction warning light is flashing, reduce the rate of acceleration to help the system restore traction of the drive wheels with the road surface. ● **SEE FIGURE 38–19.**

- **Electronic stability control.** If a vehicle is equipped with electronic stability control (ESC), also called vehicle stability control (VSC), the dash indicator lamp will flash if the system is trying to restore vehicle stability. ● **SEE FIGURE 38–20.**

- **Traction off.** If the traction control system (TCS) is turned off by the driver, an indicator lamp lights to help remind the driver that this system has been turned off and will not be able to restore traction when lost. The system reverts to on, when the ignition is turned off, and then back on as the traction off button is depressed. ● **SEE FIGURE 38–21.**

TRAC OFF

FIGURE 38–21 Traction control system has been turned off.

CRUISE

FIGURE 38–22 Indicates that the cruise control is on and able to maintain vehicle speed if set. Many vehicles use a symbol that looks like a small speedometer to indicate that the cruise control is on.

- **Cruise indicator lamp.** Most vehicles are equipped with a switch that turns on the cruise control. The cruise (speed) control system does not work unless it has been turned on to help prevent accidental engagement. When the cruise control has been turned on, the cruise indicator light is on. ● **SEE FIGURE 38–22.**

OIL PRESSURE WARNING DEVICES

OPERATION The oil pressure lamp operates through use of an oil pressure sensor unit, which is screwed into the engine block, and grounds the electrical circuit and lights the dash warning lamp in the event of low oil pressure, that is, 3 to 7 psi (20 to 50 kilopascals [kPa]). Normal oil pressure is generally between 10 and 60 psi (70 and 400 kPa). Some vehicles are equipped with a variable voltage oil pressure sensors rather than a simple pressure switch. ● **SEE FIGURE 38–23.**

OIL PRESSURE LAMP DIAGNOSIS To test the operation of the oil pressure warning circuit, unplug the wire from the oil pressure sending unit, usually located near the oil filter, with the ignition switch on. With the wire disconnected from the sending unit, the warning lamp should be off. If the wire is touched to a ground, the warning lamp should be on. If there

FIGURE 38–23 A typical oil pressure sending unit provides a varying amount of resistance as engine oil pressure changes. The output from the sensor is a variable voltage.

The Low Oil Pressure Story

After replacing valve cover gaskets on a Chevrolet V-8, the technician discovered that the oil pressure warning lamp was on. After checking the oil level and finding everything else okay, the technician discovered a wire pinched under the valve cover.

The wire went to the oil pressure sending unit. The edge of the valve cover had cut through the insulation and caused the current from the oil lamp to go to ground through the engine. Normally the oil lamp comes on when the sending unit grounds the wire from the lamp.

The technician freed the pinched wire and covered the cut with silicone sealant to prevent corrosion damage.

is *any* doubt of the operation of the oil pressure warning lamp, always check the actual engine oil pressure using a gauge that can be screwed into the opening that is left after unscrewing the oil pressure sending unit. For removing the sending unit, special sockets are available at most auto parts stores, or a 1 in. or 1 1/16 in. 6-point socket may be used for most units.

TEMPERATURE LAMP DIAGNOSIS

The "hot" lamp, or engine coolant overheat warning lamp, warns the driver whenever the engine coolant temperature is between 248°F and 258°F (120°C and 126°C). This temperature is slightly below the boiling point of the coolant in a properly operating cooling system. The temperature sensor on older models was separate from the sensor used by the engine computer. However, most vehicles now use the engine coolant temperature (ECT) sensor for engine temperature gauge operation. To test this sensor, use a scan tool to verify proper engine temperature and follow the vehicle manufacturer's recommended testing procedures. ● **SEE FIGURE 38–24.**

BRAKE WARNING LAMP

All vehicles sold in the United States after 1967 must be equipped with a dual braking system and a dash-mounted warning lamp to signal the driver of a failure in one part of the hydraulic brake system. The switch that operates the warning lamp is called a **pressure differential switch.** This switch is usually the center portion of a multipurpose brake part called a **combination valve.** If there is unequal hydraulic pressure in the braking system, the switch usually provides a ground path for the brake warning lamp, and the lamp comes on. ● **SEE FIGURE 38–25.**

Unfortunately, the dash warning lamp is often the same lamp as that used to warn the driver that the parking brake is on. The warning lamp is usually operated by using the parking brake lever or brake hydraulic pressure switch to complete the ground for the warning lamp circuit. If the warning lamp is on, first check if the parking brake is fully released. If the parking brake is fully released, the problem could be a defective parking brake switch or a hydraulic brake problem. To test for which system is causing the lamp to remain on, simply unplug the wire from the valve or switch. If the wire on the pressure differential switch is disconnected and the warning lamp remains on, then the problem is due to a defective or misadjusted parking brake switch. If, however, the warning lamp goes out when the wire is removed from the brake switch, then the problem is due to a hydraulic brake fault that caused the pressure differential switch to complete the

FIGURE 38–24 A temperature gauge showing normal operating temperature between 180°F and 215°F, depending on the specific vehicle and engine.

FIGURE 38–25 Typical brake warning light switch located on or near the master brake cylinder.

FIGURE 38–26 The red brake warning lamp can be turned on if the brake fluid level is low.

warning lamp circuit. The red brake warning lamp also can be turned on if the brake fluid is low. ● **SEE FIGURE 38–26** for an example of a brake fluid level sensor.

ANALOG DASH INSTRUMENTS

An analog display uses a needle to show the value, whereas a digital display uses numbers. Analog electromagnetic dash instruments use small electromagnetic coils that are connected to a sending unit for such things as fuel level, water temperature, and oil pressure. The sensors are the same regardless of the type of display used. The resistance of the sensor varies with what is being measured. ● **SEE FIGURE 38–27** for typical electromagnetic fuel gauge operation.

FIGURE 38–27 Electromagnetic fuel gauge wiring. If the sensor wire is unplugged and grounded, the needle should point to "E" (empty). If the sensor wire is unplugged and held away from ground, the needle should point to "F" (full).

COOLANT TEMPERATURE   TACHOMETER   SPEEDOMETER

CLASS 2

PIN 2   DLC

FIGURE 38–28 A typical instrument display uses data from the sensors over serial data lines to the individual gauges.

NETWORK COMMUNICATION

DESCRIPTION Many instrument panels are operated by electronic control units that communicate with the engine control computer for engine data such as revolutions per minute (RPM) and engine temperature. These electronic **instrument panels (IPs)** use the voltage changes from variable-resistance sensors, such as that of the fuel gauge, to determine fuel level. Therefore, even though the sensor in the fuel tank is the same, the display itself may be computer controlled. The data is transmitted to the instrument cluster as well as to the powertrain control module through serial data lines. Because all sensor inputs are interconnected, the technician should always follow the factory recommended diagnostic procedures. ● **SEE FIGURE 38–28.**

STEPPER MOTOR ANALOG GAUGES

DESCRIPTION Most analog dash displays use a stepper motor to move the needle. A **stepper motor** is a type of electric motor that is designed to rotate in small steps based on the signal from a computer. This type of gauge is very accurate.

OPERATION A digital output is used to control stepper motors. Stepper motors are direct current motors that move in fixed steps or increments from de-energized (no voltage) to fully energized (full voltage). A stepper motor often has as many as 120 steps of motion. When using a stepper motor that is controlled by the PCM, it is very easy for the PCM to keep

STEP 1

STEP 2

FIGURE 38–29 Most stepper motors use four wires which are pulsed by the computer to rotate the armature in steps.

track of the stepper motor's position. By counting the number of steps that have been sent to the stepper motor, the PCM can determine its relative position. While the PCM does not actually receive a feedback signal from the stepper motor, it knows how many steps forward or backward the motor should have moved.

A typical stepper motor uses a permanent magnet and two electromagnets. Each of the two electromagnetic windings is controlled by the computer. The computer pulses the windings and changes the polarity of the windings to cause the armature of the stepper motor to rotate 90 degrees at a time. Each 90-degree pulse is recorded by the computer as a "count" or "step," which explains the name given to this type of motor. ● **SEE FIGURE 38–29.**

NOTE: Many electronic gauge clusters are checked at key on where the dash display needles will be commanded to 1/4, 1/2, 3/4, and full positions before returning to their normal readings. This self-test allows the service technician to check the operation of each individual gauge, even though replacing the entire instrument panel cluster is usually necessary to repair an inoperative gauge.

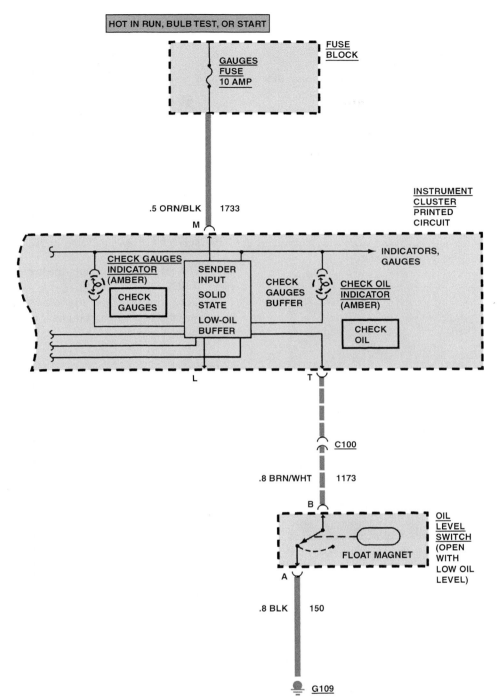

FIGURE 38–30 The ground for the "check oil" indicator lamp is controlled by the electronic low-oil buffer. Even though this buffer is connected to an oil level sensor, the buffer also takes into consideration the amount of time the engine has been stopped and the temperature of the engine. The only way to properly diagnose a problem with this circuit is to use the procedures specified by the vehicle manufacturer. Besides, only the engineer who designed the circuit knows for sure how it is supposed to work.

DIAGNOSIS The dash electronic circuits are often too complex to show on a wiring diagram. Instead, all related electronic circuits are simply indicated as a solid box with "electronic module" printed on the diagram. Even if all the electronic circuits were shown on the wiring diagram, it would require the skill of an electronics engineer to determine exactly how the circuit was designed to work. ● **SEE FIGURE 38–30.**

Note that the grounding for the "check oil" dash indicator lamp is accomplished through an electronic buffer. The exact conditions, such as amount of time since the ignition was shut off, are unknown to the technician. To correctly diagnose problems with this type of circuit, technicians must read, understand, and follow the written diagnostic procedures specified by the vehicle manufacturer.

HEAD-UP DISPLAY

The **head-up display (HUD)** is a supplemental display that projects the vehicle speed and sometimes other data, such as turn signal information, onto the windshield. The projected image looks as if it is some distance ahead, making it easy for the driver to see without having to refocus on a closer dash display. ● **SEE FIGURES 38–31 AND 38–32.**

The head-up display can also have the brightness controlled on most vehicles that use this type of display. The HUD unit is installed in the instrument panel (IP) and uses a mirror to

FIGURE 38–33 A typical head-up display (HUD) unit.

project vehicle information onto the inside surface of the windshield. ● **SEE FIGURE 38–33.**

Follow the vehicle manufacturer's recommended diagnostic and testing procedures if any faults are found with the head-up display.

FIGURE 38–31 A typical head-up display showing zero miles per hour, which is actually projected on the windshield from the head-up display in the dash.

NIGHT VISION

PARTS AND OPERATION Night vision systems use a camera that is capable of observing objects in the dark to assist the driver while driving at night. The primary night viewing illumination devices are the headlights. The night vision option uses a head-up display (HUD) to improve the vision of the driver beyond the scope of the headlights. Using a HUD display allows the driver to keep eyes on the road and hands on the wheel for maximum safety.

Besides the head-up display, the night vision camera uses a special thermal imaging or infrared technology. The camera is mounted behind the grill in the front of the vehicle. ● **SEE FIGURE 38–34.**

FIGURE 38–32 The dash-mounted control for the head-up display on this Cadillac allows the driver to move the image up and down on the windshield for best viewing.

FIGURE 38–34 A night vision camera behind the grille of a Cadillac.

The camera creates pictures based on the heat energy emitted by objects rather than from light reflected on an object as in a normal optical camera. The image looks like a black and white photo negative when hot objects (higher thermal energy) appear light or white, and cool objects appear dark or black. Other parts of the night vision system include:

- **On/off and dimming switch.** This allows the driver to adjust the brightness of the display and to turn it on or off as needed.
- **Up/down switch.** The night vision HUD system has an electric tilt adjust motor that allows the driver to adjust the image up or down on the windshield within a certain image.

CAUTION: Becoming accustomed to night vision can be difficult and may take several nights to get used to looking at the head-up display.

DIAGNOSIS AND SERVICE The first step when diagnosing a fault with the night vision system is to verify the concern. Check the owner manual or service information for proper operation. For example, the Cadillac night vision system requires the following actions to function.

1. The ignition has to be in the on (run) position.
2. The Twilight Sentinel photo cell must indicate that it is dark.
3. The headlights must be on.
4. The switch for the night vision system must be on and the brightness adjusted so the image is properly displayed.

The night vision system uses a camera in the front of the vehicle that is protected from road debris by a grille. However, small stones or other debris can get past the grille and damage the lens of the camera. If the camera is damaged, it must be replaced as an assembly because no separate parts are available. Always follow the vehicle manufacturer's recommended testing and servicing procedures.

DIGITAL ELECTRONIC DISPLAY OPERATION

TYPES

- Mechanical or electromechanical dash instruments use cables, mechanical transducers, and sensors to operate a particular dash instrument.
- Digital dash instruments use various electric and electronic sensors that activate segments or sections of an electronic display. Most electronic dash clusters use a computer chip and various electronic circuits to operate and control the internal power supply, sensor voltages, and display voltages.
- Electronic dash display systems may use one or more of several types of displays: light-emitting diode (LED), liquid crystal display (LCD), vacuum tube fluorescent (VTF), and cathode ray tube (CRT).

FIGURE 38–35 (a) Symbol and line drawing of a typical light-emitting diode (LED). (b) Grouped in seven segments, this array is called a seven-segment LED display with a common anode (positive connection). The dash computer toggles the cathode (negative) side of each individual segment to display numbers and letters. (c) When all segments are turned on, the number 8 is displayed.

LED DIGITAL DISPLAYS All diodes emit some form of energy during operation; the **light-emitting diode (LED)** is a semiconductor that is constructed to release energy in the form of light. Many colors of LEDs can be constructed, but the most popular are red, green, and yellow. Red is difficult to see in direct sunlight; therefore, if an LED is used, most vehicle manufacturers use yellow. Light-emitting diodes can be arranged in a group of seven, which then can be used to display both numbers and letters. ● **SEE FIGURE 38–35.**

An LED display requires more electrical power than other types of electronic displays. A typical LED display requires 30 mA for each *segment;* therefore, each number or letter displayed could require 210 mA (0.210 A).

LIQUID CRYSTAL DISPLAYS Liquid crystal displays **(LCDs)** can be arranged into a variety of forms, letters, numbers, and bar graph displays.

FIGURE 38–36 A typical navigation system. This Honda/ Acura system uses some of the climate control functions as well as the trip information on the display.

- LCD construction consists of a special fluid sandwiched between two sheets of polarized glass. The special fluid between the glass plates will permit light to pass if a small voltage is applied to the fluid through a conductive film laminated to the glass plates.

- The light from a very bright halogen bulb behind the LCD shines through those segments of the LCD that have been polarized to let the light through, which then show numbers or letters. Color filters can be placed in front of the display to change the color of certain segments of the display, such as the maximum engine speed on a digital tachometer.

CAUTION: Be careful, when cleaning an LCD, not to push on the glass plate covering the special fluid. If excessive pressure is exerted on the glass, the display may be permanently distorted. If the glass breaks, the fluid will escape and could damage other components in the vehicle as a result of its strong alkaline nature. Use only a soft, damp cloth to clean these displays.

- The major disadvantage of an LCD digital dash is that the numbers or letters are slow to react or change at low temperatures. ● **SEE FIGURE 38–36.**

VACUUM TUBE FLUORESCENT DISPLAYS   The
vacuum tube fluorescent (VTF) display is a popular automotive and household appliance display because it is very bright and can easily be viewed in strong sunlight. The usual VTF display is green, but white is often used for home appliances.

- The VTF display generates its bright light in a manner similar to that of a TV screen, where a chemical-coated

light-emitting element called a **phosphor** is hit with high-speed electrons.

- VTF displays are very bright and must be dimmed by use of dense filters or by controlling the voltage applied to the display. A typical VTF dash is dimmed to 75% brightness whenever the parking lights or headlights are turned on. Some displays use a photocell to monitor and adjust the intensity of the display during daylight viewing. Most VTF displays are green for best viewing under most lighting conditions.

CATHODE RAY TUBE   A **cathode ray tube (CRT)** dash
display, which is similar to a television tube or LCD display, permits the display of hundreds of controls and diagnostic messages in one convenient location.

Using the touch-sensitive cathode ray tube, the driver or technician can select from many different displays, including those of radio, climate, trip, and dash instrument information. The driver can readily access all of these functions. Further diagnostic information can be displayed on the CRT if the proper combination of air-conditioning controls is touched. The diagnostic procedures for these displays involve pushing two or more buttons at the same time to access the diagnostic menu. Always follow the factory service manual recommendations.

COLD CATHODE FLUORESCENT DISPLAYS   Cold
cathode fluorescent lighting (CFL) models are used by many vehicle manufacturers for backlighting. Current consumption ranges from 3 to 5 mA (0.003 to 0.005 A) with an average life of 40,000 hours. CFL is replacing conventional incandescent light bulbs.

ELECTRONIC ANALOG DISPLAYS   Most analog dash
displays since the early 1990s are electronically or computer controlled. The sensors may be the same, but the sensor information is sent to the body or vehicle computer through a data BUS, and then the computer controls current through small electromagnets that move the needle of the gauge. ● **SEE FIGURE 38–37.** A scan tool often is needed to diagnosis the operation of a computer-controlled analog dash instrument display.

WOW DISPLAY   When a vehicle equipped with a digital
dash is started, all segments of the electronic display are turned on at full brilliance for 1 or 2 seconds. This is commonly called the **WOW display,** and is used to show off the brilliance of the display. If numbers are part of the display, the number 8 is shown, because this number uses all segments of a number display. Technicians can also use the WOW display to determine if all segments of the electronic display are functioning correctly.

(a)

(b)

(c)

FIGURE 38–37 (a) View of the vehicle dash with the instrument cluster removed. Sometimes the dash instruments can be serviced by removing the padded dash cover (crash pad) to gain access to the rear of the dash. (b) The front view of the electronic analog dash display. (c) The rear view of the dash display showing that there are a few bulbs that can be serviced, but otherwise the unit is serviced as an assembly.

🔧 **TECH TIP**

The Bulb Test

Many ignition switches have six positions. Notice the *bulb test* position (between "on" and "start"). When the ignition is turned to "on" (run), some dash warning lamps are illuminated. When the bulb test position is reached, additional dash warning lamps often are lighted. Technicians use this ignition switch position to check the operation of fuses that protect various circuits. Dash warning lamps are not all powered by the same fuses. If an electrical component or circuit does not work, the power side (fuse) can be quickly checked by observing the operation of the dash lamps that share a common fuse with the problem circuit. Consult a wiring diagram for fuse information on the exact circuit being tested. ● **SEE FIGURES 38–38 AND 38–39.**

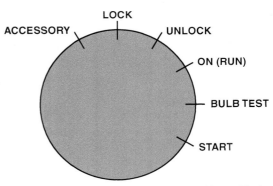

FIGURE 38–38 Typical ignition switch positions. Notice the bulb check position between "on" (run) and "start." These inputs are often just voltage signal to the body control module and can be checked using a scan tool.

ELECTRONIC SPEEDOMETERS

OPERATION Electronic dash displays ordinarily use an electric vehicle speed sensor driven by a small gear on the output shaft of the transmission. These speed sensors contain a permanent magnet and generate a voltage in proportion to the vehicle speed. These speed sensors are commonly called **permanent magnet (PM) generators.** ● **SEE FIGURE 38–40.**

The output of a PM generator speed sensor is an AC voltage that varies in frequency and amplitude with increasing vehicle speed. The PM generator speed signal is sent to the instrument cluster electronic circuits. These specialized electronic circuits include a buffer amplifier circuit that converts the variable sine wave voltage from the speed sensor to an on/off signal that can be used by other electronic circuits to indicate a vehicle's speed. The vehicle speed is then displayed by either an electronic needle-type speedometer or by numbers on a digital display.

FIGURE 38–39 Many newer vehicles place the ignition switch on the dash and incorporate antitheft controls. Note the location of the accessory position.

VEHICLE SPEED
(VS) SENSOR

FIGURE 38–40 A vehicle speed sensor located in the extension housing of the transmission. Some vehicles use the wheel speed sensors for vehicle speed information.

 REAL WORLD FIX

The Speedometer Works as if It Is a Tachometer

The owner of a Lincoln Town Car complained that all of a sudden the speedometer needle went up and down with engine speed rather than vehicle speed. In fact, the speedometer needle went up and down with engine speed even though the gear selector was in "park" and the vehicle was not moving. After hours of trouble-shooting, the service technician went back and started checking the basics and discovered that the alternator had a bad diode. The technician measured over 1 volt AC and over 10 amperes AC ripple current using a clamp-on AC/DC ammeter. Replacing the alternator restored the proper operation of the speedometer.

 TECH TIP

The Soldering Gun Trick

Diagnosing problems with digital or electronic dash instruments can be difficult. Replacement parts generally are expensive and usually not returnable if installed in the vehicle. A popular trick that helps isolate the problem is to use a soldering gun near the PM generator.

A PM generator contains a coil of wire. As the magnet inside revolves, a voltage is produced. It is the *frequency* of this voltage that the dash (or engine) computer uses to calculate vehicle speed.

A soldering gun plugged into 110 volts AC will provide a strong *varying* magnetic field around the soldering gun. This magnetic field is constantly changing at the rate of 60 cycles per second. This frequency of the magnetic field induces a voltage in the windings of the PM generator. This induced voltage at 60 hertz (Hz) is converted by the computer circuits to a miles per hour (mph) reading on the dash.

To test the electronic speedometer, turn the ignition to "on" (engine off) and hold a soldering gun near the PM generator.

CAUTION: The soldering gun tip can get hot, so hold it away from wiring or other components that may be damaged by the hot tip.

If the PM generator, wiring, computer, and dash are okay, the speedometer should register a speed, usually 54 mph (87 km/h). If the speedometer does not work when the vehicle is driven, the problem is in the PM generator drive.

If the speedometer does not register a speed when the soldering gun is used, the problem could be caused by the following:

1. Defective PM generator (check the windings with an ohmmeter)
2. Defective (open or shorted) wiring from the PM generator to the computer
3. Defective computer or dash circuit

ELECTRONIC ODOMETERS

PURPOSE AND FUNCTION An odometer is a dash display that indicates the total miles traveled by the vehicle. Some dash displays also include a trip odometer that can be reset and used to record total miles traveled on a trip or the distance traveled between fuel stops. Electronic dash displays can use either an electrically driven mechanical odometer or a digital display odometer to indicate miles traveled. On mechanical type odometers, a small electric motor, called a stepper motor,

The Toyota Truck Story

The owner of a Toyota truck complained that several electrical problems plagued the truck, including the following:

1. The cruise (speed) control would kick out intermittently.
2. The red brake warning lamp would come on, especially during cold weather.

   The owner had replaced the parking brake switch, thinking that was the cause of the red brake warning lamp coming on.

   An experienced technician checked the wiring diagram in service information. Checking the warning lamp circuit, the technician noticed that the same wire went to the brake fluid level sensor. The brake fluid was at the minimum level. Filling the master cylinder to the maximum level with clean brake fluid solved both problems. The electronics of the cruise control stopped operation when the red brake warning lamp was on as a safety measure.

Look for Previous Repairs

A technician was asked to fix the speedometer on a Pontiac Grand Am that showed approximately double the actual speed. Previous repairs had included a new vehicle speed (VS) sensor and computer. Nothing made any difference. The customer stated that the problem happened all of a sudden. After hours of troubleshooting, the customer just happened to mention that the automatic transmission (transaxle) had been repaired shortly before the speedometer problem. The root cause of the problem was discovered when the technician learned that a final drive assembly from a 4T60-E transaxle had been installed on the 3T-40 transaxle. The 4T60-E final drive assembly has 13 reluctor teeth whereas the 3T-40 has 7 teeth. This difference in the number of teeth caused the speedometer to read almost double the actual vehicle speed. After the correct part was installed, the speedometer worked correctly. The technician now always asks if there has been any recent work performed in the vehicle prior to any diagnosis.

is used to turn the number wheels of a mechanical-style odometer. A pulsed voltage is fed to this stepper motor, which moves in relation to the miles traveled. ● **SEE FIGURE 38–41.**

Digital odometers use LED, LCD, or VTF displays to indicate miles traveled. Because total miles must be retained when

(a)

(b)

FIGURE 38–41 (a) Some odometers are mechanical and are operated by a stepper motor. (b) Many vehicles are equipped with an electronic odometer.

the ignition is turned off or the battery is disconnected, a special electronic chip must be used that will retain the miles traveled.

These special chips are called **nonvolatile random-access memory (NVRAM).** *Nonvolatile* means that the information stored in the electronic chip is not lost when electrical power is removed. Some vehicles use a chip called **electronically erasable programmable read-only memory (EEPROM).** Most digital odometers can read up to 999,999.9 miles or kilometers (km), and then the display indicates error. If the chip is damaged or exposed to static electricity, it may fail to operate and "error" may appear.

SPEEDOMETER/ODOMETER SERVICE If the speedometer and odometer fail to operate, check the following:

- The speed sensor should be the first item checked. With the vehicle safely raised off the ground and supported, check vehicle speed using a scan tool. If a scan tool is not available, disconnect the wires from the speed sensor near the output shaft of the transmission. Connect a multimeter

REAL WORLD FIX

Electronic Devices Cannot Swim

The owner of a Dodge minivan complained that after the vehicle was cleaned inside and outside, the temperature gauge, fuel gauge, and speedometer stopped working. The vehicle speed sensor was checked and found to be supplying a square wave signal that changed with vehicle speed. A scan tool indicated a speed, yet the speedometer displayed zero all the time. Finally, the service technician checked the body computer to the right of the accelerator pedal and noticed that it had been wet, from the interior cleaning. Drying the computer did not fix the problem, but a replacement body computer fixed all the problems. The owner discovered that electronic devices do not like water and that computers cannot swim.

set on AC volts to the terminals of the speed sensor and rotate the drive wheels with the transmission in neutral. A good speed sensor should indicate approximately 2 volts AC if the drive wheels are rotated by hand.

- If the speed sensor is working, check the wiring from the speed sensor to the dash cluster. If the wiring is good, the instrument panel (IP) should be sent to a specialty repair facility.
- If the speedometer operates correctly but the mechanical odometer does not work, the odometer stepper motor, the number wheel assembly, or the circuit controlling the stepper motor is defective. If the digital odometer does not operate but the speedometer operates correctly, then the dash cluster must be removed and sent to a specialized repair facility. A replacement chip is available only through authorized sources; if the odometer chip is defective, the original number of miles must be programmed into the replacement chip.

ELECTRONIC FUEL LEVEL GAUGES

OPERATION Electronic fuel level gauges ordinarily use the same fuel tank sending unit as that used on conventional fuel gauges. The tank unit consists of a float attached to a variable resistor. As the fuel level changes, the resistance of the sending unit changes. As the resistance of the tank unit changes, the dash-mounted gauge also changes. The only difference between a digital fuel level gauge and a conventional needle type is in the display. Digital fuel level gauges can be either numerical (indicating gallons or liters remaining in the tank) or a bar graph display. ● **SEE FIGURE 38–42.**

FIGURE 38–42 A fuel tank module assembly that contains the fuel pump and fuel level sensor in one assembly.

The diagnosis of a problem is the same as that described earlier for conventional fuel gauges. If the tests indicate that the dash unit is defective, usually the *entire* dash gauge assembly must be replaced.

NAVIGATION AND GPS

PURPOSE AND FUNCTION The **global positioning system (GPS)** uses 24 satellites in orbit around the earth to provide signals for navigation devices. GPS is funded and controlled by the U.S. Department of Defense (DOD). While the system can be used by anyone with a GPS receiver, it was designed for and is operated by the U.S. military. ● **SEE FIGURE 38–43.**

BACKGROUND The current global positioning system was developed after a civilian airplane from Korean Airlines, Flight 007, was shot down as it flew over Soviet territory in 1983. The system became fully operational in 1991. Civilians were granted use of GPS that same year, but with less accuracy than the system used by the military.

Until 2000, the nonmilitary use of GPS was purposely degraded by a computer program called selection availability (S/A) built into the satellite transmission signals. After 2000, the S/A has been officially turned off, allowing nonmilitary users more accurate position information from the GPS receivers.

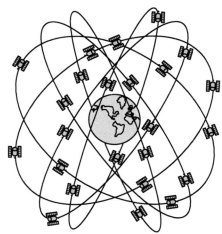

FIGURE 38–43 Global positioning systems use 24 satellites in high earth orbit whose signals are picked up by navigation systems. The navigation system computer then calculates the location based on the position of the satellite overhead.

FIGURE 38–44 A typical GPS display screen showing the location of the vehicle.

 FREQUENTLY ASKED QUESTION

Does the Government Know Where I Am?

No. The navigation system uses signals from the satellites and uses the signals from three or more to determine position. If the vehicle is equipped with OnStar, then the vehicle position can be monitored by the use of the cellular telephone link to OnStar call centers. Unless the vehicle has a cellular phone connection to the outside world, the only people who will know the location of the vehicle are the persons inside the vehicle viewing the navigation screen.

NAVIGATION SYSTEM PARTS AND OPERATION

Navigation systems use the GPS satellites for basic location information. The navigation controller located in the rear of the vehicle uses other sensors, including a digitized map to display the location of the vehicle.

- **GPS satellite signals.** These signals from at least three satellites are needed to locate the vehicle.
- **Yaw sensor.** This sensor is often used inside the navigation unit to detect movement of the vehicle during cornering. This sensor is also called a "g" sensor because it measures force; 1 g is the force of gravity.
- **Vehicle speed sensor.** This sensor input is used by the navigation controller to determine the speed and distance the vehicle travels. This information is compiled and compared to the digital map and GPS satellite inputs to locate the vehicle.
- **Audio output/input.** Voice-activated factory units use a built-in microphone at the center top of the windshield and the audio speakers speech output.

Navigation systems include the following components.

1. Screen display ● **SEE FIGURE 38–44.**
2. GPS antenna
3. Navigation control unit, usually with map information on a DVD

   The DVD includes street names and the following information.

1. Points of interest (POI), including automated teller machines (ATMs), restaurants, schools, colleges, museums, shopping, and airports, as well as vehicle dealer locations.
2. Business addresses and telephone numbers, including hotels and restaurants (If the telephone number is listed in the business telephone book, it can usually be displayed on the navigation screen. If the telephone number of the business is known, the location can be displayed.)

   NOTE: Private residences or cellular telephone numbers are not included in the database of telephone numbers stored on the navigation system DVD.

3. Turn-by-turn directions to addresses that are selected by:
   - Points of interest (POI)
   - Typed in using a keyboard shown on the display

   The navigation unit then often allows the user to select the fastest way to the destination, as well as the shortest way, or how to avoid toll roads. ● **SEE FIGURE 38–45.**

DIAGNOSIS AND SERVICE   For the correct functioning of the navigation system, three inputs are needed.
   - Location
   - Direction
   - Speed

   The navigation system uses the GPS satellite and map data to determine a location. Direction and speed are determined by the navigation computer from inputs from the satellite, plus the yaw sensor and vehicle speed sensor. The following symptoms may occur and be a customer complaint. Knowing how the system malfunctions helps to determine the most likely cause.

FIGURE 38-45 A typical navigation display showing various options. Some systems do not allow access to these functions if the vehicle is in gear and/or moving.

FIGURE 38-46 A screen display of a navigation system that is unable to acquire usable signals from GPS satellites.

🔧 **TECH TIP**

Window Tinting Can Hurt GPS Reception

Most factory-installed navigation systems use a GPS antenna inside the rear back glass or under the rear package shelf. If a metalized window tint is applied to the rear glass, the signal strength from the GPS satellites can be reduced. If the customer concern includes inaccurate or nonfunctioning navigation, check for window tint.

🔧 **TECH TIP**

Touch Screen Tip

Most vehicle navigation systems use a touch screen for use by the driver (or passenger) to input information or other on-screen prompts. Most touch screens use infrared beams projected from the top and bottom plus across the screen to form a grid. The system detects where on the screen a finger is located by the location of the beams that are cut. Do not push harder on the display if the unit does not respond, or damage to the display unit may occur. If no response is detected when lightly depressing the screen, rotate the finger to cause the infrared beams to be cut.

- If the vehicle icon jumps down the road, a fault with the vehicle speed (VS) sensor input is usually indicated.
- If the icon rotates on the screen, but the vehicle is not being driven in circles, a fault with the yaw sensor or yaw sensor input to the navigation controller is likely.
- If the icon goes off course and shows the vehicle on a road that it is not on, a fault with the GPS antenna is the most common reason for this situation.

❓ **FREQUENTLY ASKED QUESTION**

What Is Navigation Enhanced Climate Control?

Some vehicles, such as the Acura RL, use data from the navigation system to help control the automatic climate control system. Data about the location of the vehicle includes:

- **Time and date.** This information allows the automatic climate control system to determine where the sun is located.
- **Direction of travel.** The navigation system can also help the climate control system determine the direction of travel.

As a result of the input from the navigation system, the automatic climate control system can control cabin temperature in addition to various other sensors in the vehicle. For example, if the vehicle was traveling south in the late afternoon in July, the climate control system could assume that the passenger side of the vehicle would be warmed more by the sun than the driver's side and could increase the airflow to the passenger side to help compensate for the additional solar heating.

Sometimes the navigation system itself will display a warning that views from the satellite are not being received. Always follow the displayed instructions. ● **SEE FIGURE 38-46.**

PARTS AND OPERATION OnStar is a system that includes the following functions.

1. Cellular telephone
2. Global positioning antenna and computer

FIGURE 38–47 The three-button OnStar control is located on the inside rearview mirror. The left button (telephone handset icon) is pushed if a hands-free cellular call is to be made. The center button is depressed to contact an OnStar advisor and the right emergency button is used to request that help be sent to the vehicle's location.

OnStar is standard or optional on most General Motors vehicles and selected other brands and models, to help the driver in an emergency or to provide other services. The cellular telephone is used to communicate with the driver from advisors at service centers. The advisor at the service center is able to see the location of the vehicle as transmitted from the GPS antenna and computer system in the vehicle on a display. OnStar does not display the location of the vehicle to the driver unless the vehicle is also equipped with a navigation system.

Unlike most navigation systems, the OnStar system requires a monthly fee. OnStar was first introduced in 1996 as an option on some Cadillac models. Early versions used a handheld cellular telephone while later units used a group of three buttons mounted on the inside rearview mirror and a hands-free cellular telephone. ● **SEE FIGURE 38–47.**

The first version used analog cellular service while later versions used a dual mode (analog and digital) service until 2007. Since 2007, all OnStar systems use digital cellular service, which means that older systems that were analog only need to be upgraded.

The OnStar system includes the following features, which can vary depending on the level of service desired and cost per month.

- **Automatic notification of airbag deployment.** If the airbag is deployed, the advisor is notified immediately and attempts to call the vehicle. If there is no reply, or if the occupants report an emergency, the advisor will contact emergency services and give them the location of the vehicle.
- **Emergency services.** If the red button is pushed, OnStar immediately locates the vehicle and contacts the nearest emergency service agency.
- **Stolen vehicle location assistance.** If a vehicle is reported stolen, a call center advisor can track the vehicle.
- **Remote door unlock.** An OnStar advisor can send a cellular telephone message to the vehicle to unlock the vehicle if needed.

- **Roadside assistance.** When called, an OnStar advisor can locate a towing company or locate a provider who can bring gasoline or change a flat tire.
- **Accident assistance.** An OnStar advisor is able to help with the best way to handle an accident. The advisor can supply a step-by-step checklist of the things that should be done plus call the insurance company, if desired.
- **Remote horn and lights.** The OnStar system is tied into the lights and horn circuits so an advisor can activate them if requested to help the owner locate the vehicle in a parking lot or garage.
- **Vehicle diagnosis.** Because the OnStar system is tied to the PCM, an OnStar advisor can help with diagnosis if there is a fault detected. The system works as follows:

  - The malfunction indicator light (MIL) (check engine) comes on to warn the driver that a fault has been detected.
  - The driver can depress the OnStar button to talk to an advisor and ask for a diagnosis.
  - The OnStar advisor will send a signal to the vehicle requesting the status from the powertrain control module (PCM), as well as the controller for the antilock brakes and the airbag module.
  - The vehicle then sends any diagnostic trouble codes to the advisor. The advisor can then inform the driver about the importance of the problem and give advice as to how to resolve the problem.

DIAGNOSIS AND SERVICE The OnStar system can fail to meet the needs of the customer if any of the following conditions occur.

1. Lack of cellular telephone service in the area
2. Poor global positioning system (GPS) signals, which can prevent an OnStar advisor from determining the position of the vehicle
3. Transport of the vehicle by truck or ferry so that it is out of contact with the GPS satellite in order for an advisor to properly track the vehicle

If all of the above are okay and the problem still exists, follow service information diagnostic and repair procedures. If a new vehicle communication interface module (VCIM) is installed in the vehicle, the electronic serial number (ESN) must be tied to the vehicle. Follow service information instructions for the exact procedures to follow.

BACKUP CAMERA

PARTS AND OPERATION A **backup camera** is used to display the area at the rear of the vehicle in a screen display on the dash when the gear selector is placed in reverse. Backup cameras are also called *reversing cameras* or *rearview cameras*.

Backup cameras are different from normal cameras because the image displayed on the dash is flipped so it is a mirror image of

FIGURE 38–48 A typical view displayed on the navigation screen from the backup camera.

FIGURE 38–49 A typical fisheye-type backup camera usually located near the center on the rear of the vehicle near the license plate.

the scene at the rear of the vehicle. This reversing of the image is needed because the driver and the camera are facing in opposite directions. Backup cameras were first used in large vehicles with limited rearward visibility, such as motor homes. Many vehicles equipped with navigation systems today include a backup camera for added safety while backing. ● **SEE FIGURE 38–48.**

The backup camera contains a wide-angle or fisheye lens to give the largest viewing area. Most backup cameras are pointed downward so that objects on the ground, as well as walls, are displayed. ● **SEE FIGURE 38–49.**

DIAGNOSIS AND SERVICE   Faults in the backup camera system can be related to the camera itself, the display, or the connecting wiring. The main input to the display unit comes from the transmission range switch which signals the backup camera when the transmission is shifted into reverse.

To check the transmission range switch, perform the following:

1. Check if the backup (reverse) lights function when the gear selector is placed in reverse with the key on, engine off (KOEO).

2. Check that the transmission/transaxle is fully engaged in reverse when the selector is placed in reverse.

Most of the other diagnosis involves visual inspection, including:

1. Check the backup camera for damage.
2. Check the screen display for proper operation.
3. Check that the wiring from the rear camera to the body is not cut or damaged.

Always follow the vehicle manufacturer's recommended diagnosis and repair procedures.

BACKUP SENSORS

COMPONENTS   Backup sensors are used to warn the driver if there is an object behind the vehicle while backing. The system used in General Motors vehicles is called **rear park assist (RPA),** and includes the following components.

- Ultrasonic object sensors built into the rear bumper assembly
- A display with three lights usually located inside the vehicle above the rear window and visible to the driver in the rearview mirror
- An electronic control module that uses an input from the transmission range switch and lights the warning lamps needed when the vehicle gear selector is in reverse

OPERATION   The three-light display includes two amber lights and one red light. The following lights are displayed depending on the distance from the rear bumper.

- One amber lamp will light when the vehicle is in reverse and traveling at less than 3 mph (5 km/h) and the sensors detect an object 40 to 60 in. (102 to 152 cm) from the rear bumper. A chime also sounds once when an object is detected, to warn the driver to look at the rear parking assist display. ● **SEE FIGURE 38–50.**

FIGURE 38–50 A typical backup sensor display located above the rear window inside the vehicle. The warning lights are visible in the inside rearview mirror.

Check for Repainted Bumper

The ultrasonic sensors embedded in the bumper are sensitive to paint thickness because the paint covers the sensors. If the system does not seem to be responding to objects, and if the bumper has been repainted, measure the paint thickness using a nonferrous paint thickness gauge. The maximum allowable paint thickness is 6 mils (0.006 in. or 0.15 mm).

FIGURE 38–51 The small round buttons in the rear bumper are ultrasonic sensors used to sense distance to an object.

- Two amber lamps light when the distance between the rear bumper and an object is between 20 and 40 in. (50 and 100 cm) and the chime will sound again.

- Two amber lamps and the red lamp light and the chime sounds continuously when the distance between the rear bumper and the object is between 11 and 20 in. (28 and 50 cm).

If the distance between the rear bumper and the object is less than 11 in. (28 cm), all indicator lamps flash and the chime will sound continuously.

The ultrasonic sensors embedded in the rear bumper "fire" individually every 150 milliseconds (27 times per second). ● **SEE FIGURE 38–51.**

The sensors fire and then receive a return signal and arm to fire again in sequence from the left sensor to the right sensor.

Each sensor has the following three wires.

1. An 8 volt supply wire from the RPA module, used to power the sensor
2. A reference low or ground wire
3. A signal line, used to send and receive commands to and from the RPA module

DIAGNOSIS   The rear parking assist control module is capable of detecting faults and storing diagnostic trouble codes (DTCs). If a fault has been detected by the control module, the red lamp flashes and the system is disabled. Follow service information diagnostic procedures because the rear parking assist module cannot usually be accessed using a scan tool. Most systems use the warning lights to indicate trouble codes.

LANE DEPARTURE WARNING SYSTEM

PARTS AND OPERATION   The **lane departure warning system (LDWS)** uses cameras to detect if the vehicle is crossing over lane marking lines on the pavement. Some systems use two cameras, one mounted on each outside rearview mirror. Some systems use infrared sensors located under the front bumper to monitor the lane markings on the road surface.

The system names also vary according to vehicle manufacturer, including:

Honda/Acura: lane keep assist system (LKAS)
Toyota/Lexus: lane monitoring system (LMS)
General Motors: lane departure warning (LDW)
Ford: lane departure warning (LDW)
Nissan/Infiniti: lane departure prevention (LDP) system

If the cameras detect that the vehicle is starting to cross over a lane dividing line, a warning chime will sound or a vibrating mechanism mounted in the driver's seat cushion is triggered on the side where the departure is being detected. This warning will not occur if the turn signal is on in the same direction as detected. ● **SEE FIGURE 38–52.**

FIGURE 38–52 A lane departure warning system often uses cameras to sense the road lines and warns the driver if the vehicle is not staying within the lane, unless the turn signal is on.

DIAGNOSIS AND SERVICE Before attempting to service or repair a lane departure warning system fault, check service information for an explanation on how the system is supposed to work. If the system is not working as designed, perform a visual inspection of the sensors or cameras, checking for damage from road debris or evidence of body damage, which could affect the sensors. After a visual inspection, follow the vehicle manufacturer's recommended diagnosis procedures to locate and repair the fault in the system.

ELECTRONIC DASH INSTRUMENT DIAGNOSIS AND TROUBLESHOOTING

If one or more electronic dash gauges do not work correctly, first check the WOW display that lights all segments to full brilliance whenever the ignition switch is first switched on. If *all* segments of the display do *not* operate, then the entire electronic cluster must be replaced in most cases. If all segments operate during the WOW display but do not function correctly afterwards, the problem is most often a defective sensor or defective wiring to the sensor.

All dash instruments except the voltmeter use a variable-resistance unit as a sensor for the system being monitored. Most new-vehicle dealers are required to purchase essential test equipment, including a test unit that permits the technician to insert various fixed-resistance values in the suspected circuit. For example, if a 45 ohm resistance is put into the fuel gauge circuit that reads from 0 to 90 ohms, a properly operating dash unit should indicate one-half tank. The same tester can produce a fixed signal to test the operation of the speedometer and tachometer. If this type of special test equipment is not available, the electronic dash instruments can be tested using the following procedure.

1. With the ignition switched off, unplug the wire(s) from the sensor for the function being tested. For example, if the oil pressure gauge is not functioning correctly, unplug the wire connector at the oil pressure sending unit.

2. With the sensor wire unplugged, turn the ignition switch on and wait until the WOW display stops. The display for the affected unit should show either fully lighted segments or no lighted segments, depending on the make of the vehicle and the type of sensor.

3. Turn the ignition switch off. Connect the sensor wire lead to ground and turn the ignition switch on. After the WOW display, the display should be the opposite (either fully on or fully off) of the results in step 2.

TESTING RESULTS If the electronic display functions fully on and fully off with the sensor unplugged and then grounded, the problem is a defective sensor. If the electronic display fails to function fully on and fully off when the sensor wire(s) are opened and grounded, the problem is usually in the wiring from the sensor to the electronic dash or it is a defective electronic cluster.

CAUTION: Whenever working on or *near* any type of electronic dash display, always wear a wire attached to your wrist (wrist strap) connected to a good body ground to prevent damaging the electronic dash with static electricity.

TECH TIP

Keep Stock Overall Tire Diameter

Whenever larger (or smaller) wheels or tires are installed, the speedometer and odometer calibration are also thrown off. This can be summarized as follows:

- **Larger diameter tires.** The speed showing on the speedometer is slower than the actual speed. The odometer reading will show fewer miles than actual.
- **Smaller diameter tires.** The speed showing on the speedometer is faster than the actual speed. The odometer reading will show more miles than actual.

General Motors trucks can be recalibrated with a recalibration kit (1988–1991) or with a replacement controller assembly called a digital ratio adapter controller (DRAC) located under the dash. It may be possible to recalibrate the speedometer and odometer on earlier models, before 1988, or vehicles that use speedometer cables by replacing the drive gear in the transmission. Check service information for the procedure on the vehicle being serviced.

MAINTENANCE REMINDER LAMPS

Maintenance reminder lamps indicate that the oil should be changed or that other service is required. There are numerous ways to extinguish a maintenance reminder lamp. Some require the use of a special tool. Always check the owner manual or service information for the exact procedure for the vehicle being serviced. For example, to reset the oil service reminder light on many General Motors vehicles, you have to perform the following:

STEP 1 Turn the ignition key on (engine off).

STEP 2 Depress the accelerator pedal three times and hold it down on the fourth.

STEP 3 When the reminder light flashes, release the accelerator pedal.

STEP 4 Turn the ignition key to the off position.

STEP 5 Start the engine and the light should be off.

1 Observe the fuel gauge. This General Motors vehicle shows an indicated reading of slightly above one-half tank.

2 Consult the factory service manual for the specifications, wire color, and recommended test procedure.

3 From the service manual, the connector for the fuel gauge-sending unit was located under the vehicle near the rear. A visual inspection indicated that the electrical wiring and connector were not damaged or corroded.

4 To test resistance of the sending unit (tank unit) use a digital multimeter and select ohms (V).

5 Following the schematic in the service manual the sending unit resistance can be measured between the pink and the black wires in the connector.

6 The meter displays 50 ohms or slightly above the middle of the normal resistance value for the vehicle of 0 Ω (empty) to 90 Ω (full).

CONTINUED ▶

7 To check if the dash unit can move, the connector is unplugged with the ignition key on (engine off).

8 As the connector is disconnected, the needle of the dash unit moves toward full.

9 After a couple of seconds, the needle disappears above the full reading. The open connector represented infinity ohms and normal maximum reading occurs when the tank unit reads 90 ohms. If the technician does not realize that the needle could disappear, an incorrect diagnosis could be made.

10 To check if the dash unit is capable of reading empty, a fuse jumper wire is connected between the signal wire at the dash end of the connector and a good chassis ground.

11 A check of a dash unit indicated that the needle does accurately read empty.

12 After testing, reconnect the electrical connectors and verify for proper operation of the fuel level gauge.

1. Most digital and analog (needle-type) dash gauges use variable-resistance sensors.

2. Dash warning lamps are called telltale lamps.

3. Many electronically operated or computer-operated dash indicators require that a service manual be used to perform accurate diagnosis.

4. Permanent magnet (PM) generators produce an AC signal and are used for vehicle speed and wheel speed sensors.

5. Navigation systems and warning systems are part of the driver information system on many vehicles.

REVIEW QUESTIONS

1. How does a stepper motor analog dash gauge work?

2. What are LED, LCD, VTF, and CRT dash displays? Describe each.

3. How do you diagnose a problem with a red brake warning lamp?

4. How do you test the dash unit of a fuel gauge?

5. How does a navigation system determine the location of the vehicle?

CHAPTER QUIZ

1. Two technicians are discussing a fuel gauge on a General Motors vehicle. Technician A says that if the ground wire connection to the fuel tank sending unit becomes rusty or corroded, the fuel gauge will read lower than normal. Technician B says that if the power lead to the fuel tank sending unit is disconnected from the tank unit and grounded (ignition on), the fuel gauge should go to empty. Which technician is correct?
   a. Technician A only
   b. Technician B only
   c. Both Technicians A and B
   d. Neither Technician A nor B

2. If an oil pressure warning lamp on a General Motors vehicle is on all the time, yet the engine oil pressure is normal, the problem could be a _____.
   a. Defective (shorted) oil pressure sending unit (sensor)
   b. Defective (open) oil pressure sending unit (sensor)
   c. Wire shorted-to-ground between the sending unit (sensor) and the dash warning lamp
   d. Both a and c

3. When the oil pressure drops to between 3 and 7 psi, the oil pressure lamp lights by _____.
   a. Opening the circuit
   b. Shorting the circuit
   c. Grounding the circuit
   d. Conducting current to the dash lamp by oil

4. A brake warning lamp on the dash remains on whenever the ignition is on. If the wire to the pressure differential switch (usually a part of a combination valve or built into the master cylinder) is unplugged, the dash lamp goes out. Technician A says that this is an indication of a fault in the hydraulic brake system. Technician B says that the problem is probably due to a stuck parking brake cable switch. Which technician is correct?
   a. Technician A only   b. Technician B only
   c. Both Technicians A and B   d. Neither Technician A nor B

5. A customer complains that every time the lights are turned on in the vehicle, the dash display dims. What is the most probable explanation?
   a. Normal behavior for LED dash displays
   b. Normal behavior for VTF dash displays
   c. Poor ground in lighting circuit causing a voltage drop to the dash lamps
   d. Feedback problem most likely caused by a short-to-voltage between the headlights and dash display

6. Technician A says that LCDs may be slow to work at low temperatures. Technician B says that an LCD dash display can be damaged if pressure is exerted on the front of the display during cleaning. Which technician is correct?
   a. Technician A only   b. Technician B only
   c. Both Technicians A and B   d. Neither Technician A nor B

7. Technician A says that backup sensors use LEDs to detect objects. Technician B says that a backup sensor will not work correctly if the paint is thicker than 0.006 in. Which technician is correct?
   a. Technician A only
   b. Technician B only
   c. Both Technicians A and B
   d. Neither Technician A nor B

8. Technician A says that metal-type tinting can affect the navigation system. Technician B says most navigation systems require a monthly payment for use of the GPS satellite. Which technician is correct?
   a. Technician A only
   b. Technician B only
   c. Both Technicians A and B
   d. Neither Technician A nor B

9. Technician A says that the data displayed on the dash can come from the engine computer. Technician B says that the entire dash assembly may have to be replaced even if just one unit fails. Which technician is correct?
   a. Technician A only
   b. Technician B only
   c. Both Technicians A and B
   d. Neither Technician A nor B

10. How does changing the size of the tires affect the speedometer reading?
    a. A smaller diameter tire causes the speedometer to read faster than actual speed and more than actual mileage on the odometer.
    b. A smaller diameter tire causes the speedometer to read slower than the actual speed and less than the actual mileage on the odometer.
    c. A larger diameter tire causes the speedometer to read faster than the actual speed and more than the actual mileage on the odometer.
    d. A larger diameter tire causes the speedometer to read slower than the actual speed and more than the actual mileage on the odometer.

chapter 39

HORN, WIPER, AND BLOWER MOTOR CIRCUITS

OBJECTIVES: **After studying Chapter 39, the reader will be able to:** • Prepare for ASE Electrical/Electronic Systems (A6) certification test content area "G" (Horn and Wiper/Washer Diagnosis and Repair) and content area "H" (Accessories Diagnosis and Repair). • Describe how the horn operates. • List the components of a wiper circuit. • Explain how the blower motor can run at different speeds. • Discuss how to diagnosis faults in the horn, wiper, and blower motor circuits.

KEY TERMS: • Horns 449 • Pulse wipers 451 • Rain sense wipers 458 • Series-wound field 451 • Shunt field 451 • Variable-delay wipers 451 • Windshield wipers 451

HORNS

PURPOSE AND FUNCTION **Horns** are electric devices that emit a loud sound used to alert other drivers or persons in the area. Horns are manufactured in several different tones ranging from 1,800 to 3,550 Hz. Vehicle manufacturers select from various horn tones for a particular vehicle sound. ● SEE **FIGURE 39–1.**

When two horns are used, each has a different tone when operated separately, yet the sound combines when both are operated.

HORN CIRCUITS Automotive horns usually operate on full battery voltage wired from the battery, through a fuse, switch, and then to the horns. Most vehicles use a horn *relay*. With a relay, the horn button on the steering wheel or column completes a circuit to ground that closes a relay, and the heavy current flow required by the horn then travels from the relay to the horn. Without a horn relay, the high current of the horns must flow through the steering wheel horn switch. ● SEE **FIGURE 39–2.**

The horn relay is also connected to the body control module, which "beeps" the horn when the vehicle is locked or unlocked, using the key fob remote.

HORN OPERATION A vehicle horn is an actuator that converts an electrical signal to sound. The horn circuit includes an armature (a coil of wire) and contacts that are attached to a diaphragm. When energized, the armature causes the diaphragm to move up which then opens a set of contact points that de-energize the armature circuit. As the diaphragm moves down, the contact points close, re-energize the armature circuit, and the diaphragm moves up again. This rapid opening and closing of the contact points causes the diaphragm to

FIGURE 39–1 Two horns are used on this vehicle. Many vehicles use only one horn, often hidden underneath the vehicle.

FIGURE 39–2 A typical horn circuit. Note that the horn button completes the ground circuit for the relay.

vibrate at an audible frequency. The sound created by the diaphragm is magnified as it travels through a trumpet attached to the diaphragm chamber. Most horn systems typically use one or two horns, but some have up to four. Those with multiple horns use both high- and low-pitch units to achieve a harmonious tone. Only a high-pitched unit is used in single-horn applications. The horn assembly is marked with an "H" or "L" for pitch identification.

HORN SYSTEM DIAGNOSIS
There are three types of horn failure.

- No horn operation
- Intermittent operation
- Constant operation
- Weak or low volume sound

If a horn does not operate at all, check for the following:

- Burned fuse or fusible link
- Open circuit
- Defective horn
- Faulty relay
- Defective horn switch
- Poor ground (horn mounting)
- Corroded or rusted electrical connector

If a horn operates intermittently, check for the following:

- Loose contact at the switch
- Loose, frayed, or broken wires
- Defective relay

HORN SOUNDS CONTINUOUSLY
A horn that sounds continuously and cannot be shut off is caused by horn switch contacts that are stuck closed, or a short-to-ground on the control circuit. This may be the result of a defective horn switch or a faulty relay. Stuck relay contacts keep the circuit complete so the horn sounds constantly. Disconnect the horn and check continuity through the horn switch and relay to locate the source of the problem.

INOPERATIVE HORN
To help determine the cause of an inoperative horn, use a fused jumper wire and connect one end to the positive post of the battery and the other end to the wire terminal of the horn itself. Also use a fused jumper wire to substitute a ground path to test or confirm a potential bad ground circuit. If the horn works with jumper wires connected, check ground wires and connections.

- If the horn works, the problem is in the circuit supplying current to the horn.
- If the horn does not work, the horn itself could be defective or the mounting bracket may not be providing a good ground.

HORN SERVICE
When a horn malfunctions, circuit tests are made to determine if the horn, relay, switch, or wiring is the source of the failure. Typically, a digital multimeter (DMM) is used to perform voltage drop and continuity checks to isolate the failure.

- **Switch and relay.** A momentary contact switch is used to sound the horn. The horn switch is mounted to the steering wheel in the center of the steering column on some models, and is part of a multifunction switch installed on the steering column.

    CAUTION: If steering wheel removal is required for diagnosis or repair of the horn circuit, follow service information procedures for disarming the airbag circuit prior to steering wheel removal, and for the specified test equipment to use.

    On most late-model vehicles, the horn relay is located in a centralized power distribution center along with other relays, circuit breakers, and fuses. The horn relay bolts onto an inner fender or the bulkhead in the engine compartment of older vehicles. Check the relay to determine if the coil is being energized and if current passes through the power circuit when the horn switch is depressed.

    Obtain an electrical schematic of the horn circuit and use a voltmeter to test input, output, and control voltage.

- **Circuit testing.** Circuit testing involves the following steps.

    STEP 1   Make sure the fuse or fusible link is good before attempting to troubleshoot the circuit.

    STEP 2   Check that the ground connections for the horn are clean and tight. Most horns ground to the chassis through the mounting bolts. High ground circuit resistance due to corrosion, road dirt, or loose fasteners may cause no, or intermittent, horn operation.

    STEP 3   On a system with a relay, test the power output circuit and the control circuit. Check for voltage available at the horn, voltage available at the relay, and continuity through the switch. When no relay is used, there are two wires leading to the horn switch, and a connection to the steering wheel is made with a double contact slip ring. Test points on this system are similar to those of a system with a relay, but there is no control circuit.

HORN REPLACEMENT
Horns are generally mounted on the radiator core support by bolts and nuts or sheet metal screws. It may be necessary to remove the grille or other parts to access the horn mounting screws. If a replacement horn is required, attempt to use a horn of the same tone as the original. The tone is usually indicated by a number or letter stamped on the body of the horn. To replace a horn, simply remove the fasteners and lift the old horn from its mounting bracket.

Clean the attachment area on the mounting bracket and chassis before installing the new horn. Some models use a corrosion-resistant mounting bolt to ensure a ground connection. ● **SEE FIGURE 39–3.**

FIGURE 39-3 Horns typically mount to the radiator core support or bracket at the front of the vehicle.

WINDSHIELD WIPER AND WASHER SYSTEM

PURPOSE AND FUNCTION **Windshield wipers** are used to keep the viewing area of the windshield clean of rain. Windshield wiper systems and circuits vary greatly between manufacturers as well as between models. Some vehicles combine the windshield wiper and windshield washer functions into a single system. Many minivans and sport utility vehicles (SUVs) also have a rear window wiper and washer system that works independently of the windshield system. In spite of the design differences, all windshield and rear window wiper and washer systems operate in a similar fashion.

COMPUTER CONTROLLED Most wipers since the 1990s have used the body computer to control the actual operation of the wiper. The wiper controls are simply a command to the computer. The computer may also turn on the headlights whenever the wipers are on, which is the law in some states. ● **SEE FIGURE 39-4.**

WIPER AND WASHER COMPONENTS A typical combination wiper and washer system consists of the following:

- Wiper motor
- Gearbox
- Wiper arms and linkage
- Washer pump
- Hoses and jets (nozzles)
- Fluid reservoir
- Combination switch
- Wiring and electrical connectors
- Electronic control module

The motor and gearbox assembly is wired to the wiper switch on the instrument panel or steering column or to the wiper control module. ● **SEE FIGURE 39-5** on page 453.

Some systems use either a one- or two-speed wiper motor, whereas others have a variable-speed motor.

WINDSHIELD WIPER MOTORS The windshield wipers ordinarily use a special two-speed electric motor. Most are compound-wound motors, a motor type, which provides for two different speeds.

- **Series-wound field**
- **Shunt field**

One speed is achieved in the series-wound field and the other speed in the shunt wound field. The wiper switch provides the necessary electrical connections for either motor speed. Switches in the mechanical wiper motor assembly provide the necessary operation for "parking" and "concealing" of the wipers. ● **SEE FIGURE 39-6** for a typical wiper motor assembly.

- **Wiper motor operation.** Most wiper motors use a permanent magnet motor with a low speed 1 brush and a high speed 1 brush. The brushes connect the battery to the internal windings of the motor, and the two brushes provide for two different motor speeds.

  The ground brush is directly opposite the low-speed brush. The high-speed brush is off to the side of the low-speed brush. When current flows through the high-speed brush, there are fewer turns on the armature between the hot and ground brushes, and therefore the resistance is less. With less resistance, more current flows and the armature revolves faster. ● **SEE FIGURES 39-7 AND 39-8** on page 453.

- **Variable wipers.** The **variable-delay wipers** (also called **pulse wipers**) use an electronic circuit with a variable resistor that controls the time of the charge and discharge of a capacitor. The charging and discharging of the capacitor controls the circuit for the operation of the wiper motor. ● **SEE FIGURE 39-9** on page 454.

HIDDEN WIPERS Some vehicles are equipped with wipers that become hidden when turned off. These wipers are also called *depressed wipers*. The gearbox has an additional linkage arm to provide depressed parking for hidden wipers. This link extends to move the wipers into the park position when the motor turns in reverse of operating direction. With depressed park, the motor assembly includes an internal park switch. The park switch completes a circuit to reverse armature polarity in the motor when the windshield wiper switch is turned off. The park circuit opens once the wiper arms are in the park position.

FIGURE 39–4 A circuit diagram is necessary to troubleshoot a windshield wiper problem.

Instead of a depressed park feature, some systems simply extend the cleaning arc below the level of the hood line.

WINDSHIELD WIPER DIAGNOSIS
Windshield wiper failure may be the result of an electrical fault or a mechanical problem, such as binding linkage. Generally, if the wipers operate at one speed setting but not another, the problem is electrical.

To determine if there is an electrical or mechanical problem, access the motor assembly and disconnect the wiper arm linkage from the motor and gearbox. Depending on the type of vehicle, this procedure may involve:

- Removing body trim panels from the covered areas at the base of the windshield to gain access to the linkage connectors
- Switching the motor on to each speed (If the motor operates at all speeds, the problem is mechanical. If the motor still does not operate, the problem is electrical.)

If the wiper motor does not run at all, check for the following:

- Grounded or inoperative switch
- Defective motor
- Circuit wiring fault
- Poor electrical ground connection

FIGURE 39–5 The motor and linkage bolt to the body and connect to the switch with a wiring harness.

FIGURE 39–6 A typical wiper motor with the housing cover removed. The motor itself has a worm gear on the shaft that turns the small intermediate gear, which then rotates the gear and tube assembly, which rotates the crank arm (not shown) that connects to the wiper linkage.

FIGURE 39–7 A wiring diagram of a two-speed windshield wiper circuit using a three-brush, two-speed motor. The dashed line for the multifunction lever indicates that the circuit shown is only part of the total function of the steering column lever.

FIGURE 39–8 A wiring diagram of a three-speed windshield wiper circuit using a two-brush motor, but both a series-wound and a shunt field coil.

FIGURE 39–9 A variable pulse rate windshield wiper circuit. Notice that the wiring travels from the passenger compartment through pass-through grommets to the underhood area.

PARK POSITION

OTHER POSITION

C	A
D	B

TERMINAL	OPERATION SPEED
C	LOW
A	HIGH

FIGURE 39–10 A wiper motor connector pin chart.

If the motor operates but the wipers do not, check for the following:

- Stripped gears in the gearbox or stripped linkage connection
- Loose or separated motor-to-gearbox connection
- Loose linkage to the motor connection

If the motor does not shut off, check for the following:

- Defective park switch inside the motor
- Defective wiper switch
- Poor ground connection at the wiper switch

WINDSHIELD WIPER TESTING When the wiper motor does not operate with the linkage disconnected, perform the following steps to determine the fault. ● **SEE FIGURE 39–10.**

To test the wiper system, perform the following steps.

STEP 1 Refer to the circuit diagram or a connector pin chart for the vehicle being serviced to determine the test points for voltage measurements.

STEP 2 Switch the ignition on and set the wiper switch to a speed at which the motor does not operate.

STEP 3 Check for battery voltage available at the appropriate wiper motor terminal for the selected speed. If voltage is available to the motor, an internal motor problem is indicated. No voltage available indicates a switch or circuit failure.

STEP 4 Check for proper ground connections.

How Do Wipers Park?

Some vehicles have wiper arms that park lower than the normal operating position so that they are hidden below the hood when not in operation. This is called a *depressed park position*. When the wiper motor is turned off, the park switch allows the motor to continue to turn until the wiper arms reach the bottom edge of the windshield. Then the park switch reverses the current flow through the wiper motor, which makes a partial revolution in the opposite direction. The wiper linkage pulls the wiper arms down below the level of the hood and the park switch is opened, stopping the wiper motor.

STEP 5 Check that battery voltage is available at the motor side of the wiper switch. If battery voltage is available, the circuit is open between the switch and motor. No voltage available indicates either a faulty switch or a power supply problem.

STEP 6 Check for battery voltage available at the power input side of the wiper switch. If voltage is available, the switch is defective. Replace the switch. No voltage available to the switch indicates a circuit problem between the battery and switch.

WINDSHIELD WIPER SERVICE Wiper motors are replaced if defective. The motor usually mounts on the bulkhead (firewall). Bulkhead-mounted units are accessible from under the hood, while the cowl panel needs to be removed to service a motor mounted in the cowl. ● **SEE FIGURE 39–11.**

COWL PANEL

WIPER MOTOR ASSEMBLY

PLENUM

FIGURE 39–11 The wiper motor and linkage mount under the cowl panel on many vehicles.

FIGURE 39–12 A single wiper arm mounts directly to the motor on most rear wiper applications.

After gaining access to the motor, removal is simply a matter of disconnecting the linkage, unplugging the electrical connectors, and unbolting the motor. Move the wiper linkage through its full travel by hand to check for any binding before installing the new motor.

Rear window wiper motors are generally located inside the rear door panel of station wagons, or the rear hatch panel on vehicles with a hatchback or liftgate. ● SEE FIGURE 39–12.

After removing the trim panel covering the motor, replacement is essentially the same as replacing the front wiper motor.

Wiper control switches are either installed on the steering column or on the instrument panel.

Steering column wiper switches, which are operated by controls on the end of a switch stalk (usually called a *multifunction switch*), require partial disassembly of the steering column for replacement.

PULSE WIPE SYSTEMS Windshield wipers may also incorporate a delay, or intermittent operation, feature commonly called pulse wipe. The length of the delay, or the frequency of the intermittent operation, is adjustable on some systems. Pulse wipe systems may rely on simple electrical controls, such as a variable-resistance switch, or be controlled electronically through a control module.

With any electronic control system, it is important to follow the diagnosis and test procedures recommended by the manufacturer for that specific vehicle.

A typical pulse, or interval, wiper system uses either a governor or a solid-state module that contains either a variable resistor or rheostat and capacitor. The module connects into the electrical circuitry between the wiper switch and wiper motor. The variable resistor or rheostat controls the length of the interval between wiper pulses. A solid-state pulse wipe timer regulates the control circuit of the pulse relay to direct current to the motor at the prescribed interval. ● SEE FIGURE 39–13.

The following troubleshooting procedure applies to most models.

STEP 1 If the wipers do not run at all, check the wiper fuse, fusible link, or circuit breaker and verify that voltage is available to the switch.

STEP 2 Refer to a wiring diagram of the switch to determine how current is routed through it to the motor in the different positions.

① RATCHET RELEASE SOLENOID
   (OPERATED WHEN WASH SWITCH DEPRESSED)
② WASHER OVERRIDE SWITCH
   (CLOSED DURING WASH CYCLE)
③ HOLDING SWITCH
   (OPEN AT THE END OF EACH SWEEP)

FIGURE 39–13 Circuit diagram of a rheostat-controlled, electronically timed interval wiper.

STEP 3 Disconnect the switch and use fused jumper wires to apply power directly to the motor on the different speed circuits.
   ■ If the motor now runs, the problem is in the switch or module.
   ■ Check for continuity in the circuit for each speed through the control-to-ground if the wiper motor runs at some, but not all, speeds.

WINDSHIELD WASHER OPERATION Most vehicles use a positive-displacement or centrifugal-type washer pump located in the washer reservoir. A momentary contact switch, which is often part of a steering column–mounted combination switch assembly, energizes the washer pump. Washer pump switches are installed either on the steering column or on the instrument panel. The nozzles can be located on the bulkhead or in the hood depending on the vehicle.

WINDSHIELD WASHER DIAGNOSIS Inoperative windshield washers may be caused by the following:
   ■ Blown fuse or open circuit
   ■ Empty reservoir
   ■ Clogged nozzle
   ■ Broken, pinched, or clogged hose
   ■ Loose or broken wire
   ■ Blocked reservoir screen
   ■ Leaking reservoir
   ■ Defective pump

TECH TIP

Use a Scan Tool to Check Accessories

Most vehicles built since 2000 can have the lighting and accessory circuits checked using a scan tool. A technician can use the following:

- Factory scan tool, such as:
  - Tech 2 or Multiple Diagnostic Interface (MDI) (General Motors vehicle)
  - DRB III or Star Scan or Star Mobile or WiTech (Chrysler-Jeep vehicles)
  - New Generation Star or IDS (Ford)
  - Honda Diagnostic System (HDS)
  - TIS Tech Stream (Toyota/Lexus)
- Enhanced aftermarket scan tool that has body bidirectional control capability, including:
  - Snap-on Modis, Solus, or Verus
  - OTC Genisys
  - Autoengenuity

  Using a bidirectional scan tool allows the technician to command the operation of electrical accessories such as windows, lights, and wipers. If the circuit operates correctly when commanded by the scan tool and does not function using the switch(es), follow service information instructions to diagnose the switch circuits.

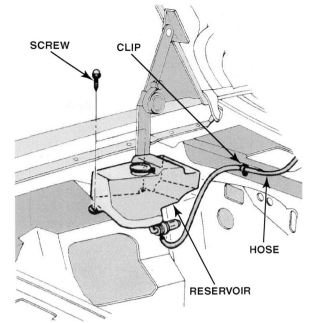

FIGURE 39–14 Disconnect the hose at the pump and operate the switch to check a washer pump.

FIGURE 39–15 Washer pumps usually install into the reservoir and are held in place with a retaining ring.

To diagnose the washer system, follow service information procedures that usually include the following steps.

STEP 1 To quick check any washer system, make sure the reservoir has fluid and is not frozen, and then disconnect the pump hose and operate the washer switch.

> **NOTE: Always use good-quality windshield washer fluid from a closed container to prevent contaminated fluid from damaging the washer pump. Radiator antifreeze (ethylene glycol) should never be used in any windshield wiper system.**

● **SEE FIGURE 39–14.**

STEP 2 If fluid squirts from the pump, the delivery system is at fault, not the motor, switch, or circuitry.

STEP 3 If no fluid squirts from the pump, the problem is most likely a circuit failure, defective pump, or faulty switch.

STEP 4 A clogged reservoir screen also may be preventing fluid from entering the pump.

WINDSHIELD WASHER SERVICE When a fluid delivery problem is indicated, check for:

- Blocked, pinched, broken, or disconnected hose
- Clogged nozzles
- Blocked washer pump outlet

If the pump motor does not operate, check for battery voltage available at the pump while operating the washer switch. If voltage is available and the pump does not run, check for continuity on the pump ground circuit. If there is no voltage drop on the ground circuit, replace the pump motor.

If battery voltage is not available at the motor, check for power through the washer switch. If voltage is available at and through the switch, there is a problem in the wiring between the switch and pump. Perform voltage drop tests to locate the fault. Repair the wiring as needed and retest.

Washer motors are not repairable and are simply replaced if defective. Centrifugal or positive-displacement pumps are located on or inside the washer reservoir tank or cover and secured with a retaining ring or nut. ● **SEE FIGURE 39–15.**

RAIN SENSE WIPER SYSTEM

PARTS AND OPERATION **Rain sense wiper** systems use a sensor located at the top of the windshield on the inside to detect rain droplets. This sensor is called the *rain sense module (RSM)* by General Motors. It determines and adjusts the time delay of the wiper based on how much moisture it detects on the windshield. The wiper switch can be left on the sense position all of the time and if no rain is sensed, the wipers will not swipe. ● **SEE FIGURES 39–16 AND 39–17.**

The control knob is rotated to the desired wiper sensibility level.

The microprocessor in the RSM sends a command to the body control module (BCM). RSM is a triangular-shaped black plastic housing. Fine openings on the windshield side of the housing are fitted with eight convex clear plastic lenses. The unit contains four infrared (IR) diodes, two photocells, and a microprocessor.

The IR diodes generate IR beams that are aimed by four of the convex optical lenses near the base of the module through the windshield glass. Four additional convex lenses near the top of the RSM are focused on the IR light beam on the outside of the windshield glass and allow the two photocells to sense changes in the intensity of the IR light beam. When sufficient moisture accumulates, the RSM detects a change in the monitored IR light beam intensity. The RSM processes the signal BCM over the data BUS to command a swipe of the wiper.

DIAGNOSIS AND SERVICE If there is a complaint about the rain sense wipers not functioning correctly, check the owner manual to be sure that they are properly set and adjusted. Also, verify that the windshield wipers are functioning correctly on all speeds before diagnosing the rain sensor circuits. Always follow the vehicle manufacturer's recommended diagnosis and testing procedures.

FIGURE 39–16 A typical rain sensing module located on the inside of the windshield near the inside rearview mirror.

FIGURE 39–17 The electronics in the rain sense wiper module can detect the presence of rain drops under various lighting conditions.

BLOWER MOTOR

PURPOSE AND FUNCTION The same blower motor moves air inside the vehicle for:

1. Air conditioning
2. Heat
3. Defrosting
4. Defogging
5. Venting of the passenger compartment

The motor turns a squirrel cage-type fan. A squirrel cage-type fan is able to move air without creating a lot of noise. The fan switch controls the path that the current follows to the blower motor. ● **SEE FIGURE 39–18.**

PARTS AND OPERATION The motor is usually a permanent magnet, one-speed motor that operates at its maximum speed with full battery voltage. The switch gets

FIGURE 39–18 A squirrel cage blower motor. A replacement blower motor usually does not come equipped with the squirrel cage blower, so it has to be switched from the old motor.

FIGURE 39-19 A typical blower motor circuit with four speeds. The three lowest fan speeds (low, medium-low, and medium-high) use the blower motor resistors to drop the voltage to the motor and reduce current to the motor. On high, the resistors are bypassed. The "high" position on the fan switch energizes a relay, which supplies the current for the blower on high through a fusible link.

current from the fuse panel with the ignition switch on, and then directs full battery voltage to the blower motor for high speed and to the blower motor through resistors for lower speeds.

VARIABLE SPEED CONTROL

The fan switch controls the path of current through a resistor pack to obtain different fan speeds of the blower motor. The electrical path can be:

- Full battery voltage for high-speed operation
- Through one or more resistors to reduce the voltage and the current to the blower motor which then rotates at a slower speed

The resistors are located near the blower motor and mounted in the duct where the airflow from the blower can cool the resistors. The current flow through the resistor is controlled by the switch and often uses a relay to carry the heavy current (10 to 12 amperes) needed to power the fan. Normal operation includes:

- **Low speed.** Current flows through three resistors in series to drop the voltage to about 4 volts and 4 amperes.
- **Medium speed.** Current is directed through two resistors in series to lower the voltage to about 6 volts and 6 amperes.
- **Medium-high speed.** Current is directed through one resistor resulting in a voltage of about 9 volts and 9 amperes.
- **High speed.** Full battery voltage, usually through a relay, is applied to the blower motor resulting in a current of about 12 amperes.

● **SEE FIGURES 39-19 AND 39-20.**

FIGURE 39-20 A typical blower motor resistor pack used to control blower motor speed. Some blower motor resistors are flat and look like a credit card and are called "credit card resistors".

NOTE: Most Ford and some other vehicles place the blower motor resistors on the ground side of the motor circuit. The location of the resistors does not affect the operation because they are connected in series.

Some blower motors are electronically controlled by the body control module (BCM) and include electronic circuits to achieve a variable speed. ● **SEE FIGURE 39-21.**

BLOWER MOTOR DIAGNOSIS

If the blower motor does not operate at any speed, the problem could be any of the following:

1. Defective ground wire or ground wire connection
2. Defective blower motor (not repairable; must be replaced)
3. Open circuit in the power-side circuit, including fuse, wiring, or fan switch

TECH TIP

The 20 Ampere Fuse Test

Most blower motors operate at about 12 A on high speed. If the bushings (bearings) on the armature of the motor become worn or dry, the motor turns more slowly. Because a motor also produces counterelectromotive force (CEMF) as it spins, a slower-turning motor will actually draw more amperes than a fast-spinning motor.

If a blower motor draws too many amperes, the resistors or the electronic circuit controlling the blower motor can fail. Testing the actual current draw of the motor is sometimes difficult because the amperage often exceeds the permissible amount for most digital meters.

One test recommended by General Motors Co. is to unplug the power lead to the motor (retain the ground on the motor) and use a fused jumper lead with one end connected to the battery's positive terminal and the other end to the motor terminal. Use a 20 A fuse in the test lead, and operate the motor for several minutes. If the blower motor is drawing more than 20 A, the fuse will blow. Some experts recommend using a 15 A fuse. If the 15 A fuse blows and the 20 A fuse does not, then you know the approximate blower motor current draw.

FIGURE 39–21 A brushless DC motor that uses the body computer to control the speed. *(Courtesy of Sammy's Auto Service, Inc.)*

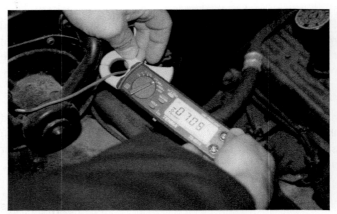

FIGURE 39–22 Using a mini AC/DC clamp-on multimeter to measure the current draw of a blower motor.

If the blower works on lower speeds but not on high speed, the problem is usually an inline fuse or high-speed relay that controls the heavy current flow for high-speed operation. The high-speed fuse or relay usually fails as a result of internal blower motor bushing wear, which causes excessive resistance to motor rotation. At slow blower speeds, the resistance is not as noticeable and the blower operates normally. The blower motor is a sealed unit, and if defective, must be replaced as a unit. The squirrel cage fan usually needs to be removed from the old motor and attached to the replacement motor. If the blower motor operates normally at high speed but not at any of the lower speeds, the problem could be melted wire resistors or a defective switch.

The blower motor can be tested using a clamp-on DC ammeter. ● **SEE FIGURE 39–22.**

Most blower motors do not draw more than 15 A on high speed. A worn or defective motor usually draws more current than normal and could damage the blower motor resistors or blow a fuse if not replaced.

ELECTRICAL ACCESSORY SYMPTOM GUIDE

The following list will assist technicians in troubleshooting electrical accessory systems.

Blower Motor Problem	Possible Causes and/or Solutions
Blower motor does not operate.	1. Blown fuse 2. Poor ground connection on blower motor 3. Defective motor (Use a fused jumper wire connected between the positive terminal of the battery and the blower motor power lead connection [lead disconnected] to check for blower motor operation.) 4. Defective control switch 5. Resistor block open or defective blower motor control module
Blower motor operates only on high speed.	1. Open in the resistors located in the air box near the blower motor 2. Stuck or defective high-speed relay 3. Defective blower motor control switch
Blower motor operates in lower speed(s) only, no high speed.	1. Defective high-speed relay or blower high-speed fuse **NOTE: If the high-speed fuse blows a second time, check the current draw of the motor and replace the blower motor if the current draw is above specifications. Check for possible normal operation if the rear window defogger is not in operation; some vehicles electrically prevent simultaneous operation of the high-speed blower and rear window defogger to help reduce the electrical loads.**

Windshield Wiper or Washer Problem	Possible Causes and/or Solutions
Windshield wipers are inoperative.	1. Blown fuse 2. Poor ground on the wiper motor or the control switch 3. Defective motor or linkage problem
Windshield wipers operate on high speed or low speed only.	1. Defective switch 2. Defective motor assembly 3. Poor ground on the wiper control switch
Windshield washers are inoperative.	1. Defective switch 2. Empty reservoir or clogged lines or discharge nozzles 3. Poor ground on the washer pump motor

Horn Problem	Possible Causes and/or Solutions
Horn(s) are inoperative.	1. Poor ground on horn(s) 2. Defective relay (if used); open circuit in the steering column 3. Defective horn (Use a fused jumper wire connected between the positive terminal of the battery and the horn [horn wire disconnected] to check for proper operation of the horn.)
Horn(s) produce low volume or wrong sound.	1. Poor ground at horn 2. Incorrect frequency of horn
Horn blows all the time.	1. Stuck horn relay (if used) 2. Short-to-ground in the wire to the horn button

1. Horn frequency can range from 1,800 to 3,550 Hz.
2. Most horn circuits use a relay, and the current through the relay coil is controlled by the horn switch.
3. Most windshield wipers use a three-brush, two-speed motor.
4. Windshield washer diagnosis includes checking the pump both electrically and mechanically for proper operation.
5. Many blower motors use resistors wired in series to control blower motor speed.
6. A good blower motor should draw less than 20 A.

REVIEW QUESTIONS

1. What are the three types of horn failure?
2. How is the horn switch used to operate the horn?
3. How do you determine if a windshield wiper problem is electrical or mechanical?
4. Why does a defective blower motor draw more current (amperes) than a good motor?

CHAPTER QUIZ

1. Technician A says that a defective high-speed blower motor relay could prevent high-speed blower operation, yet allows normal operation at low speeds. Technician B says that a defective (open) blower motor resistor can prevent low-speed blower operation, yet permit normal high-speed operation. Which technician is correct?
   a. Technician A only
   b. Technician B only
   c. Both Technicians A and B
   d. Neither Technician A nor B

2. To determine if a windshield wiper problem is electrical or mechanical, the service technician should _____.
   a. Disconnect the linkage arm from the windshield wiper motor and operate the windshield wiper
   b. Check to see if the fuse is blown
   c. Check the condition of the wiper blades
   d. Check the washer fluid for contamination

3. A weak-sounding horn is being diagnosed. Technician A says that a poor ground connector at the horn itself can be the cause. Technician B says an open relay can be the cause. Which technician is correct?
   a. Technician A only
   b. Technician B only
   c. Both Technicians A and B
   d. Neither Technician A nor B

4. What controls the operation of a pulse wiper system?
   a. Resistor that controls current flow to the wiper motor
   b. Solid-state (electronic) module
   c. Variable-speed gem set
   d. Transistor

5. Which pitch horn is used for a single horn application?
   a. High pitch
   b. Low pitch

6. The horn switch on the steering wheel on a vehicle that uses a horn relay _____.
   a. Sends electrical power to the horns
   b. Provides the ground circuit for the horn
   c. Grounds the horn relay coil
   d. Provides power (12 V) to the horn relay

7. A rain sense wiper system uses a rain sensor that is usually mounted _____.
   a. Behind the grille
   b. Outside of the windshield at the top
   c. Inside the windshield at the top
   d. On the roof

8. Technician A says a blower motor can be tested using a fused jumper lead. Technician B says a blower motor can be tested using a clamp-on ammeter. Which technician is correct?
   a. Technician A only
   b. Technician B only
   c. Both Technicians A and B
   d. Neither Technician A nor B

9. A defective blower motor draws more current than a good motor because the _____.
   a. Speed of the motor increases
   b. CEMF decreases
   c. Airflow slows down, which decreases the cooling of the motor
   d. Both a and c

10. Windshield washer pumps can be damaged if _____.
    a. Pure water is used in freezing weather
    b. Contaminated windshield washer fluid is used
    c. Ethylene glycol (antifreeze) is used
    d. All of the above

chapter 40
ACCESSORY CIRCUITS

OBJECTIVES: **After studying Chapter 40, the reader will be able to:** • Prepare for ASE Electrical/Electronic Systems (A6) certification test content area "H" (Accessories Diagnosis and Repair). • Explain how the body control module or body computer controls the operation of electrical accessories. • Explain how cruise control operates and how to diagnose the circuit. • Describe how power door locks, windows, and seats operate. • Describe how a keyless remote can be reprogrammed. • Explain how the theft deterrent system works.

KEY TERMS: • Adjustable pedals 477 • Backlight 468 • CHMSL 465 • Control wires 472 • Cruise control 463 • Direction wires 472 • Electric adjustable pedals (EAP) 477 • ETC 466 • HomeLink 470 • Independent switches 470 • Key fob 479 • Lockout switch 470 • Lumbar 473 • Master control switch 470 • Peltier effect 476 • Permanent magnet electric motors 470 • Rubber coupling 473 • Screw jack assembly 473 • Thermoelectric device (TED) 476 • Window regulator 471

CRUISE CONTROL

PARTS INVOLVED **Cruise control** (also called *speed control*) is a combination of electrical and mechanical components designed to maintain a constant, set vehicle speed without driver pressure on the accelerator pedal. Major components of a typical cruise control system include the following:

1. **Servo unit.** The servo unit attaches to the throttle linkage through a cable or chain.

   The servo unit controls the movement of the throttle by receiving a controlled amount of vacuum from a control module. ● **SEE FIGURE 40–1.**

   Some systems use a stepper motor and do not use engine vacuum.

2. **Computer or cruise control module.** This unit receives inputs from the brake switch, throttle position (TP) sensor, and vehicle speed sensor. It operates the solenoids or stepper motor to maintain the set speed.

3. **Speed set control.** A speed set control is a switch or control located on the steering column, steering wheel, dash, or console. Many cruise control units feature coast, accelerate, and resume functions. ● **SEE FIGURE 40–2.**

4. **Safety release switches.** When the brake pedal is depressed, the cruise control system is disengaged through use of an electrical or vacuum switch, usually located on the brake pedal bracket. Both electrical and vacuum releases are used to be certain that the cruise control system is released, even in the event of failure of one of the release switches.

☠ **WARNING**

Most vehicle manufacturers warn in the owner manual that cruise control should not be used when it is raining or if the roads are slippery. Cruise control systems operate the throttle and, if the drive wheels start to hydroplane, the vehicle slows, causing the cruise control unit to accelerate the engine. When the engine is accelerated and the drive wheels are on a slippery road surface, vehicle stability will be lost and might possibly cause a crash.

CRUISE CONTROL OPERATION A typical cruise control system can be set only if the vehicle speed is 30 mph or more. In a noncomputer-operated system, the transducer contains a low-speed electrical switch that closes when the speed-sensing section of the transducer senses a speed exceeding the minimum engagement speed.

NOTE: Toyota-built vehicles do not retain the set speed in memory if the vehicle speed drops below 25 mph (40 km/h). The driver is required to set the desired speed again. This is normal operation and not a fault with the cruise control system.

When the set button is depressed on the cruise control, solenoid values on the servo unit allow engine vacuum to be applied to one side of the diaphragm, which is attached to the

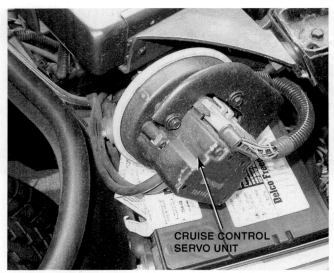

FIGURE 40–1 This cruise control servo unit has an electrical connection with wires that go to the cruise control module or the vehicle computer, depending on the vehicle. The vacuum hoses supply engine manifold vacuum to the rubber diaphragm that moves the throttle linkage to maintain the preset speed.

 TECH TIP

Bump Problems

Cruise control problem diagnosis can involve a complex series of checks and tests. The troubleshooting procedures vary among manufacturers (and year), so a technician should always consult a service manual for the exact vehicle being serviced. However, every cruise control system uses a brake safety switch and, if the vehicle has manual transmission, a clutch safety switch. The purpose of these safety switches is to ensure that the cruise control system is disabled if the brakes or the clutch is applied. Some systems use redundant brake pedal safety switches, one electrical to cut off power to the system and the other a vacuum switch used to bleed vacuum from the actuating unit.

If the cruise control "cuts out" or disengages itself while traveling over bumpy roads, the most common cause is a misadjusted brake (and/or clutch) safety switch(es). Often, a simple readjustment of these safety switches will cure the intermittent cruise control disengagement problems.

CAUTION: Always follow the manufacturer's recommended safety switch adjustment procedures. If the brake safety switch(es) is misadjusted, it could keep pressure applied to the master brake cylinder, resulting in severe damage to the braking system.

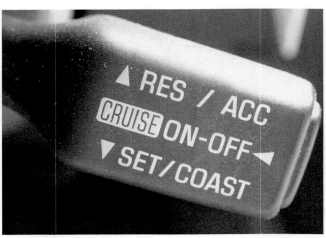

FIGURE 40–2 A cruise control used on a Toyota/Lexus.

throttle plate of the engine through a cable or linkage. The servo unit usually contains two solenoids to control the opening and closing of the throttle.

- One solenoid opens and closes to control the passage, which allows engine vacuum to be applied to the diaphragm of the servo unit, increasing the throttle opening.
- One solenoid bleeds air back into the sensor chamber to reduce the throttle opening.

The throttle position (TP) sensor or a position sensor, inside the servo unit, sends the throttle position information to the cruise control module.

Most computer-controlled cruise control systems use the vehicle's speed sensor input to the engine control computer for speed reference. Computer-controlled cruise control units also use servo units for throttle control, control switches for driver control of cruise control functions, and both electrical and vacuum brake pedal release switches. ● SEE FIGURE 40–3.

TROUBLESHOOTING CRUISE CONTROL

Cruise control system troubleshooting is usually performed using the step-by-step procedure as specified by the vehicle manufacturer.

The usual steps in the diagnosis of an inoperative or incorrectly operating mechanical-type cruise control include the following:

STEP 1 Use a factory or enhanced scan tool to retrieve any cruise control diagnostic trouble codes (DTCs). Perform bidirectional testing if possible using the scan tool.

STEP 2 Check that the cruise control fuse is not blown and that the cruise control dash light is on when the cruise control is turned on.

STEP 3 Check for proper operation of the brake and/or clutch switch.

FIGURE 40-3 Circuit diagram of a typical electronic cruise control system.

STEP 4 Inspect the throttle cable and linkage between the sensor unit and the throttle plate for proper operation without binding or sticking.

STEP 5 Check the vacuum hoses for cracks or other faults.

STEP 6 Check that the vacuum servo unit (if equipped), using a hand-operated vacuum pump, can hold vacuum without leaking.

STEP 7 Check the servo solenoids for proper operation, including a resistance measurement check.

 TECH TIP

Check the Third Brake Light

On many General Motors vehicles, the cruise control will not work if the third brake light is out. This third brake light is called the **center high-mounted stop light (CHMSL).** Always check the brake lights first if the cruise control does not work on a General Motors vehicle.

FIGURE 40–4 A typical electronic throttle with the protective covers removed.

FIGURE 40–5 A trailer icon lights on the dash of this Cadillac when the transmission trailer towing mode is selected.

ELECTRONIC THROTTLE CRUISE CONTROL

PARTS AND OPERATION   Many vehicles are equipped with an **electronic throttle control (ETC)** system. Vehicles equipped with such a system do not use throttle actuators for the cruise control. The ETC system operates the throttle under all engine operating conditions. An ETC system uses a DC electric motor to move the throttle plate that is spring loaded to a partially open position. The motor actually closes the throttle at idle against spring pressure. The spring-loaded position is the default position and results in a high idle speed. The powertrain control module (PCM) uses the input signals from the *accelerator pedal position (APP)* sensor to determine the desired throttle position. The PCM then commands the throttle to the necessary position of the throttle plate. ● SEE FIGURE 40–4.

The cruise control on a vehicle equipped with an electronic throttle control system consists of a switch to set the desired speed. The PCM receives the vehicle speed information from the vehicle speed (VS) sensor and uses the ETC system to maintain the set speed.

DIAGNOSIS AND SERVICE   Any fault in the APP sensor or ETC system will disable the cruise control function. Always follow the specified troubleshooting procedures, which will usually include the use of a scan tool to properly diagnose the ETC system.

RADAR CRUISE CONTROL

PURPOSE AND FUNCTION   The purpose of a radar cruise control system is to give the driver more control over the vehicle by keeping an assured clear distance behind the vehicle in front. If the vehicle in front slows, the radar cruise

TECH TIP

Use Trailer Tow Mode

Some customers complain that when using cruise control while driving in hilly or mountainous areas that the speed of the vehicle will sometimes go 5 to 8 mph below the set speed. The automatic transmission then downshifts, the engine speed increases, and the vehicle returns to the set speed. To help avoid the slowdown and rapid acceleration, ask the customer to select the trailer towing position. When this mode is selected, the automatic transmission downshifts almost as soon as the vehicle speed starts to decrease. This results in a smoother operation and is less noticeable to both the driver and passengers. ● SEE FIGURE 40–5.

control detects the slowing vehicle and automatically reduces the speed of the vehicle to keep a safe distance. Then if the vehicle speeds up, the radar cruise control also allows the vehicle to increase to the preset speed. This makes driving in congested areas easier and less tiring.

TERMINOLOGY   Depending on the manufacturer, radar cruise control is also referred to as the following:

- **Adaptive cruise control** (Audi, Ford, General Motors, and Hyundai)
- **Dynamic cruise control** (BMW, Toyota/Lexus)
- **Active cruise control** (Mini Cooper, BMW)
- **Autonomous cruise control** (Mercedes)

It uses forward-looking radar to sense the distance to the vehicle in front and maintains an assured clear distance. This type of cruise control system works within the following conditions.

1. Speeds from 20 to 100 mph (30 to 161 km/h)
2. Designed to detect objects as far away as 500 ft (150 m)

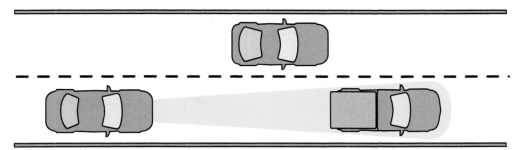

FIGURE 40–6 Radar cruise control uses sensors to keep the distance the same even when traffic slows ahead.

FIGURE 40–7 Most radar cruise control systems use radar, both long and short range. Some systems use optical or infrared cameras to detect objects.

 FREQUENTLY ASKED QUESTION

Will Radar Cruise Control Set Off My Radar Detector?

It is doubtful. The radar used for radar cruise control systems operates on frequencies that are not detectable by police radar detector units. Cruise control radar works on the following frequencies.

- 76 to 77 GHz (long range)
- 24 GHz (short range)

The frequencies used for the various types of police radar include:

- X-band: 8 to 12 GHz
- K-band: 24 GHz
- Ka-band: 33 to 36 GHz

The only time there may be interference is when the radar cruise control, as part of a precollision system, starts to use short-range radar (SRR) in the 24 GHz frequency. This would trigger the radar detector but would be an unlikely event and just before a possible collision with a vehicle coming toward you.

The cruise control system is able to sense both distance and relative speed. ● **SEE FIGURE 40–6.**

PARTS AND OPERATION   Radar cruise control systems use long-range radar (LRR) to detect faraway objects in front of the moving vehicle. Some systems use a short-range radar (SRR) and/or infrared (IR) or optical cameras to detect distances

for when the distance between the moving vehicle and another vehicle in front is reduced. ● **SEE FIGURE 40–7.**

The radar frequencies include:

- 76 to 77 GHz (long-range radar)
- 24 GHz (short-range radar)

PRECOLLISION SYSTEM

PURPOSE AND FUNCTION   The purpose and function of a precollision system is to monitor the road ahead and prepare to avoid a collision, and to protect the driver and passengers. A precollision system uses components of the following systems.

1. The long-range and short-range radar or detection systems used by a radar cruise control system to detect objects in front of the vehicle
2. Antilock brake system (ABS)
3. Adaptive (radar) cruise control
4. Brake assist system

TERMINOLOGY   Precollision systems can be called various names depending on the make of the vehicle. Some commonly used names for a precollision or precrash system include:

- **Ford/Lincoln:** Collision Warning with Brake Support
- **Honda/Acura:** Collision Mitigation Brake System (CMBS)
- **Mercedes-Benz:** Pre-Safe or Attention Assist
- **Toyota/Lexus:** Pre-Collision System (PCS) or Advanced Pre-Collision System (APCS)

FIGURE 40–8 A precollision system is designed to prevent a collision first, and then interacts to prepare for a collision if needed.

- **General Motors:** Pre-Collision System (PCS)
- **Volvo:** Collision Warning with Brake Support or Collision Warning with Brake Assist

OPERATION   The system functions by monitoring objects in front of the vehicle and can act to avoid a collision by the following actions.

- Sounds an alarm
- Flashes a warning lamp
- Applies the brakes and brings the vehicle to a full stop (if needed), if the driver does not react
  - ● **SEE FIGURE 40–8.**

If the system is unable to prevent a collision, the system will perform the following actions.

1. Apply the brakes full force to reduce vehicle speed as much as possible
2. Close all windows and the sunroof to prevent the occupants from being ejected from the vehicle
3. Move the seats to an upright position
4. Raise the headrest (if electrically powered)
5. Pretension the seat belts
6. Airbags and seat belt tensioners function as designed during the collision

HEATED REAR WINDOW DEFOGGERS

PARTS AND OPERATION   An electrically heated rear window defogger system uses an electrical grid baked on the glass that warms the glass to about 85°F (29°C) and clears it of fog or frost. The rear window is also called a **backlight.** The rear window defogger system is controlled by a driver-operated switch and a timer relay. ● **SEE FIGURE 40–9.**

The timer relay is necessary because the window grid can draw up to 30 A, and continued operation would put a strain on the battery and the charging system. Generally, the timer relay permits current to flow through the rear window grid for only 10 minutes. If the window is still not clear of fog after 10 minutes, the driver

FIGURE 40–9 A switch and relay control current through the heating grid of a rear window defogger.

can turn the defogger on again, but after the first 10 minutes any additional defogger operation is limited to 5 minutes.

PRECAUTION   Electric grid-type rear window defoggers can be damaged easily by careless cleaning or scraping of the inside of the rear window glass. Short, broken sections of the rear window grid can be repaired using a special epoxy-based electrically conductive material. If more than one section is damaged or if the damaged grid length is greater than approximately 1.5 in. (3.8 cm), a replacement rear window glass may be required to restore proper defogger operation.

The electrical current through the grids depends, in part, on the temperature of the conductor grids. As the temperature decreases, the resistance of the grids decreases and the current flow increases, helping to warm the rear glass. As the temperature of the glass increases, the resistance of the conductor grids increases and the current flow decreases. Therefore, the defogger system tends to self-regulate the electrical current requirements to match the need for defogging.

NOTE: Some vehicles use the wire grid of the rear window defogger as the radio antenna. Therefore, if the grid is damaged, radio reception can also be affected.

HEATED REAR WINDOW DEFOGGER DIAGNOSIS
Troubleshooting a nonfunctioning rear window defogger unit involves using a test light or a voltmeter to check for voltage to

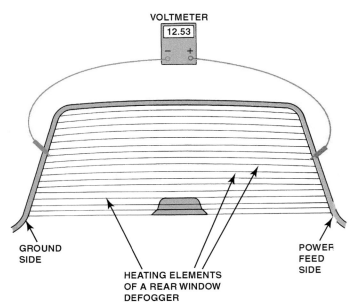

VOLTMETER

12.53

GROUND
SIDE

POWER
FEED
SIDE

HEATING ELEMENTS
OF A REAR WINDOW
DEFOGGER

FIGURE 40–10 A rear window defogger electrical grid can be tested using a voltmeter to check for a decreasing voltage as the meter lead is moved from the power side toward the ground side. As the voltmeter positive lead is moved along the grid (on the inside of the vehicle), the voltmeter reading should steadily decrease as the meter approaches the ground side of the grid.

TECH TIP

The Breath Test

It is difficult to test for the proper operation of all grids of a rear window defogger unless the rear window happens to be covered with fog. A common trick that works is to turn on the rear defogger and exhale onto the outside of the rear window glass. In a manner similar to that of people cleaning eyeglasses with their breath, this procedure produces a temporary fog on the glass so that all sections of the rear grids can quickly be checked for proper operation.

the grid. If no voltage is present at the rear window, check for voltage at the switch and relay timer assembly. A poor ground connection on the opposite side of the grid from the power side can also cause the rear defogger not to operate. Because most defogger circuits use an indicator light switch and a relay timer, it is possible to have the indicator light on, even if the wires are disconnected at the rear window grid. A voltmeter can be used to test the operation of the rear window defogger grid. ● SEE **FIGURE 40–10.**

With the negative test terminal attached to a good body ground, carefully probe the grid conductors. There should be a decreasing voltage reading as the probe is

MASKING
TAPE

FIGURE 40–11 The typical repair material contains conductive silver-filled polymer, which dries in 10 minutes and is usable in 30 minutes.

moved from the power ("hot") side of the grid toward the ground side of the grid.

REPAIR OR REPLACEMENT If there is a broken grid wire, it can be repaired using an electrically conductive substance available in a repair kit.

Most vehicle manufacturers recommend that grid wire less than 2 in. (5 cm) long be repaired. If a bad section is longer than 2 in., the entire rear window will need to be replaced. ● SEE **FIGURE 40–11.**

HEATED MIRRORS

PURPOSE AND FUNCTION The purpose and function of heated outside mirrors is to heat the surface of the mirror, which evaporates moisture on the surface. The heat helps keep ice and fog off the mirrors, to allow for better driver visibility.

PARTS AND OPERATION Heated outside mirrors are often tied into the same electrical circuit as the rear window defogger. Therefore, when the rear defogger is turned on, the heating grid on the backside of the mirror is also turned on. Some vehicles use a switch for each mirror.

DIAGNOSIS The first step in any diagnosis procedure is to verify the customer concern. Check the owner's manual or service information for the proper method to use to turn on the heated mirrors.

NOTE: Heated mirrors are not designed to melt snow or a thick layer of ice.

If a fault has been detected, follow service information instructions for the exact procedure to follow. If the mirror itself is found to be defective, it is usually replaced as an assembly instead of being repaired.

HOMELINK GARAGE DOOR OPENER

OPERATION HomeLink is a device installed in many new vehicles that duplicates the radio-frequency code of the original garage door opener. The frequency range which HomeLink is able to operate is 288 to 418 MHz. The typical vehicle garage door opening system has three buttons that can be used to operate one or more of the following devices.

1. Garage doors equipped with a radio transmitter electric opener
2. Gates
3. Entry door locks
4. Lighting or small appliances

The devices include both fixed-frequency devices, usually older units, and rolling (encrypted) code devices. ● **SEE FIGURE 40–12.**

PROGRAMMING A VEHICLE GARAGE DOOR OPENER

When a vehicle is purchased, it must be programmed using the transmitter for the garage door opener or other device.

NOTE: The HomeLink garage door opening controller can only be programmed by using a transmitter. If an automatic garage door system does not have a remote transmitter, HomeLink cannot be programmed.

Normally, the customer is responsible for programming the HomeLink to the garage door opener. However, some customers may find that help is needed from the service department. The steps that are usually involved in programming HomeLink in the vehicle to the garage door opener are as follows:

STEP 1 Unplug the garage door opener during programming to prevent it from being cycled on and off, which could damage the motor.

STEP 2 Check that the frequency of the handheld transmitter is between 288 and 418 MHz.

FIGURE 40–12 Typical HomeLink garage door opener buttons. Notice that three different units can be controlled from the vehicle using the HomeLink system.

STEP 3 Install new batteries in the transmitter to be assured of a strong signal being transmitted to the HomeLink module in the vehicle.

STEP 4 Turn the ignition on, engine off (KOEO).

STEP 5 While holding the transmitter 4 to 6 in. away from the HomeLink button, press and hold the HomeLink button while pressing and releasing the handheld transmitter every two seconds. Continue pressing and releasing the transmitter until the indicator light near the HomeLink button changes from slow blink to a rapid flash.

STEP 6 Verify that the vehicle garage door system (HomeLink) button has been programmed. Press and hold the garage door button. If the indicator light blinks rapidly for two seconds and then comes on steady, the system has been successfully programmed using a rolling code design. If the indicator light is on steady, then it has been successfully programmed to a fixed-frequency device.

DIAGNOSIS AND SERVICE If a fault occurs with the HomeLink system, first verify that the garage door opener is functioning correctly. Also, check if the garage door opener remote control is capable of operating the door. Repair the garage door opener system as needed.

If the problem still exists, attempt reprogramming the HomeLink vehicle system, being sure that the remote has a newly purchased battery.

POWER WINDOWS

SWITCHES AND CONTROLS Power windows use electric motors to raise and lower door glass. They can be operated by both a **master control switch** located beside the driver and additional **independent switches** for each electric window. Some power window systems use a **lockout switch** located on the driver's controls to prevent operation of the power windows from the independent switches. Power windows are designed to operate only with the ignition switch in the on (run) position, although some manufacturers use a time delay for accessory power after the ignition switch is turned off. This feature permits the driver and passengers an opportunity to close all windows or operate other accessories for about 10 minutes or until a vehicle door is opened after the ignition has been turned off. This feature is often called *retained accessory power*.

POWER WINDOW MOTORS Most power window systems use **permanent magnet (PM) electric motors.** It is possible to run a PM motor in the reverse direction simply by reversing the polarity of the two wires going to the motor. Most power window motors do not require that the motor be grounded to the body (door) of the vehicle. The ground for all the power windows is most often centralized near the driver's master control switch. The up-and-down motion of the individual window motors is controlled by double-pole, double-throw

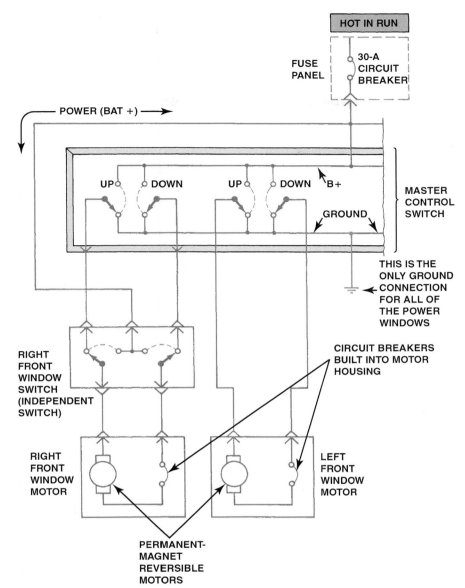

FIGURE 40–13 A typical power window circuit using PM motors. Control of the direction of window operation is achieved by directing the polarity of the current through the nongrounded motors. The only ground for the entire system is located at the master control (driver's side) switch assembly.

(DPDT) switches. These DPDT switches have five contacts and permit battery voltage to be applied to the power window motor, as well as reverse the polarity and direction of the motor. Each motor is protected by an electronic circuit breaker. These circuit breakers are built into the motor assembly and are not a separate replaceable part. ● SEE FIGURE 40–13.

The power window motors rotate a mechanism called a **window regulator.** The window regulator is attached to the door glass and controls opening and closing of the glass. Door glass adjustments such as glass tilt and upper and lower stops are usually the same for both power and manual windows. ● SEE FIGURE 40–14.

AUTO DOWN/UP FEATURES Many power windows are equipped with an auto down feature that allows windows to be lowered all of the way if the control switch is moved to a detent or

held down for longer than 0.3 second. The window will then move down all the way to the bottom, and then the motor stops.

Many vehicles are equipped with the auto up feature that allows the driver to raise the driver's side or all windows in some cases, with just one push of the button. A sensor in the window motor circuit measures the current through the motor. The circuit is opened if the window touches an object, such as a hand or finger. When the window reaches the top or hits an object, the current through the window motor increases. When the upper limit amperage draw is reached, the motor circuit is opened and the window either stops or reverses. Most newer power windows use network communications modules to operate the power windows, and the switches are simply voltage signals to the module which supplies current to the individual window motors. ● SEE FIGURE 40–15.

FIGURE 40–14 An electric motor and a regulator assembly raise and lower the glass on a power window.

TECH TIP

Programming Auto Down Power Windows

Many vehicles are equipped with automatic operation that can cause the window to go all the way down (or up) if the switch is depressed beyond a certain point or held for a fraction of a second. Sometimes this feature is lost if the battery in the vehicle has been disconnected. Although this programming procedure can vary depending on the make and model, many times the window(s) can be reprogrammed without using a scan tool by simply depressing and holding the down button for 10 seconds. If the vehicle is equipped with an auto up feature, repeat the procedure by holding the button up for 10 seconds. Always check exact service information for the vehicle being serviced.

FIGURE 40–15 A master power window control panel with the buttons and the cover removed.

TROUBLESHOOTING POWER WINDOWS

Before troubleshooting a power window problem, check for proper operation of all power windows. Check service information for the exact procedure to follow. In a newer system, a scan tool can be used to perform the following:

- Check for B (body) or U (network) diagnostic trouble codes (DTCs)
- Operate the power windows using the bidirectional control feature
- Relearn or program the operation of the power windows after a battery disconnect

For older systems, if one of the **control wires** that run from the independent switch to the master switch is cut (open), the power window may operate in only one direction. The window may go down but not up, or vice versa. However, if one of the **direction wires** that run from the independent switch to the motor is cut

(open), the window will not operate in either direction. The direction wires and the motor must be electrically connected to permit operation and change of direction of the electric lift motor in the door.

1. If *both* rear door windows fail to operate from the independent switches, check the operation of the window lockout (if the vehicle is so equipped) and the master control switch.

2. If one window can move in one direction only, check for continuity in the control wires (wires between the independent control switch and the master control switch).

3. If *all* windows fail to work or fail to work occasionally, check, clean, and tighten the ground wire(s) located either behind the driver's interior door panel or under the dash on the driver's side. A defective fuse or circuit breaker could also cause all the windows to fail to operate.

4. If one window fails to operate in both directions, the problem could be a defective window lift motor. The window could be

stuck in the track of the door, which could cause the circuit breaker built into the motor to open the circuit to protect the wiring, switches, and motor from damage. To check for a stuck door glass, attempt to move (even slightly) the door glass up and down, forward and back, and side to side. If the window glass can move slightly in all directions, the power window motor should be able to at least move the glass.

5. Always refer to and follow service information when diagnosing power window circuits.

POWER SEATS

PARTS AND OPERATION   A typical power-operated seat includes a reversible electric motor and a transmission assembly that may have three solenoids and six *drive cables* that turn the six seat adjusters. A six-way power seat offers seat movement forward and backward, plus seat cushion movement up and down at the front and the rear. The drive cables are similar to speedometer cables because they rotate inside a cable housing and connect the power output of the seat transmission to a gear or screw jack assembly that moves the seat. ● **SEE FIGURE 40–16.**

A **screw jack assembly** is often called a *gear nut*. It is used to move the front or back of the seat cushion up and down.

A **rubber coupling**, usually located between the electric motor and the transmission, and prevents electric motor damage in the event of a jammed seat. This coupling is designed to prevent motor damage.

Most power seats use a permanent magnet motor that can be reversed by simply reversing the polarity of the current sent to the motor by the seat switch. ● **SEE FIGURE 40–17.**

POWER SEAT MOTOR(S)   Most PM motors have a built-in circuit breaker or PTC circuit protector to protect the motor from overheating. Many Ford power seat motors use three separate armatures inside one large permanent magnet field housing. Some power seats use a series-wound electric motor with two separate field coils, one field coil for each direction of rotation. This type of power seat motor typically uses a relay to control the direction of current from the seat switch to the corresponding field coil of the seat motor. This type of power seat can be identified by the "click" heard when the seat switch is changed from up to down or front to back, or vice versa. The click is the sound of the relay switching the field coil current. Some power seats use as many as eight separate PM motors that operate all functions of the seat, including headrest height, seat length, and side bolsters, in addition to the usual six-way power seat functions.

NOTE: Some power seats use a small air pump to inflate a bag (or bags) in the lower part of the back of the seat, called the lumbar, because it supports the lumbar section of the spine. The lumbar section of the seat can also be changed, using a lever or knob that the driver can move to change the seat section for the lower back.

MEMORY SEAT   Memory seats use a potentiometer to sense the position of the seat. The seat position can be programmed into the body control module (BCM) or memory seat module and stored by position number 1, 2, or 3. The driver pushes the desired button and the seat moves to the stored position. ● **SEE FIGURE 40–18** on page 475.

On some vehicles, the memory seat position is also programmed into the remote keyless entry key fob.

FIGURE 40–16 A power seat uses electric motors under the seat, which drive cables that extend to operate screw jacks (up and down) or gears to move the seat forward and back.

FIGURE 40-17 A typical power seat circuit diagram. Notice that each motor has a built-in electronic (solid-state) PTC circuit protector. The seat control switch can change the direction in which the motor(s) runs by reversing the direction in which the current flows through the motor.

 TECH TIP

Easy Exit Seat Programming

Some vehicles are equipped with memory seats that allow the seat to move rearward when the ignition is turned off to allow easy exit from the vehicle. Vehicles equipped with this feature include an *exit/entry* button that is used to program the desired exit/entry position of the seat for each of two drivers.

If the vehicle is not equipped with this feature and only one driver primarily uses the vehicle, the second memory position can be programmed for easy exit and entry. Simply set position 1 to the desired seat position and position 2 to the entry/exit position. Then, when exiting the vehicle, press memory 2 to allow easy exit and easy entry the next time. Press memory 1 when in the vehicle to return the seat memory to the desired driving position.

TROUBLESHOOTING POWER SEATS Power seats are usually wired from the fuse panel so they can be operated without having to turn the ignition switch to on (run). If a power

seat does not operate or make any noise, the circuit breaker (or fuse, if the vehicle is so equipped) should be checked first. The steps usually include:

STEP 1 Check service information for the exact procedure to follow when diagnosing power seats. If the seat relay clicks, the circuit breaker is functioning, but the relay or electric motor may be defective.

STEP 2 Remove the screws or clips that retain the controls to the inner door panel or seat and check for voltage at the seat control.

STEP 3 Check the ground connection(s) at the transmission and clutch control solenoids (if equipped). The solenoids must be properly grounded to the vehicle body for the power seat circuit to operate.

If the power seat motor runs but does not move the seat, the most likely fault is a worn or defective rubber clutch sleeve between the electric seat motor and the transmission.

If the seat relay clicks but the seat motor does not operate, the problem is usually a defective seat motor or defective wiring between the motor and the relay. If the power seat uses a motor relay, the motor has a double reverse-wound field for reversing the motor direction. This type of electric motor must be properly grounded. Permanent magnet motors do not require grounding for operation.

FIGURE 40–18 A typical memory seat module showing the three-wire potentiometer used to determine seat position.

 TECH TIP

What Every Driver Should Know About Power Seats

Power seats use an electric motor or motors to move the position of the seat. These electric motors turn small cables that operate mechanisms that move the seat. *Never* place rags, newspapers, or any other object under a power seat. Even ice scrapers can get caught between moving parts of the seat and can often cause serious damage or jamming of the power seat.

NOTE: Power seats are often difficult to service because of restricted working room. If the entire seat cannot be removed from the vehicle because the track bolts are covered, attempt to remove the seat from the top of the power seat assembly. These bolts are almost always accessible regardless of seat position.

ELECTRICALLY HEATED SEATS

PARTS AND OPERATION Heated seats use electric heating elements in the seat bottom, as well as in the seat back in many vehicles. The heating element is designed to warm the seat and/or back of the seat to about 100°F (37°C) or close to normal body temperature (98.6°F). Many heated seats also include a high-position or a variable temperature setting, so the temperature of the seats can therefore be as high as 110°F (44°C).

A temperature sensor in the seat cushion is used to regulate the temperature. The sensor is a variable resistor which changes with temperature and is used as an input signal to a heated seat control module. The heated seat module uses the seat temperature input, as well as the input from the high-low (or variable) temperature control, to turn the current on or off to the heating element in the seat. Some vehicles are equipped with heated seats in both the rear and the front seats.

FIGURE 40–19 The heating element of a heated seat is a replaceable part, but service requires that the upholstery be removed. The yellow part is the seat foam material and the entire white cover is the replaceable heating element. This is then covered by the seat material.

DIAGNOSIS AND SERVICE   When diagnosing a heated seat concern, start by verifying that the switch is in the on position and that the temperature of the seat is below normal body temperature. Using service information, check for power and ground at the control module and to the heating element in the seat. Most vehicle manufacturers recommend replacing the entire heating element if it is defective. ● **SEE FIGURE 40–19.**

HEATED AND COOLED SEATS

PARTS AND OPERATION   Most electrically heated and cooled seats use a **thermoelectric device (TED)** located under the seat cushion and seat back. The thermoelectric device consists of positive and negative connections between two ceramic plates. Each ceramic plate has copper fins to allow the transfer of heat to air passing over the device and directed into the seat cushion. The thermoelectric device uses the **Peltier effect,** named after the inventor, Jean C. A. Peltier, a French clockmaker. When electrical current flows through the module, one side is heated and the other side is cooled. Reversing the polarity of the current changes which side is heated. ● **SEE FIGURE 40–20.**

Most vehicles equipped with heated and cooled seats use two modules per seat, one for the seat cushion and one for the seat back. When the heated and cooled seats are turned on, air is forced through a filter and then through the thermoelectric modules. The air is then directed through passages in the foam of the seat cushion and seat back. Each thermoelectric device has a temperature sensor, called a thermistor. The control module uses sensors to determine the temperature of the fins in the thermoelectric device so the controller can maintain the set temperature.

FIGURE 40–20 A Peltier effect device is capable of heating or cooling, depending on the polarity of the applied current.

🔧 **TECH TIP**

Check the Seat Filter

Heated and cooled seats often use a filter to trap dirt and debris to help keep the air passages clean. If a customer complains of a slow heating or cooling of the seat, check the air filter and replace or clean as necessary. Check service information for the exact location of the seat filter and for instructions on how to remove and/or replace it.

DIAGNOSIS AND SERVICE   The first step in any diagnosis is to verify that the heated-cooled seat system is not functioning. Check the owner's manual or service information for the specified procedures. If the system works partially, check the air filter, usually located under the seat for each thermoelectric device. A partially clogged filter can restrict airflow and reduce the heating or cooling effect. If the system control indicator light is not on or the system does not work at all, check for power and ground at the thermoelectric devices. Always follow the vehicle manufacturer's recommended diagnosis and service procedures.

HEATED STEERING WHEEL

PARTS INVOLVED   A heated steering wheel usually consists of the following components.

- Steering wheel with a built-in heater in the rim
- Heated steering wheel control switch
- Heated steering wheel control module

OPERATION   When the steering wheel heater control switch is turned on, a signal is sent to the control module and electrical current flows through the heating element in the rim of the steering wheel. ● **SEE FIGURE 40–21.**

FIGURE 40-21 The heated steering wheel is controlled by a switch on the steering wheel in this vehicle.

The system remains on until the ignition switch is turned off or the driver turns off the control switch. The temperature of the steering wheel is usually calibrated to stay at about 90°F (32°C), and it requires three to four minutes to reach that temperature depending on the outside temperature.

DIAGNOSIS AND SERVICE Diagnosis of a heated steering wheel starts with verifying that the heated steering wheel is not working as designed.

NOTE: Most heated steering wheels do not work if the temperature inside the vehicle is about 90°F (32°C) or higher.

If the heated steering wheel is not working, follow the service information testing procedures which would include a check of the following:

1. Check the heated steering wheel control switch for proper operation. This is usually done by checking for voltage at both terminals of the switch. If voltage is available at only one of the two terminals of the switch and the switch has been turned on and off, an open (defective) switch is indicated.

2. Check for voltage and ground at the terminals leading to the heating element. If voltage is available at the heating element and the ground has less than 0.2-volt drop to a good chassis ground, the heating element is defective. The entire steering wheel has to be replaced if the element is defective.

Always follow the vehicle manufacturer's recommended diagnosis and testing procedures.

ADJUSTABLE PEDALS

PURPOSE AND FUNCTION **Adjustable pedals**, also called **electric adjustable pedals (EAP)**, place the brake pedal and the accelerator pedal on movable brackets that are motor operated. A typical adjustable pedal system includes the following components.

FIGURE 40-22 A typical adjustable pedal assembly. Both the accelerator and the brake pedal can be moved forward and rearward by using the adjustable pedal position switch.

 TECH TIP

Check the Remote

The memory function may be programmed to a particular key fob remote, which would command the adjustable pedals to move to the position set in memory. Always check both remote settings before attempting to repair a problem that may not be a problem.

- **Adjustable pedal position switch.** Allows the driver to position the pedals
- **Adjustable pedal assembly.** Includes the motor, threaded adjustment rods, and a pedal position sensor
  - **SEE FIGURE 40-22.**

The position of the pedals, as well as the position of the seat system, is usually included as part of the memory seat function and can be set for two or more drivers.

DIAGNOSIS AND SERVICE The first step when there is a customer concern about the functioning of the adjustable pedals is to verify that the unit is not working as designed. Check the owner manual or service information for the proper operation. Follow the vehicle manufacturer's recommended troubleshooting procedure. Many diagnostic procedures include the use of a factory scan tool with bidirectional control capabilities to test this system.

REAL WORLD FIX

The Case of the Haunted Mirrors

The owner complained that while driving, either one or the other outside mirror would fold in without any button being depressed. Unable to verify the customer concern, the service technician looked at the owner's manual to find out exactly how the mirrors were supposed to work. In the manual, a caution statement said that if the mirror is electrically folded inward and then manually pushed out, the mirror will not lock into position. The power folding mirrors must be electrically cycled outward, using the mirror switches to lock them in position. After cycling both mirrors inward and outward electrically, the problem was solved. ● **SEE FIGURES 40–23 AND 40–24.**

FIGURE 40–23 Electrically folded mirror in the folded position.

FIGURE 40–24 The electric mirror control is located on the driver's side door panel on this Cadillac Escalade.

OUTSIDE FOLDING MIRRORS

Mirrors that can be electrically folded inward are a popular feature, especially on larger sport utility vehicles. A control inside is used to fold both mirrors inward when needed, such as when entering a garage or close parking spot. For diagnosis and servicing of outside folding mirrors, check service information for details.

ELECTRIC POWER DOOR LOCKS

Electric power door locks use a permanent magnet (PM) reversible motor to lock or unlock all vehicle door locks from a control switch or switches.

The electric motor uses a built-in circuit breaker and operates the lock-activating rod. PM reversible motors do not require grounding because, as with power windows, the motor control is determined by the polarity of the current through the two motor wires. ● **SEE FIGURE 40–25.**

FIGURE 40–25 A typical electric power door lock circuit diagram. Note that the control circuit is protected by a fuse, whereas the power circuit is protected by a circuit breaker. As with the operation of power windows, power door locks typically use reversible permanent magnet (PM) nongrounded electric motors. These motors are geared mechanically to the lock-unlock mechanism.

Some two-door vehicles do *not* use a power door lock relay because the current flow for only two PM motors can be handled through the door lock switches. However, most four-door vehicles and vans with power locks on rear and side doors use a relay to control the current flow necessary to operate four or more power door lock motors. The door lock relay is controlled by the door lock switch and is commonly the location of the one and only *ground* connection for the entire door lock circuit.

KEYLESS ENTRY

Even though some Ford vehicles use a keypad located on the outside of the door, most keyless entry systems use a wireless transmitter built into the key or key fob. A **key fob** is a decorative tab or item on a key chain. ● **SEE FIGURE 40–26.**

The transmitter broadcasts a signal that is received by the electronic control module, which is generally mounted in the trunk or under the instrument panel. ● **SEE FIGURE 40–27.**

The electronic control unit sends a voltage signal to the door lock actuator(s) located in the doors. Generally, if the transmitter unlock button is depressed once, only the driver's door is unlocked. If the unlock button is depressed twice, then all doors unlock.

ROLLING CODE RESET PROCEDURE Many keyless remote systems use a rolling code type of transmitter and receiver. In a conventional system, the transmitter emits a certain fixed frequency, which is received by the vehicle control module. This single frequency can be intercepted and rebroadcast to open the vehicle.

A rolling code type of transmitter emits a different frequency every time the transmitter button is depressed and then rolls over to another frequency so that it cannot be intercepted. Both the transmitter and the receiver must be kept in synchronized order so that the remote will function correctly.

FIGURE 40–26 A key fob remote with the cover removed showing the replaceable battery.

FIGURE 40–27 A typical vehicle showing the location of the various components of the remote keyless entry system.

If the transmitter is depressed when it is out of range from the vehicle, the proper frequency may not be recognized by the receiver, which did not roll over to the new frequency when the transmitter was depressed. If the transmitter does not work, try to resynchronize the transmitter to the receiver by depressing and holding both the lock and the unlock button for 10 seconds when within range of the receiver.

KEYLESS ENTRY DIAGNOSIS A small battery powers the transmitter, and a weak battery is a common cause of remote power locks failing to operate. If the keyless entry system fails to operate after the transmitter battery has been replaced, check the following items.

- Mechanical binding in the door lock
- Low-vehicle battery voltage
- Blown fuse
- Open circuit to the control module
- Defective control module
- Defective transmitter

PROGRAMMING A NEW REMOTE If a new or additional remote transmitter is to be used, it must be programmed to the vehicle. The programming procedure varies and may require the use of a scan tool. Check service information for the exact procedure to follow. ● **SEE CHART 40–1.**

PROGRAMMING A NEW REMOTE

MAKE/MODEL	NOTES	PROCEDURE
Acura RSX MDX 3.2TL RSX **Honda** Accord Civic CR-V Odyssey	Be careful to maintain the time limits between steps. Ensure that the hood, tailgate, and doors are closed. Aim the transmitter at the receiver in the power window master switch. The keyless receiver can store up to three codes. If a fourth code is stored, the first code that was input will be erased.	1. Turn the ignition on. 2. Within 1 to 4 seconds, press the lock or unlock button. 3. Within 1 to 4 seconds, turn the ignition off. 4. Repeat steps 1 through 3 two more times. 5. Within 1 to 4 seconds, turn the ignition on (fourth time). 6. Within 1 to 4 seconds, press the lock or unlock button. 7. The door lock actuators should cycle. 8. Press the lock or unlock button a second time within 1 to 4 seconds to store the code. 9. For additional transmitters, repeat steps 6, 7, and 8. 10. Turn the ignition off and remove the key to exit programming mode.
BMW All models with transmitter in key head	Up to four transmitters can be programmed. All transmitters to be programmed must be programmed at the same time. This procedure erases all learned transmitters.	1. Use the vehicle key to unlock the central locking system. 2. Enter the vehicle and close all doors. 3. Put the key in the ignition and switch the ignition switch to position 1 and then back to off, within 5 seconds. 4. Press and hold key button 2 (arrow button). 5. While holding button 2, press button 1 (BMW logo) three times within 10 seconds. 6. Release button 2. 7. The locks will cycle to confirm programming. 8. Repeat steps 4 through 7 within 30 seconds for any additional transmitters. 9. After 30 seconds with no button pressed the programming mode will exit.
Buick Rendezvous Lucerne LaCrosse **Chevrolet** Blazer Impala Monte Carlo Uplander	A scan tool is required. A total of four transmitters can be learned. All transmitters to be programmed must be programmed at the same time. Activating program mode erases previously learned codes.	1. Install a scan tool and access the BCM Special Functions, Lift Gate Module (LGM), or Module Setup; Program Key Fobs menu. 2. Press the start key on the scan tool. 3. Press and hold both the lock and unlock buttons on the first transmitter. Within 5 to 10 seconds the scan tool will report that the transmitter is programmed. 4. Repeat step 3 to program up to four transmitters. 5. Turn off and remove the scan tool to exit programming mode.

CHART 40–1

Remote keyless programming steps for popular vehicles. Procedures may also apply to similar vehicles by the same manufacturer. Always refer to service information for specific vehicles.

PROGRAMMING A NEW REMOTE

MAKE/MODEL	NOTES	PROCEDURE
Pontiac Grand Prix Montana **Saturn** Relay		
Buick Rainier **Cadillac** Escalade **Chevrolet** C/K Trucks Suburban Tahoe Trailblazer **Saab** 9-7 (some)	Fobs can also be programmed with a scan tool. All fobs to be used must be programmed at the same time. The first fob learned will be fob 1 and the second that is learned will be fob 2.	1. Enter the vehicle and close all the doors. 2. Insert the key into the ignition lock. 3. Press and hold the door unlock switch, then turn the ignition on, off, then release the unlock switch. 4. The door locks will cycle one time to confirm programming mode. 5. Press and hold the lock and unlock buttons on the key fob for about 15 seconds. 6. The locks will cycle once when the fob has been learned. 7. Repeat steps 5 and 6 to program any additional fobs. 8. Turn the ignition key to run, to exit the programming mode.
Cadillac CTS SRX	All programmed key fobs will be erased. All transmitters to be programmed must be relearned during this procedure. Up to four fobs can be programmed. The first to be learned will be fob 1 and the second to be learned will be fob 2.	1. Install the scan tool and turn the ignition on. 2. Navigate to the Body, RFA (or RCDLR), Special Functions; Program Key Fobs menu. 3. Follow the directions on the scan tool to program the transmitters.
Cadillac Deville Seville **Pontiac** Bonneville Grand Am	Up to four transmitters can be programmed All fobs to be used must be programmed at the same time. The first fob learned will be fob 1 and the second that is learned will be fob 2.	1. Install a scan tool and turn on the ignition. 2. Navigate to the Remote Function Actuator (RFA) module: Special function, Program Key Fobs menu to activate program mode. 3. The doors will lock and unlock to indicate programming mode. 4. Press and hold the lock and unlock buttons on the fob. The door locks will cycle to indicate the fob has been learned. 5. Repeat step 4 for any additional fobs. 6. To exit programming mode, turn off and remove the scan tool.
Cadillac STS XLR **Chevrolet** Corvette	A scan tool can also be used to program key fobs. This procedure will take 30 minutes to complete. All programmed key fobs will be erased. All transmitters to be programmed must be relearned during this procedure. Up to four fobs can be programmed. The first to be learned will be fob 1 and the second to be learned will be fob 2.	1. Start with the vehicle off. 2. Place the fob to be learned in the console pocket with the buttons facing forward. 3. Insert the vehicle key into the driver's door lock cylinder and cycle the key five times within 5 seconds. The DIC will display "OFF/ACC TO LEARN." 4. Press the OFF/ACC part of the ignition button. 5. The DIC will display "WAIT 10 MINUTES," then count down to zero, 1 minute at a time. The display will change to "OFF/ACC TO LEARN." 6. Repeat steps 4 and 5 two more times for a total of 30 minutes. 7. When the DIC displays "OFF/ACC TO LEARN" for the fourth time, press the OFF/ACC button again; the DIC will display "READY FOR FOB 1." 8. When fob 1 has been learned, a beep will be heard and the DIC will display "READY FOR FOB 2." 9. Remove fob 1 from the pocket and insert fob 2. A beep will be heard when that fob has been learned. 10. Repeat steps 8 and 9 for additional fobs. 11. To exit programming, press the OFF/ACC portion of the ignition button.

CHART 40-1 (CONTINUED)

CONTINUED

MAKE/MODEL	NOTES	PROCEDURE
Chevrolet Cavalier Equinox Malibu SSR S/T Trucks **Saab** 9–7 (some models) **Saturn** Vue	A scan tool is required. Up to four transmitters can be programmed. On vehicles with personalization features, the transmitters are numbered 1 and 2. The first transmitter programmed will become driver 1 and the second will become driver 2.	1. Install the scan tool and navigate to the BCM or RFA menu, Special Functions; select Program Key Fobs. 2. Select Add/Replace Key Fob to program a new or additional fob. 3. Select Clear Memory and Program All Fobs option to replace all fobs or to recode driver 1 and driver 2 fobs. 4. Follow the scan tool instructions to complete the programming.
Chevrolet Venture van GM "U" vans	All fobs to be used must be programmed at the same time. Up to four transmitters can be programmed. If the BCM displays DTCs in step 5, they may have to be resolved before programming can continue.	1. With the ignition key out of the ignition, remove the BCM PRGRM fuse from the passenger side fuse block. 2. Enter the vehicle and close all doors. 3. Insert the key and turn the ignition to ACC. 4. The seat belt indicator and chime will activate two, three, or four times, depending on the type of BCM in the vehicle. 5. Turn the key off and then back to ACC within 1 second. If the BCM has any stored DTCs, they will be displayed by the chime and belt indicator at this time. 6. Open and close any door. The chime will sound to indicate programming mode. 7. Press and hold the fob lock and unlock buttons for about 14 seconds. The BCM will sound the chime when the fob has been learned. 8. Repeat step 7 for up to four total transmitters. 9. After programming, remove the ignition key and replace the BCM PRGRM fuse.
Chrysler PT Cruiser Concorde	A scan tool is required if there are no functioning transmitters. Maximum of four transmitters can be programmed. Programming mode will exit after 30 seconds.	1. Turn ignition to run and wait until the chimes stop or fasten seat belt to cancel chimes. 2. Using any original working transmitter, press and hold the unlock button for 4 to 10 seconds. 3. While holding the unlock button, press the panic button for 1 second. Chime will sound to indicate programming mode is ready. 4. Press and release any button on the transmitters to be programmed. All transmitters should be programmed at this time, including previously programmed transmitters. A chime will sound after each programming success. 5. Turn the ignition off to exit programming.
Chrysler Sebring Town and Country **Dodge** Pickup R1500 Stratus R/T Caravan Dakota Durango	Programming is by scan tool or by "customer learn" mode. If no functioning transmitter is available the scan tool must be used. Programming mode will cancel 60 seconds after the chimes stop in step 3. All programming must be completed within this time period.	CUSTOMER LEARN MODE 1. Turn ignition to run and wait until the chimes stop or fasten seat belt to cancel chimes. 2. Using any original working transmitter, press and hold the unlock button for 4 to 10 seconds. 3. While holding the unlock button, press the panic button for 1 second. Chime sound for 3 seconds to indicate programming mode is ready. 4. Press lock and unlock buttons together for 1 second and release.

CHART 40–1 (CONTINUED)

PROGRAMMING A NEW REMOTE

MAKE/MODEL	NOTES	PROCEDURE
Jeep Liberty	Up to four transmitters can be stored.	5. Press and release any button on the same transmitter. If the code is successfully learned, the chime will sound. 6. To program additional transmitters, repeat steps 4 and 5. 7. Turn ignition off.
Ford Focus	Maximum of four transmitters can be programmed. All transmitters must be programmed at the same time. Programming mode will exit if: • The engine is started. • The 10 second time expires. • Four transmitters are programmed.	1. Enter vehicle. Close all doors. 2. Turn ignition switch from ACC to run, four times within 6 seconds. 3. Turn ignition switch to off. 4. Chime will sound to indicate ready to program. 5. Within 10 seconds press any button on the transmitter. A chime will indicate code accepted. 6. To program additional transmitters repeat step 5.
Ford F150 Pickup Explorer Taurus Escape Expedition Excursion Ranger **Lincoln** Navigator **Mazda** B2300 **Mercury** Mountaineer Mariner	All transmitters must be programmed at the same time. RKE transmitters can also be programmed using a scan tool. Programming mode will exit if: • The key is turned off. • The 20 second time expires. • The maximum number of transmitters are programmed (depends on vehicle).	1. Electrically unlock the doors using the RKE transmitter of door lock switch. 2. Turn the key from off to run, eight times within 10 seconds, ending with the key on. The module will lock and unlock the doors, indicating program mode. 3. Within 20 seconds press any button on the transmitter. The locks will cycle to indicate the transmitter has been learned. 4. Repeat step 3 for any additional RKE transmitters. 5. Turn the key off to exit the programming mode.
Infiniti G20 G35 FX35 Q45	Key fob codes can be checked and changed using a scan tool. If step 2 is done too fast, the system will not enter programming mode. Up to five key fobs can be registered. If more than five are input, the oldest ID code will be overwritten. It is possible to enter the same key code into all five memories. This can be used to erase the ID code of a fob that has been lost, if needed.	1. Enter the vehicle and close all doors. 2. Insert and then completely remove key from the ignition cylinder more than six times within 10 seconds. Hazard warning lamps will flash twice to indicate programming mode is active. 3. Insert the key and turn the ignition to ACC. 4. Press any key on the fob once. The hazard warning lamps will flash twice to indicate that the code is stored. 5. To end programming mode open the driver's door. If programming additional fobs proceed to step 6 (don't open the driver's door). 6. To enter an additional code unlock and then lock the driver's door using the window main switch. 7. Press any button on the additional fob. The hazard warning lamps will flash twice to indicate the code is learned. 8. To enter another key fob code repeat steps 6 and 7. 9. Open the driver's door to end programming mode.

CHART 40-1 (CONTINUED)

CONTINUED

PROGRAMMING A NEW REMOTE

MAKE/MODEL	NOTES	PROCEDURE
Lincoln Town Car Continental Navigator **Mercury** Grand Marquis	All RKE transmitters must be programmed at the same time. RKE transmitters can also be programmed using a scan tool. Additional transmitters must be programmed within 7 seconds or the process will have to be repeated from step 1. Wait at least 20 seconds after exiting programming mode to test the RKE transmitters.	1. Turn the key from off to run, eight times (four times for early systems) within 10 seconds, ending with the key on. The module will lock and unlock the doors, indicating program mode. 2. Press any button on the transmitter. Doors will lock and unlock to confirm programming success. 3. To program additional repeat step 2 within 7 seconds. 4. Wait 7 seconds or turn the key off to exit programming mode.
Mazda 5 6	Start with the key out and all doors, trunk lid, and lift gate closed. A total of three transmitters can be programmed. Previously programmed transmitters may be erased during this procedure. If possible, program all desired transmitters at the same time.	1. Open the driver's side door. 2. Put the key in the ignition lock and turn the ignition to on and back to lock, three times (ending in the lock position with the key in the ignition). 3. Close and then open the driver's door three times, ending with the door open. The door locks will lock and unlock. 4. Push the unlock button on the transmitter twice. Door locks will lock and unlock to verify programming is okay. 5. Repeat step 4 for any additional transmitter to be programmed. 6. When the last transmitter to be programmed has been learned, push the unlock button twice on that transmitter to exit programming mode.
Mazda 626 Millenia Protégé	Start with the key out and all doors, trunk lid, and lift gate closed. A total of three transmitters can be programmed. Previously programmed transmitters may be erased during this procedure. If possible, program all desired transmitters at the same time. Protégé will cycle locks instead of sounding a buzzer.	1. Open the driver's side door. 2. Put the key in the ignition lock and turn the ignition to on and back to lock, three times, then remove the key. 3. Close and then open the driver's door three times, ending with the door open. A buzzer will sound from the CPU. 4. Push any button on the transmitter twice. Buzzer will sound once to verify programming is okay. 5. Repeat step 4 for any additional transmitter to be programmed. 6. When the last transmitter to be programmed has been learned, push any button twice on that transmitter. The buzzer will sound twice to exit programming mode.
Nissan Altima Armada Frontier Maxima Murano Titan	Key fob codes can also be checked and changed using a scan tool. If step 2 is done too fast, the system will not enter programming mode. Up to five key fobs can be registered. If more than five are input, the oldest ID code will be overwritten. It is possible to enter the same key code into all five memories. This can be used to erase the ID code of a fob that has been lost, if needed.	1. Enter the vehicle and close all doors. 2. Insert and then completely remove key from the ignition cylinder more than six times within 10 seconds. Hazard warning lamps will flash twice to indicate programming mode is active. 3. Insert the key and turn the ignition to ACC. 4. Press any key on the fob once. The hazard warning lamps will flash twice to indicate that the code is stored. 5. To end programming mode, open the driver's door. If programming additional fobs proceed to step 6 (don't open the driver's door). 6. To enter an additional code unlock and then lock the driver's door using the window main switch. 7. Press any button on the additional fob. The hazard warning lamps will flash twice to indicate the code is learned. 8. To enter another key fob code repeat steps 6 and 7. 9. Open the driver's door to end programming mode.

CHART 40–1 (CONTINUED)

MAKE/MODEL	NOTES	PROCEDURE

Pontiac
Vibe
Scion
xB
Toyota
Camry
Corolla
	Up to four transmitters can be programmed.
	
	If more than four transmitters are programmed, the oldest transmitter code will be overwritten.
	
	There are four programming modes:
	• Add mode: Used to program additional transmitters
	• Rewrite mode: Erases all previously programmed transmitters
	• Confirmation mode: Indicates how many transmitters are already programmed
	• Prohibition mode: Erases all learned codes and disables the wireless entry system
	
	In confirmation mode, if no codes are stored the door locks will cycle five times.
	
	Open any door to exit the programming mode.
		1. Enter the vehicle, key out of ignition, close all doors except the driver's door.
		2. Insert and remove the key from the ignition twice within 5 seconds.
		3. Close and open the driver's door twice within 40 seconds and then insert the key and remove it.
		4. Close and open the driver's door twice again, then insert the ignition key and close the door.
		5. Turn the key from lock to on and back to lock to select the programming mode:
		  • One time for add mode (go to step 6)
		  • Two times for rewrite mode (go to step 6)
		  • Three times for confirmation mode (go to step 10)
		  • Five times for prohibition mode (see step 11)
		6. Remove the key from the ignition.
		7. The doors will lock-unlock once for add mode or twice for rewrite mode.
		8. To program a transmitter, press lock and unlock buttons for 1.5 seconds and release; then within 3 seconds press either button for more than 1 second to confirm programming:
		  • One lock-unlock cycle indicates okay.
		  • Two lock-unlock cycles indicates not okay; repeat this step.
		9. Repeat step 8 to program additional transmitters.
		10. In confirmation mode the number of lock-unlock cycles will indicate the number of codes already stored and programming mode will exit. Example: Two cycles indicates two codes are stored.
		11. If prohibition mode is selected the locks will cycle five times and programming mode will exit.

Pontiac G6 **Saturn** Ion L300	A scan tool is used to program key fobs. Up to four transmitters can be programmed. If any key fob is programmed, all fobs must be programmed at the same time. On vehicles with personalization features, the transmitters are numbered 1 and 2. The first transmitter programmed will become driver 1 and the second will become driver 2.	1. Install the scan tool and navigate to the Program Key Fobs menu. 2. Select the number of fobs to be programmed. 3. Press and hold the lock and unlock buttons on the first fob to be programmed. The locks should cycle to indicate okay. NOTE: This fob becomes driver 1 key fob. 4. Repeat step 3 for the second fob. This fob becomes driver 2 key fob. 5. Repeat step 3 for any other key fobs to be programmed. 6. Turn off and remove the scan tool to exit programming.
Saab 9-2	Up to four transmitters can be programmed.	1. Sit in the driver's seat and close all doors. 2. Open and close the driver's door. 3. Turn the ignition switch from on to lock, 10 times within 15 seconds. The horn will chirp to indicate programming mode. 4. Open and close the driver's door. 5. Press any button on the fob to be programmed. 6. The horn will chirp two times to indicate that the transmitter has been learned. 7. Repeat steps 4, 5, and 6 for any additional transmitters. 8. To exit from programming mode remove the key from the ignition. The horn should chirp three times to confirm.

CHART 40-1 (CONTINUED)

CONTINUED

MAKE/MODEL	NOTES	PROCEDURE
Subaru Forester Impreza Legacy Outback Tribeca	A scan tool is used to program RKE codes. Up to four RKE transmitters can be registered. The eight-digit code is on the plastic bag of a new transmitter on the circuit board inside the transmitter.	1. Install the scan tool and navigate to the keyless transmitter ID registration menu. 2. Input the transmitter eight-digit ID number into the scan tool. 3. When the number is correct, press yes. 4. The scan tool will display "ID registration done" when the ID is programmed. 5. Follow the scan tool menus to program additional transmitters.

Toyota
Tundra
Sequoia
Lexus
GS 430
RX 300
	Up to four transmitters can be programmed.
	
	If more than four transmitters are programmed, the oldest transmitter code will be overwritten.
	
	There are four programming modes:
	• Add mode: Used to program additional transmitters
	• Rewrite mode: Erases all previously programmed transmitters
	• Confirmation mode: Indicates how many transmitters are already programmed
	• Prohibition mode: Erases all learned codes and disables the wireless entry system
	
	In confirmation mode, if no codes are stored the door locks will cycle five times.
	
	Open any door to exit the programming mode.
		1. Enter the vehicle, key out of ignition, close all doors except the driver's door.
		2. Insert and remove the key from the ignition key cylinder.
		3. Use the driver's door lock control switch to lock and unlock the doors five times, at about 1 second intervals.
		4. Close and open the driver's door.
		5. Use the driver's door lock control switch to lock and unlock the doors five times, at about 1 second intervals.
		6. Insert the ignition key.
		7. Turn the key from lock to on and back to lock to select the programming mode:
		  • One time for add mode (go to step 10)
		  • Two times for rewrite mode (go to step 10)
		  • Three times for confirmation mode (go to step 12)
		  • Five times for prohibition mode (see step 13)
		8. Remove the key from the ignition.
		9. The doors will lock-unlock once, twice, three times of five times to confirm the mode.
		10. To program a transmitter press lock and unlock buttons for 1.5 seconds and release; then within 3 seconds press either button for more than 1 second to confirm programming:
		  One lock-unlock cycle indicates okay.
		  Two lock-unlock cycles indicates not okay; repeat this step.
		11. Repeat step 10 to program additional transmitters.
		12. In confirmation mode the number of lock-unlock cycles will indicate the number of codes already stored and programming mode will exit. Example: Two cycles indicates two codes are stored.
		13. If prohibition mode is selected the locks will cycle five times and programming mode will exit.

CHART 40–1

Remote keyless programming steps for popular vehicles. Procedures may also apply to similar vehicles by the same manufacturer. Always refer to service information for specific vehicles.

ANTITHEFT SYSTEMS

PARTS AND OPERATION Antitheft devices flash lights or sound an alarm if the vehicle is broken into or vandalized. In addition to the alarm, some systems prevent the engine from starting by disabling the starter, ignition, or fuel system once the antitheft device is activated. Others permit the engine to start, but then disable it after several seconds. Switches in the doorjambs, trunk, and hood provide an input signal to the control module should an undesirable entry occur on a typical system. Some antitheft systems are more complex and also have electronic sensors that trigger the alarm if there is a change in battery current draw, a violent vehicle motion, or if glass is broken. These sensors also provide an input signal to the control module, which may be a separate antitheft unit or incorporated into the PCM or BCM. ● **SEE FIGURE 40–28** on page 360 for an example of a shock sensor used in an antitheft alarm system.

FIGURE 40–28 A shock sensor used in alarm and antitheft systems. If the vehicle is moved, the magnet will move relative to the coil, inducing a small voltage that will trigger the alarm.

ANTITHEFT SYSTEM DIAGNOSIS Most factory-installed antitheft systems are integrated with several other circuits to form a complex, multiple-circuit system. The major steps are as follows:

1. It is essential to have accurate diagrams, specifications, and test procedures for the specific model being serviced.

2. The easiest way to reduce circuit complexity is to use the wiring diagram to break the entire system into its subcircuits, then check only those related to the problem.

3. If any step indicates that a subcircuit is not complete, check the power source, ground, components, and wiring in that subcircuit.

Many systems use a computer chip in the plastic part of the key. Most systems are electronically regulated and have a self-diagnostic program. This self-diagnostic program is generally accessed and activated using a scan tool. Diagnostic and test procedures are similar as for any of the other electronic control systems used on the vehicle.

ANTITHEFT SYSTEM TESTING AND SERVICE Before performing any diagnostic checks, make sure that all of the following electrical devices function correctly.

- Parking and low-beam headlights
- Dome and courtesy lights
- Horn
- Electric door locks

Circuit information from these devices often provides basic inputs to the control module. If a problem is detected in any of these circuits, such as a missing signal or a signal that is out of range, the control module disables the antitheft system and may record a diagnostic trouble code (DTC).

If all of the previously mentioned devices are operational, check all the circuits leading to the antitheft control module. Make sure all switches are in their normal or off positions. Doorjamb switches complete the ground circuit when a door is opened. ● SEE FIGURE 40–29.

FIGURE 40–29 Door switches, which complete the ground circuit with the door open, are a common source of high resistance.

FIGURE 40–30 A special tool is needed to diagnose a General Motors VATS security system and special keys that contain a resistor pellet.

Frequently, corrosion that builds up on the switch contacts prevents the switch from operating properly. Conduct voltage drop tests to isolate faulty components and circuit problems. Repair as needed and retest to confirm that the system is operational. Follow procedures from the manufacturer to clear DTC records, and then run the self-diagnostic program to verify repairs. Some system diagnostic procedures specify the use of special testers. ● SEE FIGURE 40–30.

● SEE CHART 40–2 for programming procedures for selected vehicles.

KEY PROGRAMMING PROCEDURES

MAKE/MODEL	NOTES	PROCEDURES
Chrysler Pacifica Town and Country PT Cruiser Sebring 300 Some other models **Dodge** Caravan Durango Magnum Neon Pickup Stratus **Jeep** Liberty Grand Cherokee Some other models	Programming is by scan tool or by "customer learn" mode. Customer learn mode requires at least two functioning Sentry keys. If no functioning Sentry keys are available, the scan tool and the vehicle PIN number are required for programming. Both the immobilizer and RKE are programmed with this procedure. Only a blank key transponder can be programmed. Once programmed, the key cannot be used in another vehicle. The customer learn mode will exit after each key is programmed. The complete procedure must be completed for each key to be programmed. A total of eight keys can be programmed by the Sentry Key Remote Entry Module (four on some models).	**CUSTOMER LEARN MODE** 1. Using a blank Sentry key, cut the key to match the lock cylinder code. 2. Insert one of the two valid keys into the ignition and turn the ignition on. 3. After 3 seconds, but before 15 seconds expire, turn off the ignition and remove the key. 4. Within 15 seconds insert the second valid key and turn the ignition on. 5. Within 10 seconds a chime will sound and/or the indicator lamp will flash, indicating customer learn mode is active. 6. Within 60 seconds turn the ignition off, insert the blank Sentry key, and turn the ignition on. 7. After about 10 seconds a single chime will sound and the indicator lamp will stay on solid for about 3 seconds; this indicates the key has been programmed.
Ford Taurus Some other models **Lincoln** Some models **Mercury** Grand Marquis Milan Montego	This procedure requires two or more programmed keys. If two programmed keys are not available a scan tool must be used. Maximum of eight keys can be programmed. Repeat the complete procedure for each key to be learned. If the programming is not successful the antitheft indicator will flash and the vehicle will not start. Leave the key on for 30 seconds and then retry the procedure.	1. Using the first programmed key, turn the ignition from off to run. Leave the switch in run for at least 3 seconds but not more than 10 seconds. 2. Turn the switch to off. Within 10 seconds repeat step 1 with the second programmed key. 3. Turn the ignition switch off. 4. Within 20 seconds, insert the un-programmed key and turn the ignition switch from off to run. 5. After 3 seconds, attempt to start the vehicle. If the programming is successful the vehicle will start and the antitheft indicator will light for 3 seconds and go out.
Ford Crown Victoria Some other models	This procedure requires two or more programmed keys. If two programmed keys are not available a scan tool must be used. Maximum of eight keys can be programmed.	1. Using the first programmed key, turn the ignition from off to run. Leave the switch in run for 1 second. 2. Turn the switch to off. Within 5 seconds repeat step 1 with the second programmed key. 3. Turn the ignition switch off.

CHART 40-2

Immobilizer or vehicle theft deterrent key learn procedures for some popular vehicles.

KEY PROGRAMMING PROCEDURES

MAKE/MODEL	NOTES	PROCEDURES
	Repeat the complete procedure for each key to be learned. If the programming is not successful the antitheft indicator will flash and the vehicle will not start. Leave the key on for 30 seconds and then retry the procedure.	4. Within 10 seconds, insert the un-programmed key and turn the ignition switch from off to run. 5. After 1 second, attempt to start the vehicle. If the programming is successful the vehicle will start and the antitheft indicator will light for 3 seconds and go out.
General Motors Passkey Passkey II (except vehicles with BCM)	The Passkey decoder will learn the first pellet read when the decoder module is first installed. This learned value cannot be changed. A Passkey Interrogator special tool is needed to read key pellet resistance when replacing keys. The tool will read out a code number related to the pellet resistance. PELLET CODE / RESISTANCE 1 / 402 2 / 523 3 / 681 4 / 887 5 / 1,130 6 / 1,470 7 / 1,870 8 / 2,370 9 / 3,010 10 / 3,740 11 / 4,750 12 / 6,040 13 / 7,500 14 / 9,530 15 / 11,800	**NEW DECODER MODULE** 1. Install the new decoder module. 2. Insert the key and start the vehicle to program the pellet code into the new module. **DUPLICATE KEY** 1. Use the Interrogator tool to read the existing key code. 2. Obtain a key with the matching pellet code and cut the key to match the original key. **LOST KEY** 1. The Interrogator tool must be used to determine the stored code. 2. Cut a blank key so that the ignition can be turned. 3. Access the lock cylinder 2 wire connector and connect it to the Interrogator. 4. Alternately select each of the 15 code positions on the Interrogator until the vehicle starts. This is then the correct pellet code. 5. Obtain the correct coded key and cut it to fit.
General Motors Passkey II (vehicles with BCM)	On vehicles with a body control module (BCM) the Passkey II pellet code is stored in the BCM. The BCM can learn the pellet code of a replacement key using a scan tool or this procedure. Make sure that the battery is fully charged. If the learning procedure is not successful check the system for codes and repair.	1. Insert the key to be learned and turn the ignition on. Leave the switch on for 11 minutes. The security lamp will be on or flashing during this time. 2. When the security lamp goes off turn the ignition off for 30 seconds. 3. Repeat step 1 two more times. 4. Turn the ignition off for 30 seconds. 5. Attempt to start the vehicle. The vehicle should start and run if the learn is successful.
General Motors Passkey III Passkey III+	Quick-Learn requires at least one programmed master (black) key. Keys can be learned with a scan tool. If no programmed master key is available the 30 minute Auto Learn procedure must be used.	**QUICK LEARN** 1. Insert a programmed master key and turn on the ignition. 2. Turn the ignition off and remove the key. 3. Within 10 seconds insert the key to be learned and turn the ignition on. 4. The key is now programmed.

CHART 40-2 (CONTINUED)

CONTINUED

KEY PROGRAMMING PROCEDURES

MAKE/MODEL	NOTES	PROCEDURES
	Auto Learn procedure will erase all learned keys. Make sure that the battery is fully charged. On vehicles with a driver information center (DIC) a "STARTING DISABLED DUE TO THEFT" message will display during the 10 minute timer.	**30 MINUTE AUTO LEARN** 1. Insert the new master key and turn on the ignition. The security lamp should be on and then turn it off after 10 minutes. 2. Turn the ignition off for 5 seconds. 3. Repeat steps 1 and 2 two more times (30 minutes total). 4. From the off position turn on and start the vehicle. 5. The vehicle should start and run, indicating the key has been learned.
General Motors Passlock (early systems)	Passlock systems do not have coded keys. Replacement or new keys do not have to be learned. Early Passlock systems pass an "R" code to the instrument cluster and then the IPC sends a password on to the PCM. Perform this procedure if replacing the instrument cluster, lock cylinder, or PCM.	1. After parts are installed, attempt to start the vehicle. 2. The vehicle should start and stall. 3. Leave the key on and wait until the flashing theft lamp stays on steady. 4. Attempt to start the vehicle again. It should start and continue to run. 5. The theft lamp should flash for 10 seconds and then go out to indicate the password has been learned.
General Motors Passlock (later models)	Replacement or additional keys do not have to be learned. Programming is necessary if the Passlock sensor, BCM, or PCM has been replaced. A scan tool can also be used to program the Passlock system. ● **SEE FIGURE 40–31** on page 492.	1. Turn the ignition on and attempt to start the vehicle. 2. The vehicle will not start. Release the key to on. Wait about 10 minutes for the security lamp to go off. 3. Turn off the ignition for 5 seconds. 4. Repeat steps 1 through 3 two more times. 5. For a fourth time turn the key on and start the vehicle. The vehicle should start and run, indicating that the lock code has been learned.
Honda	A programmed key, scan tool, and password are required to program keys.	1. Connect the scan tool and navigate to the ADD and DELETE KEYS menu. 2. Follow the instructions on the scan tool to add or delete keys as needed.
Hyundai	A scan tool can be used to program keys. A special ID key is needed to program new or additional keys.	1. Using the ID key, turn the ignition on then off. 2. Using the key to be programmed, turn the ignition on then off. This will program the key. 3. Repeat step 2 for any additional keys.
Toyota Camry Land Cruiser Some other earlier models	Up to seven master (black) keys can be learned. An already learned master key must be used to initiate the procedure. Keys can also be programmed with a scan tool.	1. Insert a programmed master key into the ignition switch. 2. Within 15 seconds, press and release the accelerator pedal five times. 3. Within 20 seconds, press and release the brake pedal six times. 4. Remove the master key. 5. Within 10 seconds, insert the key to be programmed into the lock cylinder and press and release the accelerator pedal one time. 6. The security indicator should flash for about 1 minute and then go out to indicate that the key has been learned. 7. To program additional keys repeat steps 5 and 6 within 10 seconds.

CHART 40–2 (CONTINUED)

Immobilizer or vehicle theft deterrent key learn procedures for some popular vehicles.

KEY PROGRAMMING PROCEDURES

MAKE/MODEL	NOTES	PROCEDURES
Toyota Corolla Matrix Tacoma Sienna RAV4 Some other late models **Lexus** LS430 Some other models	Up to five keys can be learned. A scan tool should be used to register keys.	1. Insert a programmed master key into the ignition and turn the ignition on. 2. Install the scan tool and navigate to the IMMOBILIZER, TRANSP CODE REG. screen. Follow the instructions on the scan tool. 3. The security indicator will turn on. Within 20 seconds, remove the master key. 4. Within 10 seconds, insert the new key to be programmed. 5. The security indicator will blink for 60 seconds and then go off when the key is learned.

CHART 40-2 (CONTINUED)

ELECTRICAL ACCESSORY SYMPTOM GUIDE

Cruise Control Problem	Possible Causes and/or Solutions
Cruise (speed) control is inoperative.	1. Blown fuse 2. Defective or misadjusted electrical or vacuum safety switch near the brake pedal arm 3. Lack of engine vacuum to servo or transducer 4. Defective transducer; defective speed control switch
Cruise (speed) control speed is incorrect or variable.	1. Misadjusted activation cable 2. Defective or pinched vacuum hose 3. Misadjustment of transducer

Power Windows Problem	Possible Causes and/or Solutions
Power windows are inoperative.	1. Defective (blown) fuse (circuit breaker) 2. Defective relay (if used) 3. Poor ground for master control switch 4. Poor connections at switch(es) or motor(s) 5. Open circuit (usually near the master control switch) 6. Defective lockout switch
One power window is inoperative.	1. Defective motor; defective or open control switch 2. Open or loose wiring to the switch or the motor
Only one power window can be operated from the master switch.	1. Poor connection or open circuit in the control wire(s)

Power Seats Problem	Possible Causes and/or Solutions
Power seats are inoperative, no click or noise.	1. Defective circuit breaker 2. Poor ground at the switch or relay (if used) 3. Open in the wiring between the switch and relay (if used); defective switch 4. Defective solenoid(s) or wiring 5. Defective door switch
Power seats are inoperative, click is heard.	1. "Flex" in the cables from the motor(s) to check for motor operation (If flex is felt, the motor is trying to operate the gear nut or the screw jack.) 2. Binding or obstruction 3. Defective motor (The click is generally the relay sound.) 4. Defective solenoid(s) or wiring to the solenoid(s)
All power seat functions are operative except one.	1. Defective motor 2. Defective solenoid or wiring to the solenoid

CONTINUED

Electric Power Door Lock Problem	Possible Causes and/or Solutions	Rear Window Defogger Problem	Possible Causes and/or Solutions
Power door locks are inoperative.	1. Defective circuit breaker, fuse, or wiring to the switch or relay (if used) 2. Defective relay (if used); defective switch 3. Defective door lock solenoid or ground for solenoid (if solenoid operated) 4. Open in the wiring to the door lock solenoid or the motor 5. Mechanical obstruction of the door lock mechanism	Rear window defogger is inoperative.	1. Proper operation by performing breath test and/or voltmeter (Check at the power side of the rear window grid.); defective relay or timer assembly 2. Defective switch 3. Open ground connection at the rear window grid (● SEE FIGURE 40–32.) NOTE: If there is an open circuit (power side or ground side), the dash indicator light will still operate in most cases.
Only one door lock is inoperative.	1. Defective switch; poor ground on the solenoid (if solenoid operated) 2. Defective door lock solenoid or motor; poor electrical connection at the motor or solenoid	Rear window defogger cleans only a portion of the rear window.	1. Broken grid wire(s) or poor electrical connections at either the power side or the ground side of the wire grid

FIGURE 40–31 The Passlock series of General Motors security systems uses a conventional key. The magnet is located in the ignition lock cylinder and triggers the Hall-effect sensors.

FIGURE 40–32 Corrosion or faults at the junction between the wiring and the rear window electrical grid are the source of many rear window defogger problems. Many radios use the rear window defogger grid as an antenna so a fault here could cause radio reception problems.

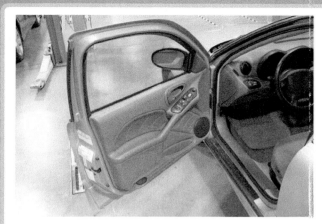

1 Looking at the door panel there appears to be no visible fasteners.

2 Gently prying at the edge of the light shows that it snaps in place and can be easily removed.

3 Under the red "door open" warning light is a fastener.

4 Another screw is found under the armrest.

5 A screw is removed from the bezel around the interior door handle.

6 The electric control panel is held in by clips.

CONTINUED ▶

7 Another screw is found after the control panel is removed.

8 The panel beside the outside mirror is removed by gently prying.

9 A gentle tug and the door panel is removed.

10 The sound-deadening material also acts as a moisture barrier and would need to be removed to gain access to the components inside the door.

11 Carefully inspect the door panel clips before reinstalling the door panel.

12 Align and press the door panel clips into the openings and reinstall all of the fasteners and components.

1. Most power windows and power door locks use a permanent magnet motor that has a built-in circuit breaker and is reversible. The control switches and relays direct the current through the motors.

2. The current flow through a rear window defogger is often self-regulating. As the temperature of the grid increases, its resistance increases, reducing current flow. Some rear window defoggers are also used as radio antennas.

3. Radar cruise control systems use many of the same components as the precollision system.

4. Remote keyless entry systems use a wireless transmitter built into the key fob to operate the power door lock.

5. Factory antitheft systems must function properly to allow the engine to crank and/or start.

REVIEW QUESTIONS

1. How do power door locks on a four-door vehicle function with only one ground wire connection?

2. How does a rear window defogger regulate how much current flows through the grids based on temperature?

3. What is the usual procedure to follow to resynchronize a remote keyless entry transmitter?

4. How do heated and cooled seats operate?

CHAPTER QUIZ

1. The owner of a vehicle equipped with cruise control complains that the cruise control often stops working when driving over rough or bumpy pavement. Technician A says the brake switch may be out of adjustment. Technician B says a defective servo unit is the most likely cause. Which technician is correct?
   a. Technician A only
   b. Technician B only
   c. Both Technicians A and B
   d. Neither Technician A nor B

2. Technician A says that the cruise control on a vehicle that uses an electronic throttle control (ETC) system uses a servo to move the throttle. Technician B says that the cruise control on a vehicle with ETC uses the APP sensor to set the speed. Which technician is correct?
   a. Technician A only
   b. Technician B only
   c. Both Technicians A and B
   d. Neither Technician A nor B

3. All power windows fail to operate from the independent switches but all power windows operate from the master switch. Technician A says the window lockout switch may be on. Technician B says the power window relay could be defective. Which technician is correct?
   a. Technician A only
   b. Technician B only
   c. Both Technicians A and B
   d. Neither Technician A nor B

4. Technician A says that a defective ground connection at the master control switch (driver's side) could cause the failure of all power windows. Technician B says that if *one* control wire is disconnected, all windows will fail to operate. Which technician is correct?
   a. Technician A only
   b. Technician B only
   c. Both Technicians A and B
   d. Neither Technician A nor B

5. A typical radar cruise control system uses _____.
   a. Long-range radar (LRR)
   b. Short-range radar (SRR)
   c. Electronic throttle control system to control vehicle speed
   d. All of the above

6. When checking the operation of a rear window defogger with a voltmeter, _____.
   a. The voltmeter should be set to read AC volts
   b. The voltmeter should read close to battery voltage anywhere along the grid
   c. Voltage should be available anytime at the power side of the grid because the control circuit just completes the ground side of the heater grid circuit
   d. The voltmeter should indicate decreasing voltage when the grid is tested across the width of the glass

7. PM motors used in power windows, mirrors, and seats can be reversed by _____.
   a. Sending current to a reversed field coil
   b. Reversing the polarity of the current to the motor
   c. Using a reverse relay circuit
   d. Using a relay and a two-way clutch

8. If only one power door lock is inoperative, a possible cause is a _____.
   a. Poor ground connection at the power door lock relay
   b. Defective door lock motor (or solenoid)
   c. Defective (open) circuit breaker for the power circuit
   d. Defective (open) fuse for the control circuit

9. A keyless remote control stops working. Technician A says the battery in the remote could be dead. Technician B says that the key fob may have to be resynchronized. Which technician is correct?
   a. Technician A only
   b. Technician B only
   c. Both Technicians A and B
   d. Neither Technician A nor B

10. Two technicians are discussing antitheft systems. Technician A says that some systems require a special key. Technician B says that some systems use a computer chip in the key. Which technician is correct?
    a. Technician A only
    b. Technician B only
    c. Both Technicians A and B
    d. Neither Technician A nor B

chapter 41
AUTOMATIC TEMPERATURE CONTROL SYSTEMS

OBJECTIVES: **After studying Chapter 41, the reader should be able to:** • Describe the purpose and function of automatic temperature control (ATC) systems. • Discuss the various types of sensors used in automatic temperature control systems. • Explain how the electrical and electronic part of the ATC system works. • Discuss how to diagnose the electrical ATC system faults.

KEY TERMS: • Ambient temperature sensor 498 • Air management system 500 • Automatic air conditioning system 497 • Automatic climatic control system 497 • Automatic temperature control (ATC) system 497 • Blend door 501 • Compressor speed sensor 499 • Discharge Air Temperature (DAT) Sensor 498 • Dual-position actuator 501 • Dual-Zone Systems 503 • Engine coolant temperature (ECT) sensor 499 • Evaporator temperature (EVT) sensor 498 • Infrared (IR) sensors 499 • In-vehicle temperature sensor 498 • Heating ventilation and air conditioning (HVAC) 497 • Mode door 502 • Negative temperature coefficient (NTC) 498 • Outside air temperature (OAT) sensor 498 • Pressure transducer 499 • Relative humidity (RH) sensor 500 • Smart motor 504 • Smart control head 504 • Sun Load sensor 498 • Temperature-blend door 502 • Temperature door 501 • Three-position actuator 501 • Variable-position actuator 501

AUTOMATIC TEMPERATURE CONTROL SYSTEM

PURPOSE AND FUNCTION The purpose and function of the **heating, ventilation, and air conditioning (HVAC)** system is to provide comfortable temperature and humidity levels inside the passenger compartment. Proper temperature control to enhance passenger comfort during heating should maintain air temperature at the foot level about 7°F to 14°F (4°C to 8°C) above the temperature around the upper body. This is accomplished by directing the heated airflow to the floor. During A/C operation, the upper body should be cooler, so the airflow is directed to the instrument panel registers. Most new HVAC systems use an electronic control head and some use electronic blower speed control, radiator fan, and control of compressor displacement.

OPERATION **Automatic Temperature Control (ATC) System** is also called **automatic climatic control system** or **automatic air conditioning system.** With an automatic temperature control system (ATC), the driver can turn the automatic controls on or off and select the desired temperature. The ATC will adjust the following:

- Blower speed
- Temperature door
- Air inlet door

FIGURE 41–1 The automatic climatic control display is part of the navigation screen on this vehicle.

- Mode door to achieve the proper temperature
- Control the air conditioning compressor operation
  ● **SEE FIGURE 41–1.**

SENSORS

PURPOSE AND FUNCTION The purpose of using sensors is to provide information to the HVAC controller regarding the conditions outside as well as inside the vehicle. Sensors provide data about the following:

- Different conditions that can affect temperature conditions within the vehicle.
- Temperature setting at the control head.
- Operation of the A/C system.
- Operation of the engine.

Pressure and temperature sensors are used to determine the condition in the air conditioning system so that the controller can

- Provide the most efficient use of energy.
- Provide a comfortable interior environment for the driver and passengers.
- Reduce the load on the engine and electrical system as much as possible to improve fuel economy.

OUTSIDE AIR TEMPERATURE SENSOR The **outside air temperature (OAT) sensor,** also called the **ambient temperature sensor,** measures outside air temperature and is often mounted at the radiator shroud or in the area behind the front grill. ● SEE FIGURE 41–2.

An ambient sensor is a thermistor that is mounted in the air stream passing through the front of the vehicle or the airflow entering the HVAC case.

- Most automotive thermistors are of the **negative temperature coefficient (NTC)** type; the resistance changes in an inverse or negative relationship with temperature.
- The resistance is low when the temperature is high.
- This sensor is used to determine the outside air temperature that is displayed on the dash.
  ● SEE FIGURE 41–3.

IN-VEHICLE TEMPERATURE SENSOR The **in-vehicle temperature sensor** is often mounted behind the instrument panel, and a set of holes or a small grill allows air to pass

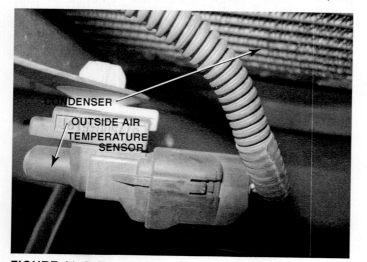

FIGURE 41–2 The outside air temperature sensor is mounted on the radiator core support in front of the A/C condenser on this vehicle.

FIGURE 41–3 The outside air temperature in displayed on the navigation screen on this vehicle and uses the information from the outside air temperature sensor.

by it. Air from the blower motor passes through the venturi of the aspirator and pulls in-vehicle air past the thermistor. This tube is called an aspirator tube and is connected to the blower housing. Blower operation produces airflow through the aspirator and past the sensor.● SEE FIGURE 41–4.

DISCHARGE AIR TEMPERATURE SENSOR The **discharge air temperature (DAT)** sensor is used to measure the temperature of the air leaving the dash vents.

- This discharge air temperature can be used to determine the proper temperature position or control compressor output.
- This sensor reading is used by the controller, which compares the discharge temperature reading with the temperature set by the driver. The control module calculates the temperature difference and automatically adjusts the HVAC system to minimize this temperature difference.

EVAPORATOR TEMPERATURE SENSOR The **evaporator temperature (EVT) sensor** is used to measure the air temperature leaving the evaporator. Evaporator air temperature can be used to determine the proper temperature position or control compressor output. The long probe of this sensor passes between the evaporator fins. It provides an evaporator temperature input to the HVAC controller.

SUN LOAD SENSOR The **sun load sensor** (also called a *solar sensor*) is normally mounted on top of the instrument panel and is used to measure radiant heat load that might cause an increase of the in-vehicle temperature. Bright sunshine provides a signal to the Electronic Control Module (ECM) that things are going to get hotter. Sun load sensors are photodiodes that change their electrical conductivity based on the level of sunlight striking the sensor.

FIGURE 41–4 The airflow from the blower causes airflow to flow past the in-vehicle temperature sensor.

A typical sun load sensor uses a 5-volt operating voltage and produces an output signal voltage based on the intensity of the light.

- Dark = 0.3 volts
- Bright sunshine = 3.0 volts
  - ● **SEE FIGURE 41–5.**

INFRARED SENSORS **Infrared (IR) sensors** are mounted in the control head or overhead in the headliner. They monitor the surface temperature of the head and chest area of the driver and passenger. The system will adjust the temperature and position of the airflow depending on the temperature they measure and the settings on the control head. The detector

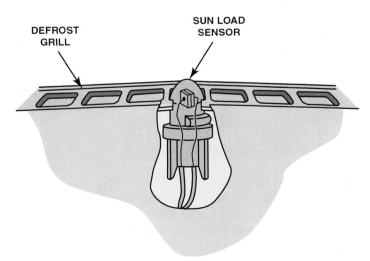

FIGURE 41–5 Sun load sensors are usually located at the top of the instrument panel.

does not emit an infrared beam but instead measures the infrared rays that are emitted from the person's body.

COMPRESSOR SPEED SENSOR The air conditioning (A/C) **compressor speed sensor,** also called a *lock* or *belt lock* sensor, is used so the ECM will know if the compressor is running, and by comparing the compressor and engine speed signals, the ECM can determine if the compressor clutch or drive belt is slipping excessively. It prevents a locked-up compressor from destroying the engine drive belt, which, in turn, can cause engine overheating or loss of power steering. If the ECM detects an excessive speed differential for more than a few seconds, it will turn the compressor off. The sensor can be either a magnetic type or a Hall-effect sensor. Check service information for details about the sensor for the vehicle being serviced.

ENGINE COOLANT TEMPERATURE SENSOR The **engine coolant temperature (ECT) sensor** is a thermistor and measures the temperature of the engine coolant and is usually located near the engine thermostat. The ECT sensor is used to keep the system from turning on the heater before the coolant is warmed up and is often called *cold engine lockout*. ● **SEE FIGURE 41–6.**

PRESSURE TRANSDUCERS A **pressure transducer** can be used in the low- and/or high-pressure refrigerant line. The transducer converts the system pressure into an electrical signal that allows the ECM to monitor pressure. The pressure signal can be used by the controller to

- Cycle the compressor to prevent evaporator freeze-up
- Change orifice tube size
- Change the compressor displacement

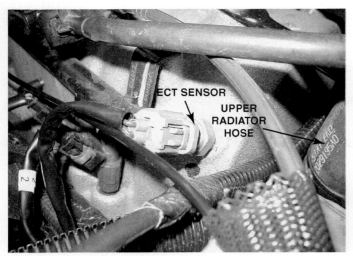

FIGURE 41-6 The engine coolant temperature sensor is usually located near the engine thermostat so it can accurately measure the temperature of the coolant.

FIGURE 41-7 Some automatic HVAC system use the information from the factory navigation system to fine tune the interior temperature and airflow needs based on location and the direction of travel.

- Shut off the compressor or speedup cooling fan operation because of high pressures
- Prevent compressor operation if the refrigerant level is low or empty

The pressures of the refrigerant systems can be checked by looking at the scan tool scan data of a factory or factory-level scan tool. ● SEE CHART 41-1 for some sample pressures and what they could indicate.

AIR QUALITY SENSORS Some systems use an *air quality sensor*, which detects hydrocarbons (HC) or ozone (O_3). HC can come from vehicle engine exhaust or decaying animal material and often produces offensive odors. Ozone is an irritant to the respiratory system. When the system detects an air quality issue, it automatically switches to using mostly inside air, about 80%, and reduces the amount of outside air entering the system to about 20% from the normal 80% level. This reduces the amount of outside air that is being brought into the passenger compartment until the system detects healthy outside air.

LOW SIDE PRESSURE	HIGH SIDE PRESSURE	CONDITION
25–35 PSI	170–200 PSI	Normal operation
Low	Low	Low refrigerant charge level
Low	High	Restriction in high-side line
High	High	System is overcharged.
High	Low	Restriction in the low-side line

CHART 41-1

Sample refrigerant system pressures and possible causes as shown from the pressure sensors and displayed on a scan tool. Check service information for the exact procedures to follow if the pressures are not correct.

RELATIVE HUMIDITY SENSOR A few vehicles use a **relative humidity (RH) sensor** to determine the level of in-vehicle humidity. High RH increases the cooling load. A relative humidity sensor uses the capacitance change of a polymer thin film capacitor to detect the relative amount of moisture in the air. A dielectric polymer layer absorbs water molecules through a thin metal electrode and causes capacitance change proportional to relative humidity. The thin polymer layer reacts very fast, usually in less than 5 seconds to 90% of the final value of relative humidity. The sensor responds to the full range from 0% to 100% relative humidity. The output of the sensor is sent to the HVAC controller, which uses the information to control the air inlet door and the air conditioning compressor operation to achieve the desired level of humidity (20% to 40%) in the passenger compartment.

GPS SENSOR A few vehicles that are equipped with a global positioning system (GPS) for navigation will have a sun position strategy that tracks the angle of the sunlight entering the vehicle. Cooler in-vehicle temperatures are required if the vehicle is positioned so sunlight enters through the windshield or side windows. ● SEE FIGURE 41-7.

AIRFLOW CONTROL

NEED FOR AIRFLOW CONTROL The system that controls the airflow to the passenger compartment is called the **air management system** or *air distribution system*. Air flows into the housing (case) that contains the evaporator and heater core from two possible inlets.

1. **Outside air,** often called *fresh air*
2. **Inside air,** usually called *recirculation* (recirc)

AIRFLOW CONTROL DOORS

From the case, the air can travel to one or more of three possible outlets. Airflow is usually controlled by three or more doors. Air flow inside the case can travel to one or more of three possible outlets.

The doors control:

- Air inlet to select outside or inside air inlet (often called the *recirculation* or *inlet* door)
- Temperature/blend to adjust air temperature (often just called the **blend door** or **temperature door**)
- Mode door to select air discharge location (direct air to the defrosters, the floor, or to the dash vents).
- **SEE FIGURE 41-8.**

A multispeed blower is included in this system to force air through the HVAC case when the vehicle is moving at low speeds or to increase the airflow at any speed.

CONTROLLING AIRFLOW

The amount or volume of HVAC air is controlled by blower speed. Higher speeds move more air. The inlet and outlet directions of the airflow and the discharge air temperature are controlled by swinging, sliding, or rotating doors. Most systems use a door (flap) that swings about 45° to 90°.

The duct system can be divided into three major sections:

1. *air inlet*
2. *plenum,* where the cold and hot air are mixed, and
3. *air distribution.*

Most doors are very simple and require little maintenance. A temperature-blend door is positioned at any place between the stops, wherever needed to produce the proper air temperature. Reducing the HVAC assembly size usually reduces the weight. Several designs of doors include:

- Sliding mode door (also called a *rolling door).*
- Some of these door designs roll up, somewhat like a window shade, and unroll to block a passage.
- Another design uses a *rotary door.* This pan-shaped door has openings at the side and edge, and the door rotates about 100° to one of four different positions. Each position directs airflow to the desired outlet(s).

FIGURE 41-8 The three major portions of the A/C and heat system are air inlet, plenum, and air distribution. The shaded portions show the paths of the four control doors.

ACTUATORS

PURPOSE AND FUNCTION

HVAC actuators are electric or mechanical devices that move doors to provide the needed airflow at the correct time and location. Actuators include:

- Electric motors that operate the air/temperature doors, also called *flaps.*
- Feedback circuits that provide position information to the HVAC controller.

TYPES OF ACTUATORS

An actuator is a part that moves the vanes or valves. Actuators used in air conditioning systems are either electric or vacuum operated and include three different types.

1. **Dual-Position Actuator.** A **dual-position actuator** is able to move either open or closed. An example of this type of actuator is the recirculation door, which can be either open or closed.

2. **Three-Position Actuator.** A **three-position actuator** is able to provide three air door positions, such as the bi-level door, which could allow defrost only, floor only, or a mixture of the two.

3. **Variable-Position Actuator.** A **variable-position actuator** is capable of positioning a valve in any position. All variable position actuators use a *feedback potentiometer*, which is used by the controller to detect the actual position of the door or valve.
- **SEE FIGURE 41-9.**

ELECTRIC ACTUATOR MOTORS

Electric actuator motors are used to move air doors. Electric door actuators can be either continuous-position or two-position units (open or closed). Variable-position actuators can stop anywhere in their range and need a feedback circuit so the ECM will know their position. The temperature-blend door is operated by an

FIGURE 41-9 Three electric actuators can be easily seen on this demonstration unit. However, accessing these actuators in a vehicle can be difficult.

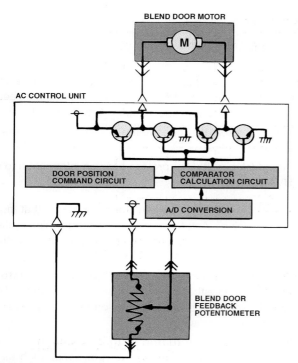

FIGURE 41–10 The feedback circuit signals the AC control unit with the blend door position.

electric servomotor (continuous-position actuator) that can move the door to any position called for to produce an air mix of the desired temperature. Some systems have the ability to count the actuator motor commutator segments so it is able to determine how far the motor revolves. A small current-flow reduction occurs as the space between the commutator bars passes under the brushes of a DC motor. This system needs no feedback circuit, but a calibration procedure must be performed if a motor or HVAC controller is replaced. Newer systems have an output from the ECM to each of the controlled actuators or outputs. ● **SEE FIGURE 41–10.**

- **Temperature Control Actuators.** The heater core is placed downstream from the evaporator in the airflow so that air can be routed either through or around it and one or two doors are used to control this airflow. This door is usually called the **temperature-blend door.** Some other names that are used depending on the vehicle manufacturer include the following:
  - *air mix door*
  - *temperature door*
  - *blend door*
  - *diverter door*
  - *bypass door*
- **Mode control actuators.** Some vehicles include ducts to transfer air to the rear seat area, and some vehicles include ducts to demist the vehicle's side windows with warm air. Airflow to these ducts is controlled by one or more **mode doors** controlled by the function lever or buttons. Mode doors are also called *function, floor-defrost,* or *panel-defrost* doors. Mode/function control sets the doors as follows:

- **A/C:** in-dash registers with outside air inlet
- **Max A/C:** in-dash registers with recirculation
- **Heat:** floor level with outside air inlet
- **Max Heat:** floor level with recirculation
- **Bi-level:** both in-dash and floor discharge
- **Defrost:** windshield registers

Many control heads also provide for in-between settings, which combine some of these operations. In many systems, a small amount of air is directed to the defroster ducts when in the heat mode, and while in defrost mode a small amount of air goes to the floor level.

- **Inlet Air control door actuators.** Air can enter the duct system from either the plenum chamber in front of the windshield (outside air) or return register (inside air). The return register is often positioned below the right end of the instrument panel. (The right and left sides of the vehicle are always described as seen by the driver.) The *inlet air control door* can also be called the
  - *fresh air door,*
  - *recirculation door, or*
  - *outside air door*

This door is normally positioned so it allows airflow from one source while it shuts off the other. It can be positioned to allow outside air to enter

- While shutting off the recirculation opening
- To allow air to return or recirculate from inside the vehicle while shutting off outside (fresh) air
- To allow a mix of outside air and return air.

In most vehicles, the door is set to the outside air position in all function lever positions except off, max heat, and max A/C. Max A/C and max heat settings position the door to recirculate in-vehicle air. ● **SEE FIGURE 41–11.**

DUAL-ZONE SYSTEMS In many vehicles, the HVAC system is capable of supplying discharge air of more than one temperature to different areas in the vehicle. This type

FLOOR PANEL
DOOR ACTUATOR
(BEHIND SHIELD)

BLEND DOOR
ACTUATOR

AMBIENT
TEMPERATURE
SENSOR

BLOWER SPEED
CONTROLLER

FRESH AIR
DOOR
ACTUATOR

FIGURE 41–11 A typical HVAC system showing some of the airflow door locations.

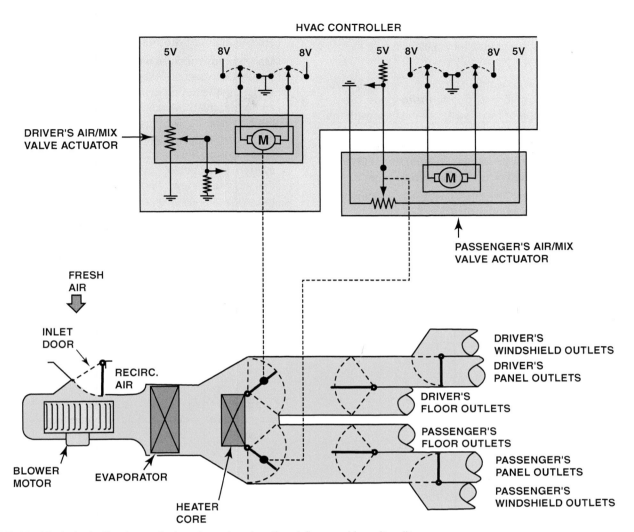

FIGURE 41-12 A dual-climate control system showing the airflow and how it splits.

of system is usually referred to as **Dual-Zone Systems** and allows the driver and front seat passenger to set their own desired temperature. Dual-zone systems contain two separately commanded temperature-blend doors. The temperature difference between the driver and front seat passenger can be up to 30°F (16°C), usually with settings between 60°F (16°C) minimum and 90°F (32°C) maximum.● **SEE FIGURE 41-12.**

Tri-Zone and *Quad-Zone* systems are usually found in passenger vans, sport utility vehicles, and luxury cars, which allow the passengers in the rear of the vehicle to control the temperature at their location.

AUTOMATIC HVAC CONTROLS

OPERATION The HVAC control head or panel is mounted in the instrument cluster. The control head provides the switches and levers needed to control the different aspects of the heating and A/C system, which include:

- HVAC system on and off
- A/C on/off
- Outside or recirculated air
- A/C, defrost, or heating mode
- Temperature desired
- Blower speed

COMPRESSOR CONTROLS Most air conditioning compressors use an electromagnetic clutch. A coil of wire inside the clutch creates a strong magnetic field that when activated connects the input shaft of the compressor to the drive pulley. Most electromagnetic coil assemblies have between 3 and 4 ohms of resistance. According to Ohm's law, about 3 to 4 amperes of current are required to energize the air conditioning compressor clutch. All electrical circuits require the following to operate:

1. A voltage source
2. Protection (fuse)

3. Control (switch)

4. An electrical load (the air conditioning compressor clutch)

5. A ground connection

All five of these must be working before current (amperes) can flow, causing the compressor clutch to engage. Some systems may connect one or more switches in series with the compressor clutch so that all have to be functioning before the compressor clutch can be engaged. A low- and high-pressure switch or sensor may also be an input to the PCM or HVAC controller for use in controlling the compressor.

- **Low-pressure switch:** This pressure switch is electrically closed only if there is 8 to 24 PSI (55 to 165 kPa) of refrigerant pressure. This amount of pressure means that the system is sufficiently charged to provide lubrication for the compressor.

- **High-pressure switch:** This pressure switch is located in the high-pressure side of the A/C system. If the pressure exceeds a certain level, typically 375 PSI (2,600 kPa), the pressure switch opens, thereby preventing possible damage to the air conditioning system due to excessively high pressure.

- **A/C relay:** The relay supplies power to the compressor.

CONTROL MODULE

The control module used for automatic climatic control systems can be referred by various terms depending on the exact make and module of vehicle. Some commonly used terms include the following:

- ECM (Electronic Control Module)
- BCM (Body control module)
- HVAC control module (often is built into the smart control head)
- HVAC controller or programmer

The control modules are programmed to open or close circuits to the actuators based on the values of the various sensors. Although it is unable to handle the electric current for devices such as the compressor clutch or blower motor, the control module can operate relays. These relays in turn control the electric devices. Units that use small current flows, such as a light-emitting diode (LED) or digital display, can operate directly from the control module.

An ECM is programmed with various strategies to suit the requirements of the particular vehicle. For example, when A/C is requested by the driver of a vehicle with a relatively small engine, the ECM will probably increase the engine idle RPM. On this same vehicle, the ECM will probably shut off the compressor clutch during wide-open throttle (WOT).

- On other vehicles, the ECM might shut off the compressor clutch at very high speeds to prevent the compressor from spinning too fast.

- In some cases, part of the A/C and heat operating strategy is built into the control head and are called **smart control heads.** In some cases, door operating strategy is built into the door operating motors, and these are called **smart motors.**

- Many control modules are programmed to run a test sequence, called *self-diagnosis*, at start-up (when the ignition key is turned on). If improper electrical values are found, the ECM indicates a failure often by blinking the A/C indicator light at the control head. Some ECMs also monitor the system during operation and indicate a failure or stop the compressor if there is a problem. One system, for example, notes the frequency of clutch cycling that indicates a low refrigerant charge level. If there are too many clutch cycles during a certain time period, the control module will shut off the compressor and set a diagnostic trouble code (DTC). **SEE FIGURE 41–13.**

CONTROLLING AIR TEMPERATURE Most HVAC systems are considered *reheat* systems in that the incoming air is chilled as it passes through the evaporator. The air is then heated as part or all of the flow passes through the heater core so it reaches the desired in-vehicle temperature. Chilling the incoming air is a good method of removing water vapor to reduce humidity, but it is not the most efficient method to get cool air. There is an increasing trend to use an electronically controlled variable displacement compressor with an air temperature sensor after the evaporator. Compressor displacement is adjusted to cool the evaporator just enough to cool the air to the desired temperature, which reduces the load on the compressor and improves fuel economy.

? **FREQUENTLY ASKED QUESTION**

Why Is the Blower Speed So High?

This question is often asked by passengers when riding in a vehicle equipped with automatic climatic control. The controller does command a high blower speed if:

- The outside temperature is low and the engine coolant temperature is hot enough to provide heat. The high blower speed is used to warm the passenger compartment as quickly as possible then when the temperature has reached the preset level, then the blower speed is reduced to maintain the preset temperature.

- The outside temperature is hot and the air conditioning compressor is working to provide cooling. The high speed blower is used to circulate air through the evaporator in an attempt to cool the passenger compartment as quickly as possible. Once the temperature reaches close to the preset temperature, the blower speed is reduced to keep the temperature steady.

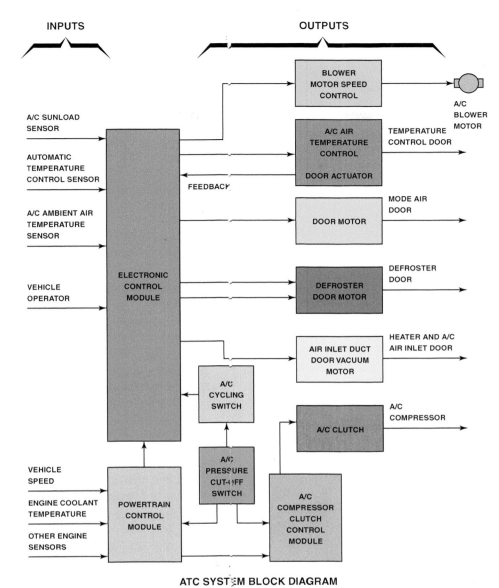

INPUTS

OUTPUTS

A/C SUNLOAD SENSOR

AUTOMATIC TEMPERATURE CONTROL SENSOR

A/C AMBIENT AIR TEMPERATURE SENSOR

VEHICLE OPERATOR

ELECTRONIC CONTROL MODULE

FEEDBACK

BLOWER MOTOR SPEED CONTROL

A/C BLOWER MOTOR

A/C AIR TEMPERATURE CONTROL DOOR ACTUATOR

TEMPERATURE CONTROL DOOR

DOOR MOTOR

MODE AIR DOOR

DEFROSTER DOOR MOTOR

DEFROSTER DOOR

AIR INLET DUCT DOOR VACUUM MOTOR

HEATER AND A/C AIR INLET DOOR

A/C CYCLING SWITCH

A/C CLUTCH

A/C COMPRESSOR

VEHICLE SPEED

ENGINE COOLANT TEMPERATURE

OTHER ENGINE SENSORS

POWERTRAIN CONTROL MODULE

A/C PRESSURE CUT-OFF SWITCH

A/C COMPRESSOR CLUTCH CONTROL MODULE

ATC SYSTEM BLOCK DIAGRAM

FIGURE 41–13 A block diagram showing the inputs to the electronic control assembly and the outputs; note that some of the outputs have feedback to the ECM.

AIR FILTRATION

PURPOSE AND FUNCTION Many newer systems include an HVAC air filter, usually called a cabin filter, in the air distribution system. Cabin filter can be located outside the air inlet and are serviced under the hood, or between blower and evaporator which are serviced from under the dash. ● **SEE FIGURE 41–14.**

This filter can also be referred to as

- *interior filter*
- *ventilation filter*
- *micron filter*
- *particulate filter*
- *pollen filter*

The cabin filter removes small dust or pollen particles from the incoming airstream. These filters require periodic replacement and if they are not serviced properly, can cause an airflow reduction when they become plugged.

UNDER HOOD

GLOVE COMPARTMENT

FIGURE 41–14 A cabin filter can be accessed either through the glove compartment or under the hood on most vehicles.

REAL WORLD FIX

Cabin Filter Fault

The owner of a 2008 Ford Escape complained that the air conditioning system was not cooling the inside of the vehicle and there seemed to be no airflow from the dash vents yet the blower motor could be heard running. A quick visual inspection of the cabin air with access under the hood showed that the cabin filter was almost completely blocked with paper, leaves, and debris. The vehicle had almost 80,000 miles on the odometer and the way it looked, the air filter had never been replaced. Most vehicle manufacturers recommend replacement of the cabin air filter about every three years or every 36,000 miles. Replacing the cabin air filter restored proper operation of the A/C system.

TYPES OF CABIN FILTERS There are two types of filter media.

1. **Particle filters.** Particle filters remove solid particles such as dust, soot, spores, and pollen using a special paper or nonwoven fleece material; they can trap particles that are about 3 microns or larger.

2. **Adsorption filters.** Adsorption filters remove noxious gases and odors using an activated charcoal media with the charcoal layer between layers of filter media.

These two filter types can be combined into a combination or two-stage filter. The filter media can have an electrostatic charge to make it more efficient.

AUTOMATIC CLIMATIC CONTROL DIAGNOSIS

DIAGNOSTIC PROCEDURE If a fault occurs in the automatic climatic system, check service information for the specified procedure to follow for the vehicle being checked. Most vehicle service information includes the following steps:

STEP 1 Verify the customer concern. Check that the customer is operating the system correctly. For example, most automatic systems cannot detect when the defrosters are needed so most systems have a control that turns on the defroster(s).

STEP 2 Perform a thorough visual inspection of the heating and cooling system for any obvious faults.

STEP 3 Use a factory scan tool or a factory level aftermarket scan tool and check for diagnostic trouble codes (DTCs).

NOTE: Older systems can be accessed using the buttons on the control panel and then the diagnostic trouble codes and system data are displayed. Check service information for the exact procedures to follow for the vehicle being serviced.

STEP 4 If there are stored diagnostic trouble codes, follow service information instructions for diagnosing the system. **SEE CHART 41–2** for sample diagnostic trouble codes (DTCs).

STEP 5 If there are no stored diagnostic trouble codes, check scan tool data for possible fault areas in the system.

FREQUENTLY ASKED QUESTION

What are the Symptoms of a Broken Blend Door?

Blend doors can fail and cause the following symptoms:

- Clicking noise from the actuator motor assembly as it tries to move a broken door.
- Outlet temperature can change from hot to cold or from cold to hot at any time especially when cornering because the broken door is being forced one way or the other due to the movement of the vehicle.
- A change in the temperature when the fan speed is changed. The air movement can move the broken blend door into another position which can change the vent temperature.

If any of these symptoms are occurring, then a replacement blend door is required. For details regarding an alternative repair option visit www.heatertreater.net.

SCAN TOOL BIDIRECTIONAL CONTROL Scan tools are the most important tool for any diagnostic work on all vehicles.

Scan tools can be divided into two basic groups:

1. **Factory scan tools.** These are the scan tools required by all dealers that sell and service a specific brand of vehicle. Examples of factory scan tools include:
   - **General Motors**—TECH 2. ● **SEE FIGURE 41–15.**
   - **Ford**—WDS (Worldwide Diagnostic System) and IDS (Integrated Diagnostic Software).
   - **Chrysler**—DRB-III, Star Scan or WiTECH
   - **Honda**—HDS or Master Tech
   - **Toyota**—Master Tech; Tech Stream

   All factory scan tools are designed to provide bidirectional capability, which allows the service technician the opportunity to operate components using the scan tool, thereby confirming that the component is able to work when commanded.

ATC-RELATED DIAGNOSTIC TROUBLE CODES

BODY DIAGNOSTIC TROUBLE CODE (DTC)	DESCRIPTION
B0126	Right Panel Discharge Temperature Fault
B0130	Air Temperature/Mode Door Actuator Malfunction
B0131	Right Heater Discharge Temperature Fault
B0145	Auxiliary HAVC Actuator Circuit
B0159	Outside Air Temperature Sensor Circuit Range/Performance
B0160	Ambient Air Temperature Sensor Circuit
B0162	Ambient Air Temperature Sensor Circuit
B0164	Passenger Compartment Temperature Sensor #1 (Single Sensor or LH) Circuit Range/Performance
B0169	In-Vehicle Temp Sensor Failure (passenger—not used)
B0174	Output Air Temperature Sensor #1 (Upper Single or LH) Circuit Range/Performance
B0179	Output Air Temperature Sensor #2 (Lower Single or LH) Circuit Range/Performance
B0183	Sun load Sensor Circuit
B0184	Solar Load Sensor #1 Circuit Range (sun load)
B0188	Sun load Sensor Circuit
B0189	Solar Load Sensor #2 Circuit Range (sun load)
B0229	HVAC Actuator Circuit
B0248	Mode Door Inoperative Error
B0249	Heater/Defrost/AC Door Range Error
B0263	HVAC Actuator Circuit
B0268	Air/Inlet Door Inoperative Error
B0269	Air Inlet Door Range Error
B0408	Temperature Control #1 (Main/Front) Circuit Malfunction
B0409	Air Mix Door #1 Range Error
B0414	Air Temperature/Mode Door Actuator Malfunction
B0418	HVAC Actuator Circuit
B0419	Air Mix Door #2 Range Error
B0423	Air Mix Door #2 Inoperative Error
B0424	Air Temperature/Mode Door Actuator Malfunction
B0428	Air Mix Door #3 Inoperative Error

CHART 41-2

Sample automatic climatic control diagnostic trouble codes.

FIGURE 41–15 A TECH 2 scan tool is the factory scan tool used on General Motors vehicles.

ATC components that may be able to be controlled or checked using a scan tool include:

- Blower speed control (faster and slower to check operation)
- Command the position of airflow doors to check for proper operation and to check for proper airflow from the vents and ducts
- Values of all sensors
- Pressures of the refrigerant in the high and low sides of the systems

2. **Aftermarket scan tools.** These scan tools are designed to function on more than one brand of vehicle. Examples of aftermarket scan tools include:

- **Snap-on** (various models, including the Ethos, Modis, and Solus)
- **OTC** (various models, including Pegasus, Genisys, and Task Master). ● **SEE FIGURE 41–16.**

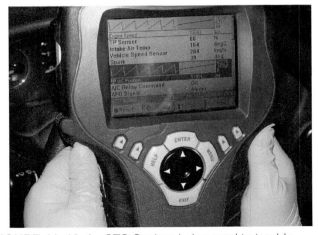

FIGURE 41–16 An OTC Genisys being used to trouble-shoot a vehicle. This scan tool can be used on most makes and models of vehicles and is capable of diagnosing other computer systems in the vehicles such as the automatic temperature control system as well as the antilock braking system (ABS) and airbag systems.

SENSOR	TYPICAL VALUE
Inside air temperature sensor	−40°F to 120°F (−40°C to 49°C)
Ambient air temperature sensor	−40°F to 120°F (−40°C to 49°C)
Engine coolant temperature (ECT) sensor	40°F to 250°F (−40°C to 121°C)
Sun load Sensor	0.3 volts (dark) 3.0 volts (bright)
Evaporator temperature sensor	Usually 34°F to 44°F (1°C to 7°C)
Relative Humidity sensor	0% to100%

CHART 41–3

Typical sensors and values that may be displayed on a scan tool. Check service information for the exact specifications for the vehicle being serviced.

- **AutoEnginuity** and other programs that use a laptop or handheld computer for the display.

While many aftermarket scan tools can display most if not all of the parameters of the factory scan tool, there can be a difference when trying to troubleshoot some faults.

SCAN TOOL DATA   Scan data related to the automatic climatic control system can be confusing. Typical data and their meaning are shown in ● **CHART 41–3.**

SUMMARY

1. Automatic temperature control (ATC) systems use sensors to detect the conditions both inside and outside the vehicle.
2. The sensors used include the following:
   - Sun load sensor
   - Evaporator temperature sensor
   - Ambient air temperature (outside air temperature) sensor
   - In-vehicle temperature sensor
   - Infrared Sensors
   - Engine coolant temperature (ECT) sensor
3. Pressure transducers detect the pressures in the refrigerant system.
4. Some systems use a compressor speed sensor to detect if the drive belt or compressor clutch is slipping.

5. The heater core is placed downstream from the evaporator in the airflow so that air can be routed either through or around it and one or two doors are used to control this airflow. This door is called the *temperature-blend door.*
6. In many vehicles, the HVAC system is capable of supplying discharge air of more than one temperature to different areas in the vehicle. This type of system is usually referred to as *Dual-Zone Climate Control Systems.*
7. The diagnostic steps include:
   - Verify the customer concern
   - Perform a thorough vial inspection
   - Retrieve diagnostic trouble codes (DTCs)
   - Check the data as displayed on a scan tool to determine what sensors or actuators are at fault

REVIEW QUESTIONS

1. What are the sensors used in a typical automatic temperature control (ATC) system?
2. What are the three airflow sections in a typical HVAC system?

3. Why is a feedback potentiometer used on an electric actuator?
4. What is the purpose of the aspirator tube in the in-vehicle temperature sensor section?

1. In heating mode, where is the airflow directed?
   a. Dash vents
   b. Floor
   c. Windshield
   d. Both b and c

2. Which sensor is also called the ambient air temperature sensor?
   a. Outside air temperature (OAT)
   b. Inside vehicle temperature
   c. Discharge air temperature
   d. Evaporator outlet temperature

3. What is the most common type of sun load sensor?
   a. Potentiometer
   b. Negative temperature coefficient (NTC) thermistor
   c. Photodiode
   d. Positive temperature coefficient (PTC) thermistor

4. An actuator can be capable of how many position(s)?
   a. Two
   b. Three
   c. Variable
   d. All of the above

5. Some cabin filters contain _____ to absorb odors.
   a. Perfume
   b. Activated charcoal
   c. Paper filter material
   d. Synthetic fibers

6. Which sensor might use an aspirator tube?
   a. Inside vehicle temperature
   b. Outside air temperature (OAT)
   c. Discharge air temperature
   d. Evaporator outlet temperature

7. Technician A says that some cabin filters are accessible behind the glove compartment. Technician B says that some cabin filters are accessible from under the hood. Which technician is correct?
   a. Technician A only
   b. Technician B only
   c. Both technicians A and B
   d. Neither technician A nor B

8. Automatic temperature control (ATC) diagnostic trouble codes are usually what type?
   a. P codes
   b. B codes
   c. C codes
   d. U codes

9. The control module used for automatic climatic control systems is called _____.
   a. ECM
   b. BCM
   c. HVAC control module
   d. Any of the above depending on the make and model of vehicle

10. A feedback potentiometer is used to _____.
    a. Provide feedback to the driver as to where the controls are set
    b. Provide feedback to the controller as to the location of a door or valve
    c. Give temperature information about the outside air temperature to the dash display
    d. Any of the above depending on the exact make and model of vehicle

AIRBAG AND PRETENSIONER CIRCUITS

OBJECTIVES: **After studying Chapter 42, the reader will be able to:** • Prepare for ASE Electrical/Electronic Systems (A6) certification test content area "H" (Accessories Diagnosis and Repair). • List the appropriate safety precautions to be followed when working with airbag systems. • Describe the procedures to diagnose and repair common faults in airbag systems. • Explain how the passenger presence system works.

KEY TERMS: • Airbag 512 • Arming sensor 512 • Clockspring 515 • Deceleration sensor 514 • Dual-stage airbags 515 • EDR 522 • Integral sensor 514 • Knee airbags 518 • Occupant detection systems (ODS) 520 • Passenger presence system (PPS) 520 • Pretensioners 510 • SAR 512 • Side airbags 521 • SIR 512 • Squib 512 • SRS 512

SAFETY BELTS AND RETRACTORS

SAFETY BELTS Safety belts are used to keep the driver and passengers secured to the vehicle in the event of a collision. Most safety belts include three-point support and are constructed of nylon webbing about 2 in. (5 cm) wide. The three support points include two points on either side of the seat for the belt over the lap and one crossing over the upper torso, which is attached to the "B" pillar or seat back. Every crash consists of three types of collisions.

    Collision 1: The vehicle strikes another vehicle or object.
    Collision 2: The driver and/or passengers hit objects
        inside the vehicle if unbelted.
    Collision 3: The internal organs of the body hit other
        organs or bones, which causes internal injuries.

If a safety belt is being worn, the belt stretches, absorbing a lot of the impact, thereby preventing collision with other objects in the vehicle and reducing internal injuries. ● **SEE FIGURE 42–1.**

BELT RETRACTORS Safety belts are also equipped with one of the following types of retractors.

- Nonlocking retractors, which are used primarily on recoiling
- Emergency locking retractors, which lock the position of the safety belt in the event of a collision or rollover

- Emergency and web speed-sensitive retractors, which allow freedom of movement for the driver and passenger but lock if the vehicle is accelerating too fast or if the vehicle is decelerating too fast.
    ● **SEE FIGURE 42–2** for an example of an inertia-type seat belt locking mechanism.

SAFETY BELT LIGHTS AND CHIMES All late-model vehicles are equipped with a safety belt warning light on the dash and a chime that sounds if the belt is not fastened. ● **SEE FIGURE 42–3.**

Some vehicles will intermittently flash the reminder light and sound a chime until the driver and sometimes the front passenger fasten their safety belts.

PRETENSIONERS A **pretensioner** is an explosive (pyrotechnic) device that is part of the seat belt retractor assembly and tightens the seat belt as the airbag is being deployed. The purpose of the pretensioning device is to force the occupant back into position against the seat back and to remove any slack in the seat belt. ● **SEE FIGURE 42–4.**

CAUTION: The seat belt pretensioner assemblies must be replaced in the event of an airbag deployment. Always follow the vehicle manufacturer's recommended service procedure. Pretensioners are explosive devices that could be ignited if voltage is applied to the terminals. Do not use a jumper wire or powered test light around the wiring near the seat belt latch wiring. Always follow the vehicle manufacturer's recommended test procedures.

STOPPING DISTANCE OF DRIVER AND VEHICLE

1 FT

FORCE ON 160 LB. DRIVER IS 4800 LB. (30 G'S)

STOPPING DISTANCE OF DRIVER → 1.5 FT

STOPPING DISTANCE OF VEHICLE → 1 FT

SEAT BELT STRETCH

FORCE ON 160 LB. DRIVER IS 3200 LB. (20 G'S)

(a)

CRASH SCENARIO WITH VEHICLE STOPPING IN ONE FOOT DISTANCE FROM A SPEED OF 30 MPH.

(b)

FIGURE 42–1 (a) Safety belts are the primary restraint system. (b) During a collision the stretching of the safety belt slows the impact to help reduce bodily injury.

REST

WEIGHT

ACTIVE

FIGURE 42–2 Most safety belts have an inertia-type mechanism that locks the belt in the event of rapid movement.

FIGURE 42–3 A typical safety belt warning light.

SEAT BELT PRETENSIONER CABLE

EXPLOSIVE CHARGE

TUBE

FIGURE 42–4 A small explosive charge in the pretensioner forces the end of the seat belt down the tube, which removes any slack in the seat belt.

FRONT AIRBAGS

PURPOSE AND FUNCTION   **Airbag** passive restraints are designed to cushion the driver (or passenger, if the passenger side is so equipped) during a frontal collision. The system consists of one or more nylon bags folded up in compartments located in the steering wheel, dashboard, interior panels, or side pillars of the vehicle. During a crash of sufficient force, pressurized gas instantly fills the airbag and then deploys out of the storage compartment to protect the occupant from serious injury. These airbag systems may be known by many different names, including the following:

1. **Supplemental restraint system (SRS)**
2. **Supplemental inflatable restraints (SIR)**
3. **Supplemental air restraints (SAR)**

Most airbags are designed to supplement the safety belts in the event of a collision, and front airbags are meant to be deployed only in the event of a frontal impact within 30 degrees of center. Front (driver and passenger side) airbag systems are *not* designed to inflate during side or rear impact. The force required to deploy a typical airbag is approximately equal to the force of a vehicle hitting a wall at over 10 mph (16 km/hr).

The force required to trigger the sensors within the system prevents accidental deployment if curbs are hit or the brakes are rapidly applied. The system requires a substantial force to deploy the airbag to help prevent accidental inflation.

PARTS INVOLVED   ● **SEE FIGURE 42-5** for an overall view of the parts included in a typical airbag system.

The parts include:

1. Sensors
2. Airbag (inflator) module
3. Clockspring wire coil in the steering column
4. Control module
5. Wiring and connectors

OPERATION   To cause inflation, the following events must occur.

- To cause a deployment of the airbag, two sensors must be triggered at the same time. The **arming sensor** is used to provide electrical power, and a *forward* or *discriminating sensor* is used to provide the ground connection.
- The arming sensor provides the electrical power to the airbag heating unit, called a **squib,** inside the inflator module.
- The squib uses electrical power and converts it into heat for ignition of the propellant used to inflate the airbag.
- Before the airbag can inflate, however, the squib circuit also must have a ground provided by the forward or the discriminating sensor. In other words, two sensors (arming and forward sensors) *must* be triggered *at the same time* before the airbag will be deployed. ● **SEE FIGURE 42-6.**

FIGURE 42-5 A typical airbag system showing many of the components. The SDM is the "sensing and diagnostic module" and includes the arming sensor as well as the electronics that keep checking the circuits for continuity and the capacitors that are discharged to deploy the air bags.

TYPES OF AIRBAG INFLATORS   There are two different types of inflators used in airbags.

1. **Solid fuel.** This type uses sodium azide pellets and, when ignited, generates a large quantity of nitrogen gas that quickly inflates the airbag. This was the first type used and is still commonly used in driver and passenger side airbag inflator modules. ● **SEE FIGURE 42-7.** The squib is the electrical heating element used to ignite the gas-generating material, usually sodium azide. It requires about 2 A of current to heat the heating element and ignite the inflator.

2. **Compressed gas.** Commonly used in passenger side airbags and roof-mounted systems, the compressed gas system uses a canister filled with argon gas, plus a small percentage of helium at 3,000 psi (435 kPa). A small igniter ruptures a burst disc to release the gas when energized. The compressed gas inflators are long cylinders that can be installed inside the instrument panel, seat back, door panel, or along any side rail or pillar of the vehicle. ● **SEE FIGURE 42-8.**

FIGURE 42–8 This shows a deployed side curtain airbag on a training vehicle.

FIGURE 42–6 A simplified airbag deployment circuit. Note that both the arming sensor and at least one of the discriminating sensors must be activated at the same time. The arming sensor provides the power, and either one of the discriminating sensors can provide the ground for the circuit.

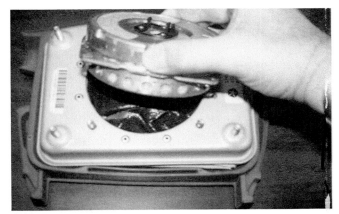

FIGURE 42–7 The inflator module is being removed from the airbag housing. The squib, inside the inflator module, is the heating element that ignites the pyrotechnic gas generator that rapidly produces nitrogen gas to fill the airbag.

Once the inflator is ignited, the nylon bag quickly inflates (in about 30 ms or 0.030 second) with nitrogen gas generated by the inflator. During an actual collision accident, the driver is being thrown forward by the driver's own momentum toward the steering wheel. The strong nylon bag inflates at the same time. Personal injury is reduced by the spreading of the stopping force over the entire upper-body region. The normal collapsible steering column remains in operation and collapses in a collision when equipped with an airbag system. The bag is equipped with two large side vents that allow the bag to deflate immediately after inflation, once the bag has cushioned the occupant in a collision.

TIMELINE FOR AIRBAG DEPLOYMENT Following are the times necessary for an airbag deployment in milliseconds (each millisecond is equal to 0.001 second or 1/1,000 of a second).

1. Collision occurs: 0.0 ms
2. Sensors detect collision: 16 ms (0.016 second)
3. Airbag is deployed and seam cover rips: 40 ms (0.040 second)
4. Airbag is fully inflated: 100 ms (0.100 second)
5. Airbag deflated: 250 ms (0.250 second)

In other words, an airbag deployment occurs and is over in about a quarter of a second.

SENSOR OPERATION All three sensors are basically switches that complete an electrical circuit when activated. The sensors are similar in construction and operation, and the *location* of the sensor determines its name. All airbag sensors are rigidly mounted to the vehicle and *must* be mounted with the arrow pointing toward the front of the vehicle to ensure that the sensor can detect rapid forward deceleration.

There are three basic styles (designs) of airbag sensors.

1. **Magnetically retained gold-plated ball sensor.** This sensor uses a permanent magnet to hold a gold-plated steel ball away from two gold-plated electrical contacts. ● **SEE FIGURE 42–9.**

   If the vehicle (and the sensor) stops rapidly enough, the steel ball is released from the magnet because the inertia force of the crash was sufficient to overcome the magnetic pull on the ball and then makes contact with the two gold-plated electrodes. The steel ball only remains in contact with the electrodes for a relatively short time because the steel ball is drawn back into contact with the magnet.

2. **Rolled up stainless-steel ribbon-type sensor.** This sensor is housed in an airtight package with nitrogen gas inside to prevent harmful corrosion of the sensor parts. If the vehicle (and the sensor) stops rapidly, the stainless-steel roll "unrolls" and contacts the two gold-plated contacts.

FIGURE 42–9 An airbag magnetic sensor.

FIGURE 42–10 Some vehicles use a ribbon-type crash sensor.

Once the force is stopped, the stainless-steel roll will roll back into its original shape. ● SEE FIGURE 42–10.

3. **Integral sensor.** Some vehicles use electronic **deceleration sensors** built into the inflator module, called **integral sensors.** For example, General Motors uses the term *sensing and diagnostic module* (*SDM*) to describe their integrated sensor/module assembly. These units contain an accelerometer-type sensor which measures the rate of deceleration and, through computer logic, determines if the airbags should be deployed. ● SEE FIGURE 42–11.

TWO-STAGE AIRBAGS   Two-stage airbags, often called advanced airbags or smart airbags, use an accelerometer-type of sensor to detect force of the impact. This type of sensor measures the actual amount of deceleration rate of the vehicle and is used to determine whether one or both elements of a two-stage airbag should be deployed.

■ **Low-stage deployment.** This lower force deployment is used if the accelerometer detects a low-speed crash.

■ **High-stage deployment.** This stage is used if the accelerometer detects a higher speed crash or a more rapid deceleration rate.

■ **Both low- and high-stage deployment.** Under severe high-speed crashes, both stages can be deployed.
   ● SEE FIGURE 42–12.

FIGURE 42–11 A sensing and diagnostic module that includes an accelerometer.

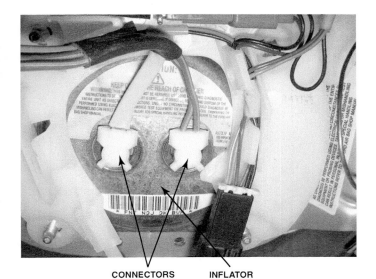

CONNECTORS
TO EACH STAGE

INFLATOR
MODULE

FIGURE 42–12 A driver's side airbag showing two inflator connectors. One is for the lower force inflator and the other is for the higher force inflator. Either can be ignited or both at the same time if the deceleration sensor detects a severe impact.

 SAFETY TIP

Dual-Stage Airbag Caution

Many vehicles are equipped with **dual-stage airbags** (two-stage airbags) that actually contain two separate inflators, one for less severe crashes and one for higher speed collisions. These systems are sometimes called *smart airbag systems* because the accelerometer-type sensor used can detect how severe the impact is and deploy one or both stages. If one stage is deployed, the other stage is still active and could be accidentally deployed. A service technician cannot tell by looking at the airbag whether both stages have deployed. Always handle a deployed airbag as if it has not been deployed and take all precautions necessary to keep any voltage source from getting close to the inflator module terminals.

WIRING Wiring and connectors are very important for proper identification and long life. Airbag-related circuits have the following features.

- All electrical wiring and conduit for airbags are colored yellow.
- To ensure proper electrical connection to the inflator module in the steering wheel, a coil assembly is used in the steering column. This coil is a ribbon of copper wires that operates much like a window shade when the steering wheel is rotated. As the steering wheel is rotated, this coil, usually called a **clockspring,** prevents the lack of continuity between the sensors and the inflator assembly that might result from a horn-ring type of sliding conductor.

 TECH TIP

Pocket the Ignition Key to Be Safe

When replacing any steering gear such as a rack-and-pinion steering unit, be sure that no one accidentally turns the steering wheel. If the steering wheel is turned without being connected to the steering gear, the airbag wire coil (clockspring) can become off center. This can cause the wiring to break when the steering wheel is rotated after the steering gear has been replaced. To help prevent this from occurring, simply remove the ignition key from the ignition and keep it in your pocket while servicing the steering gear.

- Inside the yellow plastic airbag connectors are gold-plated terminals which are used to prevent corrosion.
  - ● **SEE FIGURE 42–13.**

Most airbag systems also contain a diagnostic unit that often includes an auxiliary power supply, which is used to provide the current to inflate the airbag if the battery is disconnected from the vehicle during a collision. This auxiliary power supply normally uses capacitors that are discharged through the squib of the inflation module. When the ignition is turned off these capacitors are discharged. Therefore, after a few minutes an airbag system will not deploy if the vehicle is hit while parked.

AIRBAG DIAGNOSIS TOOLS AND EQUIPMENT

SELF-TEST PROCEDURE The electrical portion of airbag systems is constantly checked by the circuits within the airbag-energizing power unit or through the airbag controller. The electrical airbag components are monitored by applying a small-signal voltage from the airbag controller through the various sensors and components. Each component and sensor uses a resistor in parallel with the load or open sensor switch for use by the diagnostic signals. If continuity exists, the testing circuits will measure a small voltage drop. If an open or short circuit occurs, a dash warning light is lighted and a possible diagnostic trouble code (DTC) is stored. Follow exact manufacturer's recommended procedures for accessing and erasing airbag diagnostic trouble codes.

Diagnosis and service of airbag systems usually require some or all of the following items.

- Digital multimeter (DMM)
- Airbag simulator, often called a load tool
- Scan tool
- Shorting bar or shorting connector(s)

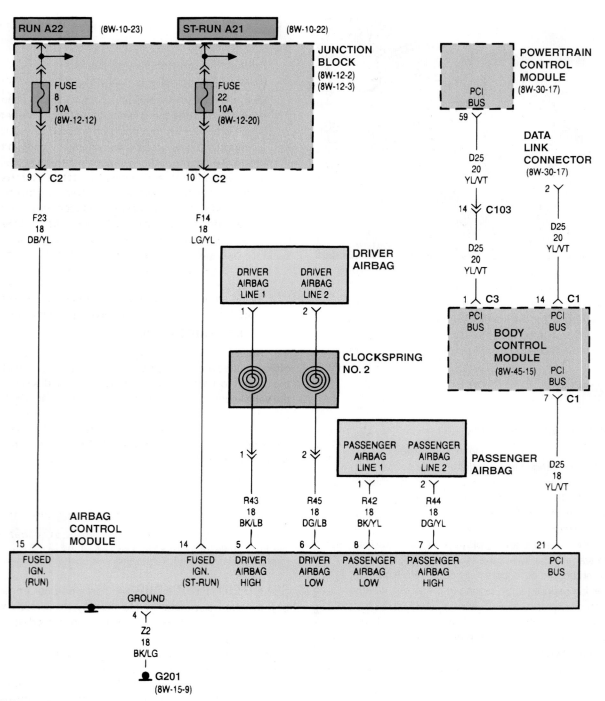

FIGURE 42–13 The airbag control module is linked to the powertrain control module (PCM) and the body control module (BCM) on this Chrysler system. Notice the airbag wire connecting the module to the airbag through the clockspring. Both power, labeled "driver airbag high" and ground, labeled "driver airbag low" are conducted through the clockspring.

- Airbag system tester
- Vehicle-specific test harness
- Special wire repair tools or connectors, such as crimp-and-seal weatherproof connectors

● **SEE FIGURE 42–14.**

CAUTION: Most vehicle manufacturers specify that the negative battery terminal be removed when testing or working around airbags. Be aware that a memory saver device used to keep the computer and radio memory alive can supply enough electrical power to deploy an airbag.

FIGURE 42–14 An airbag diagnostic tester. Included in the plastic box are electrical connectors and a load tool that substitutes for the inflator module during troubleshooting.

 FREQUENTLY ASKED QUESTION

What Are Smart Airbags?

Smart airbags use the information from sensors to determine the level of deployment. Sensors used include:

- **Vehicle speed (VS) sensors.** This type of sensor has a major effect on the intensity of a collision. The higher the speed is, the greater the amount of impact force.
- **Seat belt fastened switch.** If the seat belt is fastened, as determined by the seat belt buckle switch, the airbag system will deploy accordingly. If the driver or passenger is not wearing a seat belt, the airbag system will deploy with greater force compared to when the seat belt is being worn.
- **Passenger seat sensor.** The sensor in the seat on the passenger's side determines the force of deployment. If there is not a passenger detected, the passenger side airbag will not deploy on the vehicle equipped with a passenger seat sensor system.

PRECAUTIONS   Take the following precautions when working with or around airbags.

1. Always follow all precautions and warning stickers on vehicles equipped with airbags.
2. Maintain a safe working distance from all airbags to help prevent the possibility of personal injury in the unlikely event of an unintentional airbag deployment.
   - Side impact airbag: 5 in. (13 cm) distance
   - Driver front airbag: 10 in. (25 cm) distance
   - Passenger front airbag: 20 in. (50 cm) distance
3. In the event of a collision in which the bag(s) is deployed, the inflator module *and* all sensors usually must be replaced to ensure proper future operation of the system.
4. Avoid using a self-powered test light around the yellow airbag wiring. Even though it is highly unlikely, a self-powered test light could provide the necessary current to accidentally set off the inflator module and cause an airbag deployment.
5. Use care when handling the inflator module section when it is removed from the steering wheel. Always hold the inflator away from your body.
6. If handling a deployed inflator module, always wear gloves and safety glasses to avoid the possibility of skin irritation from the sodium hydroxide dust, which is used as a lubricant on the bag(s), that remains after deployment.
7. Never jar or strike a sensor. The contacts inside the sensor may be damaged, preventing the proper operation of the airbag system in the event of a collision.
8. When mounting a sensor in a vehicle, make certain that the arrow on the sensor is pointing toward the front of the vehicle. Also be certain that the sensor is securely mounted.

AIRBAG SYSTEM SERVICE

DIS-ARMING   The airbags should be dis-armed, (temporarily disconnected), whenever performing service work on any of the follow locations.

- Steering wheel
- Dash or instrument panel
- Glove box (instrument panel storage compartment)

Check service information for the exact procedure, which usually includes the following steps.

STEP 1   Disconnect the negative battery cable.

STEP 2   Remove the airbag fuse (has a yellow cover).

STEP 3   Disconnect the yellow electrical connector located at the base of the steering column to disable the driver's side airbag.

STEP 4   Disconnect the yellow electrical connector for the passenger side airbag.

This procedure is called "disabling air bags" in most service information. Always follow the vehicle manufacturer's specified procedures.

DIAGNOSTIC AND SERVICE PROCEDURE   Airbag system components and their location in the vehicle vary according to system design, but the basic principles of testing are the same as for other electrical circuits. Use service information to determine how the circuit is designed and the correct sequence of tests to be followed.

- Some airbag systems require the use of special testers. The built-in safety circuits of such testers prevent accidental deployment of the airbag.

Why Change Knee Bolsters If Switching to Larger Wheels?

Larger wheels and tires can be installed on vehicles, but the powertrain control module (PCM) needs to be reprogrammed so the speedometer and other systems that are affected by a change in wheel/tire size can work effectively. When 20 in. wheels are installed on General Motors trucks or sport utility vehicles (SUVs), GM specifies that replacement knee bolsters be installed. Knee bolsters are the padded area located on the lower part of the dash where a driver or passenger's knees would hit in the event of a front collision. The reason for the need to replace the knee bolsters is to maintain the crash testing results. The larger 20 in. wheels would tend to be forced further into the passenger compartment in the event of a front-end collision. Therefore to maintain the frontal crash rating standard, the larger knee bolsters are required.

WARNING: Failure to perform the specified changes when changing wheels and tires could result in the vehicle not being able to provide occupant protection as designed by the crash test star rating that the vehicle originally achieved.

- If such a tester is not available, follow the recommended alternative test procedures specified by the manufacturer.
- Access the self-diagnostic system and check for diagnostic trouble code (DTC) records.
- The scan tool is needed to access the data stream on most systems.

SELF-DIAGNOSIS All airbag systems can detect system electrical faults, and if found will disable the system and notify the driver through an airbag warning lamp in the instrument cluster. Depending on circuit design, a system fault may cause the warning lamp to fail to illuminate, remain lit continuously, or flash. Some systems use a tone generator that produces an audible warning when a system fault occurs or if the warning lamp is inoperative.

The warning lamp should illuminate with the ignition key on and engine off as a bulb check. If not, the diagnostic module is likely disabling the system. If the airbag warning light remains on, the airbags may or may not be disabled, depending on the specific vehicle and the fault detected. Some warning lamp circuits have a timer that extinguishes the lamp after a few seconds. The airbag system generally does not require service unless there is a failed component. However, a steering wheel–mounted airbag module is routinely removed and replaced in order to service switches and other column-mounted devices.

KNEE AIRBAGS Some vehicles are equipped with **knee airbags** usually on the driver's side. Use caution if working under the dash and always follow the vehicle manufacturer's specified service procedures.

DRIVER SIDE AIRBAG MODULE REPLACEMENT

For the specific model being serviced, carefully follow the procedures provided by the vehicle manufacturer to disable and remove the airbag module. Failure to do so may result in serious injury and extensive damage to the vehicle. Replacing a discharged airbag is costly. The following procedure reviews the basic steps for removing an airbag module. Do not substitute these general instructions for the specific procedure recommended by the manufacturer.

1. Turn the steering wheel until the front wheels are positioned straight ahead. Some components on the steering column are removed only when the front wheels are straight.
2. Switch the ignition off and disconnect the negative battery cable, which cuts power to the airbag module.
3. Once the battery is disconnected, wait as long as recommended by the manufacturer before continuing. When in doubt, wait at least 10 minutes to make sure the capacitor is completely discharged.
4. Loosen and remove the nuts or screws that hold the airbag module in place. On some vehicles, these fasteners are located on the back of the steering wheel. On other vehicles, they are located on each side of the steering wheel. The fasteners may be concealed with plastic finishing covers that must be pried off with a small screwdriver to access them.
5. Carefully lift the airbag module from the steering wheel and disconnect the electrical connector. Connector location varies: Some are below the steering wheel behind a plastic trim cover; others are at the top of the column under the module. ● **SEE FIGURES 42–15 AND 42–16.**
6. Store the module pad side up in a safe place where it will not be disturbed or damaged while the vehicle is being serviced. Do not attempt to disassemble the airbag module. If the airbag is defective, replace the entire assembly.

When installing the airbag module, make sure the clockspring is correctly positioned to ensure module-to-steering-column continuity. ● **SEE FIGURE 42–17.**

Always route the wiring exactly as it was before removal. Also, make sure the module seats completely into the steering wheel. Secure the assembly using new fasteners, if specified.

FRONT VIEW

HORN BUTTONS
STEERING WHEEL
CRUISE CONTROL BUTTONS
HORN WIRING HARNESS
STEERING COLUMN
CRUISE CONTROL WIRING HARNESS
AIR BAG ELECTRICAL CONNECTOR
AIR BAG MODULE

FIGURE 42–15 After disconnecting the battery and the yellow connector at the base of the steering column, the airbag inflator module can be removed from the steering wheel and the yellow airbag electrical connector at the inflator module disconnected.

SHORTING BARS

SHORTING BARS

FIGURE 42–16 Shorting bars are used in most airbag connectors. These spring-loaded clips short across both terminals of an airbag connector when it is disconnected to help prevent accidental deployment of the airbag. If electrical power was applied to the terminals, the shorting bars would simply provide a low-resistance path to the other terminal and not allow current to flow past the connector. The mating part of the connector has a tapered piece that spreads apart the shorting bars when the connector is reconnected.

SAFETY WHEN MANUALLY DEPLOYING AIRBAGS

Airbag modules cannot be disposed of unless they are deployed. Do the following to prevent injury when manually deploying an airbag.

- When possible, deploy the airbag outside of the vehicle. Follow the vehicle manufacturer's recommendations.

FIGURE 42–17 An airbag clockspring showing the flat conductor wire. It must be properly positioned to ensure proper operation.

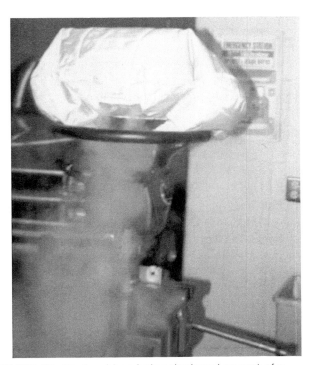

FIGURE 42–18 An airbag being deployed as part of a demonstration in an automotive laboratory.

- Follow the vehicle manufacturer's procedures and equipment recommendations.
- Wear the proper hearing and eye protection.
- Deploy the airbag with the trim cover facing up.
- Stay at least 20 ft (6 m) from the airbag. (Use long jumper wires attached to the wiring and routed outside the vehicle to a battery.)
- Allow the airbag module to cool.
  - ● SEE FIGURE 42–18.

OCCUPANT DETECTION SYSTEMS

PURPOSE AND FUNCTION The U.S. Federal Motor Vehicle Safety Standard 208 (FMVSS) specifies that the passenger side airbag be disabled or deployed with reduced force under the following conditions. This system is referred to as an **occupant detection system (ODS)** or the **passenger presence system (PPS)**.

- When there is no weight on the seat and no seat belt is fastened, the passenger side airbag will not deploy and the passenger airbag light should be off. ● SEE FIGURE 42–19.

- The passenger side airbag will be disabled and the disabled airbag light will be on if only 10 to 37 lb (4.5 to 17 kg) is on the passenger seat, which would generally represent a seated child.

- If 38 to 99 lb (17 to 45 kg) is detected on the passenger seat, which represents a child or small adult, the airbag will deploy at a decreased force.

- If 99 lb (45 kg) or more is detected on the passenger seat, the airbag will deploy at full force, depending on the severity of the crash, speed of the vehicle, and other factors which may result in the airbag deploying at a reduced force.

  ● **SEE FIGURE 42–20.**

TYPE OF SEAT SENSOR The passenger presence system (PPS) uses one of three types of sensors.

- **Gel-filled bladder sensor.** This type of occupant sensor uses a silicone-filled bag that has a pressure sensor attached. The weight of the passenger is measured by the pressure sensor, which sends a voltage signal to the module controlling the airbag deployment. A safety belt tension sensor is also used with a gel-filled bladder system to monitor the tension on the belt. The module then uses the information from both the bladder and the seat belt sensor to determine if a tightened belt may be used to restrain a child seat. ● SEE FIGURE 42–21.

- **Capacitive strip sensors.** This type of occupant sensor uses several flexible conductive metal strips under the seat cushion. These sensor strips transmit and receive a low-level electric field, which changes due to the weight of the front passenger seat occupant. The module determines the weight of the occupant based on the sensor values.

- **Force-sensing resistor sensors.** This type of occupant sensor uses resistors, which change their resistance based on the stress that is applied. These resistors are part of the seat structure, and the module can determine the weight of the occupant based on the change in the resistance of the sensors. ● SEE FIGURE 42–22.

FIGURE 42–19 A dash warning lamp will light if the passenger side airbag is off because no passenger was detected by the seat sensor.

FIGURE 42–20 The passenger side airbag "on" lamp will light if a passenger is detected on the passenger seat.

FIGURE 42–21 A gel-filled (bladder-type) occupant detection sensor showing the pressure sensor and wiring.

FIGURE 42-22 A resistor-type occupant detection sensor. The weight of the passenger strains these resistors, which are attached to the seat, thereby signaling to the module the weight of the occupant.

FIGURE 42-23 A test weight is used to calibrate the occupant detection system on a Chrysler vehicle.

CAUTION: Because the resistors are part of the seat structure, it is very important that all seat fasteners be torqued to factory specifications to ensure proper operation of the occupant detection system. A *seat track position (STP) sensor* **is used by the airbag controller to determine the position of the seat. If the seat is too close to the airbag, the controller may disable the airbag.**

DIAGNOSING OCCUPANT DETECTION SYSTEMS
A fault in the system may cause the passenger side airbag light to turn on when there is no weight on the seat. A scan tool is often used to check or calibrate the seat, which must be empty, by commanding the module to rezero the seat sensor. Some systems, such as those on Chrysler vehicles, use a unit that has various weights along with a scan tool to calibrate and diagnose the occupant detection system. ● **SEE FIGURE 42-23.**

SEAT AND SIDE CURTAIN AIRBAGS

SEAT AIRBAGS Side and/or *curtain airbags* use a variety of sensors to determine if they need to be deployed. **Side airbags** are mounted in one of two general locations.

FIGURE 42-24 A typical seat (side) airbag that deploys from the side of the seat.

  TECH TIP

Aggressive Driving and OnStar
If a vehicle equipped with the OnStar system is being driven aggressively and the electronic stability control system has to intercede to keep the vehicle under control, OnStar may call the vehicle to see if there has been an accident. The need for a call from OnStar usually will be determined if the accelerometer registers slightly over 1 g-force, which could be achieved while driving on a race track.

■ In the side bolster of the seat (● **SEE FIGURE 42-24.**)

■ In the door panel

Most side airbag sensors use an electronic accelerometer to detect when to deploy the airbags, which are usually mounted to the bottom of the left and right "B" pillars (where the front doors latch) behind a trim panel on the inside of the vehicle.

CAUTION: Avoid using a lockout tool (e.g., a "slim jim") in vehicles equipped with side airbags to help prevent damage to the components and wiring in the system.

SIDE CURTAIN AIRBAGS Side curtain airbags are usually deployed by a module based on input from many different sensors, including a lateral acceleration sensor and wheel speed sensors. For example, in one system used by Ford, the ABS controller commands that the brakes on one side of the vehicle be applied, using down pressure while monitoring the wheel speed sensors. If the wheels slow down with little brake pressure, the controller assumes that the vehicle could roll over, thereby deploying the side curtain airbags.

EVENT DATA RECORDERS

PARTS AND OPERATION   As part of the airbag controller on many vehicles, the **event data recorder (EDR)** is used to record parameters just before and slightly after an airbag deployment. The following parameters are recorded.

- Vehicle speed
- Brake on/off
- Seat belt fastened
- G-forces as measured by the accelerometer

Unlike an airplane event data recorder, a vehicle unit is not a separate unit and does not record voice conversations and does not include all crash parameters. This means that additional crash data, such as skid marks and physical evidence at the crash site, will be needed to fully reconstruct the incident.

The EDR is embedded into the airbag controller and receives data from many sources and at varying sample rates. The data is constantly being stored in a memory buffer and not recorded into the EPROM unless an airbag deployment has been commanded. The combined data is known as an *event file*. The airbag is commanded on, based on input mainly from the accelerometer sensor. This sensor, usually built into the airbag controller, is located inside the vehicle. The accelerometer calculates the rate of change of the speed of the vehicle. This determines the acceleration rate and is used to predict if that rate is high enough to deploy the frontal airbags. The airbags will be deployed if the threshold g-value is exceeded. The passenger side airbag will also be deployed unless it is suppressed by either of the following:

- No passenger is detected.
- The passenger side airbag switch is off.

DATA EXTRACTION   Data extraction from the event data recorder in the airbag controller can only be achieved using a piece of equipment known as the Crash Data Retrieval System, manufactured by Vetronics Corporation. This is the only authorized method for retrieving event files and only certain organizations are allowed access to the data. These groups or organizations include:

- Original equipment manufacturer's representatives
- National Highway Traffic Safety Administration
- Law enforcement agencies
- Accident reconstruction companies

Crash data retrieval must only be done by a trained crash data retrieval (CDR) technician or analyst. A technician undergoes specialized training and must pass an examination. An analyst must attend additional training beyond that of a technician to achieve CDR analyst certification.

SUMMARY

1. Airbags use a sensor(s) to determine if the rate of deceleration is enough to cause bodily harm.
2. All airbag electrical connectors and conduit are yellow and all electrical terminals are gold plated to protect against corrosion.
3. Always follow the manufacturer's procedure for disabling the airbag system prior to any work performed on the system.
4. Frontal airbags only operate within 30 degrees from center and do not deploy in the event of a rollover, side, or rear collision.
5. Two sensors must be triggered at the same time for an airbag deployment to occur. Many newer systems use an accelerometer-type crash sensor that actually measures the amount of deceleration.
6. Pretensioners are explosive (pyrotechnic) devices which remove the slack from the seat belt and help position the occupant.
7. Occupant detection systems use sensors in the seat to determine whether the airbag will be deployed and with full or reduced force.

REVIEW QUESTIONS

1. What are the safety precautions to follow when working around an airbag?
2. What sensor(s) must be triggered for an airbag deployment?
3. How should deployed inflation modules be handled?
4. What is the purpose of pretensioners?

1. A vehicle is being repaired after an airbag deployment. Technician A says that the inflator module should be handled as if it is still live. Technician B says gloves should be worn to prevent skin irritation. Which technician is correct?
   a. Technician A only
   b. Technician B only
   c. Both Technicians A and B
   d. Neither Technician A nor B

2. A seat belt pretensioner is _____.
   a. A device that contains an explosive charge
   b. Used to remove slack from the seat belt in the event of a collision
   c. Used to force the occupant back into position against the seat back in the event of a collision
   d. All of the above

3. What conducts power and ground to the driver's side airbag?
   a. Twisted-pair wires
   b. Clockspring
   c. Carbon contact and brass surface plate on the steering column
   d. Magnetic reed switch

4. Two technicians are discussing two-stage airbags. Technician A says that a deployed airbag is safe to handle regardless of which stage caused the deployment of the airbag. Technician B says that both stages ignite, but at different speeds depending on the speed of the vehicle. Which technician is correct?
   a. Technician A only
   b. Technician B only
   c. Both Technicians A and B
   d. Neither Technician A nor B

5. Where are shorting bars used?
   a. In pretensioners
   b. At the connectors for airbags
   c. In the crash sensors
   d. In the airbag controller

6. Technician A says that a deployed airbag can be repacked, reused, and reinstalled in the vehicle. Technician B says that a deployed airbag should be discarded and replaced with an entire new assembly. Which technician is correct?
   a. Technician A only
   b. Technician B only
   c. Both Technicians A and B
   d. Neither Technician A nor B

7. What color are the airbag electrical connectors and conduit?
   a. Blue
   b. Red
   c. Yellow
   d. Orange

8. Driver and/or passenger front airbags will only deploy if a collision occurs how many degrees from straight ahead?
   a. 10 degrees
   b. 30 degrees
   c. 60 degrees
   d. 90 degrees

9. How many sensors must be triggered at the same time to cause an airbag deployment?
   a. One
   b. Two
   c. Three
   d. Four

10. The electrical terminals used for airbag systems are unique because they are _____.
    a. Solid copper
    b. Tin-plated heavy-gauge steel
    c. Silver plated
    d. Gold plated

TIRE PRESSURE MONITORING SYSTEMS

OBJECTIVES: **After studying Chapter 43, the reader will be able to:** • Explain why a tire-pressure monitoring system is used. • Discuss the TREAD Act. • List the two types of TPMS sensors. • Describe how to program or relearn TPMS sensors. • List the tools needed to service a tire-pressure monitoring system.

KEY TERMS: • Active mode 528 • Alert mode 528 • Cold placard inflation pressure 524 • Delta pressure method 531 • Initialization 526 • Relearn 526 • Sleep mode 528 • Storage mode 529 • Tire-pressure monitoring system (TPMS) 524 • Transmitter ID 530 • TREAD Act 526

NEED FOR TIRE PRESSURE MONITORING

BACKGROUND A **tire-pressure monitoring system (TPMS)** is a system that detects a tire that has low inflation pressure and warns the driver. A tire-pressure monitoring system was first used when run-flat tires were introduced in the 1990s. A driver was often not aware that a tire had gone flat after a puncture. Because a run-flat tire is designed to be driven a limited distance and at limited speed after it loses air pressure, a method of alerting the driver had to be found. There were two systems used, indirect and direct, until the 2008 model year when the use of direct-reading pressure systems was required by law.

LOW TIRE PRESSURE EFFECTS Low-tire inflation pressures have led to all of the following:

- Reduces fuel economy due to increased rolling resistance of the tires—3 PSI below specifications results in an increase of 1% in fuel consumption
- Reduces tire life—3 PSI below specifications results in a decrease of 10% of tire life
- Increases the number of roadside faults, which have been estimated to be 90% related to tire issues
- Reduces handling and braking efficiency
- Hundreds of deaths and thousands of personal injuries are due to problems associated with low-tire inflation pressure.

COLD PLACARD INFLATION PRESSURE The term **cold placard inflation pressure** is used in service information to indicate the specified tire inflation pressure. The "placard" is the driver's side door jamb sticker that shows the tire size and the specified tire inflation pressure. The pressure stated is measured when the tires are cold or at room temperature, which is about 70°F (21°C). ● **SEE FIGURE 43–1.**

The tires become warmer while the vehicle is being driven, so tires should be checked before the vehicle has been driven or allowed to cool after being driven. Tire inflation pressure changes 1 PSI for every 10 degrees. ● **SEE CHART 43–1.**

FIGURE 43–1 The tire pressure placard (sticker) on the driver's side door or door jamb indicates the specified tire pressure.

TEMPERATURE	TIRE PRESSURE (PSI)	CHANGE FROM COLD PLACARD INFLATION PRESSURE
120°F (49°C)	37	+5
110°F (43°C)	36	+4
100°F (38°C)	35	+3
90°F (32°C)	34	+2
80°F (27°C)	33	+1
70°F (21°C)	32	0
60°F (16°C)	31	−1
50°F (10°C)	30	−2
40°F (4°C)	29	−3
30°F (−1°C)	28	−4
20°F (−7°C)	27	−5
10°F (−12°C)	26	−6
0°F (−18°C)	25	−7
−10°F (−23°C)	24	−8
−20°F (−29°C)	23	−9

CHART 43–1
The effects of outside temperature on tire inflation, assuming a placard pressure of 32 PSI.

INDIRECT TPMS

PURPOSE AND FUNCTION Indirect tire-pressure monitoring systems do not measure the actual tire pressure. Instead, the system uses the wheel speed sensors to detect differences in the speed of the wheels. The indirect system uses the wheel speed sensors to check the rolling speed of each of the tires. If a tire is underinflated, the following occurs:

- A tire that is underinflated will have a smaller diameter than a properly inflated tire. ● SEE FIGURE 43–2.
- An underinflated tire will rotate faster than a properly inflated tire.

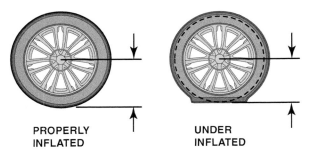

PROPERLY INFLATED   UNDER INFLATED

FIGURE 43–2 A tire with low inflation will have a shorter distance (radius) between the center of the wheel and the road and will therefore rotate faster than a tire that is properly inflated.

FIGURE 43–3 The speeds of the diagonally opposed wheels are added together and then compared to the other two wheels to check if one tire is rotating faster.

COMPENSATION FOR CORNERING When a vehicle turns a corner, the outside wheels rotate faster than the inside wheels. To compensate for this normal change in wheel rotation speed, the indirect tire-pressure monitoring system checks the diagonally opposed wheels. ● SEE FIGURE 43–3.

If the calculation of the diagonal wheel speed indicates that one of the wheels is rotating faster than the other, the TPMS warning light is illuminated.

ADVANTAGES Advantages for using the indirect system include:

- This system does not require additional components, such as tire-pressure sensors.
- This system is easily added to existing vehicles that were equipped with four-wheel speed sensors.
- It is low cost.

DISADVANTAGES Disadvantages for using the indirect system include:

- System cannot detect if all four tires are underinflated.
- Use of a space-saver spare tire may trigger the warning light.
- Cannot detect if more than one tire is low.
- Does not meet the Federal Highway Traffic Safety Standard (FMVSS) 138, which requires the system to be able to detect if any tire is underinflated by 25%.

DIAGNOSIS OF INDIRECT TPMS The diagnosis of an indirect tire-pressure monitoring system includes the following steps:

STEP 1 Verify the fault.
- If the TPMS warning light is on but not flashing, this indicates that the system has detected a tire with low inflation pressure.
- If the TPMS warning light flashes, this indicates that the system has detected a fault. Check service information for the specified steps to follow.

STEP 2 If the system has detected low tire pressure, check and adjust the tire pressure to that listed on the door pillar placard or factory specifications as stated in the owner's manual or service information.

STEP 3 Determine and correct the cause of the underinflated tire.

FIGURE 43–4 The indirect tire-pressure monitoring system has a reset switch that should be depressed after rotating or replacing tires.

RELEARN (RESET) PROCEDURES

After checking that all four tires are the same size and condition, the system may require resetting, also called **relearn** or **initialization.** Check service information for the exact steps to follow, which could include driving the vehicle over an extended period of time. The procedure usually includes the following:

- Inflate all four tires to the placard inflation pressure.
- Depress and hold the reset switch for 3 seconds. ● **SEE FIGURE 43–4.** The TPMS warning lamp should flash three times.
- Drive the vehicle so the ABS controller can learn the new "good" values. Typical driving times include:
  - Ford—20 minutes of driving
  - Toyota—30 to 60 minutes of driving
  - General Motors—60 minutes of driving

Check service information for the exact procedure to follow. Many service technicians ask the vehicle owner to drive the vehicle instead of taking the technician's time.

TREAD ACT

The **Transportation Recall Enhancement, Accountability and Documentation (TREAD) Act** requires that all vehicles be equipped with a tire-pressure monitoring system that will warn the driver in the event of an underinflated tire. This act was passed due to many accidents that were caused at least in part to underinflated tires. These accidents resulted in many deaths.

Congress passed the TREAD Act on November 1, 2000. The National Highway Traffic Safety Administration (NHTSA) requires the installation of tire-pressure monitoring systems (TPMSs) in passenger vehicles and light trucks manufactured after September 1, 2007 (2008 model year).

The NHTSA ruling is part one of a two-part final ruling.

- Part one establishes a new Federal Motor Vehicle Safety Standard (FMVSS) 138 that requires tire-pressure monitoring systems be installed in passenger vehicles and light trucks to warn the driver when a tire is 25% below the cold placard pressure.
- Part two includes the requirement to equip vehicles with a tire-pressure monitoring system that was phased-in starting in 2004. The phase-in included:
  - 20% from October 5, 2005 to August 31, 2006
  - 70% from September 1, 2006 to August 31, 2007
  - 100% from September 1, 2007 (2008 model year vehicles)

FMVSS 138 requires all cars, trucks, and vans with a gross vehicle weight rating (GVWR) of 10,000 pounds or less to illuminate a warning lamp within 10 minutes when the inflation pressure drops 25% or more from the vehicle manufacturer's specified cold tire inflation pressure as printed on the door placard.

WARNING LAMP The FMVSS 138 specifies that the driver must be warned of a low-tire inflation pressure by turning on an amber warning lamp. The warning lamp must also come on during a bulb check. The spare tire is not required to be monitored, but many vehicle manufacturers do equip full-size spare tires with a pressure sensor.

- If the TPMS warning lamp is on at start-up, the system has detected a tire with low inflation pressure.
- If the TPMS warning lamp is flashing for 60 to 90 seconds, a system fault has been detected.

TWENTY-FIVE PERCENT RULE The TREAD Act specifies that the driver be warned if any tire inflation pressure drops by 25% or more from the cold placard pressure. ● **SEE CHART 43–2.**

COLD PLACARD INFLATION PRESSURE (PSI)	WARNING LIGHT PRESSURE (−25%)	PSI LOW
40	30.0	10.0
39	29.3	9.7
38	28.5	9.5
37	27.8	9.2
36	27.0	9.0
35	26.3	8.7
34	25.5	8.5
33	24.8	8.2
32	24	8.0
31	23.3	7.7
30	22.5	7.5
29	21.8	7.2
28	21	7.0

CHART 43–2

Placard inflation pressure compared with the pressure when the TPMS triggers a warning light.

Industry experts think that 25% is too low and that this generally means that a tire has to be lower by about 8 PSI to trigger a warning light. All experts agree that tire pressure should be checked at least every month and kept at the specified cold placard inflation pressure.

FIGURE 43–6 A conventional valve stem is on the right compared with a rubber TPMS sensor stem on the left. Notice the tapered and larger brass stem. The rubber TPMS sensor also uses a longer cap that makes it easy for a technician to spot that this is not a conventional rubber valve stem.

IDENTIFYING A VEHICLE WITH TPMS

All vehicles sold in the United States since the 2008 model year must be equipped with a tire-pressure sensor. If the tire/wheel assembly has a tire-pressure monitoring system (TPMS) valve-type sensor, it can usually be identified by the threaded portion of the valve stem. ● SEE FIGURE 43–5.

RUBBER TIRE VALVE STEMS   Some TPMS sensors are black rubber like a conventional valve core but it uses a tapered brass section and a longer cap. ● SEE FIGURE 43–6. If the cap is short then it does not have a stem-mounted tire-pressure

Some replacement tires use steel body plies and could therefore block the low-level radio frequency signal sent from the tire-pressure sensor. Before installing replacement tires, check that the tires are safe and recommended for use on vehicles equipped with a direct-type tire-pressure monitoring system.

sensor. However, the wheel may be equipped with a wheel-mounted sensor, so care should still be taken to avoid damaging the sensor during service.

ALUMINUM TIRE VALVE STEMS   If the vehicle has an aluminum tire valve stem, it is equipped with a direct tire-pressure monitoring system. The valve stem itself is the antenna for the sensor.

FIGURE 43–5 A clear plastic valve-stem tire-pressure monitoring sensor, showing the round battery on the right and the electronic sensor and transistor circuits on the left.

TPMS PRESSURE SENSORS

TYPES   All direct TPMS sensors transmit tire inflation pressure to a module using a radio frequency (RF) signal. There are two basic designs used in direct pressure-sensing systems.

These sensors are manufactured by a variety of manufacturers, including:

- Beru
- Lear
- Pacific
- Schrader
- Siemens
- TRW

Each sensor uses a 3-volt lithium ion battery that has a service life of 7 to 10 years.

1. **Valve stem-mounted sensor**—This type of sensor uses the valve stem as the transmitter. The correct (nickel plated) valve core *must* be used in the aluminum valve stem. If a conventional brass valve is used, moisture in the air will cause corrosion between the two different metals.

2. **Banded sensor**—Banded sensors are installed in the drop well of the wheel and banded or clamped to keep them secure. Early banded sensors, such as those used in Corvettes equipped with run-flat tires, were piezoelectric and did not require a battery. All newer banded sensors include a battery. ● **SEE FIGURE 43–7.**

MODES OF OPERATION   Tire-pressure sensors operate in three modes of operation:

1. **Active mode**—When the sensor inside detects that the vehicle is traveling above 20 mph (32 km/h), the sensor transmits once every minute.

2. **Sleep mode**—When the vehicle is stopped, the sensor "goes to sleep" to help improve battery life. In this mode, the transmitter still will broadcast tire inflation information every hour or every 6 hours, depending on the sensor.

3. **Alert mode**—Alert mode is triggered if a rapid change in inflation pressure is detected. In alert (or rapid mode), the tire inflation pressure is sent about every second (every 800 milliseconds on some sensors).

FIGURE 43–7 The three styles of TPMS sensors most commonly found include the two stem-mounted (rubber and aluminum, left and top), and the banded style (right).

TPMS SENSOR OPERATION

Depending on the type and manufacturer, tire-pressure monitoring sensors can be any of several different designs. The TREAD Act does not specify the type or operation of the pressure sensors, only that the system must be capable of measuring tire inflation pressure and light the TPMS warning lamp. The types of sensors include:

- **Continuous-wave-type sensor**—designed to signal a tester when exposed to 5 to 7 seconds of continuous 125 KHz wave signal.
- **Magnetically-triggered-type sensor**—designed to trigger a tester if exposed to a powerful magnetic force.
- **Pulse-width-modulated-type sensor**—designed to be triggered when exposed to modulated wave 125 KHz signal.

TECH TIP

Check the TPMS Sensors Before and After Service

It is wise to check that all of the tire-pressure monitoring system sensors are working before beginning service work. For example, if the tires need to be rotated, the sensors will have to be reprogrammed for their new location. If a tire-pressure monitoring sensor is defective, the procedure cannot be performed. Use an aftermarket or original equipment tire-pressure monitoring sensor tester, as shown in ● **FIGURE 43–8.**

Then the tire-pressure sensors should be checked again after the service to make sure that they are working correctly before returning the vehicle to the customer.

FIGURE 43–8 A typical tire-pressure monitoring system tester. The unit should be held near the tire and opposite the valve stem if equipped with a wheel-mounted sensor, and near the valve stem if equipped with a valve-stem-type sensor.

TECH TIP

? FREQUENTLY ASKED QUESTION

Does a TPMS Sensor Work before Being Installed?

No. New tire-pressure warning sensors (transmitters) are shipped in **storage mode.** This mode prevents the battery from becoming discharged while in storage. When the transmitter is installed in a wheel/tire assembly and the tire is inflated to more than 14 PSI (97 kPa), the transmitter automatically cancels storage mode. Once a transmitter has canceled storage mode, it cannot enter this mode again. Therefore, once a sensor has been installed and the tire inflated above 14 PSI, the clock is ticking on battery life.

The sensor also can vary according to the frequency at which it transmits tire-pressure information to the receiver in the vehicle. The two most commonly used frequencies are:

- 315 MHz
- 433.92 MHz (commonly listed as 434 MHz)

TPMS RECEIVER

The wireless TPMS receiver is housed in one of the following locations, depending on the vehicle:

- Remote keyless entry (RKE) receiver
- Body control module (BCM)
- Door module
- Individual antennas near each wheel well. These individual antennas then transmit tire-pressure information to the driver information center.
  ● **SEE FIGURE 43–9.**

FIGURE 43–9 Some vehicles display the actual measured tire pressure for each tire on a driver information display.

TECH TIP

Check the Spare Tire

Many vehicles equipped with a full-size spare tire also have a TPMS sensor. If the inflation pressure decreases enough, the system will trigger the TPMS warning light. This is confusing to many vehicle owners who have checked all four tires and found them to be properly inflated. This fault often occurs during cold weather when the tire inflation pressure drops due to the temperature change. Most 2008 and newer vehicles equipped with a full size spare tire will come equipped with a TPMS sensor in the spare.

DIRECT TPMS DIAGNOSIS

WARNING LIGHT ON If the TPMS warning light is on and not flashing, the system has detected a tire that has low inflation pressure. ● **SEE FIGURE 43–10.**

If the TPMS light is on, perform the following steps:

STEP 1 Check the door placard for the specified tire inflation pressure.

STEP 2 Check all tires using a known-accurate tire-pressure gauge.

STEP 3 Inflate all tires to the specified pressure.

NOTE: Some systems will trigger the TPMS warning light if a tire is overinflated. An overinflated tire is also a safety-related problem.

FIGURE 43–10 A tire-pressure warning light can vary depending on the vehicle, but includes a tire symbol.

WARNING LIGHT FLASHING If the TPMS warning lamp is flashing on and off, the system has detected a fault in the system. Faults could include:

- Defective wheel sensors, such as a sensor with a dead battery.
- A fault in the receiver, such as in the remote keyless entry module.

Check service information for the exact procedure to follow if the TPMS warning lamp is flashing. Always follow the specified diagnostic and service procedures.

INSTALLING A NEW PRESSURE SENSOR

When installing a new pressure sensor either because it failed or was damaged, the new sensor has to be relearned. This process is usually done with either:

- A scan tool
- A TPMS tester

The identification number on each sensor must be recorded before being installed, so it can register to a specific location on the vehicle. All four sensor identification numbers usually have to be entered into the tool within 300 seconds (five minutes). On some vehicles, all four sensors must be relearned even if only one sensor is replaced.

TPMS DIAGNOSTIC TOOLS

SCAN TOOLS Scan tools can be used for TPMS service if the scan tool is an original equipment tool for the vehicle make or if an aftermarket scan tool has original equipment-compatible software to access the chassis or body functions of the vehicle. A scan tool is used to perform the following functions:

1. **Register TPMS sensors**—A replacement TPMS transmitter has an 8-digit number, called the **transmitter ID,** on each valve/transmitter assembly. ● SEE FIGURE 43–11.
2. **Perform initialization**—This step assigns a transmitter ID to the correct position on the vehicle, such as right front (RF). ● SEE FIGURE 43–12.
3. **Monitor sensor values**—TPMS transmitters send information to the controller including:
   - Sensor identification
   - Tire inflation pressure
   - Tire air temperature (some sensors)
   - Sensor battery voltage (some sensors)

VALVE CAP

VALVE STEM

RIM SEAL

HOLE TO ALLOW AIR INTO TIRE

HOLE TO ALLOW AIR INTO SENSOR

SENSOR BODY TO PROTECT ELECTRONICS

FIGURE 43–11 The parts of a typical stem-mounted TPMS sensor. Notice the small hole used to monitor the inflation pressure. The use of stop-leak can easily clog this small hole.

ID NUMBER (3RD LINE) HEXADECIMAL 8 DIGIT

FIGURE 43–12 When replacing a TPMS sensor, be sure to record the sensor ID because this needs to be entered into the system through the use of a tester or scan tool.

TPMS SENSOR ACTIVATIONS

ACTIVATING THE SENSOR A tire-pressure monitoring system sensor needs to be activated to verify that the sensor actually works. This should be performed before any tire or wheel service is performed. There are three methods used to activate a TPMS sensor to cause it to send a signal that can be captured to verify proper operation. These activation methods include:

1. **Using a magnet** (aluminum wheels and stem-mounted sensors only) ● **SEE FIGURE 43–13.**

2. **Changing inflation pressure** (usually requires lowering the inflation pressure by 5 to 10 PSI) This method is called the **delta pressure method.** The term *delta* refers to a change and is named for the Greek letter delta (Δ).

3. **Triggered by a handheld TPMS tester** that transmits a signal to wake up the sensor. There are two formats used, depending on the sensor. They include:

   - 125 KHz constant or continuous pulse
   - 125 KHz pulse-width-modulated pulse

HANDHELD TESTERS Several manufacturers produce handheld testers to reset the sensors. These tools are used to perform the following functions:

   - TPMS sensor activation
   - TPMS sensor relearn
   - To program a new TPMS sensor

Tools are available from the following companies:

   - OTC (http://www.otctools.com)
   - Bartec (http://www.bartecusa.com)
   - Snap-on (http://www.snapon.com)

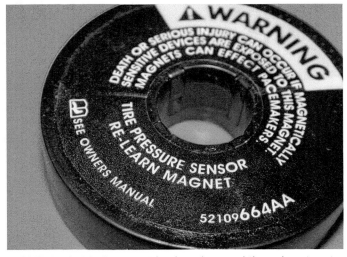

FIGURE 43–13 A magnet is placed around the valve stem to reprogram some stem-mounted tire-pressure sensors.

TPMS RELEARN PROCEDURE

The following procedure will allow the service technician to reprogram the TPMS after tire rotation on a General Motors vehicle without using a scan tool.

1. With KOEO (key on, engine off), the "lock" and "unlock" buttons on the key fob should be simultaneously pressed and held. The horn will chirp within 10 seconds, indicating the receiver is in programming mode. The programming procedure must now be completed within five minutes, with no more than one minute between programming.

   NOTE: If the horn does not chirp at the start of this procedure, the TPMS option has not been enabled. A scan tool is needed to enable the system.

2. At the left front wheel, the special magnet tool must be held over the valve stem to force the sensor to transmit its code. The horn will chirp once, indicating the system has recognized the sensor. The next sensor must be programmed within one minute.

3. The remaining sensors should be programmed in the following order: RF, RR, LR. The horn will chirp once when each sensor has been detected. It will chirp twice to indicate completion of the programming process.

TPMS SENSOR SERVICE TOOLS

ITEMS NEEDED Whenever servicing a tire/wheel assembly that has a direct TPMS system, certain items are needed. When a stem-mounted sensor is removed, the following items are needed:

1. **Information**—Check service information for the exact procedure to follow for the vehicle being serviced. Vehicles and sensors are different for different vehicles.

2. **Digital tire-pressure gauge**—Many mechanical tire-pressure gauges are not accurate. An old mechanical gauge may be used to ensure that all tires are inflated to the same pressure, but the pressure may not be accurate. ● **SEE FIGURE 43–14.**

3. **Tire valve core torque wrench**—This calibrated tool ensures that the valve core is tightened enough to prevent air loss, but not too tight to cause harm. The

FIGURE 43–14 Always use an accurate, known-good tire-pressure gauge. Digital gauges are usually more accurate than mechanical gauges.

recommended torque is 3 to 5 in.-lb (0.34 to 0.56 N.m).
● SEE FIGURE 43–15.

4. **Tire valve nut torque wrench**—Most are 11 or 12 mm in size and the torque ranges from 30 to 90 in.-lb (4.25 to 10.0 N.m).

5. **Sensor service kit**—If a pressure sensor is going to be reused, the following service parts must be replaced:

- Cap
- Valve core (nickel plated only)
- Nut
- Grommet

These parts are usually available individually or in an assortment package. Pressure sensor and kit information can be found at the following websites:

- http://www.schrader-bridgeport.com
- http://www.myerstiresupply.com
- http://www.rubber-inc.com
  ● SEE FIGURE 43–16.

FIGURE 43–15 A clicker-type valve core tool ensures that the valve core is tightened to factory specifications.

All TPMS Sensors Will Fail

All TPMS pressure sensors will fail because they contain a battery that has a service life of 7 to 10 years. What does this mean to the service technician? This means that if new tires are being installed on a 5- or 6-year-old vehicle equipped with tire-pressure sensors, then the customer should be notified that the TPMS sensors could fail almost anytime.

 FREQUENTLY ASKED QUESTION

Can TPMS sensors be switched to new wheels?

Maybe. It depends on the style of the new or replacement wheels as to whether the sensors will fit or not. Some vehicles are designed to allow for a second set of sensors such as for winter tires. Many Lexus vehicles can be programmed to use set #1 or set #2. It is best to check before purchasing new wheels. Another set of TPMS sensors could be a major added expense.

FIGURE 43–16 An assortment of service parts that include all of the parts needed to service a stem-mounted TPMS sensor being installed after removal for a tire replacement or repair.

1. Low-tire inflation pressure can cause a decrease in fuel economy, reduced tire life, and increase the chance of tire failure.

2. The designated tire inflation pressure is stated on the driver's side door jamb placard.

3. Tire inflation pressure drops 1 PSI for every 10 degrees drop in temperature.

4. The indirect tire-pressure monitoring system uses the wheel speed sensors to detect a low tire.

5. The TREAD Act, also called the Federal Motor Vehicle Safety Standard 138, specifies that all cars, trucks, and vans under 10,000 pounds gross vehicle weight rating (GVWR) must be equipped with a direct pressure-sending tire-pressure monitoring system after September 1, 2007 (2008 model year vehicles).

6. The two basic types of TPMS sensors include:
   - Valve stem-mounted
   - Banded

7. After a tire rotation, the sensors need to be reset or relearned.

8. Special tools are recommended to relearn, activate, or service a tire-pressure monitoring system.

REVIEW QUESTIONS

1. How does the use of wheel speed sensors detect a tire with low inflation pressure?

2. What is the difference between faults when the TPMS warning lamp is on compared with when it is flashing?

3. What is the percentage of vehicles that each vehicle manufacturer must equip with TPMS?

4. TPMS pressure sensors can be made by what manufacturer?

5. What are the three modes of sensor operation?

6. What information is sent to the TPMS controller from the sensor?

7. After removing a stem-type pressure sensor to replace a tire or perform a tire repair, what should be replaced?

CHAPTER QUIZ

1. A tire with lower than specified inflation pressure could lead to what condition?
   a. Reduced fuel economy
   b. Reduced tire life
   c. Increased chances of roadside faults or accidents
   d. All of the above

2. Which tire inflation information should be checked to determine the proper tire inflation pressure?
   a. Cold placard inflation pressure
   b. The maximum pressure as stated on the sidewall of the tire
   c. 32 PSI in all tires
   d. Any of the above

3. Two technicians are discussing tire pressure and temperature. Technician A says that tire pressure will drop 1 PSI for every 10 degrees drop in temperature. Technician B says that the tire pressure will increase as the vehicle is being driven. Which technician is correct?
   a. Technician A only
   b. Technician B only
   c. Both Technicians A and B
   d. Neither Technician A nor B

4. Two technicians are discussing the indirect tire-pressure monitoring system. Technician A says that it was used by some vehicle manufacturers on vehicles before the 2008 model year. Technician B says that it uses the speeds of the RF and LR tires and compares the rotating speeds of the LF and RR tires to detect a low tire. Which technician is correct?
   a. Technician A only
   b. Technician B only
   c. Both Technicians A and B
   d. Neither Technician A nor B

5. The FMVSS 138 law requires that the driver be notified if the tire inflation pressure drops how much?
   a. 30%   b. 25%
   c. 20%   d. 15%

6. The two basic types of direct TPMS sensors include _____.
   a. Rubber stem and aluminum stem
   b. Beru and Schrader
   c. Stem-mounted and banded
   d. Indirect and direct

7. What mode does a direct pressure sensor enter when the vehicle is stopped?
   a. Sleep mode
   b. Storage mode
   c. Alert mode
   d. Active mode

8. To activate or learn a direct pressure sensor, what does the service technician need to do?
   a. Enter learn mode and use a magnet
   b. Enter learn mode and decrease inflation pressure
   c. Use a handheld tester
   d. Any of the above depending on the vehicle and system

9. What does the "delta pressure method" mean?
   a. Change the inflation pressure
   b. Activate the sensor so it broadcasts the pressure to the scan tool
   c. Inflating the tire to the specified pressure
   d. Using a handheld tester to read the pressure as reported by the sensor

10. What type of valve core is used in stem-mounted sensors?
    a. Brass
    b. Nickel plated
    c. Steel
    d. Aluminum

chapter 44

ELECTRONIC SUSPENSION SYSTEMS

OBJECTIVES: **After studying Chapter 44, the reader will be able to:** • Prepare for ASE Suspension and Steering (A4) certification test content area "B" (Suspension System Diagnosis and Repair). • Describe how suspension height sensors function. • Explain the use of the various sensors used for electronic suspension control. • Discuss the steering wheel position sensor. • Explain how solenoids and actuators are used to control the suspension.

KEY TERMS: • Actuator 535 • Air suspension (AS) 543 • Armature 542 • Automatic level control (ALC) 543 • CCVRTMR 549 • Computer command ride (CCR) 541 • Desiccant 549 • Driver selector switch 541 • EBCM 537 • ECU 535 • Electromagnet 541 • Handwheel position sensor 537 • Height sensor 536 • Input 535 • Lateral accelerometer sensor 539 • LED 536 • Magneto-rheological (MR) 549 • Mode select switch 543 • Motor 542 • MRRTD 549 • Output 535 • Perform ride mode 545 • Photocell 536 • Phototransistor 536 • Pulse width 541 • Pulse-width modulation 541 • Real-time dampening (RTD) 537 • RPO 546 • RSS 537 • Selectable ride (SR) 541 • Solenoid 541 • Solenoid controlled damper 546 • Stabilitrak 546 • Steering wheel position sensor 537 • Touring ride mode 545 • Vehicle stability enhancement system (VSES) 539 • VS sensor 538 • Yaw rate sensor 540

THE NEED FOR ELECTRONIC SUSPENSIONS

Since the mid-1980s, many vehicle manufacturers have been introducing models with electronic suspension controls that provide a variable shock stiffness or spring rate. The main advantage of electronic controls is that the suspension can react to different conditions. The system provides a firm suspension feel for fast cornering and quick acceleration and braking, with a soft ride for cruising. ● **SEE FIGURE 44–1.**

ELECTRONIC SUSPENSION CONTROLS AND SENSORS

Sensors and switches provide **input** to the electronic control module (ECM), or system computer. The ECM, which may also be referred to as the **electronic control unit (ECU),** is a small computer that receives input in the form of electrical signals from the sensors and switches and provides **output** electrical signals to the system actuators. ● **SEE FIGURE 44–2.** The electrical signal causes an **actuator** to perform some type of mechanical action.

CONVENTIONAL SUSPENSION

ELECTRONICALLY CONTROLLED SUSPENSION

FIGURE 44–1 An electronically controlled suspension system can help reduce body roll and other reactions better than most conventional suspension systems.

FIGURE 44–2 Input devices monitor conditions and provide information to the electronic control module, which processes the information and operates the actuators to control the movement of the suspension.

HEIGHT SENSOR

FIGURE 44–3 A typical electronic suspension height sensor, which bolts to the body and connects to the lower control arm through a control link and lever.

HEIGHT SENSORS Sensors, which are the input devices that transmit signals to the ECM, monitor operating conditions and component functions. A **height sensor** senses the vertical relationship between the suspension component and the body. Its signal indicates to the ECM how high the frame or body is, or how compressed the suspension is. A number of sensor designs are used to determine ride height, including a **photocell** type of sensor. ● SEE FIGURE 44–3.

FIGURE 44–4 When suspension action moves the lever, it rotates the slotted disc and varies how much of the photo transistor is exposed to the LEDs, which vary the input signal.

Four height sensors, one at each wheel, deliver an input signal to the ECM. All four sensors are similar and use a control link, lever, slotted disc, and four photo interrupters to transmit a signal. Each photo interrupter consists of a **light-emitting diode (LED)** and a **phototransistor,** which reacts to the LED.

Inside the sensor, the LEDs and phototransistors are positioned opposite each other on each side of the slotted disc. ● SEE FIGURE 44–4. When the system is activated, the ECM applies voltage to the LEDs, which causes them to illuminate. Light from an LED shining on the phototransistor causes the transistor to generate a voltage signal. Signals generated by the phototransistors are delivered to the ECM as an input that reflects ride height.

As suspension movement rotates the disc, the slots or windows on the disc either allow light from the LEDs to shine on the phototransistors or prevent it. The windows are positioned in such a manner that, in combination with the four LEDs and transistors, the sensor is capable of generating 16 different levels of voltage. This variable voltage, which is transmitted to the ECM as an input signal, directly corresponds to 1 of 16 possible positions of the suspension. This input signal tells the ECM the position of the suspension in relation to the body. Whether the input voltage signal is increasing or decreasing allows the ECM to determine if the suspension is compressing or extending.

The ECM can also determine the relative position of the body to the suspension, or the attitude of the vehicle, from the four height sensors. Comparing front-wheel input signals to those of the rear wheels determines the amount of pitch caused by forces of acceleration or deceleration. A side-to-side comparison allows the ECM to determine the amount of body roll generated by cornering force.

GENERAL MOTORS ELECTRONIC SUSPENSION SENSORS There are five different sensors found on electronic suspension systems, and GM vehicles can have between one and four of these sensors, depending on the system.

FIGURE 44–5 Typical suspension position sensor.

FIGURE 44–6 A three-wire suspension position sensor schematic.

Depending on the vehicle, the *suspension position sensor* may be called by a different name. It can be called:

- An automatic level control sensor
- An electronic suspension position sensor
- A position sensor
- An air suspension sensor

The sensor provides the control module with information regarding the relative position and movement of suspension components. The common mounting location is between the vehicle body and the suspension control arm. ● **SEE FIGURE 44–5.**

The operation of the sensor is either an air suspension sensor two-wire type or a potentiometer three-wire type. The **air suspension** sensor is also known as a *linear Hall-effect* sensor. The air suspension sensor operation consists of a moveable iron core linked to the components. As the core moves, it varies the inductance of the internal sensor coil relative to suspension position.

The suspension control module energizes and de-energizes the coil approximately 20 times a second, thereby measuring sensor inductance as it relates to suspension position. The potentiometer three-wire sensor requires reference and ground voltage. Similar to the throttle position (TP) sensor, it produces a variable analog voltage signal. ● **SEE FIGURE 44–6.**

As the suspension moves up or down, an arm moves on the suspension position sensor through a ball-and-cup link. ● **SEE FIGURE 44–7.**

Suspension position sensor voltage changes relative to this movement. The sensor receives a 5-volt reference signal from the control module. The position sensor returns a voltage signal between 0 and 5 volts depending on suspension arm position.

NOTE: Some systems may require sensor learning or "reprogramming" after replacement. For instance, the sensor used on the Tahoe or Suburban needs to be programmed if replaced. Always check service information for the details and procedures to follow when replacing a sensor on the suspension.

FIGURE 44–7 A suspension height sensor.

STEERING WHEEL POSITION SENSOR Depending on the vehicle, the **steering wheel position sensor** may also be called a **handwheel position sensor.** The function of this sensor is to provide the control module with signals relating to steering wheel position, the speed and direction of handwheel position.

The sensor is found on most **real-time dampening (RTD)** and **road-sensing suspension (RSS)** applications. The sensor is typically located at the base of the steering column. Always refer to service information for vehicle-specific information. ● **SEE FIGURES 44–8 AND 44–9.**

The handwheel sensor produces two digital signals, which are used by the **electronic brake control module (EBCM).** These signals are produced as the steering wheel is rotated. The sensor can also produce more than two signals. As an example, the Cadillac Escalade handwheel sensor produces one analog and three digital signals.

FIGURE 44–8 The steering wheel position (handwheel position) sensor wiring schematic and how the signal varies with the direction that the steering wheel is turned.

FIGURE 44–9 The handwheel position sensor is located at the base of the steering column.

The sensor uses a 5-volt signal reference. Analog signal voltage values increase or decrease, between 0 and 5 volts, as the steering wheel is moved left and right of center. The digital signal is also a standard power-to-ground circuit as shown in the schematic.

FIGURE 44–10 Steering wheel (handwheel) position sensor schematic.

There are three possible digital signals:

- Phase A
- Phase B
- Index pulse

These signals provide the suspension control module with steering wheel speed and direction information. Digital signals are either high or low, 5 volts or 0 volts. ● SEE FIGURE 44–10.

The Tech 2 provides DTC faults for this sensor. If there is an intermittent concern with a steering wheel position sensor, select Tech 2 snapshot and slowly turn the steering wheel lock to lock. After the snapshot is complete, plot the analog sensor voltage to see if the signal dropped out. Any dropout is an indication of an intermittent problem.

VEHICLE SPEED SENSOR   The **vehicle speed (VS) sensor** is used by the EBCM to help control the suspension system. The vehicle speed sensor is a magnetic sensor and generates an analog signal whose frequency increases as the speed increases. The ride is made firmer at high speeds and during braking and acceleration and less firm at cruise speeds. ● SEE FIGURE 44–11.

PRESSURE SENSOR   A pressure transducer (sensor) is typically mounted on the compressor assembly. This sensor is typically found on suspension systems that use a compressor assembly. The main function of the pressure sensor is to provide feedback to the suspension control module about the operation of the compressor. The sensor assures both that a minimum air pressure is maintained in the system and that a maximum value is not exceeded. A pressure transducer (sensor) is typically mounted on the compressor assembly. This sensor is typically found on systems such as air suspension, real-time damping, and road-sensing suspension that use a compressor assembly. ● SEE FIGURE 44–12.

FIGURE 44–11 The VS sensor information is transmitted to the EBCM by Class 2 serial data.

FIGURE 44–12 An air pressure sensor.

The operation of the pressure sensor requires a 5-volt reference, a ground, and a signal wire to provide feedback to the control module. The voltage output on the signal wire will vary from 0 to 5 volts based upon pressure in the system. A high voltage indicates high pressure and low voltage indicates a low pressure.

LATERAL ACCELEROMETER SENSOR The function of the **lateral accelerometer sensor** is to provide the suspension control module with feedback regarding vehicle cornering forces. This type of sensor is also called a G-sensor, with the letter "G" representing the force of gravity. For example, when a vehicle enters a turn, the sensor provides information as to how hard the vehicle is cornering. This information is processed by the suspension control module to provide appropriate damping on the inboard and outboard dampers during cornering events. The lateral accelerometer sensor is found on the more complex suspensions systems, such as RTD and RSS systems that incorporate the **vehicle stability enhancement system (VSES)**.

This sensor can be either a stand-alone unit or combined with the yaw rate sensor. Typically, the sensor is mounted in the passenger compartment under a front seat, center console, or package shelf.

The sensor produces a voltage signal of 0 to 5 volts as the vehicle maneuvers left or right through a curve. The signal is an

FIGURE 44–13 A schematic showing the lateral acceleration sensor and the EBCM.

FIGURE 44–14 The lateral accelerometer sensor (G-sensor) is usually located under the center console.

input to the EBCM. If zero lateral acceleration, the sensor input is 2.5 volts. Check service information for specific codes that can be set.

If driving the vehicle and the voltage values increase or decrease during cornering events, this indicates proper operation. ● SEE FIGURE 44–13.

YAW RATE SENSOR
The **yaw rate sensor** provides information to the suspension control module and the EBCM. This information is used to determine how far the vehicle has deviated from the driver's intended direction. The yaw sensor is used on vehicles equipped with Electronic Stability Control (ESC).

This sensor can be either a stand-alone unit or combined with the lateral accelerometer sensor. Typically, the sensor is mounted in the passenger compartment under the front seat, center console, or on the rear package shelf.

The sensor produces a voltage signal of 0 to 5 volts as the vehicle yaw rate changes. The voltage signal is an input to the EBCM. The yaw rate input to the EBCM indicates the number of degrees that the vehicle deviates from its intended direction.

TECH TIP

The Lateral Acceleration Sensor Needed to Control the Electronic Suspension

The lateral acceleration sensor is one part of the group of sensors which provide the information needed for the suspension to be able to react to driver commands and road conditions. Using just the steering wheel position sensor would not be enough information for the suspension controller to determine the cornering loads. ● SEE FIGURE 44–14.

For example, with a 0-degree yaw rate, the sensor output is 2.5 volts. During an emergency maneuver, the signal will vary above or below 2.5 volts. This sensor does set DTC codes. These codes can be found in service information. ● SEE FIGURE 44–15.

FIGURE 44–15 Yaw rate sensor showing the typical location and schematic.

DRIVER SELECTOR SWITCH The **driver selector switch** is a two- or three-mode switch, usually located in the center console, and is an input to the suspension control module.

The switch that is used to select either touring (soft) or performance (firm) ride is found on the **Selectable Ride (SR)** and the **Computer Command Ride (CCR)** systems. The mode select switch status is generally displayed on a scan tool. The three-position switch is used on the Corvette RTD system, and allows the driver to select three modes of operation:

- Tour
- Sport
- Performance

ELECTRONIC SUSPENSION SYSTEM ACTUATORS

Each actuator in an electronically controlled suspension system receives output signals from the ECM and responds to these signals, or commands, by performing a mechanical action. Actuators are usually inductive devices that operate using an electromagnetic field. A simple **electromagnet** consists of a soft iron core with a coil of wire, usually copper, wrapped around it. ● **SEE FIGURE 44–16.**

Electrical current traveling through the coiled wire creates a magnetic field around the core. All magnets are polarized; that is, they have a north, or positive, and a south, or negative, pole. When the opposite poles of two magnets are placed near each other—positive-to-negative—the magnets attract each other. Place the same poles together, positive-to-positive or negative-to-negative, and the magnets repel each other. ● **SEE FIGURE 44–17.** Magnets also attract and are attracted to certain types of metals, especially iron and steel.

When an electromagnet has more than one coil, the stronger primary coil can induce voltage into the weaker secondary coil. This inductive transfer occurs even though there is no physical connection between the two coils.

SOLENOIDS In a **solenoid,** the core of the electromagnet also acts as a plunger to open and close a passage or to move a linkage. Solenoids are cylindrically shaped with a metal plate at one end and open at the other end to allow the plunger to move in and out. The electromagnetic coils are placed along the sides of the cylinder. A preload spring forces the plunger toward one end of the device when the solenoid is de-energized, or there is no current in the coil.

When the solenoid is energized, current passes through the coil and magnetizes the core. The magnetized core is attracted to the metal plate and the strength of the magnetic field overcomes spring force to pull the plunger inward. ● **SEE FIGURE 44–18.** When the electrical current switches off, the solenoid de-energizes and spring force returns the plunger to its rest position.

An airflow control valve is an example of a solenoid used in an electronically controlled suspension. ● **SEE FIGURE 44–19.** As the solenoid plunger extends and retracts, it opens and closes air passages between the system air-pressure tank and the air springs. The position of the plunger determines whether the springs receive more pressure or whether pressure bleeds out of them. Increasing the pressure in the air springs lifts the body higher, and decreasing the pressure by bleeding air from the springs lowers the body.

Solenoids are digital devices that are either on or off. However, the ECM can vary the amount a solenoid opens by pulsing the output signal to the coil. If the signal is rapidly switched on and off, spring and magnetic forces do not have enough time to react and effectively move the plunger between the signal changes. The amount of time the current is on compared to the amount of time it is off is called **pulse width,** and the control of a solenoid using this pulsing-on-and-off method is called **pulse-width modulation.**

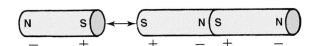

FIGURE 44–17 When magnets are near each other, like poles repel and opposite poles attract.

SOLENOID

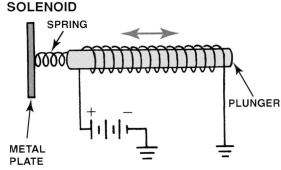

FIGURE 44–18 When electrical current magnetizes the plunger in a solenoid, the magnetic field moves the plunger against spring force. With no current, the spring pushes the plunger back to its original position.

ELECTROMAGNET

FIGURE 44–16 A magnetic field is created whenever an electrical current flows through a coil of wire wrapped around an iron core.

SOLENOID OFF

PLUNGER

PRESSURIZED
AIR

TO RIGHT
AIR SPRING
VALVE

TO LEFT
AIR SPRING
VALVE

SOLENOID ON

PLUNGER

PRESSURIZED
AIR

TO RIGHT
AIR SPRING
VALVE

TO LEFT
AIR SPRING
VALVE

FIGURE 44–19 This air supply solenoid blocks pressurized air from the air spring valves when off. The plunger pulls upward to allow airflow to the air spring valves when the solenoid is energized.

ACTUATOR MOTORS If a current-carrying conductor is placed in a magnetic field, it tends to move from the stronger field area to the weaker field area. A **motor** uses this principle to convert electrical energy into mechanical movement. Electrical current is directed through the field coils on the motor frame to create a magnetic field within the frame. By applying an electrical current to the **armature,** which is inside the motor frame, the armature rotates from a strong field area to a weaker field area. Armature movement can in turn move another part, such as a gear, pulley, or shaft, attached to it.

Located at the top mount of the air spring variable shock assembly of each wheel, the suspension control actuator moves a control rod that regulates air pressure to the spring,

STATOR
COIL

PERMANENT MAGNET

SHOCK
ABSORBER
CONTROL
ROD

AIR SPRING VALVE
CONTROL ROD

FIGURE 44–20 An actuator motor uses a permanent magnet and four stator coils to drive the air spring control rod.

which determines ride height. The actuator is an electromagnetic device consisting of four stator coils and a permanent magnet core. ● **SEE FIGURE 44–20.**

The ECM applies current to two stator coils at a time to create opposing magnetic fields around the core, which causes the core to rotate into a new position. Which coils are energized determines how far and in which direction the core rotates. ● **SEE FIGURE 44–21.** By switching current from one pair of coils to the other, the ECM moves the core into a new position, and a third position is available by reversing the polarity of the coils.

A gear at the base of the permanent magnet connects to a rod that operates the air valve to the air spring. The gear also drives another gear, which operates the control rod of the variable shock absorber. Therefore, the three positions of the suspension control actuator motor provide three shock absorber stiffness settings in addition to a variable air spring.

TYPES OF ELECTRONIC SUSPENSION

The types of electronic suspension systems used on General Motors vehicles, as examples, include:

1. Selectable Ride
2. Automatic Level Control
3. Air Suspension
4. Computer Command Ride
5. Real-Time Dampening/Road-Sensing Suspension
6. Vehicle Stability Enhancement System
7. Magneto-Rheological Suspension (F55)

SELECTABLE RIDE (SR) The Selectable Ride (SR) system is the most basic of the electronic systems offered

FIGURE 44–21 The stator coils of the actuator are energized in three ways to provide soft, medium, or firm ride from the air springs and shock absorbers.

FIGURE 44–22 Selectable Ride as used on Chevrolet and GMC pickup trucks.

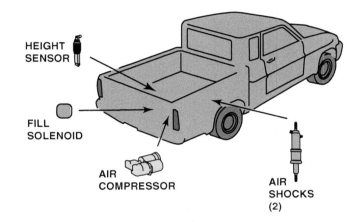

FIGURE 44–23 ALC maintains the same ride height either loaded or unloaded by increasing or decreasing the air pressure in the rear air shocks.

by General Motors. Selectable Ride (SR) allows the driver to choose between two distinct damping levels:

- Firm
- Normal

SR is found on Chevrolet and GMC full-size pickup trucks. ● SEE FIGURE 44–22.

A switch is used to control four electronically controlled gas-charged dampers. The **mode select switch** activates the bi-state (two settings) dampers at all four corners of the vehicle, allowing the driver to select vehicle ride characteristics. The system is either energizing or de-energizing the bi-state dampers to provide a firm or normal ride.

AUTOMATIC LEVEL CONTROL The **Automatic Level Control (ALC)** system automatically adjusts the rear height

of the vehicle in response to changes in vehicle loading and unloading. Automatic Level Control is found on many General Motors vehicles. ALC controls rear leveling by monitoring the rear suspension position sensor and energizing the compressor to raise the vehicle or energizing the exhaust valve to lower the vehicle. ALC has several variations across the different platforms. ● SEE FIGURE 44–23.

AIR SUSPENSION (AS) **Air Suspension (AS)** is a system very similar to the ALC system. The purpose of the AS system includes:

1. Keep the vehicle visually level
2. Provide optimal headlight aiming
3. Maintain optimal ride height

The AS system includes the following components:

- An air suspension compressor assembly
- Rear air springs
- Air suspension sensors

The AS system is designed to maintain rear trim height within 3/16 inch (4 mm) in all loading conditions, and the leveling function will deactivate if the vehicle is overloaded.

FIGURE 44–24 A typical schematic showing the air suspension compressor assembly and sensor.

The AS system also includes an accessory air inflator found in the rear cargo area. ● **SEE FIGURE 44–24.**

VARIABLE-RATE AIR SPRINGS In an air spring system with ordinary shock absorbers, the ECM uses the air springs to control trim height and is used on many Ford, Mercury, and Lincoln vehicles.

The three height sensors transmit a signal to the ECM that reflects trim height at each axle. ● **SEE FIGURE 44–25.** The ignition and brake light switches tell the ECM whether the ignition switch is on or off, and if the brake pedal is depressed. The dome light switch indicates whether any doors are open.

The on/off switch disables the air spring system to avoid unexpected movement while towing or servicing the vehicle.

CAUTION: Failure to turn off the system will cause the air springs to be vented when the vehicle is hoisted. This will cause the vehicle to drop almost to the ground when the vehicle is lowered. This can cause damage to the air springs and/or to the vehicle. The shut-off switch is usually located in the trunk.

The ECM receives information from the height sensors indicating that the trim height is too high or too low, and it energizes the actuators to add or bleed air from the air springs. The system actuators can still operate for up to an hour after the ignition is switched off.

Any time the ignition is switched to the "run" position, the ECM raises the vehicle, if necessary, within the first 45 seconds. If trim height is too high and the vehicle must be lowered, the ECM delays doing so for 45 seconds after the ignition is switched on.

An air compressor with a regenerative dryer provides the air change required to inflate the air springs on the air suspension system, and a vent solenoid is used to relieve air pressure and deflate the springs. ● **SEE FIGURE 44–26.**

By energizing the compressor relay, the ECM directs current to turn on the compressor motor when trim height needs to be raised. The ECM command to lower the vehicle is an electrical signal that opens the vent solenoid to bleed air pressure out of the system. ● **SEE FIGURE 44–27.**

GENERAL MOTORS COMPUTER COMMAND RIDE
The General Motors Computer Command Ride (CCR) system controls ride firmness by automatically controlling an actuator in each of the four struts to increase ride firmness as speed increases.

The three damping modes are:

- Comfort
- Normal
- Sport

FIGURE 44–25 The typical variable-rate air spring system uses three height sensors, two in the front and one in the rear, to monitor trim height and to provide input signals to the ECM.

FIGURE 44–26 The air spring compressor assembly is usually mounted on rubber cushions to help isolate it from the body of the vehicle. All of the air entering or leaving the air springs flows through the regenerative air dryer.

FIGURE 44–27 A solenoid valve at the top of each spring regulates airflow into and out of the air spring.

Damping mode selection is controlled by the CCR control module according to vehicle speed conditions, driver select switch position, and any error conditions that may exist.

In the **perform ride mode,** the system will place the damping level in the firm mode regardless of vehicle speed.

In the **touring ride mode,** the damping level depends on vehicle speed. ● **SEE FIGURE 44–28.**

FIGURE 44–28 Schematic showing Computer Command Ride (CCR) system.

REAL-TIME DAMPENING AND ROAD-SENSING SUSPENSION

Real-time dampening (RTD) independently controls a solenoid in each of the four shock absorbers in order to control the vehicle ride characteristics and is capable of making changes within milliseconds (0.001 second).

Road-sensing suspension (RSS), along with ALC, controls damping forces in the front struts and rear shock absorbers in response to various road and driving conditions.

RTD and RSS incorporate the following components:

■ An electronic suspension control module,
■ Front and rear suspension position sensors,
■ Bi-state dampers,
■ A ride select switch, and
■ An air compressor is used on some models.

● **SEE FIGURES 44–29 AND 44–30.**

FIGURE 44–29 Schematic showing the shock control used in the RSS system.

FIGURE 44–30 Bi-state dampers (shocks) use a solenoid to control fluid flow in the unit to control compression and rebound actions.

TECH TIP

Check the RPO Code

Whenever working on the suspension system check the **RPO (regular production option)** code for the type of suspension used. For example, the F55 RPO may be called by a different name depending on the make and model of vehicle. Also, service procedures will be different on the same vehicle depending on whether it is equipped with an F45 or an F55 system. The General Motors vehicle RPO codes are on a sticker on the spare tire cover in the trunk or in the glove compartment.

BI-STATE AND TRI-STATE DAMPERS The bi-state damper is also known as a **solenoid controlled damper.** Bi-state dampers are found on the RTD, RSS, and SR systems. Each of the suspension dampers used in these systems have an integral solenoid. The solenoid valve provides various amounts of damping by directing hydraulic damping fluid in the suspension shock absorber or strut. ● **SEE FIGURE 44–31.**

FIGURE 44–31 Solenoid valve controlled shock absorber circuit showing the left front (LF) shock as an example.

The General Motors version of ESC is called the vehicle stability enhancement system (VSES) and includes an additional level of vehicle control to the EBCM. VSES is also known as **Stabilitrak.**

The purpose of the vehicle stability enhancement system along with the antilock brake system (ABS) is to provide vehicle stability enhancement during oversteer or understeer conditions.

The pulse-width modulation (PWM) voltage signal from the suspension control module controls the amount of current flow through each of the damper solenoids. With a low PWM signal de-energized, more hydraulic damping fluid is allowed to bypass the main suspension damper passage, resulting in a softer damping mode.

As the PWM signal increases, or is energized, the damping mode becomes more firm. ● **SEE FIGURE 44–32.**

FIGURE 44–32 A typical CCR module schematic.

FIGURE 44–33 The three dampening modes of a CCR shock absorber.

FIGURE 44–34 Integral shock solenoid.

NOTE: If the suspension module does not control the shock absorber solenoid, a full soft damping mode results. In some system malfunctions, the module may command one or all of the damper solenoids to a full soft damping.

The main difference between a tri-state damper and a bi-state damper is that the tri-state damper uses an electrical actuator, whereas the bi-state damper is solenoid controlled.

The three damping modes include:

- Comfort
- Normal
- Sport

A tri-state damper has an integral electrical strut actuator that rotates a selector valve to change the flow of hydraulic damping fluid. ● SEE FIGURE 44–33.

The CCR module controls the operation of the strut actuators to provide the three damping modes.

The strut position input provides feedback to the CCR module. The strut position input is compared to the commanded actuator position to monitor system operation. ● SEE FIGURE 44–34.

? FREQUENTLY ASKED QUESTION

What Are Self-Leveling Shocks?

A German company, ZF Sachs, supplies a self-leveling shock absorber to several vehicle manufacturers, such as Chrysler for use on the rear of minivans, plus BMW, Saab, and Volvo. The self-leveling shocks are entirely self-contained and do not require the use of height sensors or an external air pump. ● SEE FIGURE 44–35.

The shock looks like a conventional shock absorber but contains the following components:

- Two reservoirs in the outer tube
- An oil reservoir (low-pressure reservoir)
- A high-pressure chamber

Inside the piston rod is the pump chamber containing an inlet and an outlet valve. When a load is placed in the rear of the vehicle, it compresses the suspension and the shock absorber. When the vehicle starts to move, the internal pump is activated by the movement of the body. Extension of the piston rod causes oil to be drawn through the inlet valve into the pump. When the shock compresses, the oil is forced through the outlet valve into the high-pressure chamber. The pressure in the oil reserve decreases as the pressure in the high-pressure chamber increases. The increasing pressure is applied to the piston rod, which raises the height of the vehicle.

When the vehicle's normal height is reached, no oil is drawn into the chamber. Because the shock is mechanical, the vehicle needs to be moving before the pump starts to work. It requires about 2 miles of driving for the shock to reach the normal ride height. The vehicle also needs to be driven about 2 miles after a load has been removed from the vehicle for it to return to normal ride height.

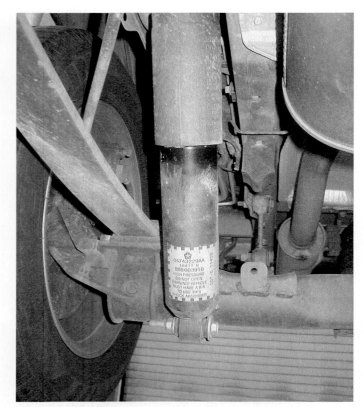

FIGURE 44–35 A typical ZF Sachs self-leveling shock, as used on the rear of a Chrysler minivan.

AUTOMATIC LEVEL CONTROL (ALC)

Vehicles that have an air inflator system as part of the ALC system also have an air inflator switch. The air inflator switch is an input to the ALC and AS system. The inflator switch is used to control the air inflator system operation and provides a signal to the ALC or AS module to initiate compressor activation.

With the ignition on, the driver can turn the system to ON. The switch will command the compressor to run for up to 10 minutes, allowing time to inflate a tire or other items requiring air.

NOTE: There are no DTCs associated with compressor assembly.

INFLATOR OR COMPRESSOR RELAY   The suspension control module energizes the relay to activate the compressor motor. This adjusts the rear trim height as needed. The suspension control module controls the compressor relay for normal operation or for the accessory air inflator.

To avoid compressor overheating, the timer within the suspension control module limits the compressor run time to 10 minutes. ● SEE FIGURE 44–36.

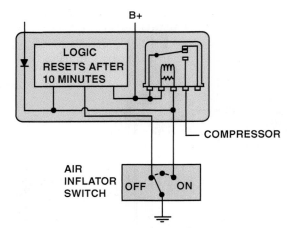

FIGURE 44–36 Schematic of the ALC system.

On RTD or RSS systems with a compressor, the scan tool may display DTCs associated with compressor relay operation. On some vehicle applications, the scan tool will display data relating to relay operation and can be used to command the relay to verify proper operation.

COMPRESSOR   The compressor is a positive-displacement air pump and can generate up to 150 lbs. of pressure per square inch (PSI). The compressor is found on the ALC, AS, RTD, and RSS systems. A 12-volt permanent magnet motor drives the compressor. The compressor supplies compressed air to the rear air shock absorbers or struts to raise the vehicle. ● SEE FIGURE 44–37.

AIR DRYER.   Within the compressor is an air dryer. The air dryer is responsible for removing moisture from the compressor system. Improper air dryer operation can cause a premature failure in the system if an air line restriction occurs due to

FIGURE 44–37 Air compressor assembly can be located at various locations depending on the vehicle.

excessive moisture build-up. A dryer on the output side of the compressor contains silica gel **desiccant,** which removes moisture from the discharge air before it travels through the nylon air hoses to the air chamber of the rear shocks.

EXHAUST SOLENOID. The exhaust solenoid, which is located on the compressor, relieves pressure in the system. The ground-side switched exhaust solenoid has three main functions:

1. It releases compressed air from the shock absorbers or air springs to lower the vehicle body.

2. It relieves compressor head pressure. By exhausting air, it protects compressor start-up from high head pressure, which can possibly cause fuse failure.

3. The solenoid acts as a pressure relief valve, which limits overall system pressure.

The special functions on many scan tools can be used to command the solenoid and to verify its operation. ● **SEE FIGURES 44–38 AND 44–39.**

FIGURE 44–38 The exhaust solenoid is controlled by the rear integration module (RIM).

FIGURE 44–39 Schematic showing the rear integration module (RIM) and how it controls the ALC compressor.

MAGNETO-RHEOLOGICAL (MR) SUSPENSION

MR fluid shocks use a working fluid inside the shock that can change viscosity rapidly depending on electric current sent to an electromagnetic coil in each device. The fluid is called **magneto-rheological (MR)** and is used in monotube-type shock absorbers. This type of shock and suspension system is called the **magneto-rheological real-time damping (MRRTD)** or **chassis continuously variable real-time dampening magneto-rheological suspension (CCVRTMR).**

Under normal operating conditions, the fluid flows easily through orifices in the shock and provides little dampening. When a large or high-frequency bump is detected, a small electrical current is sent from the chassis controller to an electromagnetic coil in each shock and the iron particles in the fluid respond within 3 milliseconds (ms), aligning themselves in fiberlike strands. ● **SEE FIGURES 44–40 AND 44–41.**

This causes the MR fluid to become thick like peanut butter and increases the firmness of the shock. This type of shock absorber is used to control squat during acceleration and brake dive as well as to reduce body roll during cornering by the chassis controller. ● **SEE FIGURE 44–42.**

FIGURE 44–40 Vehicles that use magneto-rheological shock absorbers have a sensor located near each wheel, as shown on this C6 Corvette.

FIGURE 44–41 The controller for the magneto-rheological suspension system on a C6 Corvette is located behind the right front wheel.

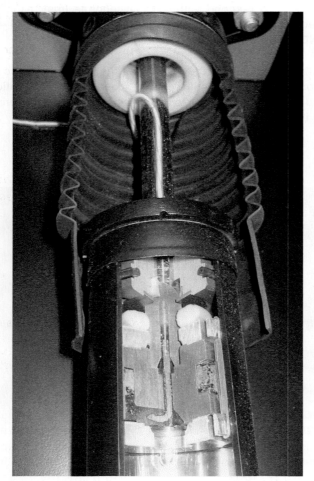

FIGURE 44–42 A cutaway of a magneto-rheological shock absorber as displayed at the Corvette Museum in Bowling Green, Kentucky.

Can Computer-Controlled Shock Absorbers and Struts Be Replaced with Conventional Units?

Maybe. If the vehicle was manufactured with or without electronic or variable shock absorbers, it may be possible to replace the originals with the standard replacement units. The electrical connector must be disconnected, and this may cause the control system to store a diagnostic trouble code (DTC) and/or turn on a suspension fault warning light on the dash. Some service technicians have used a resistor equal in resistance value of the solenoid or motor across the terminals of the wiring connector to keep the controller from setting a DTC. All repairs to a suspension system should be done to restore the vehicle to like-new condition, so care should be exercised if replacing electronic shocks with nonelectronic versions.

TROUBLESHOOTING REAR ELECTRONIC LEVELING SYSTEMS

The first step with any troubleshooting procedure is to check for normal operation. Some leveling systems require that the ignition key be on (run), while other systems operate all the time. Begin troubleshooting by placing approximately 300 lb (135 kg) on the rear of the vehicle. If the compressor does not operate, check to see if the sensor is connected to a rear suspension member and that the electrical connections are not corroded.

Also check the condition of the compressor ground wire. It must be tight and free of rust and corrosion where it attaches to the vehicle body. If the compressor still does not run, check to see if 12 volts are available at the power lead to the compressor. If necessary, use a fused jumper wire directly from the positive (+) of the battery to the power lead of the compressor. If the compressor does not operate, it must be replaced.

If the ride height compressor runs excessively, check the air compressor, the air lines, and the air shocks (or struts) with soapy water for air leaks. Most air shocks or air struts are not repairable and must be replaced. Most electronic leveling systems provide some adjustments of the rear ride height by adjusting the linkage between the height sensor and the rear suspension. ● **SEE FIGURE 44–43.**

FIGURE 44–43 Most electronic level-control sensors can be adjusted, such as this General Motors unit.

SUMMARY

1. General Motors uses seven types of electronic suspension under many different names.
2. Suspension height sensors and steering wheel (handwheel) position sensors are used in many systems.
3. A vehicle speed sensor signal is used to control the suspension at various speeds.
4. Many electronic suspension systems use a lateral accelerometer sensor, which signals the suspension computer when the vehicle is rapidly accelerating, braking, or cornering.
5. Solenoids and motors are used to control the suspension movement by moving valves in the shock absorbers or air springs.
6. An air pump and air shocks are used to raise the rear of the vehicle to compensate for a heavy load.

REVIEW QUESTIONS

1. What type of sensor is usually used on electronically controlled suspensions to sense the height of the vehicle?
2. Why is the vehicle speed sensor used as input for many electronic suspension systems?
3. What is a lateral accelerometer sensor and why is it used?
4. Why does the output side of the suspension air compressor contain a desiccant?

CHAPTER QUIZ

1. What type of sensor is used as a height sensor on vehicles equipped with an electronically controlled suspension?
   a. Hall-effect
   b. Photo cell
   c. Potentiometer
   d. All of the above

2. Which sensors do most vehicles use if equipped with electronic suspension?
   a. Height sensors
   b. Steering wheel position sensors
   c. Lateral accelerometer sensors
   d. All of the above

3. A lateral acceleration sensor is used to provide the suspension control module with feedback regarding _____ force.
   a. Cornering
   b. Acceleration
   c. Braking
   d. All of the above

4. A steering wheel position sensor is being discussed. Technician A says that the sensor is used to determine the direction the steering wheel is turned. Technician B says that the sensor detects how fast the steering wheel is turned. Which technician is correct?
   a. Technician A only
   b. Technician B only
   c. Both Technicians A and B
   d. Neither Technician A nor B

5. Technician A says that an electronic control module used in the suspension system is the same as that used for engine control. Technician B says that most electronically controlled suspension systems use a separate electronic control module. Which technician is correct?
   a. Technician A only
   b. Technician B only
   c. Both Technicians A and B
   d. Neither Technician A nor B

6. What type of actuator is used on electronically controlled suspensions?
   a. Solenoid
   b. Electric motor
   c. Either a or b
   d. Neither a nor b

7. Why is the typical rear load-leveling system connected to the ignition circuit?
   a. To keep the system active for a given time after the ignition is switched off
   b. To prevent the system from working unless the ignition key is on
   c. To keep the compressor from running for an extended period of time
   d. All of the above

8. A magneto-rheological suspension system uses_____.
   a. An electronic controller
   b. a sensor at each wheel
   c. an electromagnetic coil in each shock
   d. All of the above

9. The firm setting is usually selected by the electronic suspension control module whenever which of the following occurs?
   a. High speed
   b. Rapid braking
   c. Rapid acceleration
   d. All of the above

10. Which of the following is the least likely sensor to cause an electronic suspension fault?
   a. Yaw sensor
   b. Throttle position (TP) sensor
   c. Steering wheel position sensor
   d. Vehicle speed sensor

chapter 45

ELECTRIC POWER STEERING SYSTEMS

OBJECTIVES: **After studying Chapter 45, the reader should be able to:** • Describe the purpose and function of electric power steering system. • Discuss the various types of electric power steering systems. • Explain how electric power steering systems operate. • Discuss how to diagnose system faults. • Explain service procedures for electric power steering systems.

KEY TERMS: • Brake pedal position (BPP) sensor 558 • Column-mounted electric power steering (C-EPS) 553 • Direct-drive electric power steering (D-EPS) 553 • Electric power-assisted steering (EPAS) 553 • Electric power steering (EPS) 553 • Electro-hydraulic power steering (EHPS) 557 • Pinion-mounted electric power steering system (P-EPS) 553 • Power steering control module (PSCM) 555 • Rack-and-pinion electric power steering (R-EPS) 553 • Self-parking 557 • Steering position sensor (SPS) 556 • Steering shaft torque sensor 555

ELECTRIC POWER STEERING OVERVIEW

PURPOSE AND FUNCTION   Many of today's vehicles use **electric power steering (EPS)** systems, which is also called **electric power-assisted steering (EPAS)**. Electric power steering takes the place of hydraulic components that were previously used by using an electric motor to provide power assist effort.

ADVANTAGES   The advantages include:

- Improved fuel economy. Ford and Honda both state that fuel economy improves 3% to 5% in the absence of a power steering pump and the weight of the hydraulic system needed for conventional hydraulically operated power steering systems.

- Increase in usable power. Ford estimates that by using electric power steering instead of a conventional hydraulic system results in a three horsepower increase in engine output without any other changes.

- Allows the vehicle manufacturer to save vehicle weight and complexity because there is no need for all of the hydraulic lines and engine-driven pump.

- Improved cold weather starting because of reduced engine load without the drag of a power steering pump.

- Simple two-wire connection in many cases, making vehicle assembly and vehicle service easier.

TYPES OF EPS SYSTEMS   There are two basic types of EPS systems:

1. **Rack mounted.** The rack-mounted system has the assist motor attached to the rack and is often called a **rack-and-pinion electric power steering (R-EPS)** system. Another design has the assist motor surrounding the rack and this style is called a **direct-drive electric power steering (D-EPS)** system. ● **SEE FIGURE 45–1.**

2. **Column mounted. Column-mounted electric power steering (C-EPS)** has sensors and the assist motor located inside the vehicle so they are not exposed to the heat and outside elements as is the rack-mounted system. This is the most commonly used type and involves using a manual rack-and-pinion steering gear assembly with a motor assist in the steering column. While not directly mounted on the column itself, another type of electric power steering is the **pinion-mounted electric power steering system (P-EPS)** system. This system has the assist motor connected to the pinion shaft of the rack-and-pinion steering gear. ● **SEE FIGURE 45–2.**

EPS SYSTEM PARTS AND OPERATION

TYPES OF MOTOR USED   Most electric power steering units use a DC electric motor. Some operate from 42 volts while others operate from 12 volts. The Toyota system on a Prius uses a DC motor, reduction gear, and torque sensor, all mounted to the steering column. ● **SEE FIGURE 45–3.**

FIGURE 45–1 A rack mounted electric power steering gear on a Lexus RX 400 h taken from underneath the vehicle.

FIGURE 45–2 Honda electric power steering unit cutaway, which is an example of pinion-mounted electric power steering system.

FIGURE 45–3 A Toyota Prius EPS assembly. (Courtesy of Tony Martin)

EPS CONTROL UNIT The electric power steering (EPS) is controlled by the EPS electronic control unit (ECU), which calculates the amount of needed assist based on the input from the steering torque sensor. The steering torque sensor is a noncontact sensor that detects the movement and torque applied to the torsion bar. The torsion bar twists when the drive exerts torque to the steering wheel, and the more torque applied, the farther the bar will twist. This generates a higher-voltage signal to the EPS ECU. The EPS control unit can vary the amperage to the assist motor based on input from the torque and steering wheel sensors. The control unit also monitors the temperature of the motor and can reduce the amount of power assist if the motor temperature increases too much. ● **SEE FIGURE 45–4.**

The steering shaft torque sensor and the steering wheel position sensor are serviced as an assembly and are not individually replaceable. The steering column assembly does not include the power steering motor and module assembly. Column-mounted EPS systems use detection rings to measure the differences in relative motion between the upper (input) and lower (output) steering column shafts. Detection rings 1 and 2 are mounted on the input shaft and detection ring 3 is mounted on the output shaft. The input shaft and the output shaft are connected by a torsion bar. When the steering wheel is turned, the difference in relative motion between detection rings 2 and 3 is sensed by the detection coil and it sends two signals to the EPS ECU. These two signals are called Torque Sensor Signal 1 and Torque Signal 2. The EPS ECU uses these signals to control the amount of assist, and also uses the signals for diagnosis.

NOTE: If the steering wheel, steering column, or steering gear is removed or replaced, the system must be recalibrated, which resets the zero point of the torque sensors.

FIGURE 45–4 The torque sensor converts the torque the driver is applying to the steering wheel into a voltage signal.

FIGURE 45–5 A cross-sectional view of a Honda electric power steering (EPS) gear showing coils 1 and 2 of the torque sensor.

FIGURE 45–6 The Power Steering Control Module (PSCM) is attached to the motor of the electric power steering assembly.

The Honda electric power steering uses an electric motor to provide steering assist, and torque sensor is used to measure road resistance and the direction that the driver is turning the steering wheel. The torque sensor input and the vehicle speed are used by the EPS controller to supply the EPS motor with the specified current to help assist the steering effort. ● SEE FIGURE 45–5.

The motor turns the pinion shaft using a worm gear. The worm gear is engaged with the worm wheel so that the motor turns the pinion shaft directly when providing steering assist. If a major fault were to occur, the control module would first try to maintain power-assisted steering even if some sensors had failed. If the problem is serious, then the vehicle can be driven and steered manually. The EPS control unit will turn on the EPS dash warning light if a fault has been detected. A fault in the system will *not* cause the malfunction indicator light (MIL) to come on because that light is reserved for emission-related faults only. However, another warning light may be turned on to warn the driver of a problem with the electric power steering system. Fault codes can be retrieved by using a scan tool. Check service information for the exact procedures to follow when diagnosing electric power steering faults.

EPS INPUTS AND OUTPUTS The EPS system includes the following components and input signals from sensors and output signals to actuator components:

- Powertrain Control Module (PCM)
- Body control module (BCM)
- Power steering control module (PSCM)
- Battery voltage
- Steering shaft torque sensor

- Steering wheel position sensor
- Power steering motor
- Driver information center (DIC)
- Serial data communications circuits to perform the system functions

The **power steering control module (PSCM)** and the power steering motor are serviced as an assembly and are serviced separately from the steering column assembly. ● SEE FIGURE 45–6.

The steering shaft torque sensor and the steering wheel position sensor are not serviced separately from each other or from the steering column assembly. The steering column assembly does not include the power steering motor and module assembly.

STEERING SHAFT TORQUE SENSOR

The PSCM uses the **steering shaft torque sensor** as a main input for determining steering direction and the amount of assist needed. The steering column has an input shaft, from the steering wheel to the torque sensor, and an output shaft, from the torque sensor to the steering shaft coupler. The input and output shafts are separated by a section of torsion bar, where the torque sensor is located. The torque sensor includes two different sensors in one housing. The sensors are used to detect the direction the steering wheel is being rotated.

- When torque is applied to the steering column shaft during a right turn, the sensor signal 1 voltage increases, while the signal 2 voltage decreases.
- When torque is applied to the steering column shaft during a left turn, the sensor signal 1 voltage decreases, while the signal 2 voltage increases.

The PSCM recognizes this change in signal voltage as steering direction and steering column shaft torque.

FIGURE 45-7 Schematic showing the electric power steering and the torque/position sensor.

STEERING WHEEL POSITION SENSOR

The PSCM uses the **steering position sensor (SPS)** to determine the steering system on-center position. Because the power steering motor provides a slight amount of return-to-center assist, the PSCM will command the power steering motor to the steering system center position and not beyond. The sensor is a 5-volt dual-analog signal device with a signal voltage range of 0 to 5 volts. The sensor's signal 1 and signal 2 voltage values will increase and decrease within 2.5 to 2.8 volts of each other as the steering wheel is turned. ● **SEE FIGURE 45-7.**

POWER STEERING MOTOR

The power steering motor is a 12-volt brushless DC reversible motor with a 65-amp rating. The motor assists steering through a worm gear and reduction gear located in the steering column housing. The motor draws about 750 to 1,000 watts or about 1 horsepower at full assist. The motor itself is usually replaced as an assembly or can be included with the control unit.

POWER STEERING CONTROL MODULE (PSCM)

PURPOSE AND FUNCTION The PSCM uses a combination of steering shaft torque sensor input, vehicle speed, calculated

system temperature, and steering tuning to determine the amount of steering assist.

OPERATION When the steering wheel is turned, the PSCM uses signal voltage from the steering shaft torque sensor to detect the amount of torque and steering direction being applied to the steering column shaft and then commands the proper amount of current to the power steering motor. The PSCM receives a vehicle speed message from the PCM by way of the serial data communications circuit. At low speeds, more assist is provided for easy turning during parking maneuvers, and at higher speeds, less assist is provided for improved road feel and directional stability.

FAULT DETECTION The PSCM and the power steering motor are not designed to handle 65 amps continuously. If the power steering system is exposed to excessive amounts of static steering conditions, the PSCM will go into a protection mode to avoid thermal damage due to overheating of the power steering components. In this mode, the PSCM will limit the amount of current commanded to the power steering motor, which reduces system temperature and steering assist levels.

EPS DIAGNOSIS

The PSCM has the ability to detect malfunctions within the power steering system. Any malfunction detected will cause the driver information center to display the *power steering* warning message and/or the *service vehicle soon* indicator.

The PSCM must also be set up with the correct steering tunings, which are different in relation to the vehicle's power train configuration, model type, and tire and wheel size. A factory or aftermarket factory-level scan tool is needed to retrieve data

 REAL WORLD FIX

The Hard Steering Chevrolet HHR

The owner of a Chevrolet HHR complained that the steering wheel was harder to turn after the battery was jump started. The tow truck driver did not know what to do and advised the owner to take it to a shop to have it looked at but the driver did not think that jump starting the vehicle could affect the power steering. A technician at the shop determined that the electric power steering did not work because of a blown fuse. Apparently, the vehicle was jump started by connecting the positive jump cable to the main terminal toward the rear of the engine compartment instead of the terminal designed to be used to jump start the vehicle as the battery is located at the rear of this vehicle. ● **SEE FIGURE 45-8.**

After the blown fuse was replaced, the electric power steering worked correctly.

FIGURE 45–8 The blown fuse is the yellow 60-amp fuse next to the terminal at the top.

DIAGNOSTIC TROUBLE CODE (DTC)	DESCRIPTION OF FAULT
C1511; C1512; C1513; C1514	Torque sensor fault detected
C 1521	Short in motor circuit
U0073	EPS control module lost communications

CHART 45–1

Sample diagnostic trouble codes (DTCS) for the electric power steering system.

and to perform relearn procedures if the unit is replaced. Always check service information for the exact procedures to follow when diagnosing and serving the electric power steering system.

EPS DTCS Most electric power steering diagnostic trouble codes will be "C" codes for chassis-related faults or "U" codes for data communication faults. ● **SEE CHART 45–1** for some sample DTCs.

SELF-PARKING SYSTEM

PURPOSE AND FUNCTION Several vehicle manufacturers offer a **self-parking** feature that uses the electric power steering to steer the vehicle. The driver has control of the brakes.

SENSORS INVOLVED Most systems use the following sensors:

- Wheel speed sensor (WSS)
- Steering-angle sensor
- Ultrasonic sensors, which are used to plot a course into a parking space

SELF-PARK OPERATION Some systems, such as those manufactured by Valeo for Volkswagen, allow the driver to control the accelerator as well as the brakes, making it possible to add power to park uphill. The Toyota/Lexus system stops working if the accelerator is depressed during a self-parking event. The Toyota/Lexus system is camera based and uses the navigation system to display the parking spot with touch screen controls. The system displays a green video box to indicate that the spot is large enough and a red box to indicate that the spot is too small. The driver positions a yellow flag on the video screen to mark the front corner of the parking spot and then the vehicle backs into the space at idle speed. The driver may have to complete the parking event by straightening the vehicle and pulling forward in the spot in some vehicles.

DIAGNOSIS AND TESTING Self-parking systems use many sensors to achieve the parking event, and a fault in any one sensor will disable self-parking. Before trying to diagnose a self-parking fault, be sure that the driver is operating the system as designed. For example, the self-parking event is cancelled if the accelerator pedal is depressed on some units. Always follow the factory-recommended diagnostic and testing procedures.

ELECTRO-HYDRAULIC POWER STEERING

PURPOSE AND FUNCTION Electro-hydraulic power steering is used on the Chevrolet Silverado mild hybrid truck and on the Mini Cooper. This system uses an electric motor to drive a hydraulic pump. The **electro-hydraulic power steering (EHPS)** module controls the power steering motor, which has the function of providing hydraulic power to the brake booster and the steering gear. A secondary function includes the ability to improve fuel economy by operating on a demand basis and the ability to provide speed-dependent variable-effort steering. The EHPS module controls the EHPS power pack, which is an integrated assembly consisting of the following components:

- Electric motor
- Hydraulic pump
- Fluid reservoir
- Reservoir cap
- Fluid-level sensor
- Electronic controller
- Electrical connectors

● **SEE FIGURE 45–9.**

EHPS MODULE The electro-hydraulic power steering (EHPS) module is operated from the 36-volt (nominal) power supply. The EHPS module uses class 2 for serial communications. A 125-amp, 36-volt fuse is used to protect

FIGURE 45–9 An electro-hydraulic power steering assembly on a Chevrolet hybrid pickup truck.

the EHPS module. If this fuse were to blow open, the EHPS system would not operate and communication codes would be set by the modules that communicate with the EHPS module. The Powertrain Control Module (PCM) is the gateway that translates controller area network (CAN) messages into class

2 messages when required for diagnostic purposes. The EHPS module receives the following messages from the CAN bus:

- Vehicle speed
- Service disconnect status
- PRNDL (shift lever) position
- Torque converter clutch (TCC)/cruise dump signal (gives zero-adjust brake switch position)

The EHPS module receives several signals through wiring. The signals received and used by the EHPS module include:

- The digital steering wheel speed signals from the steering wheel sensor mounted on the steering column. The steering wheel speed sensor output contains three digital signals that indicate the steering wheel position. The signals are accurate to within 1°. The index output references a steering wheel position of 0° plus or minus 10° (steering wheel centered) and is repeated every 360° of steering wheel rotation.
- An analog brake pedal position signal from the brake-pedal-mounted **brake pedal position (BPP) sensor.** The BPP sensor outputs an analog signal, referenced to 5 volts, that increases or decreases with brake pedal depression. The electrical range of the BPP sensor motion is −55° to +25°. The mechanical range of the BPP sensor is −70° to +40°.

SUMMARY

1. The use of electric power steering compared to conventional power steering results in more available engine power and improved fuel economy.
2. The two basic types of EPS include the rack-mounted and the column-mounted system
3. The most commonly used system uses a manual rack-and-pinion gear with a column-mounted motor assist.
4. The sensors needed include the steering wheel position sensor and the steering shaft torque sensor.
5. Some vehicles that use electric power steering are capable of performing self-parking.
6. A few vehicles use an electric motor to power a hydraulic pump for steering assist.

REVIEW QUESTIONS

1. What are the types of electric power steering systems?
2. What sensors are needed for EPS systems?
3. What are the advantages of using an electric power steering system?

CHAPTER QUIZ

1. The two basic types of electric power steering include _____.
   a. Engine mounted and column mounted
   b. Column mounted and rack mounted
   c. Electro-hydraulic and rack mounted
   d. Engine driven and battery powered

2. The advantages of electric power steering compared to hydraulic power steering include _____.
   a. Less weight
   b. Improved fuel economy
   c. Increase usable engine power
   d. All of the above

3. What type of motor is used in most electric power steering (EPS) systems?
   a. AC brush type
   b. DC brushless
   c. Stepper
   d. None of the above

4. Two technicians are discussing electric power steering (EPS) systems. Technician A says that some systems operate on 12 volts. Technician B says that some systems operate on 42 volts such as some hybrid electric vehicles. Which technician is correct?
   a. Technician A only
   b. Technician B only
   c. Both technicians A and B
   d. Neither technician A nor B

5. Self-park systems use what sensors and EPS to achieve the parking maneuver?
   a. Wheel speed sensors (WSS)
   b. Steering wheel position sensor
   c. Ultrasonic sensors
   d. All of the above

6. A typical electric motor used in electric power steering systems produces about how much power?
   a. ¼ horsepower
   b. ¼ horsepower
   c. ¾ horsepower
   d. One horsepower

7. What is the relationship between the power steering control module (PSCM) and the powertrain control module (PCM)?
   a. Usually wired between the two
   b. No connection between the two
   c. Uses data lines (CAN) between the two modules
   d. Mounted together on the electric power steering (EPS) motor

8. Electro-hydraulic power steering systems use _____.
   a. An electric motor to power a hydraulic pump
   b. A conventional hydraulic power steering gear
   c. An engine-driven hydraulic power steering pump and an electric motor steering gear
   d. Both a and b

9. If a fault is detected in the electric power steering system, what dash light is turned on?
   a. The "check engine" light
   b. The "service vehicle soon" light
   c. The power steering warning light
   d. Either b or c

10. What diagnostic equipment is usually needed to diagnose faults or relearn the electric power steering system?
    a. Special electronic diagnostic equipment designed to test each specific system
    b. Factory or factory-level scan tool
    c. A breakout box
    d. A 12-volt test light

chapter 46

ELECTRONIC STABILITY CONTROL SYSTEMS

OBJECTIVES: **After studying Chapter 46, the reader will be able to:** • Prepare for Brakes (A5) ASE certification test content area "F" (Antilock Brake System Diagnosis and Repair). • Discuss how an electronic stability system works. • List the sensors needed for the ESC system. • Explain how the ESC system helps keep the vehicle under control. • Describe how a traction control system works. • List the steps in the diagnostic process for ESC and TC system faults.

KEY TERMS: • Electronic brake control module (EBCM) 562 • ESC 560 • Hand-wheel position sensor 562 • Lateral acceleration sensor 562 • Oversteer 560 • Positive slip 564 • Sine with dwell (SWD) test 561 • Steering wheel position sensor 562 • Telltale light 560 • Traction control (TC) 564 • Understeer 560 • Vehicle speed (VS) sensor 562 • Yaw rate sensor 563

THE NEED FOR ELECTRONIC STABILITY CONTROL

PURPOSE AND FUNCTION **Electronic stability control (ESC)** is a system designed to help drivers to maintain control of their vehicles in situations where the vehicle is beginning to lose control. Keeping the vehicle on the road prevents run-off-road crashes, which are the conditions that lead to most single-vehicle accidents and rollovers.

SYSTEM REQUIREMENTS The ESC is defined as a system that has all of the following features:

1. Helps vehicle directional stability by applying and adjusting individual wheel brakes to help bring the vehicle back to the intended direction.
2. Uses sensors to determine when the vehicle is not under control.
3. Uses a steering wheel position sensor to determine the intended direction of the driver.
4. Operates at all vehicle speeds, except at low speeds where loss of control is unlikely.

The electronic stability control (ESC) system applies individual wheel brakes to bring the vehicle under control if either of the following conditions occur:

- **Oversteering**—In this condition, the rear of the vehicle tends to move outward or breaks loose, resulting in the vehicle spinning out of control. This condition is also

called *loose*. If the condition is detected during a left turn, the ESC system would apply the right front brake to bring the vehicle back under control.

- **Understeering**—In this condition, the front of the vehicle tends to continue straight ahead when turning, a condition that is also called *plowing* or *tight*. If this condition is detected during a right turn, the ESC system would apply the right rear wheel brake to bring the vehicle back under control. ● **SEE FIGURE 46–1.**

NOTE: When the brakes are applied during these corrections, a thumping sound and vibration may be sensed.

TELLTALE LAMP. The ESC lamp, called a **telltale light,** is required to remain on for as long as the malfunction exists, whenever the ignition is in "On" ("Run") position. The ESC malfunction telltale will flash to indicate when the ESC system is operating to help restore vehicle stability.

ESC SWITCH. Some, but not all, vehicle manufacturers install a switch to temporarily disable or limit the ESC functions. This allows the driver to disengage ESC or limit the operation when the full ESC might not be needed such as:

- When a vehicle is stuck in sand/gravel
- When the vehicle is being operated on a racetrack for maximum performance

The electronic stability control system is turned back on when the ignition is turned off and then back on and is in the default position.

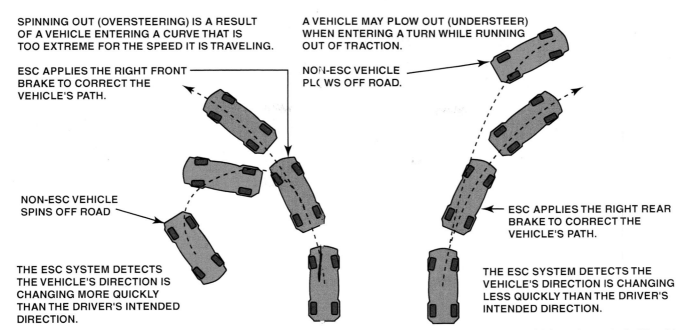

SPINNING OUT (OVERSTEERING) IS A RESULT OF A VEHICLE ENTERING A CURVE THAT IS TOO EXTREME FOR THE SPEED IT IS TRAVELING.

A VEHICLE MAY PLOW OUT (UNDERSTEER) WHEN ENTERING A TURN WHILE RUNNING OUT OF TRACTION.

ESC APPLIES THE RIGHT FRONT BRAKE TO CORRECT THE VEHICLE'S PATH.

NON-ESC VEHICLE PLOWS OFF ROAD.

NON-ESC VEHICLE SPINS OFF ROAD

ESC APPLIES THE RIGHT REAR BRAKE TO CORRECT THE VEHICLE'S PATH.

THE ESC SYSTEM DETECTS THE VEHICLE'S DIRECTION IS CHANGING MORE QUICKLY THAN THE DRIVER'S INTENDED DIRECTION.

THE ESC SYSTEM DETECTS THE VEHICLE'S DIRECTION IS CHANGING LESS QUICKLY THAN THE DRIVER'S INTENDED DIRECTION.

FIGURE 46–1 The electronic stability control (ESC) system applies individual wheel brakes to keep the vehicle under control of the driver.

FEDERAL MOTOR VEHICLE SAFETY STANDARD (FMVSS) NO. 126

Federal Motor Vehicle Safety Standard (FMVSS) No. 126 (June 26, 2008), Electronic Stability Control Systems, requires that all passenger cars, multipurpose passenger vehicles, trucks, and buses that have a gross vehicle weight rating (GVWR) of 10,000 pounds (4,536 kg) or less to be equipped with an electronic stability control (ESC) system by September 1, 2011 (2012 model year vehicles).

The ESC system must meet the following requirements

1. The ESC system must be able to apply all four brakes individually. This means that the vehicle must be equipped with a four-channel antilock braking system (ABS) which uses a wheel speed sensor at each wheel.

2. The ESC must be programmed to work during all phases of driving including acceleration, coasting, and deceleration (including braking).

3. The ESC system must work when the antilock brake system (ABS) or Traction Control is activated.

SINE WITH DWELL TEST

The standardized test used to determine if an electronic stability control system functions okay is called the **sine with dwell (SWD) test.** A vehicle is driven at 50 mph (80 km/h) and driven on a curved course that looks like a sine wave or the letter "S"

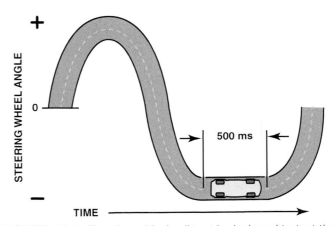

FIGURE 46–2 The sine with dwell test is designed to test the electronic stability control (ESC) system to determine if the system can keep the vehicle under control.

on its side. Then the vehicle is held in a straight-ahead position for 0.5 second (500 milliseconds) and before being steered back onto the curved section of the test. ● **SEE FIGURE 46–2.**

> **? FREQUENTLY ASKED QUESTION**
>
> **Can a Vehicle with a Modified Suspension Pass the Test?**
>
> Yes, if the system is properly engineered. To be sure, check with the company offering a suspension test to verify that the vehicle will still be able to pass the sine with dwell (SWD) test. This ensures that any changes are within the range where the ESC system can control the vehicle during emergency maneuvers. ● **SEE FIGURE 46–3.**

FIGURE 46–3 Using a simulator is the most cost-effective way for vehicle and aftermarket suspension manufacturers to check that the vehicle is able to perform within the FMVSS No. 126 standard for vehicle stability.

The quick changes involved in this test are designed to upset the chassis of the vehicle and cause the electronic stability control system to act to keep the vehicle under control during the entire test.

NAMES OF VARIOUS ESC SYSTEMS

Stability control systems are offered under the following names:

- **Acura:** Vehicle Stability Assist (VSA)
- **Audi:** Electronic Stabilization Program (ESP)
- **BMW:** Dynamic Stability Control (DSC), including Dynamic Traction Control
- **Chrysler:** Electronic Stability Program (ESP)
- **Dodge:** Electronic Stability Program (ESP)
- **Ferrari:** Controllo Stabilita (CST)
- **Ford:** AdvanceTrac and Interactive Vehicle Dynamics (IVD)
- **General Motors:** StabiliTrak (except Corvette—Active Handling)
- **Hyundai:** Electronic Stability Program (ESP)
- **Honda:** Electronic Stability Control (ESC), Vehicle Stability Assist (VSA), and Electronic Stability Program (ESP)
- **Infiniti:** Vehicle Dynamic Control (VDC)
- **Jaguar:** Dynamic Stability Control (DSC)
- **Jeep:** Electronic Stability Program (ESP)
- **Kia:** Electronic Stability Program (ESP)
- **Land Rover:** Dynamic Stability Control (DSC)

- **Lexus:** Vehicle Dynamics Integrated Management (VDIM) with Vehicle Stability Control (VSC) and Traction Control (TRAC) systems
- **Lincoln:** Advance Trak
- **Maserati:** Maserati Stability Program (MSP)
- **Mazda:** Dynamic Stability Control (DSC)
- **Mercedes:** Electronic Stability Program (ESP)
- **Mercury:** AdvanceTrak
- **Mini Cooper:** Dynamic Stability Control (DSC)
- **Mitsubishi:** Active Skid and Traction Control MULTIMODE
- **Nissan:** Vehicle Dynamic Control (VDC)
- **Porsche:** Porsche Stability Management (PSM)
- **Rover:** Dynamic Stability Control (DSC)
- **Saab:** Electronic Stability Program (ESP)
- **Saturn:** StabiliTrak
- **Subaru:** Vehicle Dynamics Control Systems (VDCS)
- **Suzuki:** Electronic Stability Program (ESP)
- **Toyota:** Vehicle Dynamics Integrated Management (VDIM) with Vehicle Stability Control (VSC)
- **Volvo:** Dynamic Stability and Traction Control (DSTC)
- **VW:** Electronic Stability Program (ESP)

ESC SENSORS

STEERING WHEEL POSITION SENSOR Depending on the vehicle, the **steering wheel position sensor** may also be called a **hand-wheel position sensor.** The function of this sensor is to provide the driver's intended direction with signals relating to steering wheel position, speed, and direction. ● **SEE FIGURES 46–4 AND 46–5.**

VEHICLE SPEED SENSOR The **vehicle speed (VS) sensor** is used by the **Electronic Brake Control Module (EBCM)** to help control the suspension system. The vehicle speed sensor is a magnetic sensor and generates an analog signal whose frequency increases as the speed increases. ● **SEE FIGURE 46–6.**

LATERAL ACCELERATION SENSOR The function of the **lateral acceleration sensor** is to provide the suspension control module with feedback regarding vehicle cornering forces. This type of sensor is also called a G-sensor, with the letter "G" representing the force of gravity. For example, when a vehicle enters a turn, the sensor provides information as to how hard the vehicle is cornering. This information is processed by the suspension control module to provide appropriate damping on the inboard and outboard dampers during cornering events.

This sensor can be either a stand-alone unit or combined with the yaw rate sensor.

HAND-WHEEL
POSITION SENSOR

SENSOR LOCATION

FIGURE 46–4 The hand-wheel position sensor is usually located at the base of the steering column.

FIGURE 46–6 The VS sensor information is transmitted to the EBCM by Class 2 serial data.

STEERING WHEEL
POSITION SENSOR

ELECTRONIC
BRAKE TRACTION
CONTROL MODULE
(EBTCM)

PHASE SIGNAL

SENSOR
SIGNAL A

B+

REFERENCE
VOLTAGE

SENSOR
SIGNAL B

GROUND

5V

VOLTAGE
SENSING
CIRCUIT

FIGURE 46–5 Hand-wheel (steering wheel) position sensor schematic.

FIGURE 46–7 A schematic showing the lateral acceleration sensor and EBCM.

Typically, the sensor is mounted in the passenger compartment:

- under a front seat
- in the center console
- on the package shelf

● **SEE FIGURE 46–7.**

YAW RATE SENSOR The **yaw rate sensor** provides information to the suspension control module and the EBCM. This information is used to determine how far the vehicle has deviated from the driver's intended direction.

This sensor can be either a stand-alone unit or combined with the lateral acceleration sensor. Typically, the sensor is

TECH TIP

Quick and Easy Lateral Acceleration Sensor Test

Most factory scan tools will display the value of sensors, including the lateral acceleration sensor. However, the sensor value will read zero unless the vehicle is cornering. A quick and easy test of the sensor is to simply unbolt the sensor and rotate it 90 degrees with the key on engine off. ● **SEE FIGURE 46–8.** Now the sensor is measuring the force of gravity and should display 1.0 G on the scan tool. If the sensor does not read close to 1.0 G or reads zero all of the time, the sensor or the wiring is defective.

FIGURE 46–8 A lateral acceleration sensor is usually located under the center console and can be easily checked by unbolting it and turn it on its side while monitoring the sensor value using a scan tool. When it is on its side the sensor value should read one G.

mounted in the passenger compartment under the front seat, in the center console, or on the rear package shelf.

This sensor does set DTC codes. These codes can be found in service information. ● SEE FIGURE 46–9.

TRACTION CONTROL

PURPOSE AND FUNCTION Traction control (TC) can be separate or used as part of the electronic stability control (ESC) system. Traction control allows an ABS system to control wheel spin during acceleration. When tires lose traction during acceleration, it is called **positive slip.**

Low-speed traction control uses the braking system to limit positive slip up to a vehicle speed of about 30 mph (48 km/h). Traction control is usually a part of the electronic stability control system. ● SEE FIGURE 46–10.

Traction control uses the same wheel speed sensors as ABS, but requires additional programming in the control

FIGURE 46–9 Yaw rate sensor showing the typical location and schematic.

FIGURE 46–10 Typical traction control system that uses wheel speed sensor information and the engine controller (PCM) to apply the brakes at lower speeds and also reduce engine power applied to the drive wheels.

module so the system monitors wheel speed continuously, not just when braking. Traction control also requires:

- Additional solenoids in the hydraulic modulator so the brake circuits to the drive wheels can be isolated from the non-drive wheels when braking is needed to control wheel spin.

- Use of a pump and accumulator to generate and store pressure for traction control braking. If a wheel speed sensor detects wheel spin in one of the drive wheels during acceleration, the control module energizes a solenoid that allows stored fluid pressure from the accumulator to apply the brakes on the wheel that is spinning. This slows the wheel that is spinning and redirects engine torque through the differential to the opposite drive wheel to restore traction.

Traction control works just as well on front-wheel-drive vehicles as it does on rear-wheel-drive vehicles.

SYSTEM COMPONENTS
The main controller for the traction can include one of the following, depending on make, model, and year of vehicle:

1. The body control module (BCM)
2. The powertrain control module (PCM)
3. The antilock brake system controller

The controller uses inputs from several sensors to determine if a loss of traction is occurring. The input signals used for traction control include:

- **Throttle position (TP) sensor** —This indicates the position of the throttle, which is the driver command for power.
- **Wheel speed sensor (WSS)** —The controller monitors all four wheel speed sensors. If one wheel is rotating faster than the other, this indicates that the tire is slipping or has lost traction.
- **Engine speed (RPM)** —This information is supplied from the engine controller powertrain control module (PCM) and indicates the speed of the engine.
- **Transmission range switch** —Determines which gear the driver has selected so that the PCM can take corrective action.

TRACTION CONTROL OPERATION
The outputs of the traction control system can include one or more of the following:

- Retard ignition timing to reduce engine torque.
- Decrease the fuel injector pulse-width to reduce fuel delivery to the cylinder to reduce engine torque.
- Reduce the amount of intake air if the engine is equipped with an electronic throttle control (ETC). Reduced airflow will reduce engine torque.
- Upshift the automatic transmission/transaxle. If the transmission is shifted into a higher gear, the torque applied to the drive wheels is reduced.

Most traction control systems are capable of reducing positive wheel slip at all vehicle speeds. Most speed traction control systems use accelerator reduction and engine power reduction to limit slip before applying the brakes to the wheel that is spinning. This action helps reduce the possibility of overheating the brakes if the vehicle were being driven on an icy or snow-covered road. ● **SEE FIGURE 46–11.**

Therefore the controller usually performs actions to restore traction in the following order:

1. Reduces engine torque to the drive wheels. This can include some or all of the following:
   - Retard spark timing
   - Reduce injector on-time (pulse-width)
   - Close or reduce the throttle opening
   - Shift the automatic transmission to a higher gear
2. Applying individual wheel brakes to slow or stop the wheel from spinning. The ABS controller supplies to the wheel brake only the pressure that is required to prevent tire slipping during acceleration. The amount of pressure

FIGURE 46–11 Wheel speed sensor information is used to monitor if a drive wheel is starting to spin.

FIGURE 46–12 A traction control or low traction light on the dash is confusing to many drivers. When the lamp is on or flashing, it indicates that a low traction condition has been determined and the traction control system is working to restore traction. A flashing traction dash light does not indicate a fault.

varies according to the condition of the road surface and the amount of engine power being delivered to the drive wheels. A program inside the controller will disable traction control if brake system overheating is likely to occur.

3. Lights a low traction or traction control warning light on the dash.

● **SEE FIGURE 46–12.**

TRACTION ACTIVE LAMP
On most applications, a "TRAC CNTL" indicator light or "TRACTION CONTROL ACTIVE" message flashes on the instrumentation when the system is engaging traction control. This helps alert the driver that the wheels are losing traction. In most applications, the message does not mean there is anything wrong with the system—unless the ABS warning lamp also comes on, or the traction control light remains on continuously.

Does Traction Control Engage Additional Drive Wheels?

When the term *traction control* is used, many people think of four-wheel-drive or all-wheel-drive vehicles and powertrains. Instead of sending engine torque to other drive wheels, it is the purpose and function of the traction control system to prevent the drive wheel(s) from slipping during acceleration. A slipping tire has less traction than a nonslipping tire—therefore, if the tire can be kept from slipping (spinning), more traction will be available to propel the vehicle. Traction control works with the engine computer to reduce torque delivery from the engine, as well as the controller to apply the brakes to the spinning wheel if necessary to regain traction.

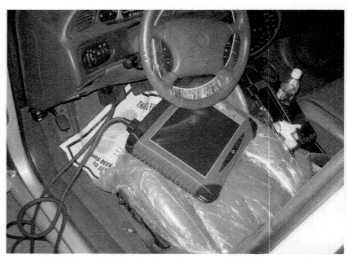

FIGURE 46–13 The use of a factory scan tool is often needed to diagnose the ESC system.

TRACTION DEACTIVATION SWITCH Many vehicles with traction control have a dash-mounted switch that allows the driver to deactivate the system when desired (as when driving in deep snow). An indicator light shows when the system is on or off, and may also signal the driver when the traction control system is actively engaged during acceleration.

ESC/TC DIAGNOSIS

Because the electronic stability control (ESC) and traction control (TC) systems use some of the same sensors and controllers, the diagnosis for them is about the same. To diagnose faults with either system, follow the recommended procedures found in service information. The usual procedure involves the following steps.

STEP 1 **Verify the customer concern (complaint).** This step includes trying to duplicate what the customer or driver is concerned about the system. If the traction control or ESC light is flashing, this indicates that it is trying to bring the vehicle under control. This may be normal operation if the following conditions exist:
- Icy or slippery road conditions
- Worn tires that lack traction

STEP 2 **Perform a thorough visual inspection** including:
- Check that all tires are the same size and tread depth.

NOTE: Using a spare tire on the drive wheel could cause the traction control and/or ESC amber warning light to flash because the controller is seeing that the smaller tire is rotating faster than the other side.

STEP 3 **Check service information** for the specified procedure to follow to retrieve diagnostic trouble codes. Most vehicles require the use of a factory-brand scan tool. ● **SEE FIGURE 46–13.**

STEP 4 **Follow the troubleshooting procedure** as specified to fix the root cause of the problem. This means following the instructions displayed on the scan tool or service information. The steps usually include all or many of the following:
- Brake fluid level
- Wheel speed sensor resistance
- Fault with the base brake system, such as air in the lines that could prevent the traction control controller from applying the wheel brakes

STEP 5 **Repair the fault.**

STEP 6 **Road test the vehicle** under the same conditions that were performed to verify the fault to be sure that the fault has been repaired.

SUMMARY

1. The purpose and function of the electronic stability control (ESC) system is to help maintain directional stability under all driving conditions by applying individual wheel brakes as needed to restore control.

2. The Federal Motor Vehicle Safety Standard (FMVSS) number 126 requires that all vehicles with a gross vehicle weight of less than 10,000 pounds be equipped with ESC by September 1, 2011.

3. The ESC can be switched off but will default to on when the ignition is turned back on.

4. The sine with dwell test (SWD) is the standard test used to test electronic stability control systems.

5. Electronic stability control sensors include steering wheel position sensor, vehicle speed sensor, lateral acceleration sensor, and yaw rate sensor.

6. Traction control (TC) systems use a variety of actions to help achieve traction of the drive wheels during acceleration, including retarding ignition timing, upshifting the transmission, and applying individual wheel brakes.

7. Diagnosis of the ESC or TC system involves the following steps:
   a. Verify the customer concern.
   b. Perform a thorough visual inspection.
   c. Check service information for specified test procedures.
   d. Follow specified testing procedures.
   e. Repair the fault.
   f. Perform a roadtest to verify the repair.

REVIEW QUESTIONS

1. What is the difference between oversteering and understeering?

2. What is the "sine with dwell" test?

3. What are some of the other names used to identify an electronic stability control (ESC) system?

4. What sensors are used in the electronic stability control system?

5. What action does the traction control system perform to help the drive wheels maintain traction during acceleration?

6. What is the typical diagnostic procedure to follow when troubleshooting a fault with the electronic stability control or traction control system?

CHAPTER QUIZ

1. The electronic stability control (ESC) system requires that the vehicle be equipped with what type of brake system?
   a. Four-wheel disc brakes
   b. Four-channel ABS
   c. Three-channel ABS
   d. Front disc with rear drum brakes

2. Which Federal Motor Safety Standard requires electronic stability control to be on all vehicles by 2011?
   a. 126
   b. 113
   c. 109
   d. 101

3. What is the name of the standard test that is performed to verify ESC operation?
   a. ESC plus
   b. Vehicle stability enhancement test
   c. Sine with dwell
   d. Anti-skid test

4. What other name is used to describe an electronic stability control (ESC) system?
   a. Vehicle Stability Assist (VSA)
   b. Electronic Stability Program (ESP)
   c. Vehicle Dynamic Control (VDC)
   d. Any of the above

5. Which sensor is used by the ESC controller to determine the driver's intended direction?
   a. Yaw sensor
   b. Steering wheel (hand-wheel) position sensor
   c. Vehicle speed (VS) sensor
   d. Lateral acceleration sensor

6. A diagnostic trouble code (DTC) has been set for a fault with lateral acceleration sensor or circuit. What test could be performed to check if the sensor is working?
   a. Unplug it and see if the scan tool reads 1.0 G
   b. Disconnect the sensor and hold it sideways to see if a scan tool reads 0.0 G
   c. Disconnect the sensor and hold it sideways to see if a scan tool reads 1.0 G
   d. Drive the vehicle in a circle to see if the scan tool reads 0.0 G

7. A lateral acceleration sensor is usually located where in the vehicle?
   a. Under the front seat
   b. In the center console
   c. On the package shelf
   d. Any of the above locations

8. If a vehicle tends to continue straight ahead while cornering, this condition is called _____.
   a. Understeer
   b. Plowing
   c. Tight
   d. All of the above

9. Traction control uses the antilock braking system and other devices to limit _____ of the drive wheels during acceleration.
   a. Positive slip
   b. Negative slip

10. A traction control system can often control all except _____.
   a. Limit engine torque delivered to the drive wheel
   b. Engage four-wheel drive
   c. Upshift the automatic transmission
   d. Apply the wheel brake to the wheel that is losing traction

INTRODUCTION TO HYBRID VEHICLES

OBJECTIVES: After studying Chapter 47, the reader will be able to: • Describe the different types of hybrid electric vehicles. • Explain how a hybrid vehicle is able to achieve an improvement in fuel economy compared to a conventional vehicle design. • Discuss the advantages and disadvantages of the various hybrid designs. • Describe HEV components, including motors, energy sources, and motor controllers. • Discuss the operation of a typical hybrid electric vehicle.

KEY TERMS: • Assist hybrid 576 • BAS 572 • BEV 568 • EV 568 • Full hybrid 576 • HEV 568 • HOV lane 574 • Hybrid 575 • ICE 568 • Idle stop mode 575 • Medium hybrid 576 • Micro-hybrid drive 574 • Mild hybrid 575 • Motoring mode 573 • Parallel-hybrid design 571 • Power-assist mode 575 • Quiet mode 575 • Series-hybrid 570 • Series-parallel hybrid 572 • Strong hybrid 576 • ZEV 569

HYBRID VEHICLE

DEFINITION OF TERMS   A hybrid vehicle is one that uses two different methods to propel the vehicle. A hybrid electric vehicle, abbreviated **HEV** uses both an internal combustion engine and an electric motor to propel the vehicle. Most hybrid vehicles use a high-voltage battery pack and a combination electric motor and generator to help or assist a gasoline engine. The **internal combustion engine (ICE)** used in a hybrid vehicle can be either gasoline or diesel, although only gasoline-powered engines are currently used in hybrid vehicles. An electric motor is used to help propel the vehicle, and in some designs, is capable of propelling the vehicle alone without having to start the internal combustion engine. A hybrid electric vehicle does not need to be plugged into an outlet because the internal combustion engine powers a generator to keep the high-voltage battery charged.

BACKGROUND   In the early years of vehicle development, many different types of propulsion systems were used, including:

- steam engine powered
- gasoline engine powered
- electric motor powered

Early electric vehicles (**EVs**) were also called **battery electric vehicles (BEV).** These early electric vehicles used lead–acid batteries, an electric traction motor, and a mechanical controller. A traction motor is an electric motor used to rotate the drive wheels and propel vehicle. The vehicle moves as a result of the traction between the wheel and the road surface to transmit the torque needed to move the vehicle.

ELECTRIC VEHICLES

EARLY ELECTRIC VEHICLES   The controller was operated by the driver and allowed different voltages to be applied to the electric motor, depending on the needs of the driver. For an example, assume that an early electric vehicle used six 6-volt batteries. If the batteries are connected in series, the negative terminal of one battery is connected to the positive terminal of the second battery. Two 6-volt batteries connected in series result in 12 volts, but the same current as one of the batteries. If two 6-volt 500-amp hour batteries were connected in series, then the output would be 12 volts and 500-amp hours. If the batteries were connected in parallel, the current of each battery is increased, but the voltage remains the same. If two 6-volt 500-amp hour batteries were connected in parallel, then the voltage would be six volts, but the capacity would be 1,000 amp hours.

The old electric vehicle mechanical controller was able to switch all six batteries in various combinations of series and parallel configurations to achieve lower voltage for slow speeds and higher voltages for higher speeds.

Electric vehicles did not have a long range and needed to have the batteries charged regularly, which meant that electric vehicles could only be used for short distances. In fact electric vehicles were almost more popular than steam power in 1900 when steam had 40% of the sales and electric had 38% of the sales. The gasoline-powered cars represented only 22% of the vehicles sold.

NOTE: Due to the oil embargo of 1973 and increased demand for alternative energy sources, Congress enacted Public Law 94–413, the _Electric and Hybrid Vehicle Research, Development, and Demonstration Act of 1976,_ which was designed to promote new technologies.

FIGURE 47–1 View of the components of the General Motors electric vehicle (EV1). Many of the features of this vehicle, such as regenerative braking, currently used on hybrid vehicles were first put into production on this vehicle.

NEWER ELECTRIC VEHICLES In the late 1990s, several vehicle manufacturers produced electric vehicles, using electronic controllers to meet the demands for zero emission vehicles as specified by law in California at the time. Electric vehicles were produced by Ford, Toyota, Nissan, and General Motors. Legislation was passed in California that included the following revisions within the **zero emissions vehicle (ZEV)** mandate.

As a direct result of the California zero-emission vehicle mandate originally calling for 10% ZEV, General Motors developed the Electric Vehicle 1, known as EV1, and it was leased to customers in California and Arizona. ●**SEE FIGURE 47–1 AND 47-2.**

By 2010, there were several electric vehicles for sale although often in limited parts of the country and in limited numbers. Electric vehicles include the Tesla, Nissan Leaf, and Chevrolet VOLT as well as plug-in hybrid electric vehicles such as the Toyota Prius.

FIGURE 47–2 General Motors EV1 without a body.

DRIVING AND OWNING A HYBRID ELECTRIC VEHICLE

DRIVING A HYBRID VEHICLE   Driving a hybrid electric vehicle is the same as driving any other conventional vehicle. In fact, many drivers and passengers are often not aware they are driving or riding in a hybrid electric vehicle. Some unique characteristics that the driver may or may not notice include:

- After the internal combustion engine has achieved normal operating temperature and other conditions are met, the engine will stop when the vehicle slows down and stops. This condition may cause some concern to some drivers who may think that the engine has stalled and then may try to restart it.

- The brake pedal may feel different, especially at slow speeds of about 5 mph and 15 mph when slowing to a stop. It is at about these speeds that the brake system switches from regenerative braking to actually applying brake force to the mechanical brakes. A slight surge or pulsation may be felt at this time. This may or may not be felt and is often not a concern to drivers.

- The power steering works even when the engine stops because all hybrid electric vehicles use an electric power steering system.

- Some hybrid electric vehicles are able to propel the vehicle using the electric motor alone, resulting in quiet, almost eerie operation.

- If a hybrid electric vehicle is being driven aggressively and at a high rate of acceleration, there is often a feeling that the vehicle is not going to slow down when the accelerator pedal is first released. This is caused by two factors:

  1. The inertia of the rotor of the electric motor attached to the crankshaft of the ICE results in the engine continuing to rotate after the throttle has been closed.

  2. The slight delay that occurs when the system switches the electric motor from powering the vehicle to generating (regenerative braking). While this delay would rarely be experienced, and is not at all dangerous, for a fraction of a second it gives a feeling that the accelerator pedal did not react to a closed throttle.

OWNING A HYBRID ELECTRIC VEHICLE

- The fuel economy will be higher compared to a similar-type vehicle, especially if driven in city-type driving conditions where engine stop and regenerative braking really add to the efficiency of a hybrid electric vehicle. However, the range of the hybrid version may be about the same as the conventional version of the same vehicle because the hybrid version usually has a smaller fuel tank capacity.

- A hybrid electric vehicle will cost and weigh more than a conventional vehicle. The increased cost is due to the batteries, electric motor(s), and controllers used plus the additional components needed to allow operation of the heating and air conditioning systems during idle stop periods. The cost is offset in part by returning improved fuel economy as well as government energy credits awarded at the time of purchase for some new-technology vehicles. It may take many years of operation before the extra cost is offset by cost savings from the improved fuel economy. However, many owners purchase a hybrid electric vehicle for other reasons besides fuel savings, including a feeling that they are helping the environment and love of the high technology involved.

CLASSIFICATIONS OF HYBRID ELECTRIC VEHICLES

SERIES HYBRID   The types of hybrid electric vehicles include series, parallel, and series-parallel designs. In a **series-hybrid design,** sole propulsion is by a battery-powered electric motor, but the electric energy for the batteries comes from another on-board energy source, such as an internal combustion engine. In this design, the engine turns a generator and the generator can either charge the batteries or power an electric motor that drives the transmission. The internal combustion engine never powers the vehicle directly. ● **SEE FIGURES 47–3 AND 47–4.**

FIGURE 47–3 A drawing of the power flow in a typical series-hybrid vehicle.

FIGURE 47–4 This diagram shows the components included in a typical series-hybrid design. The solid-line arrow indicates the transmission of torque to the drive wheels. The dotted-line arrows indicate the flow of electrical current.

The engine is only operated to keep the batteries charged. Therefore, the vehicle could be moving with or without the internal combustion engine running. Series-hybrid vehicles also use regeneration braking to help keep the batteries charged. The Chevrolet VOLT is an example of a series-hybrid design.

The engine is designed to just keep the batteries charged, and therefore, is designed to operate at its most efficient speed and load. An advantage of a series-hybrid design is that no transmission, clutch, or torque converter is needed.

A disadvantage of a series-hybrid design is the added weight of the internal combustion engine to what is basically an electric vehicle. The engine is actually a heavy on-board battery charger. Also, the electric motor and battery capacity have to be large enough to power the vehicle under all operating conditions, including climbing hills.

All power needed for heating and cooling must also come from the batteries so using the air conditioning in hot weather and the heater in cold weather reduces the range that the vehicle can travel on battery power alone.

PARALLEL HYBRID In a **parallel-hybrid design,** multiple propulsion sources can be combined, or one of the energy sources alone can drive the vehicle. In this design, the battery and engine are both connected to the transmission.

The vehicle using a parallel-hybrid design can be powered by the internal combustion engine alone, by the electric motor alone (full hybrids only), or by a combination of engine and electric motor propulsion. In most cases, the electric motor is used to assist the internal combustion engine. One of the advantages of using a parallel hybrid design is that by using an electric motor or motors to assist the internal combustion engine, the engine itself can be smaller than would normally be needed. ● **SEE FIGURES 47–5 AND 47–6.**

 FREQUENTLY ASKED QUESTION

How Fast Does the Motor-Generator Turn the Engine When Starting?

The typical starter motor used on a conventional gasoline or diesel engine rotates the engine from 100 to 300 revolutions per minute (RPM). Because the typical engine idles at about 600 to 700 RPM, the starter motor is rotating the engine at a speed slower than it operates. This makes it very noticeable when starting because the sound is different when cranking compared to when the engine actually starts and runs.

However, when the motor-generator of a hybrid electric vehicle rotates the engine to start it, the engine is rotated about 1,000 RPM, which is about the same speed as when it is running. As a result, engine cranking is just barely heard or felt. The engine is either running or not running, which is a truly unique sensation to those not familiar with the operation of hybrid electric vehicles (HEVs).

FREQUENTLY ASKED QUESTION

Is a Diesel-Hybrid Electric Vehicle Possible?

Yes, using a diesel engine instead of a gasoline engine in a hybrid electric vehicle is possible. While the increased efficiency of a diesel engine would increase fuel economy, the extra cost of the diesel engine is the major reason this combination is not currently in production.

FIGURE 47-5 The power flow in a typical parallel-hybrid vehicle.

DRIVE POWER | ----- ELECTRIC POWER

SERIES-PARALLEL HYBRID The Toyota and Ford hybrids are classified as **series-parallel hybrids** because they can operate using electric motor power alone or with the assist of the ICE. Series-parallel hybrids combine the functions of both a series and a parallel design.

The internal combustion engine may be operating even though the vehicle is stopped if the electronic controller has detected that the batteries need to be charged. ● **SEE FIGURE 47-7.**

NOTE: The internal combustion engine may or may not start when the driver starts the vehicle depending on the temperature of the engine and other conditions. This can be confusing to some who are driving a hybrid electric vehicle for the first time and sense that the engine did not start when they tried to start the engine.

TRANSMISSION OF TORQUE | ----- ELECTRICAL CURRENT

FIGURE 47-6 Diagram showing the components involved in a typical parallel-hybrid vehicle. The solid-line arrows indicate the transmission of torque to the drive wheels, and the dotted-line arrows indicate the flow of electrical current.

NOTE: A parallel-hybrid design could include additional batteries to allow for plug-in capability, which could extend the distance the vehicle can travel using battery power alone.

One disadvantage of a parallel-hybrid design is that complex software is needed to seamlessly blend electric and ICE power. Another concern about the parallel-hybrid design is that it had to be engineered to provide proper heating and air-conditioning system operation when the ICE stops at idle.

BELT ALTERNATOR STARTER SYSTEMS

PARTS AND OPERATION The belt system, commonly called the **belt alternator starter (BAS),** is the least expensive system that can be used and still claim that the vehicle is a hybrid. For many buyers, cost is a major concern and the BAS system allows certain hybrid features without the cost associated with an entire redesign of the engine and powertrain. Consumers will be able to upgrade from conventional models to BAS hybrids at a reasonable cost and will get slightly better fuel economy.

GENERATOR

GASOLINE ENGINE

BATTERY

INVERTER

MOTOR

POWER SPLIT DEVICE

DRIVE WHEELS

REDUCTION GEAR

▬▬ DRIVE POWER   ┄┄ ELECTRIC POWER

FIGURE 47–7 A series-parallel hybrid design allows the vehicle to operate in electric motor mode only or in combination with the internal combustion engine.

The BAS concept is to replace the belt-driven alternator with an electric motor that serves as a generator and a motor. When the engine is running the motor, acting as a generator, it will charge a separate 36-volt battery (42-volt charging voltage). When the engine needs to be started again after the engine has been stopped at idle to save fuel (idle stop), the BAS motor is used to crank the engine by taking electrical power from the 36-volt battery pack and applies its torque via the accessory belt, and cranks the engine instead of using the starter motor.

NOTE: A BAS system uses a conventional starter motor for starting the ICE the first time, and only uses the high-voltage motor-generator to start the ICE when leaving idle stop mode.

The motor-generator is larger than a standard starter motor so more torque can be generated in the cranking mode, also referred to as the **motoring mode.** The fast rotation of the BAS allows for quicker starts of the engine, and makes the start/stop operation possible. Having the engine shut off when the vehicle is at a stop saves fuel. Of course, the stopping of the engine does create a sense that the engine has stalled, which is a common concern to drivers unfamiliar with the operation of hybrid vehicles.

A typical BAS system will achieve a 8% to 15% increase in fuel economy, mostly affecting the city mileage with little, if any, effect on the highway mileage. On extremely small vehicles, the belt alternator starter might nudge a vehicle into the mild hybrid category. The BAS system is the type used in the Saturn VUE hybrid SUV. ● **SEE FIGURES 47–8 AND 47–9.**

MICRO-HYBRID DRIVE SYSTEM One of the major fuel-saving features of a hybrid electric vehicle is the idle stop mode, in which the internal combustion engine is stopped, instead of idling, while in traffic.

FIGURE 47–8 This chart shows what is occurring during various driving conditions in a BAS-type hybrid.

ADVANCED NICKEL-METAL HYDRIDE HYBRID BATTERY PACK, WITH AUTO DISCONNECT (LOCATED UNDER THE REAR SEAT)

ENGINE CONTROL MODULE WITH HYBRID SUPERVISORY SOFTWARE

POWER ELECTRONICS WITH INVERTER AND DC/DC CONVERTER

MODIFIED 4T45E AUTOMATIC TRANSMISSION WITH AUXILIARY PUMP

MOTOR/GENERATOR WITH 3-PHASE CABLES

DUAL TENSIONER ASSEMBLIES

FIGURE 47–9 The components of a typical belt alternator-starter (BAS) system.

? FREQUENTLY ASKED QUESTION

Can Hybrids Use the HOV Lane?

In most locations the answer is yes, but it depends on the type of hybrid vehicle. The **high-occupancy vehicle (HOV) lane** in many cities is reserved for use by vehicles that are carrying more than one occupant as a way to encourage carpooling and the use of public transportation. In California, only those hybrids classified as being high-fuel-economy models and those meeting certain emission ratings qualify. Those that do qualify, such as the Toyota Prius, are issued stickers that show that they are entitled to be in the HOV lane even if there is just the driver in the vehicle. High-performance hybrids, such as the Honda Accord hybrid, do not meet the specified fuel economy rating to allow the owners to be issued HOV stickers, which are also limited as to how many in the entire state can be issued. ● **SEE FIGURE 47–10.**

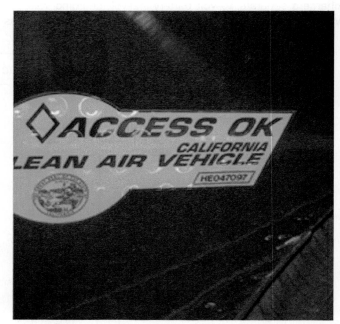

FIGURE 47–10 This sticker on a hybrid vehicle allows the driver to use the high-occupancy vehicle (HOV) lanes even if there is only one person in the vehicle as a way to increase demand for hybrid vehicles in California.

One simple system developed by Valeo uses a starter/alternator that is used as a conventional alternator when the engine is running, and as a starter to start the engine by transmitting power through the drive belt system. This type of system is often called a **micro-hybrid-drive system.** ● **SEE FIGURE 47–11.**

The only mechanical addition needed is a special belt tensioner that allows two-directional belt travel and can be fitted to almost any existing gasoline or diesel engine. The fuel and exhaust emission savings are proportional to the amount of idle time and can save up to 6% during city driving conditions.

FIGURE 47–11 A combination starter/alternator is used to provide idle stop function to conventional vehicles. This very limited and low cost system is called a micro-hybrid drive.

COMMON FEATURES OF MOST HYBRIDS

The following are the most common features of hybrids that improve fuel economy:

- **Idle stop.** The **idle stop mode** turns off the engine when the vehicle is stopped. When the brake is released, the engine immediately starts. This ensures that the vehicle is not using fuel, nor creating CO_2 emissions, when the engine is not required to propel the vehicle.
- **Regenerative braking.** When decelerating, the braking system captures the energy from the vehicle's inertia and converts it to electrical energy which is stored in the battery or other device for later use. Regenerative braking helps keep the batteries charged.
- **Power assist.** The electric motor provides extra power using electrical current drawn from the battery to assist the internal combustion engine during acceleration. This **power-assist mode** enables the vehicle to use a smaller, more fuel-efficient engine without giving up vehicle performance.
- **Engine-off drive-electric vehicle mode.** The electric motor propels the vehicle at lower speeds. This mode is often called the motoring mode. Because the internal combustion engine is not being used during acceleration, no fuel is being used and no emissions are being released. When the hybrid is in this mode, it is essentially an electric vehicle.

LEVELS OF HYBRID VEHICLES

The term **hybrid** refers to a type of vehicle. However, there are different levels of "hybridization" among hybrids on the market. Different vehicle manufacturers use various hybrid technologies.

MILD HYBRID A **mild hybrid** will incorporate idle stop and regenerative braking but is not capable of using the electric motor to propel the vehicle on its own without help from the internal combustion engine. A mild hybrid system has the advantage of costing less, but saves less fuel compared to a full hybrid vehicle and usually uses a 42-volt electrical motor and battery package (36-volt batteries, 42-volt charging).

 TECH TIP

Watch Out for Motoring Mode

When a hybrid electric vehicle is operating at low speeds, it is often being propelled by the electric motor alone, sometimes called motoring mode. As a result, the vehicle is very quiet and is said to be operating in **quiet mode.**

During this time, the driver should be aware that the vehicle is not making any sound and should be careful when driving in congested areas. Service technicians should also be extremely careful when moving a hybrid electric vehicle around the shop due to the silence of the vehicle.

Hybrid Features by Make/Model

Make/Model	Idle Stop	Regen-erative Braking	Motor Assist	Engine-Off Drive—EV Mode
2004-2007 Chevrolet Silverado 1500/GMC Sierra Hybrid	✓	✓		
Ford Escape and Mercury Mariner Hybrid	✓	✓	✓	✓
Honda Accord Civic Hybrid	✓	✓	✓	
Honda Insight	✓	✓	✓	
Toyota Prius	✓	✓	✓	✓
Saturn VUE	✓	✓	✓	
Toyota Highlander/ Lexus RX hybrids.	✓	✓	✓	✓

An example of this type of hybrid is the General Motors Silverado pickup truck and the Saturn VUE. The fuel savings for a mild type of hybrid design is about 8% to 15%.

MEDIUM HYBRID   A **medium hybrid** uses 144- to 158-volt batteries that provide for engine stop/start, regenerative braking, and power assist. Like a mild hybrid, a typical medium hybrid is not capable of propelling the vehicle from a stop using battery power alone. Examples of a medium hybrid vehicle include the Honda Insight, Civic, and Accord. The fuel economy savings are about 20% to 25% for medium hybrid systems.

FULL HYBRID   A **full hybrid,** also called a **strong hybrid,** uses idle stop regenerative braking, and is able to propel the vehicle using the electric motor(s) alone.

Each vehicle manufacturer has made its decision on which hybrid type to implement based on its assessment of the market niche for a particular model. Examples of a full or strong hybrid include the Ford Escape SUV, Toyota Highlander, Lexus RX400h, Lexus GS450h, Toyota Prius, and Toyota Camry. The fuel economy savings are about 30% to 50% for full hybrid systems.

 FREQUENTLY ASKED QUESTION

What Is an Assist Hybrid?

An assist hybrid-electric vehicle is a term used to describe a vehicle where the electric motor is not able to start moving the vehicle on electric power alone. This type of hybrid would include all mild hybrids (36 to 42 volts), as well as the medium hybrids that use 144- to 158-volt systems.

EFFICIENCIES OF ELECTRIC MOTORS AND INTERNAL COMBUSTION ENGINES

- An electric motor can have efficiency (including controller) of over 90%, while a gasoline engine only has efficiency of 35% or less.
- An ICE does not have the overload capability of an electric motor. That is why the rated power of an internal combustion engine is usually much higher than required for highway cruising. Operating smoothly at idle speed produces a much lower efficiency than operating at a higher speed.
- Maximum torque of an internal combustion engine is reached at intermediate speed and the torque declines as speed increases further.
- There is a maximum fuel efficiency point in the speed range for the ICE, and this speed is optimized by many hybrid vehicle manufacturers by using a transmission that keeps the engine speed within the most efficient range.

ELECTRIC MOTORS   Electric motors offer ideal characteristics for use in a vehicle because of the following factors:

- Constant power over all speed ranges
- Constant torque at low speeds needed for acceleration and hill-climbing capability
- Constant torque below base speed
- Constant power above base speed
- Only single gear or fixed gear is needed in the electric motor transmission

SUMMARY

1. Hybrids use two different power sources to propel the vehicle.
2. A mild hybrid with a lower voltage system (36 to 50 volts) is capable of increasing fuel economy and reducing exhaust emissions but is not capable of using the electric motor alone to propel the vehicle.
3. A medium hybrid uses a higher voltage than a mild hybrid (140 to 150 volts) and offers increased fuel economy over a mild hybrid design but is not capable of operating using the electric motor alone.
4. A full or strong hybrid uses a high-voltage system (250 to 650 volts) and is capable of operating using the electric motor(s) alone and achieves the highest fuel economy improvement of all types of hybrids.
5. Early in vehicle history, electric vehicles were more popular than either steam- or gasoline-powered vehicles.
6. Legislation passed in California in 1998, which mandated zero-emission vehicles (ZEVs), caused the vehicle manufacturers to start producing electric vehicles. When the law was changed to allow the substitution of other vehicles that produced lower emissions, but not zero, it helped promote the introduction of hybrid electric vehicles (HEVs).
7. A hybrid vehicle is defined as having two power sources to propel the vehicle.
8. Electric motors are perfect for vehicle use because they produce torque at lower speed, whereas internal combustion engines need to have an increased speed before they produce maximum power and torque.

1. What are the advantages and disadvantages of a series-hybrid design?

2. What type of hybrid electrical vehicle is a Toyota Prius and Ford Escape hybrid?

3. What are the advantages and disadvantages of mild, medium, and full hybrid vehicles?

4. Why does a BAS system cost less than the other types of hybrid vehicles?

5. What are the four modes of operation of a typical hybrid vehicle?

CHAPTER QUIZ

1. The GM EV1 was what type of vehicle?
   a. Totally electric powered
   b. A first-generation hybrid electric vehicle (HEV)
   c. A series-type HEV
   d. A parallel-type HEV

2. Which type of hybrid uses 36 to 42 volts?
   a. Mild hybrid
   b. Medium hybrid
   c. Full hybrid
   d. Strong hybrid

3. Which type of hybrid is capable of propelling the vehicle using just the electric motor?
   a. BAS type
   b. Strong (full) hybrid
   c. Medium hybrid
   d. Mild hybrid

4. About how fast does a motor-generator crank the internal combustion engine?
   a. About 1000 RPM
   b. About 2000 RPM
   c. About 150 to 300 RPM
   d. About 400 to 600 RPM

5. Which type of hybrid electric design costs the least?
   a. Strong hybrid design
   b. Series-hybrid design
   c. Parallel-hybrid design
   d. BAS design

6. Which type of hybrid electric vehicle has idle stop operation?
   a. Strong hybrids only
   b. Strong, mild, and medium hybrids
   c. Mild hybrids only
   d. Medium hybrids only

7. Technician A says that most hybrids require that they be plugged into an electrical outlet at night to provide the electrical power to help propel the vehicle. Technician B says that the internal combustion engine in an HEV will often stop running when the vehicle is stopped. Which technician is correct?
   a. Technician A only
   b. Technician B only
   c. Both Technicians A and B
   d. Neither Technician A nor B

8. Technician A says that most hybrids use the series hybrid design. Technician B says that some hybrids have 42-volt batteries. Which technician is correct?
   a. Technician A only
   b. Technician B only
   c. Both Technicians A and B
   d. Neither Technician A nor B

9. Electric motors are better than an internal combustion engine to propel a vehicle because _____.
   a. They produce high torque at low speeds
   b. They do not burn fuel and therefore do not release carbon dioxide into the environment
   c. They are quiet
   d. All of the above are correct

10. All of the following are characteristic of a hybrid electric vehicle (HEV), *except* _____.
    a. High voltages (safety issue)
    b. Lower fuel economy
    c. Lower amount of carbon dioxide released to the atmosphere
    d. Quiet

chapter 48

REGENERATIVE BRAKING SYSTEMS

OBJECTIVES: **After studying Chapter 48, the reader will be able to:** • Describe how regenerative braking works. • Explain the principles involved in regenerative braking. • Discuss the parts and components involved in regenerative braking systems. • Describe the servicing precautions involved with regenerative brakes.

KEY TERMS: • Base brakes 579 • Brake pedal position (BPP) 582 • Electrohydraulic brake (EHB) 580 • F = ma 578 • Force 578 • G 585 • Inertia 578 • Kinetic energy 578 • Mass 578 • Regen 579 • Regeneration 579 • Torque 579

INTRODUCTION

When test driving a hybrid vehicle the driver may notice that there is a slight surge or pulsation that occurs at lower speeds usually about 5 to 20 mph (8 to 32 km/h). The brakes may also be touchy and seem to be very sensitive to the brake force applied to the brake pedal. This is where the regenerative braking system stops regenerating electricity for charging the batteries and where the mechanical (friction) brakes take over. This chapter describes how this system works and how the various components of a hybrid electric vehicle (HEV) work together to achieve the highest possible efficiency.

  FREQUENTLY ASKED QUESTION

What Is the Difference Between Mass and Weight?

Mass is the amount of matter in an object. One of the properties of mass is inertia. Inertia is the resistance of an object to being put in motion and the tendency to remain in motion once it is set in motion. The weight of an object is the force of gravity on the object and may be defined as the mass times the acceleration of gravity.

Therefore, mass means the property of an object and weight is a force.

PRINCIPLES OF REGENERATIVE BRAKING

INERTIA, FORCE, AND MASS   If a moving object has a mass, it has **inertia.** Inertia is the resistance of an object to change its state of motion. In other words, an object in motion tends to stay in motion and an object at rest tends to stay at rest unless acted on by an outside force.

A hybrid electric vehicle reclaims energy by converting the energy of a moving object, called **kinetic energy,** into electric energy. According to basic physics:

A **force** applied to move an object results in the equation:

$$F = ma$$

where:

F = force
m = mass
a = acceleration

The faster an object is accelerated, the more force that has to be applied. Energy from the battery (watts) is applied to the coil windings in the motor. These windings then produce a magnetic force on the rotor of the motor, which produces torque on the output shaft. This torque is then applied to the wheels of the vehicle by use of a coupling of gears and shafts. When the wheel turns, it applies a force to the ground, which due to friction between the wheel and the ground, causes the vehicle to move along the surface.

All vehicles generate **torque** to move the wheels to drive the vehicle down the road. During this time, it is generating friction and losses. When standard brakes are applied, it is just another friction device that has specially designed material to handle the heat from friction, which is applied to the drums and rotors that stop the wheel from turning. The friction between the wheel and the ground actually stops the vehicle. However, the energy absorbed by the braking system is lost in the form of heat and cannot be recovered or stored for use later to help propel the vehicle.

RECLAIMING ENERGY IN A HYBRID
On a hybrid vehicle that has regenerative brakes, the kinetic energy of a moving vehicle can be reclaimed that would normally be lost due to braking. Using the inertia of the vehicle is the key. Inertia is the kinetic energy that is present in any moving object. The heavier the object, and the faster it is traveling, the greater the amount of energy and therefore, the higher the inertia. It is basically what makes something difficult to start moving and what makes something hard to stop moving. Inertia is the reason energy is required to change the direction and speed of the moving object.

TRANSFERRING TORQUE BACK TO THE MOTOR
Inertia is the fundamental property of physics that is used to reclaim energy from the vehicle. Instead of using 100% friction brakes (**base brakes**), the braking torque is transferred from the wheels back into the motor shaft. One of the unique things about most electric motors is that electrical energy can be converted into mechanical energy and also mechanical energy can be converted back into electrical energy. In both cases, this can be done very efficiently.

Through the use of the motor and motor controller, the force at the wheels transfers torque to the electric motor shaft. The magnets on the shaft of the motor (called the rotor—the moving part of the motor) move past the electric coils on the stator (the stationary part of the motor), passing the magnetic fields of the magnets through the coils, producing electricity. Simply stated, the electric motor(s) becomes a generator to recharge the batteries during braking. This process is called **regeneration, regen,** or simply "reclaiming energy."

PRINCIPLES INVOLVED
Brakes slow and stop a vehicle by converting kinetic energy, the energy of motion, into heat energy, which is then dissipated to the air. Fuel is burned in the internal combustion engine to make heat, which is then converted to mechanical energy and finally this is used to create kinetic energy in the moving vehicle. The goal of regenerative braking is to recover some of that energy, store it, and then use it to put the vehicle into motion again. It is estimated that regenerative braking can eventually be developed to recover about half the energy wasted as braking heat. Depending on the type of vehicle, this would reduce fuel consumption by 10% to 25% below current levels.

Regenerative braking can be extremely powerful and can recover about 20% of the energy normally wasted as brake heat. Regenerative braking has the following advantages:

- Reduces the drawdown of the battery charge
- Extends the overall life of the battery pack
- Reduces fuel consumption

All production hybrid electric vehicles use regenerative braking as a method to improve vehicle efficiency, and this feature alone provides the most fuel economy savings. How much energy is reclaimed depends on many factors, including weight of the vehicle, speed, and the rate of deceleration. ● **SEE FIGURE 48–1.**

The amount of kinetic energy in a moving vehicle increases with the square of the speed. This means that at 60 mph, the kinetic energy is four times the energy of 30 mph. The speed is doubled (times 2) and the kinetic energy is squared (2 times 2 equals 4). ● **SEE FIGURE 48–2.**

The efficiency of the regenerative braking is about 80%, which means that only about 20% of the inertia energy is wasted to heat. There are losses when mechanical energy is converted to electrical energy by the motor/generator(s) and then some energy is lost when it is converted into chemical energy in the high-voltage batteries.

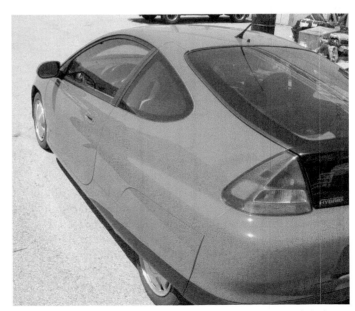

FIGURE 48–1 This Honda Insight hybrid electric vehicle is constructed mostly of aluminum to save weight.

FIGURE 48–2 A Toyota Prius hybrid electric vehicle. This sedan weighs more and therefore has greater kinetic energy than a smaller, lighter vehicle.

FIGURE 48–3 The electronic brake control unit (EBU) is shown on the left (passenger side) and the brake hydraulic unit is shown on the right (driver's side) on this Ford Escape system.

FIGURE 48–4 A typical brake curve showing the speed on the left and the percentage of regenerative braking along the bottom. Notice that the base brakes are being used more when the vehicle speed is low.

TYPES OF REGENERATIVE BRAKING SYSTEMS

Two different regeneration designs include:

■ **Series regeneration.** In series regenerative braking systems, the amount of regeneration is proportional to the brake pedal position. As the brake pedal is depressed further, the controller used to regulate the regenerative braking system computes the torque needed to slow the vehicle as would occur in normal braking. As the brake pedal is depressed even further, the service brakes are blended into the regenerative braking to achieve the desired braking performance based on brake pedal force and travel. Series regenerative braking requires active brake management to achieve total braking to all four wheels. This braking is more difficult to achieve if the hybrid electric vehicle uses just the front or rear wheels to power the vehicle. This means that the other axle must use the base brakes alone, whereas the drive wheels can be slowed and stopped using a combination of regenerative braking and base brake action. All series regenerative braking systems use an **electrohydraulic brake (EHB)** system, which includes the hydraulic control unit that manages the brake cylinder pressures, as well as the front-rear axle brake balance. Most hybrid vehicles use this type of regenerative braking system. ● **SEE FIGURE 48–3.**

The regenerative braking system mainly uses the regenerative capability, especially at higher vehicle speeds, and then gradually increases the amount of the base braking force at low vehicle speeds.

 FREQUENTLY ASKED QUESTION

Are the Friction Brakes Used During Regenerative Braking?

Yes. Most hybrid vehicles make use of the base (friction) brakes during stopping. The amount of regenerative braking compared to the amount of friction braking is determined by the electronic brake controller. It is important that the base brakes be used regularly to keep the rotors free from rust and ready to be used to stop the vehicle. A typical curve showing the relative proportion of brake usage is shown in ● **FIGURE 48–4.**

■ **Parallel regeneration.** A parallel regenerative braking system is less complex because the base (friction) brakes are used along with energy recovery by the motors becoming generators. The controller for the regenerative braking system determines the amount of regeneration that can be achieved based on the vehicle speed. Front and rear brake balance is retained because the base brakes are in use during the entire braking event. The amount of energy captured by a parallel regenerative braking system is less than from a series system. As a result, the fuel economy gains are less.

 FREQUENTLY ASKED QUESTION

How Does the Computer Change a Motor to a Generator So Quickly?

The controller of the drive motors uses a varying frequency to control power and speed. The controller can quickly change the frequency, and can therefore change the operation of a typical AC synchronous motor from propelling the vehicle (called motoring) to a generator. ● **SEE FIGURE 48–5.**

 FREQUENTLY ASKED QUESTION

Do Regenerative Brake Systems Still Use a Parking Brake?

Yes. Regenerative braking systems work while the vehicle is moving and supplements but does not replace the conventional brake system including the parking brake system.

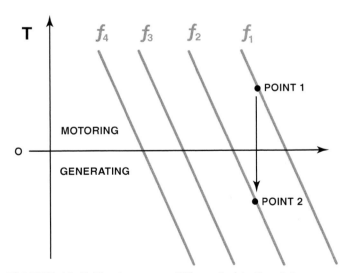

FIGURE 48–5 The frequency ("f") applied to the stator windings of an AC synchronous motor can be varied to create either forward torque ("T") or regenerative braking. If the frequency is changed from point 1 to point 2 as shown on the chart, the torque is changed from motoring (powering the vehicle) to generating and this change can be made almost instantly by the controller.

BATTERY CHARGING DURING REGENERATION

BACKGROUND Kinetic energy can be converted into electrical energy with a generator and it can be returned to the high-voltage batteries and stored for later use. Electric regenerative braking has its roots in the "dynamic brakes" used on electric trolley cars in the early Twentieth Century.

In the early electric trolley cars, the driver's control handle had a position that cut power to the electric motors and supplied a small, finely controlled excitation current to the motors' field windings. This turned the motors into generators that were driven by the motion of the trolley car. Increasing the magnetic field current increased the generating load, which slowed the trolley car, and the current being generated was routed to a set of huge resistors. These resistors converted the current to heat, which was dissipated through cooling fins. By the 1920s, techniques had been developed for returning that current to the power grid, making it available to all the other trolley cars in the system, reducing the load on the streetcar system's main generator by as much as 20%.

Regenerative braking systems are still being used in cities around the world. It is relatively easy to feed the current generated from braking into an on-board high-voltage battery system. The challenge was to make those components small enough to be practical, but still have enough storage capacity to be useful. A big breakthrough came with the development of the electronically controlled permanent-magnet motors.

PARTS AND OPERATION Motors work by activating electromagnets in just the right position and sequence. A conventional DC motor has groups of wire windings on the armature that act as electromagnets. The current flows through each winding on the armature only when the brushes touch its contacts located on the commutator. Surround the armature with a magnetic field and apply current to just the windings that are in the right position, and the resulting magnetic attraction causes the armature to rotate. The brushes lose contact with that set of windings just as the next set comes into the right position. Together, the brushes and rotation of the armature act like a mechanical switch to turn on each electromagnet at just the right position.

Another way to make a motor, instead of using electromagnets on the armature, is to use permanent magnets. Because it is impossible to switch the polarity of permanent magnets, the polarity of the field windings surrounding them needs to be switched. This is a brushless, permanent-magnet motor and the switching is only possible with the help of electronic controls that can switch the current in the field windings fast enough. The computer-controlled, brushless, permanent-magnet motor is ideal for use in electric vehicles. When connected to nickel-metal hydride (NiMH) batteries that can charge and discharge very quickly, the package is complete.

FREQUENTLY ASKED QUESTION

What Do Regenerative Brakes Look Like?

Regenerative brakes use the rotation of the wheels applied to the electric traction (drive) motor to create electricity. Therefore the brakes themselves look the same as conventional brakes because the hydraulic brakes are still in place and work the same as conventional brakes. The major difference is that the standard wheel brakes work mostly at low vehicle speeds whereas conventional brakes work at all speeds. As a result, the brakes on a hybrid electric vehicle should last many times longer than the brakes on a conventional vehicle.

LIMITATIONS OF REGENERATIVE BRAKES There are some limitations that will always affect even the best regenerative braking systems including:

- It only acts on the driven wheels.
- The system has to be designed to allow for proper use of the antilock braking system.
- The batteries are commanded to be kept at a maximum of about 60%, plus or minus 20%, which is best for long battery life and to allow for energy to be stored in the batteries during regenerative braking. If the batteries were allowed to be fully charged, then there would be no place for the electrical current to be stored and the conventional friction brakes alone have to be used to slow and stop the vehicle. Charging the batteries over 80% would also overheat the batteries.

So far its use is limited to electric or hybrid electric vehicles, where its contribution is to extend the life of the battery pack, as well as to save fuel.

REGENERATIVE BRAKING SYSTEMS

DASH DISPLAY The Toyota Prius is equipped with a center dash LCD that shows how many watt-hours of regeneration have occurred every 5 minutes. These are indicated by small "suns" that appear on the display and each sun indicates 50 watt-hours. When a sun appears, enough power has been put back into the battery to run a 50-watt lightbulb for an hour. Depending on the driver and the traffic conditions, some drivers may not be seeing many suns on the display, which indicates that the regeneration is not contributing much energy back to the batteries. The battery level also gives an indication of how much regeneration is occurring. The battery state-of-charge (SOC) is also displayed.

REGENERATIVE BRAKE COMPONENTS It is the ABS ECU that handles regenerative braking, as well as ABS functions, sending a signal to the hybrid ECU as to how much regeneration to impose. But how does the ABS ECU know what to do?

Rather than measuring brake pedal travel, which could vary with pad wear, the system uses pressure measuring sensors to detect master cylinder pressure. Some systems use a **brake pedal position (BPP)** sensor as an input signal to the brake ECU. The higher the master cylinder pressure, the harder the driver is pushing on the brake pedal.

If the driver is pushing only gently, the master cylinder piston displacement will be small and the hydraulic brakes will be only gently applied. In this situation, the ECU knows that the driver wants only gentle deceleration and instructs the hybrid ECU to apply only a small amount of regeneration. However, as master cylinder pressure increases, so does the amount of regeneration that can automatically be applied.

There are four pressure sensors in the braking system and two pressure switches. However, it is the master cylinder pressure sensor that is most important. ● **SEE FIGURES 48–6 AND 48–7.**

TECH TIP

"B" Means Braking

All Toyota hybrid vehicles have a position on the gear selector marked "B." This position is to be used when descending steep grades and the regenerative braking is optimized. This position allows the safe and controlled descent without having the driver use the base brakes. Having to use the base brakes only wastes energy that could be captured and returned to the batteries. It can also cause the brakes to overheat. ● **SEE FIGURE 48–8.**

FIGURE 48–6 The Toyota Prius regenerative braking system component showing the master cylinder and pressure switches.

FIGURE 48–7 The Ford Escape regenerative braking system, showing all of the components. Notice the brake pedal position sensor is an input to the ECU, which controls both the brake and traction control systems.

FIGURE 48–8 The "B" position on the shift display on this Lexus RX 400h means braking. This shifter position can be selected when descending long hills or grades. The regenerative braking system will be used to help keep the vehicle from increasing in speed down the hill without the use of the base brakes.

HOW THE REGENERATION SYSTEM WORKS

To keep the hybrid electric vehicles feeling as much like other vehicles as possible, the hybrids from Toyota and Honda have both the regeneration and conventional brakes controlled by the one brake pedal. In the first part of its travel, the brake pedal operates the regenerative brakes alone, and then as further pressure is placed on the pedal, the friction brakes come into play as well. The current Honda Civic Hybrid mixes the two brake modes together imperceptibly, whereas the first model Toyota Prius, for example, has more of a two-stage pedal.

Regeneration also occurs only when the throttle has been fully lifted. In the Hybrid Civic, it is like decelerating in fourth gear (in a five- or six-speed transaxle), while in the Prius models it feels less strong.

The wear of the hydraulic brakes and pads will also be reduced. The base brakes are still used when descending long hills, though as the battery becomes more fully charged, regeneration progressively reduces its braking action and the hydraulic brakes then do more and more of the work. Regeneration switches off at low speeds, so the disc brake pads and rotors stay clean and fully functional.

NOTE: One of the major concerns with hybrid vehicles is rust and corrosion on the brake rotors and drums. This occurs on hybrids because the base brakes are usually only used at low vehicle speeds.

The amount of regeneration that occurs is largely dictated by the output of the master cylinder pressure sensor. The ECU looks at the brake pressure signal from the sensor when the brake pedal switch is not triggered and uses this as the starting value. When the brake pedal is pushed, it then checks the difference between the starting value and the "brake pedal on" value and sets the regeneration value, according to this difference.

The voltage output of the pressure sensor ranges from about 0.4 to 3.0 volts, rising with increasing pressure. Service information states that a fault will be detected if the voltage from the sensor is outside of the range of 0.14V to 4.4V, or if

FIGURE 48–9 The ABS ECU on a Toyota Prius uses the brake switch and pressure sensor inputs to control the regenerative braking system. The circuit includes a voltage signal from the sensor, the regulated 5V supply to it, the input from the brake light switch (12V when the brakes are on), and the ground connection.

the voltage output of the sensor is outside a certain ratio to its nominally 5V supply voltage. ●SEE FIGURE 48–9.

ELECTRIC MOTOR BECOMES A GENERATOR When a motor is used for regenerative braking, it acts as a generator and produces an alternating current (AC). The AC current needs to be rectified (converted) to DC current to go into the batteries. Each of the three main power wires coming out of the motor needs two large diodes. The two large diodes on each main wire do the job of converting the AC into DC.

Regenerative braking is variable. In the same way as the accelerator pedal is used to adjust the speed, the braking is varied by reducing the speed.

There are deceleration programs within the Powertrain Control Module (PCM), which varies the maximum deceleration rates according to vehicle speed and battery state-of-charge (SOC).

FREQUENTLY ASKED QUESTION

Can an On-Vehicle Brake Lathe Be Used on a Hybrid Electric Vehicle?

Yes. When a brake rotor needs to be machined on a hybrid electric vehicle, the rotor is being rotated. On most hybrids, the front wheels are also connected to the traction motor that can propel the vehicle and generate electricity during deceleration and braking. When the drive wheels are being rotated, the motor/generator is producing electricity. However, unless the high-voltage circuit wiring has been disconnected, no harm will occur.

DECELERATION RATES

Deceleration rates are measured in units of "feet per second per second." What it means is that the vehicle will change in velocity during a certain time interval divided by the time interval. Deceleration is abbreviated "ft/sec" (pronounced "feet per second, per second" or "feet per second squared") or meters per sec^2 (m/s^2) in the metric system. Typical deceleration rates include the following.

- Comfortable deceleration is about 8.5 ft/sec^2 (3 m/s^2).
- Loose items in the vehicle will "fly" above 11 ft/sec^2 (3.5 m/s^2).
- Maximum deceleration rates for most vehicles and light trucks range from 16 to 32 ft/sec^2 (5 to 10 m/s^2).

An average deceleration rate of 15 ft/sec^2 (FPSPS) (3 m/s^2) can stop a vehicle traveling at 55 mph (88 km/h) in about 200 ft (61 m) and in less than 4 seconds. Deceleration is also expressed in units called a **g.** One g is the acceleration of gravity, which is 32 feet per second per second.

With a conventional hydraulic braking system, the driver can brake extremely gently, thereby only imperceptibly slowing the vehicle. A typical hybrid using regenerative braking will normally indicate a 0.1 g (about 3 ft/sec^2) deceleration rate when the throttle is released and the brake pedal has not been applied. This rate is what a driver would normally expect to occur when the accelerator pedal is released. This slight deceleration feels comfortable to the driver, as well as the passengers, because this is what occurs in a nonhybrid vehicle that does not incorporate regenerative braking. When the brake pedal is pressed, the deceleration increases to a greater value than 0.1 g, which gives the driver the same feeling of deceleration that would occur in a conventional vehicle. Maximum deceleration rates are usually greater than 0.8 g and could exceed 1 g in most vehicles. ●SEE FIGURE 48–10.

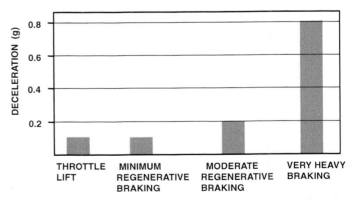

FIGURE 48–10 This graph compares the figures: at the far left a throttle lift typically giving about 0.1 g deceleration; second from the left a minimum regenerative braking of about 0.1 g; second from the right, a moderate regenerative braking is about 0.2 g; and on the far right a hard emergency stop resulting in braking of (at least) 0.8 g, which uses both the regenerative braking system, as well as the base hydraulic brake system.

FIGURE 48-11 This Honda valve train photo shows the small spring used to absorb the motion of the rocker arm when the cam is switched to a lobe that has zero lift. This action causes the valves to remain closed thereby reducing engine braking, which increases the amount of energy that can be captured by the regenerative braking system when the vehicle is slowing. The powertrain control module controls this valve action through a solenoid valve in response to inputs from the throttle position (TP) sensor and vehicle speed information.

ENGINE DESIGN CHANGES RELATED TO REGENERATIVE BRAKING

Some hybrid vehicles, such as the second-generation Honda Civic and Accord, use a variation of the VTEC valve actuation system to close all of the valves in three cylinders in both the V-6 and the inline four cylinder engines during deceleration. This traps some exhaust in the cylinders and because no air enters the pistons, the cylinders do not have anything to compress. As a result, the engine does not cause any engine braking and therefore allows more of the inertia of the moving vehicle to be converted to electrical energy due to regenerative braking. ● **SEE FIGURE 48-11.**

SERVICING REGENERATIVE BRAKING SYSTEMS

ROUTINE BRAKE SERVICE Routine brake service such as replacing the brake pads and shoes is the same on an HEV equipped with regenerative brakes as it is on a conventional vehicle.

UNIQUE MASTER CYLINDERS Most hybrid electric vehicles use unique master cylinders that do not look like

FIGURE 48-12 A master cylinder from a Toyota Highlander hybrid electric vehicle.

conventional master cylinders. Some use more than one brake fluid reservoir and others contain sensors and other components, which are often not serviced separately. ● **SEE FIGURE 48-12.**

FORD ESCAPE PRECAUTIONS On the Ford Escape hybrid system, the regenerative braking system checks the integrity of the brake system as a self-test. After a certain amount of time, the brake controller will energize the hydraulic control unit and check that pressure can be developed in the system.

- This is performed when a door is opened as part of the wake-up feature of the system.
- The ignition key does not have to be in the ignition for this self-test to be performed.
- This is done by developing brake pressure for short periods of time.

 FREQUENTLY ASKED QUESTION

When Does Regenerative Braking Not Work?

There is one unusual situation where regenerative braking will not occur. What happens if, for example, the vehicle is at the top of a long hill and the battery charge level is high? In this situation, the controller can only overcharge the batteries. Overcharging is not good for the batteries, so the controller will disable regenerative braking and use the base brakes only. This is one reason why the SOC of the batteries is kept below 80% so regenerative braking can occur.

FIGURE 48–13 When working on the brakes on a Ford Escape or Mercury Mariner hybrid vehicle, disconnect the black electrical connector on the ABS hydraulic control unit located on the passenger side under the hood.

CAUTION: To prevent physical harm or causing damage to the vehicle when serving the braking system, the technician should do the following:

1. In order to change the brake pads, it is necessary to enter the "Pad Service Mode" on a scan tool and disable the self-test. This will prevent brake pressure from being applied.
2. Disconnect the wiring harness at the hydraulic control unit. ● **SEE FIGURE 48–13.**
3. Check service information regarding how to cycle the ignition switch to enter the Pad Service Mode.

SUMMARY

1. All moving objects that have mass (weight) have kinetic energy.
2. The regenerative braking system captures most of the kinetic energy from the moving vehicle and returns this energy to high-voltage batteries to be used later to help propel the vehicle.
3. The two types of regenerative braking include parallel and series.
4. Brushless DC and AC induction motors are used in hybrid electric vehicles to help propel the vehicle and to generate electrical energy back to the batteries during braking.
5. Most hybrid electric vehicles use an electrohydraulic braking system that includes pressure sensors to detect the pressures in the system.
6. The controller is used to control the motors and turn them into a generator as needed to provide regenerative braking.

REVIEW QUESTIONS

1. What is inertia?
2. What is the difference between series and parallel regenerative braking systems?
3. What happens in the regenerative braking system when the high-voltage batteries are fully charged?
4. Describe what occurs when the driver starts to brake on a hybrid electric vehicle equipped with regenerative braking.

CHAPTER QUIZ

1. Which type of regenerative braking system uses an electrohydraulic system?
   a. Series
   b. Parallel
   c. Both series and parallel
   d. Neither series nor parallel

2. Kinetic energy is _____.
   a. The energy that the driver exerts on the brake pedal
   b. The energy needed from the batteries to propel a vehicle
   c. The energy in any moving object
   d. The energy that the motor produces to propel the vehicle

3. Inertia is _____.
   a. The energy of any moving object that has mass (weight)
   b. The force that the driver exerts on the brake pedal during a stop
   c. The electric motor force that is applied to the drive wheels
   d. The force that the internal combustion engine and the electric motor together apply to the drive wheels during rapid acceleration

4. Technician A says that the Powertrain Control Module (PCM) or controller can control the voltage to the motor(s) in a hybrid electric vehicle. Technician B says that the PCM or controller can control the electric motors by varying the frequency of the applied current. Which technician is correct?
   a. Technician A only
   b. Technician B only
   c. Both Technicians A and B
   d. Neither Technician A nor B

5. During braking on a hybrid electric vehicle equipped with regenerative braking system, what occurs when the driver depresses the brake pedal?
   a. The friction brakes are only used as a backup and not used during normal braking.
   b. The motors become generators.
   c. The driver needs to apply a braking lever instead of depressing the brake pedal to energize the regenerative braking system.
   d. The batteries are charged to 100% SOC.

6. Technician A says that a front-wheel-drive hybrid electric vehicle can only generate electricity during braking from the front wheel motor(s). Technician B says that the antilock braking system (ABS) is not possible with a vehicle equipped with a regenerative braking system. Which technician is correct?
   a. Technician A only
   b. Technician B only
   c. Both Technicians A and B
   d. Neither Technician A nor B

7. In a regenerative braking system, which part of the electric motor is being controlled by the computer?
   a. The rotor
   b. The stator
   c. Both the rotor and the stator
   d. Neither the rotor nor the stator

8. In a Toyota Prius regenerative braking system, how many pressure *sensors* are used?
   a. One
   b. Two
   c. Three
   d. Four

9. In a Toyota Prius regenerative braking system, how many pressure *switches* are used?
   a. One
   b. Two
   c. Three
   d. Four

10. Two technicians are discussing deceleration rates. Technician A says that a one "g" stop is a gentle slowing of the vehicle. Technician B says that a stopping rate of 8 ft/sec^2 is a severe stop. Which technician is correct?
   a. Technician A only
   b. Technician B only
   c. Both Technicians A and B
   d. Neither Technician A nor B

chapter 49

HYBRID SAFETY AND SERVICE PROCEDURES

OBJECTIVES: **After studying Chapter 49, the reader will be able to:** • Safely de-power a hybrid electric vehicle. • Safely perform high-voltage disconnects. • Understand the unique service issues related to HEV high-voltage systems. • Correctly use appropriate personal protective equipment (PPE). • Perform routine vehicle service procedure on a hybrid electric vehicle. • Explain hazards while driving, moving, and hoisting a hybrid electric vehicle.

KEY TERMS: • ANSI 589 • ASTM 589 • CAT III 591 • DMM 590 • Floating ground 592 • HV 589 • HV cables 589 • IEC 590 • Lineman's gloves 589 • NiMH 594 • OSHA 589 • Service plug 593

HIGH-VOLTAGE SAFETY

NEED FOR CAUTION There have been electrical systems on vehicles for over 100 years. Technicians have been repairing vehicle electrical systems without fear of serious injury or electrocution. However, when working with hybrid electric vehicles, this is no longer true. It is now possible to be seriously injured or electrocuted (killed) if proper safety procedures are not followed.

Hybrid electric vehicles and all electric vehicles use **high-voltage (HV)** circuits that if touched with an unprotected hand could cause serious burns or even death.

IDENTIFYING HIGH-VOLTAGE CIRCUITS **High-voltage cables** are identified by color of the plastic conduit and include:

- **Blue or yellow.** 42 volts (not a shock hazard but an arc will be maintained if a circuit is opened)
- **Orange.** 144 to 600 volts or higher

WARNING

Touching circuits or wires containing high voltage can cause severe burns or death.

HIGH-VOLTAGE SAFETY EQUIPMENT

RUBBER GLOVES Before working on the high-voltage system of a hybrid electric vehicle, be sure that high-voltage **lineman's gloves** are available. Be sure that the gloves are rated at least 1,000 volts and class "0" by ANSI/ASTM. The **American National Standards Institute (ANSI)** is a private, nonprofit organization that administers and coordinates the U.S. voluntary standardization and conformity assessment system. ASTM International, originally known as the **American Society for Testing and Materials (ASTM),** was formed over a century ago, to address the need for component testing in industry. The **Occupational Safety and Health Administration (OSHA)** requirements specify that the HV gloves get inspected every six months by a qualified glove inspection laboratory. Use an outer leather glove to protect the HV rubber gloves. Inspect the gloves carefully before each use. High voltage and current (amperes) in combination is fatal. ● **SEE FIGURES 49–1 AND 49–2.**

NOTE: The high-voltage insulated safety gloves must be recertified every six months to remain within Occupational Safety and Health Administration (OSHA) guidelines.

FIGURE 49–1 Rubber lineman's gloves protect the wearer from a shock hazard.

FIGURE 49–2 Wearing leather gloves over the lineman's gloves helps protect the rubber gloves from damage.

Before using the rubber gloves, they should be tested for leaks using the following procedure:

1. Roll the glove up from the open end until the lower portion of the glove begins to balloon from the resulting air pressure. Be sure to "lean" into the sealed glove to raise the internal air pressure. If the glove leaks any air, discard the gloves. ● **SEE FIGURE 49–3.**

2. The gloves should not be used if they show any signs of wear and tear.

WARNING

Cables and wiring are orange in color. High-voltage insulated safety gloves and a face shield must be worn when carrying out any diagnostics involving the high-voltage systems or components.

FIGURE 49–3 Checking rubber lineman's gloves for pinhole leaks.

CAT III-RATED DIGITAL MULTIMETER Hybrid electric vehicles are equipped with electrical systems whose voltages can exceed 600 volts DC. A CAT III-certified **digital multimeter (DMM)** is required for making measurements on these high-voltage systems.

The **International Electrotechnical Commission (IEC)** has several categories of voltage standards for meter and meter leads. These categories are ratings for over-voltage protection and are rated CAT I, CAT II, CAT III, and CAT IV. The higher the category (CAT) rating, the greater the protection to the technician when measuring high-energy voltage. Under each category there are various voltage ratings.

CAT I   Typically a CAT I meter is used for low-voltage measurements, such as voltage measurements at wall outlets in the home. Meters with a CAT I rating are usually rated at 300 to 800 volts. CAT I is for relatively low-energy levels, and while the voltage level to be high enough for use when working on a hybrid electric vehicle, the protective energy level is lower than what is needed.

CAT II   A higher-rated meter that would be typically used for checking voltages at the circuit-breaker panel in the home. Meters with a CAT II rating are usually rated at

FIGURE 49–4 Be sure to only use a meter that is CAT III-rated when taking electrical voltage measurements on a hybrid electric or electric vehicle.

300 to 600 volts. CAT II rated meters have similar voltage ratings as the other CAT ratings, but the energy level of protection is higher with a CAT II compared to a CAT I.

CAT III CAT III is the minimum-rated meter that should be used for hybrid vehicles. Meters with a CAT III rating are usually rated at 600 to 1,000 volts and the highest energy level which is needed to protect the service technician.

CAT IV CAT IV meters are for clamp-on meters only. A clamp-on meter is used to measure current (amperes) in a circuit by placing the clamp around the wire carrying the current. If a clamp-on meter also has meter leads for voltage measurements, that part of the meter will be rated as CAT III.

INSULATION TESTER An electrical insulation tester, such as the Fluke 1587, is used to test for electrical continuity between the high-voltage wires or components and the body of the vehicle. If a hybrid electric vehicle has been involved in any type of collision or any other incident where damage could occur to the insulation, the high-voltage system should be checked. An insulation tester is more expensive than a digital meter. This means that an individual service technician often does not purchase one, but any technician or service shop that works on hybrid electric vehicles should have one available.

EYE PROTECTION Eye protection should be worn when testing for high voltage, which is considered by many experts to be over 60 volts. Eye protection should include the following features:

1. Plastic frames (avoid metal frames as these are conductive and could cause a shock hazard)
2. Side shields
3. Meet the standard ANSI Z87.1

Most hybrid electric systems use voltages higher than this threshold. If the system has not been powered down or has not

FIGURE 49–5 The meter leads should also be CAT III-rated when checking voltages on a hybrid electric vehicle.

had the high-voltage system disabled, a shock hazard is always possible. Even when the high-voltage system has been disconnected, there is still high voltage in the HV battery box.

NOTE: Some vehicle manufacturers specify that full face shields be worn instead of safety glasses when working with high voltage circuits or components.

SAFETY CONES Ford requires that cones be placed at the four corners of any hybrid electric vehicle when service work on the high voltage system is being performed. They are used to establish a safety zone around the vehicles so that other technicians will know that a possible shock hazard may be present.

FIBERGLASS POLE Ford requires that a ten foot insulated fiberglass pole be available outside the safety zone to be used to pull a technician away from the vehicle in the unlikely event of an accident where the technician is shocked or electrocuted.

ELECTRIC SHOCK POTENTIAL

LOCATIONS WHERE SHOCKS CAN OCCUR Accidental and unprotected contact with any electrically charged ("hot" or "live") high-voltage component can cause serious injury or death. However, receiving an electric shock from a hybrid vehicle is highly unlikely because of the following:

1. Contact with the battery module or other components inside the battery box can occur only if the box is damaged and the contents are exposed, or the box is opened without following proper precautions.
2. Contact with the electric motor can occur only after one or more components are removed.
3. The high-voltage cables can be easily identified by their distinctive orange color, and contact with them can be avoided.
4. The system main relays (SMRs) disconnect power from the cables the moment the ignition is turned off.

LOCATIONS OF AUXILIARY BATTERIES ● SEE

CHART 49–1 for a summary of the locations of auxiliary batteries.

As a rule of thumb, the auxiliary battery is usually a flood-type if it is located under the hood and an AGM-type if it is in the trunk area.

FIGURE 49–6 The Ford Escape Hybrid instrument panel showing the vehicle in park and the tachometer on "EV" instead of 0 RPM. This means that the gasoline engine could start at any time depending on the state-of-charge of the high-voltage batteries and other factors.

☠ WARNING

Power remains in the high-voltage electrical system for up to 10 minutes after the HV battery pack is shut off. Never touch, cut, or open any orange high-voltage power cable or high-voltage component without confirming that the high-voltage has been completely discharged.

🔧 TECH TIP

Silence Is Not Golden

Never assume the vehicle is shut off just because the engine is off. When working with a Toyota or Lexus hybrid electric vehicle, always look for the **READY** indicator status on the dash display. The vehicle is shut off when the **READY** indicator is off.

The vehicle may be powered by:

1. The electric motor only.
2. The gasoline engine only.
3. A combination of both the electric motor and the gasoline engine.

The vehicle computer determines the mode in which the vehicle operates to improve fuel economy and reduce emissions. The driver cannot manually select the mode. ● SEE FIGURE 49–6.

🔧 TECH TIP

High Voltage Is Insulated from the Vehicle Body

Both positive and negative high-voltage power cables are isolated from the metal chassis, so there is no possibility of shock by touching the metal chassis. This design is called a **floating ground.**

A ground fault monitor continuously monitors for high-voltage leakage to the metal chassis while the vehicle is running. If a malfunction is detected, the vehicle computer will illuminate the master warning light in the instrument cluster and the hybrid warning light in the LCD display. The HV battery pack relays will automatically open to stop electricity flow in a collision sufficient to activate the SRS airbags.

HYBRID VEHICLE AUXILIARY BATTERY CHART

VEHICLE	AUXILIARY BATTERY TYPE	AUXILIARY BATTERY LOCATION
Honda Insight Hybrid	Flooded lead acid	Underhood; center near bulkhead
Honda Civic Hybrid	Flooded lead acid	Underhood; driver's side
Honda Accord Hybrid	Flooded lead acid	Underhood; driver's side
Ford Escape Hybrid	Flooded lead acid	Underhood; driver's side
Toyota Prius Hybrid (2001–2003)	Absorbed glass mat (AGM)	Trunk; driver's side
Toyota Prius Hybrid (2004–2007)	Absorbed glass mat (AGM)	Trunk; passenger side
Toyota Highlander Hybrid	Flooded lead acid	Underhood; passenger side
Toyota Camry Hybrid	Absorbed glass mat (AGM)	Trunk; passenger side
Lexus RX 400h Hybrid	Flooded lead acid	Underhood; passenger side
Lexus GS 450h Hybrid	Absorbed glass mat (AGM)	Trunk; driver's side
Chevrolet/GMC Hybrid Pickup Truck	Flooded lead acid	Underhood; driver's side

CHART 49–1

As a rule of thumb, the auxiliary battery is usually a flood-type if it is located under the hood and an AGM-type if it is in the trunk area.

DE-POWERING THE HIGH-VOLTAGE SYSTEM

THE NEED TO DE-POWER THE HV SYSTEM During routine vehicle service work there is no need to go through any procedures needed to de-power or to shut off the high-voltage circuits. However, if work is going to be performed on any of the following components then service information procedures must be followed to prevent possible electrical shock and personal injury.

- The high-voltage (HV) battery pack
- Any of the electronic controllers that use orange cables such as the inverter and converters
- The air-conditioning compressor if electrically driven and has orange cables attached

To safely de-power the vehicle always follow the instructions found in service information for the exact vehicle being serviced. The steps usually include:

STEP 1 Turn the ignition off and remove the key (if equipped) from the ignition.

WARNING

Even if all of the above steps are followed, there is still a risk for electrical shock at the high-voltage batteries. Always follow the vehicle manufacturer's instructions exactly and wear high-voltage gloves and other specified personal protective equipment (PPE).

FREQUENTLY ASKED QUESTION

When Do I Need to De-Power the High-Voltage System?

During routine service work, there is no need for a technician to de-power the high-voltage system. The only time when this process is needed is if service repairs or testing is being performed on any circuit that has an orange cable attached. These include:

- AC compressor if electrically powered
- High-voltage battery pack or electronic controllers

The electric power steering system usually operates on 12 volts or 42 volts and neither is a shock hazard. However, an arc will be maintained if a 42-volt circuit is opened. Always refer to service information if servicing the electric power steering system or any other system that may contain high voltage.

CAUTION: If a push-button start is used, remove the key fob at least 15 feet (5 meters) from the vehicle to prevent the vehicle from being powered up.

STEP 2 Remove the 12-volt power source to the HV controller. This step could involve:
- Removing a fuse or a relay
- Disconnecting the negative battery cable from the auxiliary 12-volt battery

STEP 3 Remove the high-voltage (HV) fuse or **service plug** or switch.

COLLISION AND REPAIR INDUSTRY ISSUES

JUMP STARTING The 12-volt auxiliary battery may be jump started if the vehicle does not start. The 12-volt auxiliary battery is located under the hood or in the cargo (trunk) area of some HEVs. Using a jump box or jumper cable from another vehicle, make the connections to the positive and negative battery terminals. ●**SEE FIGURE 49–7.**

On the 2004+ Toyota Prius vehicles, there is a stud located under the hood that can be used to jump start the auxiliary battery, which is located in the truck. ●**SEE FIGURE 49–8.**

NOTE: The high-voltage battery pack cannot be jump started on most HEVs. One exception is the Ford Escape/Mercury Mariner hybrids that use a special "jump-start" button located behind the left kick panel.

RESCUE VEHICLE

FIGURE 49–7 Jump starting a 2001–2003 Toyota Prius using a 12-volt supply to boost the 12-volt auxiliary battery in the trunk.

FIGURE 49-8 The underhood 12-volt jump-start terminal on this 2004+ Toyota Prius has a red plastic cover with a "+" sign. The positive booster cable clamp will attach directly to the vertical metal bracket.

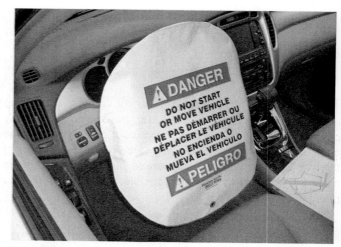

FIGURE 49-9 Using a warning cover over the steering wheel helps others realize that work is being performed on the high-voltage system and that no one is to attempt to start or move the vehicle.

When this button is pushed, the auxiliary battery is used to boost the HV battery through a DC-DC converter.

MOVING AND TOWING A HYBRID

TOWING If a disabled vehicle needs to be moved a short distance (to the side of the road, for example) and the vehicle can still roll on the ground, the easiest way is to shift the transmission into neutral and manually push the vehicle. To transport a vehicle away from an emergency location, a flatbed truck should be used if the vehicle might be repaired. If a flatbed is not available, the vehicle should be towed by wheel-lift equipment with the front wheels off the ground (FWD hybrid electric vehicles only). Do not use sling-type towing equipment. In the case of 4WD HEVs such as the Toyota Highlander, only a flatbed vehicle should be used.

MOVING THE HYBRID VEHICLE IN THE SHOP After an HEV has been serviced, it may be necessary to push the vehicle to another part of the shop or outside as parts are ordered. Make sure to tape any orange cable ends that were disconnected during the repair procedure. Permanent magnets are used in all the drive motors and generators and it is possible that a high-voltage arc could occur as the wheels turn and produce voltage. Another way to prevent this is to use wheel dollies. A sign that says "HIGH VOLTAGE—DO NOT TOUCH" could also be added to the roof of the vehicle. Remove the keys from the vehicle and keep in a safe location.
● **SEE FIGURES 49-9 AND 49-10.**

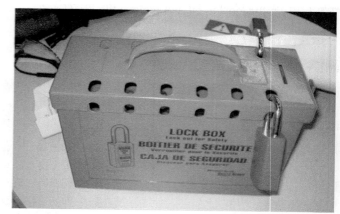

FIGURE 49-10 A lock box is a safe location to keep the ignition keys of a hybrid electric vehicle while it is being serviced.

? FREQUENTLY ASKED QUESTION

Will the Heat from Paint Ovens Hurt the High-Voltage Batteries?

Nickel-metal hydride (NiMH) batteries may be damaged if exposed to high temperatures, such as in a paint oven. The warning labels on hybrid vehicles specify that the battery temperature not exceed 146°F (63°C). Therefore be sure to check the temperature of any paint oven before allowing a hybrid electric vehicle into one that may be hotter than specified. Check service information for details on the vehicle being repaired.

REMOVING THE HIGH-VOLTAGE BATTERIES

PRECAUTIONS The HV battery box should always be removed as an assembly, placed on a rubber-covered work bench, and handled carefully. Every other part, especially the capacitors, should be checked for voltage reading while wearing HV rubber gloves. Always check for voltage as the components become accessible before proceeding. When removing high-voltage components, it is wise to use insulated tools. ● **SEE FIGURE 49–11.**

STORING THE HIGH-VOLTAGE BATTERIES If a hybrid is to be stored for any length of time, the state of charge of the HV batteries must be maintained. If possible, start the vehicle every month and run it for at least 30 minutes to help recharge the HV batteries. This is necessary because NiMH batteries suffer from self-discharge over time. High-voltage battery chargers are expensive and may be hard to find. If the HV battery SOC was over 60% when it was put into storage, the batteries may be stored for about a month without a problem. If, however, the SOC is less than 60%, a problem with a discharged HV battery may result.

HOISTING A HYBRID VEHICLE When hoisting or using a floor jack, pay attention to the lift points. Orange cables run under the vehicle just inside the fame rails on most hybrids. ● **SEE FIGURE 49–12.**

Some Honda hybrid vehicles use an aluminum pipe painted orange that includes three HV cables for the starter/generator and also three more cables for the HV air-conditioning compressor. If any damage occurs to any high-voltage cables, the MIL will light up and a no-start will result if the PCM senses a fault. The cables are not

---

FIGURE 49–11 Insulated tools, such as this socket set, would provide an additional margin of safety to the service technician when working around high-voltage components and systems.

FIGURE 49–12 The high-voltage wiring on this Honda hybrid is colored orange for easy identification.

repairable and are expensive. The cables can be identified by an orange outer casing, but in some cases, the orange casing is not exposed until a black plastic underbelly shield is removed first.

HV BATTERY DISPOSAL The hybrid electric vehicle manufacturers are set up to ship NiMH battery packs to a recycling center. There is an 800 number located under the hood or on the HV battery pack that can be used to gain information on how to recycle these batteries.

Always follow the proper safety procedures, and then minor service to hybrid vehicles can be done with a reasonable level of safety.

TECH TIP

High-Voltage Battery SOC Considerations

NiMH batteries do not store well for long lengths of time. After a repair job, or when the HV system has been powered down by a technician and powered up again, do not be surprised if a warning lamp lights, diagnostic trouble codes are set, and the MIL are illuminated. If everything was done correctly, a couple road tests may be all that is required to reset the MIL. The HV battery indicator on the dash may also read zero charge level. After a road test, the HV battery level indicator will most likely display the proper voltage level.

ROUTINE SERVICE PROCEDURES

DIAGNOSIS PROCEDURES Hybrid electric vehicles should be diagnosed the same as any other type of vehicle. This means following a diagnostic routine, which usually includes the following steps:

STEP 1 Verify the customer concern.

STEP 2 Check for diagnostic trouble codes (DTCs). An enhanced or factory level scan tool may be needed to get access to codes and sub-codes.

STEP 3 Perform a thorough visual inspection. If a DTC is stored, carefully inspect those areas that might be the cause of the trouble code.

STEP 4 Check for technical service bulletins (TSBs) that may relate to the customer concern.

STEP 5 Follow service information specified steps and procedures. This could include checking scan tool data for sensors or values that are not within normal range.

STEP 6 Determine and repair the root cause of the problem.

STEP 7 Verify the repair and clear any stored diagnostic trouble codes unless in an emission testing area. If in an emission test area, drive the vehicle until the powertrain control module (PCM) passes the fault and turns off the malfunction indicator lamp (MIL) thereby allowing the vehicle to pass the inspection.

STEP 8 Complete the work order and record the "three Cs" (complaint, cause, and correction).
● **SEE FIGURE 49–13.**

OIL CHANGE Performing an oil change is similar to changing oil in any vehicle equipped with an internal combustion engine.

However, there are several items to know when changing oil in a hybrid electric vehicle including:

- **Use vehicle manufacturer's recommended hoisting locations.** Use caution when hoisting a hybrid electric vehicle and avoid placing the pads on or close to the orange high-voltage cables that are usually located under the vehicle.

- **Always use the specified oil viscosity.** Most hybrid electric vehicles require either:

  SAE 0W-20

  SAE 5W-20

  Using the specified oil viscosity is important because the engine stops and starts many times and using the incorrect viscosity not only can cause a decrease in fuel economy but also could cause engine damage. ● **SEE FIGURE 49–14.**

- **Always follow the specified procedures.** Be sure that the internal combustion engine (ICE) is off and that the "READY" lamp is off. If there is a smart key or the vehicle has a push-button start, be sure that the key fob is at least 15 feet (5 meters) away from the vehicle to help prevent the engine from starting accidentally.

COOLING SYSTEM SERVICE Performing cooling system service is similar to performing this service in any vehicle equipped with an internal combustion engine. However, there are several items to know when servicing the cooling system on a hybrid electric vehicle including:

- **Always check service information for the exact procedure to follow.** The procedure will include the following:

  1. **The specified coolant.** Most vehicle manufacturers will recommend using premixed coolant because using water (half of the coolant) that has minerals could cause corrosion issues.

FIGURE 49–13 A scan tool display showing two hybrid-related faults in this Ford Escape hybrid.

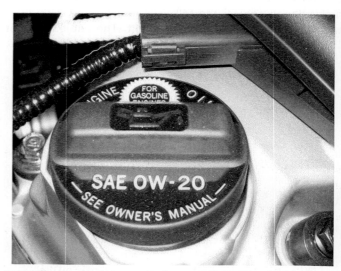

FIGURE 49–14 Always use the specified viscosity of oil in a hybrid electric vehicle not only for best fuel economy but also because of the need for fast lubrication because of the engine (idle) stop feature.

2. **The specified coolant replacement interval.** While this may be similar to the coolant replacement interval for a conventional vehicle, always check to be sure that this service is being performed at the specified time or mileage interval.

3. **The specified precautions.** Some Toyota Prius HEVs use a coolant storage bottle that keeps the coolant hot for up to three days. Opening a coolant hose could cause the release of this hot coolant and can cause serious burns to the technician.

4. Always read, understand, and follow all of the service information instructions when servicing the cooling system on a hybrid electric vehicle.

 REAL WORLD FIX

A Bad Day Changing Oil

A shop owner was asked by a regular customer who had just bought a Prius if the oil could be changed there. The owner opened the hood, made sure the filter was in stock (it is a standard Toyota filter used on other models), and said yes. A technician with no prior knowledge of hybrids drove the warmed-up vehicle into the service bay. The internal combustion engine never started, as it was in electric (stealth) mode at the time. Not hearing the engine running, the technician hoisted the vehicle into the air, removed the drain bolt, and drained the oil into the oil drain unit. When the filter was removed, oil started to fly around the shop. The engine was in "standby" mode during the first part of the oil change. When the voltage level dropped, the onboard computer started the engine so that the HV battery could recharge. The technician should have removed the key to keep this from happening. Be sure that the "ready" light is off before changing the oil or doing any other service work that may cause personal harm or harm to the vehicle if the engine starts.

AIR FILTER SERVICE Performing air filter service is similar to performing this service in any vehicle equipped with an internal combustion engine. However, there are several items to know when servicing the air filter on a hybrid electric vehicle including:

1. Always follow the service information recommended air filter replacement interval.

2. For best results use the factory type and quality air filter.

3. Double-check that all of the air ducts are securely fastened after checking or replacing the air filter.

AIR-CONDITIONING SERVICE Performing air-conditioning system service is similar to performing this service in any vehicle equipped with an internal combustion engine. However, there are several items to know when servicing the air-conditioning system on a hybrid electric vehicle including:

1. Many hybrid electric vehicles use an air-conditioning compressor that uses high voltage from the high-voltage (HV) battery pack to operate the compressor either all of the time, such as many Toyota/Lexus models, or during idle stop periods, such as on Honda hybrids.

2. If the system is electrically driven, then special refrigerant oil is used that is nonconductive. This means that a separate recovery machine should be used to avoid the possibility of mixing regular refrigerant oils in with the oil used in hybrids.

3. Always read, understand, and follow all of the service information instructions when servicing the air-conditioning system on a hybrid electric vehicle.

STEERING SYSTEM SERVICE Performing steering system service is similar to performing this service in any vehicle equipped with an internal combustion engine. However, there are several items to know when servicing the steering system on a hybrid electric vehicle including:

1. Check service information for any precautions that are specified to be followed when servicing the steering system on a hybrid electric vehicle.

2. Most hybrid electric vehicles use an electric power steering system. These can be powered by one of two voltages:

   - **12 volts**—These systems can be identified by the red or black wiring conduit and often use an inverter that increases the voltage to operate the actuator motor (usually to 42 volts). While this higher voltage is contained in the controller and should not create a shock hazard, always follow the specified safety precautions and wear protective high-voltage gloves as needed.

   - **42 volts**—These systems use a yellow or blue plastic conduit over the wires to help identify the possible hazards from this voltage level. This voltage level is not a shock hazard but can maintain an arc if a circuit carrying 42 volts is opened.

BRAKING SYSTEM SERVICE Performing braking system service is similar to performing this service in any vehicle equipped with an internal combustion engine. However, there are several items to know when servicing the braking system on a hybrid electric vehicle including:

1. Check service information for any precautions that are specified to be followed when servicing the braking system on a hybrid electric vehicle.

2. All hybrid electric vehicles use a regenerative braking system, which captures the kinetic energy of the moving vehicle and converts it to electrical energy and is sent

to the high-voltage battery pack. The amount of current produced during hard braking can exceed 100 amperes. This current is stored in the high-voltage battery pack and is then used as needed to help power the vehicle.

3. The base brakes used on hybrid electric vehicles are the same as any other conventional vehicle except for the master cylinder and related control systems. There is no high-voltage circuits associated with the braking system as the regeneration occurs inside the electric drive (traction) motors and is controlled by the motor controller.

4. The base brakes on many hybrid vehicles are often found to be stuck or not functioning correctly because the brakes are not doing much work and can rust.

NOTE: Always check the base brakes whenever there is a poor fuel economy complaint heard from an owner of a hybrid vehicle. Often when a disc brake caliper sticks, the brakes drag but the driver is not aware of any performance problems but the fuel economy drops.

TIRES Performing tire-related service is similar to performing this service in any vehicle equipped with an internal combustion engine. However, there are several items to know when servicing tires on a hybrid electric vehicle including:

1. Tire pressure is very important to not only the fuel economy but also on the life of the tire. Lower inflation pressure increases rolling resistance and reduces load carrying capacity and tire life. Always inflate the tires to the pressure indicated on the door jamb sticker or found in service information or the owner's manual.

2. All tires create less rolling resistance as they wear. This means that even if the same identical tire is used as a replacement, the owner may experience a drop in fuel economy.

3. Tires can have a big effect on fuel economy. It is best to warn the owner that replacement of the tires can and often will cause a drop in fuel economy, even if low rolling resistance tires are selected.

4. Try to avoid using tires that are larger than used from the factory. The larger the tire, the heavier it is and it takes more energy to rotate, resulting in a decrease in fuel economy.

5. Follow normal tire inspections and tire rotation intervals as specified by the vehicle manufacturer.

FIGURE 49–15 This 12-volt battery under the hood on a Ford Fusion hybrid is a flooded cell type auxiliary battery.

AUXILIARY BATTERY TESTING AND SERVICE

Performing auxiliary battery service is similar to performing this service in any vehicle equipped with an internal combustion engine. However, there are several items to know when servicing the auxiliary battery on a hybrid electric vehicle including:

1. Auxiliary 12-volt batteries used in hybrid electric vehicles are located in one of two general locations.
   - **Under the hood**—If the 12-volt auxiliary battery is under the hood it is generally a flooded-type lead–acid battery and should be serviced the same as any conventional battery. ● **SEE FIGURE 49–15.**
   - **In the passenger or trunk area**—If the battery is located in the passenger or trunk area of the vehicle, it is usually of the absorbed glass mat (AGM) design. This type of battery requires that a special battery charger that limits the charging voltage be used.

2. The auxiliary 12-volt battery is usually smaller than a battery used in a conventional vehicle because it is not used to actually start the engine unless under extreme conditions on Honda hybrids only.

3. The 12-volt auxiliary battery can be tested and serviced the same as any battery used in a conventional vehicle.

4. Always read, understand, and follow all of the service information instructions when servicing the auxiliary battery on a hybrid electric vehicle.

1 The cuff of the rubber glove should extend at least 1/2 inch beyond the cuff of the leather protector.

2 To determine correct glove size, use a soft tape to measure around the palm of the hand. A measurement of 9 inches would correspond with a glove size of 9.

3 The glove rating and the date of the last test should be stamped on the glove cuff.

4 Start with a visual inspection of the glove fingertips, making sure that no cuts or other damage is present.

5 The damage on this glove was easily detected with a simple visual inspection. Note that the rubber glove material can be damaged by petroleum products, detergents, certain hand soaps, and talcum powder.

6 Manually inflate the glove to inspect for pinhole leaks. Starting at the cuff, roll up the glove and trap air at the finger end. Listen and watch carefully for deflation of the glove. If a leak is detected, the glove must be discarded.

CONTINUED ▶

7 Petroleum on the leather protector's surfaces will damage the rubber glove underneath.

8 Glove powder (glove dust) should be used to absorb moisture and reduce friction.

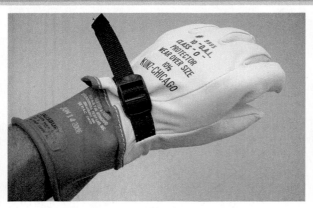

9 Put on the gloves and tighten the straps on the back of the leather protectors.

10 Technicians MUST wear HV gloves and leather protectors whenever working around the high-voltage areas of a hybrid electric vehicle.

11 HV gloves and leather protectors should be placed in a canvas storage bag when not in use. Note the ventilation hole at the bottom of this bag.

12 Make sure that the rubber gloves are not folded when placed in the canvas bag. Folding increases mechanical stress on the rubber and can lead to premature failure of the glove material.

SUMMARY

1. Personal protective equipment (PPE) for work on hybrid electric vehicles includes the wearing of high-voltage rubber gloves rated at 1,000 volts or more worn with outer leather gloves to help protect the rubber gloves.
2. A digital meter that meets CAT III standards should be used when working around the high-voltage section of a hybrid electric vehicle.
3. Safety glasses and a face shield should be worn whenever working around the high-voltage circuits of a hybrid electric vehicle.
4. The high-voltage system can be shut off at the battery pack by simply being certain that the ignition is off. Disconnecting the 12-volt battery is additional security that the high-voltage circuits are de-powered.
5. When servicing a hybrid electric vehicle, always observe safety procedures.

REVIEW QUESTIONS

1. What are the recommended items that should be used when working with the high-voltage circuits of a hybrid electric vehicle?
2. What actions are needed to disable the high-voltage (HV) circuit?
3. What are the precautions that service technicians should adhere to when servicing hybrid electric vehicles?

CHAPTER QUIZ

1. Rubber gloves should be worn whenever working on or near the high-voltage circuits or components of a hybrid electric vehicle. Technician A says that the rubber gloves should be rated at 1,000 volts or higher. Technician B says that leather gloves should be worn over the high-voltage rubber gloves. Which technician is correct?
   a. Technician A only
   b. Technician B only
   c. Both Technicians A and B
   d. Neither Technician A nor B
2. A CAT-III certified DMM should be used whenever measuring high-voltage circuits or components. The CAT III rating relates to _____.
   a. High voltage
   b. High energy
   c. High electrical resistance
   d. Both a and b
3. All of the following will shut off the high voltage to components and circuits, except _____.
   a. Opening the driver's door
   b. Turning the ignition off
   c. Disconnecting the 12-volt auxiliary battery
   d. Removing the main fuse, relay, or HV plug
4. If the engine is not running, Technician A says that the high-voltage circuits are de-powered. Technician B says that all high-voltage wiring is orange-colored. Which technician is correct?
   a. Technician A only
   b. Technician B only
   c. Both Technicians A and B
   d. Neither Technician A nor B
5. Which statement is false about high-voltage wiring?
   a. Connects the battery pack to the electric controller
   b. Connects the controller to the motor/generator
   c. Is electrically grounded to the frame (body) of the vehicle
   d. Is controlled by a relay that opens if the ignition is off
6. What routine service procedure could result in lower fuel economy, which the owner may discover?
   a. Using the wrong viscosity engine oil
   b. Replacing tires
   c. Replacing the air filter
   d. Either a or b

7. Two technicians are discussing jump starting a hybrid electric vehicle. Technician A says that the high-voltage (HV) batteries can be jumped on some HEV models. Technician B says that the 12-volt auxiliary battery can be jumped using a conventional jump box or jumper Which technician is correct?
   a. Technician A only
   b. Technician B only
   c. Both Technicians A and B
   d. Neither Technician A nor B

8. What can occur if a hybrid electric vehicle is pushed in the shop?
   a. The HV battery pack can be damaged
   b. The tires will be locked unless the ignition is on
   c. Damage to the electronic controller can occur
   d. High voltage will be generated by the motor/generator

9. Nickel-metal hydride (NiMH) batteries can be damaged if exposed to temperatures higher than about _____.
   a. 150°F (66°C)
   b. 175°F (79°C)
   c. 200°F (93°C)
   d. 225°F (107°C)

10. How should nickel-metal hydride (NiMH) batteries be disposed?
    a. In regular trash
    b. Call an 800 number shown under the hood of the vehicle for information
    c. Submerged in water and then disposed of in regular trash
    d. Burned at an EPA-certified plant

FUEL CELLS AND ADVANCED TECHNOLOGIES

OBJECTIVES: After studying Chapter 50, the reader will be able to: • Explain how a fuel cell generates electricity. • Discuss the advantages and disadvantages of fuel cells. • List the types of fuel cells. • Explain how ultracapacitors work. • Describe the advantages and disadvantages of electric vehicles. • Discuss alternative energy sources.

KEY TERMS: • Double-layer technology 608 • Electrolysis 603 • Electrolyte 605 • Energy carrier 603 • Energy density 605 • Farads 608 • Fuel cell 605 • Fuel cell hybrid vehicle (FCHV) 604 • Fuel-cell stack 605 • Fuel cell vehicle (FCV) 604 • Homogeneous Charge Compression Ignition (HCCI) 612 • Hydraulic Power Assist (HPA) 612 • Inverter 609 • Low-grade heat 607 • Membrane Electrode Assembly (MEA) 605 • NEDRA 615 • Plug-in hybrid electric vehicle (PHEV) 613 • Polymer Electrolyte Fuel Cell (PEFC) 605 • Proton Exchange Membrane (PEM) 605 • Range 614 • Specific energy 603 • Ultracapacitor 608 • Wheel motors 609 • Wind farms 615

FUEL-CELL TECHNOLOGY

WHAT IS A FUEL CELL? A **fuel cell** is an electrochemical device in which the chemical energy of hydrogen and oxygen is converted into electrical energy. The principle of the fuel cell was first discovered in 1839 by Sir William Grove, a Welsh physician. In the 1950s, NASA put this principle to work in building devices for powering space exploration vehicles. In the present day, fuel cells are being developed to power homes and vehicles while producing low or zero emissions. ● **SEE FIGURE 50–1.**

The chemical reaction in a fuel cell is the opposite of **electrolysis.** Electrolysis is the process in which electrical current is passed through water in order to break it into its components, hydrogen and oxygen. While energy is required to bring about electrolysis, this same energy can be retrieved by allowing hydrogen and oxygen to reunite in a fuel cell. It is important to note that while hydrogen can be used as a fuel, it is **not** an energy source. Instead, hydrogen is only an **energy carrier,** as energy must be expended to generate the hydrogen and store it so it can be used as a fuel.

In simple terms, a fuel cell is a hydrogen-powered battery. Hydrogen is an excellent fuel because it has a very high **specific energy** when compared to an equivalent amount of fossil fuel. One kilogram (kg) of hydrogen has three times the energy content as one kilogram of gasoline. Hydrogen is the most abundant element on earth, but it does not exist by itself in nature. This is because its natural tendency is to react with oxygen in the atmosphere to form water (H_2O). Hydrogen is also found in many other compounds, most notably hydrocarbons, such as natural gas or crude oil. In order to store hydrogen for use as a fuel, processes must be undertaken to separate it from these materials. ● **SEE FIGURE 50–2.**

BENEFITS OF A FUEL CELL A fuel cell can be used to move a vehicle by generating electricity to power electric drive motors, as well as powering the remainder of the vehicle's electrical system. Since they are powered by hydrogen and oxygen, fuel cells by themselves do not generate carbon

FIGURE 50–1 Ford Motor Company has produced a number of demonstration fuel-cell vehicles based on the Ford Focus.

FIGURE 50–2 Hydrogen does not exist by itself in nature. Energy must be expended to separate it from other, more complex materials.

FIGURE 50–3 The Mercedes-Benz B-Class fuel-cell car was introduced in 2005.

FIGURE 50–4 The Toyota FCHV is based on the Highlander platform and uses much of Toyota's Hybrid Synergy Drive (HSD) technology in its design.

emissions such as CO_2. Instead, their only emissions are water vapor and heat, and this makes the fuel cell an ideal candidate for a ZEV (zero-emission vehicle).

A fuel cell is also much more energy-efficient than a typical internal combustion engine. While a vehicle powered by an internal combustion engine (ICE) is anywhere from 15% to 20% efficient, a fuel-cell vehicle can achieve efficiencies upwards of 40%. Another major benefit of fuel cells is that they have very few moving parts and have the potential to be very reliable. A number of OEMs have spent many years and millions of dollars in order to develop a low-cost, durable, and compact fuel cell that will operate satisfactorily under all driving conditions. ● **SEE FIGURE 50–3.**

A **fuel-cell vehicle (FCV)** uses the fuel cell as its only source of power, whereas a **fuel-cell hybrid vehicle (FCHV)** would also have an electrical storage device that can be used to power the vehicle. Most new designs of fuel-cell vehicles are now based on a hybrid configuration due to the significant increase in efficiency and driveability that can be achieved with this approach. ● **SEE FIGURE 50–4.**

FUEL-CELL CHALLENGES While major automobile manufacturers continue to build demonstration vehicles and work on improving fuel-cell system design, no vehicle powered by a fuel cell has been placed into mass production. There are a number of reasons for this, including:

- High cost
- Lack of refueling infrastructure
- Safety perception
- Insufficient vehicle range
- Lack of durability
- Freeze starting problems
- Insufficient power density

All of these problems are being actively addressed by researchers, and significant improvements are being made. Once cost and performance levels meet that of current vehicles, fuel cells will be adopted as a mainstream technology. ● **SEE CHART 50–1.**

	PAFC (PHOSPHORIC ACID FUEL CELL)	PEM (POLYMER ELECTROLYTE MEMBRANE)	MCFC (MOLTEN CARBONATE FUEL CELL)	SOFC (SOLID OXIDE FUEL CELL)
Electrolyte	Orthophosphoric acid	Sulfonic acid in polymer	Li and K carbonates	Yttrium-stabilized zirconia
Fuel	Natural gas, hydrogen	Natural gas, hydrogen, methanol	Natural gas, synthetic gas	Natural gas, synthetic gas
Operating Temp.	360–410°F	176–212°F	1100–1300°F	1200–3300°F
	180–210°C	80–100°C	600–700°C	650–1800°C
Electric Efficiency	40%	30–40%	43–44%	50–60%
Manufacturers	ONSI Corp.	Avista, Ballard, Energy Partners, H-Power, International, Plug Power	Fuel Cell Energy, IHI, Hitachi, Siemens	Honeywell, Siemens-Westinghouse, Ceramic
Applications	Stationary power	Vehicles, portable power, small stationary power	Industrial and institutional power	Stationary power, military vehicles

CHART 50–1

Fuel-cell types and their temperature operating range.

TYPES OF FUEL CELLS

There are a number of different types of fuel cells, and these are differentiated by the type of **electrolyte** that is used in their design. Some electrolytes operate best at room temperature, whereas others are made to operate at up to 1800°F. See the accompanying chart showing the various fuel-cell types and applications.

The fuel-cell design that is best suited for automotive applications is the **Proton Exchange Membrane (PEM)**. A PEM fuel cell must have hydrogen for it to operate, and this may be stored on the vehicle or generated as needed from another type of fuel.

PEM FUEL CELLS

DESCRIPTION AND OPERATION

The Proton Exchange Membrane fuel cell is also known as a **Polymer Electrolyte Fuel Cell (PEFC)**. The PEM fuel cell is known for its lightweight and compact design, as well as its ability to operate at ambient temperatures. This means that a PEM fuel cell can start quickly and produce full power without an extensive warmup period. The PEM is a simple design based on a membrane that is coated on both sides with a catalyst such as platinum or palladium. There are two electrodes, one located on each side of the membrane. These are responsible for distributing hydrogen and oxygen over the membrane surface, removing waste heat, and providing a path for electrical current flow. The part of the PEM fuel cell that contains the membrane, catalyst coatings, and electrodes is known as the **Membrane Electrode Assembly (MEA)**.

The negative electrode (anode) has hydrogen gas directed to it, while oxygen is sent to the positive electrode (cathode). Hydrogen is sent to the negative electrode as H_2 molecules, which break apart into H^+ ions (protons) in the presence of the catalyst. The electrons (e^-) from the hydrogen atoms are sent through the external circuit, generating electricity that can be utilized to perform work. These same electrons are then sent to the positive electrode where they rejoin the H^+ ions that have passed through the membrane and have reacted with oxygen in the presence of the catalyst. This creates H_2O and waste heat, which are the only emissions from a PEM fuel cell. ●**SEE FIGURE 50–5.**

NOTE: It is important to remember that a fuel cell generates direct current (DC) electricity as electrons only flow in one direction (from the anode to the cathode).

FUEL-CELL STACKS

A single fuel cell by itself is not particularly useful, as it will generate less than 1 volt of electrical potential. It is more common for hundreds of fuel cells to be built together in a **fuel-cell stack.** In this arrangement, the fuel cells are connected in series so that total voltage of the stack is the sum of the individual cell voltages. The fuel cells are placed end-to-end in the stack, much like slices in a loaf of bread. Automotive fuel-cell stacks contain upwards of 400 cells in their construction. ●**SEE FIGURE 50–6.**

FIGURE 50–5 The polymer electrolyte membrane only allows H^1 ions (protons) to pass through it. This means that electrons must follow the external circuit and pass through the load to perform work.

FIGURE 50–6 A fuel-cell stack is made up of hundreds of individual cells connected in series.

The total voltage of the fuel-cell stack is determined by the number of individual cells incorporated into the assembly. The current-producing ability of the stack, however, is dependent on the surface area of the electrodes. Since output of the fuel-cell stack is related to both voltage and current (voltage × current = power), increasing the number of cells or increasing the surface area of the cells will increase power output. Some fuel-cell vehicles will use more than one stack, depending on power output requirements and space limitations.

DIRECT METHANOL FUEL CELLS

High-pressure cylinders are one method of storing hydrogen onboard a vehicle for use in a fuel cell. This is a simple and lightweight storage method, but often does not provide sufficient vehicle driving range. Another approach has been to fuel a modified PEM fuel cell with liquid methanol instead of hydrogen gas. ●**SEE FIGURE 50–7.**

Methanol is most often produced from natural gas and has a chemical symbol of CH_3OH. It has a higher **energy density** than gaseous hydrogen because it exists in a liquid state at normal temperatures, and is easier to handle since no compressors or other high-pressure equipment is needed.

FIGURE 50–7 A direct methanol fuel cell uses a methanol/water solution for fuel instead of hydrogen gas.

FIGURE 50–8 A direct methanol fuel cell can be refueled similar to a gasoline-powered vehicle.

This means that a fuel-cell vehicle can be refueled with a liquid instead of high-pressure gas, which makes the refueling process simpler and produces a greater vehicle driving range. ● **SEE FIGURE 50–8.**

Unfortunately, direct methanol fuel cells suffer from a number of problems, not the least of which is the corrosive nature of methanol itself. This means that methanol cannot be

stored in existing tanks and thus requires a separate infrastructure for handling and storage. Another problem is "fuel crossover," in which methanol makes its way across the membrane assembly and diminishes performance of the cell. Direct methanol fuel cells also require much greater amounts of catalyst in their construction, which leads to higher costs. These challenges are leading researchers to look for alternative electrolyte materials and catalysts to lower cost and improve cell performance.

NOTE: Direct methanol fuel cells are not likely to see service in automotive applications. However, they are well suited for low-power applications, such as cell phones or laptop computers.

FUEL-CELL VEHICLE SYSTEMS

HUMIDIFIERS Water management inside a PEM fuel cell is critical. Too much water can prevent oxygen from making contact with the positive electrode; too little water can allow the electrolyte to dry out and lower its conductivity. The amount of water and where it resides in the fuel cell is also critical in determining at how low a temperature the fuel cell will start, because water freezing in the fuel cell can prevent it from starting. The role of the humidifier is to achieve a balance where it is providing sufficient moisture to the fuel cell by recycling water that is evaporating at the cathode. The humidifier is located in the air line leading to the cathode of the fuel-cell stack. ● **SEE FIGURE 50–9.**

Some newer PEM designs manage the water in the cells in such a way that there is no need to pre-humidify the incoming reactant gases. This eliminates the need for the humidifier assembly and makes the system simpler overall.

FUEL-CELL COOLING SYSTEMS Heat is generated by the fuel cell during normal operation. Excess heat can lead to

FIGURE 50–9 Powertrain layout in a Honda FCX fuel-cell vehicle. Note the use of a humidifier behind the fuel-cell stack to maintain moisture levels in the membrane electrode assemblies.

a breakdown of the polymer electrolyte membrane, so a liquid cooling system must be utilized to remove waste heat from the fuel-cell stack. One of the major challenges for engineers in this regard is the fact that the heat generated by the fuel cell is classified as **low-grade heat.** This means that there is only a small difference between the temperature of the coolant and that of the ambient air. Heat transfers very slowly under these conditions, so heat exchangers with a much larger surface area must be utilized. ● **SEE FIGURE 50–10.**

In some cases, heat exchangers may be placed in other areas of the vehicle when available space at the front of the engine compartment is insufficient. In the case of the Toyota FCHV, an auxiliary heat exchanger is located underneath the vehicle to increase the cooling system heat-rejection capacity. ● **SEE FIGURE 50–11.**

 FREQUENTLY ASKED QUESTION

When Is Methanol Considered to Be a "Carbon-Neutral" Fuel?

Most of the methanol in the world is produced by reforming natural gas. Natural gas is a hydrocarbon, but does not increase the carbon content of our atmosphere as long as it remains in reservoirs below the earth's surface. However, natural gas that is used as a fuel causes extra carbon to be released into the atmosphere, which is said to contribute to global warming. Natural gas is not a carbon-neutral fuel, and neither is methanol that is made from natural gas.

Fortunately, it is possible to generate methanol from biomass and wood waste. Methanol made from renewable resources is carbon neutral, because no extra carbon is being released into the earth's atmosphere than what was originally absorbed by the plants used to make the methanol.

FIGURE 50–10 The Honda FCX uses one large radiator for cooling the fuel cell, and two smaller ones on either side for cooling drive train components.

FIGURE 50–11 Space is limited at the front of the Toyota FCHV engine compartment, so an auxiliary heat exchanger is located under the vehicle to help cool the fuel-cell stack.

An electric water pump and a fan drive motor are used to enable operation of the fuel cell's cooling system. These and other support devices use electrical power that is generated by the fuel cell, and therefore tend to decrease the overall efficiency of the vehicle.

AIR SUPPLY PUMPS Air must be supplied to the fuel-cell stack at the proper pressure and flow rate to enable proper performance under all driving conditions. This function is performed by an onboard air supply pump that compresses atmospheric air and supplies it to the fuel cell's positive electrode (cathode). This pump is often driven by a high-voltage electric drive motor.

FUEL-CELL HYBRID VEHICLES Hybridization tends to increase efficiency in vehicles with conventional drive trains, as energy that was once lost during braking and otherwise normal operation is instead stored for later use in a high-voltage battery or **ultracapacitor.** This same advantage can be gained by applying the hybrid design concept to fuel-cell vehicles. Whereas the fuel cell is the only power source in a fuel-cell vehicle, the fuel-cell hybrid vehicle (FCHV) relies on both the fuel cell and an electrical storage device for motive power. Driveability is also enhanced with this design, as the electrical storage device is able to supply energy immediately to the drive motors and overcome any "throttle lag" on the part of the fuel cell.

SECONDARY BATTERIES. All hybrid vehicle designs require a means of storing electrical energy that is generated during regenerative braking and other applications. In most FCHV designs, a high-voltage nickel-metal hydride (NiMH) battery pack is used as a secondary battery. This is most often located near the back of the vehicle, either under or behind the rear passenger seat. ● **SEE FIGURE 50–12.** The secondary battery is built similar to a fuel-cell stack, because it is made up of many low-voltage cells connected in series to build a high-voltage battery.

ULTRACAPACITORS. An alternative to storing electrical energy in batteries is to use ultracapacitors. A capacitor is best known as an electrical device that will block DC current, but allow AC to pass. However, a capacitor can also be used to store electrical energy, and it is able to do this without a chemical reaction. Instead, a capacitor stores electrical energy using the principle of electrostatic attraction between positive and negative charges.

Ultracapacitors are built very different from conventional capacitors. Ultracapacitor cells are based on **double-layer technology,** in which two activated-carbon electrodes are immersed in an organic electrolyte. The electrodes have a very large surface area and are separated by a membrane that allows ions to migrate but prevents the electrodes from touching. ● **SEE FIGURE 50–13.** Charging and discharging occurs as ions move within the electrolyte but no chemical reaction takes place. Ultracapacitors can charge and discharge quickly and efficiently, making them especially suited for electric assist applications in fuel-cell hybrid vehicles.

Ultracapacitors that are used in fuel-cell hybrid vehicles are made up of multiple cylindrical cells connected in parallel.

FIGURE 50–12 The secondary battery in a fuel-cell hybrid vehicle is made up of many individual cells connected in series, much like a fuel-cell stack.

FIGURE 50–13 The Honda ultracapacitor module and construction of the individual cells.

FIGURE 50–14 An ultracapacitor can be used in place of a high-voltage battery in a hybrid electric vehicle. This example is from the Honda FCX fuel-cell hybrid vehicle.

● **SEE FIGURE 50–14.** This results in the total capacitance being the sum of the values of each individual cell. For example, ten 1.0-**farad** capacitors connected in parallel will have a total capacitance of 10.0 farads. Greater capacitance means greater electrical storage ability, and this contributes to greater assist for the electric motors in a fuel-cell hybrid vehicle.

Ultracapacitors have excellent cycle life, meaning that they can be fully charged and discharged many times without degrading their performance. They are also able to operate over a wide temperature range and are not affected by low temperatures to the same degree as many battery technologies. The one major downside of ultracapacitors is a lack of specific energy, which means that they are best suited for sudden bursts of energy as opposed to prolonged discharge cycles. Research is being conducted to improve this and other aspects of ultracapacitor performance.

FUEL-CELL TRACTION MOTORS. Much of the technology behind the electric drive motors being used in fuel-cell vehicles was developed during the early days of the California ZEV mandate. This was a period when battery-powered electric vehicles were being built by the major vehicle manufacturers in an effort to meet a legislated quota in the state of California. The ZEV mandate rules were eventually relaxed to allow other types of vehicles to be substituted for credit, but the technology that had been developed for pure electric vehicles was now put to work in these other vehicle designs.

FIGURE 50–15 Drive motors in fuel-cell hybrid vehicles often use stator assemblies similar to ones found in Toyota hybrid electric vehicles. The rotor turns inside the stator and has permanent magnets on its outer circumference.

The electric traction motors used in fuel-cell hybrid vehicles are very similar to those being used in current hybrid electric vehicles. The typical drive motor is based on an AC synchronous design, which is sometimes referred to as a DC brushless motor. This design is very reliable as it does not use a commutator or brushes, but instead has a three-phase stator and a permanent magnet rotor. ● SEE FIGURE 50–15. An electronic controller (inverter) is used to generate the three-phase high-voltage AC current required by the motor. While the motor itself is very simple, the electronics required to power and control it are complex.

Some fuel-cell hybrid vehicles use a single electric drive motor and a transaxle to direct power to the vehicle's wheels. It is also possible to use **wheel motors** to drive individual wheels. While this approach adds a significant amount of unsprung weight to the chassis, it allows for greater control of the torque being applied to each individual wheel. ● SEE FIGURE 50–16.

TRANSAXLES. Aside from the hydrogen fueling system, fuel-cell hybrid vehicles are effectively pure electric vehicles in that their drive train is electrically driven. Electric motors work very well for automotive applications because they produce high torque at low RPMs and are able to maintain a consistent power output throughout their entire RPM range. This is in contrast to vehicles powered by internal combustion engines, which produce very little torque at low RPMs and have a narrow range where significant horsepower is produced.

ICE-powered vehicles require complex transmissions with multiple speed ranges in order to accelerate the vehicle quickly and maximize the efficiency of the ICE. Fuel-cell hybrid vehicles use electric drive motors that require only a simple reduction in their final drive and a differential to send power to the drive wheels. No gear shifting is required and mechanisms such as torque converters and clutches are done away with completely. A reverse gear is not required either, as the electric drive motor is simply powered in the opposite direction.

HEAT VENTS TO DISSIPATE HEAT GENERATED BY THE FUEL CELL AND ELECTRONICS

UNIVERSAL DOCKING CONNECTION CONNECTS TO BODY CONTROL SYSTEMS

MECHANICAL LOCKS SECURE THE BODY TO THE SKATEBOARD

FUEL-CELL STACKS AND HYDROGEN STORAGE TANKS

FOUR WHEEL MOTORS PROPEL THE VEHICLE

FIGURE 50–16 The General Motors "Skateboard" concept uses a fuel-cell propulsion system with wheel motors at all four corners.

FIGURE 50–17 The electric drive motor and transaxle assembly from a Toyota FCHV. Note the three orange cables, indicating that this motor is powered by high-voltage three-phase alternating current.

The transaxles used in fuel-cell hybrid vehicles are extremely simple with few moving parts, making them extremely durable, quiet, and reliable. ● SEE FIGURE 50–17.

POWER CONTROL UNITS. The drive train of a fuel-cell hybrid vehicle is controlled by a power control unit (PCU), which controls fuel-cell output and directs the flow of electricity between the various components. One of the functions of the PCU is to act as an **inverter,** which changes direct current from the fuel-cell stack into three-phase alternating current for use in the vehicle drive motor(s). ● SEE FIGURE 50–18.

Power to and from the secondary battery is directed through the power control unit, which is also responsible for maintaining the battery pack's state of charge and for controlling and directing the output of the fuel-cell stack. ● SEE FIGURE 50–19.

During regenerative braking, the electric drive motor acts as a generator and converts kinetic (moving) energy of the

FIGURE 50–18 The power control unit (PCU) on a Honda FCX fuel-cell hybrid vehicle is located under the hood.

FIGURE 50–19 Toyota's FCHV uses a power control unit that directs electrical energy flow between the fuel cell, battery, and drive motor.

vehicle into electricity for recharging the high-voltage battery pack. The PCU must take the three-phase power from the motor (generator) and convert (or *rectify*) this into DC voltage to be sent to the battery. DC power from the fuel cell will also be processed through the PCU for recharging the battery pack.

A DC-to-DC converter is used in hybrid-electric vehicles for converting the high voltage from the secondary battery pack into the 12 volts required for the remainder of the vehicle's electrical system. Depending on the vehicle, there may also be 42 volts required to operate accessories such as the electric-assist power steering. In fuel-cell hybrid vehicles, the DC-to-DC converter function may be built into the power control unit, giving it full responsibility for the vehicle's power distribution.

HYDROGEN STORAGE One of the pivotal design issues with fuel-cell hybrid vehicles is how to store sufficient hydrogen onboard to allow for reasonable vehicle range. Modern drivers have grown accustomed to having a minimum of 300 miles between refueling stops, a goal that is extremely difficult to achieve when fueling the vehicle with hydrogen. Hydrogen has

a very high energy content on a pound-for-pound basis, but its energy density is less than that of conventional liquid fuels. This is because gaseous hydrogen, even at high pressure, has a very low physical density (mass per unit volume). ● **SEE FIGURE 50–20.**

A number of methods of hydrogen storage are being considered for use in fuel-cell hybrid vehicles. These include high-pressure compressed gas, liquefied hydrogen, and solid storage in metal hydrides. Efficient hydrogen storage is one of the technical issues that must be solved in order for fuel cells to be adopted for vehicle applications. Much research is being conducted to solve the issue of onboard hydrogen storage.

HIGH-PRESSURE COMPRESSED GAS. Most current fuel-cell hybrid vehicles use compressed hydrogen that is stored in tanks as a high-pressure gas. This approach is the least complex of all the storage possibilities, but also has the least energy density. Multiple small storage tanks are often used rather than one large one in order to fit them into unused areas of the vehicle. One drawback with this approach is that only cylinders can be used to store gases at the required pressures. This creates a good deal of unused space around the outside of the cylinders and leads to further reductions in hydrogen storage capacity. It is common for a pressure of 5000 psi (350 bar) to be used, but technology is available to store hydrogen at up to 10,000 psi (700 bar). ● **SEE FIGURE 50–21.**

3 HIGH-PRESSURE HYDROGEN STORAGE TANKS

FIGURE 50–20 This GM fuel-cell vehicle uses compressed hydrogen in three high-pressure storage tanks.

GLASS FIBER
CARBON FIBER
ALUMINUM

FIGURE 50–21 The Toyota FCHV uses high-pressure storage tanks that are rated at 350 bar. This is the equivalent of 5,000 pounds per square inch.

The tanks used for compressed hydrogen storage are typically made with an aluminum liner wrapped in several layers of carbon fiber and an external coating of fiberglass. In order to refuel the compressed hydrogen storage tanks, a special high-pressure fitting is installed in place of the filler neck used for conventional vehicles. ● SEE FIGURE 50–22. There is also a special electrical connector that is used to enable communication between the vehicle and the filling station during the refueling process. ● SEE FIGURE 50–23.

The filling station utilizes a special coupler to connect to the vehicle's high-pressure refueling fitting. The coupler is placed on the vehicle fitting, and a lever on the coupler is rotated to seal and lock it into place.

LIQUID HYDROGEN. Hydrogen can be liquefied in an effort to increase its energy density, but this requires that it be stored in cryogenic tanks at −423°F (−253°C). This increases vehicle range, but impacts overall efficiency, as a great deal of energy

FIGURE 50–22 The high-pressure fitting used to refuel a fuel-cell hybrid vehicle.

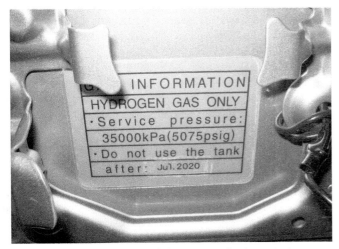

FIGURE 50–23 Note that high-pressure hydrogen storage tanks must be replaced in 2020.

FIGURE 50–24 GM's Hydrogen3 has a range of 249 miles when using liquid hydrogen.

FIGURE 50–25 Refueling a vehicle with liquid hydrogen.

is required to liquefy the hydrogen and a certain amount of the liquid hydrogen will "boil off" while in storage.

One liter of liquid hydrogen only has one-fourth the energy content of 1 liter of gasoline. ● SEE FIGURES 50–24 AND 50–25.

SOLID STORAGE OF HYDROGEN. One method discovered to store hydrogen in solid form is as a metal hydride, similar to how a nickel-metal hydride (NiMH) battery works.

 TECH TIP

Hydrogen Fuel = No Carbon

Most fuels contain hydrocarbons or molecules that contain both hydrogen and carbon. During combustion, the first element that is burned is the hydrogen. If combustion is complete, then all of the carbon is converted to carbon dioxide gas and exits the engine in the exhaust. However, if combustion is not complete, carbon monoxide is formed, plus leaving some unburned carbon to accumulate in the combustion chamber. ● SEE FIGURE 50–26.

FIGURE 50–26 Carbon deposits, such as these, are created by incomplete combustion of a hydrocarbon fuel.

A demonstration vehicle features a lightweight fiber-wrapped storage tank under the body that stores 3 kg (about 6.6 pounds) of hydrogen as a metal hydride at low pressure. The vehicle can travel almost 200 miles with this amount of fuel. One kilogram of hydrogen is equal to 1 gallon of gasoline. Three gallons of water will generate 1 kilogram of hydrogen.

A metal hydride is formed when gaseous hydrogen molecules disassociate into individual hydrogen atoms and bond with the metal atoms in the storage tank. This process uses powdered metallic alloys capable of rapidly absorbing hydrogen to make this occur.

HYDRAULIC HYBRID STORAGE SYSTEM

Ford Motor Co. is experimenting with a system it calls **Hydraulic Power Assist (HPA).** This system converts kinetic energy to hydraulic pressure, and then uses that pressure to help accelerate the vehicle. It is currently being tested on a four-wheel-drive (4WD) Lincoln Navigator with a 4.0-L V-8 engine in place of the standard 5.4-L engine.

A variable-displacement hydraulic pump/motor is mounted on the transfer case and connected to the output shaft that powers the front drive shaft. The HPA system works with or without 4WD engaged. A valve block mounted on the pump contains solenoid valves to control the flow of hydraulic fluid. A 14-gallon, high-pressure accumulator is mounted behind the rear axle, with a low-pressure accumulator right behind it to store hydraulic fluid. The master cylinder has a "deadband," meaning the first few fractions of an inch of travel do not pressurize the brake system. When the driver depresses the brake pedal, a pedal movement sensor signals the control unit, which then operates solenoid valves to send hydraulic fluid from the low-pressure reservoir to the pump. The pumping action slows the vehicle, similar to engine compression braking, and the fluid is pumped into the high-pressure reservoir. Releasing the brake and pressing on the accelerator signals the control unit to send that

high-pressure fluid back to the pump, which then acts as a hydraulic motor and adds torque to the drive line. The system can be used to launch the vehicle from a stop and/or add torque for accelerating from any speed.

While the concept is simple, the system itself is very complicated. Additional components include:

- Pulse suppressors
- Filters
- An electric circulator pump for cooling the main pump/motor

Potential problems with this system include leakage problems with seals and valves, getting air out of the hydraulic fluid system, and noise. In prototype stages the system demands different driving techniques. Still, this system was built to prove the concept, and the engineers believe that these problems can be solved and that a control system can be developed that will make HPA transparent to the driver. A 23% improvement in fuel economy and improvements in emissions reduction were achieved using a dynamometer set for a 7,000-pound vehicle. While the HPA system could be developed for any type of vehicle with any type of drive train, it does add weight and complexity, which would add to the cost.

HCCI

Homogeneous Charge Compression Ignition (HCCI) is a combustion process. HCCI is the combustion of a very lean gasoline air–fuel mixture without the use of a spark ignition. It is a low-temperature, chemically controlled (flameless) combustion process. ● **SEE FIGURE 50–27.**

HCCI combustion is difficult to control and extremely sensitive to changes in temperature, pressure, and fuel type. While the challenges of HCCI are difficult, the advantages include having a gasoline engine being able to deliver 80% of diesel efficiency (a 20% increase in fuel economy) for 50% of the cost. A diesel engine using HCCI can deliver gasoline-like emissions. Spark and injection timing are no longer a factor as they are in a conventional port-fuel injection system.

While much research and development needs to be performed using this combustion process, it has been shown to give excellent performance from idle to mid-load, and from ambient to warm operating temperatures as well as cold-start and run capability. Because an engine only operates in HCCI mode at light throttle settings, such as during cruise conditions at highway speeds, engineers need to improve the transition in and out of the HCCI mode. Work is also being done on piston and combustion chamber shape to reduce combustion noise and vibration that is created during operation in the HCCI operating mode.

Ongoing research is focusing on improving fuel economy under real-world operating conditions as well as controlling costs.

DIESEL ENGINE
(COMPRESSION IGNITION)

FUEL
INJECTOR

HOT REGIONS
CREATES NO$_x$ AND
SOOT (PM) EMISSIONS

GASOLINE ENGINE
(SPARK IGNITED)

HOT REGIONS
CREATES NO$_x$
EMISSIONS

HCCI ENGINE
(HOMOGENEOUS CHARGE
COMPRESSION IGNITION)

LOW TEMPERATURE
COMBUSTION RESULTS
IN REDUCED EMISSIONS

FIGURE 50–27 Both diesel and conventional gasoline engines create exhaust emissions due to high peak temperatures created in the combustion chamber. The lower combustion temperatures during HCCI operation result in high efficiency with reduced emissions.

PLUG-IN HYBRID ELECTRIC VEHICLES

A **plug-in hybrid electric vehicle (PHEV)** is a hybrid electric vehicle that is designed to be plugged into an electrical outlet at night to charge the batteries. By charging the batteries in the vehicle, it can operate using electric power alone (stealth mode) for a longer time, thereby reducing the use of the internal combustion engine (ICE). The less the ICE is operating, the less fuel is consumed and the lower the emissions. At the present time, plug-in hybrids are not offered by any major manufacturer but many conventional HEVs are being converted to plug-in hybrids by adding additional batteries.

If a production plug-in hybrid is built, it should be able to get about twice the fuel economy of a conventional hybrid. The extra weight of the batteries will be offset, somewhat, by the reduced weight of a smaller ICE. At highway speeds, fuel efficiency is affected primarily by aerodynamics, and therefore the added weight of the extra batteries is equal to one or two additional passengers and thus would only slightly reduce fuel economy. Recharging will normally take place at night during cheaper off-peak hours. Counting fuel and service, the total lifetime cost of ownership will be lower than a conventional gasoline-powered vehicle.

There are emissions related to the production of the electricity, which are called *well-to-wheel emissions*. These emissions, including greenhouse gases, are far lower than those of gasoline, even for the national power grid, which is 50% coal. Vehicles charging off-peak will use power from plants that cannot be turned off at night and often use cleaner sources such

as natural gas and hydroelectric power. Plug-in hybrids could be recharged using rooftop photovoltaic systems, which would create zero emissions.

THE FUTURE FOR ELECTRIC VEHICLES

The future of electric vehicles depends on many factors, including:

1. The legislative and environmental incentives to overcome the cost and research efforts to bring a usable electric vehicle to the market.

2. The cost of alternative energy. If the cost of fossil fuels increases to the point that the average consumer cannot afford to drive a conventional vehicle, then electric vehicles (EVs) may be a saleable alternative.

3. Advancement in battery technology that would allow the use of lighter-weight and higher-energy batteries.

COLD-WEATHER CONCERNS Past models of electric vehicles such as the General Motors electric vehicle (EV1) were restricted to locations such as Arizona and southern California that had a warm climate, because cold weather is a major disadvantage to the use of electric vehicles for the following reasons:

■ Cold temperatures reduce battery efficiency.

■ Additional electrical power from the batteries is needed to heat the batteries themselves to be able to achieve reasonable performance.

- Passenger compartment heating is a concern for an electric vehicle because it would require the use of resistance units or other technology that would reduce the range of the vehicle.

HOT-WEATHER CONCERNS Batteries do not function well at high temperatures, and therefore some type of battery cooling must be added to the vehicle to allow for maximum battery performance. This would then result in a reduction of vehicle range due to the use of battery power needed just to keep the batteries working properly. Besides battery concerns, the batteries would also have to supply the power needed to keep the interior cool as well as all of the other accessories. These combined electrical loads represent a huge battery drain and reduce the range of the vehicle.

RECHARGING METHODS AND CONCERNS How far an electric vehicle can travel on a full battery charge is called its **range.** The range of an electric vehicle depends on many factors, including:

- Battery energy storage capacity
- Vehicle weight
- Outside temperature
- Terrain (driving in hilly or mountainous areas requires more energy from the battery)
- Use of air conditioning and other electrical devices

Because electric vehicles have a relatively short range, charging stations must be made available in areas where these vehicles are driven.

Plug-in hybrid electric vehicles help over come the "range anxiety" experienced by drivers of pure electric vehicles. A plug-in hybrid vehicle uses more batteries than a conventional hybrid electric vehicle to extend its range using battery power alone. ● **SEE FIGURE 50–28.**

VEHICLE CHARGING

CHARGING LEVELS There are three levels of chargers that can used to charge a plug-in hybrid electric vehicle (PHEV) or electric vehicle (EV). The three levels include:

- **Level 1** Level 1 uses 110- to 120- volt standard electric outlet and is capable of charging a Chevrolet Volt extended range electric vehicle in 10 hours or more. The advantage is that there is little if any installation cost as most houses are equipped with 110-volt outlets and can charge up to 16 amperes.

- **Level 2** Level 2 chargers use 220 to 240 volts to charge the same vehicle in about 4 hours. Level 2 chargers can be added to most houses, making recharging faster (up to 80 amperes) when at home, and are the most commonly used charging stations available at stores and college. Adding a level 2 charging outlet to the garage for access can cost $2,000 or more depending on the location and the wiring of the house or apartment.

- **Level 3** Level 3 charging stations use 440 volts and can charge most electric vehicles to 80% charge in less than 30 minutes. This high charge rate may be harmful to battery life. Always follow the charging instructions and recommendations as stated in the owner's manual of the vehicle being charged. Level 3 chargers charge the vehicle using direct current (DC) at a rate up to 125 amperes. A Level 3 charger station can cost $50,000 or more, making this type of charger most suitable where facilities will be selling the service of rapidly charging the vehicle. ● **SEE FIGURE 50–29.**

SAE STANDARD PLUG Most electric (Nissan Leaf) and plug-in hybrid vehicles (Chevrolet Volt and Toyota Prius) use a standard plug. The standard plug meets the specification as designated by SAE standard J1772. ● **SEE FIGURES 50–29** and **50–30.**

FIGURE 50–28 A typical electric vehicle charging station on the campus of a college in southern California.

LEVEL 3 CONNECTOR   SAE JI772 LEVEL 1 AND LEVEL 2 CONNECTOR

FIGURE 50–29 A cutaway view of a Nissan Leaf electric vehicle showing the two charging connectors. Both of these connectors are located in the center of the vehicle in the front making plugging in the cable easy to access.

AC LINE 2

AC LINE 1

SAFETY
(PROXIMITY
DETECTION)

GROUND

CONTROL
PILOT

FIGURE 50-30 The SAE J1772 plug is used on most electric and plug-in hybrid electric vehicles and is designed to work with Level 1(110–120 volt) and Level 2 (220–240 volt) charging.

 FREQUENTLY ASKED QUESTION

What Is NEDRA?

NEDRA is the **National Electric Drag Racing Association** that holds drag races for electric-powered vehicles throughout the United States. The association does the following:

1. Coordinates a standard rule set for electric vehicle drag racing, to balance the needs and interests of all those involved in the sport.
2. Sanctions electric vehicle drag racing events, to:
   • Make the events as safe as possible.
   • Record and maintain official records.
   • Maintain consistency on a national scale.
   • Coordinate and schedule electric vehicle drag racing events.
3. Promotes electric vehicle drag racing to:
   • Educate the public and increase people's awareness of electric vehicles while eliminating any misconceptions.
   • Have fun in a safe and silent drag racing environment.
   ● **SEE FIGURE 50–31.**

 WIND POWER

Wind power is used to help supplement electric power generation in many parts of the country. Because AC electricity cannot be stored, this energy source is best used to reduce the use of natural gas and coal to help reduce CO_2 emis-

(a)

(b)

FIGURE 50–31 (a) The motor in a compact electric drag car. This 8-inch-diameter motor is controlled by an electronic controller that limits the voltage to 170 volts to prevent commutator flash-over yet provides up to 2,000 amperes. This results in an amazing 340,000 watts or 455 Hp. (b) The batteries used for the compact drag car include twenty 12-volt absorbed glass mat (AGM) batteries connected in series to provide 240 volts.

sions. Wind power is most economical if the windmills are located where the wind blows consistently above 8 miles per hour (13 km/h). Locations include the eastern slope of mountain ranges, such as the Rocky Mountains, or on high ground in many states. Often, wind power is used as supplemental power in the evenings when it is most needed, and is allowed to stop rotating in daylight hours when the power is not needed. Windmills are usually grouped together to form **wind farms,** where the product is electrical energy. Energy from wind farms can be used to charge plug-in hybrid vehicles, as well as for domestic lighting and power needs. ● **SEE FIGURES 50–32 AND 50–33.**

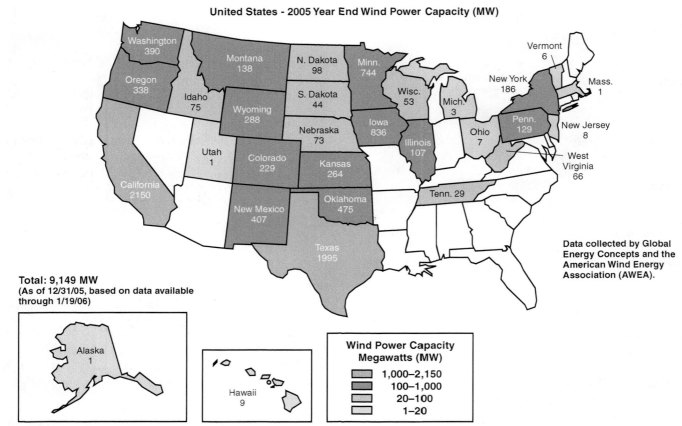

United States - 2005 Year End Wind Power Capacity (MW)

Washington 390
Montana 138
N. Dakota 98
Minn. 744
Vermont 6
Oregon 338
Idaho 75
Wyoming 288
S. Dakota 44
Wisc. 53
Mich. 3
New York 186
Mass. 1
Nebraska 73
Iowa 836
Illinois 107
Ohio 7
Penn. 129
New Jersey 8
Utah 1
Colorado 229
Kansas 264
West Virginia 66
California 2150
New Mexico 407
Oklahoma 475
Tenn. 29
Texas 1995

Data collected by Global Energy Concepts and the American Wind Energy Association (AWEA).

Total: 9,149 MW
(As of 12/31/05, based on data available through 1/19/06)

Alaska 1

Hawaii 9

Wind Power Capacity Megawatts (MW)
- 1,000–2,150
- 100–1,000
- 20–100
- 1–20

FIGURE 50–32 Wind power capacity by area. (Courtesy of U.S. Department of Energy)

FIGURE 50–33 A typical wind generator that is used to generate electricity.

HYDROELECTRIC POWER

Hydroelectric power is limited to locations where there are dammed rivers and hydroelectric plants. However, electricity can and is transmitted long distances—so that electricity generated at the Hoover Dam can be used in California and other remote locations. Electrical power from hydroelectric sources can be used to charge plug-in hybrid electric vehicles, thereby reducing emissions that would normally be created by burning coal or natural gas to create electricity. However, hydroelectric plants are limited as to the amount of power they can produce, and constructing new plants is extremely expensive. ● SEE FIGURE 50–34.

FIGURE 50–34 The Hoover Dam in Nevada/Arizona is used to create electricity for use in the southwest United States.

1. The chemical reaction inside a fuel cell is the opposite of electrolysis in that electricity is created when hydrogen and oxygen are allowed to combine in the fuel cell.
2. A fuel cell produces electricity and releases heat and water as the only by-products.
3. The major disadvantages of fuel cells include:
   - High cost
   - Lack of hydrogen refueling stations
   - Short range
   - Freezing-temperature starting problems
4. Types of fuel cells include PEM (the most commonly used), PAFC, MCFC, and SOFC.
5. Ultracapacitors are an alternative to batteries for the storage of electrical energy.
6. A gasoline-powered engine can be more efficient if it uses a homogeneous charge compression ignition (HCCI) combustion process.
7. Plug-in hybrid electric vehicles could expand the range of hybrid vehicles by operating on battery power alone.
8. Wind power and hydroelectric power are being used to recharge plug-in hybrids and provide electrical power for all uses, without harmful emissions.

REVIEW QUESTIONS

1. How does a fuel cell work?
2. What are the advantages and disadvantages of fuel cells?
3. What are the uses of the various types of fuel cells?
4. How does an ultracapacitor work?
5. What are the advantages and disadvantages of using hydrogen?
6. What alternative power sources could be used for vehicles?

CHAPTER QUIZ

1. A fuel cell produces electricity from _____ and _____.
   a. Gasoline/oxygen
   b. Nitrogen/hydrogen
   c. Hydrogen/oxygen
   d. Water/oxygen
2. What are the by-products (emissions) from a fuel cell?
   a. Water
   b. CO_2
   c. CO
   d. Nonmethane hydrocarbon
3. Which type of fuel cell is the most likely to be used to power vehicles?
   a. PAFC
   b. PEM
   c. MCFC
   d. SOFC
4. Which liquid fuel could be used to directly power a fuel cell?
   a. Methanol
   b. Ethanol
   c. Biodiesel
   d. Unleaded gasoline
5. Which is *not* a function of an ultracapacitor?
   a. Can pass AC current
   b. Can be charged with DC current
   c. Discharges DC current
   d. Can pass DC current
6. Hydrogen is commonly stored at what pressure?
   a. 100,000 psi
   b. 50,000 psi
   c. 5,000 psi
   d. 1,000 psi
7. Hydrogen storage tanks are usually constructed from _____.
   a. Steel
   b. Aluminum
   c. Carbon fiber
   d. Both b and c
8. HCCI is a process that eliminates what parts or components in a gasoline engine?
   a. Fuel tank
   b. Battery
   c. Fuel injectors
   d. Ignition system
9. A plug-in hybrid is different from a conventional hybrid electric vehicle because it has _____.
   a. A built-in battery charger
   b. Li Ox batteries
   c. More batteries
   d. Bigger motor/generator
10. Which energy source(s) is (are) currently being used to help reduce the use of fossil fuels?
    a. Hydrogen
    b. Wind power
    c. Hydroelectric power
    d. Both b and c

GLOSSARY

3-minute charge test   A method used to test batteries. Not valid for all types of batteries.

4 WAL   An abbreviation for four-wheel antilock. The Kelsey-Hayes EBC4 braking system used on General Motors trucks.

ABS   See *Antilock braking system*.

AC coupling   A signal that passes the AC signal component to the meter, but blocks the DC component. Useful to observe an AC signal that is normally riding on a DC signal; for example, charging ripple.

AC motor   An electric motor that is powered by AC (alternating current).

AC synchronous motor   An electric motor that uses a three-phase stator coil with a brushless permanent magnet rotor. Another term for DC brushless motor.

Acceleration slip regulation (ASR)   A name for a traction control system used on some General Motors vehicles.

Accumulator   A temporary location for fluid under pressure.

AC/DC clamp-on DMM   A type of meter that has a clamp that is placed around the wire to measure current.

ACIM   AC Induction Motor. See *Induction motor*.

ACM   Active Control Engine Mount. ACMs are computer controlled and are designed to dampen unusual vibrations during ICE start/stop.

Active sensor   A type of wheel speed sensor that produces a digital output signal.

Active crossover   A type of crossover that uses electronic components to block certain frequencies.

Active mode   The mode where a tire pressure sensor is transmitting tire inflation pressure information after the vehicle reaches 20 MPH or faster and at a rate of once every minute.

Actuator   An electromechanical device that performs mechanical movement as commanded by a controller.

Adhesive-lined heat shrink tubing   A type of heat shrink tubing that shrinks to one-third of its original diameter and has glue inside.

Adjustable pedals   Brake and accelerator pedals are mounted on a moveable support that allows them to be moved by the driver.

Adjustable wrench   A wrench that has a moveable jaw to allow it to fit many sizes of fasteners.

AFS   *Active Front headlight System.* A name for the system that causes the headlights to turn when cornering.

Aftermarket parts   Parts that are used in the repair of vehicles that are made by a company other than the same company who made the original factory-installed part.

AGM   Absorbed glass mat. AGM batteries are lead-acid batteries, but use an absorbent material between the plates to hold the electrolyte. AGM batteries are classified as valve-regulated lead-acid (VRLA) batteries.

AGST   Above ground storage tank, used to store used oil.

Ah   Ampere-hour. A battery capacity rating.

Air compressor   A piece of shop equipment that uses an electric motor to power an air compressor, which is stored in a pressure tank for use in the shop.

Air drill   A drill powered by compressed air.

Air filter   An element usually constructed of pleated paper that filters dirt from the air entering the engine. Most air filters are designed to trap dirt particles that are larger than 20 microns in size.

Air gap   The distance between the wheel speed sensor and the reluctor wheel.

Air management system   The term used to describe the airflow management through a automotive HVAC system.

Air ratchet   An air-operated hand tool that rotates a socket.

Air suspension (AS)   A type of suspension that uses air springs instead of metal or fiberglass springs.

Airbag   An inflatable fabric bag that deploys in the event of a collision that is severe enough to cause personal injury.

Air-blow gun   A handheld nozzle attached to a compressed air hose to apply air pressure to a component or device.

ALB   Abbreviation for antilock brakes. See also *Antilock braking system*.

Alert mode   An operating mode of a tire pressure sensor that causes the dash warning lamp to flash in the event of a rapid decrease in tire inflation pressure.

Alkaline battery   A battery that uses an alkaline (pH greater than 7) electrolyte solution.

Alternator   An electric generator that produces alternating current; also called an *AC generator*.

Alternator output test   A test used to test the amperage output of an alternator. This test usually involves the use of a carbon pile tester or similar unit that applies a load to the electrical system.

Alternator whine   A noise made by an alternator with a defective diode(s).

AM   Amplitude modulation, a type of radio transmission.

Amber ABS warning lamp   The dash warning lamp that lights (amber color) if a fault in the antilock braking system (ABS) is detected.

Ambient temperature sensor   A sensor usually located behind the grille of the vehicle used to monitor the outside air temperature. Used as an input for the outside air temperature dash display and to the automatic climatic control system.

American wire gauge (AWG)   A method used to measure wire diameter.

Ammeter   An electrical test instrument used to measure amperes (unit of the amount of current flow).

Ampere   The unit of the amount of current flow. Named for André Ampère (1775–1836).

Ampere hours (Ah)   A method used to rate battery capacity.

Ampere-turns   The unit of measurement for electrical magnetic field strength.

Analog   A type of dash instrument that indicates values by use of the movement of a needle or similar device. An analog signal is continuous and variable.

Analog-to-digital (AD) converter An electronic circuit that converts analog signals into digital signals that can then be used by a computer.

ANC Active noise control. ANC is a function of the vehicle's sound system, and is designed to generate sound pulses that "cancel" undesirable noises from the engine compartment.

Anode The positive electrode; the electrode toward which electrons flow.

ANSI The American National Standards Institute (ANSI) is a private, nonprofit organization that administers and coordinates the U.S. voluntary standardization and conformity assessment system.

Antilock braking system (ABS) A system that is capable of pulsing the wheel brakes if lockup is detected to help the driver maintain control of the vehicle.

APO Auxiliary power outlet. APOs are 120-volt AC electrical outlets located on a vehicle such as the GM parallel hybrid truck.

APP Accelerator pedal position sensor. Also known as an accelerator pedal sensor (APS).

Apprentice program A program where a person enrolls to learn a trade under the direction of a journeyman plus includes classroom training in addition to on-the-job training.

APS Accelerator pedal sensor. Also known as an accelerator pedal position (APP) sensor.

Armature The rotating unit inside a DC generator or starter, consisting of a series of coils of insulating wire wound around a laminated iron core.

Arming sensor A sensor used in an air bag circuit that is most sensitive and completes the circuit first among the two sensors that are needed to deploy an air bag.

Asbestosis A health condition where asbestos causes scar tissue to form in the lungs, causing shortness of breath.

ASE Abbreviation for the National Institute for Automotive Service Excellence, a nonprofit organization for the testing and certification of vehicle service technicians.

ASE Certified Master Automobile Technician A person who has taken and passed ASE certification tests for A1 through A8 and has had the specified work experience.

ASTM American Society for Testing and Materials (ASTM), was formed over a century ago, to address the need for component testing in industry.

ASR See *Acceleration slip regulation*.

Assist hybrid A hybrid electric vehicle design that utilizes regenerative braking and idle stop but cannot propel the vehicle in electric-only mode. A assist (mild) hybrid drive typically operates below 50 volts.

Atmospheric pressure Pressure exerted by the atmosphere on all things (14.7 pounds per square inch at sea level).

Atom The atom is the smallest unit of matter that consists of a nucleus surrounded by negatively charged electrons.

AT-PZEV Advanced Technology Partial-Zero-Emission Vehicle.

Auto link A type of automotive fuse.

Automatic air-conditioning system A system that uses sensors and actuators to maintain a preset temperature inside a vehicle.

Automatic climatic control system See *automatic temperature control system*.

Automatic level control (ALC) A General Motors term for a rear suspension system that used air shocks and a height sensor used to keep the rear of the vehicle level under all load conditions.

Automatic temperature control (ATC) system A system that uses sensors and actuators to maintain a preset temperature inside a vehicle.

Automatic transmission fluid An oil specifically designed for use in automatic transmissions that can vary according to make, model, and year of vehicle. Abbreviated ATF.

Auxiliary battery The 12-volt battery in a hybrid electric vehicle.

Aviation tin snips Cutters designed to cut sheet metal.

Backlight Light that illuminates the test tool's display from the back of the LCD. Also the rear window of a vehicle.

Backup camera A camera mounted on the rear of the vehicle that is used to display what is behind a vehicle when the gear selector is placed in reverse.

BAS Battery alternator starter. A type of mild (assist) hybrid that uses a larger than normal alternator/starter combination to provide assist tot eh ICE and start the ICE when in idle-stop mode.

Base The name for the section of a transistor that controls the current flow through the transistor.

Battery cables Cables that attach to the positive and negative terminals of the battery.

Battery electrical drain test A test to determine if a component or circuit is draining the battery.

Battery module A number of individual cells (usually six) connected in series. NiMH cells produce 1.2 volts, so most NiMH battery modules produce 7.2 volts.

Battery vent The external air intake vent for the battery cooling system in a Ford Escape hybrid.

Baud rate The speed at which bits of computer information are transmitted on a serial data stream. Measured in bits per second (bps).

BCI Battery Council International. This organization establishes standards for batteries.

BCM Battery condition monitor module. On Honda HEVs, the BCM is responsible for providing information on high-voltage battery condition to other modules on the vehicle network.

Beam-type torque wrench A type of wrench that displays the torque being applied to a fastener by the position of a deflective pointer and a scale, indicating the amount of torque.

Bearing splitter A two-part steel device used between a bearing and a gear or other component, which is used to remove the bearing using a hydraulic press.

Bench grinder An electric motor with a grinding stone and/or wire brush attached at both ends of the armature and mounted on a bench.

Bench testing A test of a component such as a starter before being installed in the vehicle.

Bench vise A vise mounted to a bench

BEV Battery electric vehicle.

BHP Brake horsepower. BHP is horsepower as measured on a dynamometer.

BIN number A U.S. federal rating of emissions. The lower the BIN number, the cleaner the exhaust emission is.

Binary system A computer system that uses a series of zeros and ones to represent information.

Bipolar transistor A type of transistor that has a base, emitter, and collector.

BJB Battery junction box. The power distribution box located near the battery in the ICE compartment.

Blend door An air mix valve located in the air distribution box of a vehicle's HVAC system. The blend door is responsible for "blending" air from the A/C evaporator with warm air from the heater core to deliver air at the proper temperature at the outlet ducts.

Blower motor An electric motor used to move air through the vehicle's HVAC system.

Bluetooth A short range wireless communication standard named after a Danish king that had a bluetooth.

BNC connector Coaxial-type input connector. Named for its inventor, Neil Councilman.

BOB See *Break out box*.

Body The steel structure of the vehicle that includes the doors, hood, fenders, and rear section.

Body-on-frame A type of vehicle construction that uses a steel frame to support the drivetrain (engine, transmission, and drive axle assembly), a separate body that is attached to the frame.

Boost converter An electronic component that increases voltage from a DC power source. Toyota's THS II system utilizes a boost converter to increase electric drive motor efficiency.

Bound electrons Electrons that are close to the nucleus of the atom.

Box-end wrench A type of wrench that has the end enclosed so that it can grip around the head of a bolt or nut.

BPM (brake pressure modulator) A part of the Bosch ABS hydraulic control unit.

BPMV (brake pressure modulator valve) A part of the hydraulic control unit used in a Delphi DBC-7 ABS system.

BPP (brake pedal position) A sensor used to detect the position of the brake pedal. Used in most regenerative braking systems.

Braided ground straps Ground wires that are not insulated and braided to help increase flexibility and reduce RFI.

Brake balance control system The component in a brake system that ensures that the wheel brakes are applied quickly and balanced among all four wheels for safe operation.

Brake fluid A non-petroleum-based fluid called polyglycol used in hydraulic brake systems.

Brake fluid level sensor A sensor used in the brake fluid reservoir to detect when brake fluid is low and turns on the red brake warning light on the dash.

Brake lights Lights at the rear of the vehicle which light whenever the brake pedal is depressed.

Brake warning lights Include the red brake warning light and the amber ABS warning light.

Branches Electrical parts of a parallel circuit.

Break-out box (BOB) An electrical tester that connects to a connector or controller and allows access to each terminal so testing can be performed using a meter or scope.

Breaker bar A handle used to rotate a socket; also called a *flex handle*.

Brush-end housing The end of a starter or generator (alternator) where the brushes are located.

Brushes Carbon or carbon-copper connections used to pass electrical current to a rotating assembly such as an armature in a starter motor or a rotor in a generator (alternator).

Brushless motor An electric motor that does not use brushes or a commutator. Instead, brushless motors are typically constructed with permanent magnets in the rotors and are powered by three-phase alternating current.

Bulb test A test to check the operation of certain circuits controlled by the ignition switch.

Bump cap A hat that is plastic and hard to protect the head from bumps.

Burn in A process of operating an electronic device for a period ranging from several hours to several days.

Bus An electrical network which ties several modules together.

Bypass tube A tube located in the ICE water jacket that allows coolant to bypass the radiator and be sent directly to the water pump inlet when the thermostat is closed.

CA Cranking amperes. A battery rating.

CAA Clean Air Act. Federal legislation passed in 1970 and updated in 1990 that established national air quality standards.

CAB See *Controller antilock brake*.

Cabin filter A filter located in the air intake of a vehicle's HVAC system. A cabin filter prevents particulate matter from entering the cabin air space.

Calibration codes Codes used on many powertrain control modules.

California Air Resources Board (CARB) A state of California agency which regulates the air quality standards for the state.

CAN Controller Area Network, a type of serial data transmission.

Candlepower A rating of the amount of light produced by a light source such as a light bulb.

Capacitance Electrical capacitance is a term used to measure or describe how much charge can be stored in a capacitor (condenser) for a given voltage potential difference. Capacitance is measured in farads or smaller increments of farads such as microfarads.

Carbon monoxide (CO) A colorless, odorless, and highly poisonous gas. It is formed by the incomplete combustion of gasoline.

Casting number An identification code cast into an engine block or other large cast part of a vehicle.

CAT III An electrical measurement equipment rating created by the International Electrotechnical Commission (IEC). CAT III indicates the lowest level of instrument protection that should be in place when performing electrical measurements on hybrid electric vehicles.

Catalytic converter An emission control device located in the exhaust system that changes HC and CO into harmless H_2O and CO_2. A three-way catalyst NOx is also divided into harmless separate nitrogen (N_2) and Oxygen (O_2).

Cathode The negative electrode.

CCA Cold Cranking Amperes. A rating of a battery tested at zero degree F.

CCD Chrysler Collision Detection. A type of module communication used in early Chrysler vehicles until about 2004.

CCVRTMR Chassis Continuously Variable Real-Time dampening Magneto-Rheological suspension. A type of electronic suspension used on some General Motors vehicles.

Cell An individual segment of a battery that includes a negative electrode, a positive electrode, and the electrolyte solution. Batteries are made up of a number of cells connected in series. A group of negative and positive plates to form a cell capable of producing 2.1 V.

CEMF Counter electromotive force.

CFL Cathode fluorescent lighting.

CFR Code of Federal Regulations.

Change of state The process where a material absorbs or releases heat energy to change between solid, liquid, and gaseous states.

Channel A term used to describe a wheel brake being controlled by the antilock brake system controller.

Charge indicator A hydrometer built into one battery cell that gives a visual indication of the battery's state of charge.

Charging voltage test An electrical test using a voltmeter and an ammeter to test the condition of the charging circuit.

Chassis The frame, suspension, steering, and machinery of a motor vehicle.

Cheater bar A pipe or other object used to lengthen the handle of a ratchet or breaker bar. Not recommended to be used as the extra force can cause the socket or ratchet to break.

Chisel A sharpened tool used with a hammer to separate two pieces of an assembly.

CHMSL Centrally High Mounted Stop Light; the third brake light.

Circuit A circuit is the path that electrons travel from a power source, through a resistance, and back to the power source.

Circuit breakers A mechanical unit that opens an electrical circuit in the event of excessive flow.

Clamping diode A diode installed in a circuit with the cathode toward the positive. The diode becomes forward biased when the circuit is turned off, thereby reducing the high voltage surge created by the current flowing through a coil.

Class 2 A type of BUS communication used in General Motors vehicles.

Claw poles The magnetic points of a generator (alternator) rotor.

Clock generator A crystal that determines the speed of computer circuits.

Clock in The act of recording the time when a technician reports for work or when work is started on a vehicle.

Clock time The time charged to complete a service procedure, which is determined by the actual time spent.

Clockspring A flat ribbon of wire used under the steering wire to transfer airbag electrical signals. May also carry horn and steering wheel control circuits depending on make and model of vehicle.

Close-end An end of a wrench that grips all sides of the fastener.

Clutch Any device that is made to couple one mechanism with another to cause each to rotate at the same speed.

CMOS Complementary metal oxide semiconductor.

Coil A device that has wire wrapped around a core and used to create a magnetic field.

Cold chisel A type of chisel used to remove rivets or to break off fasteners.

Cold cranking amperes The number of amperes that can be supplied by the battery at 0°F for 30 seconds while the battery maintains a voltage of at least 1.2 volts per cell.

Cold placard inflation pressure The designated tire inflation pressure that all tires should be inflated to and located on or near the driver's door.

Cold solder joint A type of solder joint that was not heated to high-enough temperature to create a good electrical connection. Often a dull gray appearance rather than shiny for a good solder connection.

Collector The name of one section of a transistor.

Color shift A term used to describe the change in the color of an HID arc tube assembly over time.

Column-mounted electric power steering (C-EPS) A type of electric power steering where the motor is attached to the steering column.

Control current The current at the base of a transistor which is used to control the emitter-collector current.

Combination circuit Another name for a series-parallel electrical circuit.

Combination valve A valve used in the brake system that performs more than one function, such as a pressure differential switch, metering valve, and/or proportioning valve.

Combination wrench A wrench that is open ended at one end and has a box end at the other end.

Commission pay Income to a service technician determined by the number of hours that a flat-rate manual states in the time it should take multiplied by the hourly rate of the technician.

Commutator The name for the copper segments of the armature of a starter or DC generator. The revolving segments of the commutator collect the current from or distribute it to the brushes.

Commutator segments The name for the copper segments of the armature of a starter or DC generator.

Commutator-end housing The end of a starter motor that contains the commutator and brushes. Also called the brush-end housing.

Complete circuit A type of electrical circuit that has continuity and current will flow if connected to power and ground.

Composite headlight A type of headlight that uses a separate, replaceable bulb.

Compound circuit Another name for a series-parallel electrical circuit.

Compression spring A spring which is part of a starter drive that acts on the starter pinion gear.

Compressor speed sensor A sensor used to measure the speed of the air-conditioning compressor.

Computer command ride (CCR) A type of electronic suspension used in some General Motors vehicles.

Condenser Also called a capacitor; stores an electrical charge.

Conductance The plate surface area in a battery that is available for chemical reaction. Battery condition can be assessed using a measurement of its conductance.

Conductor A material that conducts electricity and heat. A metal that contains fewer than four electrons in its atoms' outer shell.

Connector The plastic part of a wiring connector where metal electrical terminals plug in.

Continuity Instrument setup to check wiring, circuits, connectors, or switches for breaks (open circuit) or short circuits (closed circuit).

Continuity light A test light that has a battery and lights if there is continuity (electrical connection) between the two points that are connected to the tester.

Control wires The wires in a power window circuit that are used to control the operation of the windows.

Controller A term used to describe a module or a computer used to control a system or a part of a vehicle.

Controller antilock brake (CAB) The term used by Chrysler for their ABS.

Conventional theory The theory that electricity flows from positive (+) to negative (−).

Coolant The liquid mixture in the engine cooling system.

Coolant heat storage system A system used on the second-generation Toyota Prius that stores hot coolant in order to warm the ICE prior to a cold start.

Coolant recovery reservoir An external storage tank for the ICE cooling system. Collects coolant as the ICE warms up and supplies coolant to the system as the ICE cools down.

Cooperative education A training program that includes on-the-job plus classroom training.

Core A part that is returned to a parts store and which will be turned over to a company to be repaired or remanufactured.

Core charge An amount of money paid when a rebuildable part is purchased and refunded when the worn or defective part is returned to the parts store.

Coulomb A measurement of electrons. A coulomb is 6.28 × 101 (6.28 billion billion) electrons.

Counter electromotive force (cemf) A voltage produced by a rotating coil such as a starter motor where the armature is being moved through a magnetic field.

Country of origin The first number of the vehicle identification number (VIN), which identifies where the vehicle was assembled.

Courtesy lights General term used to describe all interior lights.

CPA Connector Position Assurance. A clip used to help hold the two parts of an electrical connector together.

CPU Central processor unit.

Creep aid A function of some hybrid electric vehicles that keeps the vehicle's base brakes applied briefly after the ICE leaves idle stop mode to allow for smooth starts.

Creeper A small platform mounted on short casters designed for a service technician to lie down and maneuver under a vehicle.

Crimp and seal connectors A type of electrical connector that has glue inside which provides a weather-proof seal after it is heated.

Critical thinking A term used to describe the thought process used to help make sound decisions.

Crossover An electronic circuit that separates frequencies in a sound (audio) system.

Crowfoot socket A type of socket that slips onto the side of the bolt or nut. Used where direct access from the top is restricted.

CRT Cathode ray tube. A type of display which is commonly used in TVs.

Cruise control A system that maintains the desired vehicle speed. Also called speed control.

Customer pay (CP) The amount that the customer pays for a repair.

Cut zone Areas of a vehicle that can be cut by a first responder.

Cycle life The number of times a battery can be charged and discharged without suffering significant degradation in its performance.

Cylinder deactivation A phase of internal combustion engine operation in which the valves of certain cylinders are disconnected from the valve train and remain closed. This allows the ICE to operate on fewer cylinders for greater fuel economy and efficiency.

Cylindrical cell A battery cell that is constructed similar to a D cell.

Damper disc The coupling between the ICE's flywheel and the transmission in a hybrid electric vehicle. The damper disc is designed similar to the hub in a clutch disc and is made to absorb torsional vibration.

Darlington pair Two transistors electrically connected to form an amplifier. This permits a very small current flow to control a large current flow. Named for Sidney Darlington, a physicist at Bell Laboratories from 1929 to 1971.

dB An abbreviation for decibel, a measure of relative noise level.

DC brushless motor An electric motor that uses a three-phase stator coil with a brushless permanent magnet rotor. Another term for AC synchronous motor.

DC coupling A signal transmission that passes both AC and DC signal components to the meter.

DC motor An electric motor powered by direct current (DC). DC motors typically utilize brushes and a commutator on a wire wound armature.

DC-to-DC converter An electronic component found in a hybrid electric vehicle that converts high-voltage DC to 12-volts DC for charging the auxiliary battery.

Dead-blow hammer A type of hammer that has lead shot (small pellets) inside a steel housing, which is then covered with a plastic covering. Used to apply a blunt force to an object.

Deceleration sensor A sensor mounted to the body or frame of a vehicle that detects and measures the deceleration of the vehicle. Used to control the activation of the air bags and vehicle stability systems.

Decibels (dB) A unit of the magnitude of sound.

Deep cycle Discharging a battery completely and then recharging it. Most battery technologies do not tolerate deep cycling.

Delta pressure method A procedure to reset or relearn tire pressure monitoring systems (TPMS) by changing the air pressure in the tire until the controller senses the change.

Delta winding A type of stator winding where all three coils are connected in a triangle shape. Named for the triangle-shaped Greek capital letter.

Desiccant A dryer on the output side of the compressor contains silica gel which removes any moisture from the system. Used in an electronic system where an air compressor is used to inflate air shocks.

Despiking diode Another name of clamping diode.

DFCO Deceleration fuel cut-off. An engine control function that cuts fuel to the ICE cylinders when the vehicle is decelerating.

Diagonal pliers Pliers designed to cut wire and to remove cotter keys. Also called *side cuts* or *dike pliers*.

DIC Driver Information Center. The instrument panel readout on a GM vehicle that provides extra information about vehicle operation and diagnostics.

Die grinder   A handheld air-operated tool used with a grinding stone or a wire brush.

Dielectric   An insulator used between two conductors to form a capacitor.

Digital computer   A computer that uses on and off signals only. Uses an A-to-D converter to change analog signals to digital before processing.

Diode   An electrical device that allows current to flow in one direction only.

Dipstick   A long thin piece of metal used to determine the level of engine oil or automatic transmission fluid.

Direct-drive electric power steering (D-EPS)   A type of electric power steering where the motor is attached to the steering rack.

Direction wires   The wires from the control switch to the lift motor on a power window circuit. The direction of current flow through these wires determines which direction the window moves.

Discharge Air Temperature (DAT) Sensor   A temperature sensor located at the outlet of the evaporator.

Displacement   The total volume displaced or swept by the cylinders in an internal combustion engine.

Distracter   An answer on a multiple choice test that is not the correct answer.

Division   A specific segment of a waveform, as defined by the grid on the display.

DMM   Digital multimeter. A digital multimeter is capable of measuring electrical current, resistance, and voltage.

Doping   The adding of impurities to pure silicon or germanium to form either P- or N-type material.

DOT   Abbreviation for the Department of Transportation.

DOT 3   Rating of the most commonly specified brake fluid.

DOT 4   A brake fluid rating for polyglycol.

DOT 5.1   The highest rated polyglycol brake fluid.

DOT 5   Silicone brake fluid rating.

Double cut method   The cutting of 12-volt battery cables where each cable is cut twice. After the first cut is made, another cut is made about 2 inches from the first cut.

Double-cut file   A file that has two rows of teeth that cut at an opposite angle.

Double-layer technology   Technology used to build ultracapacitors. Involves the use of two carbon electrodes separated by a membrane.

Double overhead camshaft (DOHC)   An engine design with two camshafts above each line of cylinders—one for the exhaust valves and one for the intake valves.

DPDT   Double-pole, double-throw switch.

DPST   Double pole, single-throw switch.

Drive-by-wire   Another term for electronic throttle control. See *ETC*.

Drive-end (DE) housing   The end of a starter motor that has the drive pinion gear.

Drive shaft   A shaft that transfers engine torque from the output of the transmission to the rear axle (differential) assembly.

Drive size   The size in fractions of an inch of the square drive for sockets.

Driver selector switch   A switch inside the vehicle that allows the driver to select the firmness of the suspension.

DRL   Daytime running lights. Lights that are located in the front of the vehicle and come on whenever the ignition is on. In some vehicles the vehicle has to be moving before they come on. Used as a safety device on many vehicles and required in many counties such as Canada since 1990.

Dry charged   Emptying the electrolyte from a fully charged lead-acid battery in order to store or ship it. Dry-charged batteries are refilled with electrolyte before being put back into service.

DSO   Digital storage oscilloscope.

Dual inline pins (DIP)   A type of electronic chip that has two parallel lines of pins.

Dual-position actuator   An actuator used in a heating ventilation and air-conditioning (HVAC) system that has two positions.

Dual-stage airbags   Airbags that can deploy either with minimum force or full force or both together based on the information sent to the airbag controller regarding the forces involved in the collision.

Dual-Zone Systems   A type of HVAC system that has separate temperature controls for the passenger and driver's side of the vehicle.

Duty cycle   The percentage of time a unit is turned on.

DVOM   Digital volt-ohm-milliammeter.

Dynamic voltage   Voltage measured with the circuit energized and current flowing through the circuit.

E & C   Entertainment and comfort.

Easy out   A tool used to extract a broken bolt.

EBCM (electronic brake control module)   The name General Motors uses to describe the control module used on the ABS unit.

EBTCM (electronic brake traction control module)   The term used to describe the valve body and control module of an ABS unit.

ECA   Electronic control module. The name used by Ford to describe the computer used to control spark and fuel on older model vehicles.

ECB   Electronically controlled braking system. The system used on Toyota HEVs that controls the operation of the vehicle's base brakes and regenerative braking systems.

ECM   Electronic control module. A generic term for a computer or controller used in a vehicle.

ECU   Electronic Control Unit. A generic term for a vehicle computer.

eCVT   Electronic continuously variable transmission. An electric motor is used in conjunction with a planetary gearset to provide an infinite number of gear ratios.

EDR   Event data recorder. The hardware and software used to record vehicle information before, during, and after an airbag deployment.

EEPROM   See *E^{2}PROM*.

E^{2}PROM   Electronically erasable programmable read-only memory. A type of memory that can be electronically erased and reprogrammed.

EHB   Electro-hydraulic brake. A unit used on all vehicles that use series-type regenerative braking and is used to control brake cylinder pressure as well as front-to-rear brake balance.

EHCU (electrohydraulic control unit)   General Motors ABS control module for four-wheel antilock braking systems.

EHPS   Electro-hydraulic power steering. A 42-volt assist unit that provides pressurized fluid for power steering and brakes in a GM Parallel Hybrid Truck.

Electric adjustable pedals (EAP)   A system that uses an electric motor to move both the accelerator and the brake pedal forward or rearward by the driver using a position control switch.

Electric secondary fluid pump   An electrically driven auxiliary pump used in automatic transmissions for hybrid-electric vehicles. This pump is energized when the ICE is in idle stop mode to maintain transmission pressures.

Electrical load   Applying a load to a component such as a battery to measure its performance.

Electrical noise   Electrical interference sometimes caused by the arcing of brushes on the commutator in a DC motor.

Electrical potential   Another term to describe voltage.

Electricity   The movement of free electrons from one atom to another.

Electrochemistry   The term used to describe the chemical reaction that occurs inside a battery to produce electricity.

Electrode   A solid conductor through which current enters or leaves a substance, such as a gas or liquid.

Electrolysis   The process in which electric current is passed through water in order to break it into hydrogen and oxygen gas.

Electrolyte   Any substance that, in solution, is separated into ions and is made capable of conducting an electric current. An example of electrolyte is the acid solution of a lead-acid battery.

Electromagnetic   The magnetic field around an electromagnet which consists of a soft iron core surrounded by a coil of wire. Electrical current flowing through the coiled wire creates a magnetic field around the core.

Electromagnetics   The science or application of electromagnetic principles.

Electromagnetism   A magnetic field created by current flow through a conductor.

Electromotive force (EMF)   The force (pressure) that can move electrons through a conductor.

Electron theory   The theory that electricity flows from negative (−) to positive (+).

Element   All matter is made from slightly over 100 individual components called elements. The smallest particle that an element can be broken into and still retain the properties of that element is known as an atom.

EM   Electric machine. A term used to describe any device that converts mechanical energy into electrical energy or vice versa.

EMF   See *Electromotive force*.

EMI   Electromagnetic interference. An undesirable electronic signal. It is caused by a magnetic field building up and collapsing, creating unwanted electrical interference on a nearby circuit.

Emitter   The name of one section of a transistor. The arrow used on a symbol for a transistor is on the emitter and the arrow points toward the negative section of the transistor.

Energy density   A measure of the amount of energy that can be stored in a battery relative to the volume of the battery container. Energy density is measured in terms of Watt-hours per liter (Wh/L).

Energy recirculation   A term used to describe the Toyota THS-II system's ability to propel the vehicle using either MG1 or MG2 depending on which is most efficient at the time.

Engine coolant temperature (ECT) sensor   A sensor used to measure the temperature of the coolant in the engine.

Engine stand   A floor mounted-frame usually equipped with casters on which an engine can be attached and rotated.

Entrepreneur   A person who owns a business.

Environmental Protection Agency (EPA)   A federal government agency that oversees the enforcement of laws related to the environment. Included in these laws are regulations on the amount and content of automotive emissions.

EPA   Environmental Protection Agency.

EPAS   Electric power assist steering. Also known as EPS (electric power steering).

EPM   Electrical Power Management. A General Motors term used to describe a charging system control sensor and the control of the generator (alternator) output based on the needs of the vehicle.

EPS   Electric power steering. Also known as EPAS (electric power assist steering).

ESC   Electronic stability control.

ESD   Electrostatic discharge. Another term for ESD is static electricity.

ETC   Electronic throttle control. The intake system throttle plate is controlled by a servo motor instead of a mechanical linkage. Also known as drive-by-wire.

ETR   Electronically tuned radio. A type of radio now used in all vehicles that use electronics to tune the frequencies instead of using a variable capacitor.

EV   Electric vehicle. A term used to describe battery-powered vehicles.

Evaporator   An A/C system component that absorbs heat from the air in the vehicle's passenger compartment.

Evaporator drain   An outlet at the bottom of the evaporator housing that allows condensed water to flow out of the passenger compartment.

Evaporator Temperature (EVT) Sensor   A sensor used in automatic temperature control systems used to measure the temperature of the evaporator.

Exhaust gas recirculation (EGR)   The process of passing a small, measured amount of exhaust gas back into the engine to reduce combustion temperatures and formation of NOx (oxides of nitrogen).

Extension   A socket wrench tool used between a ratchet or breaker bar and a socket. When using a scope, an external trigger is used to start the recording of an event based on a voltage changed in another (external) circuit.

External trigger   When using an oscilloscope connecting when the scope is to be triggered or started is connected to another circuit when the one being measured.

Eye wash station   A water fountain designed to rinse the eyes with a large volume of water.

F = MA   A formula for inertia. The force (F) of an object in motion is equal to the mass (M) times the acceleration (A).

Farad   A unit of capacitance, symbolized as F. A 1-farad capacitor can store 1 coulomb of electrons when 1 volt of potential is applied to its terminals.

FAS Flywheel Alternator Starter. A term used to describe the motor-generator located between the ICE and the transmission on a GM parallel hybrid truck.

Feedback The reverse flow of electrical current through a circuit or electrical unit that should not normally be operating. This feedback current (reverse-bias current flow) is most often caused by a poor ground connection for the same normally operating circuit.

Feeler gauge A set of precision thickness steel blades used to measure a gap. Also called a *thickness gauge*.

FET Field effect transistor. A type of transistor that is very sensitive and can be harmed by static electricity.

Fiber optics The transmission of light through special plastic that keeps the light rays parallel even if the plastic is tied in a knot.

FICA A payroll deduction (Federal Insurance Contribution Act, also known as Social Security).

Field coils Coils or wire wound around metal pole shoes to form the electromagnetic field inside an electric motor.

Field housing The part of a starter that supports the field coils.

Field poles The magnets used as field coils in a starter motor.

Files A metal smoothing tool.

Fire blanket A fire-proof wool blanket used to cover a person who is on fire and smother the fire.

Fire extinguisher classes The types of fires that a fire extinguisher is designed to handle is referred to as fire class.

Fitting wrench A wrench that is used to remove the fitting holding a brake line or other line. Also called a *line wrench* or *flare-nut wrench*.

Flagging The act of recording the time and the description of the work completed on a vehicle.

Flare-nut wrench A type of wrench used to remove brake lines.

Flat rate Pay based on the amount of time published in a labor guide rather than using the actual amount of time spent on the repair.

Flat-tip screwdrivers A screwdriver used to remove and insert screws that have a single slot. Also called a *straight blade screwdriver*.

Floating ground system An electrical system that uses a ground that is not connected to the chassis of the vehicle.

Flooded cell A battery cell with electrodes immersed in liquid electrolyte.

Floor jack A hydraulic jack mounted on casters or steel wheels and used to lift a vehicle.

Flux Magnetic lines of force.

Flux density The density of the magnetic lines of force around a magnet or other object.

Flux lines Individual magnetic lines of force.

FM Frequency modulation, which is a type of radio transmission.

Force A unit that indicates the effort used against an object and measured in pounds or Newtons.

Formal evaluation Usually a written evaluation conducted by a supervisor that tries to identify areas of strengths as well as areas of an employee that may need to be improved as part of continuous improvement of the shop or dealer.

Forward bias Current flow in normal direction. Used to describe when current is able to flow through a diode.

Frame The structural part of a vehicle that uses a frame to support the drivetrain and the body.

Free electrons The outer electrons in an atom that has fewer than four electrons in it outer orbit.

Frequency The number of times a waveform repeats in one second, measured in Hertz (Hz), frequency band.

Fuel cell An electrochemical device that converts the energy stored in hydrogen gas into electricity, water, and heat.

Fuel-cell hybrid vehicle (FCHV) A vehicle that uses a fuel cell to create electricity which is then stored in a high-voltage battery that is used to provide electrical power to an electric motor which propels the vehicle.

Fuel-cell stack A collection of individual fuel cells "stacked" end-to-end, similar to slices of bread.

Fuel-cell vehicle (FCV) A vehicle that uses a fuel cell to create electricity which is then stored in a high-voltage battery and used to propel a vehicle using an electric motor.

Full hybrid A hybrid electric vehicle that utilizes high voltages (200 volts and above) and is capable of propelling the vehicle using "all-electric" mode at low speeds. Also known as a "strong" hybrid.

Fuse An electrical safety unit constructed of a fine tin conductor that will melt and open the electrical circuit if excessive current flows through the fuse.

Fuse link A safety device used on a solvent washer which would melt and cause the lid to close in the event of a fire. A type of fuse used to control the maximum current in a circuit.

Fusible link A type of fuse that will melt and open the protected circuit in the event of a short circuit, which could cause excessive current flow through the fusible link. Most fusible links are actually wires that are four gauge sizes smaller than the wire of the circuits being protected.

G force The amount of force applied to an object by gravity.

Gassing The release of hydrogen and oxygen gas from the plates of a battery during charging or discharging.

Gate The voltage applies to the gate of an field effect transistor (FET) controls the output of the FET.

Gauss gauge A gauge used to measure the unit of magnetic induction or magnetic intensity named for Karl Friedrich Gauss (1777–1855), a German mathematician.

GAWR Gross axle weight rating. A rating of the load capacity of a vehicle and included on placards on the vehicle and in the owner's manual.

Gel battery A lead-acid battery with silica added to the electrolyte to make it leak-proof and spill proof. Also called a valve-regulated lead-acid (VRLA) battery.

Generation mode A mode of operation in hybrid electric vehicles that uses engine power to generate electricity for charging the high-voltage battery.

Generator A device that converts mechanical energy into electrical energy. Also called an alternator.

Generator motor A term used to describe the smaller electric machine in a Ford Escape Hybrid transmission.

Generator output test A test used to determine the condition of a generator (alternator).

Germanium A semiconductor used in early diodes.

GFD   Ground-fault detection. A diagnostic function used to monitor the auxiliary power outlets in a GM parallel hybrid truck.

Global warming   An overall increase in the earth's temperature. Global warming is thought to be caused by an increased concentration of greenhouse gases in the earth's atmosphere.

GMLAN   General Motors Local Area Network. GM's term for CAN used in GM vehicles.

GMM   Graphing multimeter.

GPS   Global positioning system. A government program of 24 satellites which transmit signals and used by receivers to determine their location.

Graticule   The series of squares on the face of a scope. Usually 8 by 10 on a screen.

Green zone   The area of the tachometer face on a Ford Escape Hybrid that indicates the vehicle is operating in "all-electric" or "stealth" mode.

Grid   The lead-alloy framework (support) for the active materials of an automotive battery.

Gross pay   Total amount of income earned before deductions.

Ground   The lowest possible voltage potential in a circuit. In electrical terms, a ground is the desirable return circuit path. Ground can also be undesirable and provide a shortcut path for a defective electrical circuit.

Ground brushes   The brushes in a starter motor that carry current to the housing of the starter or ground.

Ground (return) path   The electrical return path that the current flows through in a complete circuit.

Ground plane   A part of antenna that is metal and usually the body of the vehicle.

Grounded   An electrical fault where the current is going to ground rather than through the load and then to ground.

Growler   Electrical tester designed to test starter and DC generator armatures.

GVWR   Gross vehicle weight rating. The total weight of the vehicle, including the maximum cargo.

Hacksaw   A saw that uses a replaceable blade and is used to cut a variety of materials depending on the type of blade used.

Handwheel position sensor   A sensor that detects the position as well as the direction and speed that the driver is rotating the steering wheel. Used as an input to the electronic suspension and electronic stability control system.

Hazard warning   A sticker or decal warning that a hazard is close.

Hazardous waste material   Chemicals such as waste oil and solvents that are no longer being used by a shop and may pose a danger to environment or people.

HCCI   See *Homogeneous-charge compression ignition*.

HCM   Hybrid Control Module. The module in a GM parallel hybrid truck that is responsible for all hybrid vehicle functions.

HCU   See *Hydraulic control unit*.

Heat exchanger   A device such as a radiator or condenser that is used to absorb or reject heat from a fluid passing through it.

Heat shrink tubing   A type of rubber tubing that shrinks to about half of its original diameter when heated. Used over a splice during a wire repair.

Heat sink   A device used to dissipate heat from electronic components.

Heater core   A cooling system component that is responsible for transferring heat from the ICE coolant to the air flowing into the passenger compartment.

Heating, ventilation, and air conditioning (HVAC)   The term used to describe the heating and air-conditioning system in a vehicle.

Height sensor   A sensor used in an electronic suspension system that detects the height of the suspension.

Helper pump   An electric water pump used to circulate coolant through a hybrid electric vehicle's heater core when the ICE is in idle stop mode.

HEPA   High Efficiency Particulate Air filter.

HEPA vacuum   High efficiency particulate air filter vacuum used to clean brake dust.

Hertz   A unit of measurement of frequency. One Hertz is one cycle per second, abbreviated Hz. Named for Heinrich R. Hertz, a nineteenth-century German physicist.

HEV   Hybrid electric vehicle. Describes any vehicle that uses more than one source of propulsion.

HID   High Intensity Discharge. A type of headlight that uses high voltage to create an arc inside the arc tube assembly which then produces a blue-white light.

High impedance test meter   A digital meter that has at least 10 million ohms of internal resistance as measure between the test leads with the meter set to read volts.

High resistance   A type of electrical fault that causes a recued amount of current flow.

High-pass filter   A filter in an audio system that blocks low frequencies and only allows high frequencies to pass through to the speakers.

Hold-in winding   One of two electromagnetic windings inside a solenoid; used to hold the movable core into the solenoid.

Hole theory   A theory which states that as an electron flows from negative (−) to positive (+), it leaves behind a hole. According to the hole theory, the hole would move from positive (+) to negative (−).

Holes   *See Hole theory*.

HomeLink   A brand name of a system used and included in many new vehicles to operate the automatic garage door opener.

Homogeneous-charge compression ignition (HCCI)   A low-temperature combustion process that involves air–fuel mixtures being burned without the use of spark ignition.

Horn   An electro-mechanical device that creates a loud sound when activated.

Housing expense   Includes rent or mortgage payment, plus heat, light, and other utility expenses.

HPA   See *Hydraulic power assist*.

HUD   Head-up display.

HV   High voltage. Applies to any voltage above 50 volts.

HV battery   High-voltage battery. Hybrid electric vehicles use NiMH battery packs that are rated up to 330 volts DC.

HV cables   Vehicle cables that carry high voltage.

HVTB   High-voltage traction battery. The high-voltage battery in a Ford Escape Hybrid.

Hybrid   Abbreviated version of hybrid electric vehicle (HEV).

Hybrid flasher   A type of flasher unit that can operate two or more bulbs at a constant rate.

Hydraulic power assist (HPA)   A hybrid vehicle configuration that utilizes hydraulic pumps and accumulators for energy regeneration.

Hydraulic press   A piece of shop equipment usually mounted on the floor, which uses a hydraulic cylinder to remove and install pressed-on components, such as bearings.

Hydrocarbons (HC)   Any of a number of compounds of carbon and hydrogen used as fuel, such as gasoline. High levels of hydrocarbons in tailpipe emissions are a result of unburned fuel. When combined with NOx and sunlight, they form smog.

Hydrometer   An instrument used to measure the specific gravity of a liquid. A battery hydrometer is calibrated to read the expected specific gravity of battery electrolyte.

ICE   Internal combustion engine.

ICU (Integrated control unit)   Chrysler's name for the hydraulic modulator and pump assembly used in the Teves Mark 20 non-integral four-wheel ABS system.

Idle stop mode   A phase in hybrid electric vehicle operation in which the internal combustion engine shuts off during idle operation. The ICE typically restarts the moment the brake pedal is released.

IEC   International Electrotechnical Commission.

IGBT   Insulated gate bipolar transistors. IGBTs are the primary switching devices for the inverter in a hybrid electric vehicle.

Ignition control module (ICM)   The electronic control module that controls the charging and discharging of the ignition coil(s).

IMA   Integrated Motor Assist. Describes the motor-generator located between the ICE and the transmission on Honda hybrid electric vehicles.

Impact wrench   An air-operated hand tool used to install and remove threaded fasteners.

Impedance   The resistance of a coil of wire, measured in ohms.

Impeller   The mechanism in a water pump that rotates to produce coolant flow.

Impurities   Doping elements used in the construction of diodes and transistors.

Incandescent light   A type of light that uses an incandescent rather than a fluorescent or LED light source.

Incentive pay   See Commission pay.

Independent switches   Switch located at each door and used to raise or lower the power window for that door only.

Induction motor   An AC motor in which electromagnetic induction is used to generate a magnetic field in the rotor without the need for brushes. Also known as an AC asynchronous motor.

Inductive ammeter   A type of ammeter that is used as a Hall Effect senor in a clamp that is used around a conductor carrying a current.

Inertia   The tendency of an object to resist changes in motion. An object at rest tends to stay at rest, and an object in motion tends to stay in motion unless acted on by an outside force.

Informal evaluation   A process of evaluation that is usually not written but instead is based on observation and verbal communications of an employer of an employee.

Infrared (IR) sensors   A type of sensor used in many automatic air-conditioning systems that are used to detect the temperature of the passenger areas.

Initialization   A procedure that resets or relearns where each tire sensor is located after a tire rotation.

Input   Information on data from sensors to an electronic controller is called input. Sensors and switches provide the input signals.

Input conditioning   What the computer does to the input signals to make them useful; usually includes an analog-to-digital converter and other electronic circuits that eliminate electrical noise.

Insulated bolt cutters   Bolt cutters that are electrically insulated to protect the first responders from a potential electrical shock.

Insulated brushes   Brushes used in a starter motor that connect to battery power through the solenoid.

Insulated path   The power side of an electrical circuit.

Insulator   A material that does not readily conduct electricity and heat. A nonmetal material that contains more than four electrons in its atom's outer shell.

Intake manifold   The part that delivers air to all of the individual cylinders from one throttle body unit.

Integral ABS   An antilock braking system that includes the master cylinder, booster, ABS solenoids, and accumulator(s) all in one unit.

Integral sensor   A term used to describe a crash sensor that is built into the airbag control module.

Integrated circuit (IC)   An electronic circuit that contains many circuits all in one chip.

Internal resistance   The resistance to current flow that exists inside the battery. Battery condition can be assessed using an internal resistance measurement.

Inter-Provincial (IP) Certificate   A certificate required to work on vehicles in all Canadian provinces except Quebec and British Columbia.

In-Vehicle Temperature Sensor   A thermistor used to measure the temperature of the interior of a vehicle and used in automatic air-conditioning systems.

Inverter   An electronic device used to convert DC (direct current) into AC (alternating current).

IOD   Ignition off draw. A Chrysler term used to describe battery electrical drain or parasitic draw.

Ion   An atom with an excess or deficiency of electrons forming either a negative or a positive charged particle.

IP   Abbreviation for instrument panel.

IPM   Interior permanent magnet. Describes the arrangement of the permanent magnets on the inside of the rotor shell in an AC synchronous electric motor.

IPU   Intelligent power unit. Describes the collection of modules responsible for control of the motor-generator in the Honda IMA system.

ISO   International Standards Organization.

Isolating Decoupler Pulley (IDP)   A pulley on an alternator that contains a roller one-way clutch which helps reduce drive belt noise and movement.

Isolation solenoid   A solenoid used in an antilock braking system to isolate the master cylinder from the wheel brakes.

IVR   Instrument voltage regulator.

Jack stand   See Safety stand.

Job shadowing   A term used to describe when someone is observing a person at work to see what is involved in the trade during a course of a day.

Jobber   A name used to describe a store where automotive parts are sold to shops and individuals.

Julian date   The number of the day of the year. Also called *JD*.

Jumper cables   Heavy-gauge (4 to 2/0) electrical cables with large clamps, used to connect a vehicle that has a discharged battery to a vehicle that has a good battery.

Junction   The point where two types of materials join.

KAM   Keep alive memory.

Kelvin (K)   A temperature scale where absolute zero is zero degrees. Nothing is colder than absolute zero.

Key fob   A decorative unit attached to keys. Often includes a remote control to unlock/lock vehicles.

Keyword   A type of network communications used in many General Motors vehicles.

Kilo (k)   Means 1,000; abbreviated k or K.

Kinetic energy   The energy of motion. Any object (or mass) in motion has kinetic energy.

Kirchhoff's current law   A law that states "The current flowing into any junction of an electrical circuit is equal to the current flowing out of that junction."

Kirchhoff's voltage law   A law about electrical circuits that states: "The voltage around any closed circuit is equal to the sum (total) of the resistances."

Knee airbags   Airbags that are located inside a panel behind the lower instrument panel to help protect the knees in the event of a frontal collision.

kW   Abbreviation for kilowatt, a measure of power. One kilowatt is 1,000 watts, and 746 watts is equivalent to 1 horsepower.

Labor guides   A book or service information that provides the time that is needed to perform a service or repair operation.

Lateral accelerometer sensor   A type of sensor used to detect cornering forces and used as an input from electronic stability control systems.

LCD   Liquid-crystal display.

LDWS   Lane departure warning system.

Least likely questions   A type of question asked on the ASE certification tests.

LED   Light-emitting diode. A high-efficiency light source that uses very little electricity and produces very little heat.

LED test light   A test light used by technicians to test for voltage that has high impedance and uses an LED with a 470 ohm resistor to control current through the tester.

Left-hand rule   A method of determining the direction of magnetic lines of force around a conductor. The left-hand rule is used with the electron flow theory (− flowing to +).

Legs   Another name for the branches of a parallel circuit.

Lenz's Law   The relative motion between a conductor and a magnetic field is opposed by the magnetic field of the current it has induced.

LEV   Low emission vehicle.

Leyden jar   A device first used to store an electrical charge. The first type of capacitor.

Lineman's gloves   Type of gloves worn by technicians when working around high-voltage circuits. Usually includes a rubber inner glove rated at 1,000 volts and a protective leather outer glove when used for hybrid electric vehicle service.

Li-poly   Lithium-polymer battery design. A type of solid state battery that shows promise for EV and HEV applications.

Load   A term used to describe a device when an electrical current is flowing through it.

Load test   A type of battery test where an electrical load is applied to the battery and the voltage is monitored to determine the condition of a battery.

Load tester   A device for applying a heavy current load to a battery in order to assess its current-producing ability.

Lock tang   A mechanical tab that is used to secure a terminal into a connector. This lock tang must be depressed to be able to remove the terminal from the connector.

Locking pliers   Pliers that can be used to grasp an object and then be locked into position. Often called by a popular brand name VISE-GRIPS®.

Lockout switch   A lock placed on the circuit breaker box to insure that no one turns on the electrical circuit while repairs are being made.

Lodestone   A type of iron ore that exists as a magnet in its natural state.

Logic probe   A type of tester that can detect either power or ground. Most testers can detect voltage but most of the others cannot detect if a ground is present without further testing.

Low-grade heat   Cooling system temperatures that are very close to the temperature of the ambient air, resulting in lowered heat transfer efficiency.

Low-pass filter   A device used in a audio system that blocks high frequencies and only allows low frequencies to pass to the speakers.

Low-water loss battery   A type of battery that uses little water in normal service. Most batteries used in cars and light trucks use this type of battery.

LPA (low pressure accumulator)   A spring-loaded temporary storage reservoir used to hold brake fluid. Part of the electrohydraulic control unit of a Kelsey-Hayes EBC4 4WAL antilock brake system.

Lumbar   The lower section of the back.

Magnetic flux   The lines of force produced in a magnetic field.

Magnetic induction   The transfer of the magnetic lines of force to another nearby metal object or coil of wire.

Magnetism   A form of energy that is recognized by the attraction it exerts on other materials.

Magneto-rheological (MR)   A working fluid inside the shock that can change viscosity rapidly depending on electric current sent to an electromagnetic coil in each device.

Maintenance-free battery   A type of battery that does not require routine adding of water to the cells. Most batteries used in cars and light truck are maintenance free design.

Malfunction indicator lamp (MIL)   This amber dash board warning light may be labeled "check engine" or "service engine soon."

Mass   A measure of the amount of material contained in an object. Gravity acts on a mass to give it weight.

Master control switch   The control switch for the power windows located near the driver who can operate all of the windows.

MCA   Marine cranking amps. A battery specification.

MCM   Motor control module. The module in a Honda HEV that controls the operation of the IMA unit.

MDM   Motor drive module. The module in a Honda HEV that controls the flow of current to and from the IMA unit. The MDM is controlled by the MCM (motor control module).

MEA   See *Membrane electrode assembly*.

Medium hybrid   A hybrid electric vehicle design that utilizes "medium" voltage levels (between 50 and 200 volts). Medium hybrids use regenerative braking and idle stop but are not capable of starting the vehicle from a stop using electric mode.

Mega (M)   Million. Used when writing larger numbers or measuring large amount of resistance.

Membrane electrode assembly (MEA)   The part of the PEM fuel cell that contains the membrane, catalyst coatings, and electrodes.

Meniscus   The curve shape of a liquid when in a tube. Used to determine when a battery has been properly filled with distilled water.

Mentor   An experienced technician who offers to help a beginning technician learn all aspects of the trade.

Mercury   A heavy metal that is liquid at room temperature.

Mesh spring   A spring used behind the starter pinion on a starter drive to force the drive pinion into mesh with the ring gear on the engine.

Meter accuracy   The accuracy of a meter measured in percent

Meter resolution   The specification of meter that indicates how small or fine a measurement the meter can detect and display.

Metric wire gauge   The metric method for measuring wire size in the square millimeters. This is the measure of the core of the wire and does not include the insulation.

Micro (μ)   One-millionth of a volt or ampere.

Microbe   A microorganism that is too small to be seen by the human eye.

Micro-hybrid drive   A term used to describe Belt Alternator Starter (BAS) and other mild hybrid systems.

Mild hybrid   A hybrid electric vehicle design that utilizes regenerative braking and idle stop but cannot propel the vehicle in electric-only mode. A mild hybrid drive typically operates below 50 volts.

Milli (m)   One thousandth of a volt or ampere.

Miller cycle   A four-stroke cycle engine design that utilizes the Atkinson cycle along with a forced induction system such as a supercharger.

Mode door   A door that controls the airflow through an air-conditioning system and switches the airflow to the various vents depending on the needs or the commands from the HVAC controller.

Mode select switch   A switch used to change the mode, two wheel drive or four wheel drive, of a four wheel drive vehicle.

Model year (MY)   The year of a vehicle, which may be different from the calendar year when it is sold.

Modulation   The combination of these two frequencies is referred to as modulation.

Momentary switch   A type of switch that toggles between on and off.

MOSFET   Metal Oxide Semiconductor Field Effect Transistor. A type of transistor.

Most likely   A type of test question used on ASE certification tests.

Motor   An electric device that turns as a result of an electrical current flowing through the assembly.

Motoring mode   A phase of BAS hybrid vehicle operation where the motor-generator cranks the ICE to start it.

MOV   Metal oxide varistor. An electronic device that operates like two back-to-back zener diodes.

MRRTD   Magneto-Rheological Real-Time Damping. A type of electronic suspension used on some General Motors vehicles.

MSDS   Material Safety Data Sheets.

Multigroove adjustable pliers   Pliers that are capable of grasping a wide range of object sizes; also called *water pump pliers* or by a popular brand name of Channel Locks®

Multiple choice   The type of questions used on the ASE certification tests.

Multiplexing   A process of sending multiple signals of information at the same time over a signal wire.

N.C.   Normally closed.

N.O.   Normally open.

National Institute for Automotive Service Excellence   The formal name of ASE, the company that gives technician certification tests.

NEDRA   National Electric Drag Racing Association.

Needle–nose pliers   Pliers that are equipped with pointed jaws, which allow use in restricted areas or for small parts.

Negative temperature coefficient (NTC)   A material that decreases in resistance as the temperature increases.

Net pay   Amount earned minus deductions. Also called *take home pay*.

Network   A communications system used to link multiple computers or modules.

Neutral charge   An atom that has the same number of electrons as protons.

Neutral safety switch   An electrical switch which allows the starter to be energized only if the gear selector is in neutral or park.

NiCd   Nickel-cadmium battery design. Commonly called an alkaline battery.

NiMH   Nickel-metal hydride. A battery design used for the high-voltage batteries in most hybrid electric vehicles.

NLEV   National Low-Emission Vehicle.

Node   A module and computer that is part of a communications network.

Nominal voltage   The approximate voltage of a fully charged battery cell.

Nonintegral ABS   An antilock braking system (ABS) that uses a conventional master cylinder and power brake booster.

Nonvolatile RAM   Computer memory capability that is not lost when power is removed.

NPN transistor A type of transistor that has the P-type material in the base and the N-type material is used for the emitter and collector.

NTC Negative temperature coefficient. Usually used in reference to a temperature sensor (coolant or air temperature). As the temperature increases, the resistance of the sensor decreases.

N-type material Silicon or germanium doped with phosphorus, arsenic, or antimony.

Nut splitter A hand tool designed to break a nut that is rusted onto a bolt or stud.

Nuts A female threaded fastener to be used with a bolt or stud.

NVRAM Nonvolatile random access memory.

OAD Overrunning alternator dampener.

OAP Override alternator pulley.

OBD-II On-Board Diagnosis, second generation. The standard used for all emissions-related systems of the engine since 1996 on all vehicles sold in the United States.

Occupant detection systems An airbag system that includes a sensor in the passenger seat used to detect whether or not a passenger is seated in the passenger side and the weight range of that passenger.

OE Original equipment.

Offset aviation snip A tin snip that has curved jaws allowing it to make curved cuts either left or right.

Ohm The unit of electrical resistance. Named for George Simon Ohm.

Ohm's Law An electrical law that requires 1 volt to push 1 ampere through 1 ohm of resistance.

Ohmmeter An electrical tester deigned to measure electrical resistance in ohms.

Oil filter A filter usually constructed of pleated paper in a sheet metal container that filters dirt from the engine oil.

Oil galleries A name used to describe the oil passages in an engine where pressurized oil flows to lubricate the moving parts.

Oil pan The lower part of an engine were oil is stored, usually made from stamped steel or cast aluminum.

Oil pump A pump inside an engine used to send pressurized oil to the moving parts of the engine.

Oil sump Another name for an oil pan.

OL Overload or overlimit.

On-the-job (OTJ) A term used to describe training that occurs when the worker is actually working on the job and learns from others who are doing the same or similar work.

OP-amps An abbreviation for operational amplifier. Used in circuits to control and simplify digital signals.

Open circuit Any circuit that is not complete and in which no current flows.

Open circuit voltage Voltage measured without the circuit in operation.

Open-end wrench The end of a wrench that is open to allow the wrench to be inserted onto a fastener from the side.

Oscilloscope (scope) A tester that displays voltage levels on a screen.

OSHA Occupational Safety and Health Administration. OSHA is the main federal agency responsible for enforcement of workplace safety and health legislation.

Output The command from an electronic controller to an actuator or a device.

Output drivers Transistors inside a control module used to control an output device either by applying power or ground to the device.

Outside air temperature (OAT) sensor A sensor usually located in front of the radiator at the front of the vehicle used to measure the outside air temperature. This sensor is used to display outside air temperature on the dash as well as an input to the HVAC controller for operation of the automatic air-conditioning system.

Overhead camshafts An engine design where the camshaft(s) are located above the valves in the cylinder head.

Overhead valve (OHV) An engine design where the camshaft is located in the engine block (cam in block design) and the valves are in the cylinder head over the pistons.

Override alternator pulley (OAP) An alternator (generator) drive pulley that has a one-way clutch used to smooth the operation of the alternator and reduce the stress on the drive belt.

Overrunning alternator dampener (OAD) An alternator (generator) drive pulley that has a one-way clutch and a dampener spring used to smooth the operation of the alternator and reduce the stress on the drive belt.

Overrunning clutch A part of a starter drive assembly that allows the engine to rotate faster than the starter motor to help protect the starter from harm in the event the ignition switch is held in the crank position after the engine starts.

Oversteer A condition while cornering where the rear of the vehicle breaks traction before the front resulting in a spin out-of-control condition.

Oxides of nitrogen (NOx) A primary emission produced in the combustion chamber under high temperatures when nitrogen combines with oxygen. Oxides of nitrogen contribute to the formation of smog (ground level ozone [O_3]) when combined with HC and sunlight.

Pacific fuse element A type of automotive fuse.

Parallel circuit An electrical circuit with more than one path from the power side to the ground side. Has more than one branch or leg.

Parallel hybrid A hybrid vehicle design where the electric machine (or other source of energy) assists the ICE to propel the vehicle.

Parasitic load test An electrical test that measures how much current (amperes) is draining from the battery with the ignition off and all electrical loads off.

Partitions Separations between the cells of a battery. Partitions are made of the same material as that of the outside case of the battery.

Parts counter person A term used to describe the person who works at a parts store or the parts department at a shop or dealer who gets parts for technicians or customers.

Part-time employment A term used to describe working at a job for less than the normal 40 hours per week.

PASS A word used to help remember how to use a fire extinguisher; pull pin, aim, squeeze the lever, and sweep the nozzle from side to side.

Passenger presence system (PPS) An airbag system that includes a sensor in the passenger seat used to detect whether or not a passenger is seated in the passenger side and the weight range of that passenger.

Passkey I and II A type of anti-theft system used in General Motors vehicles.

Passlock I and II A type of anti-theft system used in General Motors vehicles.

PATS Passive Anti-Theft System. A type of anti-theft system used in Ford, Lincoln, and Mercury vehicles.

PCM Powertrain control module.

PCU Power control unit. The assembly that contains the MDM and DC-to-DC converter in a Honda hybrid electric vehicle.

Peltier Effect The French scientist Peltier found that electrons moving through a solid can carry heat from one side of the material to the other side. This effect is called the Peltier effect.

Perform ride mode A firm position of the shock absorbers in a system used in some General Motors vehicles.

Permanent magnet electric motors Electric motors that use permanent magnets for the field instead of electromagnets.

Permeability The measure of how well a material conducts magnetic lines of force.

Phase-change liquid A fluid used to transfer heat efficiently from electronic components. The components are immersed in the fluid, which changes from a liquid to a vapor as it absorbs heat.

PHEV Plug-in hybrid electric vehicle.

PHT Parallel hybrid truck. A term used to describe the Chevrolet Silverado/GMC Sierra hybrid pickup truck.

PID Parameter identification. The information found in the vehicle datastream as viewed on a scan tool.

Phosphor A chemical-coated light-emitting element called a phosphor is hit with high-speed electrons, which cause it to glow and create light.

Photocell A photocell (also called solar sensor) is used to measure radiant heat load that might cause an increase of the in-vehicle temperature.

Photodiodes A type of diode used as a sun-load sensor. Connected in reverse bias, the current flow is proportional to the sun load.

Photoelectricity When certain metals are exposed to light, some of the light energy is transferred to the free electrons of the metal. This excess energy breaks the electrons loose from the surface of the metal. They can then be collected and made to flow in a conductor; this is called photoelectricity.

Photons Light is emitted form an LED by the release of energy in the form of photons.

Photoresistor A semiconductor that changes in resistance with the presence or absence of light. Dark is high resistance and light is low resistance.

Phototransistor An electronic device that can detect light and turn on or off. Used in some suspension height sensors.

Piezoelectricity The principle by which certain crystals become electrically charged when pressure is applied.

Pillars A term used to describe the supporting vertical member of the body used to support the roof.

Pinion-mounted electric power steering system (P-EPS) A type of electric power steering where the motor is attached to the steering pinion gear.

PIV Peak Inverse Voltage. A rating for a diode.

Plastic optical fiber (POF) A type of module communications transfer media used by the byteflight BUS is used in safety critical systems, such as airbags, and uses the time division multiple access (TDMA) protocol, which operates at 10 million bps.

Plug-in hybrid vehicle (PHEV) A hybrid electric vehicle utilizing batteries that can be recharged by plugging into a household electrical outlet.

PM generator A sensor that has a permanent magnet and a coil of wire and produces an analog voltage signal if a notched metal wheel passes close to the sensor.

PM starter A starter motor that uses permanent magnet field coils.

PNP transistor A type of transistor that uses N-type material for the base and P-type material for the emitter and collector.

Polarity The condition of being positive or negative in relation to a magnetic pole.

Pole The point where magnetic lines of force enter or leave a magnet.

Pole shoes The metal part of the field coils in a starter motor.

Polyglycol A term used to describe brake fluid.

Polymer Electrolyte Fuel Cell (PEFC) Another term for Proton Exchange Membrane fuel cell. See *PEM*.

Porous lead Lead with many small holes to make a surface porous for use in battery negative plates; the chemical symbol for lead is Pb.

Portable crane A piece of shop equipment that is used to lift and move heavy pieces of equipment, such as an engine.

Positive crankcase ventilation (PCV) System used to prevent corrosive blowby gases (by-products of combustion) in the crankcase from entering the atmosphere.

Positive slip A condition where a driven tire loses traction during acceleration.

Positive temperature coefficient (PTC) Usually used in reference to a conductor or electronic circuit breaker. As the temperature increases, the electrical resistance also increases.

Potentiometer A three-terminal variable resistor that varies the voltage drop in a circuit.

Power line capacitor A capacitor used to boost the output of a sound system to move the speakers especially when reproducing low frequencies.

Power path The name for the power side of electrical circuit between the power source and the electrical load.

Power source In electrical terms the battery or generator (alternator).

Power steering control module (PSCM) The controller used to control the electric power steering system which is usually mounted on the steering column near the actuator motor assembly.

Power-assist mode A phase of hybrid vehicle operation in which the ICE is assisted by the electric machine (or other source of energy) to propel the vehicle.

PPE Personal protective equipment, which can include gloves, safety glasses, and other items.

Pressure differential switch Switch installed between the two separate braking circuits of a dual master to light the dash board "brake" light in the event of a brake system failure, causing a *difference* in brake pressure.

Pressure transducer   A type of sensor that converts pressure into an electrical (voltage) signal.

Pretensioners   An explosive devices used to remove the slack from a safety belt when an airbag is deployed.

Preventative maintenance (PM)   Operations and fluid changes performed on a vehicle as part of normal maintenance to help prevent faults or worn parts.

Primary battery   Nonrechargeable battery.

Primary wire   Wire used for low voltage automotive circuits, typically 12 volts.

Processing   The act of a computer when input data is run through computer programs to determine what output is needed to be performed.

Programmable Controller Interface (PCI)   A type of network communications protocol used in Chrysler brand vehicles.

PROM   Programmable read-only memory.

Propeller shaft   A term used by many manufacturers for a drive shaft.

Protection   A term used to describe a fuse or circuit breaker in an electrical circuit.

Protocol   A term used to describe a method of communications using networks.

Proton Exchange Membrane (PEM)   Proton Exchange Membrane fuel cell. A low- temperature fuel cell known for fast starts and relatively simple construction.

PRV   See *Peak inverse voltage.*

PTC circuit protection   Usually used in reference to a conductor or electronic circuit breaker. As the temperature increases, the electrical resistance also increases.

P-type material   Silicon or germanium doped with boron or indium.

Pull-in winding   One of two electromagnetic windings inside a solenoid used to move a movable core.

Pulse train   A DC voltage that turns on and off in a series of pulses.

Pulse width   The amount of "on" time of an electronic fuel injector.

Pulse wipers   Windshield wipers that operate intermittingly. Also called delay wipers.

Punch   A hand tool designed to be used with a hammer to drive out pins.

PWM   Pulse width modulation; operation of a device by an on/off digital signal that is controlled by the time duration the device is turned on and off.

Quiet mode   A hybrid or electric vehicle being operated using electric propulsion only.

Rack-and-pinion electric power steering (R-EPS)   A type of electric power steering where the motor is attached to the steering rack.

Radiator   A cooling system component used to dissipate heat from the coolant to the surrounding air.

Radio choke   A small coil of wire installed in the power lead, leading to a pulsing unit, such as an IVR to prevent radio interference.

Rain-sense wipers   Windshield wiper that use an electronic sensor to detect the presence of rain on the windshield and start operating automatically if the wiper switch is in the Auto position.

RAM   Random access memory. A nonpermanent type of computer memory used to store and retrieve information.

Range   The distance a vehicle can travel on a full charge or full-fuel tank without recharging or refueling. Range is measured in miles or kilometers.

Ratchet   A handle used to rotate a socket, which is reversible and allows the socket to be rotated in one direction and then free movement in the opposite direction of rotation.

RBS   Regenerative braking system. A hybrid electric vehicle system that allows vehicle kinetic energy to be converted into electrical energy for charging the high-voltage battery.

RCRA   Resource Conservation and Recovery Act.

Real-time dampening (RTD)   A type of electronic suspension system used in some General Motors vehicles.

Rebuilt   See Remanufactured.

Recombinant battery   A battery design that does not release gasses during normal operation. AGM batteries are known as recombinant batteries.

Rectifier bridge   A group of six diodes, three positive (+) and three negative (−) commonly used in generators (alternators).

Relative humidity (RH) sensor   A sensor used in automatic air-conditioning systems and used by the HVAC controller to help maintain comfortable temperature and humidity inside a vehicle.

Relearn   A process where a tire pressure sensor is reset after a tire rotation.

Reference   A term used to describe the name of a person who knows you and can speak to others about your knowledge and skills.

Regen   An abbreviation for regenerative braking.

Regeneration   A process of taking the kinetic energy of a moving vehicle and converting it to electrical energy and storing it in a battery.

Regenerative braking (RGB)   A hybrid vehicle function that recovers kinetic energy while the vehicle is decelerating and stores it for later use.

Relay   An electromagnetic switch that uses a movable arm.

Release solenoid   A solenoid used to open a vent port to release pressure from a brake circuit.

Reluctance   The resistance to the movement of magnetic lines of force.

Remove and inspect (R&I)   The term used to describe what a service technician does to check on the condition of a part. The part is removed from the vehicle and inspected to judge its condition to determine if it can be repaired or needs to be replaced with a new part.

Remove and replace (R&R)   The term used to describe the replacement of a component or a part.

Removers   This term is used to describe hand tools, which are designed to remove broken studs, bolts, and other fasteners.

Renewal parts   The term used to referring to parts used to replace the original parts that came on the vehicle when it was new just as tires.

Repair order   Also called an *RO* or *work order*. Contains all vehicle and customer information and the list of service work that is to be completed.

Reserve capacity   The number of minutes a battery can produce 25 A and still maintain a battery voltage of 1.75 V per cell (10.5 V for a 12-V battery).

Residual magnetism   Magnetism remaining after the magnetizing force is removed.

Resistance   The opposition to current flow measured in ohms.

Resolver   A speed sensor that utilizes three coils to determine rotor position.

Resume   A statement of your background and experience submitted to a potential employer.

Reverse bias   When the polarity of a battery is connected to a diode backwards and no current flows.

RF   Radio frequency.

RGB   Regenerative braking.

Rheostat   A two-terminal variable resistor.

Right-to-know laws   Laws that state that employees have a right to know when the materials they use at work are hazardous.

Ripple voltage   Excessive AC voltage produced by a generator (alternator usually caused by a defective diode.

RMS   Root Mean Square. A method of displaying variable voltage signals on a digital meter.

ROM   Read-only memory.

Rosin-core solder   A type of solder for use in electrical repairs. Inside the center of the solder is a rosin that acts as a flux to clean and help the solder flow.

Rotor   The rotating part of a generator where the magnetic field is created.

RPA   Rear Park Assist. The General Motors term to describe the system used to detect objects and warn the driver when backing.

RPO   Regular production order.

RSS   Road sensing suspension. A type of electronic suspension used in some General Motors vehicles.

Rubber coupling   A flexible connection between the power seat motor and the drive cable.

RVS   Remote vehicle start. A General Motors term for the system that allows the driver to start the engine using a remote control.

RWAL   Rear wheel anti-lock. General Motors and Chrysler's version of a single-channel rear-wheel-only antilock braking system used on many rear-wheel-drive pickups and vans.

SAE   Society of Automotive Engineers.

Safety stand   A metal device with an adjustable vertical support that is designed to support a vehicle after it has been raised off the ground. Also called a *jack stand*.

SAR   Supplemental Air Restraints. Another term used to describe an airbag system.

Saturation   The point of maximum magnetic field strength of a coil.

SCR   Silicon Controller Rectifier.

Screw jack assembly   A screw jack that is used to raise or lower a power seat.

Screwdriver   A hand tool designed to remove or insert screws.

SDARS   Satellite Digital Audio Radio Services. Another term used to describe satellite radio.

Seal driver   A hand tool used with a mallet or hammer to seat seals into a seal groove.

Seal puller   A hand tool designed to remove seals.

Secondary battery   Rechargeable battery.

Sediment chamber   A space below the cell plates of some batteries to permit the accumulation of sediment deposits flaking from the battery plates. A sediment chamber keeps the sediment from shorting the battery plates.

Selectable ride (SR)   A type of electronic suspension used in some General Motors vehicles.

Self-parking   A feature used in some vehicles equipped with electric power steering that allows the vehicle to be parked without having the driver turn the steering wheel.

Self-propelled vehicles   A term used to describe the first vehicles that used a motor or engine to propel the vehicle instead of using a horse to provide the power.

Semiconductor   A material that is neither a conductor nor an insulator; has exactly four electrons in the atom's outer shell.

Serial Communication Interface (SCI)   Serial Communication Interface, a type of serial data transmission used by Chrysler.

Serial data   Data that is transmitted by a series of rapidly changing voltage signals.

Series circuit   An electrical circuit that provides only one path for current to flow.

Series circuit laws   Laws that were developed by Kirchhoff which pertain to series circuits.

Series-hybrid   A hybrid vehicle design in which there is no mechanical connection between the ICE and the drive wheels. Instead, the ICE drives a generator that is used to produce electricity for recharging the high voltage battery and for propelling the vehicle through an electric motor.

Series-parallel circuits   Any type of circuit containing resistances in both series and parallel in one circuit.

Series-parallel hybrid   A hybrid vehicle design that can operate as a series hybrid, a parallel hybrid, or both series and parallel at the same time.

Series-wound field   A typical starter motor circuit where the current through the field windings is connected in series with the armature before going to ground. Also called a series-wound starter.

Serpentine (poly V) belt   A type of accessory drive belt that is used to power several accessories from the crankshaft of the engine.

Service advisor   A person who talks to the customer about a vehicle service and completes the work order.

Service bay   A work area for a vehicle, with or without a lift. Also called a *stall*.

Service consultant   Another name for a service advisor.

Service information   Includes service manuals, owner's manuals, CD-ROM discs, Internet sites, or other sources where vehicle information is found.

Service manager   The person in charge of a shop or dealer service department.

Service plug   A high-voltage electrical disconnect device on hybrid electric vehicles. The service plug should always be disconnected whenever working on a hybrid electric vehicle's high-voltage circuits.

Servomotor   The actuator in an electronic throttle control (ETC) system. Located in the ETC throttle body.

SGCM Starter Generator Control Module. The module in a GM parallel hybrid truck that controls the current to and from the integrated starter generator.

Shim A thin metal spacer.

Shop foreman A journeyman service technician who helps solve technical problems and helps service technicians.

Short circuit A circuit in which current flows, but bypasses some or all the resistance in the circuit. A connection that results in a "copper-to-copper" connection.

Shorted A condition of being shorted, such as a short circuit.

Short-to-ground A short circuit in which the current bypasses some or all the resistance of the circuit and flows to ground. Because ground is usually steel in automotive electricity, a short to ground (grounded) is a "copper-to-steel" connection.

Short-to-voltage A circuit in which current flows, but bypasses some or all the resistance in the circuit. A circuit that results in a "copper-to-copper" connection.

Shunt A device used to divert or bypass part of the current from the main circuit.

Shunt field A field coil used in a starter motor that is not connected to the armature in series but is grounded to the starter case.

Side airbags Airbags that deploy from the either from the door panel or from the side of the seat.

Silicon A semiconductor material.

Sine with dwell (SWD) test A test used to determine if an aftermarket suspension-related part is able to still allow the electronic stability control system to control the vehicle.

Single overhead camshaft (SOHC) A type of engine design that uses a single overhead camshaft per bank of cylinder to operate both the intake and the exhaust valves.

Single-cut file A file that has just one row of cutting teeth.

SIR Supplemental inflatable restraints. Another term for air bags.

Skin effect An AC electrical effect where the current rides on the surface of the conductor instead of through the core of thee conductor.

SKIS Sentry key immobilizer system. A type of antitheft system used in Chrysler vehicles.

SLA Abbreviation for short/long arm suspension.

Sleep mode A mode of operation of a tire pressure monitoring sensor that occurs when the wheels are not rotating and is used to help extend battery life.

Sleeve A part of a micrometer that has the major measurement designations.

SLI The battery that is responsible for starting, charging, and lighting in a vehicle's electrical system.

SLI battery The battery that is responsible for starting, charging, and lighting in a vehicle's electrical system.

Slip-joint pliers A hand tool that has two positions allowing the use of two different ranges of sizes.

Slip-ring end (SRE) The end of a generator (alternator) that has the brushes and the slip rings.

Small-hole gauge A handheld measuring tool that is adjustable to fit inside small holes. A micrometer is then used to measure the gauge to determine the inside diameter of the hole. Also called a *split-ball gauge*.

Smart control head An actuator used in an automatic temperature control system that can not only power the actuators but also keep track of the location of the door and controls.

Smart motor A motor actuator used in HVAC systems that can not only move an air door but can provide feedback as to the position of the motor and the door to the controller.

SMR System main relay. The high-voltage disconnect relays used in Toyota HEVs.

Snap-ring pliers A hand tool that is designed to install or remove snap rings.

Socket A tool used to grasp the head of a bolt or nut and then rotated by a ratchet or breaker bar.

Socket adapter An adapter that allows the use of one size of driver (ratchet or breaker bar) to rotate another drive size of socket.

Soft skills A term used to describe skills needed to get along with others in the work place that are not included in the technical skills needed to actually perform the work.

Solar cells A device that creates electricity when sunlight hits a semiconductor material and electrons are released. About one kilowatt from a solar cell that is one square meter in size.

Solenoid An electromagnetic switch that has a movable core.

Solenoid controlled damper A name given to a shock absorber that can be changed electrically either in two or three positions depending on the vehicle application.

Solenoid valves Valves that are opened and closed using an electromagnetic solenoid.

Solvent Usually colorless liquids that are used to remove grease and oil.

SPDT Single pole, double throw. A type of electrical switch.

Speakers A device consisting of a magnet, coil of wire, and a cone which reproduces sounds from the electrical signals sent to the speakers from a radio or amplifier.

Specific energy The energy content of a battery relative to the mass of the battery. Specific energy is measured in Watt-hours per kilogram (Wh/kg).

Specific gravity The ratio of the weight of a given volume of a liquid divided by the weight of an equal volume of water.

Spike protection resistor A resistor usually between 300 and 500 ohms that is connected in a circuit in parallel with the load to help reduce a voltage spike caused when a current following through a coil is turned off.

Spindle The part of a micrometer that moves and contacts the object being measured.

Splice pack A term used by General Motors to describe the connection of modules in a network.

Split-ball gauge See Small hole gauge.

SPM Surface permanent magnet. A type of rotor in an AC synchronous electric motor that places the magnets on its outside circumference.

Sponge lead Lead with many small holes used to make a surface porous or sponge-like for use in battery negative plates; the chemical symbol for lead is Pb.

Spontaneous combustion A condition that can cause some materials, such as oily rags, to catch fire without a source of ignition.

SPST Single pole, single throw. A type of electrical switch.

Squib The heating element of an inflator module which starts the chemical reaction to create the gas which inflates an air bag.

Squirrel-cage rotor A rotor design utilized in AC induction motors. The conductors in the rotor are made in the shape of a squirrel cage.

SRS Supplemental restraint system. Another term for an airbag system.

SST Special service tools. Tools specified by a vehicle manufacture needed to service a vehicle or a unit repair component of a vehicle.

Stabilitrak A brand name of the General Motors Corporation electronic stability control (ESC) system.

Standard Corporate Protocol (SCP) A network communications protocol used by Ford.

State-of-charge The degree or the amount that a battery is charged. A fully charged battery would be 100% charged. Abbreviated as SOC.

State-of-health (SOH) A signal sent by modules to all of the other modules in the network indicating that it is well and able to transmit.

Starter drive A term used to describe the starter motor drive pinion gear with overrunning clutch.

Starter solenoid A type of starter motor that uses a solenoid to activate the starter drive.

Static electricity An electrical charge that builds up in insulators and then discharges to conductors.

Stator A name for three interconnected windings inside an alternator. A rotating rotor provides a moving magnetic field and induces a current in the windings of the stator.

Steering position sensor (SPS) A sensor that detects the position as well as the direction and speed that the driver is rotating the steering wheel. Used as an input to the electronic suspension and electronic stability control system.

Steering shaft torque sensor A sensor used to detect the torque being applied tot eh steering wheel by the driver for use as a input to control the electronic suspension and /or electronic stability control system.

Steering wheel position sensor A sensor that detects the position as well as the direction and speed that the driver is rotating the steering wheel. Used as an input to the electronic suspension and electronic stability control system.

Stepper motor A motor that moves a specified amount of rotation.

Stiffening capacitor See *Powerline capacitor*.

Stone wheel A grinding stone attached to a grinder used for cleaning, sharpening, or other similar operations.

Storage The process inside of a computer where data is stored before and after calculations have been made.

Straight cut aviation snip A tin snip that is designed with curved jaws that allow a straight cut through sheet metal.

Straight time The amount of time actually spent performing a service operation.

Straightedge A precision ground measuring gauge that is perfectly straight.

Strong hybrid Another term for "full hybrid." See *Full hybrid*.

Stud A short rod with threads on both ends.

Stud removal tool A hand tool used with a breaker bar or ratchet to remove what is left of a broken stud.

Subwoofer A type of speaker that is used to reproduce low-frequency sounds.

SULEV Super-Ultra-Low-Emission Vehicle.

Sulfation Permanent damage in a lead-acid battery caused by the hardening of lead sulfate on the battery plates. Sulfation takes place when a lead-acid battery is discharged for an extended period of time.

Sun Load sensor The sun load sensor (also called a solar sensor), is normally mounted on top of the instrument panel and is used to measure radiant heat load that might cause an increase of the in-vehicle temperature.

Suppression diode A diode installed in the reverse bias direction and used to reduce the voltage spike that is created when a circuit that contains a coil is opened and the coil discharges.

Surface charge A "false" charge that exists on the battery plates when a vehicle is first turned off.

SVR Sealed valve regulated. A term used to describe a type of battery that is valve-regulated lead acid or sealed lead acid.

SWCAN An abbreviation for single wire CAN (Controller Area Network).

Team leader An experienced technician who helps advise a small group of technicians who are paid according to the total amount of work completed by all members of the team.

Technical service bulletin When a problem has a correction, the vehicle manufacturer releases a technical service bulletin (TSB), which details the repair. Also called *technical service bulletin information (TSBI)*.

Technician A person who performs diagnosis and service work to a vehicle.

Technician A and B questions A type of question used on ASE certification tests.

Telltale lamp A dash warning light. Also called an idiot light.

Temperature door See *temperature-blend door*.

Temperature-blend door A door used to control airflow either through the evaporator or around it to control temperature. Also called an air-mix door, temperature door or blend door.

Terminal The metal end of a wire which fits into a plastic connector and is the electrical connection part of a junction.

Terminating resistors Resistors placed at the end of a high-speed serial data circuit to help reduce electromagnetic interference.

Test light A light used to test for voltage. Contains a light bulb with a ground wire at one end and a pointed tip at the other end.

THD Total Harmonic Distortion. A rating for an amplifier used in a sound system.

Thermistor A resistor that changes resistance with temperature. A positive-coefficient thermistor has increased resistance with an increase in temperature. A negative-coefficient thermistor has increased resistance with a decrease in temperature.

Thermocouple When two dissimilar metals are connected and heated, it creates a voltage. Used for measuring temperature.

Thermoelectric device (TED) An electrical unit that can produce heat or cold depending on the polarity of the applied current. Used in heated and cooled seats and cup holders.

Thermoelectricity The production of current flow created by heating the connection of two dissimilar metals.

Thermostat A device that controls the flow in a system such as the engine cooling system based on temperature.

Thickness gauge See Feeler gauge.

Thimble   The part of a micrometer that is rotated to move the spindle.

Three Cs   Technicians need to complete the work order by informing the customers of the three Cs—complaint (concern), cause, and the correction.

Threshold voltage   Another name for barrier voltage or the voltage difference needed to forward bias a diode.

Through bolts   The bolts used to hold the parts of a starter motor together. The long bolts go though field housing and into the drive-end housing.

Throws   The term used to describe the number of output circuits there are in a switch.

THS   Toyota Hybrid System. Two generations of THS have been produced thus far, and these are known as THS I and THS II.

Tier   A level of environmental regulation created by the EPA. Tier 1 is gradually being phased out in favor of stricter Tier 2 regulations.

Time base   The setting of the amount of time per division when adjusting a scope.

Tin snips   A hand tool used to cut sheet metal, thin cardboard, or similar material.

Tire pressure monitoring system (TPMS)   A system of sensors or calculations used to detect a tire that has low tire pressure.

TLEV   Transitional Low-Emission Vehicle.

Tone generator tester   A type of tester used to find a shorted circuit that uses a tone generator. Headphones are used along with a probe to locate where the tone stops, which indicates were in the circuit the fault is located.

Torque   Twisting force. Torque is measured in pound-feet or Newton meters.

Torque wrench   A wrench that registers the amount of applied torque.

Torx   A type of fastener that features a star-shaped indentation for a tool. A registered trade mark of the Camcar Division of Textron.

Total circuit resistance (R_T)   The total resistance in a circuit.

Touring ride mode   A mode or position used in an electronic suspension system in some General Motors vehicles.

TPMS   Tire pressure monitoring system.

TRAC   Traction control. A function of the vehicle antilock brake system that enables application of the brake on wheels that have lost traction.

Traction control (TC)   The electromechanical parts used to control wheel slip during acceleration.

Traction motor   A motor-generator in a hybrid electric vehicle that is responsible for propelling or assisting the ICE in propelling the vehicle.

Trade number   The number stamped on an automotive light bulb. All bulbs of the same trade number have the same candlepower and wattage, regardless of the manufacturer of the bulb.

Trainee   The term used to describe a person being trained.

Transaxle   A transmission used in front-wheel-drive vehicles that include the final drive (differential) within the assembly.

Transfer case   A unit containing gears used to transfer engine power to the rear wheels or to both the front and rear wheels on a vehicle equipped with four-wheel drive.

Transistor   A semiconductor device that can operate as an amplifier or an electrical switch.

Transmitter ID   The identification on a TPMS sensor.

TREAD Act   The act that created the requirement that all vehicles built after September 2007 be equipped with a direct reading tire pressure monitoring system.

Trigger level   The voltage level that a waveform must reach to start display.

Trigger slope   The voltage direction that a waveform must have to start display. A positive slope requires the voltage to be increasing as it crosses the trigger level; a negative slope requires the voltage to be decreasing.

Trouble light   A light used for close viewing of dark areas. Also called a *work light*.

Troxler effect   The Troxler effect is a visual effect where an image remains on the retina of the eye for a short time after the image has been removed. The effect was discovered in 1804 by Igney Paul Vital Troxler (1780–1866), a Swiss physician. Because of the Troxler effect, headlight glare can remain on the retina of the eye and create a blind spot.

TSB   Technical service bulletin.

TTL   Transistor-Transistor Logic.

Tube-nut wrench   See Fitting wrench.

Turns ratio   The ratio between the number of turns used in the primary winding of the coil to the number of turns used in the secondary winding. In a typical ignition coil the ratio is 100:1.

Tweeter   A type of speaker used in a audio system that is designed to transmit high-frequency sounds.

Twisted pair   A pair of wires that are twisted together from 9 to 16 turns per foot of length. Most are twisted once every inch (12 per foot) to help reduce electromagnetic inference from being induced in the wires as one wire would tend to cancel out any interference pickup by the other wire.

UART   Universal Asynchronous Receive/Transmit, a type of serial data transmission.

UBP   UART-based protocol.

ULEV   Ultra-Low-Emission Vehicle.

ULEV II   Ultra Low-Emission Vehicle certified under the Phase II LEV standard.

Ultracapacitor   A specialized capacitor technology with increased storage capacity for a given volume.

UNC   Unified national coarse.

Undercut   A process of cutting the insulation, usually mica, from between the segments of a starter commutator.

Understeer   A condition when cornering where the vehicle tends to keep going straight when the driver is turning the steering wheel.

UNF   Unified national fine.

Unibody   Another name used to describe a unit body vehicle.

Unit body   A type of vehicle construction first used by the Budd Company of Troy, Michigan, that does not use a separate frame. The body is built strong enough to support the engine and the power train, as well as the suspension and steering system. The outside body panels are part of the structure. Also see Space frame construction.

Universal joint   A joint in a steering or drive shaft that allows torque to be transmitted at an angle.

Used oil   Any petroleum-based or synthetic oil that has been used.

UST   Underground storage tank.

Utility knife   A handheld knife that uses replaceable blades.

Valence ring   The outermost ring or orbit of electrons around a nucleus of an atom.

Variable-delay wipers   Windshield wipers whose speed can be varied.

Variable-position actuator   A variable position actuator used in an automatic temperature control system is capable of positioning a valve in any position. All variable position actuators use a feedback potentiometer, which is used by the controller to detect the actual position of the door or valve.

Varistors   Resistors whose resistance depends on the amount of voltage applied to them.

VATS   Vehicle Antitheft System. A system used on some General Motors vehicles.

VDIM   Vehicle Dynamic Integrated Management. A vehicle stability control system used on Lexus HEVs.

VECI   Vehicle emission control information. This sticker is located under the hood on all vehicles and includes emission-related information that is important to the service technician.

Vehicle identification number (VIN)   Alphanumeric number identifying vehicle type, assembly plant, power train, etc.

VIN   Vehicle identification number.

Viscosity   The thickness or the resistance to flow of a liquid.

VISE GRIPS®   A brand name for locking pliers.

Voice recognition   A system which uses a microphone and a speaker connected to an electronic module which can control the operation of electronic devices in a vehicle.

Volt   A unit of electrical pressure.

Voltage drop   Voltage loss across a wire, connector, or any other conductor. Voltage drop equals resistance in ohms times current in amperes (Ohm's law).

Voltmeter   An electrical test instrument used to measure volts (unit of electrical pressure). A voltmeter is connected in parallel with the unit or circuit being tested.

VRLA   Valve regulated lead-acid battery. A sealed battery that is both spill-proof and leak-proof. AGM and gelled electrolyte are both examples of VRLA batteries.

VSC   Vehicle stability control. An electronic stability control system used on Lexus vehicles.

VSES (Vehicle Stability Enhancement System)   A General Motors term used to describe one type of electronic stability control system.

VSS (vehicle speed sensor)   This sensor, usually located at the extension housing of the transmission/transaxle, is used by the electronic control module for vehicle speed.

VTF   Vacuum tube florescence. A type of dash display.

Warehouse distributor (WD)   A company that purchases parts from the manufacturer and sells the parts to automotive parts stores.

Water jacket   The coolant passages around the cylinders that are used to absorb and transfer heat away from the ICE assembly.

Water pump   A mechanical device responsible for circulating coolant through a liquid cooling system.

Water pump pliers   See Multigroove adjustable pliers.

Watt   An electrical unit of power; 1 watt equals current (amperes) × voltage (1/746 hp).

Watt's Law   The formula for Watts is the voltage times the amperes in the circuit which represents the electrical power in the circuit.

Wheel motor   An electric motor that is mounted directly on the vehicle's wheel, eliminating the connecting drive shaft.

Wheel speed sensors (WSS)   Sensors used to detect the speed of the wheels. Used by an electronic controller for antilock brakes and/or traction control.

WHMIS   Workplace Hazardous Materials Information Systems.

Wind farm   An area of land that is populated with wind-generating windmills.

Window regulator   A mechanical device that transfers the rotating motion of the window hand crank or electric motor to a vertical motion to raise and lower a window in a vehicle.

Windshield wipers   The assembly of motor, motor control, operating linkage plus the wiper arms and blades which are used to remove rain water from the windshield.

Wire brush wheel   A wire brush wheel is often mounted on one end of a grinder and is used for cleaning parts and other similar operations.

Wiring schematic   A drawing showing the wires and the components in a circuit, using symbols to represent the components.

Work experience   Two years of work experience as a service technician is needed plus passing one or more tests to be certified by ASE.

Work light   See Trouble light.

WOW display   A dash display when it first comes on and lights all possible segments. Can be used to test the dash display for missing lighted segments.

Wrench   A hand tool used to grasp and rotate a threaded fastener.

Xenon headlights   Headlights that use an arc tube assembly that has a xenon gas inside and which produces a bright bluish light.

Yaw rate sensor   A sensor that detects when the center of a vehicle is rotating around a vertical axis. Used as an input sensor for the electronic stability control system.

Zener diode   A specially constructed (heavily doped) diode designed to operate in reverse-bias without harm up to the current limit of the diode.

ZEV   Zero-Emission Vehicle. This rating is typically only achieved by battery-powered vehicles or those powered by fuel cells.

Zinc-air   A type of battery design that uses a positive electrode of gaseous oxygen and a negative electrode made of zinc.

Index

Electricity, 155
  compared to electronics, 361
  conductors, 157–159
  conductors and resistance, 162
  conventional theory vs. electron theory, 159
  current flow, 159
  defined, 155–156
  electron shells, 156–157
  free and bound electrons, 157
  insulators, 158
  ions, 156
  magnetism and, 203
  magnets and electrical charges, 156
  path of least resistance, 180, 201
  positive and negative charges, 156
  resistors, 163–164
  semiconductors, 158
  sources
    chemical, 162
    friction, 161
    heat, 161
    light, 161
    magnetism, 162
    pressure, 161–162
  units
    amperes, 159
    ohms, 160
    volts, 159–160
    watts, 161
  See also Electromagnetism
Electro-hydraulic power steering (EHPS), 557–558
Electrochemistry, 162
Electrohydraulic brake (EHB), 580
Electrolysis, 603
Electrolytes, 288, 605
Electromagnetic energy or radio waves, 213
Electromagnetic interference (EMI), 209–211
Electromagnetism, 201–210
  defined, 201
  electromagnetic interference (EMI), 209–211
  ignition coils and, 207–209
  induction and, 206–207
  uses of, 204–205
  See also Magnetism
Electromagnets, 203
Electromotive force (EMF), 160
Electron shells, 156–157
Electron theory, vs. conventional theory, 159
Electronic analog displays, 434
Electronic brake control module (EBCM), 537, 562
Electronic components, failure causes, 371–372
Electronic conductance testing, 293
Electronic control assembly (ECA), 376
Electronic control module (ECM), 376, 536
Electronic control unit (ECU), 376, 535
Electronic fuel level gauges, 438
Electronic odometers, 436–438
Electronic serial number (ESN), 225
Electronic service information, 106–108
Electronic speedometers, 435–436
Electronic stability control (ESC) systems, 560–567
  diagnosing, 566
  Federal Motor Vehicle Safety Standard (FMVSS) No., 126, 561
  names of various systems, 562
  sensors, 562–564

sine with dwell (SWD) test, 561–562
  system requirements, 560
  traction control, 564–566
Electronic suspension systems, 535–552
  actuators, 541–542
  automatic level control (ALC), 548–549
  control and sensors, 535–541
  magneto-rheological (MR) suspension, 549–550
  need for, 535
  troubleshooting rear electronic leveling systems, 550–551
  types of, 542–548
Electronic throttle control (ETC) system, 466
Electronically erasable programmable read-only memory (EEPROM), 437
Electronics, defined, 361
Electromagnetic induction, 206
Electrons, 155–158
  moving through a conductor, 159
Electrostatic discharge (ESD), 374–375
Elements (batteries), 288
EMF. See Electromotive force
EMI. See Electromagnetic interference
Emission standards (U.S.), 113–115
Emitter, 367
Emission control system, 5–6
Employment. See Careers
Employment applications, 22
Employment plans, 20–21
Energy, 139
  acoustical energy (sound), 213
  electromagnetic energy or radio waves, 213
Energy density, 605
Engine air filter, 121
Engine coolant temperature (ECT) sensor, 380, 499
Engine design evolution, 4–5
  inline vs. V-type design, 4
  valve location design, 4
Engine fault warning, 424–425
Engine mapping, 378
Engine-off drive-electric vehicle mode, 575
Engine oil, 123
Engine performance (A8), 7, 106
Engine power management (EPM), 336
Engine repair (A1), 7
Engine speed (RPM), 380, 565
Engine stands, 89
Engine systems, 5–6
  air intake system, 5
  cooling system, 5
  emission control system, 5–6
  fuel system, 5
  ignition system, 5
  lubrication system, 5
  starting and charging system, 5
Engines, service information and, 105–106
English customary measuring system, 95
Environmental Protection Agency (EPA), Hazardous Materials Identification Guide, 65
Entertainment and comfort, 387
Entrepreneur, 16
Environmental hazards. See Hazardous materials
Environmental Protection Agency (EPA), 56–57, 58
  asbestos regulations, 58
  emission standards, 113–115
  Hazardous Materials Identification Guide, 65

W

Warehouse distributors, 33
Warranties, 9–10
Waste chart, 63–64
Water
    as conductor, 158
    as fire extinguisher, 53
    mixing with acids, 145
Water jackets, 5
Water pump, 5
Water pump pliers, 73
Water spray trick, for testing drive belts, 128
Watt, James, 169
Watts, 161, 169–170
Watt's law, 169–170
Wavelength, 213–214
Wax trick, 77
Weight metric measurements, 95
Wheel motors, 609
Wheel speed sensor (WSS), 565
WHMIS. *See* Workplace Hazardous Materials Information Systems
Wiggle test, 282
Wind chill factor, 126
Wind farms, 615
Wind power, 615–616
Window regulator, 471
Window tinting, GPS and, 440
Windshield washer fluid, 120
Windshield wiper and washer system
    components, 451–453, 461
    computer controlled, 451, 452
    hidden wipers, 451, 453
    wiper motors, 451
Windshield wipers, 119–120
Wire brush wheel, 87
Wire repair, 264–266
    aluminum wire repair, 266
    crimp-and-seal connectors, 265–266
    crimping terminals, 265
    heat shrink tubing, 265
    soldering, 264–265
Wire size schematics, 269–270, 271
Wiring
    speakers, 218–219
    See also Automotive wiring
Wiring schematics and symbols, 106, 269–279
    batteries, 270, 272
    boxed components, 274
    capacitors, 273
    circuit information, 269, 270
    circuit trouble-shooting procedure, 279–282
    color-coding, 275
    common power or ground, 278–279

    dash warning symbols, 424–427
    electric heated unit, 273, 274
    electrical components, 273
    electrical motors, 273
    electrical troubleshooting guide, 282–283
    ISO relay terminal identification, 275, 276
    locating an open circuit, 278
    momentary switches, 275
    relay operation, 275–276, 277
    relay voltage spike control, 276–277
    resistors, 273
    separate replaceable part, 274
    step-by-step troubleshooting guide, 283
    switches, 274
    terminology, 269
    transistors, 367–368
    wire size, 269–270, 271
    wiring, 270, 272–273
Wood frame construction, 2
Work, 139
    vs. torque, 140
Work habit hints, 34
Work orders, 12, 14, 15
    documenting, 31–32
    flagging, 32–33
Work times, 35
Workplace Hazardous Materials Information Systems (WHMIS), 57
WOW display, 434
Wrenches, 87–88
Writing skills, 29
Wrought alloys, 147

X

Xenon headlights, 412
XM radio, 224

Y

Yaw rate sensor, 540, 563–564
Yellow conduit, 267

Z

ZEBRA batteries, 300–301
Zener diodes, 362
    construction, 362
    despiking, 363
    operation, 362
Zero emissions vehicle (ZEV), 569
ZEV. *See* Zero emissions vehicle
Zinc-air batteries, 300